EDINBURGH UNIVERSITY PUBLICATIONS
SCIENCE AND MATHEMATICS NO. 3F

PRIMATES

COMPARATIVE ANATOMY
AND TAXONOMY

VI
CATARRHINI
CERCOPITHECOIDEA
CERCOPITHECINAE

A Monograph
by

W. C. OSMAN HILL
M.D., F.R.S.E., F.L.S., F.Z.S.

EDINBURGH
AT THE UNIVERSITY PRESS

© W. C. Osman Hill 1966
EDINBURGH UNIVERSITY PRESS
George Square, Edinburgh 8
Australia and New Zealand
Hodder & Stoughton Limited
Africa, Oxford University Press
India, P. C. Manaktala & Sons
Far East, M. Graham Brash & Son

PRINTED BY R. & R. CLARK, LTD. EDINBURGH

TO MY WIFE

PREFACE

WITH the present volume the treatment of the Old World Simian Primates is commenced. General introductions are provided to the Catarrhini as a whole and to the superfamily Cercopithecoidea. The diversification of forms within the latter necessitates some subdivision in dealing with the subgroups involved. This is particularly the case with the numerous and complex members of the genus *Cercopithecus*, which has received no comprehensive revision in recent years. Anatomical studies have further shown the desirability of separating, at subfamilial level, this genus and its immediate allies, *Miopithecus*, *Allenopithecus* and *Erythrocebus*. This means that the present volume closes conveniently with the treatment of the subfamily Cercopithecinae, and leaves the remaining Cercopithecidae (macaques, mangabeys, baboons and their fossil allies) for consideration in the subsequent volume.

The basal early Primates of the Oligocene are also considered, for the assumption that these include forms ancestral to the existing Old World simians is justified. However, it must be understood that the basic division between Cercopithecoidea and Hominoidea (the Cynomorpha and Anthropomorpha of earlier systematists) occurred very early. Whilst, therefore, *Parapithecus* may truly be a generalized ancestral form, some, at least, of the other early fossils considered may be regarded as already showing leanings towards an anthropomorph rather than a cynomorph lineage. Nevertheless, in the absence of indubitable evidence, they have been treated in this volume, on chronological grounds.

W. C. OSMAN HILL,
Yerkes Primate Research Center
January, 1966

ACKNOWLEDGMENTS

NEEDLESS to say a work such as the present would never be written without assistance from many and varied sources, and it becomes at once a duty and a pleasure to acknowledge the unstinted help received in abundance from many friends and correspondents.

Material made use of in the anatomical work, as well as in the systematic studies, has been collected over the past thirty years and more, both from private donors and through the kindness of the directors and other staff of various public zoological collections and of animal dealers. Of the public zoos I am specially indebted to those at Baltimore, Md. ; Bristol ; Chessington, Surrey ; Chester ; Colombo Museum, Ceylon ; Dehiwela, Ceylon ; Edinburgh ; London ; Miami, Fla ; Glen Helen, Isle of Man ; and San Diego, California. I would like especially to thank the following individuals associated with the above collections for the readiness with which they acceded to my frequent and bothersome requests and for the excellent state of the material supplied : Mr. A. Watson (Baltimore), Mr. R. E. Greed (Bristol), Major H. A. Snazle (Chessington), Major A. N. Weinman (Colombo Museum, Ceylon), Mr. T. S. Gillespie and Mr. A. Cunliffe (Edinburgh), Mr. G. S. Mottershead and Mr. R. J. Bloom (Chester), Dr. Gordon Hubbell (Miami) and Dr. G. H. Pournelle and Mr. Clyde Hill (San Diego). Material emanating from London was studied during my tenure of the Prosectorship of the Zoological Society.

My particular thanks are due to the authorities of the San Diego Zoo for their consideration in supplying me with much unique material (including *Allenopithecus*) over the last several years.

Among private individuals to whom I am indebted for specimens, the following should specially be mentioned : Dr. E. C. Appleby (Edinburgh), C. P. Chase (Miami), Gerald M. Durrell (Jersey), Mrs. B. Cartwright (Leamington), Mr. R. N. Fiennes (London), Mr. Hall (of Messrs. Harrods Ltd.), Dr. J. Hope (Atlanta ; now at Bedford), Dr. G. Hubbell (Miami), Mr. R. Jackson (North Wales), Professor W. E. Kershaw (Liverpool), the late Mr. J. W. Lester (London), Mr. J. J. C. Mallinson (Jersey), the late Mr. F. G. Merfield (London), Dr. J. R. Napier (London), Mr. B. Nettleden (formerly of London), Mr. R. Shingler (now of Trinidad), Professor Dr. D. Starck (Frankfurt), Dr. J. Sabater Pí (Rio Muñi), the late Sir G. Tyrrhit-Drake (Maidstone, Kent), the late Mr. C. S. Webb (Nairobi) and Mr. Andrew Wilson (Glasgow).

Material must also be acknowledged from Messrs. Glaxo Laboratories, Greenford, Middlesex (Dr. Pratt) and from King Williamstown Museum (Mr. E. T. Skead).

For the extended loan of the unique juvenile specimen (skin and skull) of *Cercopithecus hamlyni* I owe a great debt of gratitude to Dr. H. Brongersma and Mr. A. M. Husson of the Leiden Museum.

For the privilege of examining material, including numerous type specimens, and the facilities vouchsafed during my visits, I am under considerable obligation to the authorities in the mammal department of the British Museum (Natural History), and the U.S. National Museum (Smithsonian Institution, Washington, D.C.). At the former I would particularly like to acknowledge the help of Messrs. R. W. Hayman and J. E. Hill. At the latter I have been given every facility and assistance by Dr. David Johnson and his staff. At the Tring Museum, where many rewarding hours were spent, I was as usual given great assistance by Dr. J. E. Dandy, the Officer in Charge, and Mr. C. L. Rance, resident superintendent and his staff.

Among the zoological collections visited in my pursuit of living examples of unusual varieties of primates I would like to draw attention to those at Antwerp (Mr. W. Van den bergh and Dr. Agatha Gijzen), Basel (Dr. E. Lang), Chester (Mr. G. S. Mottershead and Mr. R. Bloom), Paris (M. Strazielle), Milwaukee (Dr. Speidel), St. Louis (Mr. Marlin Perkins), Washington, D.C. (Drs. T. Reed and Ted Roth) and Zürich (Professor Dr. H. Hediger), and to express my appreciation to the above-mentioned Directors and their staff who devoted their time and experience to assisting me.

For valuable information supplied at my request or obtained during discussion, I am deeply indebted to the following : Mr. J. H. Ayer (Lincoln, Nebraska), Dr. A. C. V. van Bemmel (Rotterdam), the late Angus H. Booth (Gold Coast), Mrs. Leonora Brandt (Cincinnati), M. Pierre Dandelot (Paris), Miss Jessie Dobson (Royal College of Surgeons, England), Mr. Frank Dumond (Goulds, Florida), Dr. Agatha Gijzen (Antwerp Zoo), Robert R. Grant (Academy of Natural Sciences, Philadelphia, Pa.), Mr. L. Grimmer (Washington Zoo), Dr. Bernard Grzimek (Frankfurt), Dr. A. J. Haddow (Entebbe, Uganda), the late Professor K. R. L. Hall (Bristol), Professor Dr. H. Hediger (Zürich), S/c Marvin Jones (U.S. Army), Mr. E. Maruska (Cincinnati Zoo), Dr. H. J. Kuhn (Frankfurt), M. Max Poll (Tervueren Museum), Mr. G. B. Rabb (Brookfield Zoo, Chicago), Dr. W. T. Roth (Washington, D.C.), Head-Keeper L. Smith (London Zoo), Professor Dr. D. Starck (Frankfurt), M. L. Strazielle (Paris Menagerie), the late Dr. E. Schwarz ; Dr. N. C. Tappen (Tulane University, New Orleans, La.), Mr. Bob Truett (Birmingham, Alabama), Mr. W. Van den bergh (Antwerp Zoo), Dr. Jiri Volf (Prague) and Mr. Ernest P. Walker (Washington, D.C.).

Besides the numerous authors who have kindly provided me with reprints of their publications, I have to acknowledge the help I have received in connection with special items of literature, in particular to M. M. J. Bemindt of Antwerp, M. Max Poll (Tervueren Museum), who kindly provided me with a detailed map of the Congo and to the Institut des Parcs Nationaux du Congo. I am deeply appreciative of library facilities, to the Librarian, Zoological Society of London and his staff, to the Royal Society of Medicine, to the library of Tring Museum (Miss P. M. Thomas), and to the general and medical libraries of Emory University and also to the staff of the library of the University of Georgia, Athens, Ga. The Japan Monkey Centre has provided me with important publications. The Royal Society of Edinburgh generously lent blocks for figs. 85-90.

Black-and-White photographs have been acknowledged on the individual plates. The coloured photograph of *C. pogonias pogonias* is reproduced by kind permission of Mr. Edward Maruska and the one of *C. pogonias grayi* by permission of Mr. V. Six.

For technical help I am indebted to the late W. E. Lawrence and to K. A. T. Denham in London, to Dr. R. Quinton-Cox in Atlanta and to Dr. Daris Swindler, formerly of Charleston, S.C., and, for her artistic work, to Mrs. Kay Leclerc of Atlanta.

My secretary, Miss Marie Wright has been long-suffering with extremely untidy manuscripts involving much re-typing and modification. I am grateful for her forbearance and also for help in tracing obscure references. I must also add a tribute to my publisher, especially Mr. A. Turnbull and Miss P. K. Duncan, both of whom have borne patiently with my wishes.

The greater part of the work has been assisted, since December 1962, by National Institutes of Health Grant # FR 00164, administered by Dr. Geoffrey H. Bourne, Director, Yerkes Regional Primate Research Center, whose kindly help in all matters of administration I most gratefully acknowledge.

Finally I must remind my readers of my continued indebtedness to the late Professor Frederic Wood-Jones., F.R.S.

PUBLISHER'S NOTE

The Edinburgh University Press gratefully acknowledges a generous grant made by the J. K. Young Endowment Fund (per Messrs. Wallace & Guthrie, W. S., Edinburgh) towards the cost of publication of this volume.

CONTENTS

INFRAORDER CATARRHINI

Definition 3 ; Historical 3 ; Structure : External Features 28 ;
Skeletal System 33 ; Dentition 39 ; Myology 40 ; Splanchnology 40 ;
Angeiology 46 ; Neurology 46 ; Sense Organs 46 ; Behavioural
Characters 47 ; Geographical Distribution 50 ; Geological
History 51 ; Taxonomy 54

SUPERFAMILY CERCOPITHECOIDEA

Definition 56 ; Structure : External Features 57 ; Skeletal System 62 ;
Myology 66 ; Splanchnology 70 ; Haematology 84 ; Angei-
ology 90 ; Neurology 100 ; Sense Organs 125 ; Karyology 131 ;
Reproductive Physiology 134 ; Early Development and Placenta-
tion 140 ; Behavioural Characters 147 ; Distribution 174 ;
Taxonomy 175

SYSTEMATIC LIST p. 178

FAMILY I. PARAPITHECIDAE p. 182

PARAPITHECIDAE INCERTAE SEDIS p. 188

Fossil Early CATARRHINI INCERTAE SEDIS p. 191

LIST OF PLATES

xvii

Colour Plates

LIST OF FIGURES

LIST OF TABLES

NOMENCLATURAL EMENDATION

ON p. 432 the Samango monkey has been treated under the scientific name *Cercopithecus albogularis samango* Wahlberg 1844, on the grounds that *C. labiatus* Geoffroy 1842 is a *nomen nudum*. Later search reveals that Geoffroy published two good descriptions of this monkey under the latter name, at least one of which antedates Wahlberg's designation, and must therefore replace it. The references are :

1. I. Geoffroy, 1841, *Arch. Mus. Paris*, **2**, 555.
2. I. Geoffroy, 1849, Article Cercopithèque ou Guenon, in d'Orbigny (ed.). *Dictionnaire universelle d'histoire naturelle*, **3**, p. 302.

There is some doubt as to the exact day of publication of the second article, which is, in fact, quoted in the first—presumably prior to its publication. On the title-page of the copy consulted 1849 is given as date of publication, yet the notation in the 1841 publication is given as 1842 !

NOTE

I hope I shall be forgiven for continuing to use the geographical names with which I started this series: Gold Coast (Ghana) ; Northern Rhodesia (Zambia) ; Southern Rhodesia (Rhodesia) ; Tanganyika and Zanzibar (Tanzania) ; Madagascar (Malagasy) ; Nyasaland (Malawi). It would cause confusion to use the modern names for these countries in conjunction with the old forms still used in Museums and collections and also in quotes. W.C.O.H.

Infraorder CATARRHINI

Infraorder CATARRHINI E. Geoffroy, 1812*

Old World Simian Primates

(SYN. : Catarrhina Hemprich, 1820, p. 17 : Family Simiadae, Gray, 1821, p. 296, 1870, p. 4, Fleming, 1822, p. 172, Gosse, 1848, p. 8 ; Simiae, Ogilby, 1838, Gray, 1870, p. 4, Gadow, 1898, p. 53 ; Catarrhini Latreille, 1825, p. 43, Blyth, 1847, p. 728 ; Catarrhina Owen, 1851, p. 334 ; Heopitheci, van der Hoeven, 1852–6 ; Catarrhinae, Haeckel, 1866, clx)

DEFINITION.—Simian Primates with narrow internarial septum separating external nares which are directed either forwards, downwards and forwards or even (*e.g. Homo, Nasalis*) directly downwards ; with the pollex present (except in *Colobus*) well separated from the other digits and more completely opposable than in any platyrrhine monkey ; with a formula for the permanent dentition I.$\frac{2}{2}$, C.$\frac{1}{1}$, P.$\frac{2}{2}$, M.$\frac{3}{3}$ = 32 ; with the tail, when present, never prehensile ; pterion normally with fronto-alisphenoidal contact, separating parietal from malar ; with a well-developed bony tubular external auditory meatus ; and with the large intestine provided with taeniae coli, a sigmoid flexure and a conical or bulbous caecum whose apex is never permanently hook-shaped.

HISTORICAL

Knowledge of Old World Primates of several kinds is traceable back to the ancients. Whole books (*e.g.* Lichtenstein, 1791 ; McDermott, 1938) have been written on the monkeys and apes supposedly known to the ancients ; it is therefore possible here to refer only briefly to the main points, leaving details to be considered under the individual genera.

Several species of monkeys were known, at least as early as 1500 B.C., to the ancient Egyptians, who venerated the Hamadryas Baboon (*Papio hamadryas*) and also the Anubis Baboon (*P. anubis*) as is attested, not only by depictions on their monuments, but also from their having embalmed their dead bodies. Their deities Anubis and Thoth were dog-headed or jackal-headed beings and evidently based on baboons. Secular knowledge of other species of long-tailed monkeys is further indicated on their monuments, though opinions differ as to their identity. Well known is a carving depicting the procession of a returning conqueror in which is shown a tailed monkey riding upon the neck of a giraffe—evidently intended to indicate the locality wherein the conquest had occurred. The animal is bound by a strap around its waist much as is still to be seen in the

* *Ann. Mus. Hist. nat. Paris*, xix. 87.

east, proving the animals were kept as pets.   Another sculpture, found at
Memphis and now in the Berlin Museum, shows images of monkeys on
sepulchral stones.   Ogilby (1838) * is of opinion that the species depicted is
the Nisnas (*Erythrocebus patas pyrronotus*) ; this may well be, but in view of
the former wider distribution of monkeys in northern Africa, it would seem
probable that at least one of the true guenons (the Grivet, *Cercopithecus
aethiops aethiops*) was known, and this is suggested by engravings found at
Gizeh (*vide infra* under *Cercopithecus*, p. 211).   Other coloured Egyptian
drawings represent monkeys on all fours, with the tail curved over the
back—an attitude adopted by mangabeys.   Many further examples are given
by McDermott (1938).

According to Strabo (*c.* 55 B.C.–A.D. 20) the Babylonians worshipped a
baboon and, although no primate has, to our knowledge, occurred naturally
within historic times in Mesopotamia, it is evident that monkeys were
articles of commerce—presumably from Egypt—though possibility of access
to Asiatic monkeys cannot be denied.

One of the most firmly established facts regarding ancient knowledge of
the Old World Primates is the discovery made by the Carthaginian admiral
Hanno, who, around 537–525 B.C., made a voyage round the west coast of
Africa as far as Mount Cameroon.   In the *Periplus*, published after his
return, mention is made of γορίλλοι (gorilloi) encountered on the island of
Sherboro off the coast of Sierra Leone.   Three of the beasts were captured
and their skins brought back to Carthage.   Much controversy has taken
place regarding the identity of Hanno's apes, and it is commonly accepted
that they were chimpanzees.   Winwood Reade (1864) denied this, declaring
them to be baboons (? drills—a native term probably cognate with gorilla).
But recently Stechow (1949) of München brought forward new evidence that
they were real gorillas and not chimpanzees, baboons or pygmies—a view
also expressed by McDermott (1938).

The Phoenicians, being great traders, were largely responsible for
disseminating knowledge of apes and monkeys over the Mediterranean area.
The Barbary Ape (*Macaca sylvana*) was then common in their own land and
it seems to be the species which spread, by commerce, to the European
side of the Mediterranean, where no Primate was indigenous, notably to
Italy, where the Etruscans have left numerous coloured paintings on the walls
of tombs, some of which depict apes—apparently known in the Etruscan
tongue as *arim* (rendered αρίμος in Greek) (*e.g.* the Tomba della scimmia
near Chiusi, dated *c.* 500–450 B.C., and the Tomba Golini near Orvieto).

On the other hand, much earlier (*c.* 1580–1450 B.C.) representations of
monkeys in frescoes at Cnossos, Crete, pertaining to the period known to

---

* Yerkes and Yerkes (1929) mistakenly attribute this anonymous work to the ornithologist
James Rennie (1787–1867), but Ogilby is usually regarded as author, and this is confirmed by his
own admission (*Proc. zool. Soc. Lond.*, 1843, p. 11).

archaeologists as Late Minoan I, evidently owe their inspiration to early Egyptian sources. These representations are very naturalistic, showing coloured figures of quadrupedal guenons of the greenish type which McDermott opines to be *Cercopithecus tantalus*, on account of the clearly marked white frontal band. It is more likely, on geographical grounds, that one of the other races would be the basis, as, for example, Grivet (*C. aethiops*), for *C. tantalus* has its centre of origin in Nigeria, an unlikely source for monkeys at the date in question. This is further vindicated by the representations of small greenish monkeys depicted in Egyptian monuments of the time of Rameses I (1321 B.C.) taken among booty from Ethiopia.

Apes of some kind were also known to the ancient Hebrews, among whom they were designated *koph* (קוֹף) (plural *kophim* or *qôphîm*)—evidently cognate with Arabic *keb* or *kep* and the Greek κέπος. Two references in the Old Testament * indicate that, at the time of Solomon (tenth century B.C.) apes were objects of trade, particularly with the land of Ophir—usually regarded as the land of Punt of the Egyptians (*i.e.* Somaliland), " For Solomon had at sea a navy at Tarshish, with the navy of Hiram ; once every three years came the navy of Tarshish, bringing gold and silver, ivory and apes and peacocks ". The mention of peacocks would imply that the apes might be of Asiatic origin, whilst ivory might be either Asiatic or African, though more probably the latter. However, the traditional translation of *tukkîyîm* as peacock has been questioned. It appears to have been mistaken for a similar Tamil word, and that the real meaning is again " apes "— presumably of another kind than *kophim*. There is, moreover, no other evidence of peacocks being known to the contemporary Hebrews.

There are many references to monkeys in the earlier Hellenic literature (for details *vide* McDermott *loc. cit.*). Special mention should be made perhaps of Ctesias (fl. 400 B.C.), who was physician to the Persian king Artaxerxes for seventeen years. Mainly a historian, he wrote about his experiences at the Persian court and also about India. His authority is usually regarded as somewhat questionable. His account of a race of dog-headed men in India shows his gullibility, though possibly based on distorted accounts of an Asiatic anthropoid ape. Keller (1909) has suggested the gibbon.

Aristotle (384–322 B.C.) summarized the knowledge of the Greeks anent the apes and monkeys. He uses five names which appear to represent different species, though he describes all together. Consequently there has been considerable difference of opinion among later writers as to what his terms represent. They are κῆβος, κάλλιθριξ, πίθηκος, κυνοκέφαλοι, and χοιροπίθηκος.

κῆβος (latinized later as *cepus*, *cephus*, *cebus* and other variants) is a sort of generic term and may refer to any small, tailed monkey. Buffon (1756) arbitrarily identified it with the Mona monkey (*Cercopithecus mona*) but

* III Kings, 10, 22 ; II Chronicles, 9, 21.

being a purely West African form, this is unlikely. Ogilby (1838) gives convincing evidence that it might relate to a Gelada (*Theropithecus gelada*), a native of Abyssinia, though admitting that later writers and commentators deduced it to be some other species, *e.g.* the Nisnas (*Erythrocebus patas pyrronotus*). About πίθηκος there is little doubt; it was the most familiar ape known to the ancients—the North African tailless Barbary Ape (*Macaca sylvana*).

The κάλλιθριξ (*callithrix* or *callitrix*) has given rise to more conjecture. Erroneously transferred by Buffon to the common West African Green monkey (*Cercopithecus sabaeus*) the evidence is more in favour of a beast with specially beautiful fur, hence the name. This would seem to point to another Abyssinian species, the Guereza (*Colobus abyssinicus*) whose skins were probably traded along the Nile. This view is sponsored by Ogilby.

Less doubt arises regarding the κυνοκέφαλοι, *i.e. cynocephali* or dog-headed ones. The name clearly relates to baboons and almost certainly to the Hamadryas (*Papio hamadryas*) sacred to the Egyptians.

The term χοιροπίθηκος was used incidentally later (*Hist. Anim.* lib. 2, cap. 2) and would seem to refer specifically to some form of baboon with a more pig-like snout. From the description this possibly referred to a mandrill (*Mandrillus sphynx*), which might have been brought from West Africa to Egypt or Greece by the Phoenicians. The stunted tail of the mandrill would have induced Aristotle to make comparison with the tailless πίθηκος (*vide* Ogilby, p. 435).

Megasthenes (fl. *c.* 300 B.C.), a Greek historian and geographer, having been a representative of Seleucus Nicator, King of Syria, to the court of Chandragupta (316–292 B.C.), wrote a work (now lost) on India. He mentioned a stone-rolling habit of Indian monkeys, which probably refers to the Rhesus Macaque (*Macaca mulatta*). He also described larger white animals with very long tails and black faces. This identifies them clearly as the common langur (*Semnopithecus entellus*). They inhabited the country of the Prasii (*i.e.* Western India).

Agatharchides (fl. *c.* 200–100 B.C.), author of a work entitled *De mari Erythraeo*, describes the various monkeys of that area, including the lion-faced *cepus*, as being as large as gazelles. McDermott thinks this was one of the more colourful guenons, but the description corresponds more to the Gelada. There appears in this work also the earliest mention of what could be interpreted as an anthropoid ape. It refers to two tribes inhabiting Ethiopia named *spermatophagi* (seed eaters) and *hylophagi* (wood eaters). Most of the descriptive details of both and especially of the *hylophagi* seem applicable to the chimpanzee.

Other Primates referred to by Agatharchides are the *sphinx, callithrix* and *cercopithecus*. The first is undoubtedly a baboon, probably the Hamadryas, but some authorities consider it a guenon.

Much confusion arose from the slipshod way in which later writers and commentators used Aristotle's terms but transposed their references to different animals. No two authors, moreover, used them in a uniform connotation. Most important of these later writers are Diodorus (first century B.C.), Strabo (c. 55 B.C.–A.D. 25), Pliny (A.D. 23–79), Aelian (fl. A.D. 250) and Solinus (3rd century A.D.).

Diodorus Siculus, a Greek historian, flourished in Rome at the time of Caesar and Augustus. He is regarded as the earliest naturalist of importance after Aristotle, though his works show him to have accepted data uncritically. His most important primatological observation is that female baboons carry their wombs externally—a cogent interpretation of their periodic perineal swellings.

Strabo, essentially a geographer, visited all countries between Armenia and Italy and between the Euxine and Ethiopia. Nevertheless, much of his information is second-hand. For example, from Diodorus Siculus, Strabo knew that the πίθηκος or tailless ape was abundant in North Africa and he also quotes Posidonius, who saw large numbers of them when visiting Libya, where at that time the forests extended to the coast.

On the other hand, the *cebus*, *cepus* or *cephus* of Diodorus and Strabo is more controversial. G. Cuvier, in annotating the French edition of Pliny's *Natural History*, attempts, not very successfully, to recognize them as three separate species of monkey, *i.e.* the *cepus* of Diodorus and Strabo he thinks to be the common Ethiopian baboon (*Papio anubis*), whilst the *cepus* mentioned by Agatharchides is supposedly the Hamadryas baboon, whereas Aelian's use of the name is applicable to the Patas monkey or Nisnas. Cuvier evidently did not interpret Agatharchides correctly, for this author elsewhere particularly distinguishes the *cepus* from the *cynocephalus* (Ogilby, p. 341). Strabo mentions Hermopolis as the centre of worship of the *cynocephalus*, whereas the Babylonians in the vicinity of Memphis worshipped the *cepus*. This suggests that he is using both terms for varieties of baboon as nowhere is there evidence that any other primate form was held in Egypt as sacred.

Pliny (Gaius Plinius Secundus), a native of Como, was the most celebrated naturalist of Roman times. He wrote a *Historia naturalis* in thirty-seven books and flourished during the reign of Nero, who was notorious for his fascination for maintaining collections of exotic wild animals. Pliny lists uncritically quite a collection of real and fabled creatures of primate or quasi-primate facies, such as satyrs, pygmies, cynocephali, cynoprosopi and so on, some being supposedly human or subhuman in character. It is somewhat difficult to sift the wheat from the chaff; albeit Pliny reports accurately when dealing with creatures whose existence had been well established; some of his statements could possibly be imperfect descriptions of anthropoid apes given by travellers returning from the east. This applies, for example, to his satyrs, which reputedly existed in the "tropical mountains" of India (*Catharcludorum dicitur regio*), had human faces, sometimes went on all fours, but were often bipedal. Could this be a reference to the Orang-utan or to one of the gibbons ? He also quotes one Tauron as authority for the existence of *choromandae*, having hairy bodies, amber eyes, dog-like teeth and frightful voices—clearly a suggestion of gibbon lies here. Other apes called *scyritae* he mentions on the authority of Megasthenes, who encountered them among the nomadic Indian tribes. These are characterized by having no nose, the nostrils opening as foramina directly on the face, whilst their bandy legs can be twisted in all directions ; this vaguely evokes the image of a young orang.

Pliny knew of baboons (*cynocephali*) but did not characterize them from other apes beyond commenting on their ferocity. An interesting observation made by Pliny was that tailed apes were more affected by phases of the moon. This evidently dates back to the connection between the baboon and the moon upheld by the Egyptians and was clearly an early recognition of the periodicity of the sexual swellings so conspicuous in these animals. Another attribute of monkeys noted by Pliny was their attachment to their offspring ; he declares they are so affectionate that their embraces sometimes crush the infant.

Pliny describes the *callithrix* as differing widely from ordinary apes, having a beard and a broad-based tail and not capable of survival outside its normal habitat. This further confirms the theory that the Guereza (*Colobus abyssinicus*) was meant.

Tailed apes, *cercopitheci*, were referred to by Pliny in such terms that specific diagnosis is uncertain. From India Pliny refers to men with hairy tails which must be regarded as a description of one of the Indian monkeys.

Aelian (Claudius Aelianus), a Roman, wrote in Greek, being an admirer of Plato, Aristotle, Plutarch and other earlier savants. His *De Natura animalium* contains many references to monkeys mostly based on earlier sources, *e.g.* Pythagoras and Clitarchus. His description of the *cepos* fairly conclusively indicates a Patas monkey (*Erythrocebus patas*) or, at any rate, its eastern race, the Nisnas (*q.v. antea*, p. 4). Although he gives an extensive account of *cynocephalus*, he omits mention of its sacred associations, but includes other interesting data readily applicable to the Hamadryas baboon : the ferocity and lascivious character of the old males, the educability of the young, etc. In Mauretania he mentions the panther as an enemy of the monkeys. Of Indian species his data are drawn from Ctesias, Megasthenes and Strabo, but he makes mistakes in his facts, *e.g.* reversing the colours in dealing with the Entellus Langur and increasing the tail length from three to seven feet! On the other hand, in discussing the monkeys of the land of the Prasii, he mentions one species with a beard and a lion-like tail. This could well be the earliest surviving mention of the Lion-tailed Macaque

(*Macaca silenus*) of the Malabar tract, albeit McDermott, following Keller, prefers to believe they were Langurs, since they were reported feeding on rice put out for them by the natives. A reddish Indian ape of lascivious character almost surely refers to the Rhesus Macaque. Aelian follows Pliny in his description of the satyrs, stating that they have the appearance of the creatures so called in mythology. The account is based possibly upon vague travellers' tales of gibbons or even orangs.

Gaius Julius Solinus, who probably lived during the first half of the third century A.D., is perhaps the most important of this early group as far as the history of the Primates is concerned, not only for his classification of the then known forms, but more perhaps for his influence on later writers, which extended well into the Middle Ages. His *Collectanea rerum memorabilium* contains a short description of the ancient world, with remarks on zoological as well as historical, social and religious questions. It was revised in the sixth century under the title *Polyhistor* (a term subsequently taken as the author's name, and even as a generic title for writers of his type).

Solinus refers first in general terms to the genus *simiarum* which is characterized by its ability to imitate humans, rendering them easy of capture, for hunters obtain them by pretending to smear their own eyes with bird-lime, which induces the ape to imitate them, so blinding themselves and facilitating capture. Excessive maternal attachment to the young, which are carried in the mother's arms, is another characteristic emphasized by Solinus, who also affirms that they rejoice at full moon, but grieve on the waning moon—an early recognition of some sort of lunar periodicity in simian behaviour based doubtless upon ancient observations on baboons. Following these general remarks, Solinus enumerates five distinct kinds of simians. These are :

1. *Cercopitheci* : tailed, but otherwise resembling the aforementioned, which seems to indicate that the preliminary remarks apply to a particular species only.
2. *Cynocephali* : vicious and untameable ; very numerous in Ethiopia.
3. *Sphinges* : easily domesticated ; shaggy coated and with prominent mammae.
4. *Satyri* : lively in gesture and of pleasing countenance.
5. *Callitriches* : differing from all the rest in almost every particular ; bearded and with broad tails, unable to survive outside their original habitat (Ethiopia).

No account of the monkeys known in Roman times would be complete without reference to Galen (Claudius Galenus), a Greek physician of Pergamum, who practised medicine in Rome from A.D. 164. His renown is largely based on his anatomical work, for which purpose he utilized the πίθηκος, *i.e.* Barbary Ape (*Macaca sylvana*), as being the most readily available subject in the absence of human cadavera. However, he was well acquainted also with the κυνοκέφαλος (Hamadryas baboon) and willing to use it anatomically. Other primates recognized by Galen were κῆβος, σάτυρος and λύγξ. The name *cebus* was used for any tailed monkey not included under the other terms and therefore as a generic term; it was definitely not a gibbon. Galen's satyr, on the other hand, was an Indian species, but apparently likewise not a gibbon and consequently not used in the same sense as by Pliny, Aelian or Solinus; it remains unidentified. The lynx of Galen and some other early writers is not the animal so named in modern times, but clearly an ape of some kind. The term is used by Pliny in connection with σφύγξ and probably relates to a tailed species.

Throughout, Galen compares his material structure by structure with corresponding parts in Man. He arranges his apes in descending order according to size of jaws. Of particular interest is his statement that apes are the only animals that share with Man the liability to hernia, which he attributes to their larger peritoneum. He also recommends to artists and sculptors the study of the monkey's hand as a parody of its human counter-part, thus emphasizing the early development of the idea of the ludicrous as applicable to subhuman primates.

Horapollon of Phaenebythis (in the nome of Panopolis, Egypt) wrote, during the fourth century, commentaries on Sophocles and other early Greek philosophers. His two extant books on *Hieroglyphics* (which profess to be translations from Egyptian into Greek) contain some observations on baboons, notably the fact that the Sacred Baboon (*Papio hamadryas*) undergoes a menstrual cycle. This was evidently based upon ancient Egyptian knowledge, as no reference to it is made by either Aristotle or Galen.

During the sixth century the Spanish encyclopaedist and historian Isidore of Seville published his *Etymologia*, in which he incorporated Solinus' list of known simians. He stated that the term *simia* covered five genera of apes, thus disposing of the concept that it also referred to a specific kind or breed. He modified Solinus' characterization of *cynocephali*, describing them as " similar to the apes " but with dog-like heads, leaving an impression of some confusion as to whether they were really apes or dog-headed people. There was also some vagueness about the *satyri* so that later writers often combined them with the *cynocephali*.

After the close of Roman times a period of thirteen centuries elapsed before apes or monkeys were again mentioned in European literature. During these dark ages the lamp of learning was maintained, burning albeit feebly, in the hands of Arabic-speaking peoples. These writers salvaged the remnants of Greek literature, translating it into their own tongue, but added little in the way of original observation. Among them el Kasvini (Sakarja ben Muhammed; thirteenth century), a native of northern Persia, was the contemporary of Pliny and author of a collective work entitled *The Wonders of Nature*. Based largely upon Aristotle, it includes descriptions of a number of animals unknown to the ancients, including the Orang-utan. Better known, however, was Avicenna (Ibn-sina, 980–1037), a native of Bokhara, who became a physician. He, too, relied on Aristotle under whose name *cepos* he described in general terms long-tailed monkeys.

Although during the Middle Ages in Europe no advances were made in regard to classical zoology, *i.e.* anatomical structure, taxonomy, habitat, etc., some interest in the general biology, behaviour and psychology of monkeys was evinced, albeit distorted by applications to the religious and moral concepts so characteristic of the period. These ideas were codified in the so-called Bestiaries—collections of animal stories and legends, with allegorical treatment, compiled by unknown scribes—which were popular for centuries in many lands and languages. The most celebrated of them, the *Physiologus*, dates back to the early part of the fourth century (it is referred to by Epiphanius in his controversy with Origen, one of the early church fathers who flourished during the first half of the third century), but editions continued to appear as late as the thirteenth century.

According to Janson (1952), the earliest mediaeval writer whose treatment of any primate goes beyond conventional ideas derived from Isidore or the Bestiaries is Hildegard of Bingen, a mid-twelfth century German nun who compiled a medical compendium, the *Physica*. This is largely a materia medica incorporating many supposed remedies of animal origin. One of the few animals to which remedial properties were not, however, attributed, is the ape. Notwithstanding this, the authoress discourses on many aspects of simian behaviour, recounting many similarities with Man, and drawing attention particularly to the fact that the she-ape exhibits a menstrual cycle governed by the moon. Hildegard upheld Galen's doctrine of " humours " and attributed a " hot constitution " to the ape ; but all this was tinged with ideas culled from the Bestiaries and used in support of her theological opinions, and cosmological concepts.

The thirteenth century is noted in the history of science for the labours of the encyclopaedists—clerics and scholars who attempted to commit to paper all the known facts (as well as many fancies) concerning the natural world. None made original observations, being content, for the most part, to draw upon their predecessors, especially Solinus, Isidore and others, but their labours indicate the beginnings of a revival in interest in natural phenomena. Five encyclopaedists are worthy of mention in respect of ape-lore, two Englishmen, a Fleming, a Frenchman and a German. Their varied contributions have been considered in detail by Janson (1952), but a brief reference to each is warranted here.

The most important encyclopaedic work at the turn of the thirteenth century is that of Alexander Neckham (1157–1217), a native of St. Albans, Hertfordshire, who became abbot of Cirencester. His *De naturis rerum* includes many stories concerning the attributes of apes, more especially those relating to their imitative capacities. One, which is derived from an earlier (*c.* 1200) account by Jacques de Vitry, was to the effect that monkeys could be captured by the hunter putting on boots weighted with lead, the animals watching from a distance ; he takes them off and goes away, leaving the boots behind. The apes, imitating his action, put on the boots and, being thereby impeded in their escape, readily fall to their would-be capturer. Neckham uses this story, and others of like nature, as levers to bolster his moral allegories, but also to put on record as complete a picture as was then possible of the nature and behaviour of the animal. Anecdotal material is richer in Neckham's writings than in any previous compiler's, though it is hard to determine how original this might be.

The writings of four renowned encyclopaedists enrich the literature of the mid-thirteenth century, all of whom make some reference to monkeys: these are Thomas of Cantimpré, Bartholomaeus Anglicus, Vincent de Beauvais and Albertus Magnus.

Probably earliest chronologically is Thomas of Cantimpré (born between 1186 and 1210 ; died between 1271 and 1280), a Fleming from Brabant who studied at Liège and entered the Dominican order. His *De natura rerum* was a popular encyclopaedia completed between 1228 and 1244. Thomas ably compares part for part the physical similarities between ape and man, drawing largely upon Aristotle, but denies the latter's statement of corresponding internal similarities. He contrasts the ape's lack of navel with its conspicuousness in Man ; he admits that the vulva of the female resembles that of a woman, but declares the *virga* of the male to be more like a dog's. One wonders if he was aware of the presence of a baculum, to give him this idea. As usual, all these qualities are adapted to explain and foster Christian dogma.

Bartholomew the Englishman (fl. 1250), a Franciscan cleric, had a genuine interest in natural history. His *De proprietatibus rerum*, originally issued in Cologne, comprised nineteen books and included sections on psychology, physiology, medicine, animals and other natural phenomena. His material derives from the classical writers—partly via Avicenna ; Aristotle's statement concerning the similarity of simian and human internal structure, refuted by Thomas, is here quoted without comment. Bartholomew's interpretation of the simian nature is less tinged with religious aura than that of his predecessors, albeit he refers to the ape as a " monstrous beast ", yet he credits it with a high degree of intelligence in so far as it can be taught many tricks. He avers that in diet the ape is omnivorous, resorting even to vermin, which it will pick off people's heads, a clear indication that the grooming propensity had been recognized, though misinterpreted.

Vincent de Beauvais (Vincentius Bellovacensis), another contemporary of Thomas of Cantimpré, was born probably in the later half of the twelfth century. He became a member of the Dominican order, and subprior of a monastery at Beauvais. Tutor to Louis IX and his sons, he produced an immense encyclopaedia entitled *Speculum maius*, material for which was drawn from Aristotle, Pliny, Dioscorides, the *Physiologus* and many later sources, including Thomas and Albertus Magnus. It follows the general pattern of Thomas's work, but completely lacks the moralizations. An elaborate discussion on apes occupies three chapters, but includes nothing from direct observation; in fact it would seem to have been Vincent's principle to eschew any personal ideas or opinions. Every statement is credited to its source, so that historiographically it is of greater importance than most contemporary writings.

By far the most outstanding in merit and originality, however, was the monumental *De animalibus* of Albertus Magnus (Albrecht von Bollstadt, 1193–1280), a scholastic philosopher, born in Swabia of a noble family and educated at Padua, who paid particular attention to Aristotelian learning. Receiving a doctorate from Paris, he taught there for a time, becoming a Provincial of his order and finally Bishop of Ratisbon.

Whereas, however, earlier writers had established a two-fold category of animate beings, *i.e.* Man and beasts, Albert is the first to introduce a third, namely man-like creatures (*similitudines hominis*), thus introducing the earliest conception of a missing link or an attempt to bridge the gap between human and non-human. Incidentally, the third category is regarded as the product of degradation from the human level and was consequently linked with the theological doctrine of the fall of man. It included all kinds of *monstra*, pygmies and the like, besides simians in the stricter sense.

There are scattered references to apes in Albertus's works, but most are in a chapter entitled *Symia*. This recounts all the data from Thomas of Cantimpré (except for the allegory), with a few additions borrowed from Bartholomaeus Anglicus. A single statement relating to the *spinga* (= sphinga, sphynx) seems to be based on personal observation. He identified this animal with the Meerkatze, describing it as compounded of ape and wild cat, with two black spots on its cheeks and a very long grey tail, tipped with black. Other categories of simians seem to be somewhat confused in Albertus's mind, for his groupings are not as clear-cut as in Isidore's earlier listing. Thus Albertus maintains that *cythosical* (presumably a corruption of *cercopithecus*) is a synonym of *spinga*, as is also *mamonetus*, a term derivable from the Persian name for an ape, *maimon*. Without using the name *callithrix*, he gives a correct description of the variety so named by Isidore, referring to them merely as Ethiopian apes that cannot survive outside their chosen habitat, features which point to the Guereza as being the prototype. Neither *Cynocephali* nor *Satyri* are discussed by Albertus, save that the former is intended under the appellation *canina simia*, but a chapter dealing with the *Pilosus* is possibly based on vague stories concerning an anthropoid ape, though distorted by attributes derived from pagan ideas of satyrs : *e.g.* it is shaped like a man above the waist and like a goat below ; it is relegated to the *genus symiarum*.

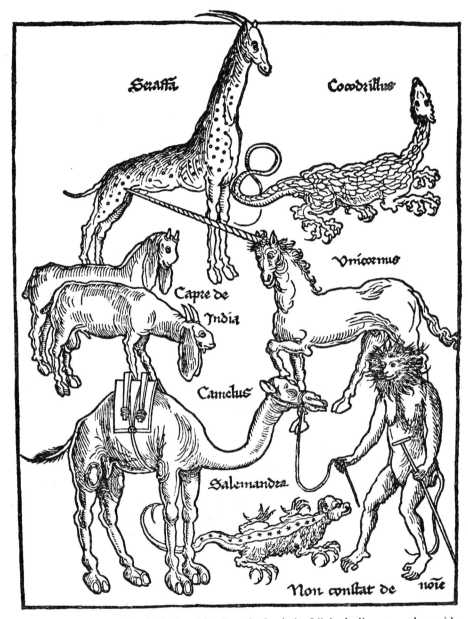

FIG. 1.—Various animals depicted by Breydenbach (1486) including an anthropoid primate presumably based on a Lion-tailed Macaque (*Macaca silenus*)

Albertus also devotes a long chapter to comparative anatomy of apes and Man, but he accepts, like his predecessors, only the presence of the attribute *ratio* as the determinant for human status.

In the thirteenth century Europeans began to travel again to distant parts, returning to write accounts of their experiences and their encounters with strange animals. Earliest among them was the Venetian Marco Polo

(?1254–1325) who, with his father and uncle, journeyed overland to China, where he spent many years, returning partly by sea. He is known to have travelled in Persia, India, Tibet, Burma, China, Japan, Java and Sumatra. He dictated his memoirs to a writer, Rusticiano of Pisa, and they were eventually published as *The Book of Ser Marco Polo*. One of his reminiscences related to the custom of the natives of Basura, a province of Java, of embalming the bodies of monkeys (? gibbons) and selling them as pygmies or mermaids—a deceitful practice still employed to tempt the unwary.

In 1486 Bernard von Breydenbach, Canon of Mainz, published his *Reyss in das gelobt Land*, one of the earliest printed books. It details his experiences in the Holy Land and contains references to giraffes and long-tailed monkeys. Yerkes and Yerkes (1929) reproduce a figure from this work showing various animals including an erect, tailed, man-like creature bearing outstanding hairs around its face. It recalls in almost every detail an illustration published by Buffon (1756) as representing a Douc (*Pygathrix nemaeus*) from Cochin China.

The Berber traveller John Leo (Leo Africanus) in the fifteenth century wrote an account of his journeying in northern and central Africa which was published (1550) in Italian. He employed the name *mone* for the first time for a monkey, and his description fits well the species now known by that name. Nevertheless he explained the term as being a generic one employed by the Moors for any long-tailed species and gave alternate spellings in Spanish and Provençal vernaculars.

By the mid-sixteenth century, when the Renaissance was well under way, we encounter the earliest encyclopaedic writers, beginning with the Swiss Konrad Gesner (1516–1565), who in his *Historiae animalium* Lib. I, *De quadrupedibus viviparis* (1551) brings Pliny up to date, adding much that is new whilst deleting the more fanciful elements from Pliny's uncritical catalogues. He also drew information from Diodorus, Avicenna and Albertus Magnus. Gesner treated all monkeys under the name *simia*, but mentions such subdivisions as *cercopithecus* (tailed forms which included guenons and macaques) and *cepus* (which seems to have been the Mona monkey). He reproduced von Breydenbach's anthropoid figure.

In Renaissance art the monkey takes its place at an early stage. Perhaps the earliest certain knowledge regarding the mangabeys is the representation of a pair of White-collared Mangabeys (*Cercocebus torquatus*) in the painting " Two monkeys " (*c.* 1562) of Pieter Bruegel the elder, now in the Berlin Museum.

Another Venetian, Gasparo Balbi, a jeweller by trade, following in the wake of the Polos, set out from Venice in 1570 for the Indies. He met with long-tailed apes worshipped by the local population in India ; passing thence to Burma he found others that resembled " mountain cats " tied to the temples. These are the earliest references since ancient times to the langurs, held sacred almost everywhere in the east.

A short time later, important new information hailed from West Africa where the Portuguese had been busily colonizing. An Englishman, Andrew Battel, was captured in 1559 and held prisoner many years by the Portuguese in Angola. An account of his adventures is published in Samuel Purchas's *His Pilgrimes* (1613, but with many later editions, of which the important one from our point of view is that of 1625). Here Battel is reported as declaring the woods to be inhabited in plenty, notably by " baboones, monkies, apes and parrots " but also by " two kinds of monsters " of which the larger was called *Pongo* and the lesser *Engeco*. The former is stated to be the size of a man. There can be little doubt that Battel's *Pongo* is the gorilla and his *Engeco* a chimpanzee.

Meanwhile in 1591 Filippo Pigafetta published the experiences of a Portuguese soldier, Odoardo Lopez (Eduardo or Duarte Lopez), who had visited the Songo (= Congo) and met with creatures that can only be identified as chimpanzees. A curious illustration accompanies Pigafetta's report, showing two long-armed tailless apes being captured whilst they were in the act of putting on the traveller's boots. This is reproduced by Huxley (1894).

It suffices to mention the names only of Gotthard Artus (1603), Prosper Alpinus (fl. 1553–1617) and Clusius (1605), all of whom made passing references to various catarrhine apes and served as sources of information for the later encyclopaedists Ray and Buffon.

New references to Asiatic anthropoid apes appear in Louis Daniel Le Compte's *Nouveaux Mémoires sur l'état présent de la Chine* (Amsterdam, 1697) where general descriptions appear both of gibbon and orang-utan. More important were the reports of Francis Pyrard de Laval (1619) and Captain Richard Jobson (1623). Pyrard de Laval visited Sierra Leone and met with an ape called *barrus*, whose description agrees closely with the chimpanzee. On the other hand, Jobson, who visited the Gambia, wrote accurately concerning " munkies " and " babownes ", though some confusion is expressed in relation to the latter. The first part of the account is accurate, but the later portion is applicable to the chimpanzee. He particularly describes the social behaviour including social hierarchy, vocal manifestations and method of carrying the young among baboons; also the nest-building propensities, which clearly stem from a knowledge of the chimpanzee.

One of the greatest advances made in the study of the great apes was the work of the Dutch anatomist Nicolaus Tulp (Tulpius) (1641) who obtained and dissected an Indian satyr, which he described sufficiently accurately and in detail to be identified as an African chimpanzee. Only a few years later Tulp's countryman Jacob Bontius (1658) wrote unmistakably about the Bornean orang, though illustrated with an inaccurate figure patently based upon a hirsute human female.

Still another restless Dutchman around this period, Olfert Dapper (1676), visited West Africa. His work, originally published in Flemish, was, in 1686, translated into French. He gives vague references to a " satyr " called by the negroes *quojas-morrou* and by the Portuguese *salvage*. It would appear to refer to a chimpanzee rather than a gorilla, an opinion which receives confirmation from his statement that thirty to forty years previously one had been sent alive to Prince Frederick Henry of the Netherlands ; and this was presumably the specimen dissected by Tulp. Dapper knew of at least two other monkeys ; they may have been guenons or mangabeys, but his descriptions are too imprecise for certainty.

Meanwhile Georg Marcgrav (1648) published in Amsterdam his *Historia rerum naturalium Brasiliae*, based on his travels in company with W. Piso, a botanist. Although this is one of the earliest works on South American zoology, it contains a few references to West African primates, especially guenons. Of special interest is the animal named *exquima*, which Ogilby (p. 346) interprets to be a Roloway (*Cercopithecus diana roloway*) since Marcgrav declared its home to be Guinea and the Congo. Buffon, however, interpreted Marcgrav's figure as showing a prehensile tail and convinced himself that the *exquima* must be a *sapajou* (*vide* vol. v, p. 359). Nevertheless, other decidedly African species are mentioned by Marcgrav ; for instance, he gives a vague description of a guenon which Linnaeus used as a basis for his *Simia cephus*, and to which Buffon gave the name *moustache*. Marcgrav is also the first to introduce the term macaque in its original Portuguese form *macac*—presumably based on a native name for some African species, although nowadays used for an Asiatic genus.

The celebrated Jesuit virtuoso Athanasius Kircher (1602–1680) contributed a chapter in the work of John Nieuhoff (1669), describing his expedition to China undertaken in 1665. It is stated that " The province of Fokien hath an animal perfectly resembling man, but longer armed and hairy all over, called *Fesse*, most swift and greedy after human flesh ", presumably a garbled account of some gibbon. Also mentioned as inhabitants of China and India are apes and baboons of a different kind, evidently large macaques and also possibly langurs.

Various other travelogues of the period were used as source books by Ray, Buffon, Pennant and other systematizers, notably the accounts of voyages by Pietro della Valle (1665), de Gennes (edited by Froger, 1698) and Andre Brué (1697) among others.

More important perhaps were the voyages (1658–1665) of Gautier Schouten to the East Indies and of Jacob Ludolf (Ludolphus) in 1682 to Abyssinia, and also the experiences of the English seaman Robert Knox (1681) in Ceylon. Schouten described the orang-utan without addition,

C

however, of any new facts, but with repetition of earlier tales derived from native sources.

Ludolf's account of his Ethiopian travels contains many quaint allusions to the monkeys found there, notably concerning baboons. He also alludes to the Guereza (*Colobus abyssinicus*) for the first time since antiquity, albeit his figure of the animal is based on a Black-pencilled Marmoset (*Hapale penicillata*). He ascribes the name *guereza* to the Amharic language; in Ethiopian it is called *foukes*.

Knox's career recalls that of his countryman Battel (*supra*, p. 16), for he was a prisoner in Ceylon for nearly twenty years. His captivity limited his observations to the central hills of the island, but gave him ample opportunity for observing the types of monkeys and their habits. He gives the earliest accurate account, under the Sinhalese epithet *wanderoo*, of the Purple-faced Monkey (*Kasi senex*) so named later by Pennant, contrasting them with the smaller reddish macaque which he affirms is called *rillowe* (a distortion of Sinhala *rilawa*).

The closing year of the seventeenth century saw the appearance of the most epoch-making contribution to primatology thus far : *The Anatomy of a Pygmie Compared with That of a Monkey, an Ape and a Man* by the English anatomist Edward Tyson. Tyson's "pygmie" was a young chimpanzee which had recently been brought from West Africa. As the title indicates, he compares the structure organ by organ with those of other known Primates and with their human counterparts also, thus anticipating modern methods of investigation.

The confusion between Asiatic and African anthropoid apes, both of which continued to be referred to as orangs, was maintained during the whole of the eighteenth century. This was initiated by Tulp, who first used the name *orang-utan*, but applied it to a chimpanzee. In spite of Tyson's work the error persisted. Numerous references to the Asiatic animal occur during the early eighteenth century, notably from Schouten (1707), Le Guat (1708), who obtained a live orang in Java but which died on its way back to Europe; Beeckman (1718) and Carreri (1727) both of whom possessed living orangs; and du Halde (1735). Carreri records the old tale of how monkeys prise open oysters by wedging stones between the valves.

Bosman (1705), on the other hand, describes various apes from West Africa, among them a *Colobus* and another that he calls *smitten*. The latter is one of the native names of the Mandrill, but Bosman's account shows some confusion with the Chimpanzee though its fawn colour seems to argue in favour of the Mandrill. Indubitable references to chimpanzees are contained in the accounts of de la Brosse (1738), Thomas Boreman (1739) and the engraver Scotin (1739). The two latter produced curious anthropomorphic figures of the animal; Boreman's account owes much to Tyson, but he evidently examined a female brought to England in 1738, whose manners he outlines in more detail. Further data are found in the writings of William Smith (1744), who relates some native stories of apes and monkeys and illustrates his account by a curious figure designated " Mandrill " which, however, again shows confusion with the anthropoid ape. Another visitor to the Guinea coast, John Barbot (1746), details the usual commonplaces of his predecessors.

This brings the history of the Old World Primates to the time of the great French compiler, G. L. Leclerc, Comte de Buffon, whose encyclopaedic *Histoire naturelle* began to appear in 1756. This great work monographs all the apes and monkeys known at the time, with reasonably good figures combined with anatomical descriptions provided by Daubenton, based on animals dying in the Jardin des Plantes. Buffon relied for much of his information on the numerous travellers to distant tropical climes, some of whom have been mentioned above ; but he also made many personal observations on animals in the royal menagerie or in private ownership.

About the same time Linnaeus was cataloguing the animal kingdom, giving short diagnoses of the recognized apes and monkeys and, for the first time, employing the binomial nomenclature, which, since 1758, has been adopted universally among zoologists. Linnaeus, however, recognized only two genera of Old World Primates as now understood, namely *Homo* and *Simia*. Under *Homo* he included both Man and the tailless anthropoids ; all other monkeys fell under his all-embracing *Simia*. (See, however, *infra* under *Cercopithecus*, p. 389.)

Worthy of mention at this point is the English painter-naturalist George Edwards, who described (1758) and illustrated a number of simians for the first time, among them the Pig-tailed Macaque (*Macaca nemestrina*). This was the basis of the *Maimon* of Buffon. Edwards also figured the monkey shortly afterwards named Talapoin by Buffon.

In 1759, according to Allamand, a Flemish naturalist, two live orangs were taken to Europe by a M. Pallavicini, and prior to their embarkation they were under observation by M. Relian, a surgeon practising in Batavia. This author remarked on the human features of these apes and bewails the lack of knowledge of the adult animal in the wild—an omission shortly to be rectified to some extent by van Wurmb (1781), to whom we also owe the first account of the Proboscis monkey (*Nasalis larvatus*). Hoppius (1760), a pupil of Linnaeus, had also lamented upon the lack of information concerning mature orangs in their natural habitat. Chimpanzees are again the subject of attention by Lt. J. Matthews, R.N., who was resident at Sierra Leone (1785–1787). He referred to them as " japanzees ". Further details on gibbons appear in the writings of de Visme (1769) and van Iperen and Schouman (1784) among several less important publications of the period.

The celebrated Dutch anatomist Camper (1770) ably followed the tradition set by Tyson ; dealing with the orang-utan as Tyson had done with the chimpanzee, comparing its structure system by system with that of Man. He paid special attention to the vocal apparatus and initiated new ideas in craniology, especially in the use of the facial angle. Another anatomist of the period was Vicq d'Azyr (1792), whose work on the comparative anatomy of the brain deserves special mention. John Hunter's work stands in a category apart from all others. Although his results remained for the most part unpublished during his lifetime its general impress on contemporary thought was immense. His approach was from the functional viewpoint and consequently of great value in the interpretation of human physiology. His knowledge of the Primates was considerable and he spared no effort to obtain specimens and to have their details recorded by artists like Stubbs, many of whose works are to be seen in the Hunterian Museum of the Royal College of Surgeons in London.

Thomas Pennant (1781), the British counterpart of Buffon, was responsible for first drawing attention to some of the species of the genus *Colobus*, skins of which he found in the museum of Sir Ashton Lever. Pennant also described and figured the Mandrill under the name Rib-faced Baboon, whilst his Wood Baboon probably pertains to the Drill (*Mandrillus leucophaeus*), though F. Cuvier later identified it with one of the black Celebesian apes.

The closing year of the eighteenth century, exactly a century later than the epoch-making work of Tyson, saw the appearance of a similar landmark : the magnificent coloured atlas of the known Primates, the work of J. Audebert (1799). In this publication the name Rhesus is applied for the first time to the common macaque of Bengal.

The early years of the nineteenth century are marked by considerable activity on the part of colonial administrators, travellers and explorers in bringing to Europe living or preserved examples of Old World Primates, and by the systematic description thereof on the part of the Parisian naturalists, E. Geoffroy Saint-Hilaire and the two Cuviers, the elder, Baron G. Cuvier, a celebrated comparative anatomist and palaeontologist, and his younger brother Fréderic, who had charge of the Paris menagerie, the contents of which served as a basis for the description and illustration of many new species of Old World Primates (F. Cuvier, 1818 *et seq.*).

Among the British, the activities of Thomas Stamford Raffles (1781–1826) stand out particularly. Raffles was administrator in the East India Company's service, becoming Governor of Java—until the island was ceded to the Dutch—and later residing in Sumatra and Singapore. Returning to England with vast zoological collections, he lived in retirement and, together with N. A. Vigors, Thomas Horsfield and others, founded in 1826 the Zoological Society of London. His contributions to knowledge of simians included new observations on the orang, on gibbons, especially the Siamang (*Symphalangus syndactylus*), on various langurs, including the Proboscis monkey and on the Pig-tailed and Crab-eating Macaques.

In earnest competition with Raffles were the French naturalists, Diard and Duvaucel, both of whom were sent out by the Cuviers on collecting expeditions in the Malayan region. Diard is to be particularly remembered for obtaining the Douc (*Pygathrix nemaeus*) from Cochin China, whilst Duvaucel gave the first good account of the Entellus monkey (*Semnopithecus entellus*) besides collecting gibbons.

Oriental zoology was furthered about this time by the researches of Hardwicke and Hodgson (who both worked on Himalayan zoology) and by Thomas Horsfield, who had worked under Raffles in Java and whose *Zoological Researches in Java* was published in 1824. In this appears the first description of the Negro Langur (*Trachypithecus cristatus*). Hodgson also discovered a new langur, namely *Semnopithecus schistaceus*. In all this new access of information relative to oriental primates, the name of Edward Blyth (1801–1873) calls for special note. As curator of the Calcutta Museum, established by the Asiatic Society of Bengal, Blyth was at the receiving end of the vast quantity of material collected over a wide area both in India and beyond. Paying special attention to monkeys, he described at least a dozen new species, including langurs from India and Ceylon (the latter forwarded to him by a local zoologist, E. Kelaart) and macaques from Burma, the Himalayas and the Andamans.

Meanwhile the Dutch had been busy in their Indonesian possessions, largely at the instigation of C. J. Temminck (1770–1858), the wealthy conservator of the Leyden Museum, who commissioned a succession of collectors to obtain material for the museum. Notable among these, from the primatological standpoint, were Kuhl, who founded a research station at Buitenzorg, and S. Müller, who discovered several new monkeys and produced an important monograph (1839–1845) on his finds in collaboration with H. Schlegel and edited by Temminck. Schlegel, who became Temminck's successor in Leyden, trained a further group of collectors, besides producing an important monograph (1876) on the then known Primates.

Earlier monographic revisions had already been completed by Jardine (1845–1846), I. Geoffroy Saint-Hilaire (1851), zoologist of the Paris Museum, and in Germany by G. L. Reichenbach (1862), J. A. Wagner (1840) and the English zoologist, J. E. Gray (1870), the last mentioned based on material in the British Museum. Subsequent to the receipt of materials from the Raffles collections, new specimens had been accumulating in London from collectors like A. R. Wallace, Müller's rival in Indonesia, and from the death of monkeys in the menagerie of the London Zoological Society that had, during their life, been described as types of new species by those assiduous members of the Society's staff, E. T. Bennett, G. R. Waterhouse, W. Ogilby and, somewhat later, P. L. Sclater.

Knowledge of Ethiopian primates was carried forward at this time as a

result of the labours of several expeditions, notably those of Hemprich and
Ehrenberg (1828–1845) in north-eastern Africa and of Rüppell (1843) in
Abyssinia. The former expedition recognized the Nisnas (*Erythrocebus
pyrronotus*) as a distinct form from the already well-known Patas (*E. patas*),
whilst Rüppell's collections included such novelties as the Gelada (*Theropithecus*) and several varieties of *Colobus*.

Many of the newer discoveries were made known by the zoologists
attached to the Paris Museum and menageries, especially the Geoffroys,
father and son, and the two Cuviers. In 1820 Desmarest published his
general work on mammals and he included the newly recognized Black
Baboon of Celebes, named *Cynocephalus niger*. This was transferred to a
new genus *Cynopithecus* by the younger Geoffroy (1835). Meantime F.
Cuvier (1823) had described the strange Celebesian macaque (*Macaca maura*),
of which other varieties were afterwards recognized by Ogilby (1840) and
Meyer (1899). I. Geoffroy, between 1834 and 1850, introduced many new
or supposedly new species to science before producing his monographic
catalogue in 1851, whilst F. Cuvier compiled a valuable atlas of the Primates
he had observed alive during his tenure of the directorship of the menagerie
in the Jardin des Plantes. Other contemporary French participators in the
furthering of our knowledge were Prince Lucien Bonaparte (who described
in 1856 a remarkable new langur, *P. potenziani*), J. Pucheran, E. Rivière
and E. de Pousargues, while A. T. Rochebrune (1883–1884) is especially
to be remembered for his monographic revision of the African *Colobus*
monkeys, of which an aberrant new species had recently (1838) been introduced to science by the Belgian zoologist P. J. van Beneden.

The year 1847 marks an epoch in the history of primatology inasmuch
as the gorilla was first officially introduced to orthodox science and its
existence established by physical evidence. Although a rather vague account
had been published by T. E. Bowdich (1819), a missionary in Ashanti, it
was left to another medical missionary, Thomas Savage (1847), to advise
the celebrated London anatomist, Richard Owen, that there was, in West
Africa, an ape larger than a chimpanzee, and of this he sent drawings of the
skull. Savage himself published a description of the animal, giving it the
name *Troglodytes gorilla* to distinguish it from *T. niger*—the name by which
the chimpanzee was then known.

Two other skulls from the Gabon, in French Equatorial Africa, were
also received by Owen and duly described, and meantime Wilson, another
missionary, forwarded a skull to Boston ; this was described and figured by
Wyman (1847). These illuminating discoveries led to an enthusiastic search
by numerous hunters for this elusive primate. Early in the field was the
notorious Paul du Chaillu, who shot several gorillas in the Gabon (1855–
1865) and wrote somewhat colourful accounts of his experiences. Many of
his stories were received with incredulity thereby stimulating others,

notably a young Englishman, Winwood Reade, to visit the gorilla country to confirm or deny these accounts. The first living gorilla reached England in 1860, but survived only a few months (*Proc. zool. Soc.*, 1876) ; a second arrived in Germany in 1876.

The later decades of the nineteenth century are remarkable for the large numbers of new and interesting Old World monkeys that came to be described, either from living specimens in European menageries or from skins collected in the field. One of the most prolific students was A. Milne-Edwards, who between 1870 and 1898 described many new Asiatic species (macaques and langurs) and also a new *Colobus* (*C. tholloni*). Most remarkable among these was a representative of a completely new genus *Rhinopithecus*, from China, collected by the renowned Père Armand David, to which Milne Edwards added a further species *R. bieti* in 1898. John Anderson also discovered new Asiatic primates incorporating these in his scholarly *Anatomical and Zoological Researches* (1878) reporting the results of two expeditions in 1868 and 1875 to western Yunnan. Likewise W. T. Blanford, a student of Indian mammals, following Jerdon, an army surgeon, revised all the then known primates of his area in the widely known series *Fauna of British India* (1888). The well-known English systematist, Oldfield Thomas, had already (1889) commenced adding to a long list of new primate forms, a subject with which his name has become associated. His activities continued for at least another thirty-five years, during which period he contributed accounts of new langurs (*e.g. Presbytis hosei, P. cruciger, P. sabana*), among others. Following on Peters, a German zoologist who first described (1879) the Crested Mangabey (*Cercocebus galeritus*), Rivière (1886) added *C. agilis*, and the Dutchman, Oudemans (1890), the remarkable new Black Mangabey (*C. aterrimus*) from the Congo. Meyer introduced new forms from the Philippines and Celebes, notably, previously unknown varieties of *Macaca maura* and of *Cynopithecus*. Lydekker (1900) added further to the catalogue of known mangabeys and around the same time Paul Matschie of the Berlin Museum vied with Oldfield Thomas in the numbers of new names introduced to describe supposedly valid species or subspecies of African monkeys and anthropoid apes—especially from the then German colonial territories. Perhaps his most outstanding contribution was the recognition in 1903 of the Mountain Gorilla (*Gorilla beringei*).

R. I. Pocock added materially to our knowledge of most groups of Primates commencing with his early studies on sexual phenomena, the careful recordings of external characters, and the reviews of difficult genera such as *Cercocebus* (1906), *Cercopithecus* (1907) and *Hylobates* (1927) as well as by his later contributions to Indian mammalogy, ending with his authoritative revision of Blanford's treatise.

Other outstanding contributions during the present century have been G. S. Miller's description (1903) of a remarkable new Langur genus (*Simias*) from the Pagi Islands near Sumatra and of a new (dwarf) type of Siamang; Rothchild's (1904) on the anthropoid apes; Dollman's (1909) on new *Colobus* species and more important still (1912) his description of the remarkable new snub-nosed monkey (*Presbytiscus*) from Tonkin.

One of the most critical modern students of Old World monkeys has been E. Schwarz (1889–1961), who systematically revised, in succession, the genera *Cercocebus* (1910, 1928), *Cercopithecus* (1926, 1928) and *Colobus* (1929); but most outstanding perhaps of all the recent additions to the primate list is his recognition in 1929 of the Pygmy Chimpanzee (*Pan paniscus*), afterwards studied in greater detail by Coolidge (1933) and Frechkop (1935). Coolidge (1929) had earlier carefully revised the genus *Gorilla*, concluding that only two recognizable forms existed.

Progress in aspects of the Catarrhini other than taxonomic was later in gaining impetus, but a steady stream of anatomical discoveries has been maintained since the earliest contributions of Volcher Coiter (1534–?1600), who published his comparative osteological studies in 1573. Notable contributors have been Claude Perrault (1613–1688), who published (1666–1699) anatomical accounts of several monkeys, while Riolan fils (1577–1657) produced a comparative osteology of monkey and Man in 1628. Buffon was ably assisted in the anatomical parts of his encyclopaedic work by L. J. M. Daubenton (1716–1799), whose studies were later supplemented, especially as regards the brain, by F. Vicq d'Azyr (1792, 1805). The contributions of Tulpius (1641), Tyson (1699), Camper (1784, 1791) and Hunter (1786) have already been mentioned (*supra*, pp. 16, 18, 20). The last mentioned left much unpublished material, some of which was ultimately made available, some say plagiarized, by his brother-in-law, Sir Everard Home.

During the nineteenth century an important discovery was that made by Otto (1825) of the peculiarities of the stomach in Colobidae, followed by more detailed studies by Owen, who also contributed to many other branches of primate anatomy, especially of the anthropoid apes.

Twentieth-century anatomical work is best reviewed in correlation with the organs concerned, but the annals of this epoch will be rendered perhaps more remarkable by the emergence of scientific behavioural studies, and such aspects as haematology, serology, caryology and other disciplines which are assisting increasingly in the determination of the phylogenetic interrelations of primate species.

Palaeontology was rather late in developing. The absence of Primates from the fossil record was, in fact, a potent weapon in the armoury of the anti-evolutionists.

Perhaps the earliest find was that of a fossil femur found by Schleiermacher (1820) in the Lower Pliocene beds at Eppelsheim, near Mainz. Its primate affinities were not recognized at the time, nor indeed until after undoubted primate fossils had been recovered from elsewhere. Although the femur was examined by Kaup, Lartet and Owen, all of whom considered it affined to the gibbons, it received no scientific name until 1895 when Pohlig designated it *Paidopithex rhenanus*.

Meantime some controversy arose, largely due to an oversight on the part of Owen (1846), as to whom credit was due for the unearthing of the earliest primate fossil.

In 1830 Hugh Falconer (1808–1865) proceeded to India as an assistant-surgeon in the East India Company's service. The following year he was posted to Sahararunpore, whence he soon made expeditions to the Siwalik Hills at the foot of the Himalayas. He determined the deposits here to be of Tertiary age, in the absence of confirmatory evidence of animal remains, prophesying that such would eventually be forthcoming. With his friend Cautley, Falconer soon had proof, and their joint researches were soon followed, before the end of 1834, by the discovery, by Baker and Durand, of the great bone-bearing beds near the valley of the Murkunda, and below Nahun. The first fossil primate material was recovered in 1836 in the form of a talus of *Semnopithecus*, and recognized as such by Falconer by November of that year, although the published description did not appear until the following year (Cautley and Falconer, 1837). Meantime, however, Baker and Durand (November 1836) had described an anthropoid mandible and another jaw fragment, affined to *Semnopithecus*, which they had re-covered from the Siwalik deposits. This material is now in the British Museum.

Meantime, unknown to Falconer, some fossil primates had been revealed in Europe. Firstly, in 1837 Lartet described an almost complete lower jaw of an ape which he attributed to *Hylobates*. This specimen had been dis-covered in freshwater Tertiary strata in southern France. It was subsequently examined by Blainville (1841), who assigned it to a position nearer the monkeys.

In England some mandibular and dental fossils were recovered during 1838 and 1839, by W. Colchester, from similar deposits on the banks of the River Deben in Suffolk. These were examined by Lyell and Owen. Owen correctly assigned them to the genus *Macacus* and supposed they were of Eocene date, but this was later (1862) retracted.

Further evidence of Miocene apes on the Continent continued to appear. Of prime importance was the large anthropoid *Dryopithecus*, the first jaw fragment and a humerus of which were recovered in 1856 at Saint Gaudens, and described and named by Lartet. Isolated teeth of the same genus were subsequently recovered from the Swabian alps. Further study in France of the gibbon-like fossil referred to above led Gervais (1849) to propose a new genus *Pliopithecus* for its reception, and twenty years later Biedermann (1869) added a second species to the genus, based on an upper jaw found

near Zürich.　An important find from the Middle Miocene lignite beds
at Monte Bamboli in Tuscany represented a large creature almost the size
of *Dryopithecus*.　It was named　*Oreopithecus* by Gervais (1872).　Some
palaeontologists placed it with the great apes, others in the Cynomorpha.　In
spite of more recent finds of the same genus, it still proves a bone of contention.　Practically the entire skeleton is now known, thanks to the energies
of the Swiss palaeontologist, J. Hürzeler.

Rich Lower Pliocene deposits, containing many simian fossils amongst
others, were revealed in the later years of the nineteenth century at Pikermi,
near Athens in Greece.　A French palaeontologist, Gaudry, forwarded to
Paris material from at least twenty-five individuals, while other remains
were taken (1838) to Münich by a soldier.　Among the latter was an almost
complete skeleton of a monkey which Wagner (1839) made the basis of a
new genus *Mesopithecus*, in so far as its teeth and skull affined it with *Semnopithecus*, while the skeleton recalled that of *Macaca*.　From beds of similar
age at Steinheim in Württemberg other *Semnopithecus*-like fossils recovered
were five mandibles which Fraas (1870) attributed to a new species, *S.
grandaevus*.　Still other fossils were yielded from Pliocene deposits at
Montpellier and named *S. monspessulanus* by Gervais.　Another fossil from
Perpignan, France, was separated by Depéret (1889) as representing a genus
Dolichopithecus.　Macaques also were apparently contemporaneous, *M.
priscus* being named by Gervais, whilst new finds from Grays, Essex, England,
were named *M. pliocenus* by Owen.

Another French palaeontologist, Lapouge, in 1894, described a fragment
from the Pliocene beds at Montpellier under the name *Anthropodus*, considering it to be from an anthropoid ape.

In the late 1870s and 1880s the importance of the Siwalik deposits to
the palaeontological history of the Primates became increasingly emphasized.
These beds included strata of both Miocene and Pliocene age.　They had
by now yielded remains of macaques, baboons and langurs, and also important
relics of larger types of anthropoid status though more generalized than the
recent forms.　R. Lydekker of the Geological Survey made new discoveries
in this field, notably of the jaws of a large ape he named *Sivapithecus*, but
the most outstanding and far-reaching developments did not take place
till the early years of the present century under the guidance of G. E.
Pilgrim and still later of American expeditions (*vide* reports by Brown,
Gregory and Hellman (1924), Lewis (1934) and Gregory and Hellman
(1939)).

Around 1900 the Oligocene deposits of the Fayûm beds in Egypt had
become known largely due to expeditions sent by Fraas of Stuttgart and
of expeditions, especially by H. F. Osborn, sponsored by the American
Museum.　The field work was carried out by Markgraf.　Results were
reported on by Osborn (1908), Schwalbe (1909), Schlosser (1911) and Stromer

(1913). Most spectacular was the mandible of *Parapithecus* named by Schlosser and studied later by Werth (1918), Gregory (1916) and others. It seemed to bridge the gap between prosimians and Catarrhini. Schlosser also created the genus *Propliopithecus* to receive fragmentary remains of a contemporary gibbon-like anthropoid, recalling the already well-known *Pliopithecus*, though much more ancient.

One of the most intriguing discoveries was that of the first so-called ape-man. Although a few fossils definitely attributable to early human beings had been known from various sites, dating from the 1848 discovery of Gibraltar Man, the phylogenetic history of human lineage was, in Darwin's time and for long afterwards, more or less conjectural. E. Haeckel, Darwin's principal protagonist in Germany, was full of conjectures and lost no time in building a picture of a hypothetical transitional being between ape and Man. He went so far as to give it a name, *Pithecanthropus alalus*. This so fired the imagination of a young Dutch anatomist, E. Dubois, that he took service in the government of the Netherlands East Indies for the sole purpose of using his spare time searching for fossil evidence to substantiate Haeckel's hypothesis. After many disappointments, he found what he was looking for, and brought back to Europe a skull cap, a femur and some teeth which he startled the world by describing as *Pithecanthropus erectus*. His finds remained long unique, in spite of other *ad hoc* expeditions, such as that of Selenka in 1908. The remainder of this story is too intricate to consider here, and may be conveniently deferred until the appropriate place in the sequel.

The only other major discovery meriting mention in this brief survey is that of the numerous fossils recovered from the bone breccias of South Africa and known collectively as the Australopithecinae. In 1925 Dart startled the scientific world by his announcement of the recovery, in 1924 from a quarry in Bechuanaland, of the almost complete skull, with a natural endocranial cast, of a being intermediate between ape and Man. He called it *Australopithecus africanus*. Dart's analysis and conclusions were severely criticized by his colleagues, largely because many of the man-like features of his specimen could be explained on grounds of its juvenility, and also possibly because, if accepted, the prevailing view that Man emerged in Asia would be undermined. Subsequent discovery by Broom, from 1936 onwards, of adult examples allied to or identical with *Australopithecus* completely changed the climate of opinion, though the exact taxonomic status of the australopithecines is still a matter for controversy. Further discoveries from East Africa by L. S. B. Leakey and his wife have been made with remarkable regularity during the last thirty years and serve to fill important gaps in the succession of primate (including human) forms from the Miocene apes *Proconsul* and *Limnopithecus* up to the Australopithecinae and Hominidae.

STRUCTURE

I. External Features

The Catarrhini include a wide variety of simian primates ranging in size from the largest existing species, the Gorilla, to the small African Talapoin (*Miopithecus*), which is scarcely larger than a squirrel-monkey (*Saimiri*). The range in size is even greater if fossil forms are taken into consideration, for *Gigantopithecus*, a fossil Orang from China, was much larger than a Gorilla, whilst *Parapithecus* was scarcely larger than a *Tarsius*. They are almost equally diverse in appearance, though on the whole they can be placed in two major categories, corresponding to the taxonomic division, Cynomorpha and Anthropomorpha, to use Huxley's classic terms. The cynomorphs are dog-shaped, *i.e.* fundamentally quadrupedal forms with the body carried normally in a horizontal (pronograde) position, with the face directed forwards and the skull hinged to the spine in such fashion that the foramen magnum is directed backwards as much as downwards. The Anthropomorpha, by contrast, present an orthograde or semi-upright posture with the skull hinged accordingly, so that the foramen magnum faces more downwards than backwards. Hence these forms—the anthropoid apes of English writers—are, to a certain degree, man-like or at least man-shaped. This is not to say, however, that the division is a particularly sharp one in the physiological sense. Cynomorph monkeys can and do raise themselves into an erect posture, especially momentarily in scanning the environment, though they do not normally progress any distance bipedally. They do, however, adopt an upright posture in sitting, the body then resting in the vertical position. Conversely anthropomorphs are not physiologically bipedal like Man. Like the cynomorphs, they rest in a vertical posture. In walking their bodies are sloped—with the shoulders considerably higher than the rump. This is due to the great disparity between the lengths of pectoral and pelvic limb, a feature which renders them orthograde or semi-erect even in quadrupedal progression—which is their usual mode of progression—except for the Hylobatidae. The last-mentioned approach Man more closely than any other of the anthropomorphs in respect of their more effective bipedality in terrestrial locomotion, as well as in their body proportions.

Reverting to the Cynomorpha, the epithet dog-shaped applies in a general way to all monkeys whether Old World or New World, but was originally and is more particularly applicable to the baboons, examples of which were termed dog-headed apes by the ancients. Their terrestrial cursorial adaptations have enhanced the dog-like appearance in many respects.

REGIONAL DETAILS (de Beaux, 1917, Pocock, 1925)

NASAL REGION.—Differs essentially from that of the Platyrrhini in the narrow nasal septum which, though broader above than below, does not separate the nares so widely. In consequence the external nares face downwards, or downwards and forwards rather than laterally. There are, however, variations. Just as in the Platyrrhini the genera *Aotes* and *Brachyteles* are stenorhine by New World standards so *Colobus* has, for an Old World monkey, a relatively broad nasal septum. In general the nose is not elevated above the general surface of the face to any great extent, but here, too, *Colobus* is exceptional, and the process seen in *Colobus* is carried to further extremes in certain of its Asiatic relatives, such as *Rhinopithecus* and *Nasalis*, with their grotesquely enlarged external noses. Certain gibbons also present some elevation of the nose, whilst in the African apes, especially *Gorilla*, though the central area of the nose is depressed, the alae are much padded so as to form broad facial prominences. Special features also distinguish the apex nasi of the baboons, where the whole muzzle departs considerably from the rounded, more or less flattened face of the more typical catarrhines.

LIPS.—Relatively deep and mobile in all forms ; in the Pongidae and *Theropithecus* they are specially mobile, being capable of considerable protrusion and eversion. The cheeks are provided with herniations of their mucous lining into the subcutaneous tissue of the throat in the Cercopithecidae, but not in the Colobidae or the Hominoidea.

EARS.—Essentially as in Platyrrhini as far as sculptural details are concerned, but vary considerably in size. They are specially large in *Pan* and in the young of baboons and macaques, but small in *Cercopithecus*, *Hylobates* and *Pongo*. Many, *e.g. Macaca, Papio*, retain some evidence of the morphological apex of the pinna in the shape of a tubercle (Darwin's or Woolner's tubercle), or prominence at the junction of the superior and posterior borders. Appearances here depend largely on the degree of rolling of the helix, this being very variable. (*Vide* Schwalbe, 1889 *a, b*, 1916 ; Wallis, 1897 ; Streeter, 1922.) In general the external ear stands well away from the head, especially in macaques, baboons and their allies, but is more adpressed in *Cercopithecus*, Colobidae, Hylobatidae, *Pongo* and *Gorilla*.

For the most part external ears are naked apart from sparse tufts on helix, tragus, antitragus, etc., but many forms present a pencil on or about the morphological apex (*e.g.* some species of *Cercopithecus*).

CHEIRIDIA.—In contrast to the Platyrrhini, the Catarrhini exhibit a fully opposable pollex, but the opposability occurs in several grades (Napier 1960, 1961). In the Miocene fossil *Proconsul*, the form of the metacarpophalangeal joint resembles that found in *Cebus* (Napier and Davis, 1959), but the angle of set of the pollex is slightly greater than in *Cebus*, and less than in *Pan*.

The fully opposable hand as found in a generalized catarrhine is distinguished from that of a platyrrhine by the independence of the pollex which, as shown by Midlo (1934), has migrated proximally, giving a deeper first interdigital cleft. There is, however, considerable variation in effectiveness of opposability, the ability to attain pulp to pulp contact of the apical pads of I and II depending on the relative lengths of the two digits. Its most perfect attainment occurs in *Homo*, and its least in *Pongo* ; in *Colobus*, with the pollex aborted, of course, the power is lacking and here the hand, as in the thumbless Ateleinae, is used purely as a hook. Napier, in the paper referred to, discusses the osteological and myological bases for the variations in manual prehensile power.

Regarding the functional anatomy of the hand, Napier (1956, 1960) has analysed the prehensile function of the human hand into two patterns, which he terms the power grip and the precision grip. In the power grip the dominant feature is the force applied, delicacy and precision being of secondary importance. In the precision grip the object is grasped between the palmar aspect of the terminal phalanx of the pollex and that of the index finger (or additional fingers), the power used being proportional to the weight of the object held.

Phylogenetically the precision grip is the more recently acquired and is scarcely indicated in Cercopithecoidea. Both grips occur in pongids, but Napier found the execution of the two differed profoundly from the pattern in the human hand on account of the disproportionate length of the thumb and fingers. Some measure of compensation for the relative ineffectiveness of the pongid grip is considered to be expressed in the phenomenon of double-locking of the fingers—a function which may be deduced from a study of passive movements of the pongid hand. Such movements compare closely with those of the human hand, except that, with the wrist-joint flexed, extension of digits is limited, while passive movements at the meta-carpo-phalangeal joints is very free and limited only by the contact of fingers and palm, the range being approximately 170° (compared with 90° in Man). Acutely flexed fingers can be locked into the cutaneous fold opposite the base of the digits and then, by further flexion, double-locked by rolling the locked digits into the palm, the apical pad of the digit then making contact with the palmar surface of the base of the intermediate phalangeal segment.

The digital formula varies slightly in the different groups, but III is always longest and I shortest, with II and IV equal or subequal and V shorter than either. All digits end in nails which vary from highly convex to very flat, that on the pollex inclining to be broader and flatter than those on other digits.

Flexure creases are well marked on the palm, the distal transverse crease commonly extending horizontally across the palm ; but in Man this crease is normally divorced into an ulnar and a radial component which do not meet, each running obliquely towards mid-palm, the radial lying more proximally and the ulnar turning distally towards the interdigital cleft between II and III—evidently a concomitant of the functional independence of the index finger. Palmar pads are not well marked, except during foetal life, but their sites are recognizable by virtue of their dermatoglyphic configurations. The latter vary greatly among the different genera and therefore need no special discussion here. (Bychowska, 1930; Wolff, 1938 *a* and *b*; Midlo and Cummins, 1942; Biegert, 1961.)

Regarding the pes, the only exceptional genus is *Homo*, where, in response to the erect posture, the grasping function has been lost, the hallux being brought into line with the remaining toes and incorporated into the weight-bearing longitudinal arch. Concomitant changes occur in other parts of the foot, notably in dermatoglyphic patterns, besides skeletal and myological adaptations (see especially Morton 1922, 1924; Wood Jones, 1944).

In all other catarrhines the pes shows the typical prehensile structure with widely divergent opposable hallux similar to that found in Platyrrhini and even in prosimians. Some intermediate states are occasionally met with in *Gorilla*, particularly the highland race (*G. beringei*) (Schultz, 1934). Digital formula of the foot, except in *Homo*, is similar to that of the manus, and the remarks made above relative to tactile pads, flexure creases and dermatoglyphics are equally applicable here.

EXTERNAL GENITALIA (see especially Wislocki, 1936).—There are many minor generic and specific differences between these organs, but a general pattern prevails throughout the Catarrhini. In the male the testes are typically postpenial in the adult and are located in a pendulous scrotum; but the degree of pendency is variable; in many forms (*e.g. Gorilla, Pongo, Cercopithecus*) it is barely more than sessile. Both scrotum and penis are typically naked or but sparsely haired. Often the genitalia are vividly coloured, the scrotum in that case often contrasting with the penis, or at all events, with the glans. In some forms (especially *Papio, Mandrillus*) vivid integumentary colours extend beyond the genitals to the circumanal region, buttocks or even beyond. Another feature, restricted to the Cercopithecoidea and the Hylobatidae, is the occurrence over the expanded ischial tuberosities of the keratinized sitting pads (ischial callosities). These are small and hidden by the surrounding fur in *Cercopithecus* and *Hylobates*, but large, and sometimes confluent in the mid-line in *Papio* and its allies, *Macaca*, etc. Vestigial callosities have been reported in individual chimpanzees and orangs, but normally in these apes they are lacking.

The penis varies greatly in form, especially the glans. It also varies in its relation to the symphysis, notably in the site at which it becomes free to enter its integumentary sheath. A baculum is present in all except *Homo*, but this varies greatly in size, being large in *Macaca* and *Papio*, small in Hominoidea.

In the female the rima pudendi is variously guarded by labial folds. In the adult well-developed labia majora are found only in the human female, at least only traces are present in other catarrhines—in contrast to the Strepsirhini and Platyrrhini. These folds, however, are better marked in the foetus and may persist for some time postnatally, *e.g.* in the great apes. In the foetus of *Macaca* and many others a transverse fold exists rostral to the clitoris (Bolk, 1907 ; confirmed by Wislocki, 1936). It bears a striking homology to the scrotum of the male and is therefore regarded as homologous with labia majora. The structure reappears at puberty in *Macaca*, *Miopithecus* and *Cercocebus* when it becomes involved in the catamenial swelling, of which it comprises the so-called pubic or pseudoscrotal lobe.

Catamenial swelling is a phenomenon found irregularly distributed among female Catarrhini. It is associated with the sexual cycle and involves a localized oedema of the skin of the perineum, often extending to include the callosities and/or the integument around them. In some forms, *e.g.* *Macaca mulatta*, the swelling also involves the basal portion of the tail, and in individual cases extends cranially along the back. The process is associated with changes in water metabolism, urinary output, etc., and is under control of the sex hormones secreted by the ovary (Krohn and Zuckerman, 1937 ; Ogston *et al.*, 1939). The swelling evolves slowly, but at the onset of the luteal phase of the cycle, when menstruation supervenes, it rapidly regresses. It remains in abeyance during pregnancy. Special peculiarities affect the swelling in *Procolobus*, where the feature, once developed at puberty, appears to be more durable and to have a more solid structure (Hill, 1952). *Vide infra*, p. 134 for further data.

Labia minora are much more frequently developed than labia majora. Their presence, however, may be confined to the ventral part of the vulva, where they become related to the clitoris, forming its praeputium and frenula, the remainder of the rima then being flush with the general perineal integument (*e.g.* in some *Cercopithecus* spp.). The clitoris varies in size ; often inconspicuous, it never approaches the proportions seen in *Ateles*, although an approach is made in some species of Hylobatidae. An os clitoridis may be present (*e.g.* in *Symphalangus*, Harms, 1956 *a*). The organ is never perforated by the urethra.

Except in *Homo*, mammary glands, during the quiescent phase, are poorly represented, and even in the gravid state and during lactation they do not form external swellings, enlarging instead diffusely subcutaneously. The only external manifestation is an enlargement of the nipples, which elongate and become pendulous. A single pectoral pair of nipples is the rule, but numerous individual examples of a supernumerary pair, either axillary or abdominal, have been reported (Schultz, 1948, who listed thirty-four cases from the literature of supernumerary nipples among catarrhines.) Of these, sixteen examples have been in *Macaca mulatta*, but other macaques (*M. irus*, *M. sinica*) and baboons have been involved, besides examples of *Cercopithecus ascanius schmidti*, *Erythrocebus*, *Hylobates*, *Symphalangus*, *Pongo* and *Pan*. In the last mentioned Matthews and Baxter (1948) record an example of polythelia in which the glands were functional. Gynaecomastia has been reported in the male Rhesus monkey, with clumps of well-formed alveoli ; in the normal male the organ consists of an uncomplicated duct system not extending beyond the base of the nipple (Folley *et al.*, 1939).

II. Skeletal System

SKULL

In the general form of the skull most catarrhines recall that of the more advanced Cebidae, as they possess the globular brain-case hafted to a relatively orthognathous facial skeleton, which has migrated back beneath the fore end of the brain case. In exceptional cases, however, varying degrees of prognathism have been secondarily evolved, the direction of forward growth being somewhat different in the genera involved. Commonly it is more or less directly forwards, *e.g.* in *Macaca, Cercocebus, Theropithecus* and *Gorilla* ; but in *Papio, Mandrillus* and related fossil forms, it is as much downwards as forwards, somewhat on the lines of the growth direction of the bill in certain charadriiform birds, such as *Gallinago* (fig. 2).

Concomitant with the prognathism, there is increase in the size of the masticating muscles and, therefore, in the areas required for their attachment. This results, in the forms concerned, in elevation of temporal and lambdoid ridges into crests of varying height, and buttressing by other bony growths such as supraorbital ridges or tori. Their ontogenetic development has been commented upon by Scott (1963).

Scott concludes that the evolution of the skull appears to be correlated with three fundamental developmental processes : (1) increase in brain size—especially in the Pongidae and *Homo* ; (2) failure of the basal angle to open out after the time of birth, with maintenance of the foetal kyphosis associated with early closure of the intrasphenoidal synchondrosis ; (3) a change in direction of growth of the septal cartilage of the nose from predominantly forward to predominantly downward. Processes (2) and (3) appear responsible for secondary features, such as early closure of the premaxillary suture and reduction of the snout.

Secondary alveolar prognathism and its concomitants are related to the development of a massive dentition superposed upon an earlier phylogenetic reduction of the snout (see also for further details and discussion in this connection, Anthony, 1952 ; Hofer, 1954 *a* and *b* ; Biegert, 1957 ; Ashton, 1957).

In the brain-case the frontal is large, but ends at the vault in a transverse or coronal suture without being carried far back between the parietals. The parietals are extensive and marked at varying levels by the temporal lines, which indicate the upper limit of the temporalis muscle. In many genera, especially in males, these gain the summit, the lines of the two sides

D

meeting in a ridge, sometimes raised into a sagittal crest (*Gorilla* shows the extreme in this respect). From the lambda a crest is formed which descends towards the mastoid region. Usually this is fused with the hinder part of the temporal line or ridge, but it may develop independently by expansion of the bone for additional attachment of muscles inserting on the nuchal plane. Again *Gorilla* shows an extreme degree of this upgrowth, whereby lambdoid crests are developed. The nuchal plane may be flattened or

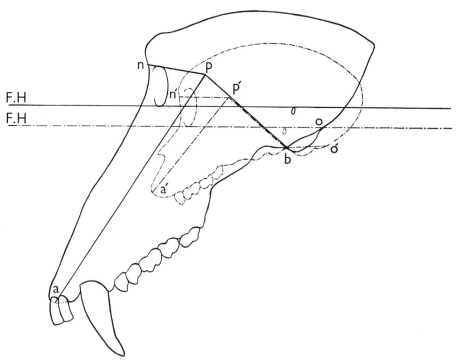

Fig. 2.—Baboon (*Papio* sp.). Outlines of crania of an adult male and an infant in norma
lateralis to demonstrate growth changes in the basicranial axis

F.H, Frankfurt horizontal; *a*, alveolon or prosthion; *b*, basion; *n*, nasion; *o*, opisthion;
p, prosphenion
Note (i) the spheno-ethmoidal angle (bpn) is more open in the adult, (ii) the foramino-basal
angle (pbo) is less open in the adult and (iii) the spheno-maxillary angle (bpa) scarcely
differs in the two animals. Based on a figure by Zuckerman (1953 *b*)

bulbous and, particularly in Hominoidea, it is pushed downwards by expansion of the parietal region, thus coming to face directly downwards, or more downwards than backwards (*e.g. Miopithecus, Pongo, Homo*).

In the temporal region the tympanic ring of the foetus and neonatus is converted into an osseous tube, which forms the skeletal support of the medial one-third at least of the auditory passage. There is no tympanic bulla. The mastoid region is laterally prominent, but only in the Hominoidea is there a downwardly growing mastoid process, and even there it is variable. The region is, however, invaded by air-space, Schultz (1952). The styloid process may or may not be ossified, but there is always a minute bony tympano-hyal.

At the pterion the commonest arrangement seems to be for the squamosal to meet the frontal, shutting the parietal from the alisphenoid, but in *Homo*, *Pongo* and most Colobidae, the alisphenoids and parietals meet. But there are many individual variations in the detailed pattern.

Somewhat the same applies to the intracranial relationships of the frontal with the presphenoid and mesethmoid. In Cynomorpha typically the frontals provide thick processes, which grow medially to meet over the presphenoid-mesethmoid junction, resulting in deep, sometimes almost tubular, olfactory fossae ; the same applies in Hylobatidae and *Gorilla*, but in *Pongo*, *Pan* and *Homo* the frontals fail to meet, leaving the prespheno-mesethmoid junction exposed from above (see especially Wood Jones, 1929 *b* ; Ashley-Montagu, 1943).

In the face the orbits are large and completely surrounded by bone, except for the superior and inferior orbital fissures. Their roofs encroach upon the cranial cavity, but with advance in size of the frontal lobes of the cerebral hemispheres, the encroachment decreases in ascending from monkeys to apes and Man. In *Homo* the encroachment is virtually nil.

Nasal bones are, except in baboons, short, flat and typically unite early with each other. Fronto-maxillary and fronto-nasal sutures are usually in alignment (cf. Platyrrhini, where the nasals advance farther up). In cynomorph monkeys, too, the nasal processes of the premaxillae ascend as far as those of the maxillae (Wood Jones, 1929 *b*). The premaxillo-maxillary suture remains open till late in life, except in *Homo*, where it becomes obscured by forward growth of the alveolar process of the maxilla to meet its fellow rostral to the premaxilla. An air-cavity (maxillary antrum) occupies the body of the maxilla.

The malar provides part of the lateral wall of the orbit, but never reaches back to articulate with the parietal ; on the inferior orbital rim, it may touch the lachrymal (*e.g.* in *Macaca*), but is usually widely separated from it. The anterior root of the zygomatic arch is projected forwards so as to lie level with M.$\underline{^2}$ (Winge, 1924).

Lachrymal and planum orbitale of ethmoid are typically separated by downgrowth of a process from the frontal to meet the maxilla. Wood Jones regards this as a catarrhine specialization on a par with the interfrontal union over the prespheno-mesethmoid junction.

The palate, even in short-faced forms, is usually elongated, narrow and parallel-sided. Only in the orthognathous races of *Homo* is it more broad than long, bordered by a horseshoe-shaped alveolar arch.

Order of suture closure is very variable among the Catarrhini, the commonest order over the vault being lambdoid, followed by sagittal and finally coronal, but in *Cercocebus*, *Macaca*, some examples of *Pongo*, and

Homo, the sagittal closes before coronal or lambdoid.   In general, sutures close at a later state in Catarrhini than in Platyrrhini and the facial unions are delayed (Chopra, 1957).   The pre-basi-sphenoid union is not obliterated until after the time of complete eruption of the permanent dentition.

The mandible is of the usual form, but its size varies in relation to the robustness of its dental armature.   It is therefore relatively weak in foetalized forms such as *Miopithecus* and *Homo*, but powerful in all its parts in *Papio*, *Gorilla* and *Pan*, other genera being intermediate in varying degree. Ankylosis at the symphysis occurs early in postnatal life.   The fundamental form of the symphyseal region may be modified in three ways : by the development of (*a*) a mandibular torus, (*b*) a simian shelf, or (*c*) a chin or mental protuberance.   The last named is a very recent acquisition confined to modern Man and some forms of Hylobatidae, especially *Symphalangus*, but a slight convexity at the lower part of the symphysis is sometimes seen in *Papio*, where it is related to the position of the developing canines.

Torus and simian shelf are both present in Pongidae and Hylobatidae, though, in the latter, the shelf is poorly developed.   The two are separated by a depression, the genial pit, in which are the openings of one or more vascular canals.   The torus is well developed in some cynomorph monkeys, while the shelf may or may not be present.

Inflection of the angular region of the mandible is very unusual but appears in *Miopithecus* and some forms of *Hylobates* (*e.g. Hylobates agilis*).

The hyoid may be represented, as in Man, by a simple horseshoe-shaped bony arch with cartilaginous or partly ossified lesser cornua springing from the junction of corpus and greater cornu.   More frequently the corpus hyoidei is variously enlarged by the expansion of the median laryngeal air sac, which fills the concavity on the pharyngeal aspect of the bone.   Both lesser and greater cornua may be ossified.

AXIAL SKELETON

The vertebral formula is variable.   Cervical vertebrae are constantly seven in number, while the thoraco-lumbar region usually includes nineteen (rarely eighteen or twenty), of which the thoracics vary from eleven to thirteen and lumbars six or seven, but a cranial shift of the pelvis, especially in the Hominoidea, may reduce these (*e.g.* lumbars reduced to three or four in *Gorilla*, five in *Homo*).   Generally only two vertebrae, more rarely three, make up the sacrum, but in Hominoidea others are added posteriorly by inclusion of vestigial post-sacrals—up to five in *Homo*.   Occasionally six-piece sacra occur in *Homo* from sacralization of the last lumbar.   Even in so-called tailless forms, *e.g. Macaca sylvana* and all the Hominoidea, a few post-sacral vertebrae are present, commonly fused in the case of the

Hominoidea into a solid coccyx. Chevron bones are commonly present on the first few post-sacral vertebrae of all tailed forms.

At least an incipient sigmoid curve is present on the spinal column; this increases in the Pongidae and attains its acme in *Homo* (see especially Cunningham, 1886).

The arch of the atlas is sometimes grooved, otherwise perforated by the vertebral artery.

In the thoracic region the neural spines are inclined backwards throughout the series in Hominoidea, but in the quadrupedal cynomorphs they commence to incline forwards from T.11 or T.12 and the forward inclination is continued thereafter through the lumbar series. Relative proportions and directions of transverse, costal, mammillary and other processes differ materially in the two main divisions of the Catarrhini.

The sternum is, in quadrupedal cynomorphs, of the elongated narrow type, but the orthograde anthropomorphs are platysternal. *Symphalangus* shows the broadest and shortest sternum of the whole primate order (Mivart, 1865). This divergence in sternal morphology is correlated with the general shape of the thorax, which is transversely narrowed and deep dorso-ventrally in leptosternal forms, broad and shallow in the platysternal apes and Man.

APPENDICULAR SKELETON

The pectoral limb skeleton may be somewhat shorter than the pelvic, but in Pongidae the reverse is the case, whilst in Hylobatidae and in *Oreopithecus* this reversed trend reaches its maximum. The change-over is linked with the replacement of a quadrupedal ambulatory or cursorial function by the orthograde or semi-orthograde bodily posture associated with a peculiar mode of progression known as brachiation, where the pectoral limbs are used more in progression than the pelvic limbs (*vide infra* under locomotor activities, p. 48). *Homo* is peculiar in retaining a pectoral limb of moderate length, combined with an elongated pelvic limb, yet adopting a completely orthograde posture.

Clavicles vary with the shape of the thorax, being narrow, slender and obliquely disposed in cynomorphs, more robust and more transversely aligned in anthropomorphs. The scapula shows correlated changes in shape, but these do not so closely correspond with the thoracic variations as might be expected. Even within the confines of a single genus (*e.g. Cercopithecus*), wide divergences occur (*vide infra*, p. 253 and fig. 34). In general, however, a scapula with a short vertebral, and long cranial and axillary borders is correlated with the quadrupedal type of thorax, whilst a scapula with long vertebral and short cranial border and acute caudal angle is associated with the broad-chested orthograde apes and Man. The spinous process **is** always more or less perpendicular to the vertebral border, varying within narrow limits.

The humerus is of the general mammalian type, varying mainly in such details as the set of the head, torsion of shaft and degree of development of tuberosities, condyles and epicondylar ridges, and the deltoid crest. The supinator crest is often strongly developed, *e.g.* in *Papio*. The entepicondylar foramen is *always* lacking (cf. Platyrrhini). Radius and ulna are separate and with increasing power of pronation become increasingly bowed apart. The head of the radius is approximately circular in outline, allowing free rotation, but the olecranon tends to be shorter than in Platyrrhini, although *Papio* is exceptional.

In the hand the pollex is inclined to become reduced in brachiating forms and even in some rapidly progressing arboreal forms, such as *Presbytis* and its allies. In *Colobus* it is lacking as an external feature, though retaining a vestigial, buried metacarpal. The hand tends to be elongated in quadrupedal cynomorphs, and in Hylobatidae and *Pongo*, but inclines towards a broader structure in *Gorilla* and Man.

An os centrale is present in the carpus, except in *Pan*, *Gorilla* and *Homo*.

The pelvis is narrow in quadrupedal (pronograde) forms, but in the orthograde apes, and especially in Man, it is broadened, and the iliac fossae become expanded to support the viscera in the new position. Even in cynomorphs, however, the iliac blade is expanded compared with its condition in most platyrrhines, providing larger areas of attachment for enlarged gluteal and iliacus muscles so important in leaping and climbing. Ischial tuberosities tend to be expanded, especially in the callosity-bearing cynomorphs, but the associated eversion is lost in the larger apes and Man.

The femoral shaft is less straight than in Strepsirhini and Platyrrhini, showing an inclination toward forward bowing. This tendency is maximal in the orthograde forms and is correlated with posterior bony buttressing by a linea aspera. A third trochanter is typically lacking, but turns up occasionally as an individual anomaly (*e.g.* in Man).

A suprapatella is not developed. Tibia and fibula are invariably separate, with long slender shafts ; but in *Gorilla* and *Pongo* they are short and robust and the tibia forwardly bowed. A synovial joint unites the distal ends of the two bones, thereby permitting freedom of movement in inversion and eversion of the foot.

Quadrupedal cynomorphs fall into Morton's metatarsi-fulcrumating group in contrast to the tarsi-fulcrumating orthograde forms. Compared with the platyrrhines, the calcaneus tends to be shortened. Phalangeal components of the digits in the terrestrial baboons and *Erythrocebus* are short relative to the metatarsals, and the hallux tends to be reduced, though retaining its grasping power. Digits are longer and the hallux more strongly opposable in the arboreal forms. In *Homo* the foot is highly specialized and modified, notably in the alignment of the hallux on the distal edge of the metatarsus alongside II, combined with its loss of the power of opposition.

The order of epiphyseal union in the long bones differs materially among the various groups of Catarrhini (Washburn, 1943). Schultz (1940, 1941) found that *Pan* and *Pongo* both differed from *Homo* in respect of the delayed union of the coracoid with the scapula and of the three components of the os innomination. Whereas also in *Homo* and Cercopithecoidea coracoid and innominate unions are preceded only by the distal humeral epiphyseal union, in the great apes they are delayed until the date of the union of epiphyses at the knee—the most retarded region of all.

The general pattern of the sequence is the same in cynomorphs as in Man. Maturation appears to proceed regionally. In the pectoral limb the elbow region matures first followed by the epiphyses of the hand and wrist and finally by the shoulder. In the pelvic limb the hip region matures earlier than the foot and ankle, the knee being last to cease growth. Axial skeletal elements mature prior to the limb girdles.

III. Dentition

Dental formula $I.\frac{2}{2}$, $C.\frac{1}{1}$, $P.\frac{2}{2}$, $M.\frac{3}{3} = 32$; of temporary dentition $D.I.\frac{2}{2}$, $D.C.\frac{1}{1}$, $D.M.\frac{2}{2} = 20$.

The difference from the platyrrhine formula is due to the loss in each jaw of a premolar, usually considered to be $P.\frac{2}{2}$, leaving $P.\frac{3}{3}$ and $P.\frac{4}{4}$.

Incisors tend to bear broadly spatulate crowns, especially in the upper jaw, and particularly $I^{\underline{1}}$. This is especially the case in the Pongidae and, to a lesser degree, in *Homo*.

Canines are typically long, with high, pointed crowns projecting beyond the occlusal surfaces of neighbouring teeth, thereby necessitating the presence of diastemata for their reception in occlusion, *i.e.* between $I^{\underline{2}}$ and the canine in the upper jaw and between canine and $P.\overline{3}$ in the lower jaw. *Homo* is exceptional in bearing reduced canines and in lacking the diastemata. A further sexual difference affects the canines of most forms, the crowns being much larger in males than females; but in gibbons they are enlarged in both sexes.

Premolars are characteristically bicuspid, but $P.\overline{3}$ is frequently modified in connection with its occlusion against the upper canine whereby it takes on a sectorial character. Molars are typically quadrituberculate both above and below. Their cusps are primitively conical elevations separated by sagittal and transverse grooves, but in the cynomorphs a bilophodont character is attained by the development of transverse ridges connecting the cusps in pairs, while the crown is constricted between the front and rear pairs. In $M.\overline{1}$ and $M.\overline{2}$ the hypoconulid is lost, but in $M.\overline{3}$ it may be developed or represented as a prominent heel.

As regards roots, all the upper premolars and molars bear three roots in Catarrhini, two labial and one lingual in position. In the lower jaw all the cheek-teeth are two-rooted, the roots being proximal and distal in position (Wood Jones, 1929 *b*). Man is exceptional in having the upper premolar roots reduced to two or even one, and lower premolars are generally single-rooted also.

Important features characterize the microstructure of the teeth of all Catarrhini, as first shown by Carter (1922). The tooth enamel of Catarrhini agrees in character with that of the Mascarene Lemuroidea inasmuch as it contains a system of tubules continuous with the dentinal tubules. The enamel proper consists of rods or prisms of granular character and with straight, even margins, separated from each other by a minimal amount of interstitial substance. This contrasts with the wavy character of the enamel prisms in platyrrhine teeth and in those of lorisiform Strepsirhini, where, moreover, the structures are separated by large quantities of interstitial material. A detailed study of the histology of the dental tissues of *Cercopithecus* has recently been published by Ockerse (1963).

IV. Myology

As with the Platyrrhini, no comprehensive account exists of the myological peculiarities of the Catarrhini. Monographs, both descriptive and comparative, have appeared on the musculature of individual species or genera, *e.g. Pan* (Wilder, 1861, Champneys, 1871, Macalister, 1871, Sperino, 1897, Ledingham, 1904); *Gorilla* (Macalister, 1873, Sommer, 1906, 1907, Raven, 1950); *Papio* (Champneys, 1871); *Mandrillus* (Pagenstecher, 1867, Sonntag, 1922), and *Macaca mulatta* (Howell and Straus, 1933), to mention but a few. There are also numerous contributions on individual muscles or muscle groups dealing with one or several species as well as incidental references in more general works. Space forbids the mention of all these at this point, but references up to 1939 are readily traced in Ruch's (1941) invaluable *Bibliographia primatologica* and thereafter in the annual issues of the section Mammalia of the *Zoological Record*.

V. Splanchnology

PERITONEUM

Although conforming to the basic pattern similar to that in the Platyrrhini, progressive changes are observable through the Catarrhine series from monkeys to Man. Firstly the mesoduodenum is entirely lost, the whole duodenum, except for a short section adjacent to the pylorus, is entirely retroperitoneal (Treves, 1885, Klaatsch, 1892; van Loghem, 1903; Straus, 1936) but a short mesoduodenum sometimes persists as an individual anomaly, as Straus found in an example of *Papio*. The free part near the pylorus forms the caudal boundary of the epiploic foramen (of Winslow), whose dorsal limit is the peritoneal covered ventral wall of the prehepatic part of the postcaval vein. The liver itself forms the cranial boundary and the ventral limit is comprised by the free border of the gastro-hepatic omentum, bearing the bile duct, hepatic artery and portal vein. The foramen leads into a capacious lesser sac dorsal to the stomach and lesser omentum. In *Cercopithecus* and its allies, the sac also extends caudally between the laminae of the greater omentum, but in more advanced forms, especially the Hominoidea, fusion of the dorsal and ventral laminae obliterates this extension of the lesser sac. At the cranial end of the lesser sac a digitiform pouch alongside the oesophagus and upon the left crus of the diaphragm persists.

Chapman (1879, 1880) claimed that the great omentum in cynomorphs shows no adhesion to the colon or with the peritoneum of the transverse colon, except in a rudimentary fashion in some macaques. This sweeping statement has justly been challenged by Straus (1936), who points out that such fusion may be extensive. Adhesion takes various forms, *e.g.* (1) fusion limited to the hepatic flexure, as van Loghem found in several instances ; (2) adhesion to transverse colon as reported by Straus in *Cercopithecus sabaeus* and *Cercocebus lunulatus* ; (3) to both ascending and transverse colon, reported by Duckworth and by Straus in *Erythrocebus* ; (4) to hepatic flexure, ascending colon and caecum (Huntington, Reider) ; (5) to most of the colon—a rare anomaly reported once for *Erythrocebus* by Straus ; or (6) the reverse anomaly where adhesion is slight so that the dorsal attachment of the omentum is traceable to the abdominal wall—reported once in *Macaca mulatta* by Straus. In all four anthropoid apes and in Man the adhesion is regularly to the whole length of the transverse colon from hepatic to splenic flexure.

Primitively the whole alimentary tract from the duodeno-jejunal flexure to the colo-rectal junction is provided with a dorsal mesentery. This varies in its dorso-ventral depth and in the course of its parietal attachment. Fundamentally the attachment takes an inverted J-shaped course with the incurved part supporting the small intestine (mesenterium proprium) and the transverse and long limbs of the J constituting the root of the mesocolon. This is the pattern found in many cynomorphs. In more advanced forms varying degrees of shortening or loss of parts of the mesocolon are presented. Extension of fixation of the colon from a primary locus at or near the hepatic flexure towards the caecum reduces the ascending mesocolon, leaving the caecum itself free on all sides but connected to the antimesenteric border of terminal ileum by a triangular (primitively anangious) peritoneal fold (mesotyphlon). In the Hominoidea further fixation of the caecum occurs, rendering it immobile ; the mesotyphlon becomes a mesoappendix. In

Man the descending mesocolon is also lost by fusion of its sinistral layer with the parietal peritoneum of the left flank. In all the Hominoidea the loss of the ascending mesocolon results in the emergence of a secondary mesentery to the jejuno-ileum. Instead of its primitive median dorsal line of attachment, a secondary oblique line is formed along the medial limit of the area of fusion of ascending mesocolon with parietal peritoneum. This line proceeds from the duodeno-jejunal flexure caudally and to the right to end at the ileo-colic junction in or near the right iliac fossa. Varying degrees of arrest in the development of this process may be retained, *e.g.* in Hylobatidae (Straus).

Digestive System

Lips become increasingly mobile in passing from cynomorphs to Man, thereby increasing their adaptability in acquisition and testing of food, and also in ministering to the increasing powers of emotional expression and modification of vocal emissions.

Palatine ridges in the lower catarrhines vary between 6 and 11, but by omitting *Papio*, with its high average of over 9, the average fluctuates between 7 and 8·1 (Schultz, 1958). In Colobidae the pattern inclines to complication through discontinuities and bifurcations of the ridges (Schultz, 1949). In all the cynomorphs ridges extend back at least to M.^{2}, but in *Cercopithecus* and *Macaca* most frequently to the palatine border. Gibbons and *Pongo* retain high numbers of ridges, but they are very variable in the latter, as also in *Pan* and *Gorilla*, where they differ on the two sides. In Man, the number of ridges varies from 2 to 8, 4 being the modal number.

The tongue is usually unpigmented, but pigment appears in some guenons, including *Erythrocebus*, whilst in Hylobatidae individual vallate and fungiform papillae may be pigmented. In shape the organ varies from spatulate to subconical, varying in conformity with jaws and dental arcades. Vallate papillae are commonly arranged in V-formation; only in Hominoidea does a Y-shaped pattern occur (also found in some Lemuridae). The apical cluster of fungiform papillae is extensive in all catarrhines and, as shown by Tuckerman (1892), are provided with taste-buds. Lateral organs vary in the different main families and are characteristic in several genera.

The stomach may be simple (Cercopithecidae, Hylobatidae, Pongidae, Hominidae) or complex (Colobidae), but *Allenopithecus* is somewhat transitional. The duodenum may be J-shaped or C-shaped and is retroperitoneal. Valvulae conniventes may be developed in some pongid genera and are constant in *Homo*. A papilla major may or may not be present and a papilla minor may occur in the absence of the major papilla.

The colon is invariably sacculated and provided with three longitudinal taeniae. These converge on the caecum and at the colo-rectal junction.

The caecum is usually conical in the quadrupedal forms and shorter, more globose in the orthograde apes, where also its apex is replaced by a vermiform appendix of varying length. In the wall of this last-named structure considerable lymphoid tissue occurs. The colon is topographically divided into ascending, transverse and descending portions, the last named often continued into an omega-shaped loop or pelvic colon which in the pongids is folded back on itself (Hill, 1949). The rectum varies in length with the length of the pelvis minor. In the orthogrades lateral flexures are developed upon it, and these are foreshadowed in some cynomorphs (Lubosch and Schaller, 1928; Hill, 1952, 1958).

In the liver multiple lobation is characteristic of the cynomorphs; the lobes tend to be reduced in the orthograde forms, except curiously in *Gorilla*. In the cynomorphs also the caudate lobe remains elongated; in the orthogrades it is reduced to a nodule on the Spigelian lobe. Reduction is maximum in gibbons. However, there are many variations in detailed form. The oesophageal notch varies in depth, being relatively shallow in baboons (Duckworth, 1915) and in the orthograde types. The liver is grossly modified in shape and dislocated by the large stomach in Colobidae. A bare area replaces the mesohepar in Hominoidea and is incipient in some cynomorphs. The gall-bladder may or may not be exposed, either completely or partially. Its duct joins the hepatic ducts and the common passage opens into the duodenum in association with the main pancreatic duct.

Respiratory Tract

The larynx is fairly uniform in general structure throughout the Catarrhini, but differs considerably in respect of the sac-like air-containing outgrowths. In the Cynomorpha a median subcutaneous air-sac clothes the front and sides of the neck. It is connected with the laryngeal cavity through the thyro-hyoid ligament (saccus laryngeus medianus superior). In the Pongidae the air-sacs are lateral outgrowths from the laryngeal ventricle, which escape from the larynx above the thyroid cartilage, enlarging in the neck and sending loculi in several directions, *e.g.* to the pectoral region and axilla, *i.e.* both in front of and behind the clavicle (saccus laryngeus lateralis). These are largest in *Pongo*; they are vestigial in Man, where they are represented by the laryngeal saccules, rarely extending beyond the cranial border of the thyroid cartilage.

As regards pulmonary lobation, the Cercopithecoidea retain the common ceboid pattern of three left and four right lobes, but there may be further subdivision. In Hylobatidae the lobes are reduced to two on the left, but four are retained on the right (Sonntag, 1924; Wood Jones, 1929 *b*). The Orang is unique in total loss of lung lobation bilaterally. In *Pan, Gorilla* and *Homo* the azygos lobe is lacking, thus reducing the number of lobes on the right lung to three.

Urogenital Organs

The right kidney is not invariably situated caudad of the left ; the left is considerably caudad, for example, in *Macaca* ; sometimes the two are at the same level. A caudad right kidney is usual in gibbons, great apes and Man. Except in Man, the kidney in unipyramidal. In all cynomorphs the pyramid is elongated and the medullary mass undivided. Division of a single pyramid into four parts occurs in gibbons, where the medullary mass is constantly subdivided (Wood Jones, 1929 *b*). A single papilla is constant in *Pongo*, but in *Pan* and *Gorilla* some subdivision of its summit has been recorded (up to eight in *Gorilla*, according to Sonntag and seven in the chimpanzee).

Although the human kidney is lobulated in the foetus and the neonatus, it soon becomes superficially smooth. External lobulation is not, however, necessarily correlated with internal lobulation by division of the medulla into several pyramids (Straus, 1934). In other Catarrhini the foetal and neonatal kidney is not superficially lobulated, as found by Anthony and Villemin (1923) in *Macaca* and *Papio*, but the same authors noted an incipient lobation in foetal *Pan* and *Gorilla*, while Deniker (1885) described in a foetal *Hylobates* a smooth right and a slightly lobulated left organ.

Testes vary considerably in relative size, being sometimes small (*Cercopithecus, Presbytis, Gorilla*) and often quite large (*e.g. Macaca, Miopithecus, Pan*) in relation to total body size, the differences not being correlated with the major groups, though specific for particular genera. See especially Schultz (1938).

The cremaster is well developed and capable of withdrawing the descended testes towards the external abdominal ring, *e.g.* in certain emotional states. Testes normally descend into a pendulous or subpendulous post-penile scrotum, but the scrotum is sessile in some genera (*e.g. Pan, Gorilla, Hylobates*). In some cynomorphs descent is delayed till relatively late in postnatal life (Harms, 1956 *a*). One or two hydatids of Morgagni are commonly present (*e.g.* in *Macaca, Cercopithecus, Mandrillus* and *Papio* ; Zuckerman and Krohn, 1937). A sinus epididymidis is usually lacking, though Ayer (1948) reports it in *Semnopithecus*. A mesepididymis is present, at any rate in cynomorphs, and here also the processus vaginalis remains open at least to the inguinal canal, and sometimes throughout the canal as a slit-like passage. The terminal part of the vas may be diverticulated, convoluted or expanded to form an ampulla. Seminal vesicles are commonly large, fusiform bodies and more complicated than in Platyrrhini (Klaar and Krasa, 1921). The prostate is bipartite with a cranial and a caudal lobe, except in

Pongo and *Homo*. Only in the last mentioned does the gland extend to the pubic side of the urethra. The cranial lobe differs in structure and function, being comparable to the coagulating gland of rodents (van Wagenen, 1936).

The size and structure of the utriculus varies greatly. Bulbo-urethral glands are large in cynomorphs, especially *Macaca*, but are smaller in Colobidae. They have never been reported in anthropomorphs in spite of diligent search. A baculum is present in all but *Homo*.

In the female, ovaries are small compared with those of Platyrrhini, and differ further in lacking the extensive interstitial luteinization. Uterine tubes are commonly coiled, with a slit-like abdominal ostium surrounded by fimbriae. Both superior and inferior mesosalpinx are present in cynomorphs. In anthropoid apes only the latter is represented, and the tubes are straighter, as in *Homo*. A minute superior mesosalpinx has, however, been noted in *Hylobates pileatus* (Wislocki, 1932 ; Matthews, 1946).

The uterus is, apart from individual congenital anomalies, invariably a uterus simplex. It is divisible into a cranial segment or " body " (corpus uteri) and a narrower cervix. The body presents a dome-like fundus sometimes showing a median depression (*e.g.* in *Macaca*). The cervix is large and complicated in some cynomorphs, but simpler in Hominoidea. The distal part of the cervix is telescoped into the vaginal vault. The vagina is lined by a highly corrugated and heavily keratinized epithelium, but details are variable. There are marked cyclical variations in structure in the ovary and in all parts of the genital tract of female Catarrhini in relation to the menstrual cycle.

DUCTLESS GLANDS

On the whole the spleen is less elongated and less flattened and less accommodated to the greater gastric curve than in Platyrrhini. Usually tetrahedral in shape, its borders and angles are more sharply defined than in Man. The organ is misplaced and modified in form in Colobidae (*e.g.* in *Nasalis*, Duckworth, 1915). In the great apes the spleen resembles the human organ, but shows some features intermediate between human and cynomorph spleens. Accessory spleens (spleniculi) sometimes occur.

In the hypophysis the pars tuberalis commonly forms a collar round the infundibulum. A " Nackenhypophyse " or posterior extension from the pars distalis over the dorsum of the pars nervosa near its junction with the infundibulum has been recorded in *Gorilla*, *Pan* and *Papio* (Hanström, 1958).

The thyroid consists of two lateral lobes which vary somewhat in position. They may or may not be connected by an isthmus.

Adrenals are invariably triangular in sagittal section. Small accessory adrenals, sometimes purely cortical, are frequently met with at various sites.

VI. Angeiology

The heart is less axially aligned than in Platyrrhini, though *Cercopithecus* still retains a relatively median heart. The branches from the aortic arch are variable ; it may be two-, three- or even four-branched (the last mentioned when a thyroidea ima arises independently, as, *e.g.*, in some examples of *Pongo* and in *Homo* as an anomaly). Only two trunks are the rule in cynomorphs, an innominate (later providing right subclavian and both carotids) and a left subclavian. In the Hominoidea the branching is variable.

VII. Neurology

Brain

In the brain the occipital lobes of the cerebrum completely cover the cerebellum dorsally and even project beyond. The cerebral hemispheres in Cynomorpha closely resemble those in higher Platyrrhini. All the principal sulci are present, the simian sulcus or Affenspalte being particularly well marked, while the area behind it is relatively smooth. In the Anthropomorpha additional sulci are generally present and the occipital region is no longer smooth. The posterior cornu of the lateral ventricle is large and marked medially by a hippocampus minor, due to the indentation of the calcarine fissure. There is also an eminentia collateralis in Hominoidea. The insula shows varying degrees of operculation, attaining its most complete submergence in *Homo*.

In the cerebellum the vermis is large compared with the lateral lobes in Cynomorpha, the reverse being the case in Hominoidea. The two groups also differ in respect of the size of flocculus and paraflocculus ; these remain well developed in the monkeys, becoming reduced in the great apes and Man.

VIII. Sense Organs

In the olfactory apparatus, aside from the external distinctions (*antea*, p. 29), the nasal fossa is much reduced in relative size and the turbinals reduced in number to three or even two. These are arranged in a vertical series one above the other. The naso-turbinal is reduced to a mere ridge (agger nasi). There is evidence of only one ectoturbinal, represented by the bulla ethmoidalis. In cynomorphs the fossa is reduced by encroachment of the two orbits, but in the anthropomorphs these are divorced, allowing secondary invasion of the interorbital area by nasal fossa. Size and distribution of accessory air sinuses differs. In all, a maxillary antrum is present, and this may be the only sinus (*e.g.* in most Cynomorpha), but in the higher forms invasion of frontal, ethmoid, sphenoid and even the palatine may occur. The route of invasion appears, however, to differ in the various genera involved. In gibbons, for example, pneumatization of frontal, ethmoid, palatine and maxilla takes place from a primary sphenoidal air-space, whereas in *Pongo* the extention is from the maxillary sinus into frontal, ethmoid, lachrymal, malar, nasal, palatine and sphenoid, in spite of the co-existence of a primary sphenoidal sinus (Cave, 1948).

As regards visual functions, the great expansion of the striate cortex of the cerebrum in all Catarrhini suggests greater visual acuity and refinement. This is further attested by elaboration of the histological details of the retina ; this in some genera (*e.g. Cercocebus*) is greater even than in Man, especially in the macular region, and notably in the density of photoreceptors and proportion of cones to rods, which relate functionally to colour perception. Optical axes are parallel, providing a basis for full stereoscopic vision. In the optic nerves about 40 per cent of fibres remain uncrossed at the chiasma. Lamination of the grey matter of the lateral geniculate body is more elaborate and better defined than in Platyrrhini—again sometimes in excess of that found in Man. As many as eight laminae have been recorded in the central part of the nucleus in *Macaca* (Le Gros Clark, 1959), although six is more usual in Catarrhini.

Differences in histological structure, *e.g.* in regard to pigment cells, have been reported in the chorioidea by Rohen (1962). The lachrymal gland is composed of two parts and in position resembles the human organ. An accessory gland within the upper eyelid (Krause's gland) has been reported in *Macaca*. A rudimentary Harderian gland has been found in the nictitating membranes of *Cercocebus* and *Macaca sylvana* by Franz (1934).

In the middle ear the Cynomorpha approximate to the Platyrrhini in the straight, feebly divergent crura of the stapes ; in the pongids the crura are curved and divergent, as in Man (Doran, 1879). The head of the malleus is club-shaped, supported on a short neck in cynomorphs, but a longer one in anthropomorphs (Werner, 1960).

Tactile vibrissae are further reduced on platyrrhine standards, being restricted in cynomorphs to short, sparsely planted facial hairs, particularly supraorbitally and on the lips. They are entirely lacking in Hominoidea, though vestiges may be found in the foetus. A transient carpal papilla has been reported even in a human foetus.

BEHAVIOURAL CHARACTERS

Behavioural patterns are amazingly diverse among Old World simians, so that a comprehensive account would be too lengthy at this stage. Details are deferred for consideration under the respective families and genera.

Regarding locomotion, for example, no common features are applicable to the whole of the Catarrhini. The main disparity occurs between the quadrupedal, arboreal leapers and runners (*e.g. Cercopithecus, Colobus*), the terrestrial pronograde cursorial forms (*Erythrocebus, Papio*) and, finally, the orthograde walkers and brachiators (*e.g. Hylobates, Pan*). A discussion on the phenomenon of brachiation is deferred (*infra*, p. 153), though the recent studies of Napier (1961, 1963), Erikson (1963), Ashton and Oxnard (1963, 1964), Oxnard (1963) and Ziegler (1964) are recommended for the attention of workers on this aspect of behaviour.

Dietetically the Catarrhini are equally varied, some species being highly catholic in their tastes, others remarkably specialized in correlation with restricted types of diet.

A major behavioural feature common, in some measure, to all the Catarrhini, is social organization—a subject upon which extensive studies, both in the field and under experimental conditions, have been made in recent

TABLE I

SOME SUGGESTED CATEGORY SYSTEMS FOR
SOCIAL BEHAVIOUR OF PRIMATES

Chance [1956]	McDowell, Davis and Steele [1956]	Scott [1958]
Sounds	Self-oriented units	Ingestive behaviour
Agonistic behaviour	Other-animal oriented units	Agonistic behaviour
Display of dominance	Inanimate object oriented units	Shelter-seeking
Copulatory behaviour	Rapid-energy-expenditure units	Sexual behaviour
Play	Visual survey units	Investigative behaviour
Bathing		Care-soliciting behaviour
Grooming		Care-giving behaviour
Erotic		Eliminative behaviour
Running		Allelomimetic behaviour
Huddling		
Social space		

Mason [1960]	Hammack [1960]	Plutchik [1962]
Approach	Shifts in location	Incorporation behaviour
Aggression	Aggression	Destruction behaviour
Sexual presentation	Cage manipulation	Reproduction behaviour
Mount	Block manipulation	Orientation behaviour
Play	Visual activity	Exploration behaviour
Visual orientation	Self grooming	Deprivation reactions
Groom	Resting	Protection behaviour
Social investigation		Rejection behaviour
Thrusting		
Social facilitation of exploration		
Withdrawal		

TABLE 2

ALTMANN'S CATALOGUE OF SOCIALLY SIGNIFICANT BEHAVIOUR PATTERNS IN *MACACA MULATTA*

1. Has erection of penis
2. Presents sexually to
3. Grasps waist of
4. Grips legs of
5. Gives pelvic thrusts to
6. Gnashes teeth
7. Grasps mounter
8. Ejaculates
9. Dismounts
10. Eats (own) ejaculate
11. Stimulates genitals manually (if reflexive : masturbates)
12. Gives ventral-embrace gesture to
13. Clings to (embraces) ventral surface of
14. Gives dorsal-embrace gesture to
15. Clings to dorsal surface of
16. Gives release-embrace gesture to
17. Stops embracing
18. Suckles (by mother)
19. Suckles from (by infant)
20. Prevents suckling on the part of
21. Shows incipient suckling from
22. Stimulates genitals orally ; fellatio
23. Holds nipple of
24. Ik, Ik, Ik . . . +spasms (frustration cry ?)
25. Plays with
26. Bites
27. Hits
28. Gives incipient chase to : lunges toward ; slaps ground toward
29. Ho ! (threat cry ?)
30. Bobs head (and thorax) toward
31. Gives open-jawed gesture toward
32. Stares at (beetle brows)
33. Looks at
34. Avoids staring at
35. Looks " apprehensively " toward
36. Eéé (fear-pain cry ?)
37. Holds tail erect
38. Grimaces toward
39. Smacks lips at
40. Krrr (?)
41. Walks toward
42. Runs toward : chases
43. Walks away from
44. Runs away from ; flees from
45. Follows
46. Walks past
47. Progresses
48. Hu, Hu, Hu (food-contentment cry ?)
49. Shakes limb
50. Presents for grooming to
51. Grooms
52. Pulls
53. Eats or drinks
54. Ignores
55. Ka ! (alarm cry ?)
56. Koo (play cry ?)

years,* while others are in progress. These are further discussed below under Cercopithecoidea (p. 165).

A useful general analysis by Plutchik (1964) has recently appeared. Plutchik adopts the definition of Baron and Littmann (1961), that social behaviour is " what one gets when behaviour of one or more individuals can be shown to be a function of the behaviour of others ", and he considers

---

* The following Catarrhini have been most intensively studied:

Macaca mulatta (Carpenter, 1942; Altmann, 1962; Koford, 1963, Southwick *et al.*, 1961 *a, b*; Southwick, 1962, 1963).

M. fuscata (Imanishi, 1957, 1960, Itani, 1959; Kawamura, 1959; *et al.*).

M. assamensis (Carpenter, 1942).

Papio sp. (Zuckerman, 1932 *c*; de Vore, 1962 *a, b*, 1963; de Vore and Washburn, 1960, 1962; Washburn and de Vore, 1961; Hall, 1960, 1961).

Semnopithecus (Jay, 1962).

Kasi (Ripley, 1964, in press).

Hylobates lar (Carpenter, 1940; Bernstein and Schusterman, 1964).

Pongo (Carpenter, 1938; Harrisson, 1962).

Pan (Nissen, 1931; Goodall, 1962, 1963; Kortlandt and Kooij, 1963).

Gorilla (Bingham, 1932; Emlen and Schaller, 1960; Schaller, 1963).

E

that such behaviour can be studied at almost any phylogenetic level (*e.g.* population dynamics, reproductive rates, etc.).

Plutchik tabulates categories of special significance in primate social behavioural patterns, as deduced from the writings of previous workers. These are here reproduced with the addition of important categories from Altmann (1962 *b*).   Tables 1 and 2.

Review summaries of recent work in the socio-biology and allied aspects of catarrhine behaviour are to be found in *Primate Social Behaviour*, edited by Southwick (1963), and more especially in the review of Mason and Rio-pelle (1964), where full bibliographies are presented.

GEOGRAPHICAL DISTRIBUTION

Catarrhini are distributed over the whole of the Old World range of the Pithecoidea (see map, fig. 13, Vol. III, p. 74).   Thus in Africa they occur throughout the tropical belt, at all altitudes short of the snow line.   Further-more they extend southwards in the subtropical zone to the Cape.   In the north the distribution is limited by the Sahara desert, but local populations (*e.g.* of *Papio* and *Erythrocebus*) range into the Sahel country, *e.g.* in the Aïr region and the Ennedi plateau.   Moreover a northward range along the Nile extended, during early historic times, into Egypt, although, at the present time, the northern limit in this region is the northern Sudan around Atbara. In Abyssinia, Grivet monkeys (*Cercopithecus aethiops aethiops*) range into the north of the country and extend eastwards thence to the Red Sea coast between Port Sudan and the Eritrean border.   In the same general area occur the Gelada (*Theropithecus*) and the Hamadryas Baboon (*Papio hama-dryas*), the latter also reappearing across the Red Sea in Arabia.

Separated by the Sahara from the other African simians, the Barbary Macaque (*Macaca sylvana*) ranges over north-western Africa and, in earlier times, extended much farther eastwards (Joleaud, 1931 ; Frechkop, 1951) ; presumably, at an earlier geological epoch, its range met that of the Asiatic macaques.   The Barbary ape also has the distinction of being the only subhuman primate surviving in Europe, where it is confined to the Rock of Gibraltar.   The European range, too, was much more extended in earlier geological ages, according to fossil evidence from the Pliocene of Western Europe, including England.

In Asia the Catarrhini affect chiefly the southern and eastern areas of the mainland and most of the islands, including Ceylon (but not the Lacca-dives or Maldives), the Andamans, Nicobars and all the Indonesian chain as far as Timor, as well as in the Philippines, Hainan, Hong Kong, Formosa and Japan.   Wallace's line is also transgressed in its northern extension in so far as macaques occur in Celebes, though not in New Guinea (*vide* Raven, 1935, p. 292, and Vol. III, pp. 72-75).

On the Asiatic mainland the western limit follows the western coast of peninsular India as far as the Kathiawar peninsula, but north of this the western extent skirts east of the arid north-western part of India until it meets the Himalayas. The foothills and southern ranges of the Himalayas are included in the catarrhine range, at least to altitudes locally of 12,000 ft. (Pocock, 1939). Eastwards, monkeys range into northern Burma, Siam, Indo-China and China, where, in Moupin, *Rhinopithecus* and *Macaca* occur in the Snowy Mountains at altitudes up to 3000 metres. Both in the Himalayas and Moupin, as well as in Japan, monkeys have been reported as thriving in places where snow periodically lies upon the trees and terrain. The Shimokita peninsula on the island of Honsyu is the northern limit of the distribution of the Japanese macaque (*Macaca fuscata*) and also of subhuman Primates throughout the world (Izawa and Nishida, 1963). From western China, macaques, related to the Rhesus, range north-eastwards skirting the headwaters of the Yang-tse in a broad swath as far as the province of Tche-li, crossing to the left bank of the Huang-ho. The lower Huang-ho Valley and the whole basin of the Yang-tse are at present uninhabited by monkeys, but the southern coastal tract, including the basin of the Si-kiang, supports a race of the Rhesus (*vide* Pocock, 1932 and Miller, 1933).

GEOLOGICAL HISTORY *

Aside from the problematic *Amphipithecus* and *Pondaungia* of the Upper Eocene of Burma, the earliest simian primates discovered in the Eastern hemisphere occur in the Oligocene beds of the Fayûm, some 100 miles inland from the Mediterranean coast of Egypt. At this epoch the area was forested and traversed by sluggish streams and supported, besides small early Catarrhini, a mammalian population comprising small rodents, and the ancestors of hyraxes, sirenians and proboscideans. Until recently only seven fragmentary specimens of early primates were known from these deposits, but these were augmented by over a hundred new specimens during recent expeditions under the auspices of Yale University (Simons, 1964).

Apart from the generalized *Parapithecus*, represented solely by a mandible, which is usually regarded as showing evidence of tarsioid origin, the Fayûm fossils already show evidence of early evolutionary divergence along two phyletic lines, one cercopithecoid and the other anthropoid (*i.e.* hominoid). Thus the recently discovered *Oligopithecus* (*infra*, p. 195) has molars which indicate that it may well be on or near the evolutionary line that gave rise to the superfamily Cercopithecoidea. On the other hand, a gibbon-like form (*Propliopithecus*) is also well represented in the Fayûm fauna. New well-preserved material of this or an allied genus was recovered in 1963 by

* See also Patterson, 1954.

the Yale expedition, and Simons believes that *Propliopithecus* is a more generalized hominoid that may be on the phyletic line leading to the great apes and Man.

During the succeeding Miocene, fossil representatives of both main groups are represented over a wide area. The most generalized cercopithecoid is probably the Lower Miocene *Mesopithecus*, originally discovered by Gaudry at Pikermi, Greece. Virtually a complete skeleton was recovered and its generalized status is manifested in so far as it presents features intermediate between the two living types represented by the macaques and the langurs. Subsequently material was recovered from East Africa and has been tentatively assigned to this genus by McInnes (1943) and by Clark and Leakey (1951).

Somewhat more recent are the remains of *Dolichopithecus*, two species of which (*D. ruscinensis* and *D. arvernensis*) were described by Depéret (1890, 1929) from the Lower Pliocene of France. In these the face is somewhat lengthened and the limbs short, suggesting an approach to the baboons. Of similar age is the fragment designated by Gervais (1947) as *Semnopithecus monspessulanus* in the belief that it was closely related to the existing langurs.

Contemporaneous with *Mesopithecus* in the Rift Valley area of East Africa and in the region around Lake Victoria, the hominoids were represented by both gibbon-like (*Limnopithecus*) and pongid types (*Proconsul*). The former differs little from the previously known and widely distributed European genus *Pliopithecus*, of which it may be no more than a subgenus (*vide* Simonetta, 1957).

Proconsul shows many features recalling the cynomorph monkeys, but also others demanding its inclusion within the Pongidae or great apes. At least three species have been recognized, one being a giant form (Clark and Leakey, *loc. cit.*).

Another important so-called synthetic form is the European genus *Oreopithecus* of the Late Miocene and early Pliocene of central Italy. Remains of this were first recovered nearly a hundred years ago and described by Gervais (1872). They were later studied by Ristori (1890), who detected resemblances in the lower jaw to *Papio* and *Cercopithecus*, while the upper jaw presented features recalling the anthropoid apes. Gregory noted resemblances between the lower cheek-teeth and those of the Fayûm genus *Apidium*, a likeness which has been amply confirmed in new material of the latter genus recovered by the Yale expeditions. Thanks to the indefatigable activities of the Swiss palaeontologist Hürzeler, numerous new and more complete skeletal remains have been recovered during the last decade. These have shown the apartness of *Oreopithecus* from other hominoids, probably warranting the erection of a separate family for its reception and indicating a divergent phyletic line paralleling in many ways that taken by the pongids.

Meantime, true man-like apes had evolved during the late Miocene and early Pliocene. A great centre of dispersal of these was in north-west India, where, in the Chinji and Nagri beds of the Siwalik Hills at the foot of the Himalayas, an abundance of fossil apes has been unearthed. These all pertain to a group known today as the Dryopithecinae, a subfamily based upon the genus *Dryopithecus*, originally founded in 1856 by Lartet upon a mandible from Saint-Gaudens, France. These dryopithecines have subsequently been shown to have occurred not only in western and central Europe, but to have migrated into Africa and also eastwards into China from the original Siwalik centre of origin. Many of the newer finds have received generic names, such as *Sivapithecus*, *Hispanopithecus*, *Austriacopithecus* and *Udabnopithecus*, but in all probability all of them, including even *Proconsul*, are reducible to the synonymy of *Dryopithecus* (*fide* Simon, 1964). One at least of the later Indian dryopithecines, namely *Ramapithecus*, which shows a more advanced dentition foreshadowing that of Man, deserves separate status.

From the mid Pliocene onwards, fossil catarrhines become more numerous. Among cynomorphs the somewhat isolated *Libypithecus* is represented by an almost complete skull from Egypt. It stands possibly in ancestral relationship to *Theropithecus*. In the Siwaliks, it is only in the more recent Dhok-Pathan zone that cynomorphs are well represented ; and here were found a *Cercopithecus* (*C. asnoti*) and a *Macaca* (*M. sivalensis*). In the uppermost Pliocene true baboons are known from the Siwaliks (*Papio falconeri*), from China (*Procynocephalus*) and from South Africa (*Parapapio*, *Dinopithecus*, *Gorgopithecus* and *Brachygnathopithecus*) and East Africa (*Simopithecus*, *Dinopithecus*).

Macaques were widely distributed in Europe during this period and numerous names have been given to them (*M. priscus*, *M. florentinus*, *M. suevicus*, *M. tolosanus*), but there is some doubt as to whether or not these are merely temporal varieties of *M. sylvana* (see *antea*, p. 50), an explanation which applies with even more force to the Pleistocene forms *M. majori* (from Sardinia) and *M. trarensis* (from Algeria).

A cranium from the Pleistocene of north Viet-nam has been described by Jouffroy (1959 *b*) as an extinct form of the Stump-tailed Macaque (*M. speciosa*).

The phyletic line leading to the true hominids was pushed back to the Pontian (early Pliocene) by Leakey's (1962) announcement of the discovery of an upper jaw of *Kenyapithecus* in East Africa. Its dentition resembles that of *Dryopithecus*, and even more of *Ramapithecus*, so that the new form occupies the gap between the last mentioned and the Australopithecinae, though closer to the former.

The name Australopithecinae has been employed for a large series of fossils, mainly from South and East Africa, but also represented by more

recent finds in Asia (Palestine, Java, China). Their exact date has always
been somewhat doubtful, but all the evidence points to their having lived
during the Middle Pleistocene. The first to be made known was *Australopithecus africanus*, described by Dart (1925) on the basis of an almost complete skull, with a natural endocranial cast, of a juvenile with complete milk
dentition plus M.$\frac{1}{1}$. Dart's insistence that this represented a truly transitional being between ape and Man led to considerable controversy which
was only cleared up after many years and the intervening recovery of further
fossils, including skulls of adults. These discoveries were the result of the
labours of Broom and Robinson. Many of the specimens received new
generic names, but recent studies have tended to reduce most of them to
synonymy. In any event all are conveniently grouped under the general
subfamilial name, Australopithecinae. From these forms to the earliest
representatives of the human family, *e.g. Pithecanthropus* of the Pleistocene
of Java and China, the transition is nowadays regarded as phylogenetically
feasible. (For further details consult the chapters by Remane and Heberer
in *Primatologia*, i. 1956, and the above-mentioned article by Simons.)

TAXONOMY

As will have been gathered from the foregoing sections, especially that
on geological history, the Catarrhini are basically divisible into two main
series, to which Huxley (1872) gave the names Cynomorpha and Anthropomorpha, respectively. The former, the dog-like quadrupedal monkeys, are
contrasted with the man-shaped orthograde forms. Simpson (1931, 1945)
gives these groups superfamily rank and alters the names, to adjust to the
current usage regarding superfamilial nomenclature, to Cercopithecoidea and
Hominoidea. Aside from other peculiarities the two groups differ fundamentally in respect of the cusp patterns of their molar crowns, these being
more specialized in the cynomorphs, where the two anterior cusps and the
two posterior cusps are each joined by transverse ridges giving a bilophodont
character. This contrasts with the simpler five-cusped anthropoid molars,
where the depressions between the cusps are arranged in the form of a **Y**
with the stem anteriorly (the so-called Y-5 or dryopithecine pattern).

Subordinate taxa are variously treated as regards status by different
authorities. Many writers treat all the existing cynomorphs under a single
family Cercopithecidae, but valid reasons support Pocock's (1926) contention
that the specialized leaf-eaters (commonly treated as the subfamily Colobinae) be raised to family rank (Colobidae), leaving the Cercopithecidae to
embrace the guenons, macaques, mangabeys and baboons. This becomes
even more imperative when, as will be discussed hereafter, the differences

within the restricted family Cercopithecidae are taken into account and designated by subfamilial rank.

The question of the status of the early fossil cynomorphs is somewhat controversial. The Oligocene *Parapithecus* is by general consensus given separate family rank, Parapithecidae, but opinions differ as to whether this is to be aligned with the Cercopithecoidea or the Hominoidea. In view of its antiquity and possible ancestral relationship to both superfamilies, a basal position seems to be called for. The taxonomic reference for the other early forms is even more questionable, but for the present those not showing definite hominoid features may most conveniently be considered alongside *Parapithecus*. The gibbon-like fossils automatically link up with the recent gibbons within the Hominoidea, where they may be treated as a separate family, Hylobatidae, though some prefer to give them subfamily rank only, and at least one writer (Simonetta, 1957) includes them in the Hominidae (see below).

The great apes constitute a well-defined family, Pongidae (Simiidae of nineteenth-century authors), but within this the fossil *Dryopithecus* and its allies constitute a clearly distinguishable subfamily (Dryopithecinae). Similarly *Australopithecus* and its allies constitute another (Australopithecinae), but whether this is to be contained within the Pongidae (where Simpson places it) or transferred to the human family (Hominidae), as several recent workers prefer, is a debatable situation.

Some (*e.g.* Simonetta, 1957) even take the view that the Pongidae are not separable at the family level from the Hominidae, treating the gibbons, great apes and Man under the family Hominidae.

Controversial also is the status of *Oreopithecus*. Although at first treated as a cynomorph, the later discovery of fresh and more complete skeletons forces us to revise the situation. There is no doubt that *Oreopithecus* stands at the parting of the ways between the two divergent evolutionary lines, the cynomorph and the anthropomorph, and yet is sufficiently distinct from either to warrant a family of its own, Oreopithecidae. The exact relationship of this to the two lines is doubtful, and one view has it that it represents an independent phyletic line, intermediate between the two that lead to the existing apes and monkeys.

Accordingly, for the present, the scheme delineated herewith is accepted as a general classification of the Catarrhini down to the subfamilial level :

Infraorder Catarrhini E. Geoffroy, 1812, p. 87

Superfamily I. *Cercopithecoidea* Simpson, 1931, p. 271 (=Cynomorpha Huxley, 1872, p. 469).

† Family 1. *Parapithecidae* Schlosser, 1911, p. 58.

Family 2. *Cercopithecidae* Gray, 1821, p. 297 (restricted).

Subfamily (a) Cercopithecinae Blanford, 1888 (Guenons).

„ (b) Cynopithecinae Mivart, 1865, p. 547 (or preferably Papioninae, based on the name of the earliest named genus) (Macaques, Mangabeys, Baboons).

Family 3. *Colobidae* Blyth, 1875, p. 9 (Langurs and Colobs).

Superfamily II. *Hominoidea* Simpson, 1931, p. 272 (=Anthropomorpha, Huxley, 1872, p. 474).

† Family 1. *Oreopithecidae* Schwalbe, 1916, p. 149.

Family 2. *Hylobatidae* Blyth, 1875, p. 1 (Gibbons).

Family 3. *Pongidae* Elliot, 1913, i, XXVII (=Simiidae Bonaparte, 1850).

† Subfamily (a) Dryopithecinae Gregory and Hellman, 1939, p. 370.
„ (b) Ponginae Allen, 1925, p. 477.
† „ (c) Australopithecinae Gregory and Hellman, 1939, p. 370.

Family 4. *Hominidae* Gray, 1825, p. 338 (Mankind).

Superfamily CERCOPITHECOIDEA Simpson, 1931

OLD WORLD MONKEYS, or CYNOMORPH CATARRHINES

(SYN.: Family Cercopithecidae Gray, 1821, p. 297; Cynocephalina, Gray, 1825, p. 9; Cercopithedae, Burnett, 1828, p. 307; Cynopithecina, Geoffroy, 1843, p. 495; Cynopithecini, Huxley, 1864, p. 671; Cynopithecinae, Mivart, 1865, p. 547; Menocerca Haeckel, 1866, p. clx; Cynomorpha, Huxley, 1871, p. 469; Cynopithecidae, Gill, 1872, p. 2; Papionidae, Blyth, 1875, p. 4; Cynopitheci, Macalister, 1878, p. 325; Cercopithecini, Winge, 1924; Lasiopygidae, Elliot, 1911, p. 341, 1913, 2, p. 115; G. M. Allen, 1925, p. 306.)

DEFINITION.—Quadrupedal plantigrade or subplantigrade catarrhines with the pelvic limbs longer than the pectorals; with more or less prominent muzzles; with large canines separated by diastemata from adjacent teeth; with the anterior lower premolar bearing a simple pointed crown and an oblique, trenchant, anterior edge biting against the upper canine; with bilophodont molar crowns; the protocones and hypocones of the upper molars equally developed (cf. Hominoidea); hairs on pectoral limbs directed distad throughout; with moderate to large naked callosities overlying the expanded ischial tuberosities; with a median laryngeal air-sac expanding over the front of the neck (at least in males); tail present or absent; thorax laterally compressed; thoraco-lumbar vertebrae exceeding eighteen; sternum narrow, elongated; pelvis narrow with iliac fossa flattened; caecum conical or globose lacking an appendix vermiformis; placenta usually bidiscoidal.

The name Cercopithecoidea is derived from what may be regarded as the type genus of the group so named, *i.e. Cercopithecus*. This name itself is of interest in so far as it signifies an ape with a tail and it is to be presumed that apes lacking or apparently lacking this appendage were already known to the ancients who first used the name (see below under historical section dealing with genus *Cercopithecus*). The distinction between tailed and tailless forms, however, is of no special genetic significance in as much as reduction of the appendage to the point of virtual disappearance has occurred independently in several different phyletic lines. Duckworth (1915) notes that as early as 1572, Volcher Coiter, a renowned comparative anatomist in his day, drew attention to the distinction between true and tailed apes in his *Analogia ossium humanorum simiae et verae et caudatae quae Cynocephali similis est, atque vulpis.*

This is not to say, therefore, that the Cercopithecoidea, as a group, are distinguished from the remaining Catarrhini by virtue of possessing a tail. Most of them certainly do, and in by far the majority the appendage is long to very long. In the more terrestrial forms shortening tends to occur, *e.g.* in baboons, in some of which, *e.g.* the Drill and Mandrill, it is reduced to a mere stump. A trend towards taillessness also appears among the macaques, a few of which are long tailed, but others show varying degrees of shortening, culminating in the Barbary Ape (*Macaca sylvana*), which is virtually tailless, at least so far as an external tail is concerned. The Celebesian macaques too show extreme reduction in the tail. On the other hand all members of the genus *Cercopithecus* and its allies, also *Cercocebus*, *Colobus* (*s. lato*) and its Asiatic relatives the langurs (*Presbytis*, etc.) are long tailed, with the sole exception of the curious short-tailed *Simias* of Pagi Island, Sumatra.

STRUCTURE

I. External Features

All Cercopithecoidea are recognizably monkeys—a statement which barely applies to every platyrrhine primate, *i.e.* all are, in general, man-shaped but quadrupedal with subequal fore- and hind-limbs terminating in elongated pentadactyl cheiridia, as opposed to the Hominoidea, where one pair of limbs is longer (usually considerably longer) than the other. The African Colobidae are exceptional in lacking the pollex, but otherwise this digit is moderately to well developed and more completely opposable than in any platyrrhine.

In general, the head is rounded with a moderately produced muzzle only, but the baboons are exceptional in the extreme elongation of the muzzle. Callosities are invariably present over the ischial tubera, and are recognizable well before birth. The tail, generally long and non-prehensile, has already been discussed above. Cheek pouches sometimes occur and where present are correlated with a simple form of stomach (Cercopithecidae), whereas if lacking (Colobidae) a specialized sacculated stomach invariably occurs.

REGIONAL DETAILS

EYES.—The eyes are, for the most part, large and deeply pigmented, but in baboons they are proportionately small to the body size.

NOSE.—The nose is typically flattened and the oval nostrils separated merely by a narrow septum. The narial openings face downwards or downwards and forwards. *Nasalis* and *Rhinopithecus* and its allies are exceptional in possessing a raised external nose, which, in the first mentioned, attains to positively grotesque proportions, at least in adult males. *Colobus* (*s. lato*) is also somewhat exceptional by normal catarrhine standards in showing

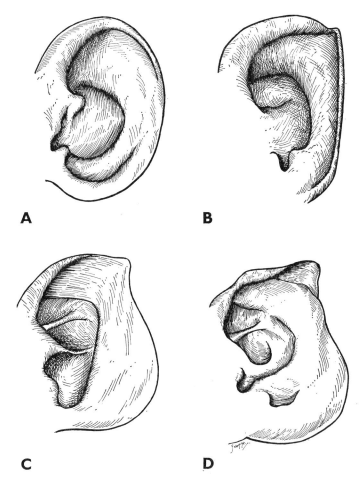

FIG. 3.—Graduated series showing variations in the form of the pinna among cynomorph monkeys : A, *Cercopithecus cephus* ; B, *Colobus polykomos polykomos* ; C, *Macaca silenus* ; D, *Papio cynocephalus*

not only slight elevation of the rhinal area but also in the relatively broad septum (cf. *Brachyteles*, Vol. V, p. 254.)

EARS.—The ears are much as in the more advanced Cebidae, being oval to rounded, but in many forms, *e.g. Macaca, Papio*, a distinct apex is developed at the junction of the superior and posterior borders of the pinna. In such cases the helical fold extends only part way along the superior border. In other cases the apical region itself is incorporated in the fold and the tip then reduced to a tubercle (Darwin's or Woolner's tubercle) or it may be altogether lacking. In any event all the parts recognized in the human auricle, except the lobule, are homologously represented in the cercopithecoid organ, and in much the same proportion to each other. Frequence of Darwinian tubercle in Catarrhini (from Keith, 1901):

	No. Examined	Present (%)
Cercopithecus	19	80
Macaca	21	95
Baboons	15	100
Langurs	29	45
Gibbons	12	0
Orang-utans	15	40
Chimpanzees	23	9
Gorillas	19	26

PELAGE.—Hair tracts have been described by Schwalbe for *Macaca irus* where a rather generalized condition occurs, lacking the complications, especially on the head, found in other members of its genus and of other genera of the suborder.

In the late foetus of *M. irus* the following data are recorded :

(*a*) Sinus hairs are restricted to four zones of the head, supraorbital region, lateral nasal region and the upper and lower lips. None occur on cheeks or interramal area and there is little or no evidence of elevation of skin at the sites of implantation.

(*b*) From the brows a cranio-caudal stream covers the crown ; laterally there is an uninterrupted stream, but on the median area a vortex may be present, for some races of *M. irus* show, in the adult, a crest in this location, though in others there is no interruption here of the cranio-caudal stream.

(*c*) The primitive cranio-caudal stream extends posteriorly along the back and on to the dorsum of the tail, but usually on the tail it divides into two lateral symmetrical subdivisions.

(*d*) No whorls appear on the flanks, nor in the upper pectoral region.

(*e*) On the pectoral limb the elbow is the site of convergence of two streams, one proceeding distally from the upper arm and the other proximally from the forearm. The hairs of the forearm are not entirely directed| disto-proximally as in the Pongidae, but take a varying oblique course from the radial border disto-proximally. But in the more proximal region the hairs become more transversely disposed and tend eventually towards the summit of the olecranon (see fig. 4 from Schwalbe).

(*f*) On the hind-limb a simple proximo-distal trend occurs.

CUTANEOUS PIGMENTATION.—This is discussed fully below under *Cercopithecus* (*infra*, p. 222).

CUTANEOUS GLANDS.—In spite of the prevalence of a distinctive body odour in most, if not all, species of Cercopithecoidea, cutaneous glands, serving as a source of scent, have generally been regarded as insignificant or lacking (Zuckerman, 1933, p. 66).

The only localized glandular apparatus is that reported by Hill (1944, 1954, 1955) associated with a specialized tuft of modified hair on the mid-sternal area in *Mandrillus*. Isolated glandular pores exuding a dark brown waxy secretion are prevalent in the inguinal region of some species of *Cercopithecus* and more sparsely elsewhere on the ventral surface.

Odours produced fall into the garlic-like category, but vary distinctly from genus to genus. They are difficult to assess, though familiarity with them permits recognition of a particular species by its aroma, *e.g.* especially characteristic are the scents of the Celebesian apes and certain groups of *Cercopithecus* and *Cercocebus*.

Circumanal glands include both apocrine and holocrine types and are more numerous according to Tachibana (1936) in lower monkeys than in the Hominoidea, and furthermore increase numerically with age. Genera studied include *Papio*, *Cynopithecus*, *Macaca*, *Cercocebus*, *Cercopithecus* and *Semnopithecus*. Further studies on cutaneous glands in *Macaca cyclops*, at fifteen different bodily sites, have been made by Yoshioka (1936) with particular reference to the quantitative representation of sweat glands and sebaceous glands.

CHEIRIDIA.—In adaptation to an arboreal existence, hands and feet contrast with those of most members of the Hominoidea in being narrow and elongated, with the digits tending to align in the sagittal axis, though capable of limited divarication. Pollex and more especially hallux are fully opposable. Interdigital webbing variable and often considerable, at least between certain digits.

Palms and soles are relatively flattened—a condition which has evoked the term " monkey-paw " to describe certain pathological wasting conditions in Man. This is due partly to lesser development of the hypothenar and thenar groups of muscles and to the partial effacement of torulae tactiles. Nevertheless the pads are well seen in the foetus and are recognizable even in the mature hand and foot, though more from the disposition of the ridge patterns upon them than by definite local elevations. Thus all the pads except the proximal thenar pad are represented in the palm.

The exposed hairless areas on palm and sole are completely covered with continuous patterns of papillary ridges, the increase being correlated with the greater tactile power required in an arboreal environment. On the digits patterns occur not only on the apical pads, but also on the proximal and intermediate segments.

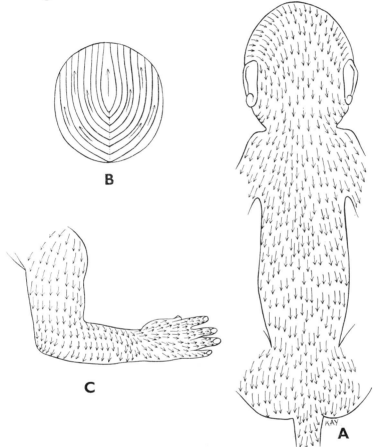

FIG. 4.—*Macaca irus*. Foetus showing hair tracts of A, dorsal surface; B, Crown; C, right pectoral limb. Redrawn from Schwalbe

Interdigital pads are also represented, but are displaced somewhat towards the tibial side on the planta. Moreover, the first interdigital is continuous with an elongated eminence extending proximally almost to the heel, possibly the equivalent of the proximal thenar pad. Similarly the fourth interdigital is confluent with the elongated but narrower hypothenar pad, which reaches the heel. Ridged skin extends backwards on to the heel.

Over the summits of the interdigital pads entwined loops (*vortices duplicati*) are frequently developed. Between these fields the volar skin is marked by parallel curved ridges which radiate distally from an origin in the carpal region.

Apical pads on the manual digits bear patterns of elliptical loops, but on the pollex especially, appearances suggest the occurrence of entwined loops termed by Schlaginhaufen (1905, 1906) *vortex duplicatus.*

On the intermediate phalangeal area ridges form transverse parallel fields or sometimes flattened arches ; they are less dense here and occasionally (as in some specimens of *Macaca irus*) fail to appear. Over the proximal phalanges the ridges course obliquely on the pollex, but on the other digits arched or looped patterns may occur.

On the plantar skin, ridge patterns are much as on the hand, but special features have been pointed out by Schlaginhaufen distinguishing the cynomorph catarrhines from the other Old World Primates, including Man, and also differing among the different groups of the Cercopithecoidea.

Particularly important is the course of a line labelled R_{13a} by Schlaginhaufen (1906). This line or radius derives from a triradius (T.13) at the base of the first interdigital pad, passing usually towards the preaxial (tibial) margin of the planta. In the cynocephalous catarrhines, however, the line cuts transversely across the sole to the postaxial (fibular) border thereby isolating the configurational fields over the remaining interdigital pads from those over the proximal pads. It would seem to be a modification which has arisen in association with the more terrestrial habits of this group of catarrhines—a suggestion which receives added support from the fact that the same arrangement exists in the terrestrial genus *Erythrocebus* (*vide* Midlo and Cummins, 1940, figs. 424-425).

II. Skeletal System

SKULL

The cranial skeleton is subject to so much variation in proportions and in other anatomical details in the various members of this group that little of a general nature can be stated. Typically the skull recalls that of such a platyrrhine monkey as *Cebus*, with a relatively globular brain-case and flattened face with large, forwardly directed orbits, reduced nasal region and relatively small mandible. Such a cranium exists in the genus *Cercopithecus* and some members of the Colobidae, but greater disproportion between facial and cerebral components becomes increasingly manifest in passing to such genera as *Macaca*, *Cercocebus* and finally the various baboons (*Papio*, etc.) where the facial elongation produces the dog-like muzzle that has been recognized since ancient times as their especial characteristic, and which exceeds all muzzle development even in the lower prosimians. It is, therefore, presumably a secondarily derived feature rather than a retained primitive condition, placing the baboons at the apex of a phyletic line rather than on the low plane, where they were placed by the early, pre-Darwinian zoologists.

On the brain-case temporal ridges are frequently developed and sometimes meet at the vertex to form a median sagittal line or even an upstanding crest. In front they diverge towards the lateral orbital rims into which they merge. Above the orbits supraorbital ridges or tori may occur and may be separated from the frontal squame by a transverse depression. Posteriorly a transverse line or crest (occipital crest) may be equally developed. Much controversy has arisen as to whether or not this is an independent structure from the sagittal or temporal crest. From a study of specific differences within the genus *Colobus* (*s. lato*) Vogel (1962) has recently shown that the development of the sagittal crest is dependent on a quantitative relation between masticatory apparatus and brain-case only within a uniform proportional type: " An alteration of the proportional type is possible within a narrow systematical category. Therefore the crista sagittalis cannot be used for phylogenetical conclusions." In the largest forms of *Colobus*, where the facial structure is greatest and the brain-case relatively small, the sagittal crest is short, confined to the lambdoid region and associated with a high occipital crest. On the other hand the small *C. verus*, with small jaws and relatively large brain-case, shows a long sagittal crest extending well forward on the frontal bone, but only a feeble occipital crest. Morphologically *C. badius* is cranially intermediate in these respects.

The orbit is separated from the temporal fossa, as in all Pithecoidea, by a bony partition. The naso-lachrymal duct opens within the orbital margin. On the medial orbital wall the lachrymal is separated by a process of maxilla from the os planum of the ethmoid. The interorbital septum is, however, narrow, especially posteriorly and in the neonatus and juvenile stages. The infraorbital canal, bearing the infraorbital nerve and vessels, is not roofed in by bone, except where the canal pierces the orbital margin to appear on the face ; there are usually several perforations which may differ in number on the two sides. Up to seven have been seen, *e.g.* in *Mandrillus sphinx* and *Cercocebus*.

On the side wall of the brain-case the squamous temporal typically projects forwards to meet the frontal over a greater or lesser distance, thus separating the alisphenoid from the antero-inferior angle of the parietal. There are, however, numerous variations even within a single genus. On the whole, the African species seem to favour the fronto-temporal pterion whilst the Oriental langurs commonly show a parieto-alisphenoid union as in Man and many prosimians. A frequent anomaly is an X-pterion, where the squamosal just touches the frontal.

In no cercopithecoid does the malar send a process on the orbital wall to meet the parietal—a typically platyrrhine specialization.

The external auditory passage is represented by a bony tube prolonged from the tympanic annulus of the newborn. An auditory bulla is lacking, though the anterior part of the petrosal may appear inflated to some degree inferiorly.

The glenoid fossa is relatively deep and the post-glenoid tubercle well developed and spinose.

In contrast to the Hominoidea a true styloid process is not developed, but a well developed stylo-mandibular ligament is present, attached above to a false styloid of uncertain homology, yet functionally equivalent to the hominid styloid (Zuckerman *et al.*, 1962).

The palate is elongated in the sagittal plane in proportion to the degree of prognathism. It is commonly parallel-sided, but in some of the smaller species (*e.g. Cercopithecus*) some posterior convergence of the alveolar processes occurs.

In very few cynomorph monkeys has the lesser hyoid cornu any ossification, but in some examples of *Cercopithecus* Flower (1870) found a short, bony ceratohyal similar to that in platyrrhine monkeys. Thyrohyals, on the contrary, are always ossified, being straight, long and transversely compressed.

The basihyal is shield-shaped, concave dorsally and strongly convex ventrally. The dorsal concavity lodges the median ventral laryngeal air-sac (saccus medianus laryngeus superior).

Post-cranial Axial Skeleton

Cervical vertebrae are invariably seven in number, but the formula in other regions varies from genus to genus. Typically thoraco-lumbars number 19 and of these the rib-bearing vertebrae may be 12 or 13. The anticlinal vertebrae is usually the tenth thoracic. Lumbars are characterized by spinose anapophyses directed backwards and slightly dorsad from the neural arches, and embracing the pre-zygapophyses of the next vertebra. Sacrals usually number three; but the postsacrals vary considerably according to variations in tail length. They may be as few as three (*Macaca*) or as many as 31 [*Semnopithecus* (Mivart)].

Spinal curvature is relatively slight, but according to Cunningham (1886) the curves met with in the human spine are sometimes seen in rudimentary degree. Thus the cervical region shows a ventral convexity, and its spinous processes tend to converge so as to form, with the intervening fibro-muscular structures, a median nuchal septum. The thoraco-lumbar region is relatively straight, but with a general arc-like trend. A more pronounced ventral convexity affects the hinder lumbar region due to the uptilting of the sacrum, to be followed by a variable amount of sacral concavity. These features are best noted in the baboons.

The thoracic cage is of the quadrupedal type, laterally compressed and deepened dorso-ventrally, but the thoracic index shows a fair range of variation. Ribs are relatively narrow, none showing the broadening characteristic of a few genera of Platyrrhini, or of the Pongidae. Similarly the sternum is of the narrow quadrupedal pattern, contrasting strongly with the latisternal Hominoidea. It consists of six ossified sternebrae, all rod-like except the manubrium, which is laterally expanded and dorso-ventrally flattened. Eight pairs of costal cartilages unite with it laterally.

Appendicular Skeleton

The clavicle is more obliquely disposed than in Man and shows a lesser degree of sinuosity. Its acromial end is flattened and directed dorsad. The sternal end is straight. A distinct impression for the subclavius is present and there is a bony ridge associated with the attachment of the deltoid muscle.

The scapula varies considerably in general outline and in details, but on the average the scapular index is high, the bone being broad in proportion to its length. Duckworth (1915) gives an approximate index (presumably for *Cercopithecus* or *Macaca*) of 118 compared with an average human index of 65. The bone thus resembles that of other quadrupedal mammals rather than that of the erect-walking type, where the pectoral limbs are freed from bearing the body weight. Nevertheless the bone is more variable than commonly supposed even within a single genus (*vide* under *Cercopithecus, infra*, p. 253).

Variations also occur in respect of the relative areas of supraspinous and infraspinous fossae, size and site of the spinous process, and development along the axillary border. A coraco-scapular notch is usually lacking and the acromion process small.

On the humerus the lateral lip of the bicipital groove is very prominent, but the medial lip is generally feebler or even lacking. An entepicondylar foramen is lacking. Differentiation at the distal end between capitellum and trochlea is less distinct than in the Hominoidea, while the form of the capitellum especially indicates that the flexion and extension movements required in quadrupedal progression have not been encroached upon by pronation and supination.

Torsion of the humeral shaft is considerable—around 100° compared with that of Carnivora (95°, Broca); the average human (European) value is 161°.

Radius and ulna articulate with each other and with the humerus so as to permit a fair degree of pronation and supination.

In the carpus the os centrale is distinct, whilst the pisiform is large, rod-like and provided with an epiphysis at its free extremity. Proximally the carpus articulates both with radius and ulna.

F

The pollex is short, due to the shortness of its individual phalanges rather than to any reduction in the metacarpal. Reduction is greater in Colobidae than Cercopithecidae, an external thumb being absent in *Colobus*.

Like the thorax the pelvis is transversely narrowed and its canal cylindrical. Innominate bones are antero-posteriorly elongated, strongly contrasting with the bones in Man and to a lesser degree with those in other Hominoidea. There is an elongated symphysis between the pubes extending back also to involve part of the ventral processes of the ischia. Ischial tuberosities are invariably large with expanded subcutaneous surfaces related to the cutaneous callosities. These vary in size, reaching their maximum development in the baboons.

In the femur the shaft is relatively straight and bears a small head and short neck. Greater and lesser trochanters are well developed, but a third trochanter is not usually present. The linea aspera is feebly developed, but a linea spiralis is commonly well marked. Lateral expansion of the distal end of the bone is less advanced than in Hominoidea, but the curvature of the condyles, when viewed from the side, is more nearly semicircular, indicating a freer range of movement than in the orthograde apes.

The narrow patella is related about equally to each femoral condyle. Posterior to the knee joint, fabellae are developed in the heads of the gastrocnemius. Additional sesamoid bones may occur, *e.g.*, in the tendon of the soleus (cyamella).

Tibia and fibula are separate and much resemble their human representatives except for certain proportional measurements. The pedal skeleton, including the tarsus, is relatively flattened, lacking the familiar arches of the human foot. Constituent bones, however, are arranged as in Man, with the exception of the hallux, which is fully opposable and articulated with the entocuneiform by a saddle-like joint. The hallux is short compared with the other digits, but as in the pollex, this is due to the shortness of the phalanges. In no case is it reduced to the extent met with in the case of the pollex. A large sesamoid (os peronaeum) is developed in the peroneus longus tendon as it passes from the lateral to the inferior surface of the cuboid bone.

III. Myology

The platysma is strongly developed and extensive, traceable, from the pectoral region forwards, over the clavicles to the mid-line of the nape and to the zygoma. Locally, where the buccal pouch protrudes in the Cercopithecidae, it is somewhat attenuated. A sphincter colli is also well developed deep to the above (Ruge, 1887). On the flanks a dorso-humeralis sheet converges towards the axilla, where it is well marked, inserting on the humerus by a tendinous band prolonged into the distal part of the deep pectoral aponeurosis. Duckworth (1915) found this muscle innervated in *Mandrillus* by fibres derived from the medial cord of the brachial plexus and by the lateral branch of the second thoracic nerve.

Facial muscles are powerfully developed, on a massive scale, associated more with the facility for grimacing than showing finer shades of expression which make the facial features of, for example, the Hominoidea, so much more delicate. These muscles are divisible into a superficial and a deep layer. The former are derivatives of the platysma and include the superficial muscles of the cranial vault, extrinsic and intrinsic ear muscles and the superficial mimetic muscles of the face. Deeper muscles are derivitives of sphincter colli. These include the buccinator-orbicularis oris system, orbicularis oculi and certain auricular and preauricular muscles. Noteworthy, is the decussation of platysma fibres below the chin—probably correlated with the presence of the buccal pouch.

In the orbit a retractor bulbi (m. choanoides) occurs constantly—an unusual finding, since the muscle, though usual in lower mammals, is lacking in *Tarsius*, Platyrrhini and in Hominoidea (Ottley, 1879).*

The anterior bellies of the two digastrics fuse to form a fan-shaped sheet connecting the two horizontal mandibular rami and are broadened behind by a fibrous arcade on to which the intermediate tendons insert (Parson's type I). A variable amount of fusion with the underlying mylohyoideus is present, due to incomplete differentiation in the embryo (Gegenbaur, 1899). Fleshy fibres of digastrics thicken towards the mandible but leave no digastric fossa marking the site of attachment. The posterior belly is related to the stylohyoideus, which divides below to embrace the intermediate tendon.

Omohyoideus lacks a central tendon. The other infrahyoid muscles exhibit nothing peculiar.

Sterno-cleido-mastoideus has usually two heads, sternal and clavicular, but the latter occasionally fails. The belly is massive and inserts above on the mastoid region and occipital bone.

In the diaphragm, arcuate ligaments are lacking or indistinct, the fleshy fibres arising locally from the fascia over quadratus lumborum. Crural origins may extend posteriorly more than usual, *e.g.* to L.4 in *Semnopithecus* (Kohlbrugge, 1897).

Perineal muscles remain very primitive in the female, proceeding very little beyond the sphincter cloacae condition. In the male, however, differentiation is as advanced as in the hominid male, but a levator penis is developed in addition, although superficial and deep transversus perinaei are not represented. Ischio-cavernosus and bulbo-cavernosus are relatively much larger than in Hominoidea. A levator ani as understood in the Hominoidea does not here exist, the caudal connections remaining in evidence and therefore functionally related to tail movements rather than to maintenance of the status of pelvic viscera.

* Except as an anomaly (*e.g.* Whitnall, 1911).

Trapezius inserts on the lateral fifth of the clavicle, and is thus widely separated from the clavicular head of the sterno-mastoid.   Beneath the acromial part of this muscle is the omo-trachelian slip (levator claviculae) which resembles that of the Pongidae.   Similarly related to the rhomboideus sheet is the occipito-scapularis or rhomboideus capitis.   Otherwise the rhomboideus sheet remains undivided.

Deltoideus has a long clavicular origin, occupying the whole ventral surface of the bone.   It may also extend along the whole length of the scapular spine as far as the vertebral border, though the more dorsal parts may become aponeurotic.   Nothing peculiar affects the other scapular muscles.

Pectoralis major usually lacks a clavicular head, its origin being confined to the sternum, though the presternal element is large, thickened and partly differentiated from the remainder.   Fibres of the two sides meet in the midline.

Fibres derived from the rectus abdominis sheath and neighbouring parts of the sternum constitute a pectoralis abdominis.   It is a derivative of the deeper pectoralis sheet (entopectoral layer).

Pectoralis minor also springs from the sternum, having no costal connections ;   it inserts by a fascial band which passes over the coracoid to the shoulder-joint capsule.   Medial to it, and arising from the hinder costal cartilages, is a pectoralis tertius, whose fibres proceed parallel to those of the preceding, and end in the fascial sheet over the capsule of the shoulder joint. Subclavius is strongly developed and less transversely aligned than in the Hominoidea.   A single costo-sternalis is present compared with two in prosimians and none in Hominoidea.

Latissimus dorsi near its insertion gives rise to the dorso-epitrochlearis or latissimo-epicondyloideus, which proceeds along the medial aspect of the brachium together with the extensors to insert on the medial epicondyle. Latissimus proper remains fleshy till near the humerus.   It lacks a scapular slip.   Its most cranial fibres pass behind the tendon of teres major of which these fibres may be an aberrant portion (Kohlbrugge, 1897 ;   Duckworth, 1915).

Biceps brachii is two-headed and lacks a lacertus fibrosus.   Coracobrachialis is generally differentiated into a long (coraco-brachialis medius) and a short portion (coraco-brachialis profundus).   The latter is usually absent in Hominoidea.   Brachialis may show incipient division at its origin ;   it varies in robusticity, being stronger in Cynopithecinae than in Cercopithecinae. There may also be some incorporation with fibres from brachio-radialis.

Triceps is always powerfully developed, especially the long head, which extends its origin some distance along the axillary border of the scapula. An anconaeus lateralis is present.

An epitrochleo-anconeus may occur as in other lower Primates but not in the Hominoidea ; it appears to be a vestige of the primitive humeral origin of flexor carpi ulnaris.

Pronator teres never shows an ulnar head, neither is there usually a radial or coronoid head for flexor digitorum sublimis (cf. Hominoidea). There is no separate flexor pollicis longus, the tendon to the pollex proceeding obliquely from the common digital flexor profundus tendon at the wrist. An accessory head of the deep flexor arising from the flexor sublimis is the rule ; it is a relic of the primitive connection between superficial and deep flexor layers.

Brachio-radialis inserts, as in Man, at the base of the radial styloid. In most Hominoidea it inserts more proximally, even as high (e.g. in gibbons) as the middle of the shaft.

Pollicial muscles differ little from those of prosimians, but each of the other digits is provided with two extensor tendons, a superficial (from extensor communis) and an independent deep tendon (extensor indicis, medius, annularis and digiti minimi).

Ectoglutaeus, as in other quadrupedal simians, is small, being thinner and less extensive than in orthograde apes. Its origin, however, is from both sacral and post-sacral vertebrae, but the latter portion forms a separate caudo-femoralis muscle. Over the ilium the ectogluteal stratum is entirely aponeurotic. Tensor fasciae latae is present, ending below in the ilio-tibial band of fascia lata. Glutaeus medius is better developed, but less bulky n proportion, than in Man. Pyriformis is undifferentiated from it. The deepest gluteal stratum may differentiate into a glutaeus minimus and a glutaeus quartus (scansorius). Gemelli completely obscure the obturator internus tendon dorsally.

On the flexor aspect the psoas is powerfully developed, but not so greatly as in orthograde forms. A psoas parvus is invariably distinct, inserting on the pubic part of the ilio-pectineal line.

Biceps femoris shows but a single head whose insertion is largely into the fascia cruris. Its origin is greatly increased by the expansion and eversion of the ischial tuberosity. Other hamstrings are almost equally affected. A tenuissimus does not occur.

The adductor mass is also well developed. Pectineus may or may not be divided longitudinally into a part supplied by the obturator nerve (medially) and one supplied by the femoral nerve, but commonly only the latter part is represented. Gracilis is both broad and strong ; its insertion may be wholly on the tibia (as in Colobidae) or partly into the deep fascia—as also may occur with the insertion of semitendinosus.

Adductor longus is large and its fleshy fibres are intermingled with tendinous bands. Adductor brevis is incompletely differentiated from ad- ductor magnus, but the latter is further divided in many cases into pubo- femoralis and ischio-condyloideus portions, the former supplied by the obturator nerve and the latter by the sciatic. Obturator externus may also show varying degrees of division into dorsal and ventral elements.

Quadriceps femoris shows the usual components, but they are different in relative proportions to those in Hominoidea. Rectus femoris is bicipital, having a large flattened acetabular head, and a small but usually distinct reflected head (*e.g.* in *Papio*). Vastus lateralis is very robust and extensive, especially around the base of the great trochanter, more so than in vastus medialis. Vastus intermedius is closely related to the last and gives few or no fibres to form a subcrureus (articularis genu). Sartorius is ribbon-like and arranged as in other Catarrhini.

Gastrocnemius shows two well-defined heads, each provided with sesamoids in their tendons of origin. Soleus arises only from the fibula, but occasionally a second or tibial head may be found. Plantaris is always present (cf. many Hominoidea) ; its tendon proceeds distally between gastrocnemius and soleus and is intimately related to the tendo Achillis. It can, however, be dissected away and traced past the calcaneus to become continuous with plantar fascia. Popliteus is well developed, and deep to it a peronaeo-tibialis (pronator tibiae or rotator fibulae) is described by Howell and Straus (1933) in *Macaca* ; they also state that it occurs in gibbons and occasionally in the larger Hominoidea.

Most cynomorphs retain the primitive mammalian condition of the flexores fibularis and tibialis with their tendons fused in the sole ; the digits being supplied more or less equally from the common tendon ; the four fibular digits receiving fibres from flexor tibialis, and the four tibial ones from flexor fibularis. The flexor accessorius bears only one head.

The plantar fascia is strongly developed compared with the one in, for example, the prosimians, due chiefly to the marked development of the aponeurosis tibialis. The aponeurosis fibularis gains a deep attachment to the proximal part of metacarpal V, and a deep intermediate aponeurosis runs towards the hallux. The central part of the aponeurosis is specially strengthened in terrestrial genera such as *Papio* (Loth, 1907 ; Duckworth, 1915).

From the deep surface of the plantar fascia arises the flexor brevis digitorum, which receives an additional deep head from the tendon of the flexor tibialis. The superficial head provides a tendon to II with an indefinite fascial expansion directed towards III but failing to meet it (Sawalischin, 1911 ; confirmed by Duckworth, 1915, in *Mandrillus*). The deep head furnishes perforated tendons to digits III, IV and V.

IV. Splanchnology

PERITONEUM

This has been considered fully in Vol. III, p. 36 *et seq.*

DIGESTIVE SYSTEM

Lips are relatively thin but mobile, sometimes excessively so, *e.g.* in *Theropithecus*, where the upper lip is capable of complete eversion so that its mucous buccal surface comes to face outwards ; its cutaneous surface being thereby apposed to the skin over the nose—a grimace peculiar to this genus.

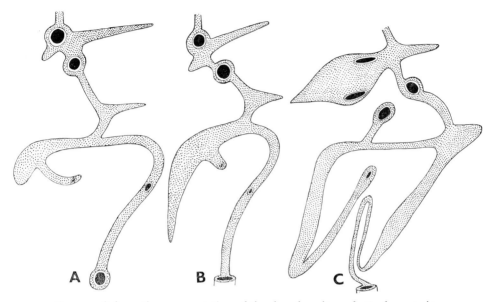

FIG. 5.—Schematic representation of the dorsal peritoneal attachments in
A, *Papio hamadryas* ; B, *Cercopithecus* and C, *Pan*

Structural details have been studied by Duckworth (1910, 1915) with special reference to baboons. Vertical sections of the lips of *Papio* show the presence of orbicularis oris extending as an attenuated band to the free margin of the lip, where it is somewhat recurved. Mucous glands are abundant here as well as near the orifice of the buccal pouch. Buccinator is spread over the wall of the latter, with platysma fibres superficial to it. These pouches open into the floor of the vestibulum oris opposite the lower premolars. The herniation of buccal mucosa, with its muscular coats, lies subcutaneously. During distension the pouch enlarges downwards and backwards beyond the lower border of the mandible. Pouches are utilized for the temporary storage of hurriedly gathered food, and occasionally receive eructated material. They are lacking in the Colobidae. The vestibule also receives the ducts of the parotid gland.

The hard palate is marked by transverse rugae which vary in number and form in the different genera. Numerous mucous glands affect the hard palate, and their openings are specially visible in the hinder half. Pigmentation, giving a bluish patchy appearance, is sometimes seen as, for example, in *Cercopithecus petaurista*. The tongue too varies in shape according to the degree of facial prognathism, being short and rounded in *Cercopithecus* and langurs, more elongated and parallel-sided in *Macaca, Cercocebus* and especially in *Papio* and *Mandrillus*. It is provided with foliate papillae and frenal lamellae, but lacks sublingua and plicae fimbriatae. The apex is truncated, and the dorsum provided with the usual types of papillae. Pigmentation occurs in some forms (*e.g. Cercopithecus, Erythrocebus*, Sonntag, 1925).

A socia parotidis is almost invariably present.

In the pharynx the tonsils are small and located in a tonsillar fossa between anterior and posterior faucial pillars. The oral and nasal moieties of the soft palate are visibly different, the former being glandular and the latter muscular. A uvula exists on the centre of the free border, this has a central glandular core surrounded by the sparse fibres of the uvular muscle (azygos uvulae).

The oesophagus has the same course and relations as it has in Man ; in the abdomen it grooves the liver deeply. Its hinder thoracic portion is, in some genera (*e.g.* Colobidae), provided with a sort of mesentery formed by apposition of the right and left halves of the mediastinal pleura over a triangular area, with its base attached to the diaphragm.

As in other Primates, striped muscle ceases short of the cardia (Gulliver, 1842).

The stomach varies enormously. Commonly, as in Cercopithecidae, it is globular or pyriform and much resembles the stomach in Hominoidea ; but in Colobidae it is grossly modified, being enlarged, sacculated and folded upon itself. This modification produces marked changes in the position and conformation of the liver and displacement of the spleen. The simpler types of stomach show a well-marked incisura angularis on the lesser curve and often also a sulcus intermedius on the greater curve. The latter also bears a well-developed omentum, carrying a variable amount of fat, and is composed of four layers of peritoneum, the two ventral being separated, by an extension of the lesser sac, from the two dorsal laminae. An attachment to the transverse colon may occur, but is usually restricted to a small area near the hepatic flexure.

Duodenum and small intestine have the same relations as in Man, the former lacking a mesentery. The mesenterium commune is common to small intestine and ascending colon, but a variable degree of fixation of the latter to the parietes is developed. Transverse and descending colons have extensive mesenteric attachments. The colon is invariably provided with three taeniae and the wall between these is highly sacculated. Traced on to the caecum the taeniae gradually widen and fuse to form a continuous longitudinal coat on the apical part of the sac. The apex is rounded, more or less frequently conical, but varies somewhat according to the degree of contraction of the muscular coat. In full contraction the apical region becomes sharply delimited from the basal part of the sac, but this state never proceeds to the formation of a permanent apical appendix vermiformis. A caeco-colic sphincter may be indicated.

The rectum is remarkably straight in most genera, although certain lateral pouchings have been described.

The liver presents features expected in a pronograde mammal, but shows several advances on the condition in Strepsirhini. The peritoneal attachment to the diaphragm is linear, contrasting with the so-called bare area characteristic of the orthograde Hominoidea. An oesophageal notch is present on the dorsal surface, but varies in depth, being deeper (and hence more primitive) in *Cercopithecus* than in *Papio*. The duodenal incisure is not present. The left lateral lobe is relatively reduced, being withdrawn from the right side of the abdomen due to the preponderance in size of the right lobe. The true caudate lobe is present, but has lost the falciform shape seen in Strepsirhini and Platyrrhini. It lies almost entirely ventral to the post-caval vein. Area of contact between the right lateral lobe and the kidney has become reduced. A new development of the left lobe, termed by Ruge (1906) *processus triangularis*, has appeared and corresponds to the tuber omentale of the Hominoidea. In all these features *Cercopithecus* is more primitive than the other cynomorphs, especially in the persistence of the large size of the left lobe, which may (unless the stomach is distended) gain contact with the spleen. In the Colobidae the liver is grossly displaced and compressed against the right side of the diaphragm by the enlarged and complicated stomach.

The two central lobes remain distinct in the colobid liver but are fused in some other genera, *e.g. Papio*.

The gall bladder varies in its relations to the right lobe, being sometimes free and sometimes partially enclosed by liver tissue. Its duct opens into the common bile duct which joins the pancreatic duct before entering the duodenum. There is, occasionally, as in Man, a second pancreatic duct opening separately more to the left and aborally, *e.g.* in *Macaca mulatta*. The two ducts are connected within the head of the pancreas by a sagittally running passage. Duodenal musculature may be specialized around the opening of the accessory duct (Singh, 1963).

RESPIRATORY SYSTEM

The larynx lies relatively high in the neck, and in consequence the cervical part of the trachea is proportionately lengthened. Thus in *Macaca mulatta* Geist (1933) found the caudal border of the cricoid level with the cranial part of the body of C.4, while the hyoid is ventral to the caudal part of the axis vertebra. The organ is relatively large, and especially so in the Colobidae, *Papio* and *Cercocebus* (Negus, 1929).

All the cartilaginous elements found in the human larynx are represented and in much the same relative proportions. The superior thyroid cornu is well developed except in *Macaca*, where, however, it establishes an articulation with the great cornu of the hyoid. Otherwise these are joined by ligament in which a *cartilago triticea* may develop. In *Papio ursinus* much elastic tissue is present in this ligament. Arytenoids are relatively small but with well-marked muscular processes. Wrisberg's cartilages are large and located near the apex of the arytenoids, separated by a notch from the nodule of Santorini.

The plica vocalis is relatively long and thin, lacking muscular fibres, and with its free edge directed towards the aditus. Duckworth, however, found the crico-thyroideus unusually extensive on the deep aspect of the thyroid cartilage, especially upwards. On the plica ventricularis there is some indication of stratification of the epithelium. Dorsally the fold contains a process from the cuneiform cartilage. The opening of the ventricle between the vocal and ventricular folds is slit-like.

A median ventral laryngeal air-sac (saccus medianus superior) is commonly present. It varies greatly in size, being smaller in females. Largest sacs occur in the Colobidae where they extend subcutaneously in the neck from the mandible to the clavicles. In other forms they remain subhyoid. They open into the laryngeal ventricle, in some cases through the base of the epiglottis.

Tracheal rings are C-shaped, with the discontinuity dorsally.

Lobation of the lungs follows the common primate pattern, there being more subdivision than in the Hominoidea, the left lung being two-lobed and the right four-lobed. On the left the lobes are apical and basal, separated by a deep interlobar fissure which takes an oblique dorso-ventral course, ending posterior to the hinder limit of the incisura cardiaca. The latter is therefore confined to the apical lobe and from its deepest penetration a further short fissure may be continued vertically some distance into the apical lobe (Narath, 1901 ; Hayek, 1960). The basal lobe is not often further subdivided, but may show additional notches or short fissures (*e.g.* in *Papio*), incising the costo-diaphragmatic border.

On the right there are apical, middle and basal lobes arranged much as in Man, with the addition of an azygos or infracardiac lobe or lobus impar, extending inwards from the basal lobe and dorsal to the intrathoracic part of the postcaval vein. Interlobar fissures include : a more or less vertical one between apical and middle lobes and an oblique one between middle and basal lobes. The two are confluent dorsally. The azygos lobe is pendulous, being attached to the basal lobe by a relatively narrow pedicle. The first interlobar fissure may be incomplete, failing to meet the oblique fissure dorsally (*e.g.* in some examples of *Macaca*). In *Erythrocebus* both fissures are short, the oblique being confined to the dorsal area and the other confined to the ventral margin. On the other hand some forms, *e.g. Macaca sinica*, show tendencies to increase the amount of fissuration. In an example of this last species a small lobule of Wrisberg has also been encountered on the medial aspect of the apical lobe.

Presence of the lobus azygos involves extension of the right pleural sac. This takes the form of a diverticulum (*sinus subpericardiacus*) which passes to the left between caval vein and oesophagus behind the base of the pericardium, thereby limiting contact between the latter and the diaphragm.

A cervical dome is sometimes developed in *Cercopithecus*; this is exceptional (Patten, 1899). Dorsal to the sternum two pleurae approach at a more cranial level than in Man and they may overlap in the midline. They remain in contact over a greater proportional distance than in the latisternal Hominoidea before finally diverging posteriorly. The left pleura diverges first over the pericardium, but the uncovered area of the latter is very limited. Dorsally the pleural sacs extend backwards beyond the last thoracic vertebra, *i.e.* as far as the fourteenth thoraco-lumbar in *Macaca*, 12-15 in *Cercopithecus*, 13-15 in *Papio* and 13-14 in *Presbytis* (Ruge, 1893).

UROGENITAL SYSTEM

Commonly the right kidney is placed more caudally than the left, but this is not invariable. In many Colobidae the reverse occurs, evidently from caudal displacement of the left gland by the enlarged stomach. Even in *Macaca* the left kidney may be a long distance caudad of the right (Wood Jones, 1929 *b*) but, on the other hand, both may be at approximately the same level, as Hill (1952) reports for *Colobus verus*. Straus and Arcadi (1958) state that this is the normal condition in Cercopithecidae. The left is sometimes heavier than the right (*Cercocebus*, *Papio*), but often the reverse is the case (*Macaca mulatta*, *Papio*, *Erythrocebus*, *Semnopithecus*; Straus and Arcadi, *loc. cit.*)

Kidneys are heavier, relative to body-weight, than in the larger Pongidae, but there are exceptions, *e.g. Macaca*, *Cercocebus galeritus*, *Trachypithecus cristatus* and *Kasi senex*. They are of the regular bean-shape, smooth-surfaced, but one pole—usually the cranial—is smaller than the other, the reverse of the usual arrangement (Straus and Arcadi, 1958, and authorities there cited). Lobulation may be present prenatally and occasionally persists, *e.g.* in *Cercocebus torquatus* (Straus). The foetal kidney, however, is smooth in Colobidae (Hill, 1952) and in *Papio ursinus* and *Macaca mulatta* (Anthony and Villemin, 1923).

Internally the kidney is invariably unipyramidal, with a single renal papilla (Straus, 1934; Freund, 1939). Of the five types of renal structure into which primate kidneys can be classified, four (types A, B, C, and D) are variants of the simple unipyramidal pattern, and all four occur in Cercopithecoidea. Type A with the pelvic surface of the medulla cranio-caudally

flattened or with a concave ledge or shelf (Nierenleiste) occurs in Cercopithecinae and Cynopithecinae, but has not been reported in any colobid monkey, except for an example of *Presbytis* mentioned by Mijsberg (1923). Type B
is similar without papilla, but divided into cranial and caudal segments by
a furrow ; it has been found in *Cercocebus*, *Papio* and *Macaca*. Type C with
a simple, low, convex papilla occurs commonly in *Macaca*, *Cercocebus*,
Cercopithecus and *Erythrocebus* but has not been reported in *Papio* or in
Colobidae. Type D, with the papilla subdivided apically into two or more
pseudo-papillae upon a single primary pyramid has been reported in individuals of most genera, and most frequently in *Papio*. Division is quite
arbitrary and has no taxonomic significance.

The area cribrosa may be diffuse, as in *Cercopithecus*, where the ducts of
Bellini are not confined to the apex of the papilla, but usually the ducts
converge to the apex, *e.g.* in *Macaca*. Sometimes they are grouped into
two or more sets in accordance with the number of false papillae (*Macaca*).
Tubi maximi or large ducts, opening independently into the cranial and
caudal angles of the renal pelvis, are extremely rare in Primates though
common in rodents and ungulates. They have been reported and figured by
Sperber (1944) in *Macaca sylvana* and *Papio*.

Cortex is thinner than medulla, but thicker proportionately than in
Hominoidea or prosimians. In *Papio* it reaches its maximum, compared with
medullary volume, where the two layers are almost equal in depth. Denzer
(1938) found in juveniles of *Macaca irus* that the cortex formed 40-45 per
cent of total renal volume.

Relations of structures at the renal hilum are commonly as in Man, but
positions of artery and ureter are reversed, according to Lineback (1933) in
Macaca mulatta.

Ureters leave the hilum caudally. The pelvis is undivided in the four
types of renal structure encountered, *i.e.* there are no calyces. The ducts
finally enter the urinary bladder dorsally or dorso-laterally.

The bladder varies much in shape according to its functional phases, but
is commonly pyriform, though Förster (1922) uses the term ellipsoid to
describe the organ in *Macaca* and *Presbytis*. It is typically located almost
entirely within the pelvis, *e.g.* in *Semnopithecus* (Ayer, 1948) *Macaca*,
Presbytis (Forster), but Hill (1952) found an almost entirely abdominal situation in *Colobus verus*. A trigone of normal shape has been reported in the
bladder of the last mentioned, but Ayer found that in *Semnopithecus* it is
reduced to a Y-shaped area. A normal trigone was found by Hill in *Macaca
mulatta*, *Cercocebus torquatus* and *Papio anubis*. A faint interureteric bar or
torus has been recorded in *Colobus verus*, but this is lacking in *Macaca
mulatta* and *Semnopithecus priam*.

Adult males invariably possess scrotal testes, but these often remain
partially retractile into the inguinal canal, and it would seem that the power-

ful cremaster is partly under voluntary control. At any rate retraction of the testes occurs during certain emotional states—presumably as a protective measure, *e.g.* in anger, fear, etc., where a fight seems imminent. In most genera, especially *Papio*, *Macaca* and *Cercocebus* testes are large in proportion to body-size, but in *Cercopithecus* and its allies and in the Colobidae they are smaller. In *Macaca mulatta* the two average 30-50 gr., but over 70 gr. may be attained *i.e.* over 0·7 per cent body-weight, nearly ten-fold the human values and exceeding practically all other subhuman primates (Schultz, 1938).

The scrotum of the adult is correspondingly large, subspherical and semi-pendulous, with no trace of median raphe, but with a median sulcus. In many genera it is vividly coloured—*e.g.* various shades of blue in the super-species *Cercopithecus aethiops*, crimson in some *Macaca* species, lilac in *Mandrillus sphinx*, mauve to sky-blue in *M. leucophaeus* (Hill, 1955 *b*), indigo in *Cercopithecus neglectus*. Scrotal integument lacks glandular specializations ; sparse hairs are frequently present.

As mentioned, the cremaster is powerfully developed with frequently a final attachment to the os pubis [Mijsberg (1923), Wislocki (1933 *b*), Miller (1947)].

The processus vaginalis remains open in the mature animal in *Macaca mulatta* and *M. nemestrina* and probably others ; but it communicates with the general peritoneal cavity by a mere slit, too restricted to permit complete withdrawal of the testis. The passage is wider in *Semnopithecus* (Ayer, 1948), but in *Colobus verus* the passage is closed (Hill, 1952).

Descent of the testes differs in some respects from that in *Homo*. Descent usually occurs prenatally in *M. mulatta*, according to Wislocki (1933 *a*), during the second half of pregnancy, and in the newborn, the gonads are usually located in a small but well-defined turgid scrotum. Sub-sequently, however, the scrotum is reduced to a flattened transverse fold, due to the return of the testes to a position near the external abdominal ring. They retain their mobility but rarely migrate beyond a parapenial position before the end of the third postnatal year. Final descent occurs during the fourth to fifth year when the scrotum shows a marked increase in volume. Experimental induction of these changes has been effected in prepubertal monkeys by injection of gonadotrophic (Engle, 1932) or androgenic (Hamilton, 1938) hormones. Harms (1956, p. 575) refers to tardy postnatal testicular descent in other cercopithecoids, *e.g.* *Nasalis*, *Papio* (descent at time of eruption of permanent dentition), *Presbytis*, *Cercopithecus* (descent at time of completion of eruption of milk dentition).

Structurally there is little to remark apart from the microscopical changes undergone during the postnatal period. These have been studied by van Wagenen and Simpson (1954) in *Macaca mulatta*. Regression of semi-niferous tubercles and Leydig's cells is associated with the testicular reascent. Growth is extremely slow between the first year and end of the third year ;

germinal epithelium is comprised solely of spermatogonia and a few spermato-
cytes. After the third year growth is rapid, the tubules doubling their
diameter, accompanied by differentiation of the interstitial tissue. Spermatogenesis occurs during the first half of the third year. Full reproductive
maturity may occur six to twelve months later in less inbred animals (Eckstein, 1948, 1959; Spiegel, 1954 (in *M. irus*); Harms, 1956).

The testicular artery has been studied in *Macaca*, *Papio* and *Mandrillus*
by Harrison (1949) who finds that in the spermatic cord the vessel is convoluted as in lower mammals (*e.g.* the dog) but there is also slight convolution
on the posterior border of the testis, and a further complexity of pattern at
the lower pole and along the anterior surface.

Of accessory structures, a sinus epididymis is reported lacking in Cercopithecidae by Mijsberg (1923), though Ayer (1948) found it in *Semnopithecus*,
yet in *Procolobus verus* Hill (*loc. cit.*) failed to identify it. Testicular appendages (hydatids of Morgagni) have been reported by Zuckerman and Krohn
(1937) in several species of *Macaca*, in *Cercopithecus*, *Papio*, *Mandrillus* and
Semnopithecus. More frequent are epididymal appendages, sessile or pedunculated, but sometimes the attachment is between testis and caput. Occasionally remnants of paramesonephric (Müllerian) ducts are also preserved,
resembling minute Fallopian tubes.

The epididymis is always well developed and its dorsal border commonly
suspended by a fold of tunica vaginalis to the parietes of the sac and continued proximally along the spermatic cord. The cauda, together with the
lower pole of the testis, is often more extensively adherent to the parietes.

The ductus deferens presents no ampulla in *Macaca*. The ejaculatory
duct is formed by union with the duct from the seminal vesicle within the
prostate. In *Semnopithecus* Ayer found a small ampulla and some diverticula-
tion of the terminal part of the ductus.

Seminal vesicles vary greatly in size according to age and physiological
state. Ayer (*loc. cit.*) found them small and fusiform in *Semnopithecus*, but
Eckstein (1958) reports larger organs in *Colobus*, recalling those in *Macaca
mulatta*, where they make contact in the median plane and are grossly
lobulated. The same appearance is seen in adults of *Papio*, *Mandrillus* and
Cercocebus.

According to Oudemans (1892) and Mijsberg (1923) vesicular glands are
composed of coiled tubes with either short lateral diverticula (as in *Semnopithecus*) or with long, coiled branches given off from the terminal part of the
main duct (*e.g.* in *Macaca mulatta*, *M. nemestrina*, *M. irus* and *Papio*).

In the prostate cranial and caudal lobes are recognizable (Mijsberg, 1923),
the former encircling the terminal parts and excretory ducts of the seminal
vesicles. The prespermatic portion lies cranial to the ejaculatory ducts. The
more compact caudal lobe is smoother and also darker in colour; it is
located entirely posterior to the ejaculatory ducts. The two main lobes are

separated by a deep cleft almost to the urethra. No prostatic tissue extends to the ventral aspect of the urethra. Cranial and caudal lobes differ histologically, the cranial part being homologous with the coagulating gland of rodents, for its secretion effects coagulation of the seminal plasma and is therefore responsible for the formation of the *bouchon vaginale* (vaginal plug) during copulation (van Wagenen, 1936). Some comparative data on the prostate in Colobidae are given by Hill (1952).

In the prostatic urethra ejaculatory ducts open upon the summit of a prominent colliculus at the same level as the semilunar opening of the transversely disposed utriculus (Oudemans, 1892). Prostatic openings are located more distally at the base of the colliculus. The utriculus recalls a small uterine cavity in *Semnopithecus* and some species of *Cercopithecus*, and is highly glandular; by contrast, in baboons and *Macaca* it is short, blind and non-glandular (Zuckerman and Parkes, 1935). The colliculus of *Semnopithecus* is slender and lined by several layers of cylindrical cells extending into side pockets. Collicular glands histologically recall prostatic alveoli (Heller and Sprinz, 1921).

Cowper's glands (gl. bulbourethrales) are well developed, lying between the prostate and the bulb of the urethra. They are rounded to pyriform and relatively larger than in Man (Oudemans, 1892; Mijsberg, 1923). They are smaller in *Semnopithecus* (Ayer, 1948).

Effects on the accessory genital structures of injections of hormones have been published by Aykroyd and Zuckerman (1938), Zuckerman and Parkes (1938) and Zuckerman and Sandys (1939).

The body of the penis is composed of the usual three cylindrical erectile bodies (*corpora cavernosa*) arranged in the normal mutual relationship. Characteristic, is the long subsymphyseal course of the corpus penis, the free portion being carried forwards (Mijsberg). In addition to the ischio- and bulbo-cavernosi, there is usually a small levator penis muscle arising from the ischium, medial to the ischio-cavernosus, and ending in a thin tendon which unites on the dorsum penis with its fellow, finally fusing with the fascia penis. It elevates and straightens the free portion of the organ.

A small baculum (*os penis, os priapi*) is invariably present within the glans, often somewhat asymmetrically disposed, especially at its distal end (*e.g.* in *Macaca* and *Papio*). The bone is rod-shaped, straight or sinuous with a blunt proximal and more pointed distal end. In length it varies in adults from 10 to 30 mm., being shorter in some macaques and guenons, longer in others, and longer still in mangabeys and baboons.

Compared with the Colobidae, ovaries in Cercopithecidae are relatively small and show less extensive interstitial lutein-forming tissue. Oval in shape, they vary somewhat according to the stage of the sexual cycle (Hartman, 1932; Frommolt, 1934); they are largest in baboons during the luteal and menstrual phases (Zuckerman and Parkes, 1932). They do not increase during pregnancy (cf. Ceboidea). The organ is partly covered by a fold of peritoneum derived from the mesosalpinx (Polak, 1908 in *Colobus*; Ayer, 1948 in *Semnopithecus*; Hill, 1952 in *Procolobus*).

MacLeod (1881) claimed germinal epithelium to be deficient in cynomorph catarrhines, but this may have been from a study of inadequately preserved material. Frommolt found it well developed. Cyclical changes in the ovary have been summarized by Brambell (1956). In a young mature female baboon ovarian follicles possess a diameter of 180μ at the end of the first phase of the cycle, gaining 310μ when the antrum appears and 6000μ at maturity, an increase of $\times 33 \cdot 3$ during the second phase.

Details have been studied in relatively few genera of cynomorphs, namely *Macaca* (Corner, 1923, 1927, 1942; Corner, Hartman and Bartelmez, 1945, all deal with relation of ovulation to menstruation and luteal formation) also the studies of Joachimovits (1931, 1935) and Frommolt (1934) on *M. mulatta* and *M. irus*; and *Papio* (Parkes, 1931; Zuckerman and Parkes, 1932). Large numbers of primordial egg cells form histologically a conspicuous cortex to the ovary beneath the tunica albuginea. More centrally lie larger follicles in various stages of ripening, also atretic follicles and corpora lutea or products of their degeneration. Binovular follicles sometimes occur. Large corpora lutea are characteristic of the second phase of the ovarian cycle. As in Hominoidea, there is little interstitial tissue. Joachimovits has reported paraganglionic cells at the ovarian hilum in *Macaca irus*.

Fallopian tubes commence with fimbriated funnels bearing slit-like ostia guarded by ovarian and uterine fimbriae of equal length. The main part of the tube is coiled and held in place by both an anterior and a posterior mesosalpinx, the former producing a fold coursing along the free border of the tube and extending beyond the tube to assist in effecting a deep ovarian bursa, which falls into category 3 of Zuckerkandl (1897). In *Papio* the tube is specially vascular after ovulation; at menstruation it carries debris supposedly derived from red blood cells (Zuckerman and Parkes).

The normally single median uterus (*uterus simplex*) varies considerably in size according to age and phases of the sexual cycle. It is vaguely divided externally into a cranial portion, the body of the uterus, and a cervix of complex structure. The cranial extremity or fundus is limited by a line drawn between the two tubal attachments. It is smooth, convex and not provided with any intercornual ligament. Along the lateral borders of the body, extending from the tubal attachments to the cranial part of the cervix is the line of attachment each side of the broad ligament, a double-layered sheet of peritoneum (mesometrium) carrying blood vessels, etc., and connecting the genital tract to the parietes. Sometimes in *Macaca*, especially in juveniles, the fundus presents a shallow median depression or notch, giving an incipiently bicornuate effect. The lumen too is vaguely bicornuate cranially, but caudal to the level of the tubes undivided.

The cervix is cylindrical with a narrow lumen and thick, folded walls. In *Macaca* the folds form projections (*colliculi*) at constant sites giving the cervical canal a tortuous course ; in *M. mulatta* there are two bends, almost right-angled (Clark and Corner, 1935 ; Sandys and Zuckerman, 1938). In *M. sinica* and *M. radiata* these colliculi are even better developed and provided with considerable glandular tissue (Zuckerman, 1930 ; Hill, 1939 *vide* also Franke, 1902). These complications are lacking in the Colobidae. Distally the external os, rounded or slit-like, opens into the vagina upon the summit of the hindmost part of the cervix which is telescoped into the vaginal vault as in *Homo*.

Changes in the uterus occur during the phases of the sexual cycle.

The vagina is thick-walled, both from muscular and epithelial development, the latter being highly rugose and keratinized. In prepubertal females it retains the embryonic condition of a solid cord (*e.g.* in *Cercopithecus*), which becomes canalized at puberty, around the age of three years. Cyclical changes affect the degree of keratinization, and these are reflected in the contents of the lumen which have been much studied by the smear technique.

Another feature of many Cercopithecidae (especially *Papio*, *Mandrillus*, *Cercocebus* and some species of *Macaca*) is the occurrence of a so-called sexual skin. This is an area of integument surrounding and including the external genitalia, sometimes extending to the tail and thighs or even, as in *M. mulatta*, to a considerable distance cranially on the back. During the resting phase of the ovarian cycle the sexual skin departs little from ordinary integument, but during the follicular phase it becomes tumescent and often highly coloured from an accumulation of fluid in the subcutaneous tissues and congestion of the cutaneous vessels. Swelling typically increases to a maximum, which coincides with ovulation. Thereafter, during the ensuing luteal phase, abrupt detumescence occurs, and the sexual skin returns to its inactive condition. There are many differences in detail, even between species of a single genus. These have been studied in a number of forms (especially *Macaca* and *Papio*) summarized by Pocock (1906), Collings (1926), Allen (1928), Zuckerman and Parkes (1930), Zuckerman (1930, 1932 *a* and *b*, 1937), Woskresensky and Ivanow (1932), Gillman (1935), Fisher, Krohn and Zuckerman (1936), Aykroyd and Zuckerman (1938), Zuckerman *et al.* (1938) and Ogston, Philpot and Zuckerman (1939). Experimental studies on sexual skin are reported by numerous workers including Parkes and Zuckerman (1931), Schoeller *et al.* (1932, 1933) on *Papio* ; Bachman *et al.* (1936) on *Macaca* ; and Zuckerman and Parkes (1939) on *Mandrillus*.

Correlation with the cyclical phases of the other parts of the reproductive system will be considered under physiology (*infra*, p. 134) whilst generic and specific differences will be treated under the appropriate genera and species.

G

Mammae are normally restricted to a single pectoral pair, though numerous individual instances of supernumerary nipples have been recorded (in 1 to 15 per cent, Speert, 1942 ; Schultz, 1948), usually situated caudal to the normal pair (*e.g.* in *Macaca*, *Papio* and *Erythrocebus*). A degree of asymmetry in position and size of nipple is not uncommon.

The glandular tissue is feebly developed except during pregnancy, being diffusely distributed in the subcutaneous tissues. Even in pregnancy the glands never produce any superficial enlargement comparable to the human condition. Details have been studied only in *Macaca mulatta* (Turner and Allen, 1933; Folley *et al.*, 1939). Before puberty a complex duct system is present, but alveolar development reaches its full expression only after ovulation and luteinization have become established. Growth follows according to the simple allometric law. In male Rhesus monkeys a simple duct system radiates a short distance from the nipple; occasionally gynecomastia has been recorded, with clumps of alveoli, and these may be experimentally induced by injection of female sex hormones (Folley *et al.*, 1939).

ENDOCRINE ORGANS

The pituitary has been studied on a comparative basis in several genera, namely *Papio*, *Macaca*, *Cynopithecus*, *Cercocebus*, *Erythrocebus* and *Cercopithecus*, the result of work by Rodriguez (1937), Köhne (1944), Dawson (1948) and Hanström (1948, 1958). Almost all the material examined has been from captive animals, the only exception being a Malbrouck monkey (*Cercopithecus pygerythrus cynosuros*) described by Hanström.

Variations concern chiefly the relationships of the pars distalis and pars tuberalis to the infundibulum. In the *C. cynosuros* examined by Hanström there was no zona tuberalis. Köhne and others have reported the pars tuberalis forming a collar round the infundibulum better developed rostrally and, beneath this, sometimes the pars distalis forms a restricted dorso-caudal bridge (*e.g.* in *M. mulatta*). Dawson and also Palay (1953) do not mention this bridge, but Palay refers to an extension formed by pars intermedia covering the rostral part of the infundibulum. Migration of intermedia cells into the processus infundibuli has been observed in *Cynopithecus*, but not in *Macaca*, *Erythrocebus* or *Cercopithecus*. A hypophyseal cleft is sometimes retained, otherwise it is obliterated or represented by a few cysts of Rathke as Hanström found in *Cercopithecus sabaeus*. In *Papio* the pars intermedia is feebly developed, covering the rostral surface only of the processus infundibuli, often locally reduced to a single cell-layer. No invasion of cells from the intermedia into the posterior lobe has been seen in *Papio* by Köhne, but Hanström has reported this in *P. hamadryas*.

Palay (1953) adduces evidence of neuro-secretory material in the neurons and cell processes of the supraoptic and paraventricular nuclei in *Macaca mulatta.* Granules of the secretion attain a larger size than in Man. They also occur in the axons of the fibres which constitute the hypothalamo-hypophyseal tract.

Thyroid lateral lobes may be independent or joined by one or more transverse bands composed of glandular tissue. In *Cynopithecus,* Forsyth (1910) records a single isthmus crossing the fifth to sixth tracheal rings. In *Cercopithecus sabaeus* two connections, at the third and twelfth rings respectively, have been noted by the same author. Two isthmi have also been recorded by Meckel (quoted by Pischinger, 1937) in *Erythrocebus* and *Papio.* Occasionally the isthmus is lacking in *Papio* (for further details consult Bargmann, 1958).

Weight of the thyroid varies from 0·232 to 0·314 gm. in *Macaca,* and from 0·407 to 0·567 gm. in *Cercocebus* (Inay *et al.,* 1940).

In *Papio,* Grafflin (1942) found the follicular epithelium to contain sudanophile fat and also yellow pigment, the latter fluorescent and mildly sudanophile. He classifies it as a wear-and-tear product (Abnutzungs-pigment). Colloid is non-fluorescent and eosinophilic.

Parathyroids, normally four in number, are rounded or ovoid nodules found on the dorsal surface of the lateral lobes of the thyroid or on its lateral margins, but are equally varied in position as in Man. Forsyth (1908) found only one pair of parathyroids in *Cercopithecus,* with a pair of accessory thyroid bodies. His *Cercopithecus campbelli* also had a single pair.

In a *Macaca nemestrina* Forsyth found, on the right, a parathyroid located at the caudal pole of the thyroid, the other at its lateral margin ; on the left there was one at the lateral margin and the other altogether posterior to the thyroid ; in addition an accessory thyroid body was found on the right between trachea and oesophagus. Three examples of *Cercopithecus sabaeus* each showed a different arrangement.

Epithelial islands have been reported within the thyroid in *Macaca* (Biedl, 1913), *Cercopithecus* (Capobianco and Maziotti, 1899) and *Papio* (Grafflin, 1942) (*vide* also Bargmann, 1958).

Grafflin (1940) declares the parathyroids in *Papio* to be irregularly lobulated in structure, made up of a single type of cell (homologous with the " principal " cell of Man and mammals generally). Later (1942) he identified four types of cell, principal, wasserhelle, dark oxyphile and pale oxyphile as in the human gland.

A thymus situated partly in the neck and partly in the thorax (Hammars' type I) pertains in *Macaca.* Inay *et al.* (1940) record the weight of the organ as 1·5-1·9 gm. in *Macaca,* 7-10 gm. in *Cercocebus.* The gland undergoes involution at puberty, as in Man (*vide* Bargmann, 1943, 1958), also in malnutrition (Sauer and Fegley, 1960).

Adrenals have been described in most genera of Old World monkeys, dating from Daubenton (1776), Vicq d'Azyr (1792), Cuvier (1805) and

Meckel (1806). More modern observations include the studies of Pettit (1896), Kolmer (1918), Hill (1930, 1933, 1952) and Bourne (1936, 1949). As in Man the organs are large during foetal life and in the neonatus, thereafter regressing rapidly from the degeneration of the so-called " foetal " cortex (Hill, 1930, 1933). In the adult, as found by Kolmer (1918) in *Macaca*, there are three cortical zones and a highly vascular central medulla. The organs are typically located in contact with the cranial pole of the corresponding kidney, but in some Colobidae they are separated, at least on the left, by a variable distance. In shape the organs vary on the two sides and also from species to species, though all the variants are based on a generally flattened pyramidal structure with a somewhat corrugated surface—except in the foetus and neonatus where the surface is smooth. Pettit found quadrangular adrenals in *Papio papio*, but in *Mandrillus* the more usual triangular outline was encountered, as previously noted by Daubenton and Vicq d'Azyr.

A curious feature in the adrenal cortex of *Cercopithecus* has been noted by Kohno (1925), namely small epithelial-lined spaces in the zona glomerulosa filled during life with serum. The remainder of the cortex was as found by Kolmer in the other monkeys, and without a connective tissue stratum at the cortico-medullary boundary.

V. Haematology

BLOOD CELLS.—The classic observations are those of Ponder *et al.* (1928, 1929) who studied blood samples from *Cercopithecus*, three species of *Macaca* and a *Papio cynocephalus*. Their results appear in Table 4, p. 86. The most striking result to be deduced from the table is the wide range of variation in the blood picture in apparently healthy monkeys, though the mean diameter of the red cells and the percentage of haemoglobin are relatively constant.

A recent summary of the haematology of the healthy macaque (*M. mulatta*) has been provided by Krise (1960), who ably summarizes earlier literature. Here, too, the wide range of variation is remarkable. Krise examined over 500 Rhesus monkeys and his results appear in Table 3, p. 85.

Supplementary data are given by Gisler *et al.* (1960).

BLOOD GROUPS.—It was long considered that the well-known phenomenon of blood groups, based on the presence of agglutinating substances in the serum, was confined to Man. It was later shown that the substances occurred in anthropoid apes, including gibbons.

Researches were extended to lower monkeys by Landsteiner and Miller (1925) who examined ten guenons, an *Erythrocebus*, four mangabeys, twenty-three macaques and eight baboons. Most of these gave negative results and none gave evidence of any true reaction, although these workers demonstrated B-like agglutinogens in the cells of several New World monkeys.

TABLE 3

HAEMATOLOGY OF 538 *MACACA MULATTA*

	No. of Observations	Mean	S.D.	Range
Erythrocytes per cu. mm.	876	5,571,900	729,780	3,110,000–8,570,000
Leucocytes ,, ,, ,,	891	12,155	5,981	1200–43,100
Haemoglobin gms/100 cc.	655	11·72	3·025	7·0–16·5
Polymorphs (per 100)	738	35·79	16·70	4–91
Lymphocytes ,,	738	60·52	17·26	7–95
Monocytes ,,	738	0·717	0·379	0–8
Eosinophils ,,	738	2·63	2·37	0–16
Basophils ,,	738	0·213	0·178	0–4
Bilobed lymphocytes (per 1000 lymphocytes)	439	0·589	0·415	0–12
Stabs (per 100 cells)	738	0·37	0·31	0–9
Haematocrit (heparinized or sequestrated)	392	37·01	6·75	12–51
Haematocrit (citrated)	42	45·47	3·85	35–53
Platelets (dry method)	119	211,744	68,100	79,900–368,640
,, (wet method)	57	344,035	71,750	250,000–750,000
Clotting time (1-tube)	27	1 min. 55 sec.	39 sec.	1 min.– 3 min. 15 sec.
,, time (resistance)	161	4·32 min.	0·36 min.	1 min.–3 min.
Sedimentation rate (per hr.)	448	0·902 mm.	2·2 mm.	0–28 mm.
Reticulocytes %	76	0·354	0·187	0·1–3·4
Plasma prothrombin time (sec.)	203	13·18	2·54	10·5–18·5
Serum prothrombin time (sec.)	174	54·12	23·57	19·1–180
Electric resistance rate (milliohms/min.)	132	5·67	2·21	0·2–13·9

Conflicting evidence was soon brought forward by Thomson and Kemp (1930) who examined fourteen macaques and two baboons, testing with the same sera used in typing human blood. They considered nine of their animals contained B receptors, but they threw doubt on their own suggestion in so far as the reaction may be due to the presence of heteroagglutinins.

TABLE 4

HAEMATOLOGY OF CERCOPITHECOIDEA

	Erythrocytes, per cu. mm.	Leucocytes, per cu. mm.	Haemo-globin %	Mean diam. Erythrocytes in Plasma	Differential Count *				
					NP	EP	BP	L	LM
Cercopithecus sabaeus	6,400,000	12,600	87	7·8	58	7	1	31	3
Macaca mulatta	5,000,000	10,400	77	8	73	3	1	18	2
Macaca irus	6,432,000	7,200	90	8	37	19	24	18	1
Macaca maura	5,000,000	7,600	88	7·9	69	2	4	23	1
Papio cyno-cephalus	6,970,000	10,400	87	7·7	65	2	1	29	2

* NP Neutrophil polymorphs; EP Eosinophil polymorphs; BP Basophil polymorphs; L Lymphocytes; LM Large mononuclears; T Transitional leucocytes.

Whatever be the true explanation, the capacity of cercopithecoid blood to absorb the anti-B agglutinin must be very low.

The failure of Landsteiner and Miller, and several subsequent workers (*e.g.* Voronoff and Alexandresco, 1930) to obtain group-specific reactions with blood samples of Old World monkeys led to the conclusion that factors A and B were lacking. In spite of the absence of A and B from the red cells, the sera of many species indicated the presence of either agglutinin anti-A or anti-B, but not both. For example, anti-A is present in *M. mulatta*, and anti-B in *Cercopithecus pygerythrus*, although group-specific reactions were obtainable with erythrocytes (Landsteiner, 1928). This was taken to indicate that the reciprocal relation between agglutinogen and agglutinin (Landsteiner's rule) did not hold in these species.

In *Macaca mulatta* Buchbinder (1933) found in the serum a substance indistinguishable from human α-iso-agglutinin, but no antigen in body-cells comparable with human isoantigens. Agglutination of rhesus erythrocytes by human serum of any of the four human blood groups is explained by Buchbinder as due to heteroagglutinins.

These puzzling features were resolved by the work of Candela *et al.* (1940) and Wiener *et al.* (1942, 1953) who extended observations to secretions and organ extracts. The presence of B-like substances was demonstrated in saliva and organ extracts of *Macaca mulatta* and this accounts for the absence of natural B-agglutinins from the serum.

Candela *et al.* (1940) first demonstrated the presence in the tissues and secretions in *Macaca mulatta* and *M. irus* of both A-like and B-like factors, accompanied by complementary agglutinins in the serum. In other words a reciprocal arrangement of agglutinogen and agglutinin, previously known only in Hominoidea, also holds true for cynomorph monkeys. Reinterpretation of earlier results on *M. mulatta* justified to Candela *et al.* the conclusion that all individuals of this species are related to group B, but that *M. irus* individuals possessed both A and B factors.

The presence of B or B-like agglutinogen in the erythrocytes of at least individual Rhesus monkeys was demonstrated by Buchi (1953).

Of considerable importance in relation to human haematology was the discovery by Landsteiner and Wiener (1940, 1941) that antiserum from rabbits that had been injected with erythrocytes from *Macaca mulatta* caused agglutination of human red cells as well as those of Rhesus monkeys. Approximately 15 per cent of human samples tested failed to react. On the basis of this immunological reaction the antigen was labelled " Rh " and human erythrocytes which reacted were termed Rh-positive and the anomalous 15 per cent Rh-negative. Later studies led to the conclusion that the Rh-factor is a complex of several antigens, each separately inherited ; as many as eight categories of agglutinogens have been established.

Clinical importance of the Rh-factors in human pathology lies in the fact that a pregnant (Rh-negative) mother can develop an anti-Rh substance to her Rh-positive foetus. This results in the haemolytic condition designated erythroblastosis foetalis in the newborn—fatal unless treated—and consequently of selective value in evolution, thus far the only function assignable to any of the blood-group factors (Wiener, 1943). The Rh-factor is transmitted as a simple mendelian dominant (Landsteiner and Wiener, 1941).

Another system of blood factors found in human erythrocytes is the MNS system (Landsteiner and Levine, 1928), and certain of these at any rate occur also in subhuman Primates. The factors M and N may occur together or separately and are transmitted by a pair of allelic genes M and N, located on a different chromosome pair from the A, B and O. They give rise to three types of blood M, N and MN. Proportionate representation of the three types differs among human races, *e.g.* a high proportion of N in Ainu and aboriginal Australians and high proportion of M in Amerinds and Eskimos. Landsteiner and Levine found M and N in the blood of anthropoid apes, but for some time subsequently, contradictory results were found with simian blood. Wiener found that these results were due to qualitative differences in the M antisera used, *e.g.* some anti-M sera agglutinated blood of *M. mulatta*, others did not. Landsteiner and Wiener (1937) and Wiener (1938) carried out tests with a variety of anti-M sera on several species and found that several different M-like antigens occur in the blood of apes and monkeys, and that the species tested could be arranged in a graded series based upon the resemblances of human blood to the M factor. Not unexpectedly the chimpanzee showed the closest resemblance. M agglutinogens were regularly found in Cercopithecoidea, but not in Platyrrhini (except for one species (*Ateles*) which reacted only with a special serum). Cercopithecoids tested included *Macaca mulatta, M. irus, Cercopithecus sabaeus, Cercocebus atys, Papio* (two species) and *Mandrillus.*

Corresponding tests made with anti-N sera have so far produced positive results only with blood from chimpanzees and not all such antisera react even here.

HAEMOGLOBINS.—Apart from changes in gaseous saturation, it has been known for a considerable time, since 1866, that there occur at least two essentially different types of haemoglobin in human blood : adult haemo-globin (haemoglobin A) and foetal haemoglobin (haemoglobin F) which differ in the nature of the globin portion of their molecules. At birth 60-80 per cent of the respiratory blood pigment is haemoglobin F, but none is formed subsequently, so it is normally replaced entirely by haemoglobin A by the age of 4 months. If, however, ability to produce haemoglobin A is impaired, haemoglobin F may continue to be produced during later child-hood or even into adult life. There are also numerous variants of haemo-globin A (S, C, D, E, G, H, I and J). Genes for haemoglobin A and its variants are multiple alleles, one locus on a single chromosome being occupied by genes for either A or one of its variants ; so genetic composition may be AA or AS, AC, etc. No pathogenicity arises, provided one A gene is present in the genetic heritage (Lehmann, 1960).

Abnormal haemoglobins in monkeys have been reported by Jacob and Tappen (1957). Samples were obtained from wild monkeys in Uganda and studied by paper electrophoresis, using human AA haemoglobin as reference point. Normal results were obtained from the blood of 37 examples of *Cercopithecus ascanius*, 3 *C. aethiops subsp.*, 6 *C. neglectus*, 2 *Colobus badius tephrosceles* and 3 *C. abyssinicus*. But in one of 5 *Cercopithecus mitis* and in all of 16 *Cercocebus albigena* tested, abnormal haemoglobins were found. Presence of two components in the abnormal examples of *C. mitis* suggests a heterozygous condition and the occurrence of more than one allele in the local population.

The abnormal haemoglobin in *Cercocebus* is a slow-moving substance and indicates a fixation in the population of a different allele from that controlling haemoglobin A, or the fixation of a modifying allele or alleles at another locus.

Subsequent studies (Jacob and Tappen, 1958) resulted in further revela-tion of abnormal haemoglobins in monkeys, besides confirmation of previous results. Two further examples of *C. mitis*, three of *C. ascanius* and one *C. l'hoesti* all proved normal, as did six out of seven *C. mona* and a sample from *Papio anubis*. On the other hand two further samples of *Cercocebus albigena* behaved as in the original experiments and so did four of *Cercocebus galeritus*, all showing the slow-moving type of haemoglobin similar in rate to human haemoglobin G. Tappen (1960) also mentions a heterozygous *Cercopithecus denti*.

The presence of haemoglobin F in *Macaca mulatta* has recently been reported by Beaven and Gratzer (1959) and by Sen *et al.* (1960). Adult monkeys, according to Sen *et al.*, contain 1-5 per cent alkali-resistant haemoglobin with an average of 2·9 per cent, contrasted with newborns where 38·8-60 per cent occurs with an average of 48·9 per cent.

OTHER BLOOD PROTEINS.—Systematic importance of the serum proteins traces back to Kraus' (1897) discovery of the precipitin reaction. Nuttall (1904), after several hundred tests, came to certain conclusions respecting blood relationships within Primates, in particular that there is a close relationship between Hominidae and Pongidae and a more distant relationship with the Cercopithecoidea. Further quantitative work on some seven species of Cercopithecoidea, compared with a single anthropoid ape (*Pan*) and single samples from a platyrrhine (*Cebus*) and a lorisoid (*Perodicticus*) was reported on by Zuckerman and Sudermann (1935). The tests proved that antiserum from an individual of any one species of cercopithecoid monkey may react no more strongly with blood from another individual of the same species than it does with that from other species or genera of the same family. In other words, interspecific relationships are no stronger than intergeneric similarities. However, the relationship of cercopithecoid with chimpanzee blood is closer than with human, although human serum does give a group reaction to anti-cercopithecoid serum, compared with negative reactions which occur with material from *Cebus* or *Perodicticus*. These workers, therefore, concluded that the serum precipitin test is only of limited value in determining genetic relationships.

Recently attention has been directed to the haptoglobins, a group of carbohydrate-containing globulins first discovered in human serum and so called from their ability to combine with haemoglobin. Beckman and Cedarmark (1960) have reported on these proteins in ten samples of *Macaca irus*, using the method of starch-gel electrophoresis. Resulting protein patterns were similar to those produced by human serum. Two different haemoglobin-combining patterns were observed identical with types Hp 1-1 and Hp 2-1 of Man. Three of the ten monkeys were type Hp 2-1 and these had a much heavier concentration of haptoglobin in the fastest zone compared with human Hp 2-1, resembling the modified Hp 2-1 of Giblett (1959).

Earlier, Arends and Rodriguez (1960) had examined twenty-seven monkeys (25 *M. mulatta*, 1 *M. irus* and a *Cebus nigrivittatus*) all of which showed type Hp 1-1, whereupon these authors suggested that this might be phylogenetically significant. Beckman and Cedarmark conclude that Hp 2-2 has not yet emerged in evolution. Evidently Hp 1-1 is the primitive condition, and it is of some interest that a high percentage of type Hp 1 genes is present in African negroes, and may have a selective value in a tropical environment.

Another serum protein, transferrin, has been identified in human serum and, like haptoglobin, exhibits genetically determined variations in the population. A comparative study of the distribution of this and other serum proteins in subhuman Primates has been commenced by Goodman *et al.* (1962) by the use of a two-dimensional zone electrophoresis ; a combination of filter-paper and starch-gel electrophoresis. Among other Primates examined have been 19 *Macaca irus*, 17 *M. mulatta* and several other macaque species. Results show that each has its own characteristic constellation of components. Patterns induced by the *Macaca* sera differed in several respects from those of *Homo* and *Pan* (which showed close similarity). Notable, in *Macaca*, was the absence of a fast-moving α-1 globin of oroso-mucoid mobility and the presence of a new component which shows mobility on filter-paper of γ-1 globulin, but which in starch migrates faster than gamma globulin and slower than transferrin.

Starch-gel patterns clearly reflect the closer affinity of *M. irus* to *M. mulatta* than to any of the other species tested, but a few features indicate their specificity. Sera of *M. irus* always showed a much larger quantity of gamma globulin. Sera of *M. mulatta* showed greater intraspecific variation than did those of *M. irus*, confirming earlier work of Bangham and Tee (reported by Allison, 1959) of a β-globulin variation among sera of *M. mulatta*.

VI. Angeiology

The pericardium is located in a relatively median position, but the leftward extension of the cardiac apex reaches at least to the lateral sternal line, usually close to the sixth costal cartilage.* In *Papio*, at least, the median position may be retained (Duckworth, 1915).

Area of contact between pericardium and diaphragm becomes more extensive than in Platyrrhini, but a subpericardial sinus (infracardiac bursa) of the right pleura is still found, limiting the dorsal extent of the pericardio-diaphragmatic contact. Frick (1960), however, reports an extension of the sinus ventrally to the chest wall in *Macaca nemestrina*, while *M. irus* shows considerable separation and laxity of the laminae of the right ligamentum phrenico-pericardiacum (lig. pericardiaco-phrenico-venosum of Ruge). Adhesion invariably occurs between pericardium and diaphragm over the cardiac apex.

Ruge's (1893) estimate of the angle subtended by the long axis of the heart with the line connecting the anterior and posterior caval veins is 52° in *Macaca irus*, compared with the much more obtuse angle seen in Hominoidea and the more acute one in the prosimians (*e.g.* 33° in *Nycticebus*). In consequence the intrathoracic course of the postcaval is shortened. Transverse diameter of the heart is greater in proportion to its axial length and dorso-ventral diameter than in lower Primates, though less than in Hominoidea. The organ is therefore more or less egg-shaped, with the narrow end forming the apex and the broad end comprised by the atria. In *Macaca* and *Erythrocebus* Frick describes the heart as elliptical, whereas in *Papio*,

---

* Range of variation fourth costal cartilage (*Mandrillus*)—seventh costal cartilage (*Erythrocebus*).

Theropithecus and *Cercopithecus* the apex is more sharply defined. *Presbytis* agrees with *Ateles* in so far as the right ventricular apex reaches almost as far as the left. For minor variations in shape the article by Frick should be consulted.

Internal arrangements within the cardiac chambers are much the same as in *Homo*, and are subject to as many individual as specific or generic differences. Walls of the atria are very thin, especially in the smaller forms ; they are thicker in *Papio* and *Theropithecus*. Even in *Cercopithecus* some thickening occurs with the presence of a basal marginal swelling in both atria marked off by a groove from the main part of the chamber. A crista terminalis occurs with musculi pectinati in the right chamber. Fasciculus Loweri (between the openings of the caval veins) and fasciculus interauricularis verticalis (between the left and right groups of pulmonary veins) are readily recognized, but not so strongly as to obscure the tuberculum intervenosum. A thin semilunar Eustachian valve is present and also a vestigial Thebesian valve.

In the right ventricle a strongly developed crista supraventricularis demarcates the conus portion from the atrio-ventricular portion of the chamber. Both are smooth-walled, the columnae carneae being confined to the apical region. Arrangement of papillary muscles is variable, and a moderator band may or may not be recognizable (Truex and Warshaw, 1942, refer to it in *Macaca mulatta*, where it occurs in under 50 per cent of hearts).

In the left ventricle the mitral valve has a large aortic and a smaller lateral or marginal cusp. A small intermediate cuspule is often present between them. Nodes of Arantius are specially distinct in the cusps of the semilunar valves of the aorta and pulmonary artery in *Papio*.

Coronary arteries have been intensively studied in *Macaca mulatta* by Chase (1938) and by Chase and de Garis (1939). In 266 hearts Chase found the usual pattern (over 50 per cent) for the right coronary, a short truncus communis extending for 2-3 mm. from the aorta to the first branch (ramus infundibularis). In approximately 40 per cent a radix communis divides into infundibular and main arteries. In about 6 per cent two separate arteries spring from the aorta. In isolated individuals still other arrangements were noted. The left coronary most frequently (over 50 per cent) is represented by circumflex and descending branches arising in common directly from the left sinus of Valsalva. In approximately 40 per cent of cases these two vessels arise from the bifurcation of a common stem of variable length. A third pattern is where two arteries arise independently from the aortic sinus (about 6 per cent). Normal termination on the diaphragmatic surface of the heart is for the left coronary to end as a ramus descendens in the posterior longitudinal sulcus, and delivering a larger atrial branch to the septum. Sometimes both arteries end in the posterior longitudinal sulcus, alternatively the ramus descendens posterior is supplied by the right coronary.

The commonest arrangement of the branches from the aortic arch is by two trunks, but occasionally three occur as in *Homo*. When two occur the first (or innominate) gives off the left common carotid and brachiocephalic which thereafter bifurcates into right common carotid and right subclavian. This arrangement (Keith's type B) was found by Keith (1895) in *Cercopithecus*, *Cercocebus* and *Presbytis*. He found some examples of *Presbytis*, however, showing his type A, where the left subclavian springs from the angle between the arch and the anonyma.

Among macaques Keith found, out of twenty-two examples (comprising *M. nemestrina*, *M. irus* and *M. speciosa*), thirteen with type A, seven with type B and two with type C aortic arch branchings.

Macaca has been studied intensively by de Garis (1936, 1938, 1941) who unfortunately uses a different categorization from Keith. In a first series of 133 macaques (115 *M. mulatta*, 10 *M. sinica*, 7 *M. irus* and 1 *M. nemestrina*) he encountered the normal human arrangement in 14 *M. mulatta*, a radix communis for anomyma and carotis sinistra in 15, a short truncus communis for anomyma and carotis sinistra in 62 (and also in the *M. nemestrina*); an intermediate truncus communis in 12 *M. mulatta*, 1 *M. sinica*, and 2 *M. irus*; a long truncus communis in 19 *M. mulatta*, 5 *M. irus* and 5 *M. sinica*. In a second series of 153 *M. mulatta* only 13 showed the human condition of the arch, 17 showed the radix communis for anomyma and carotis interna; 89 presented a short (6 mm.) truncus communis for anomyma and carotis interna; 25 had an intermediate (11 mm.) truncus communis; only 6 had the normal lower mammalian pattern with long truncus communis.

Individual variants include (i) patterns with an extremely short innominate approximating to the four-branched arch; (ii) a thyroidea ima from the left carotid or (iii) from the truncus communis.

Other cynomorph genera for which data are available are tabulated by de Garis (1941) who includes material from the literature as well as his own observations. *Cercopithecus* commonly shows a truncus communis giving off left carotid and brachiocephalic (de Garis type C) or some variant thereof, *e.g.* a medium or long truncus or even type C.3, where the right subclavian is the first branch from the truncus. The last is also recorded for *Macaca sinica* and *Papio*. *Papio* also shows the other varieties of type C. A long truncus has been seen in *Cercocebus* (two species), *Erythrocebus* and *Nasalis*. In *Nasalis* and *Cercocebus* a medium-sized truncus has also been found, whilst in *Semnopithecus entellus*, *Macaca sinica* and some individual baboons, an intermediate between C.2 and C.3 is recorded by de Garis.

As in Platyrrhini the common carotid artery has a long, unbranched course bifurcating into its terminal branches at the level of the angle of the mandible, though occasionally a thyroidea ima is given off in its early part, *e.g.* in *Macaca* and *Presbytis* (Theile, 1852; Keith, de Garis). The thyroidea superior may originate at the bifurcation as Theile found in *M. sylvana*. In any case, it is the first branch off the external carotid. The laryngeal artery usually springs directly off the carotid instead of from the superior thyroid, but it may branch off the linguo-facial trunk (Platzer, 1960). The lingual divides into a sublingualis and a profunda linguae, the former giving off an a. dorsalis linguae and muscular branches. The facial has the usual course and branches both superficial and deep to the mandible. The ascending pharyngeal may arise from the carotid bifurcation or from the external carotid. An occipital artery occasionally is lacking, and may be replaced by branches from the posterior auricular. The termination of the occipital perforates the cranial wall to end in meningeal branches. Parotid arteries are derived directly from the carotis externa. The carotid ends by bifurcation into superficial temporal and maxillary arteries. From the latter a middle meningeal is derived which passes through the foramen ovale. The parent vessel ends as the infraorbital artery.

The internal carotid courses unbranched from its origin to the point where it enters the carotid canal of the temporal bone. Here it takes the usual course, emerging to become related to the divisions of the trigeminal nerve in the cavernous sinus, through which it passes obliquely mediad and forwards, giving hypophyseal branches as it proceeds. It turns abruptly upwards anteriorly to perforate the dura. It gives off the ophthalmic artery whilst in the subarachnoid space and then divides into its terminal anterior and middle cerebral branches. The anterior cerebrals of the two sides converge and unite for a short distance; an a. communicans anterior is, therefore, lacking. Sometimes a median end branch terminates in the splenium of the corpus callosum. The middle cerebral courses within the Sylvian fissure, supplying most of the lateral aspect of the hemisphere; it has no share in the circle of Willis. The latter is constituted by anterior cerebrals, carotids, posterior communicating, posterior cerebrals and basilar arteries.

From the subclavian arises first the vertebral, which takes the usual course to the vertebrarterial foramen of C.6, thereafter ascending to the base of the skull, through the foramen magnum on to the base of the medulla. It fuses with its fellow to form the basilar artery. Parallel with the vertebral a very fine vessel ascends on the longus colli. A costo-cervical trunk was described by Theile in *Macaca sylvana*, breaking up into superior intercostal and cervicalis profunda, the former supplying the anterior 2-3 intercostal spaces. In *M. mulatta* these two vessels arise independently. An a. thoracica interna (internal mammary) arises next, from the hinder wall of the subclavia. It ends by dividing into superior epigastric and musculo-phrenic branches. In *Macaca* it gives a branch to the infrahyoid muscles. The suprascapular branch is larger and given off immediately before the subclavia crosses the scalenes. It gives off a cervicalis ascendens and, more laterally, a cervicalis superficialis. The vessel then passes over to the dorsal aspect of the scapula, ending finally in the trapezius. In *Macaca sylvana* and *M. mulatta* the truncus thyreo-cervicalis is a branch of the suprascapular, but the inferior thyroid may arise independently from the subclavian, whilst in *M. sylvana* a thyroid vessel may spring from the common carotid.

The axillary artery retains a primitive condition by providing a large subscapular trunk for the circumflex humeral and scapular branches, but the a. circumflexa humeri anterior tends to arise independently of the other two. In this the Cercopithecoidea, especially *Papio*, according to Duckworth, approach *Homo* rather than the Pongidae.

The brachial is nearly always of the superficial type, crossing the median nerve ventrally and dividing usually proximal to the elbow. In *Macaca cyclopis*, Yoshimi (1956) found it invariably penetrating the ansa n. mediani. Various types of high origin of radial and ulnar offsets ensue. Arrangements consequently resemble those of human foetuses prior to the sixth month of gestation (Duckworth). For further details see under separate genera and also Platzer (1960, p. 321); Yoshimi (1956); Wang (1960).

Relative contributions of ulnar and radial arteries to the palmar arches are variable, being more primitive in *Papio*, where the ulnar element is the lesser, compared with *Cercopithecus*, where they are equal. In *Macaca cyclopis*, Mori (1959) found a large superficial volar branch of the radial arising high in the forearm and it normally formed the major part of the superficial volar arch. Moreover the deep branch of the ulnar was also small.

The abdominal aorta follows the lumbar vertebral bodies to the left of the mid-line and bifurcates into two common iliacs at the body of the hindmost lumbar. Its first branch is the coeliac axis. This usually has three offshoots, but sometimes (as recorded by Theile, Rojecki (1889) and Grzybowsky (1926)) only two, the hepatic arising separately or in common with the anterior mesenteric. On the other hand, the last mentioned may, itself, be absorbed into the coeliac axis (*e.g.* in some specimens of *Cercopithecus sabaeus* and in various individual macaques).

The posterior mesenteric arises from the middle of the ventral surface of the aorta, gives off numerous colic branches and ends on the rectum.

Paired renals spring immediately caudal to the preceding in *Macaca sylvana* and *M. irus*. They take a transverse course with a slight caudad trend. An inferior phrenic vessel is derived from the left renal, but a right phrenic proceeds directly from the aorta. Adrenal vessels are derived from the renals in *Macaca*. Renals also provide ureteric branches. Spermatic (or ovarian) arteries are commonly derived directly from the aorta on both sides, the left arising higher than the right, but sometimes one (more commonly the left) or both may be derived from the corresponding renal. These also supply ureteric branches.

Parietal branches of the abdominal aorta include the lumbar arteries and a median sacral, which may supply the last pair of lumbars. These may, however, as Thiele found in *Macaca sylvana*, proceed from the angle between aorta and common iliac on either side.

Common iliacs may provide the last lumbars and also ilio-lumbar arteries. The internal iliacs break up into two divisions, a dorsal (or gluteal) and a ventral, the latter providing obturator, pudendal, vesical and uterine arteries.

The gluteal in *Cercopithecus*, *Cercocebus*, *Macaca*, *Papio* and *Cynopithecus*, according to Popowsky (1889), is the first branch. It passes into the buttock cranial to the pyriformis and ends in supplying gluteal muscles. It may provide the ilio-lumbar (*e.g.* in *M. mulatta*).

The obturator is normally a ventral branch of the internal iliac (*Cercopithecus*, *Cynopithecus*, *Macaca sylvana*), but sometimes it springs from the external iliac (*e.g. M. irus*, *M. mulatta*, some examples of *M. sylvana* and *Papio cynocephalus*). In the thigh it anastomoses with the medial femoral circumflex, as found in *M. mulatta* by Imai (1939). Popowsky found the uterine artery springing from the obturator in a *Cercopithecus ascanius*, whilst Thiele reported in *Macaca sylvana* the deep epigastric arising from the same vessel.

The internal pudic has the same course as in Man. It provides middle and inferior rectal (or haemorrhoidal) branches, a transversus perinaei and a bulbo-urethral artery. It ends by dividing into dorsalis penis and an a. profunda penis (*seu* clitoridis). In *Semnopithecus entellus* Popowsky found an exceptional condition where the a. dorsalis clitoridis sprang independently from the internal iliac, and it supplied the uterine artery *en route*. Inferior vesical arteries are derived in females from the uterine arteries.

Sciatic arteries commonly arise directly from the internal iliac, but sometimes from the gluteal.

Obturator arteries sometimes, *e.g.* in *Macaca irus* and *Papio cynocephalus*, are given off from the external iliac. A deep epigastric is supplied just before the external iliac proceeds into the thigh. From this an external pudendal branch may be given to the scrotum, as Popowsky found in *Cercopithecus ascanius*. A deep circumflex iliac also arises from the external iliac, but details show some variation. The ilio-lumbar may spring directly from the external iliac or from the obturator.

From the commencement of the femoral artery spring some subcutaneous branches, separately or from a common stem (*e.g.* as Rojecki and Bluntschli found in *Macaca* and *Presbytis*). Popowsky mentions superficial epigastric and superficial circumflex iliac sharing a common stem in *Macaca* and *Cercopithecus*, with superficial external pudic arising independently, except that in *C. ascanius* the last mentioned was derived from the medial femoral circumflex. Distribution of all these vessels is constant, however, and agrees with the human arrangement.

The largest branch of the femoral is invariably the lateral circumflex, but sometimes this springs from the profunda, while exceptionally its three principal branches arise separately from the parent vessel as Bluntschli (1906) found in his *Presbytis*. Bluntschli also discovered in *Macaca, Cercopithecus* and *Papio* that the lateral circumflex may be lacking and its territory taken over by the profunda. A common stem for profunda and both aa. circumflexa is another recorded variation. The medial circumflex femoral artery may arise from external iliac, internal iliac or from one of the branches of these two vessels. Occasionally it springs from the profunda femoris, or from the femoral in common with the lateral circumflex (*e.g.* in *M. sylvana*, Theile). Its territory is greater than that of its human counterpart, incorporating also part of the territory of the obturator artery.

The profunda is smaller relatively than in Hominoidea and divides almost at once into numerous muscular branches which end in the adductors and the quadriceps. Nevertheless at least two perforating branches have been reported in *Cercocebus* and one in *Cercopithecus* (Manners-Smith, 1911). Otherwise aa. perforantes arises directly from the femoral.

Platzer (1960) reports an a. genu descendens in his *M. mulatta* series arising near the terminal division of the femoral into saphenous and popliteal branches, but Bluntschli found it arising with equal frequency from the saphena, but only rarely from the popliteal.

A saphenous artery is constantly present ; Bluntschli found it lacking only in his *Presbytis*. Passing the knee between gracilis and sartorius insertions, it ends in the crural region by division into a larger anterior and smaller posterior branches. The former, as in prosimians and platyrrhines, divides further into superficial and deep divisions. The superficial branch follows the tibialis anterior to the dorsum of the foot, ending as the first dorsal interosseous of the metatarsus, which anastomoses with the plantar vessels. During its course the superficial division provides medial malleolar and medial tarsal branches. The deep division also ends on the dorsum pedis, supplying in *M. mulatta* the dorsal metatarsal branches II and III, having previously given off as collateral art. metatarsea IV. According to Popowsky and Manners-Smith an arcus dorsalis pedis is formed, although Theile failed to establish this in his *M. sylvana*.

The popliteal artery runs freely in the popliteal fat, not, as in Man, close to the capsule of the joint. The articular branches appear variable ; sometimes a single stem supplies them all ; in other cases a variable number of branches emerge from the parent trunk. In general there are proximal and distal articular branches on both medial and lateral sides of the joint and sometimes intermediate ones also. In *M. sylvana* Theile found them exactly as in Man. Occasionally an anastomosis persists between one of the articular arteries and the posterior recurrent tibial as found by Manners-Smith in *Mandrillus*. After supplying muscular twigs, the popliteal divides into tibial and peroneal terminal branches. Normally in *Macaca* the division is into anterior and posterior tibials and an a. peronaea, but in *Papio* and

Erythrocebus the division is into anterior tibial and peronaeal, where the posterior tibial is derived from the saphena. In *Macaca cyclopis* the division, according to Mizutani (1960), is into anterior tibial and a peroneo-tibial trunk which later gives off the posterior tibial traceable to the sole. The peronaeal artery commonly arises from the posterior tibial as in Man, *e.g.* in *Semnopithecus*, *Cercopithecus diana* and *C. sabaeus* (Manners-Smith). With the persistence of an a. saphena, the anterior tibial is reduced.

A well-developed superficial plantar arch occurs in *Mandrillus* (Manners-Smith). A deeper arch is normally present in most Cercopithecoidea, but the main supply to the digits is from the saphena, either by its communication to the plantar arcade, passing through the second intermetatarsal interval, or by the large perforating artery of that space (*e.g.* in *Papio* and *Mandrillus*). Some similar arrangement appears usual in *Macaca cyclopis*, with the large medial plantar branch of the posterior tibial taking the major share (Tanaka, 1961).

The face and scalp are drained by the facial and retromandibular veins (Nonaka, 1959, in *Macaca cyclopis*). The former joins the external jugular, and the latter may unite first with the facial or enter the external jugular independently.

A jugulo-cephalic trunk furnishing, with the external jugular, a complete venous ring around the clavicle, has not been observed in any Old World monkey (Platzer, 1960). Small isolated lacunae affect the superior sagittal sinus (Bluntschli, 1910). At the torcular Herophili the blood from the sagittal sinus flows in both directions.

In the arm both cephalic and basilic veins are represented. Apart from them, venous blood returns entirely by way of the venae comitantes. The brachial vein continues as the axillary and then as the subclavian. In its axillary course it receives circumflex humeral and subscapular tributaries.

In the thorax the vena azygos major empties as in Man into the superior vena cava. In *Macaca* it sometimes becomes free from the parietes within a sheath of cervical pleura whence a small lobule of Wrisberg is fashioned from the apical part of the right lung (*e.g.* in *M. sinica*, personal observation). Seib (1931/2) found no hemiazygos veins in *M. mulatta*, spaces of both sides being drained into the v. azygos major. Subcutaneous venous drainage of the chest and abdomen have been recorded for *Macaca cyclopis* by Tsubouchi (1961).

The relatively long thoracic part of the posterior vena cava has already been mentioned. The abdominal portion presents nothing unusual. In contrast to its frequency in gibbons, Keith (1896) found no examples, among fifty catarrhine monkeys, of divided post-renal segment.

The obturator vein in *Macaca* embouches into the external iliac (Imai, 1939). In the leg there are typically great and small saphenous veins draining the superficial tissues, but sometimes one or other is lacking. Nishi (1937),

H

for example, could not find the v. saphena magna in *Macaca* or *Semnopithecus*. In such cases the v. saphena parva takes over.

On the foot tibial and fibular marginal veins drain a delicate plexus from the sole. Dorsal digital veins from the four lateral toes drain the margins of the respective digits and end in two or three longitudinal vessels which unite variously to form an oblique dorsal vein. This forms anastomotic links with veins from the hallux and finally becomes continuous with the fibular root of v. saphena parva, whereas the hallucial vein forms the tibial root of the same vein (Ayukawa, 1960, in *M. cyclopis*).

LYMPHATIC SYSTEM

This has been little studied in Catarrhine monkeys. Teshima (1935) has recorded details for *Macaca mulatta* following the earlier work of Beattie (1927). Rieffenstuhl (1960) has summarized the earlier data for all primate groups.

Lymphatics from the tail flow into a common trunk which ends in the glands situated between the two common iliac veins. From the dorsum of the foot a number of collecting channels are formed which course parallel with each other up the medial side of the leg and thigh to end in a superficial inguinal group of glands. These glands also receive lymph from the external genitalia. Drainage from the inguinal glands is on the same plane as in Man. Deeper inguinal glands receive deeper lymph drainage from the penis and deeper parts of the perineum and pass their contents, in turn, to glands in the femoral canal and along the iliac vessels.

Abdominal lymphatics show some advances on arrangements in lower Primates, especially in the numbers and sites of lymphatic glands and nodes. Presence of numerous glands in the mesocolon exemplifies this, as well as the greater differentiation and wider distribution of mesenteric glands. Whereas in *Lemur* a maximum of five mesocolic nodes is the rule, in *Macaca* they increase up to 40-63 localized into outer, middle and inner (or basal) groups, compared with the sparse basal group alone present in *Lemur* (Kihara and Teshima, 1935). Important collections of ileo-colic glands occur on both dorsal and ventral aspects of the ilio-colic angle, draining the caecum and neighbouring parts of both large and small intestine. Some of them extend peripherally into the ileo-colic peritoneal folds.

A group of two to five glands is arranged at the division of the coeliac axis at the cranial border of the pancreas, and extending along the splenic artery. Inconstant smaller glands may occur along the lesser curve of the stomach and one or two nodes are frequently found at the cardia (paracardial nodes). More numerous small nodes appear in the gastro-colic omentum along the left gastric-epiploic artery. They intercept lymph from the gastric walls. On the caudal margin of the pylorus lie one or two small subpyloric nodes draining lymph from the lesser curve of the duodenum. A single node occupies the porta hepatis for collection of lymph from liver and gall-bladder. Its effluents drain to the coeliac group. The cisterna magna lies between the pillars of the diaphragm and may be represented by a series of intercommunicating dilatations of the thoracic duct, as, *e.g.*, in *Macaca sinica* (Weidenreich, Baum, and Trautmann, 1933). From here the thoracic duct usually takes the same route through the thorax as in Man. In *Macaca mulatta*, after travelling dorsal to the aorta, it proceeds obliquely leftwards at the level of T.5-7. It frequently shows segmental dilatations *en route* (cf. the figures of McClure and Silvester, 1909). In the thorax it receives lymph from intercostal spaces and from the thoracic viscera *via* the broncho-mediastinal trunks. Communication with the venous system is variable even between individuals of the same species as shown by McClure and Silvester, who classify their findings into as many as nine different patterns—opening either into the angle between external and internal jugular veins or into the angle between the united jugulars and the subclavian of the left side, with similar patterns for the right lymphatic duct. Sometimes two openings are found, one in each venous angle, in which event, as in one of McClure and Silvester's *Cercopithecus*, the jugulo-subclavian termination may be a separate trunk from the thoracic duct, and drains the homolateral pectoral limb. Two such trunks in their *Macaca nemestrina* are shown, both opening independently into the common jugular angle.

Lymph from the pectoral limb is collected by a subclavian trunk interrupted *en route* by the axillary glands, which are enveloped in the axillary fat. Lymph from the deeper structures of the forearm and hand is not interrupted by cubital lymph nodes so far as is known ; these appear first in the Pongidae (Teshima).

Lymph from the head and neck is drained into a jugular lymph trunk on either side. From the fore part of the scalp, eyelids and root of nose, collectors converge towards the ear and empty into glands in the parotid area. From the hinder scalp, occiput and external ear vessels converge towards the mastoid region and terminate in deep cervical glands, with occasional earlier interruption by retro-auricular nodes. Collectors draining the nose, upper lip and cheeks, and cheek-pouches follow the facial artery and vein behind the cheek-pouch to end in glands of the submandibular group. Teshima also found, in a single individual, a small buccinator node. From the lower lip collecting channels follow the inferior labial branch of the facial artery and terminate directly in submandibular lymph nodes. Lymph from the tongue ends directly in the upper group of deep glands, as does also that from the naso-pharynx, according to Yoffey and Drinker (1938). From the teeth, gums and lower jaw lymph vessels freely communicate between the two sides ; a submental node interrupts the anterior vessels ; otherwise the lymph proceeds to the antero-lateral group of submandibular nodes (three on each side) and then to the deep cervical glands.

VII. Neurology

Central Nervous System

The brain of most cynomorph monkeys is no larger in proportion to body size than in the more advanced Cebidae, and in some, *e.g. Papio*, it is less.* Nevertheless this discrepancy is not correlated with any diminution in mental ability ; in fact there is evidence to the contrary. In certain details, however, the catarrhine brain is remarkable for its specializations, as, for example, in the great size of the corpus callosum, which is an index not only of the great extent of the neopallium, but also of the increased expression of association areas within the cortex.

Like the Cebidae, the Cynomorpha are microsomatic and therefore show poor development of the parts of the brain connected with smell, *e.g.* reduced olfactory bulb, with long attenuated peduncular tract, yet the tuberculum olfactorium is recognizable (lacking the flattening that has occurred in pongid and human brains) and a remnant of the rhinal fissure is seen in the incisura temporalis. Olfactory commissures (anterior commissure, psalterium and fornix) are greatly reduced.

On the other hand, the visual apparatus is highly developed and its central representation markedly obtrusive, notably in its cortical (neopallial) representation. Hereby the occipital lobes of the cerebral hemispheres are produced posteriorly and, as in many cebids, completely cover the cerebellum from above. Internally it contains an extensive posterior cornu, whilst the grey substance of the pallium is marked by a well-developed stria Gennarii over that part of the cortex neighbouring the calcarine fissure (area striata). Another characteristic feature of the occipital lobe of the cynomorph hemisphere is the smooth unfissured appearance of its lateral surface. This broad smooth area is sharply demarcated anteriorly from the rest of the hemisphere (which is well sulcated) by a deep vertical sulcus, the sulcus simiarum or Affenspalte. Its depth is such that other sulci have been submerged, so that developmentally its occipital lip constitutes an operculum. Homologization with any sulcus on the human brain is difficult and controversial. Some homologized it with the outer part of the parieto-occipital, but Elliot Smith (1903, 1904) maintained it to be represented by the inconstant sulcus lunatus. At the point where the simian sulcus cuts the upper edge of the hemisphere, it is joined by the intraparietal sulcus, the two together thus forming an inverted V which embraces the upper termination of the long sinuous parallel sulcus ascending from the temporal lobe. The bifurcation of the caudal extremity of the intraparietal sulcus (transverse occipital sulcus) is submerged by the occipital operculum (variations of the sulcal pattern, especially in the

---

* For quantitative data relative to brain-weight/body-weight proportions the work of Leboucq (1928, 1929) should be consulted.

occipital area are numerous. They have been studied intensively in Asiatic cynomorphs by Kohlbrugge (1903).)

The intraparietal is also joined by the parieto-occipital sulcus which, however, exhibits extreme variation in view of its being developmentally what Elliot Smith terms a compensatory sulcus. Commonly it is a deep but simple incision at the dorso-medial edge of the hemisphere. It may be surrounded on the mesial aspect by a U-shaped system whose posterior limb is essentially parieto-occipital, whereas the cranial limb pertains to the intercalary series, being the compensatory or post-limbic fissure of Broca, and is sometimes separate from the caudal limb. Elliot Smith considers the fundamental element surrounded by this U to be analagous with the parieto-occipital ramus of the intraparietal of *Cebus*. The mesial aspect of the occipital lobe also bears the calcarine system, comprised of a deep horizontal sulcus passing back without demarcation into the stem of the T-shaped retrocalcarine. Beginning at the inferior angle of the T, and coursing a considerable distance along the lower margin of the hemisphere, is the collateral sulcus ; it ends near the rhinal fissure on the medial aspect of the temporal pole.

A very pronounced flexure in the pyriform lobe has produced the vallecula Sylvii. The portion in front of the vallecula has become much reduced and would not be recognized as part of the pyriform lobe, except for the relationship to the olfactory tract ending in the posterior part of the lobe. The anterior rhinal fissure has disappeared, but the posterior forms a distinct incisura temporalis which demarcates the pyriform lobe laterally.

On the base, the Sylvian fissure commences as a lateral extension of the vallecula and extends obliquely upwards and backwards on the lateral aspect. Its dorsal end almost touches the tip of the parallel sulcus, but it is separated by a narrow gyrus, often submerged, so that the Sylvian then appears to join the parallel superficially.

At the commencement of the Sylvian fissure is a large triangular, depressed area, the insula or island of Reil, which forms the cortical covering of the underlying corpus striatum. It is overlapped by opercula derived from neighbouring cortical areas, notably by the dorsal (fronto-parietal) operculum, and also from the temporal lobe, but there is no trace of a frontal (anterior) operculum (cf. Hominoidea). The insula is surrounded dorsally by a sulcus, the limiting sulcus of Reil, which appears homologous with the suprasylvian of other mammals. The anterior end of the dorsal limiting sulcus extends forwards on to the deep aspect of the neighbouring operculum, just lateral to the junction of Sylvian fissure and vallecula, but not as far as in the hominoid brain (sulcus transversus gyri reunientis). Anteriorly the insular area is separated from the orbital aspect of the frontal lobe by a coronally directed eminence. Its surface is crossed obliquely (parallel with the Sylvian) by a shallow sulcus which is comparable with the pseudosylvian sulcus of ordinary mammals (see especially Friant, 1947). Friant (1952, 1953) has also considered the ontogenetic history of this important region.

The orbital aspect of the frontal lobe is markedly concave. Consequently the approximation of the raised medial margins of the two hemispheres produces a keel-like appearance. The lateral elevation bounding the concavity sweeps forwards and mediad from the lateral end of the above mentioned eminence which delimits the orbital area posteriorly from the vallecula. It eventually turns abruptly mediad to form the frontal pole by uniting with the medial sagittal elevation. Upon the orbital surface occurs an orbital sulcus of varying size and conformation ; Elliot Smith considers it represents the praesylvian of other mammals. Alongside it is developed a variable pattern of compensatory foldings sometimes producing an H-shaped or triradiate arrangement.

The frontal lobe is expanded from before backwards and above down compared with that of lower Primates. It represents about 12 per cent of the total surface of the hemisphere in *Cercopithecus*, and 11·8 per cent in *Macaca* (Anthony, 1952).

There is a typical central sulcus separating the frontal lobe posteriorly from the parietal. On the frontal lobe laterally occur a simple sagitally directed inferior frontal sulcus and an arcuate (inferior praecentral). Above the latter, two small depressions represent the superior frontal sulcus, while below the central sulcus is a small plain sulcus, the inferior transverse of Eberstaller.

On the temporal lobe, besides the parallel sulcus, there occur two fragmentary depressions between it and the collateral. They are regarded as inferior temporal sulci. On the lateral aspect of the occipital lobe near the occipital pole is sometimes a shallow, horizontal sulcus, corresponding with the sulcus occipitalis lateralis of the *Cebus* brain. It is the only lateral marking on this lobe.

On the mesial surface, in addition to the calcarine and parieto-occipital fissures, there are others compensatory to the calcarine, around which they arrange themselves. A well-developed intercalary or calloso-marginal sulcus (s. genualis) is constant ; its posterior extremity is upturned. There may be a separate rostral sulcus anteriorly.

As regards cytoarchitectonics the work of Brodmann (1909) on *Macaca* shows that considerable advances have been made compared with the brain of *Hapale*, especially in the expansion of certain areas (notably Brodmann's areas 1 (a. postcentralis), 4 (a. giganto-pyramidalis) and 17 (a. striata or visual area), but also in the addition of new intercalary areas which represent association centres. These are represented in the accompanying diagram (fiig. 6), which should be compared with fig. 11 of Vol. III of this work.

Growth of the brain has been studied in *Macaca* by Zuckerman and Fisher (1938) and in *Semnopithecus* by Friant (1953).

Proportionate to the cerebral hemispheres other parts of the brain are small, especially the corpora mammillaria, interpeduncular body, and to a lesser degree the corpora geniculata and corpora quadrigemina.

The lateral geniculate body much resembles the human structure, being horseshoe to reniform in shape with a definite hilus facing downwards and

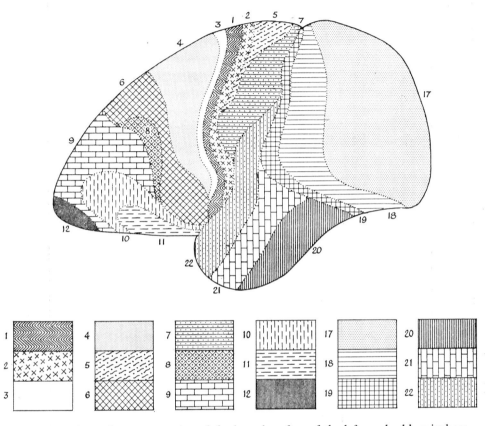

FIG. 6.—Schematic representation of the lateral surface of the left cerebral hemisphere of *Macaca* showing cytoarchitectonic areas based on the studies of Brodmann

Key to Brodmann's areas: 1, A. postcentralis intermedia; 2, A. postcentralis caudalis; 3, A. postcentralis oralis; 4, A. giganto-pyramidalis; 5, A. preparietalis; 6, A. frontalis granularis; 7, A. parietalis (association area); 8, A. frontalis; 9, A. frontalis granularis; 10, A. fronto-polaris; 11 and 12, A. praefrontalis (olfactoria); 17, A. striata; 18, A. occipitalis (visuo-psychic); 19, A. praeoccipitalis; 20, A. temporalis inferior; 21, A. temporalis media; 22, A. temporalis superior

medially. In *Macaca* it is comprised by six layers of cells separated by compact sheets of white fibres (Minkowski, 1913, 1920). Large cells occur prominently in two rows along the hilus. They are figured by Sachs (1909) and in *Cercopithecus* by Friedemann (1911).

The thalamus is somewhat smaller proportionately than in Hominoidea but presents the same general arrangement of nuclei. Number and position of dorsal nuclei are identical, but association nuclei increase in size from

TABLE 5
THALAMIC NUCLEI IN *MACACA*

Nuclear Group	Walker (1937)	Crouch (1934)	Aronsen and Papez (1934)	Clark and Boggon (1935)	Vogt (1909) Friedemann (1911) Mussen (1923)	Grunthal (1934)
Anterior Group	1. N. antero-dorsalis	Antero-dorsal n.	N. antero-dorsalis	N. antero-dorsalis	Anterior accessory nucleus	N. anterior
	2. N. antero-ventralis	Antero-ventral n.	N. anterior	N. antero-ventralis	Anterior n.	
	3. N. antero-medialis	Antero-medial n.	N. anterior	N. antero-medialis	,,	
Midline	4. N. parataenialis medialis	N. parataenialis medialis	N. parataenialis		N. parataenialis medialis	N. medianus anterior
	5. N. parataenialis lateralis	N. parataenialis lateralis	—		N. parataenialis lateralis	—
	6. N. interparataenialis	N. interparataenialis	N. paraventricularis anterior		—	N. medianus anterior l. (?)
	7. N. paraventricularis anterior	N. paraventricularis anterior	,,		—	N. medianus anterior B
	8. N. paraventricularis posterior	N. paraventricularis posterior	N. paraventricularis posterior		—	
	9. N. centralis medialis	N. centralis medialis	N. centralis medialis		—	N. medianus posterior l.
	10. N. inter-antero-medialis	N. inter-antero-medialis	—		—	N. medianus posterior B
	11. Massa grisea centralis	Central grey	N. reuniens anterior et posterior : N. rhomboideus		—	N. medianus posterior reuniens
Lateral	12. N. lateralis dorsalis	N. lateralis dorsalis	N. lateralis or N. dorsalis		La. (lateral thalamic n. superior part)	N. dorsalis posterior A
	13. N. lateralis posterior	N. lateralis posterior	N. lateralis posterior Posterior half of n. lateralis pars		Lb (upper part of lateral nucleus)	Posterior half of n. lateralis

	+n. lat. antero-med. et lat. Caudal ⅔: n. vent. antero-med. et lat. and n. lat. ant. med. et lat. / N. ventralis intermedius and postero medialis	Anterior ½ n. ventralis pars lateralis / Posterior ½ n. ventralis pars lat. and n. ventralis pars arcuata	v.a.l., r.a.m. and ant. ½ of lb / Ve, Var, Vp.	v.t.m, v.a.l., v.t.l. and ant. ½ of lb / Va and caudal part of ventricular thalamic nucleus	Anterior half of N. lateralis principalis / Posterior half of v. lateralis principalis (ventral part)
15. N. ventralis lateralis	+n. lat. antero-med. et lat. Caudal ⅔: n. vent. antero-med. et lat. and n. lat. ant. med. et lat.	Anterior ½ n. ventralis pars lateralis	v.a.l., r.a.m. and ant. ½ of lb	v.t.m, v.a.l., v.t.l. and ant. ½ of lb	Anterior half of N. lateralis principalis
16. N. ventralis posterior	N. ventralis intermedius and postero medialis	Posterior ½ n. ventralis pars lat. and n. ventralis pars arcuata	Ve, Var, Vp.	Va and caudal part of ventricular thalamic nucleus	Posterior half of v. lateralis principalis (ventral part)
Medial					
17. N. medialis dorsalis	N. medialis dorsalis	N. medialis	N. dorso-medialis	Main n. medialis	N. internus centrum medianum
18. N. centrum medianum	Centre median of Luys	N. centrum medianum	Centre median nucleus	N. centralis	N. semilunaris (Flechsig)
19. N. parafascicularis	N. parafascicularis	N. parafascicularis	N. parafascicularis	N. parafascicularis	N. parafascicularis
20. N. submedius	N. paracentralis	N. ventralis pars submedia		N. submedius	N. circularis
21. N. paracentralis	N. paracentralis	N. paracentralis		N. int. medullary lamina	N. circularis
22. N. centralis lateralis	N. centralis lateralis	N. centralis lateralis		N. int. medullary lamina	N. circularis
23. N. medialis ventralis	N. medialis ventralis	N. ventralis pars medialis		N. ventralis commissuralis medialis	N. medianus posterior 7 (?)
Posterior					
24. N. pulvinaris lateralis	Lateral n. of pulvinar	P 2		Pu	Pl
25. N. pulvinaris medialis	Medial n. of pulvinar	P 3 and P 4		Pb and Pd	
26. N. pulvinaris inferior	Inferior n. of pulvinar	P 1		Pd	—
27. N. suprageniculatus	N. suprageniculatis	N. suprageniculatus		N. suprageniculatus	—
28. N. limitans	N. limitans	N. of optic tract		N. limitans	—

macaque towards the Hominoidea in correlation with cortical advances. Aronson and Papez (1934) give the proportionate size of dorsal thalamus expressed in terms of greatest length of the human thalamus as 12·2 for *Macaca*, 12·8 for *Cercocebus* and 16·4 for *Papio*.

Walker (1937) reviewed the thalamus of *Macaca* after critically examining the results of previous workers. He concluded that the structure could be subdivided, on the basis of fibre connections and cytomorphology, into certain major and minor parts. His scheme differs essentially from those of previous students in the recognition of the anterior half of the ventral and lateral nuclear groups as anatomically and functionally different from the posterior half. This anterior part he terms nucleus ventralis lateralis. Walker's divisions are compared with the earlier schemes in Table 5, p. 104.

Clark and Northfield (1937) studied the cortical projection from the pulvinar in *Macaca* and found the latter to consist of two parts separated by a bundle of cortico-tectal fibres. One element in relation to the lateral geniculate projects to the periparastriate cortex, whilst the main element projects on to the posterior Sylvian receptor region, which is contiguous with the auditory projection area of the medial geniculate in the superior temporal gyrus. The massa intermedia is large. The tuber cinereum is thin-walled and directed caudally to end in the infundibulum. The hypothalamic area is provided with a specially rich blood supply which has been studied in detail in *Macaca* by Mergner (1961) who compares his findings with those in *Oedipomidas* and certain rodents.

In the brain-stem the pons is broadened but not sufficiently to obscure the trapezoid body. Pyramidal tracts are relatively large and prominent, and the olivary body is also distinct.

The cerebellum is relatively small. In median sagittal section it presents the usual division into three main lobes by the fissura prima in front and the fissura secunda caudally. The anterior lobe comprises the culmen (parts III and IV of Bolk). Lobulus centralis and culmen are separated by the deep sulcus postcentralis, while the sulcus postlingualis separates the lingula from the culmen.

The middle lobe also has three main divisions (i) lobulus simplex, (ii) declive +folium cacuminis +tuber valvulae and (iii) pyramid. The latter is demarcated from the tuber by the prepyramidal sulcus (the caudal limit of the middle lobe of Ingvar's scheme).

The middle lobe is expanded laterally and bent upon itself to form the lobus ansiformis which is comprised of two more or less equal-sized crura (I morphologically cranial and II morphologically caudal) united caudally, but separated elsewhere by the deep fissura intercruralis. Crus I is attached to the folium cacuminis by a slender band of nervous tissue only : crus II is connected to the tuber valvulae. The fissura prepyramidalis is traceable on to the hemisphere posterior to the last-mentioned connection as the fissura retro-tonsillaris, which demarcates the anterior limit of the large lobus paramedianus.

The posterior lobe comprises medially the uvula and the nodule separated by the sulcus uvulonodularis. Each is connected by a peduncular process (formatio vermicularis) with a group of folia. That connected with the uvula constitutes the paraflocculus, whilst that associated with the nodule is the flocculus. Together these constitute the floccular lobe—much reduced compared with that of lower mammals. The paraflocculus, however, is less reduced than the flocculus and is provided with a pedunculated appendage, the petrosal lobule, which is received into a fossa on the petrous temporal bone.

SPINAL CORD.—This differs little from the human structure, but the dural envelope is less voluminous in proportion to the size of the nerve cord than in Man. It presents cervical and lumbar enlargements. Segmentation is not apparent except for the nerve-root attachments. These vary in number according to the vertebral formula. In *Macaca mulatta* there are 34 pairs (8 cervical, 12 thoracic, 7 lumbar, 3 sacral and 4 caudal). Reduction of caudal segments to three occurs individually (Hines, 1933). Furrows and ridges are visible only on the first two cervical segments, the contours elsewhere being smooth. The cervical cord accounts for one-seventh the total length, the thoracic a little over one-third, lumbar, sacral and caudal together one-ninth. The caudal one-third is comprised by the filum terminale (Hines, *loc. cit.*). The cord extends farther down the canal in the adult than in the human adult. Few specific data are available, but Hines states that in *M. mulatta* it terminates anterior to L.5. In *M. sinica* it ends opposite the disc between L.4 and L.5, but in an *M. irus* it was found ending one vertebra cranial to this level (Hill, 1939).

PERIPHERAL NERVOUS SYSTEM

(*a*) CRANIAL NERVES

The olfactory nerve is composed of numerous filaments which perforate the cribriform plate by independent foramina.

The optic nerve is large and formed from fibres which constitute the ninth layer of the retina, which are the axons of ganglion cells of the eighth layer, together with some from the Dogiel cells of the sixth layer. In monkeys ganglion cells degenerate a few days after section of the optic nerve or tract or destruction of the lateral geniculate nucleus (Polyak, 1957). The orbital course is somewhat wavy ; complete decussation occurs at the optic chiasma.

Third, fourth and sixth nerves, according to Winckler (1932) are, in *Cercopithecus*, relatively large. The very large locomotor nerve leaves the cranium by the superior-medial part of the sphenoidal fissure after accompanying the ophthalmic nerve through the cavernous sinus along its medial border and above the abducent. Penetrating the orbit it bifurcates into superior and inferior divisions. The superior division proceeds beneath the rectus superior and accompanies it along its lateral border together with the nasal nerve; it innervates the superior rectus and gives a branch to the levator palpebrae.

The larger inferior division is directed deeply and somewhat mediad. It fails to divide until it reaches the lateral border of the optic nerve where it breaks into three. One branch passes under the optic nerve, to enter the medial rectus a short distance from its origin, supplying eight to ten twigs to the muscle. Next is a branch to the inferior rectus equalling the previous nerve in size and dividing into several twigs. Finally the branch to the inferior oblique passes between the lateral and inferior recti.

The ciliary ganglion, according to Winckler (1932), is, in *Cercopithecus*, attached to the third nerve on the branch to the inferior oblique, which supplies the short (motor) root of the ganglion (1 mm. long). The long or sympathetic root is also carried by the third nerve through the cavernous sinus and sphenoidal fissure, being derived originally from the plexus on the internal carotid artery.

Three branches of distribution emerge from the anterior pole of the ganglion. The feeblest rejoins the oculomotor and divides terminally into two: the next branch is somewhat more robust. The third and stoutest proceeds obliquely beneath the optic nerve and divides on its medial side. A symmetrical pattern of entry into the eyeball is established.

The pathetic or trochlear nerve, also very large according to Winckler, is stronger than the frontal branch of the ophthalmic. It courses in a fold of dura, which provides it with a sheath, above the superior petrosal sinus. From the posterior clinoid process it takes a direction from behind and laterally obliquely mediad and then through the sphenoidal fissure, crossing in succession the upper aspect of the superior rectus and levator palpebrae near their origins. Turning further medially it penetrates the superior oblique muscle along its upper border by 6-8 filaments.

The trigeminal is provided with a large semilunar ganglion of triangular contour, with its base directed forwards and laterally, giving rise to the three primary divisions. The ophthalmic division has the usual relation to the cavernous sinus and enters the orbit through the superior orbital fissure, only after dividing into its three terminal branches, nasociliary, frontal and lachrymal nerves. The last two are large and give the appearance of a bifurcation of the ophthalmic whilst the nasociliary is very small, arising medial and posterior to the frontal nerve.

Winckler (1932) describes the frontal in *Cercopithecus* as entering the orbit by the sphenoidal fissure along the lateral edge of the fourth nerve, but giving no anastomotic connections thereto. In the orbit it lies above the levator palpebrae and divides into three terminal branches some 1·5 cm.

behind the orbital margin, though by artificial dissection it can be made to divide much farther back. Its branches are a lateral frontal, the largest, medial frontal, and supratrochlear, the two last of equal size. The supratrochlear forms connections with the nasal.

The nasal nerve is separable back to the Gasserian ganglion, but is very thin and in close contact with the frontal. In the orbit it lies lateral to the oculomotor nerve, and accompanies its superior division under the superior rectus and levator palpebrae. Crossing the optic nerve, it divides into two unequal terminal branches, the internal nasal and the external nasal. The former proceeds between the oblique and upper border of the rectus medialis and divides into an ethmoidal filament and the internal nasal proper, which proceeds through the lamina cribrosa into the cranial fossa, whence it takes the usual course into the nasal fossa. The external nasal nerve is directed towards the supero-medial angle of the orbit where it bifurcates into an upper (infratrochlear nerve) and lower branch, the latter distributed on the dorsum nasi.

The lachrymal nerve emerges from the front of the trigeminal ganglion at the cavernous sinus, reuniting with the frontal, which it accompanies through the superior orbital fissure. In the orbit it is directed towards the supero-lateral angle of the outlet, meanwhile dividing into three branches, (i) the most medial and slenderest twig, passing through the lachrymal gland to end in the skin of the upper eyelid, (ii) a larger middle branch which passes between the superior and lateral recti to gain the centre of the lachrymal gland ; it gives a very fine branch to the gland, the remainder ending in the skin of the forehead, (iii) a lateral branch as large as the preceding which also gives a twig to the gland and then proceeds through the malar foramen to end in the overlying skin. Distribution of the lachrymal has also been studied by Lacroix (1926) in *Cercopithecus*, *Macaca* and *Papio*.

From the maxillary division of the trigeminal, a large zygomatic nerve is given off in the pterygo-palatine fossa. It proceeds with the larger infraorbital into the infraorbital canal and there divides into zygomatico-temporal and zygomatico-facial branches. The former supplies skin over the temporal fossa while the latter is distributed around the lateral palpebral canthus. Sometimes (in up to 50 per cent in *Macaca mulatta*) the zygomatico-temporal is lacking, its field being supplied by a branch from the zygomatico-facial. Also given off in the pterygo-palatine fossa are the posterior superior dental nerves. They enter canals in the posterior wall of the maxillary antrum. The anterior superior dental springs from the labial division of the infraorbital nerve as it enters the infraorbital groove. Both nerves proceed into the infraorbital canal where the dental portion diverges to supply the canine and incisor teeth (Ashton and Oxnard, 1958).

In the infraorbital groove the maxillary nerve branches into nasal and labial divisions. The latter gives a large medial and small lateral branch.

These pass through the infraorbital canals in a characteristic manner. A supero-medial canal accommodates the nasal division ; the large central canal conveys a branch of the labial division, and a small lateral opening transmits the remainder of the labial division. There are variations on this theme. Ashton and Oxnard found in two *Papio hamadryas* and in two of three specimens of *Cercopithecus* the medial branch of the infraorbital canal was divided and the nasal division of the nerve in consequence occupied two foramina. In one *Macaca mulatta* the most lateral internal opening was absent, both branches of the labial division of the nerve emerging through a single foramen. In *Papio* and in one macaque the more medial canals, transmitting branches of the labial division, divided so that labial twigs occupied at least three foramina.

On the face the nasal division provides a fine superior branch to the dorsum nasi and an inferior to the vestibulum oris. The labial division splits into a medial and a lateral series of branches of which the medial subdivides further into three twigs. Of these the most medial innervates the philtrum, some filaments crossing the midline. Lateral branches innervate the upper lip and forepart of the cheek. Some of these interlace with terminal filaments from VII (see also Bowden *et al.*, 1960).

The spinal part of the spinal accessory nerve is a mixed nerve commencing in the central axis at the caudal end of the tractus solitarius. Windle (1931) found nerve-cells both intracranially and peripherally on the rootlets and trunk of the nerve in *Macaca*.

(b) Spinal Nerves

(i) Cervical Plexus.—This has been studied extensively in a large number of cynomorph monkeys by Huntington (1897) on whose account the following remarks are based (see, however, also Brooks, 1883 ; Bolk, 1902 a).

The general pattern in formation of the plexus is much as in Man, *e.g.* by connections between the ventral primary divisions of the first four cervical nerves.

The ventral division of C.1 gives a large communication which enters the sheath of the hypoglossal nerve. This bundle divides in the sheath into a centripetal component, which continues with the hypoglossal, and another which is peripherally directed.

The centripetal bundle gives several small twigs to the recti capiti ventrales, after which it continues as a slender twig in the hypoglossal sheath, entering the anterior condylar canal.

The rest of C.1 descends to form a loop with C.2 on the ventral aspect of the lateral mass of the atlas (first or atlantal cervical ansa). Close to this junction C.2 gives off a dorsally directed branch which becomes applied to a similar branch from C.3 and these unite with the spinal accessory nerve.

The bulk of its fibres course craniad in the spinal accessory sheath but a small twig descends with the communicating branch to C.3.

The remainder of C.2 constitutes the second ansa and, after giving a ramus communicans to X and a twig to rectus capitis ventralis major, is continued into a nerve trunk which, with a similar branch from C.3, forms the ansa cervicalis profunda (communicans noni).

The third nerve, after contributing the ramus to XI and a branch to the infrahyoid muscles, is continued mainly as the great auricular nerve which incorporates in part the fibres which represent the lesser occipital nerve of *Homo*. C.3 also sends a descending branch from which are derived a cranial contribution to the superficial cervical nerve and a branch which joins one from C.4 to constitute the lower division of the superficial cervical. It also sends motor nerves to the deeper prevertebral muscles and the levator scapulae.

Additional to the above-mentioned contributions to the posterior element of the superficial cervical nerve, C.4 furnishes from near its root a large branch to the upper part of scalenus ventralis and another which is a contribution to the phrenic nerve.

The remainder of C.4, after furnishing a loop with C.5, divides into two main branches, dorso-lateral and ventro-medial. The former supplies the nerve to levator claviculae and then terminates in supra-

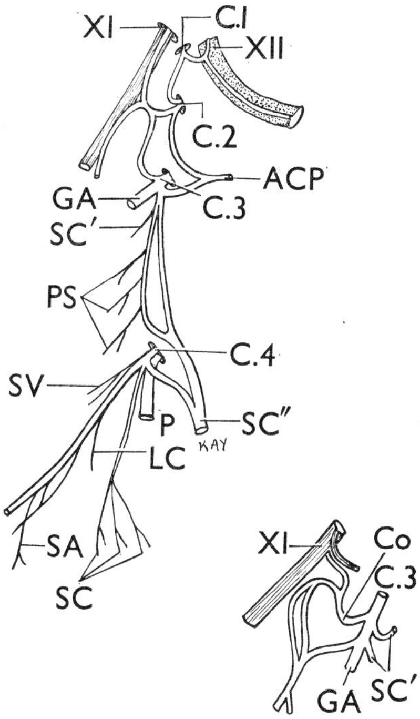

FIG. 7.—*Macaca mulatta* ♀ Cervical plexus of the right side. Based on the data of Huntington (1897)

ACP, ansa cervicalis profunda; *Co*, communicating loop; *GA*, great auricular nerve; *LC*, nerve to levator claviculae; *P*, phrenic nerve; *PS*, nerves to prevertebral muscles and levator scapulae; *SA*, supra-aeronial nerve; *SC*, supraclavicular and suprasternal nerve; *SC'*, superficial cervical nerve (upper); *SC''*, superficial cervical nerve (lower); *SV*, nerve to scalenus ventralis

cromial cutaneous branches. The ventro-medial division provides supraclavicular and suprasternal nerves.

Some variations occur in respect of the anastomotic connections with XI, which, in Huntington's view, throw possible light on the origin of the human lesser occipital nerve, which is lacking in the cynomorphs. In *M. radiata*, for example, C.3 gives, in addition to the great auricular and contribution to the superficial cervical, a large communicating ramus which passes mainly to the sternomastoid branch of XI, travelling centrally in the sheath thereof. The remainder of this branch combines, as two filaments, with the main trunk of XI, which it accompanies peripherally, but separating again and, after receiving an additional filament from C.3, constitutes a cutaneous nerve to the skin near the levator claviculae.

Great auricular nerve.—A large trunk which curves round the dorsal margin of the sternomastoid and ascends on its lateral surface to the ear, before gaining which it breaks into a leash of branches. In all forms examined these are arranged identically : (*a*) most dorsal branch supplies skin of post-auricular and mastoid regions, extending over occipital origin of trapezius to anastomose with the great occipital nerve ; (*b*) the second and largest branch runs in the cranio-auricular groove, giving branches to mastoid region, cranial aspect of anterior helix, cymba and cavitas conchae ; (*c*) a twig solely supplying the cavitas conchae inferior or posterior part of the cymba ; (*d*) innervates the floor and anterior wall of the auditory meatus ; (*e*) and (*f*) supply skin over the parotid gland in front of and below the meatus.

Superficial cervical nerve.—As noted above this is comprised of two parts, one ascending from C.3 and a transverse whose fibres originate in C.3 and C.4. The ascending division sends a twig to the skin of the parotid region and continues thereafter to divide into two terminal branches, which proceed obliquely to the anterior margin of the parotid area and to the angle of the mandible. One twig continues over the masseter to end in skin over the cheek-pouch. The transverse division passes the sternomastoid margin at a more caudal level usually in company with the suprasternal and medial supraclavicular nerves. Passing deep to the external jugular vein, the nerve sends a large, cranially directed branch innervating the cervical skin as far as the midline, and a smaller caudally directed branch which accompanies the suprasternal nerves to supply skin over the origin of sternomastoid and over the manubrium.

Descending cervical nerves.—These include the suprasternal, supraclavicular and supracromial branches of the plexus and are all derived from C.4. They are remarkable for their large size and the number of their individual branches, otherwise their distribution is much as in Man, apart from being more extensive, in so far as their territories extend caudal to the level of the nipples.

In addition, reference must be made to the ansa cervicalis profunda formed by the descendens cervicalis uniting with the descendens hypoglossi and innervating the infrahyoid muscles. The descendens hypoglossi leaves the hypoglossal nerve in front of the external carotid artery, descending obliquely on the fascial sheath of the vessel. Near the carotid bifurcation it is joined by the communicating branch from the second and third cervical nerves. The descendens cervicis is formed from the continuation of C.2 with a communication from C.3 and joins the descendens hypoglossi to form the ansa. They are easily separated by dissection, being held in a loop merely by a fascial sheath. Minor variations in the size and position of the connections, especially the form of the precarotid interlacement are reported and figured in different species by Huntington.

Typically above or in front of the point of connection between the dorsal and ventral limbs of the ansa the ventral limb is composed of two trunks proceeding in opposite directions. The ascending element derived from C.2 passes up to the point of connection with the hypoglossal whose sheath it enters to be carried peripherally, and eventually to innervate the thyro-hyoideus and genio-hyoideus muscles. The descending trunk of the ventral limb of the ansa carries the fibres from C.1. Crossing the ascending trunk, its fibres are distributed to sterno-hyoideus, sterno-thyroideus and both parts of omo-hyoideus. The nerve to the sterno-thyroid is remarkably long, continuing on the deep aspect of the muscle almost to its sternal attachment.

Phrenic nerve.—Arises typically by union of two roots respectively from C.4 and C.5, with an additional root from C.4 and C.5 combined *via* the nerve to the subclavius. Proceeding caudally on the scalenus ventralis, it crosses the medial edge of the muscle 2 cm. cranial to the first rib, passing thence ventral to, and subsequently to the medial side of, the vertebral artery. It enters the thorax, dorsal to the sternal end of the clavicle and first costo-sternal junction, where it receives the contribution from the nerve to the subclavius. The intrathoracic course is thereafter as usual.

The so-called paraphrenic nerve (comprised of filaments from C.5 which emerge from the nerve to the subclavius) has been studied by Locchi (1932) in *Macaca* and *Papio*. Apparently, as in Man, these reunite with the phrenic proper after passing ventral to the subclavian vein above the pulmonary hilum. They innervate the dorsal part of the diaphragm.

(ii) Limb Plexuses.—Compared with the Hominoidea the cynomorph monkeys show evidence of post-fixation of the limb plexuses. Thus in the brachial plexus the segmental derivation of the axillary nerve is C.6, C.7 (Kohlbrugge, 1897), compared with C.5 (or C.4 and C.5) for Man (Harris, 1904). Further, there is constantly a large contribution to the plexus from the second thoracic nerve; this is variable in Hominoidea, but never more than slight (Todd, 1912).

The same is true for the lumbo-sacral plexus. This is exemplified in the femoral nerve which derives roots from thoraco-lumbar segments 15-17 or 16-18 (Kohlbrugge) compared with 14-16 for Man (Quain). The reduction of the number of lumbar vertebrae, and hence of spinal segments in the Hominoidea is a factor to be considered here, but cannot explain the post-fixation of the brachial plexus also.

(iii) Brachial Plexus (Brooks, 1883; Harris, 1904, 1939; Ono, 1936).—Ono (1936) studied the brachial plexus in three species of macaques (*M. mulatta*, *M. cyclopis*, *M. irus*) and found the kind and manner of plaiting accorded with the human norm. Roots contributing are C.4-T.2, but while

I

C.4 and T.2 are inconstant in their association, C.5-T.1 are constant. Variations occur in the following proportions : C.5-T.2, 52·5 per cent ; C.5-T.1, 37·5 per cent ; C.4-T.2, 4 per cent. Ono concluded there was an inclination to post-fixation on human standards. Brooks (1883) found in *Macaca* the whole of C.5-C.8 involved in the plexus with a considerable contribution from C.4 and from the main trunk of T.1. The large C.4 he found to give contribution to the small C.5 just as the latter provides the phrenic nerve.

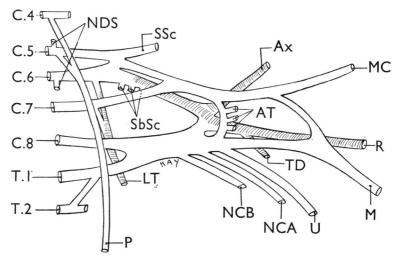

FIG. 8.—*Macaca mulatta*. Brachial plexus, based upon the findings of Ono (1936)

Ax, axillary nerve ; *AT*, anterior thoracic nerves ; *LT*, long thoracic nerve ; *M*, median nerve ; *MC*, musculo-cutaneous nerve ; *NCA*, nervus cutaneus antebrachii medialis ; *NCB*, nervus cutaneus brachii mediails ; *NDS*, dorsalis scapulae nerves ; *P*, phrenic nerve ; *R*, radial nerve ; *SbSc*, subscapular nerves ; *SSc*, suprascapular nerve ; *TD*, thoraco-dorsal nerve ; *U*, ulnar nerve

The suprascapular nerve arises exactly as in Man, except that it takes more fibres from C.6. After this, the anterior (upper) trunk divides, giving off one branch running ventral to the other. The ventral branch is longer than the trunk ; it unites with one from C.7 thereby forming the lateral cord. From the ventral side of the cord springs the lateral pectoral (external anterior thoracic) nerve and a cutaneous branch, after which the cord ends as the lateral head of the median nerve.

The dorsal division of the anterior trunk is larger than the ventral. It meets a similar branch from C.7 giving off collaterally two small subscapular nerves and then, from the point of union, a larger trunk which subdivides into a middle subscapular and a large circumflex nerve. Thereafter this union receives another contribution—from the combined C.8 and T.1—to form the very large radial nerve.

Besides this dorsal branch of the combined C.8 +T.1 another cord arises more caudal in position and of greater length. This gives off ventrally the medial thoracic and then subdivides more or less equally, the cranial being the medial head of the median, the other becoming the ulnar nerve after giving off, from its medial side, the medial cutaneous nerve. (For the musculo-cutaneous nerve, *vide infra*, p. 118.)

Of the supraclavicular branches the nerve to the subclavius is very constant (from C.6) giving off the paraphrenic as already mentioned, the fibres of which have originated from C.5.

The nerve of Bell, or long thoracic, comes from the dorsal aspect of the plexus by two heads from C.6 and C.7. Less constant in arrangement are the nerves to the rhomboids and the long subscapular. The former generally emerges from one of the heads of the long thoracic (from C.6), but it may arise directly from C.5. The long subscapular sometimes emerges from the dorsal branch of C.7 and sometimes from the radial or even more distally (*vide* Brooks for details).

The lesser internal cutaneous (medial brachial cutaneous) of human anatomy is not usually a separate entity, but replaced by a large branch of the intercosto-brachial or intercostal branch of T.2, but Brooks found it occasionally branching from the medial (antebrachial) cutaneous or from the medial pectoral nerve.

(iv) Lumbo-sacral Plexus.—In *Mandrillus sphinx* Utschneider (1892) found eight lumbar nerves, the last emerging between L.8 and S.1, but in *Macaca nemestrina* only seven lumbar nerves were present; a number also recorded for *M. mulatta* (Howell and Straus, 1933).

In *Macaca mulatta* Zuckerman (1938) reported T.12 giving rise to the subcostal nerve, but occasionally contributing a twig to L.1 for incorporation in the ilio-hypogastric nerve. L.1 is almost entirely devoted to the ilio-hypogastric, but may send a branch to L.2 to reinforce the ilio-inguinal nerve. The ilio-inguinal was found difficult to determine by Zuckerman, whose dissections did not reveal the same picture as the diagram presented by Howell and Straus (1933), where L.1-L.3 between them form two nerves coursing parallel to each other and the subcostal. Zuckerman found that, after emerging from the spine, L.2 divides into two main trunks of which the more cranial receives a twig from L.1 and the more caudal a filament from L.3. Both course around the flank parallel to the ilio-hypogastric and, like it, give dorsal branches to the dorso-lateral parts of the trunk. They evidently together correspond to the ilio-inguinal; an arrangement also found by Russell (1893). L.2 therefore has a wider field of distribution than L.1 as found also by Sherrington (1893). Rarely the ilio-inguinal arises from L.2 only, more frequently from L.1 and L.2 or L.2 and L.3. Presence of a thirteenth rib does not alter the neural segmentation.

The genito-femoral nerve normally arises from L.3 only, but sometimes (4 out of 32 with a normal number of thoraco-lumbar vertebrae in Zuckerman's series) a contribution is received from L.2 and in 7 out of 33 a branch from L.4 was found. Stimulation of the root of L.2 always effected contraction

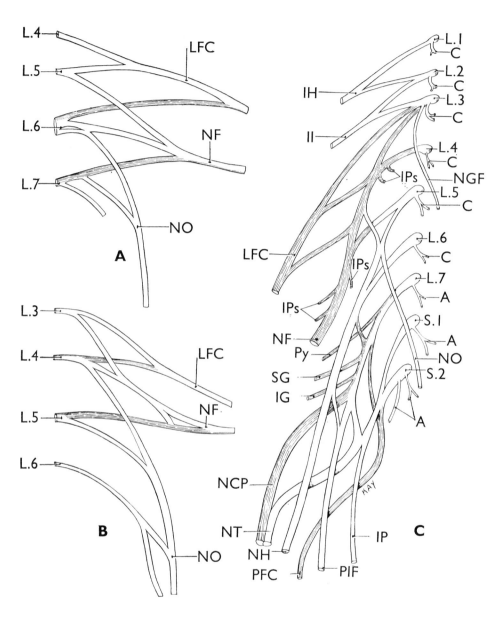

FIG. 9.—A, Left lumbar plexus of *Mandrillus sphinx*; B, The same of *Macaca nemestrina*; C, Right lumbo-sacral plexus of *Macaca mulatta*. (A & B, modified from Utschneider; C, from Howell & Straus.) A, Branches to caudal flexor musculature; C, Branches supplying psoas magnus and parvus and quadratus lumborum muscles

A, branches to caudal flexors; *C*, branches to psoas magnus, psoas parvus and quadratus lumborum; *IG*, inferior gluteal nerve; *IH*, iliohypogastric; *II*, ilioinguinal; *IP*, internal pudic nerve; *IPs*, branches to ilio-psoas; *LFC*, lateral femoral cutaneous nerve; *NCP*, common peroneal nerve; *NF*, femoral nerve; *NGF*, genito-femoral nerve; *NH*, nerve to the hamstrings; *NO*, obturator nerve; *NT*, tibial nerve; *PFC*, posterior femoral cutaneous (small sciatic nerve); *PIF*, pubo-ischio-femoral nerve (=obturator nerve); *Py*, nerves to pyriformis; *SG*, superior gluteal nerve

of the cremaster in Sherrington's (1892) experiments, even when no obvious communication with L.3 could be detected. Stimulation of L.4 in monkeys with a post-fixed plexus also induces contraction of the cremaster (Sherrington). Zuckerman and Burr (1934) did not usually find the genito-femoral emerging from the psoas as a single trunk, but coursing medially close to the sympathetic chain and then along the external iliac artery. In the region of the internal abdominal ring it divides into its terminal genital and femoral (lumbo-inguinal) branches, the former proceeding down the inguinal canal and the other continuing into Scarpa's triangle. Occasionally, however, the nerve emerges by two separate branches of L.3 through the psoas, one of which, the lumbo-inguinal, establishes communications with the sympathetic chain while the genital nerve runs caudally medial to the lateral femoral cutaneous nerve and then to the internal abdominal ring. Very rarely the genito-femoral is derived from the sympathetic trunk entirely.

The lateral cutaneous nerve of the thigh derives from L.3-L.5, but sometimes from L.3 and L.4 only, or L.4 and L.5 only, the variations being uninfluenced by the phenomena of pre- or post-fixation, or by the presence of a thirteenth rib.

Femoral and obturator nerves draw their fibres from lumbar roots 3-5, but additional fibres sometimes come from L.6, or the composition may be from L.4-L.6. The contribution from L.3 usually passes as a single trunk to the root of L.4 near the exit of the latter from the intervertebral foramen.

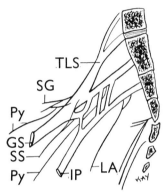

FIG. 10.—*Mandrillus leucophaeus*. Sacral plexus of the right side viewed from the pelvic aspect (redrawn from Cordier *et al.*)

GS, great sciatic nerve ;
IP, internal pudic nerve ;
LA, nerve to levator ani ;
Py, nerves to pyriformis ;
SG, superior gluteal nerve ;
SS, small sciatic nerve ;
TLS, truncus lumbo-sacralis

In the normal plexus the branch from L.5 to the lumbo-sacral trunk passes directly to the root of L.6 near the exit of the latter from the intervertebral foramen, but occasionally it receives this contribution *via* the obturator nerve. The combined structure proceeds distally and joins with a large branch from L.7 to constitute, with a similar branch from S.1, the great sciatic nerve (L.5-S.1 or L.6-S.2 or L.6-S.1).

The pudendal (internal pudic) nerve is made up of the remaining branch of S.1 joined by a large contribution from S.2 and takes the usual course to the perineum.

The *sacral plexus* in several species of baboons has been reported on by Cordier *et al.* (1936) who find that there are two distinct and separate plexuses, sciatic and pudendal, although in both *Papio hamadryas* and *Mandrillus leucophaeus* they contract anastomoses at the level of their constituent roots. Details in *Mandrillus* are depicted in fig. 10 which is based on Cordier's figure.

In long-tailed Cercopithecoidea the tail is innervated by segmental nerves that form lateral longitudinal connections which constitute a collector nerve each side of the tail. Cranially this communicates with the sacro-coccygeal plexus. In *Macaca mulatta* there are only four pairs of caudal nerves, not easily differentiated into dorsal and ventral components. Together with S.3 they are responsible for innervation of the skin and muscles of the tail (Howell and Straus, 1933).

(v) Peripheral Nerves.—Concerning peripheral nerves little of a general nature can be stated. In the arm the musculo-cutaneous nerve is often not separately definable, being incorporated in the median. Median and ulnar nerves may likewise be inseparable in the brachium, becoming distinct only at the elbow. Similarly in the forearm there may be communications between radial and ulnar nerves. Winckler (1930) has commented on the correlation between the degree of divarication of the pollex and the angle made by the thenar branch of the median nerve with its parent trunk. This angle increases as the primate scale is ascended, although an extreme degree of recurrence was found, for example, in the cebid, *Ateles*. In Cercopithecoidea the following data are presented :

	Angle between Pollex and Limb Axis	Angle of Incidence of Thenar Branch of Median Nerve	Depth of Flexor Retinaculum (mm.)
Macaca	75°	160°	20
Cercopithecus sabaeus	75°	130°	7
C. mona	70°	140°	7

Duckworth (1904) dissected the posterior interosseous nerve in *Mandrillus* à propos of the perforating branch to the pronator quadratus previously recorded in *Hylobates* by Hepburn (1892). He failed to find it, but noted slight differences in the order of emergence of various branches compared with those in *Gorilla*.

Kosinski (1927) has dealt with the cutaneous nerves of the manus, basing his remarks on *Macaca mulatta*, *Cercopithecus aethiops* and *C. cephus*. The superficial branch of the radial is responsible normally for the innervation of the radial three-and-one-half digits, but in the Rhesus and one Grivet only two-and-one-half were involved, while in all four examples of *C. cephus* this latter arrangement prevailed. In five out of seven catarrhines the ulnar nerve innervates one-and-one-half digits.

The cutaneous nerves of the pelvic limb have been described—and figured in *Macaca irus* (under the title *Cercopithecus cynomolgus*)—by Bolk (1897) in a paper mainly devoted to the Pongidae. His findings are best presented by the accompanying figure (fig. 11) based on Bolk's figs. 11, 13 and 14.

Utschneider (1892) described the lateral femoral cutaneous nerve in *Mandrillus* and *Macaca nemestrina*. In the former he found it was derived mainly from the fourth lumbar nerve joined by a smaller contribution from

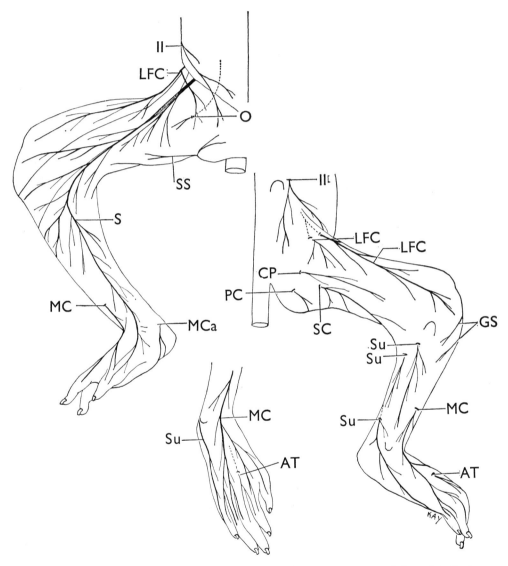

Fig. 11.—*Macaca irus* (Crab-eating Macaque). Cutaneous nerves of the pelvic limb.
Redrawn from Bolk (1897)

AT, anterior tibial nerve ; *CP*, cutaneous branch of posterior rami of sacral nerves ; *GS*, genual branches of saphenous nerve ; *II*, ilio-inguinal nerve ; *LFC*, lateral femoral cutaneous nerve ; *MC*, musculo-cutaneous nerve ; *MCa*, medial calcaneal nerve ; *O*, cutaneous branch of obturator nerve ; *PC*, perforating cutaneous nerve ; *S*, great saphenous nerve ; *SC*, cutaneous nerves from great sciatic ; *SS*, small sciatic nerve ; *Su*, sural nerves

L.5 and that the combined trunk is joined by a further twig from L.6 near the anterior ventral iliac spine. In the thigh it supplies branches to skin on both lateral and medial aspects as far as the knee. A twig to the scrotum is supplied from the medial branch. In *Macaca nemestrina* the nerve is derived from L.3 and L.4 and supplies some muscular branches to the psoas complex.

The femoral nerve in *Mandrillus*, according to Utschneider, draws its fibres from L.5-L.7, compared with L.3-L.5 in *M. nemestrina*. The contribution from L.7 in the former emerges between the psoas major and iliacus muscles, supplying twigs to both. Proceeding over the ventral aspect of iliacus, the nerve enters the thigh through the so-called lacuna muscularis and there divides into muscular and cutaneous branches of distribution. One branch supplies the pectineus, passing deep to the femoral vessels. Another goes to the sartorius and, after supplying it, perforates the muscle to end cutaneously near the knee.

A large medial branch supplies the rectus and carries on to the crural region. It communicates with the medial branch of the lateral femoral cutaneous. Other branches supply the vasti and the knee joint.

The obturator nerve, after entering the thigh *via* the obturator canal, ends in two branches. One ends in the obturator internus muscle and the adductor magnus also sending a twig to the hip joint. The other branch supplies adductores longus, brevis and gracilis, and thereafter, perforating the fascia lata, ends in the knee joint.

According to Ssokolow (1933) the sural nerves differ from the usual human pattern in not forming any anastomosis, but conform to what he terms the tibial variant of the normal human arrangement. The medial cutaneous nerve of the calf has an independent oblique course, but usually over the centre of the Achilles tendon, sends a strong connecting ramus to the tibial nerve or to the lateral plantar nerve. For the most part the lateral sural nerve is lacking, but if present gives a small number of collateral rami as in Man. The lateral nerve of the dorsum pedis is weaker than in Man. Bolk (1897) derives the fibres of this nerve entirely from the nineteenth thoraco-lumbo-sacral segment.

The musculo-cutaneous nerve of the leg has been studied by Winckler (1934) in *Cercopithecus sabaeus*. After giving filaments to the peronaeus longus it passes between the two heads of the muscle. Distally it courses between the peronaeus brevis and the peronaeus quinti digiti, which lies behind, giving two filaments to the latter prior to its becoming tendinous. In *C. mona* six to seven twigs are provided. The rest of the motor part of the nerve goes to the large belly of peronaeus brevis, which remains fleshy to the ankle. There is no deep accessory peroneal nerve.

All the bellies of the extensor digitorum brevis are supplied by the anterior tibial, which also innervates the calcaneo-cuboid joint and the two post-axial tarso-metatarsal joints.

In the foot the cutaneous innervation of the dorsum has been worked out by Winckler (1936) in *Cercopithecus* (*C. mona*, *C. sabaeus*). Apparently the small saphenous nerve gives numerous branches around the lateral malleolus and along the lateral edge of the dorsum of the foot and fifth toe. It communicates with the musculo-cutaneous. The first important branch of the latter is supplied to the tarsal region and to the lateral malleolus, anastomosing with the twigs from the lateral saphenous. Then follows a branch directed towards the last interdigital cleft. This is reinforced by a twig from the previous branch. It gives terminal branches to toes IV and V. The main nerve continues and bifurcates into medial and lateral branches, the latter ending at the third interdigital cleft. The medial branch again bifurcates, sending one branch to the medial side of the middle toe and another towards the second interdigital cleft, overlapping the field of the anterior tibial. Meanwhile the main nerve has also provided, from its preaxial side, a large branch destined for the first interdigital cleft which gives, besides the digital nerves along the contiguous margins of I and II, a dorsalis hallucis to the dorsum of the big toe ; this forms communications with the long saphenous, which courses along the medial border of the foot and big toe. The anterior tibial nerve emerges over the second interdigital cleft and furnishes collaterals for toes II and III.

Winckler found differences between *Macaca* and *Cercopithecus* in respect of the details of branching of the musculo-cutaneous nerve. The pattern is somewhat simpler in *Macaca*.

(c) AUTONOMIC NERVOUS SYSTEM

(van den Broek, 1907, 1908 ; Riegele, 1926 ; Botar, 1931 *a* and *b*, 1932 ; Kiss, 1932 ; Kuntz, 1933 ; Trumble, 1934 ; Zuckerman, 1938.)

The sympathetic is very variable in construction even within a single species, *e.g. Macaca mulatta*, or on the two sides of one individual, albeit a general anatomical plan is recognizable.

The cervical part of the main chain is closely associated with the vagus (Kiss, 1931, 1932) communicating therewith usually by two or more branches, a constant one being just caudal to the superior cervical ganglion. Rich connections are also formed between the sympathetic chain, vagus and their respective cardiac branches and the recurrent laryngeal nerves, these connections being richer on the right than on the left (Zuckerman) as found in Man by Funaoka and Shinosaki (1928).

The superior cervical ganglion in *Macaca* is a fusiform body of variable size lying ventral to the transverse elements of the second and third cervical vertebrae, parallel with the ganglion nodosum of the vagus and medial to the internal carotid artery. Its cranial pole provides two nerves, internal carotid and jugular, extending into the head, the former constituting a plexus around the artery, the latter providing two rami, one entering the jugular foramen to join the jugular ganglion, the other passing over or through the petrosal ganglion to join the tympanic plexus. Other connections from the ganglion are to the ganglion nodosum, to the hypoglossal nerve and to the first three or four cervical nerves. Branches of distribution are provided to pharynx, oesophagus and plexuses around the external and common carotid arteries (Kuntz, 1933). Nerve supply to the pharynx in *Macaca mulatta* has been carefully recorded by Sprague (1944) who found the pharyngeal plexus poorly developed, but an additional nerve, not present in Man, is supplied to the organ from the superior laryngeal branch of the vagus. Motor fibres to the pharynx and palate leave the brain *via* the bulbar accessory and lower vagus roots, and pass to the muscles by the pharyngeal branch of the vagus— except those supplying stylopharyngeus and ceratohyoideus, which are of glossopharyngeal origin.

Riegele (1926) describes a slender branch emerging from a strong connection between superior cervical and nodose ganglia. This passes caudally parallel to the main trunk and provides branches to the vagus, to the sympathetic trunk and to the second and third cervical nerve. Kuntz failed to find this branch in his dissections.

A middle cervical ganglion is usually well defined, but sometimes is comprised by two separate enlargements situated craniad to the subclavian artery. Connecting middle and inferior (or stellate) ganglia, fibres to the trunk divide to surround the artery forming the ansa subclavia. Riegele found a small ganglionic enlargement on the ventral limb of the loop. Occasionally, still other small ganglionic nodes may appear on the sympathetic trunk between the superior and middle cervical ganglia, or on the branches of communication with the vagus, or on the cardiac nerves derived from either sympathetic or vagus. Zuckerman (*loc. cit.*) records a small node on a communicating branch from the sympathetic to the recurrent laryngeal nerve in a Rhesus.

The inferior cervical or stellate ganglion is commonly a crescentic mass lying on the necks of the first two ribs, concave caudo-medially and separated from the first thoracic nerve by the superior intercostal vessels. In about 60 per cent of instances Zuckerman found the caudal horn of the stellate ganglion incorporated in the ganglion of the second space, and in one instance the third ganglion was also more or less fused with it. Branches from the stellate ganglion may be grouped into medial and lateral sets. The lateral group include grey rami communicantes to C.7 and C.8 and both grey and white rami to T.1 and to the communicating loop which commonly connects T.1 and T.2. Occasionally a grey ramus also connects with C.6. Medial branches include twigs to neighbouring blood vessels, a communication to the phrenic nerve (sometimes derived from the subclavian loop) and others to the vagus.

Occasionally the inferior cardiac branch springs from the ganglion, or from the ventral limb of the loop.

Sometimes all the cardiac branches of the sympathetic unite to form a single trunk, especially on the left. There is no constancy in the arrangement of the cardiac nerves whether from sympathetic or vagus, variations occurring from individual to individual and even on the two sides of the same animal. On the right side all cardiac nerves end in the deep cardiac plexus. On the left some of the vagal and sympathetic fibres pass to the superficial cardiac plexus, but it is not possible to state categorically which, in view of the variability.

The thoracic trunk of the sympathetic courses over the necks of the ribs beneath the pleura, exhibiting a ganglion at every segment (except the fore-most). All the ganglia are connected obliquely by white and grey rami to the corresponding spinal nerve. Sometimes these form a single bundle in each segment, but more usually grey rami lie cranial to the white. Some-times more than two rami are found in a particular segment. In the more cranial segments some communications are made to the cardiac plexuses; other twigs join the plexus gulae and plexuses on the aorta and pulmonary vessels.

Splanchnic nerves are derived from the more caudal thoracic ganglia, mainly from the last, with additional contributions from the first two or three lumbar ganglia. A more cranial origin occurs in *Semnopithecus* and *Papio* (Zuckerman). Greater, lesser and least splanchnics of human anatomy cannot usually be defined, although commonly three nerves from the last thoracic and cranial lumbar segments end in the coeliac ganglion or plexus.

The lumbar section of the sympathetic chain is continuous with the thoracic portion either behind (*i.e.* dorsal to) the diaphragm or occasionally through its fibres in a position lateral to the crura. The cord lies on the lumbar bodies ventral to the segmental lumbar vessels and usually exhibits five or six ganglia each side, though occasionally more are present. The first one or two are more accessible from the thoracic side of the diaphragm, the third being the first obviously abdominal swelling.

Occasionally adjacent lumbar ganglia become contiguous and may fuse, the fourth or fifth being the most frequently affected. In one Rhesus, Zucker-man found lumbar ganglia 3-5 fused into a single mass. Sometimes, as also occurs in the thoracic region, the ganglia are located more on the grey rami than on the main trunk. The chains of the two sides are frequently con-nected by transverse fibres. All the lumbar ganglia are connected to the segmental spinal nerves by grey rami, sometimes (*e.g.* in the caudal segments) by two or more such rami. White rami are more laterally located and pass from the segmental lumbar nerve to the ganglion of the next segment to the caudal side, and sometimes there are also connections to the second segment to the rear, *i.e.* lumbar ganglion 6 receives white rami from segments 4 and 5. The caudal limit of emergence of oblique white rami is, in slightly under

50 per cent of Rhesus monkeys, the third lumbar nerve, in the rest the fourth, except in two anomalous cases (both with twelve pairs of ribs and post-fixed lumbar plexus) where white rami passed from L.5 to the sixth lumbar ganglion. Kuntz (*loc. cit.*) found white rami connected with only the first three lumbar nerves, but the last also contained preganglionic fibres. Trumble (1934) found that the most caudal rami in macaques were associated with L.3 and occasionally with L.4. Zuckerman found the caudal limit to be L.3 in *Semnopithecus, Macaca irus, Papio papio* and *P. ursinus*. In some specimens of *Cercopithecus sabaeus, Macaca nemestrina, Mandrillus leucophaeus* and in two examples of *Papio cynocephalus* the limit was L.4. In *Papio hamadryas*, out of five specimens examined, the caudal limit was L.4 in one example which had an extra lumbar vertebra, L.3 in one of the others and L.5 in the remainder.

The sacral chain continues the lumbar sympathetic cord into the pelvis, where it lies on the ventral aspect of the sacrum. Caudally the cords of the two sides converge towards the midline ending finally in the ganglion impar which is commonly located on the first post-sacral vertebra. There are usually three paired sacral ganglia cranial to the ganglion impar.

Each of the first two sacral ganglia provides grey rami which proceed obliquely backwards to the appropriate sacral foramina. Grey rami from the hinder ganglia are multiple but very fine. There is much individual variation in the pattern of the sacral autonomic.

Prevertebral plexuses comprise the usual cardiac, pulmonary, gular, coeliac, hypogastric and pelvic plexuses, but other lesser networks are subsidiary to these. As in Man, the cardiac plexuses are arranged in superficial and deep parts, while the coronary plexuses are subsidiary to the superficial cardiac plexus.

Pulmonary plexuses are dorsal and ventral in relation to the lung hila. The ventral plexus receives fibres from X and from the deep cardiac plexus, and also, on the left, from the superficial cardiac plexus. The dorsal plexus is composed of vagal fibres and rami from thoracic sympathetic ganglia 2-4.

The coeliac or solar plexus is located around the roots of the coeliac axis and anterior mesenteric arteries ; it comprises an extensive reticulum in which are found a pair of large ganglia and a variable number of smaller ones. It receives all the splanchnic nerves and several contributions from the right vagus. From its cranial part the plexus supplies elements which form a subsidiary plexus around the phrenic vessels, which also receives filaments from the phrenic nerves. Other derived plexuses are the aortic, adrenal, renal, anterior mesenteric, spermatic (or ovarian), posterior mesenteric and hypogastric plexuses. The last-mentioned is not very conspicuous in monkeys and is made up by filaments from the aortic plexus and from the lumbar ganglia. Caudally it becomes merged in the pelvic plexuses.

Other connections of the lumbar ganglia occasionally met with are to the genito-femoral and obturator nerves, the former being the more frequently affected (Zuckerman and Burr, 1934).

Pelvic plexuses show some sexual differences in distribution, being located lateral to the rectum in the male and around the vagina in the female. Their fibres are derived from the last lumbar and first two sacral nerves *via* their visceral rami (nervi erigentes) and from the posterior mesenteric plexus *via* the hypogastric nerves. They also receive contributions from the lower lumbar sympathetic ganglia. Subsidiary plexuses extend around the pelvic vessels to supply the pelvic viscera.

VIII. Sense Organs

NOSE

The external nose has been considered already (*antea* p. 58). Here the nasal fossa alone concerns us.

Immediately within the external nares is the vestibule. This is lined by mucous membrane differing in texture and colour from that lining the main part of the nasal fossa. The latter is soft and slightly yellowish, whereas in the vestibule it is firmer and pinker. In *Cercopithecus*, at any rate, the vestibular mucosa is continued upwards on the fore part of the roof of the nasal fossa for a distance of some 10-12 mm., the edges of this tract (especially the hinder edge) being raised, and the floor excavated, giving the effect of an open tube leading upwards from the external naris. Elsewhere the external naris is margined by only a narrow zone of modified mucosa which is not as sharply demarcated from the normal nasal mucosa. In *Kasi* (and other langurs) the above-mentioned groove is converted into an almost closed tube by the further elevation of the lower rim until it makes contact, without fusing, with the upper rim, producing a scroll-like process. The tube has a large rostral opening which can be seen from without the external naris. The function of this peculiar structure is unknown. In *Papio* this scroll is replaced by a prominent fusiform projection in line with but completely distinct from the inferior conchae. The structure divides the vestibule into an upper and a lower moiety of equal dimensions without, however, forming a blind pocket like that of *Kasi*. The vestibular mucosa is sharply defined caudally by a serrated line from the general respiratory mucosa.

In the general anatomy of the nasal fossa the Cercopithecoidea follow the same plan as in the Platyrrhini. Cave (1948) considers that these two groups, together with the Hominoidea, have each undergone independent parallel evolution from the more primitive prosimian condition. In support of this is the interesting feature that, in the more primitive members of both Catarrhini and Platyrrhini, there is an interorbital septum. In the more advanced, larger-brained forms, the interorbital region has been re-invaded by the upper reaches of the nasal fossa.

In *Macaca mulatta* (Lucas, 1932; Geist, 1933) the fossa in sagittal section presents a triangular outline instead of the quadrilateral outline of the human counterpart, due to the narrower space between the frontal and presphenoid bones. As a result, the roof is angular and very restricted in the transverse dimension. Geist gives four fundamental differences separating the cynomorph fossa from that of Man, namely: the absence of the homologue of the superior concha; the lack of frontal, ethmoidal and sphenoidal accessory sinuses; the existence of a permanent communication with the buccal cavity by way of the incisive foramen; and finally the presence of a membranous septum continuous with the dorsal border of the bony septum and extending into the nasopharynx.

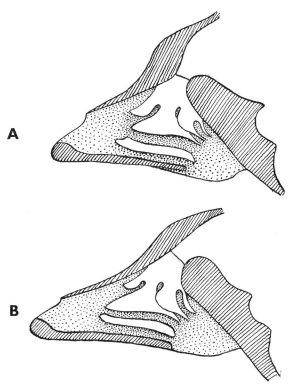

Two irregularities mark the septum, (i) a ridge marking the site of the nasopalatine nerve; this encases the nerve posteriorly but lies above it anteriorly, and (ii) a tubercle located anterior to the apex of the middle concha analagous to the agger nasi of the lateral wall in Man, serving to impede the flow of air through the fossa. The tubercle is purely mucosal in juvenile monkeys, but in adults is

FIG. 12.—Lateral wall of the right nasal fossa in A, *Papio*; B, *Mandrillus* (based on drawings found among the effects of C. Tate Regan)

associated with an elevation on the underlying cartilage.

On the lateral wall two prominent projections of the mucosa are present. These correspond in position and attachments to the middle and inferior conchae of Man. The inferior expands rapidly downwards from its superior line of attachment and is more constant in shape than the upper concha. On its deep (lateral) aspect a prominent cartilage-based projection underlies the ala nasi. The hinder extremity of the inferior concha extends a little beyond the hinder border of the hard palate. The opening of the naso-lachrymal duct opens into the fore part of the inferior meatus.

The upper concha is supported on a tongue-shaped turbinal attached to the hinder part of the lateral wall of the fossa, leaving its cranial, caudal and ventral margins free. Lucas has recorded variations in the peripheral outline of this concha. Above it lies a depression (spheno-ethmoidal recess) homologous with the human superior meatus. Beneath this concha is a prominent uncinate process surrounded posteriorly by a hiatus semilunaris, into the floor of which opens the maxillary air-sinus—the only paranasal sinus present in *Macaca*. The sinus recalls in shape that of the human embryo of 105 days described by Schaeffer (1920). Its walls are smooth even in the adult. The ostium is a small opening which forms the entrance into a canal, the ethmoidal infundibulum, which leads to the hiatus semilunaris. On the bony skull the opening into the antrum is larger ; in the fresh state the gap is filled by membrane almost to the roof of the cavity. A rudimentary superior concha may be present in *Macaca*, but is never elevated above the general level of the wall of the fossa (olfactory region), being indicated solely by a shallow horizontal depression representing the superior meatus (Lucas). It is better developed in *Cercocebus*, where it is slightly raised above the general level, and still more so in *Papio*, where a supreme meatus is also indicated.

Lucas found the ciliary currents in the nasal secretion adapted to the complex nature of the walls. In general, mucus is propelled from smaller to larger spaces in order to transmit material away from the olfactory area. Ultimately all material is impelled by ciliary action of the pars respiratoria towards the naso-pharynx. The degree of ciliary activity increases along a vertical axis from roof to floor of the fossa.

Olfactory epithelium is relatively more extensive than in Man. Lucas, in *Macaca*, found it covering the postero-superior angle of the middle meatus wall and a juxtaposed area on the lateral face of the middle concha which it does not do in Man. The same distribution has been found in *Kasi* and *Papio*.

The naso-pharyngeal canal is elongated from before backwards and lined by smooth mucous membrane. Near its roof is the slit-like orifice of the Eustachian tube. Salpingo-palatine and salpingo-pharyngeal folds are lacking, but a small tubercle at the lower edge of the opening imparts a slightly crescentic form to the ostium.

Although the maxillary is the only sinus present in *Macaca*, even this is lacking in *Papio*, though present above the true molars in *Mandrillus* according to Aubert (1929). Absence of the antrum seems to be correlated with the large space occupied by the root of the canine—compensated for in *Mandrillus* by the additional bony expansion on the dorsum of the muzzle. Aubert also describes a frontal sinus in *Cercopithecus sabaeus*, sometimes much enlarged, thereby forming a prominent swelling over the forehead—a condition I have also encountered in the same species. The sphenoid is occupied by diploe, but a small excavation within this in *C. aethiops* is interpreted by Aubert as a rudimentary sphenoidal sinus. On the other hand Weinert (1925/6) found frontal sinuses lacking in all cynomorphs he examined.

Eller (1932), however, describes, figures and gives mensurational data for the antrum of *Papio hamadryas*, comparing it with the same structure in *Macaca mulatta* at different ages. Eller's contribution also gives an account of the relationship of the antrum to neighbouring tissues and organs, especially the deciduous and permanent dentitions.

VISUAL APPARATUS (see especially Polyak, 1957; Rohen, 1962)

In Old World monkeys the conjunctiva is pigmented in the immediate vicinity of the cornea and to some degree peripherally therefrom, but varies in degree in different genera. It receives the 3-5 ducts from the lachrymal gland at the upper lateral fornix, whilst tears are withdrawn *via* the puncta lacrimalia situated at the top of a papilla on the free margin of each eyelid near the medial canthus. The caruncula lacrimalis is an area of modified conjunctiva immediately adjacent to the puncta, on a deeper level, filling the angle of the canthus. Around the caruncle is a depression, the lacus lacrimalis. A large lachrymal sac lies beneath the caruncle in a depression on the lachrymal bone and adjacent part of the nasal process of the maxilla. A small nictating membrane (see especially Bartels, 1911) projects from the medial canthus deep to the caruncle. The membrane is generally pigmented, at least on its free lateral margin and commonly more marked than in Man. It lacks the cartilaginous basis of the membrana nictitans of lower mammals.

The eyeball is relatively large, though varying somewhat according to genus. Schultz (1940) has given details for *Cercopithecus, Macaca, Papio* and *Nasalis*. In *Cercopithecus* ($\male$) the absolute volume of the globe is 3·89 c.c. In *Macaca mulatta* there is a significant sexual difference, males averaging 5·21 c.c. and females 4·30 c.c. In a male baboon Schultz found an eyeball 6·36 c.c. *Nasalis* also shows a sexual difference, but slighter than in the Rhesus, *viz.* males averaging 3·62 c.c. and females 3·43 c.c. Eyeballs do not vary in size relative to the body-weight, *e.g.* a *Cercopithecus* of 4·5 kg. or female macaques of 5·5 kg. weight have eyeballs as large as or even larger than female orangs of 37·5 kg. Ontogenetically the globe grows rapidly in early life, but slowly later so that the relative size is greater in the juvenile. It is also greater in females than males. In a small infant of *Presbytis sabana* Schultz found a ratio of eyeball to body-weight of 0·303 compared with a value of 0·064 for its mother, *i.e.* per kilogram of body-weight the infant's eye is almost five times as large as that of the adult female.

All catarrhine eyeballs are richer in pigment than those of Man (Kolmer, 1930), but in structure they are very similar in all details, even in respect of such details as those responsible for visual intensity in different regions of the retina. The same applies to the vascular arrangements but, as regards extent and refinement of the structural elements, Kolmer found the globes of *Papio* and *Cercopithecus* superior to those of *Macaca*, the latter again being slightly superior to those in Hominoidea.

The greatest differences from the eyeballs of Hominoidea are to be found in details of the iris and ciliary bodies, in particular the anterior strata of the iris being more complicated in structure than in Man. In many monkeys the iris is characterized by pigment cells of peculiar shape, forming long fusiform structures. In *Macaca* the front layer of the iris is composed of numerous small spindle-shaped cells containing dark pigment. All monkeys are provided with a dilator iridis varying considerably in thickness. The lens much resembles the human lens, but it is more flattened in *Erythrocebus*.

The retina is of the diurnal type, *i.e.* cones prevailing over rods. Kolmer tentatively commented on histochemical differences between rods and cones, suggesting microchemical differences. He succeeded in demonstrating histochemically at least two kinds of cones in *Cercopithecus diana* and in *Macaca*, and suggested some correlation with colour perception. That colour perception is of a high order in catarrhine monkeys has been ably demonstrated by Brecher (1935, 1936) who found it more advanced in, *e.g.*, *Cercocebus* than in Man. Bierens de Haan (1925), too, found that *Macaca nemestrina* could distinguish four principal colours, while Trendelenburg and Schmidt (1930) reported experiments with *M. irus* and *M. mulatta* indicating normal trichromatic colour vision of equal efficiency to that of Man. More recently Wislocki *et al.* (1952, 1954 *a*, *b*) have studied the histochemical structure of catarrhine retinae, and also other ocular structures, using various procedures confirming Kolmer's observations and adding much new information.

The outer portions of both rods and cones in *Cercopithecus* and *Mandrillus* were found by Kolmer to be extremely lengthened but he could not find any explanation for this specialization. Kolmer's findings on detailed microscopic structure of rods and cones have been supplemented by those of Sjöstrand (1959) in the electron microscopic field (see Rohen's fig. 3).

A well-marked fovea is invariably present in the Cercopithecoidea, while in *Cercopithecus diana* Kolmer found a distinct foveola. Here also was found a thin uniform ora terminalis marked by the presence of fine striated muscle fibres. An ora serrata does not exist (Henderson, 1926).

Ophthalmoscopy in *Cercopithecus*, *Cercocebus*, *Macaca*, *Cynopithecus*, *Papio* and *Mandrillus* has been reported upon by Johnson (1901). In all five species of *Macaca* examined the chorioideal vessels were very marked as orange-red streaks radiating from the optic disc. Retinal vessels are crimson and the nerve fibres semiopaque. There is considerable pigmentation, but less than in the fundus of the chimpanzee. The fundus of *Papio* resembles that of *Macaca*, but in *Mandrillus* the chorioideal vessels are even more marked, and the same applies to *Cercopithecus albogularis*. *C. diana* shows a grey fundus, the pigmentation obscuring the chorioideal vessels. In *C. sabaeus* the fundus resembles that of *Mandrillus*, but the macula has double

K

the diameter of that of any other cynomorph examined. *Cercocebus* has a fundus like that of *Macaca* whilst *Cynopithecus* exhibits a deeply pigmented fundus with heightened reflexes from the vessels and macular ring.

AUDITORY ORGAN (Werner, 1960)

The external ear has been considered above (p. 59 ; but see also Lasinski, 1960). The main feature from the taxonomic point of view is the presence of a bony external meatus which accounts for the inner two-thirds of the entire passage, the outer one-third being provided with a cartilaginous support anatomically continuous with the cartilage of the pinna.

The tympanic membrane exhibits a pars tensa and a pars (membrana) flaccida, but the latter is very restricted. The outline of the membrane is more circular in *Macaca* than in, *e.g.*, *Pongo*, where it is oval. Slight onto-genetic changes in shape may occur. The angle at which the handle of the malleus inserts on the membrane varies somewhat. Measured against the plane of the zygomata, Forster (1925) recorded angles of 60° (for *Cerco-pithecus*), 68° (for *Macaca*), indicating a much more vertical position than in any other Primate except *Tarsius* (71°) ; the angles in Platyrrhini and Hominoidea ranging around 40° to 53° at most.

Werner has supplied new figures and descriptions of the auditory ossicles of several Primates including *Macaca irus*, *Papio cynocephalus*, to replace the somewhat inadequate and outdated data of Hyrtl (1845) and Doran (1876). The ossicles of *Macaca mulatta* have also been figured stereoscopically by Gregory (1920).

The malleus presents a club-shaped head, which projects into the epi-tympanic recess. The articular surface is rounded, raised above the general level and strongly bowed medialwards. It is separated from the handle by a short, but distinct neck. On the manubrium is a short, robust, processus brevis and a well-developed muscular process. The incus is, as in other groups, subject to much individual variation, so that nothing can at present be stated as being peculiar to the bone in the Cercopithecoidea, and the same applies to the stapes. In *Macaca irus* Werner shows the stapes with a short, thick stem, with divergent, relatively weak but straight crura ending in a narrow reniform footplate. The foramen subtended by the crura and foot-plate is a rounded oval.

On the medial wall of the middle ear the promontary is a very distinct feature. A swelling in the epitympanic recess is caused by the lateral semi-circular canal above that formed by the canal for the facial nerve and above the depression containing the foramen ovalis. Sometimes the wall of the canal is in part unossified (*e.g.* in *Semnopithecus*).

The labyrinth differs little from that of other Primates, or in fact from any of the placental mammals. A valve-like structure has been described on the communication between the saccular and cochlear portions of the membranous labyrinth (Hoffman and Bost, 1930). Pigmentary deposits have been found in the perilymphatic connective tissue and also under the epithelium of the membranous labyrinth, especially in the ampulla, where a sickle-shaped deposit occurs.

Angles subtended between anterior and posterior and between anterior and lateral semicircular canals have been estimated by Berg (1903) by corrosion methods on several monkeys. His results are as follows:

	Cercop. mona	M. nemestrina	Papio hamad.

Angle between
  Ant. and post. canals
  Ant. and lat. canals
Sum
	95°
	85°
	180°
		100°
		78°
		178°
			98°
			65°
			163°

In a number of studies by Girard (1923, 1924, 1930) the relation of the plane of the lateral semicircular canal to the rest of the skull has been estimated and found to be highly variable and to give some indication of the relative growth of the facial and cranial parts of the skull, especially in such aberrant types as the baboons (*vide* Werner's fig. 17, based on Girard's studies).

The number of coils in the cochlea varies somewhat even within the same genus. The only cynomorphs examined so far have all been baboons of the genus *Papio*. Gray (1907) recorded three-and-one-quarter turns for *P. papio* whilst Hyrtl (1845) found two-and-three-quarters in *P. sphinx* and three in *P. ursinus*.

KARYOLOGY

Recent work on the chromosomes of various Primates necessitates some consideration here with reference to the taxonomic implications within the Cercopithecoidea. The most recent general review of the present state of knowledge is given by Chu and Bender (1962) and by Hamerton (1963), but as far as Cercopithecoidea are concerned the studies of Tappen (1960 a and b, 1963) and Chiarelli (1958, 1962 a and b), and authors there cited are of special value.

Chromosomes of several species of *Cercopithecus*, of *Erythrocebus*, *Cercocebus* and several species of *Macaca* and *Papio* have been studied, and results provide evidence of the interrelations of these genera and species and of their possible phylogenetic development. It would appear that there has been a reduction in numbers of chromosomes during phylogeny.

Chromosome numbers are extraordinarily uniform in the baboons, macaques and mangabeys, where the diploid number is invariably 42, whereas in *Cercopithecus* and *Erythrocebus* the number is always greater,

TABLE 6

CHROMOSOME NUMBERS IN CERCOPITHECOIDEA

	Diploid Number	Authority
Cercopithecidae		
Cercopithecinae		
Cercopithecus mitis	72	Chiarelli, 1962 *a*
Cercopithecus mona	66	Bender and Mettler, 1958
		Chu and Giles, 1957
C. campbelli	66	Chu and Bender, 1961
C. denti	66	Chu and Bender, 1962
C. petaurista buttikoferi *	66	Chu and Giles, 1957
C. ascanius	66	Tappen, 1960 *b*
C. aethiops (incl. *sabaeus*)	60	Chu and Giles, 1957
		Chiarelli, 1962 *a*
		Baylet & Grattepanche, 1964 *a* & *b*
C. diana	60	Chiarelli, 1962 *a*
C. l'hoesti	60	Chiarelli, 1962 *a*
	72	Chu and Bender, 1961
C. neglectus	60	Tappen, 1960 ; Chiarelli
C. cephus	66	Chiarelli, 1962 *a* (corrected 1964)
Allenopithecus nigroviridis	60	Chiarelli, 1962 *a*
Miopithecus talapoin	54	Chiarelli, 1962 *a*
Erythrocebus patas	54	Chu and Giles, 1961
		Tappen
		Baylet & Grattepanche, 1964 *a*
Cynopithecinae		
Macaca sylvana	42	Chiarelli, 1962 *a*
M. speciosa	42	Chiarelli, 1962 *a*
M. fuscata	42	Shiwago, 1939
M. mulatta	42	Darlington and Haque, 1955
		Chu and Giles, 1961
		Rothfils and Siminowitch, 1958
		Tappen
		Baylet & Grattepanche, 1964 *a*
M. assamensis	42	Chiarelli, 1962 *a*
M. silenus	42	Chiarelli, 1962 *a*
M. nemestrina	42	Darlington and Haque, 1955
		Chiarelli, 1962 *a*
M. radiata	42	Chiarelli, 1962 *a*
M. sinica	42	Chiarelli, 1962 *a*
M. irus	42	Chu and Bender, 1961
		Chiarelli, 1962 *a*
M. maura	42	Chiarelli, 1962 *a*
M. cyclopis	42	Makino, 1952
Cynopithecus niger	42	Chiarelli, 1962 *a*
Cercocebus torquatus	42	Chu and Giles, 1957
		Bender and Mettler, 1958
		Chiarelli
C. galeritus	42	Tappen
		Chiarelli

* Listed by the authors under *C. nictitans*

TABLE 6—*continued.*

	Diploid Number	Authority
C. albigena	42	Tappen
		Chiarelli
C. aterrimus	42	Chiarelli
Papio ursinus	42	Chiarelli
P. anubis	42	Chu and Giles, 1957
		Chiarelli
P. cynocephalus	42	Chiarelli
P. papio	42	Darlington and Haque, 1955
		Chiarelli
		Baylet & Grattepanche, 1964 *a*
P. hamadryas	42	Chiarelli
Mandrillus sphinx	42	Chu and Giles, 1957
		Chiarelli, 1962 *a*
M. leucophaeus	42	Chiarelli
Theropithecus gelada	42	Chiarelli
Colobidae		
Semnopithecus entellus	50	Makino, 1952
Trachypithecus obscurus	44	Chiarelli
Colobus ? polykomos	44	Chiarelli

though not uniformly so. Not only do the diploid numbers differ among the various species of *Cercopithecus*, but at least three different karyotypes have been recorded within the genus. These data provide further evidence, if any were required, for separating *Cercopithecus* and its allies (*Miopithecus*, *Allenopithecus*, *Erythrocebus*) from the assemblage comprised by the baboons, macaques and mangabeys.

For convenience and further reference the latest data on diploid chromosome numbers among the Cercopithecoidea are provided in Table 6.

All the chromosomes of *Macaca* are metacentric. Each species has one pair of autosomes with prominent secondary constrictions (according to Chu and Bender these are probably nucleolus organizer regions). The X chromosome is medium-sized and submetacentric; Y is also a small element with a median centromere. In *Papio* both X and Y are metacentric and the autosomes are shorter than in *Macaca*. In *Cercocebus* the karyotypes of two subspecies of *C. torquatus* have been examined by Chu and Bender (1962), and they resemble each other but are different from both *Macaca* and *Papio*, although all have the same diploid number. (For further details see Chiarelli, 1962 *b*.)

Among the species of *Cercopithecus* karyotype patterns regularly differ; those with 60 chromosomes have 6 acrocentrics, three with 66 have 12 acrocentrics, while the group with 72 has 18 acrocentrics, *i.e.* acrocentrics decrease in number *pari passu* with reduction in total chromosomes. (Hamerton, 1963.)

Work remains to be done on the shapes, sizes and relative positions of chromosomes, before final assessment can be made in regard to their value in taxonomy. All workers agree that chromosome enumeration alone is insufficient, though serving as a useful tentative indicator of Primate affinities.

An interesting side-line of genetic interest is the announcement of Park (1957) that sex chromatin in Man is first seen at 12 days in the trophoblast and at 16 days in the embryo, while in *Macaca* it appears at the tenth day in the trophoblast and the nineteenth day in the embryo.

REPRODUCTIVE PHYSIOLOGY

Menstrual Cycle (Bland Sutton, 1887; Pocock, 1906; Siepi, 1925; Collings, 1926; Allen, 1926, 1927; Hartman, 1928; Harms, 1956; Eckstein and Zuckerman, 1962). Overt expression both in appearance and behaviour during the follicular phase of the female sexual cycle reaches its maximum among certain members of the Cercopithecoidea—notably among the baboons, mangabeys and some of the macaques. Nevertheless it is not possible to give an overall statement, even for one genus, on account of the wide interspecific variations. In *Cercopithecus* and *Erythrocebus* there is little or no external sign of the follicular phase and only minimal external bleeding at menstruation. By contrast, the closely related genera *Miopithecus* and *Allenopithecus* undergo marked enlargement of the so-called sexual skin.* This is expressed, as in macaques and baboons, by a gradual enlargement of the area around the vulva and anus, reaching a maximum at the end of the follicular phase. Thereafter, the tumescence involutes in the first 24 hours of the luteal phase. The same process affects all the baboons of the genera *Papio* and *Mandrillus*, reaching its highest development in *Papio*, where a truly grotesque exuberance of the sexual skin is manifested. In *Mandrillus* the appearances are more akin to those in the female of *Cercocebus*. In *Macaca* considerable variations are exhibited among the different subgroups of the genus. Most show some form of periodic (menstrual) reddening and/or tumescence of the sexual skin (*e.g. M. mulatta, M. nemestrina*) whereas others (*e.g. M. irus*, Spiegel, 1929, 1950) exhibit this in lesser degree, even varying individually, while still others (*e.g.* the subgenus *Zati*, which includes the Bonnet and Toque monkeys, *M. radiata* and *M. sinica*) show none, but instead undergo strange internal changes affecting the vaginal contents.

Theropithecus exhibits some unique features, including a bare area of sexual skin on the pectoral region, additional to the usual perineal area. Cyclic swelling is limited but accompanied by intensification of the red

* A term first introduced by Langley and Sherrington (1891) to denominate the area which, in *Macaca mulatta*, becomes flushed during the menstrual cycle. Zuckerman *et al.* (1938) used the term to denote any region of skin which responds to oestrogenic stimulation either by reddening and/or swelling.

colouration and by the development of conspicuous cutaneous vesicles at the periphery of both pectoral and perineal areas. (Appelman, 1953, 1957; Matthews, 1956.)

TABLE 7

PERIODICITY AND DURATION OF MENSTRUATION IN CERCOPITHECOIDEA

Species	Duration of Cycle (in days)	Duration of Bleeding (in days)	
Cercopithecus aethiops	av. 31	?	Zuckerman, 1930
C. albogularis eryth-rarchus (based on behaviour)	26–30	2	Hill (unpublished)
Cercocebus atys	26–33	4–5	Zuckerman, 1930
„ „	28–46 av. 33·4 (± o·1)		Zuckerman, 1937
C. aterrimus (8 cycles studied in one ♀)	28 +	4–5	Hill (unpublished)
Macaca radiata	29, 31, 33		Zuckerman, 1930
„ „	25, 26, 31, 36	up to 10	Hartman, 1938
M. sinica	29	1–4	Hill, 1939
M. irus	28 (23–42)	3 max. 6	Spiegel, 1950
M. mulatta	28	4–6	Corner, 1923
	75% between		Allen, 1927
	23 and 33		Hartman, 1927
	(young ♀♀ less		Zuckerman, 1930
	regular than		
	mature ♀♀)		
M. nemestrina	29·5		Zuckerman, 1930
M. maura	30–40		Zuckerman, 1930
Cynopithecus niger	30·7 (28–35)		Spiegel (quoted by Harms)
Papio ursinus	41 (34–67)	4–9	Zuckerman, 1932
	42 (29–63)		Gillman, 1942
	35·6 (29–42)		Gillman and Gilbert, 1946
P. anubis	35 (30–38)		Zuckerman, 1932–3
	35 (28–38)		Zuckerman, 1937
			Siepi, 1925
P. cynocephalus	31–32		Zuckerman, 1932–7
P. hamadryas	33 (31–36)		Zuckerman, 1932–7
Mandrillus leucophaeus	32·6		Zuckerman and Parkes, 1939

Menstrual bleeding has been reported for many cynomorph species. It is often more copious than in any platyrrhine that shows the phenomenon, though varying from slight (e.g. in Colobidae) to copious (Cercocebus, Papio) and showing also individual variations in amount. Individually also, periods of amenorrhoea occur in some mature females, e.g. in Macaca sinica.

The bleeding occurs from the onset of the luteal phase and, in forms exhibiting a sexual swelling, appears during the later phases of the tumescence, continuing during the period following detumescence. The periodicity of the flow is on the average truly menstrual provided pregnancy does not supervene. Spiegel (1950) gives the average period for *Macaca irus* as 31 days, but it may vary individually from 23-42 days. The data given in Table 7 and which show ranges of variation in periodicity and in duration of the menstrual flow have been collated by Harms with my personal observations added.

Much has been written on the supposed breeding season of Old World monkeys, but the general consensus is that no such season exists. Mature males are at all times potent and females may be found in receptive condition at all times of the year. Moreover, pregnancies and births have been recorded in the wild, in the few species sufficiently well studied, during all the months of the year. Heape (1894, 1896, 1897), Hingston (1920) and Hartman (1931) believed that wild Rhesus monkeys have a restricted breeding season during September and October. Similarly, Carpenter (1942), who studied free-ranging Rhesus monkeys liberated on Santiago Island, Puerto Rico, claimed that matings occurred mainly between February and April resulting in births during August, September and October, with little or no primary sexual behaviour in the interim. Nevertheless in captivity Rhesus monkeys breed at all seasons ; but there is evidently a seasonal difference in the rate of conceptions and births (Hartman, 1931, 1932) which may give a false impression of restricted breeding season if insufficient samples are examined.

Heape (1894) also believed that one or more limited breeding seasons applies to *Semnopithecus entellus*, but Zuckerman (1931), basing his opinion on the birth records in the London Zoo, considered Heape's assertion as of doubtful value. This opinion is confirmed by personal experience with various langurs in Ceylon (Hill, 1937). However, in parts of India which experience a cold season, the langurs tend to produce their young more especially during certain months (February, March) than continuously throughout the year. This follows on matings during the colder months (McCann, 1933).

Ovulation occurs spontaneously in *Macaca mulatta* (Corner, 1923, 1932) and may be accompanied by a few erythrocytes in the vagina—recognizable only on lavage—at the mid-cycle bleeding (Hartman, 1928, 1932). It occurs around the thirteenth day of the cycle, so that the follicular phase is of 13 days' duration and the luteal (in a 28-day cycle) 15 days. Regression of the corpus luteum is demonstrable after the thirteenth day of its formation, menstruation supervening a day or two later (Corner *et al.*, 1945). In *Papio* ovulation has been shown, by laparotomy, to coincide with subsidence of the sexual skin (Zuckerman, 1930, 1937 ; Zuckerman and Parkes, 1932) but Gillman and Gilbert (1946) consider that in *P. ursinus* ovulation may precede by 2-3 days the complete deturgescence.

Puberty, as judged by the first appearance of sexual swelling, occurs in *Macaca mulatta* at the average age of 2 years $3\frac{1}{2}$ months and a mean body-weight of 3400 g., while menarche is attained at the average age of 2 years 7 months (range 27-32 months) ; (data derived from Allen, 1927 ; Hartman, 1932 ; Schultz, 1933 ; Zuckerman, van Wagenen and Gardiner, 1938 ; Eckstein, 1948 ; Smith and Rubinstein, 1940 ; Eckstein, and Zuckerman 1962). Earlier menarche (average 2 years, with the earliest variant at 1 year 5 months) were noted in van Wagenen's (1949, 1950) colony of inbred animals. Final definitive development of sexual skin swelling is not attained until 5 years with a body weight of 5000 g. The interim period is one of adolescent sterility and is characterized by irregularity of menstruation and by frequent anovular cycles. Abortion is common if pregnancy supervenes during this period. Menstruation and breeding may continue till the seventeenth or eighteenth year (Eckstein and Zuckerman, 1959).

Spiegel (1950) found that in *M. irus* the first menstruation appears at the average age of $2\frac{1}{2}$-3 years (earliest 2 years 3 months), while the period of adolescent sterility lasts from 3 months to 2 years. The male *M. irus* attains sexual maturity at $4-4\frac{1}{2}$ years.

Similar findings have been recorded for other macaques, *e.g. M. sinica* (Hill, 1939). In *M. nemestrina*, Zuckerman (1937) reported puberty at 50 months. In *Papio ursinus*, Gillman (1939) and Gillman and Gilbert (1946) noted the earliest appearance of perineal turgescence between $3\frac{1}{2}$ and 4 years of age followed by menarche after a short interval, but the turgescence increases in degree during each cycle till a maximum is attained during the next 1-2 years. A similar increasing turgescence over the first eight cycles has been observed by the present writer in *Cercocebus aterrimus* and *C. atys*.

There are no reliable data on puberty in other cynomorph genera, apart from a reference to *Semnopithecus priam* attaining puberty at 4 years (Hill, 1936).

Copulation in all cynomorph monkeys so far observed occurs with the female in the quadrupedal attitude. The male mounts from behind (*coitus more canum*), grasping the female around her flanks with his hands while his feet grasp the crural segment of her pelvic limbs. The process has been figured for *Macaca* by Friedenthal (1910) whose illustration is reproduced by Harms. Ejaculation occurs following a few rapid pelvic thrusts. In macaques and baboons the phenomenon is overt, uninhibited and diurnal, but *Cercopithecus* and the Colobidae are much more reticent. In *Cercopithecus* coitus is commonly nocturnal. Luck (1959), referring to *C. pygerythrus*, notes that the sex life is very much a private affair and in captivity breeding is not frequent. Personal experience with *C. albogularis kolbi, C. a. erythrarchus, C. cephus* and *C. aethiops* confirms this.

Insemination presumably falls into Walton's (1960) category (*d*), *i.e.* vaginal insemination with incipient copulation plug or slight seminal coagulation—a category which includes Man—but more data are needed on this question.

Pregnancy.—The gestation period is somewhat variable, even within the limits of a single species, though the average ranges around 6 months. The following data have been culled from the literature and appear in Table 8.

TABLE 8

GESTATION PERIODS IN CERCOPITHECOIDEA

Species	Duration of Gestation (days)	Authority
Macaca mulatta	163·9 (range 146–180) (av. of 30 pregnancies)	Hartman, 1932
	165·2 (range 149–180) (av. of 26 pregnancies with variable offspring)	Hartman, 1932
	168	van Wagenen, 1945
	191 (abnormally prolonged)	Eckstein, 1944
M. irus	167 (range 153–179)	Spiegel, 1950
M. nemestrina	171 (single pregnancy)	Zuckerman, 1937
M. radiata	153, 166, 169 (3 successive pregnancies in 1 ♀)	Hartman, 1932
M. sinica	180	Personal observation
M. sylvana	210	Brown, 1936
Papio hamadryas	172·2 (range 154–183)	Zuckerman and Parkes, 1932
P. ursinus	187 (range 173–193)	Gilbert and Gillman, 1951
Mandrillus sphinx	220	Jennison, 1927
	270	Auge, 1930 (quoted by Kenneth)
Cercopithecus	213	Jennison, 1927 Kenneth, 1947
C. aethiops aethiops	188	Shortridge, 1934
Semnopithecus priam	210	Hill, 1937

An indication of pregnancy, frequently, but not invariably present, is the " placental sign " described by Hartman in *Macaca*. It is represented by slight vaginal bleeding (often microscopic only) beginning the fourteenth day after conception (or 29 days after the beginning of the previous menstrual bleeding). It persists for about three weeks and is traceable to the uterine glands near the periphery of the placenta (Wislocki and Hartman, 1929). Hartman believed the reaction to be associated with implantation. The sign has been confirmed by Spiegel in *M. irus*.

Gonadotrophic hormones are present in the urine from the nineteenth to the twenty-fifth day only during pregnancy (Hamlett, 1937 ; Delfs, 1941). Pregnanediol does not occur in the urine of pregnant macaques (Marker and Hartman, 1940).

Pregnancy normally results in a single foetus, but twins have been reported on occasion in several cynomorphs, *e.g. Macaca mulatta, M. irus*

(Selenka, 1892; Schultz, 1956); *M. maura* (triplets) (Breitinger, 1951);
Papio (Knottnerus-Meyer, 1909; Hediger and Zweifel, 1962) (7 cases),
Cercopithecus (4 cases) and *Nasalis* (1 case) (Schultz, 1956) (see also Schultz,
1948). Multiple births have also been mentioned in *Semnopithecus*
(Blyth, 1843 (quoting Moor, 1810); Blanford, 1888), but these may relate
to cases of kidnapping or acceptance of the living child of a dead mother.

Parturition.—This has been fully documented for *M. mulatta* by Hartman
and for *M. irus* by Spiegel, and protocols for the whole procedure have been
published. These are reproduced by Harms (1956) and need therefore only
brief reference here (see also Vol. II, pp. 92-95).

Presentation of the foetus is typically cephalic (dorso-posterior), but
breech presentation has been recorded. Spontaneous version from breech
to cephalic position has been revealed radiographically prior to parturition
(Hartman). Face presentation has been reported in *M. mulatta* (Hill, 1955)
and in *M. irus* (Spiegel, 1950).

Spiegel divided labour in *M. irus* into three stages, each very variable in
duration. These are :

Stage 1—Eröffnungsperiod (period of opening up of birth canal).
Stage 2—Austreibungsperiod (phase of foetal expulsion).
Stage 3—Nachgeburtenperiod (passage of after-birth).

Stage 1 varies in duration 25 minutes up to 3 days, but most cases fall between
$2\frac{1}{2}$ hours and 2 days. Rupture of the membranes and escape of amniotic
fluid usually occurs at this point, but may happen earlier during stage 1.
Foetal expulsion is rapid, sometimes as low as 25 seconds, but more frequently
from 2-15 minutes, with a maximum of 28 minutes. Uterine efforts are
substantially implemented by manual assistance. After a further period
varying from 40 seconds to 11 minutes the membranes are passed and
thereafter, typically, consumed by the mother, who severs the umbilical cord
by biting.

Lactation.—Little accurate data exist on the phenomenon of lactation in
cynomorph monkeys. Nipples elongate, enlarge, and often deepen in colour,
becoming bright red or purple during the later stages of pregnancy, and
remaining so during the period of lactation. The mammary tissue enlarges
merely by peripheral spread, so that prominent or pendulous mammae are
never formed.

Hartman's (1932) experience with Rhesus monkeys led him to the average
estimate of duration of lactation as 7 months, but great variability exists,
milk sometimes being plentifully secreted after 1 year. Lactation is reduced
to 3-4 months in cases of still-birth. Amenorrhoea is usual during lactation
and non-ovulating cycles are frequent (Hartman, 1938). Nevertheless conception can occur in a lactating female (Hartman, 1931, 1932). The single
infant suckles the right and left nipples alternately, but sometimes where

these are extensile both nipples may be suckled at once (*e.g.* in *Cercopithecus pygerythrus*, *vide* Sclater, 1893 ; according to Booth (1962), however, this is the normal phenomenon in this genus).

In *M. irus* Spiegel found lactation to last $1-1\frac{1}{2}$ years, and if the female conceives again, it may carry on for several years. Lactational amenorrhoea lasts 2-13 months.

EARLY DEVELOPMENT AND PLACENTATION

Gametogenesis.—Spermatozoa of several cynomorph monkeys have been described by Retzius (1909, 1912, 1914). These are *Macaca sylvana*, *M. sinica*, *Cercocebus torquatus*, *Papio sphinx* (? *Mandrillus*), *P. cynocephalus* and *Cercopithecus aethiops*. The sperms much resemble those of Man and the more typical mammalian pattern. They are larger than in *Lemur*, surpassing all other known Primate spermatozoa except those of *Pongo*. The head is broadly ovoid, flattened in one plane, and the acrosome is not clearly distinguished from the nuclear portion of the head. The connecting piece is intermediate in length between the long prosimian and the shorter hominoid representative. The pars principalis of the tail is very long, but the pars terminalis relatively short.

Histogenesis of the sperms has been reported on for the macaque by Moreaux (1909). The process corresponds in general and as regards size relationships with that in lower mammals. The centriole in the polygonal spermatids lies superficially near the cell-membrane ; the cytoplasm is richly loaded with mitochondria. Transformation into spermatozoa involves lengthening of the nucleus and assumption of an ovoid form, with the simultaneous migration of the centriolar apparatus to one pole. The distal centriole develops a flagellum-like process at first short, but soon elongating to become the tail of the future sperm. The nucleus moves towards the surface and the cytoplasm is pushed to one side, eventually being shed. Later the distal centriole splits into two smaller bodies which separate, the distal element becoming anchored to the rapidly growing tail-piece. Mitochondria become grouped around the axial filament and produce the spiral sheath around it (see also Starck, 1956).

Histochemical studies in spermatogenesis in *Macaca*, using the periodic-acid Schiff technique, are reported by Clermont and Leblond (1955). Four phases are recognizable named successively Golgi, cap, acrosome and maturation phases. At the Golgi phase, positively staining particles appear in the idiosome and fuse to form the acrosomic granule, which exhibits an inner and an outer zone. The latter, in the second phase, expands over the nuclear membrane to become the head-cap. The inner zone persists as a small hemisphere on the nuclear surface. In the third phase the acrosomic granule enlarges to become the acrosome which now appears homogeneous. In

Macaca it shows a flat, triangular appearance, thus differing from the human sperm, where it ceases to be recognizable as a separate structure. In the final stage positive P.A.S. staining gradually diminishes.

The Ovum.—The ovum in cynomorph monkeys is much the same in size and appearance as that of other Pithecoidea (Hartman, 1929). The macaque oocyte at the conclusion of its growth has a diameter of 80μ without zona pellucida, 109μ including the zona (Starck, 1956). Details of oogenesis do not appear to have been fully worked out for any genus of Cercopithecoidea, but the first maturation division in *Macaca* has been described by Hartman and Corner (1941). Crystalline bodies have been found in the ovum of *Cercopithecus sabaeus* by Athias (1915) and of *Macaca* by Pollak (1926).

Early Developmental Stages.—Preimplantation stages for *Macaca mulatta* have been described by Corner (1923), Allen (1927, 1928), Lewis and Hartman (1933, 1941) and Hartman and Corner (1941).

Corner and Allen both studied unfertilized tubal ova. Recoveries have taken place at the tenth and fourteenth days of the menstrual cycle, but some ova have not been positively related to a fixed point in the cycle. Corner's ova still had follicle cells attached, but Allen's, which was flushed from the tube by injection from the ostium, was free of such, probably due to a longer interval since ovulation. It had, however, a highly refractive, sharply defined zona pellucida of which the innermost third was pale iridescent blue. Cytoplasm was yellowish and vesicular rather than granular under low power. High power showed it more greyish and granular. A polar body was present, but its nuclear structure not definable; nor was there any spindle remains within the ovum. Fluid was present between ovum and zona. Further non-fertilized eggs are reported by Lewis and Hartman (1933, 1941), who also give accounts of early stages of cleavage in tubal ova, eggs in the 2-cell, 4-cell and 16-cell conditions being described, and their relative ages after ovulation given (as determined by Hartman's technique of rectal palpation of the ovaries). Two-celled eggs are found at 23-49 days after ovulation, 4-celled eggs 24-52 days and a 16-celled stage at 96-144 days after ovulation. First cleavage is approximately equatorial. Second and third cleavages appear to pass through the short diameter of the cells at right angles to the first cleavage plane. Blastomeres lie parallel in the first cleavage; in the 4-celled stage the two pairs lie crosswise to each other, as in the rabbit (Gregory, 1930). A 4-celled tubal ovum of *M. nemestrina* was described by Selenka (1903) from a specimen provided by Hubrecht. In this the zona pellucida had been lost either prematurely or through the agency of preservatives. The blastomeres were approximately equal in size, but two were spherical and two oval. In the 8-celled stage the blastomeres are fairly symmetrical in arrangement, but there is some interdigitation at the primary cleavage plane.

The 1-celled stage lasts 24 hours, 2-celled from 24th to 36th hour, 3- and

4-celled stages from 36th to 48th hour; 5-, 6-, 7- and 8-celled ova from 72nd to 96th hour after ovulation.

Embryogenesis in *Macaca* has been fully documented by Heuser and Streeter (1941) in a classical contribution following on the more haphazard accounts of early isolated stages of cynomorph embryos published by Selenka (1891–2, 1898–9, 1903) on *Nasalis*, *Trachypithecus* and two species of *Macaca* (*M. nemestrina* and *M. irus*) and reviewed by Hill (1932) in his classic Croonian Lectures.

The morula stage is so far unknown, but is presumed to differ in no important respect from that of other eutherian mammals. At the ninth to tenth day after ovulation the partially segmented ovum lies free in the uterine cavity. Presumably at this time the zona pellucida is lost and very shortly thereafter, with the release of enzymes from the egg itself now in the blasto-cyst stage, erosion of the endometrium occurs and the process of implantation effected. Free blastocysts at the eighth and ninth days are described by Heuser and Streeter. The fully formed blastocyst resembles that of *Homo*, being for the most part a thin-walled sphere with one pole thickened by the presence of the amnio-embryonic mass (inner-cell mass), and separated from the cavity of the vesicle by a thin stratum of primary endoderm cells. At the stage of completion of its primary differentiation on the ninth day, the blasto-cyst has a diameter of 0·267 mm., an increase which is not due to growth, but largely to the accumulation of fluid within the vesicle.

Embedding.—Primary superficial adhesion of the blastocyst to the uterine epithelium occurs on the ninth day and has been figured by Heuser and Streeter (1941, Pl. 3). Adhesion is by the embryonic pole, near the margin of the embryonic node. Area of contact is gradually widened until a circular field, with the node at its centre, is adherent. Apposition is complete by the tenth day and invasive trophoblast reaches the uterine stroma. Cytoplasm of the maternal cells appears to be disorganized and digested by the tropho-blast, the remaining nuclei becoming clumped together, and in turn engulfed by the syncytium. Meantime the trophoblast of the embryonic pole is becoming differentiated into two layers, an outer plasmoditrophoblast and an inner cytotrophoblast.

Some active proliferation of the uterine epithelium involving not only the surface epithelium, but also that around the ducts of the uterine glands occurs in the vicinity of the implantation site, as Selenka also found in *Trachy-pithecus*.

Embedding seems to occur with almost equal frequency on the dorsal and ventral walls of the uterus, with an occasional lateral nidation, whilst cervical nidation was also once encountered in forty-four specimens studied by the American embryologists. Vascular arrangements in the uterine walls corre-spond with those described for *Homo*, the spiral arteries that supply the superficial parts of the endometrium being specially notable, together with the related venous sinuses, which play a share, with the trophoblast, in establishing the placental circulation.

With the advance of trophoblastic activity the syncytium assumes a mottled appearance due to the varied rate of assimilation of maternal tissues and the irregular differentiation of primitive trophoblast into its two components, whereby islands of the unaltered tissue are seen surrounded by differentiated trophoblast, especially whilst thickening of the trophoblastic plate occurs during the tenth and eleventh days. At this time, too, engulfment of maternal erythrocytes begins as the invading syncytium opens up the venous sinuses. These come to occupy clefts in the syncytium which, as the process advances, becomes converted into lacunae. The clefts are oriented at right angles to the disc, but lose their arrangement as they become engorged and converted into lacunae. Spiral arteries are not tapped by the invasive tissue ; these appear to serve as a mechanism for slowing down the maternal blood-flow locally. On the fifteenth day villi appear and, as the means of nourishment is thereby augmented, growth of the blastocyst is speeded up.

At this time the inner cell mass undergoes changes. Its peripheral part differentiates into the basal embryogenic portion and a region which is amniogenic. The latter cells undergo rapid division and orient themselves radially. They become separated from the amniogenic cells, which are irregularly arranged, by a cleft. This becomes filled with watery fluid. It enlarges to form the amniotic cavity, the wall at the same time being stretched to form the amnion. Dorsal closure of the amniotic cavity is sometimes incomplete, allowing it to communicate with lacunae.

Beneath the embryonic disc the layer of endoderm cells is continuous peripherally with the walls of the yolk-sac—meantime derived from cavitation in the portion of the inner cell mass beneath the embryonic disc—as shown also by Selenka (1898) in *Nasalis*. From the first, the primitive endoderm or gut primordium is discrete from the yolk-sac ; it is the product of induction from the activities of the embryogenic cells of the disc ; whereas the yolk-sac appears to arise from fibroblastic cells resembling those of the extra-embryonic mesoderm, and closely related to the exocoelomic membrane. The yolk-sac is therefore part of the system of auxiliary structures rather than part of the embryo.

The primitive streak is developed in much the same fashion as in Man. It is designated by Heuser and Streeter as the locus of the second order of specialization, the first being the segregation of the embryogenic elements from those destined for the formation of foetal membranes. The primitive streak is not correctly designated as ectoderm, but a tissue from which ectoderm, mesoderm and endoderm are all derived. It is, in fact, a remnant of the primordial germ-plasm from which derived cells are being separated and translated into centres of specialization and differentiation.

Embryonic mesoblast is not recognizable until the thirteenth day, *i.e.*

after the establishment of the gut primordium. The first mesoblast appears in the space between the gut primordium and the overlying germinal disc. The mesoblast cells become abundant by the seventeenth day and they can be determined to have emanated from the primitive streak cells. Simultaneously, the gut primordium undergoes some fragmentation, becoming more membranous in character like the lining cells of the yolk-sac. Some cells dehisce and mingle with the early mesoblast cells, the inference being that the latter are equally endodermal as ectodermal in origin. Probably the gut supplies its own mesodermal elements while those derived from the primitive streak become somatic mesoderm.

Meanwhile the older extra-embryonic mesoderm has been providing secondary outer layers to the amnion and yolk-sac (this takes place during the seventeenth to nineteenth day). That associated with the yolk-sac becomes somewhat more elaborate and engages in angiogenesis, forming in fact both blood and blood vessels.

Resemblances during early development between Cercopithecoidea and Hominoidea—they both differ from other Primates—are enumerated by Selenka (1901) and include :

(1) Precocious concrescence of the blastocyst with the uterine epithelium.
(2) Precocity in development of chorionic villi.
(3) Precocious appearance of mesoderm.
(4) Precocious closure of the amnion.
(5) Precocity in development of vitelline vessels.
(6) Tardy differentiation of germinal disc.
(7) Reduction of allantois.
(8) Secondary modification of allantoic stalk into a supporting and suspending shaft (body-stalk ; Haftstiel of German embryologists).
(9) Attachment to the preceding of the yolk-sac stalk.
(10) Pronounced retroversion of the vertebral axis up to the sixth week.

Placentation (Turner, 1878 ; Waldeyer, 1889 ; Selenka, 1898, 1901 ; Duckworth, 1907 ; Hill, 1932 ; Wislocki and Hartman, 1929 ; Wislocki and Streeter, 1938 ; Amoroso, 1952, 1961 ; Starck, 1956). (See also Vol. I, fig. 2 c.)

Important differences in placentation distinguish the Old World monkeys from the Platyrrhini. Both of course are haemochorial. The precocious activity of the trophoblast has already been mentioned ; it is also more potent in its capacity for invasion and cytolysis of the maternal tissues. Chorionic villi are mostly free instead of being situated in a nidus of vascularized syncytiotrophoblast. Their freedom permits their being bathed directly by maternal blood almost from the outset. The placental area therefore is functional as soon as the embryonic circulation is established.

Attachment and embedding take place at a relatively earlier stage, the blastocyst being smaller at this time than in any platyrrhine monkey. The area of primary contact is more localized and the area of trophoblastic proliferation similarly restricted.

Wislocki and Streeter (1938) compare the details of cynomorph placentation with the process in *Tarsius*, in platyrrhines and in the Hominoidea. They also review the earlier work on cynomorphs other than *Macaca mulatta*, notably Selenka's and Kollmann's (1900) on *M. irus*, Duckworth's on *M. nemestrina* and Selenka's on *Semnopithecus pruinosus* (= *Trachypithecus cristatus* subsp.) and *S. nasicus* (= *Nasalis larvatus*).

Definitive relations between placenta and uterus are finally established by the thirty-fifth day. The villi are now intricately branched, and have become longer, more robust and fully vascularized. The terminal trophoblastic cell-columns which form their apices abut on the necrotic zone at the junction of foetal and maternal elements. Cytotrophoblast beneath the syncytium forms a continuous spread over the decidua basalis ; it is also continuous with the cell columns. It corresponds to the trophoblastic shell of the human conceptus, but differs in the more restricted extent of the syncytial elements and in its generally simpler character. Ultimately most of the trophoblast degenerates and disappears, its breakdown products contributing to the fibrinous material at the junctional zone, though this is less marked than in the placenta of the Hominoidea. Further details on the histological and cytological features of the macaque placenta are given by Wislocki and Bennett (1943). They note especially that decidual cells are smaller and less numerous than in the human placenta.

According to Herberg (1935) maternal blood reaches the intervillous spaces through a number of large coiled arteries which enter basally and centrally beneath the disc. Blood leaves the organ marginally through a circumferential sinus, as well as basally through the floor of the intervillous spaces.

Macroscopically the cynomorph placenta is of the discoid variety and typically, as in many platyrrhines, two discs are present (bidiscoidal placenta). The primary disc receives the attachment of the umbilical cord, the secondary and sometimes smaller lobe being vascularized by vessels crossing the intervening chorion from the main disc. *Vide* Breschet's (1845) figure of the placenta of *Cercopithecus sabaeus* reproduced by Wislocki (1929). Bidiscoidal placentae have been reported in *Cercopithecus, Cercocebus, Macaca, Trachypithecus, Presbytis, Nasalis* and *Colobus*. Wislocki (1929) has classified these and given references to earlier work.

In *Papio* and *Mandrillus*, however, the placenta is invariably single and the umbilical end attached near the centre of the disc (Breschet ; Turner (1879) ; Coventry, 1923). Occasional single discs have been reported in *Macaca* (*e.g. M. irus* by Chapman, 1879 ; *M. sinica*, personal observation ; and *Presbytis cruciger*, Selenka, 1898).

Length of the umbilical cord, both relative and absolute, shows considerable variation according to the data published by Starck (1957). In a *Macaca*

L

TABLE 9

ABSOLUTE AND RELATIVE LENGTH OF UMBILICAL CORD
IN CERCOPITHECOIDEA

	Species	C.R. Length of Foetus	L. of Funis	Percentage Length of Funis/Foetus
S.	*Cercopithecus aethiops*	28	31	110
S.	,,	110	90	82
S.	,,	115	120	105
S.	,,	138	120	88
S.	,,	140	125	90
S.	,,	140	125	90
S.	,,	145	110	75
H.	*C. pygerythrus johnstoni*	106	96	85
H.	,,	115·2	125·5	108·5
H.	*C. mitis kolbi* (full term)	196	265	134·5
H.	*C. m. stuhlmanni* (full term)	190	290	152
H.	*C. mona*	71·5	104	145
H.	,,	108	145	133
H.	,,	109·6	123	114
H.	,,	128	130	101
H.	*C. petaurista buttikoferi*	20	4·8	4·1
H.	*Allenopithecus nigroviridis* (full term)	153	180	118
H.	*Macaca sylvana* (early)	41·5	31	75
H.	*M. mulatta*	91·3	87·5	95
H.	,,	159	142	112
S.	,,	181	195	108
S.	*Papio hamadryas*	33	25	80
S.	,,	85	112	130
H.	,,	160	205	129
H.	*P. hamadryas × P. papio*	190	305	106
H.	*P. hamadryas × P. anubis*	210	295	104
H.	*P. papio × P. anubis*	240	420	107·5
S.	*P. anubis*	110	132	120
H.	*Kasi senex senex*	50	80	160
H.	,,	52·5	65·4	127
H.	,,	45·8	65·6	104·8
H.	,,	64·6	93·5	104
H.	*K. s. nestor*	109	114·8	105
H.	*K. s. senex*	131	172·5	132
H.	,,	159	142	89·5
H.	,,	215	265	123
H.	*Semnopithecus priam*	75	85·2	114·5
H.	,,	117	154·7	130
H.	,,	120	170	142
H.	,,	130	154	118·5
H.	,,	153	175	114
H.	,,	171	193	112
S.	*Trachypithecus cristatus*	140	110	78
H.	*Colobus abyssinicus* (full term)	190	345	203
H.	*C. badius preussi*	74	106·5	114
	,,	99·3	157	157
H.	,,	169·6	210	124

S. = Starck's data ; H. = personal data.

mulatta foetus of 181 mm. C.R. length, the cord is 195 mm. long giving a percentage length of 108, compared with 82 per cent in a *Cercopithecus aethiops* of approximately the same size. There seems to be some change of relationship with advancing size of the foetus, as indicated by the data shown in Table 9, p. 146 taken partly from Starck's table with additions from personal records.

BEHAVIOURAL CHARACTERS

Prior to the twentieth century, information concerning the behaviour of cynomorphous monkeys was largely compiled from travellers' tales, whilst the naturalistic literature was for the most part anecdotal in character. Little or no intensive systematic field work had been undertaken and there were few data derived from observations on captive animals (*e.g.* Darwin, 1872), and none at all of an experimental nature.

Reports by travellers were often exaggerated, fanciful or distorted and, like those of du Chaillu on the gorilla, needed re-investigation by competent observers. Moreover, when serious studies came to be made, they were first directed towards the man-like apes rather than to the more numerous and more accessible cynomorphous group.

Pocock (1906) had early drawn attention to some behavioural features connected with the menstrual cycle of captive monkeys and in the late twenties the matter was considered further by Zuckerman, who also extended the scope of his work to include the social behaviour of baboons both in captivity and in the field. From this emerged his book, *The Social Life of Monkeys and Apes* (1932), which for long remained unique in its field. It summarized existing knowledge and added new concepts in connection with the organization of Primate social groups.

The American psychologist, C. R. Carpenter, conducted several field studies in free-living Primates, his *magnum opus* being the study of *Alouatta* which has already been reviewed (Vol. V, p. 84). Later he turned his attention to Old World forms, more particularly to an introduced colony of Rhesus monkeys on Caya Santiago off the east coast of Puerto Rico. His review articles of 1942 and 1950 are especially pertinent here. Incidentally a follow-up on this unique colony has been carried out by Altmann (1956–8) and by Koford (1959) and, under his direction, is being further studied by Layne, Conaway, Kaufman, Vandenburgh and Sade.

Little further progress was made, due to the international upheavals of 1939–45, and no significant advances were made until the early 1950s when a group of Japanese zoologists of Kyoto University established a Primate research centre for the study of the Japanese macaque (*Macaca fuscata*). Outstanding contributions have been made on this species by Imanishi (1957 *et seq.*), Miyadi (1959), Itani (1951 *et seq.*), Kawamura (1954), Kawai (1958), Mizuhara (1957) and others.

Arising from its importance in relation to the transmission of disease, Haddow and his associates (of the Virus Research Institute, Entebbe, Uganda) instituted a detailed field study of the ecology and behaviour of the Red-tailed Guenon (*Cercopithecus ascanius schmidti*) in East Africa and produced a series of important papers, of which Haddow's (1952) is the most significant from the present point of view.

Other African Primates in which renewed interest has recently been taken are the baboons. Intensive studies of their behaviour have especially been made by Starck and Frick (1958), Bolwig (1959), Washburn and De Vore (1961) and by Hall (1962).

Cynthia Booth (1962) has added new observations on the East African forms of *Cercopithecus* and *Colobus*, whilst Ullrich (1961) has produced a thoroughly detailed field study of *Colobus abyssinicus*.

Review articles on recent and current field work on various Primates have been published by Sahlins (1959), Imanishi (1960), Bourlière (1961), Buettner-Janusch (1962), Altmann (1962), Howell (1962), Washburn (1963) and De Vore and Lee (1963).

The experimental approach to the study of cynomorph behaviour (experimental psychology) has been developing entirely within the last few decades. The Rhesus monkey has been the subject of most of this work, though some observations have been made on baboons. Necessarily, these experiments have involved captive animals often placed in highly abnormal and artificial situations, so that critics may maintain that they have but a limited use in understanding the mental equipment of the experimental animal. The approach has been made largely by comparative psychologists, though some data have been accumulated by neuro-physiologists and students of animal behaviour in the broader sense.

Specially important are the experiments directed towards evaluation of learning capacity, reactions to strange situations and those concerned with social relations and group behaviour. The literature on these aspects of monkey behaviour up to 1940 is documented adequately by Ruch (1941), but special mention should be made of the contributions of Buytendijk and Revesz (1920, 1923), Bierens de Haan and his associates (1925 onwards), Harlow and his co-workers (1932 to the present), Kluver (1933) and the Russian school established by Kohts (1928, 1959) and the researches initiated by Yerkes in the laboratories of primate biology at Orange Park, Florida, followed up by his successors, Lashley and Nissen.

ECOLOGY : HABITAT (Tappen, 1960 ; Napier, 1962)

The great majority of cynomorph monkeys are inhabitants of tropical rain-forests, where they spend a fully arboreal existence, active by day and sleeping by night. But there are exceptions. The total range (*vide* map,

Vol. 3, p. 74) includes areas beyond the tropics (*e.g.* in North China and Japan), or within the tropics at altitudes beyond those that support typical tropical forest vegetation (*e.g.* in the Himalayas up to the snow-line, in Western China (*Rhinopithecus*) and on the rock of Gibraltar). Moreover, the wide geographical range provides ecological situations well outside the typical forest belts, many of which have been exploited by this or that genus of monkey—whereby a greater diversity of forms has evolved than was possible among New World primates. Especially notable are the terrestrial or semi-terrestrial habits adopted by many baboons, certain macaques and *Erythrocebus*, which spend all or part of their time in savannah or subdesert regions and repair to the trees, if at all, only when alarmed—indicative that the trees are their ancestral home, to the shadow of which they retire when pressed; colonization of the extra-arboreal niches is of recent origin. Certain macaques especially favour rocky situations where trees are sparse or lacking (*e.g. Macaca sylvana, M. cyclopis* and to a lesser degree *M. fuscata*).

Even confining attention to the rain-forest there is much diversification of the ecology, in so far as, within a single forest, different species have their favoured loci, and seldom or never mix even with others of the same genus (*e.g. Cercopithecus*) occupying different ecological niches.

The phenomena of distribution in relation to habitat has been more intensively studied in African monkeys than in Asiatic, and results have been ably summarized by Tappen (1960) and Napier (1962). Tappen bases his scheme on the phyto-geographical zones schematized by Moreau (1952) and modified by data obtained from Shantz and Marbut (1923).

Predominant vegetational zones in Africa are grouped by Moreau into five main biotic types, all of which are germane to the understanding of Primate distribution on the continent. These are :

1. *Arid type.* Rainfall not more than 20 ins. per annum. At least 6 months of year very dry. Trees stunted, usually deciduous and thorny. Ground cover does not persist through the year.

2. *Lowland evergreen rain forest.* Rainfall ample throughout the year. Many trees deciduous, but lack leaves for short periods only ; different species shed leaves at differing times, resulting in permanently green forest. Best seen in West Coast areas and in the Congo basin, with outlying areas eastwards to foot of Kenya highlands. Same along eastern coastal belt.

Although the western lowland coastal rain forest is continuous with the Congo forest, a portion of it along the Guinea coast is isolated by an important ecological barrier known as the Dahomey gap, which is occupied by savannah. This has an important bearing on the distribution of monkeys.

3. *Montane evergreen rain forest.* Occurs at altitudes over 5000 ft. in tropics and at progressively lower levels to the south of the tropical belt. Continuous in some places with preceding, but even so the flora is very distinct. Largest areas are in Abyssinia and the Kenya highlands, with isolated patches elsewhere, *e.g.* Mount Cameroon and an " ecological archipelago " in the east.

An intermediate sub-zone between the montane forest and the sub-alpine moorland (No. 5) is recognized by Moreau as bamboo forest.

4. *Savannah*. Includes a wide variety of landscapes varying from pure grassland to woodlands distinct from closed forests. Climatically dependent upon a

FIG. 13.—Sketch map to show main biotic divisions of Africa. Highland areas capable of supporting highland evergreen forest are marked with crosses. (After Moreau, 1952)

long dry season, too long to allow growth of rain forest even when total annual rainfall may be in fact greater than in some evergreen forests.

Rosevear (1953) considers the low humidity of the drier season rather than its absolute length, to be responsible for preventing fast growth. Trees predominantly deciduous ; ground cover is made up of perennial grasses. This type of landscape may occur anywhere from sea level up to 7000 ft. Along rivers coursing across savannah country, forested zones occur; they depend on ground water rather than rainfall; these are distinguished by Moreau as gallery-forests, and although physiognomically equivalent to the poorer evergreen lowland rain-forest, they differ floristically.

5. *Subalpine moorland*. A zone above the timber line beginning at 9000 ft. Occupies limited areas only on slopes of higher mountains. Chapin (1923) sub-divides it into two sub-zones, a lower characterized by tree-heaths, and an upper (above 12,500 ft.) characterized by giant lobelias and arborescent groundsels.

Within the broader vegetational zones various smaller microclimates have been recognized. These have been discussed by Napier (*loc. cit.*), who attempts to show how these differences have involved evolutionary adaptation of the primate inhabitants to the ecological niches provided. Adaptation has affected both morphology and behaviour. Evidence has accumulated, for example from the work of Zuckerman, Washburn and De Vore, Hall and Kummer on baboons, that the pattern of social life, more particularly on the size of the groups and the closeness of the social linkage, differs profoundly from the pattern observed in forest-dwelling species. Differences also occur in other behavioural features such as facial expression, vocalization (*teste* Andrew, 1962).

Napier laudably attempts a three-dimensional diagrammatization of the minor ecological niches in Africa. In the tropical rain-forest belt he recognizes three sub-types, namely, (1) mangrove (lining estuaries and creeks within tidal limits), (2) secondary forest, *i.e.* tropical rain-forest temporarily cultivated and then abandoned, (3) swamp-forest. Within these and the virgin forest several strata are discernible, viz.: (*a*) closed canopy, characterized by thick-stemmed lianas and herbaceous epiphytes. Many of the trees are provided with buttress roots; (*b*) the forest floor lacking grasses, but supporting ill-defined herbaceous and shrubby growth. The canopy itself presents three well-defined storeys, the highest extending up to 150 ft. or more. The middle storey (120 ft.) and the understorey (60 ft.) are progressively more extensive latitudinally.

Each of these divisions supports its typical primate fauna, adapted both morphologically and behaviourally to the particular niche. Thus, in mangrove swamps the quadrupedal *Cercopithecus* occurs, and in true swamp forest *Allenopithecus* is specially adapted. On the forest floor occur *Mandrillus* and *Cercocebus atys*. In the closed canopy *Cercocebus galeritus*, *Colobus*, *Cercopithecus mona* and other guenons inhabit the understorey; *Cercopithecus diana*, *C. mona*, *C. campbelli*, *Procolobus verus* and *Colobus polykomos* the middle storey; while the uppermost levels are inhabited solely by certain guenons such as *Cercopithecus pogonias*, *C. erythrotis*, *C. diana* and *C. nictitans*, and by *Colobus badius*, according to the geographical area concerned.

In Asia the forest belt is more restricted. The Indian subcontinent largely falls into the savannah zone, but a rain-forest tract occurs along the Malabar coast, with an outlier in south-western Ceylon. Montane forest appears along the Himalayas. Eastwards larger territories of tropical rain-forest and gallery-forests reappear in Burma and the Malay Peninsula and thence eastwards, affecting the major part of Indonesia, except for Java,

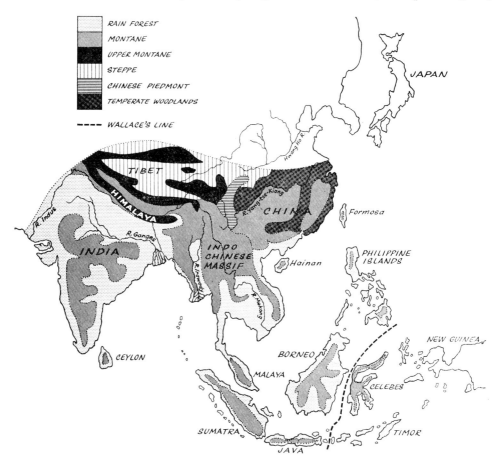

FIG. 14.—Sketch map to show biotic divisions of South Asia.
Redrawn from Sanderson (1961)

where cultivation has destroyed the pattern. The general pattern may be judged from the accompanying chart based on Sanderson (1961).

To sum up then, it transpires that recent studies have necessitated the addition of a vertical dimension to the more familiar two-dimensional distribution maps of arboreal animals, since the forest canopy presents several horizontal strata, each providing a number of differing physical environments for the arboreal fauna. Although the floristic composition of the canopy varies from place to place, the four recognizable strata appear to develop irrespective of the flora involved, *i.e.* a shrub stratum, the understorey (25-50 ft.) ; the middle storey (50-120 ft.) and the upper storey (120-150 ft.). The understorey consists of trees whose crowns form a completely closed canopy, the crowns interlacing and bound together by creepers, making together a solid mass of foliage. The middle storey is more irregular ; here and there crowns form a closed canopy, when they are in lateral contact ; but there are conspicuous gaps where the top of the lower storey is exposed. The upper storey is composed of the tallest trees, having umbrella-like crowns projecting beyond the middle storey, which is in comparative isolation. Here and there are single giants (emergents) of 200 ft. or more projecting even beyond the preceding. Lowest branches of one storey make contact with the highest of the storey below, so that the canopy provides a vertical continuum enabling certain species to pass from one horizon to another.

MOTILE ACTIVITIES

Locomotion in all cynomorph monkeys is quadrupedal, whether arboreal or terrestrial. The body is normally held in a horizontal pose and the four limbs alternate in progression. Details vary with the genus, particularly regarding the mode of transmission of body-weight through hands and feet. Typically the whole of the palmar surface and soles make contact with the substratum, but variations occur, especially in terrestrial and semi-terrestrial forms, in the direction of concentration of weight bearing on the more distal parts of the cheiridia (*e.g.* in *Cynopithecus, Papio, Mandrillus*). Retention of opposable thumb and big toe is indicative of the grasping power required in quadrupedal progress through trees. Loss of the thumb, combined with elongation of the hand and the conversion of the latter into a hook-like organ, is a specialization that parallels the phenomenon noted, *e.g.* in the Platyrrhine, *Ateles*. Among the cynomorphs it reaches its acme in *Colobus*, but the same trend is already apparent in the Asiatic leaf-monkeys. In these there is therefore an approach to that method of progression which reaches its full development only in the Pongidae and which has come to be known as brachiation from the fact that the body-weight is suspended, pendulum-wise, beneath the branches, and translation effected by swinging on the suspending arms. Owen (1859) first introduced the term brachiator in reference to the gibbons, where this mode of progression attains its maximum expression, but it was Keith (1899) who popularized the term " brachiation ", and extended its use to the larger apes which Owen had contrasted as " knuckle-walkers " (Trevor, 1963). Napier (1961, 1963) has coined the term semi-brachiators to include monkeys such as *Colobus, Nasalis* and other langurs which frequently progress by arm swinging and which thereby constitute an intermediate locomotor group. Basically the semi-brachiators are arboreal quadrupeds which spend a variable amount of time swinging by the arms and leaping with outstretched fore-limbs to gain a distant hand-hold, as described graphically for *Kasi senex* by Tennent (1861, p. 9).

Modes of leaping and of landing on target vary even within the limits of a single group (Hill, 1956). Aside from quadrupedal locomotion it must be added that the fore-limbs may, even in the most terrestrial quadrupedal forms, be temporarily relieved of the duty of transmission of body-weight. This enables the animal to rise upon its hind-limbs for purposes of scanning the horizon over tall grass or foliage, or to allow the hands freedom for exploring the environment for food or for retrieving an errant offspring otherwise out of reach. This does not, however, extend as a rule to bipedal progression, though in some cases a few steps may be taken bipedally either on the ground or in trees, for instance, if the hands are both involved at once in carrying a heavy fruit or similar spoil.

An erect attitude, however, is normally assumed in sitting. This mode of resting is not peculiar to the cynomorphs, but reaches its maximum expression among them in so far as in them only (apart from the gibbons among the Hominoidea) has the habit induced the morphological adaptation of ischial callosities. In sitting, the tail, when present, takes no share in supporting the body, but is held aside, or dependent over the substratum. In this posture the head is balanced on the spine in such a fashion as to permit the eyes, and the face generally, to be directed straight forwards without the necessity of hyperextension of the neck. This facility permits emancipation of the hands, enabling them to explore the environment, manipulate food, etc. (*vide* Hill, 1954, p. 77).

The question of aquatic locomotion in monkeys may conveniently be considered at this point. The matter is of special interest in view of recent suggestions by Hardy (1960) and Dart (1960) of the possible significance of an aquatic or semi-aquatic environment on the emergence of man and his cultures. Doubtless many cynomorphs can swim if put to it, but few monkeys readily take to water except for standing on the brink, splashing and paddling. Some macaques in zoos (especially *M. silenus*) have a predilection for discomfiting visitors by splashing water from their drinking vessels. Records of true swimming are confined to macaques (Stewart, 1886; Muir, 1910; Knottnerus-Meyer, 1928) and *Nasalis*. A newspaper report illustrated with photographs was published in 1959 showing a male Proboscis monkey swimming at sea two miles from the Bornean shore. Beebe (1934, p. 26) also reports having seen this species swimming. Interdigital webbing is, incidentally, extensive in *Nasalis*.

Among the macaques, *M. irus*, the Crab-eating Macaque, shows a habitat preference for mangrove swamps, finding much of its food in the water, and hence is often compelled to swim.

In the Monkey Jungle at Goulds, Florida, there is a free-ranging colony of Crab-eating Macaques (*Macaca irus*). At one station there is a pool of water separating animals from the public trail, and this is utilized for a spectacular display, the monkeys being induced to enter the water to retrieve food. We were shown a remarkable photograph taken from below water level of a female macaque diving for food whilst carrying her infant on her back. The mother has her eyes open, but the infant's are closed. She had evidently trained the infant to adjust to this unusual environmental change. On returning to surface the baby's head is said to reappear first, for the mother can continue below for a longer period.

Most cynomorph species are characterized by their stance, posture and attitudinizations. These vary enormously according to the species even within a single genus, and their significance is equally diverse (see especially Haddow, 1952, fig. 14). Special postures are assumed in aggressive moods, or in inviting social or sexual intercourse, whilst the tail is frequently held in characteristic postures (Hill, 1938) or moved in certain ways either (a) indicating the animals' mood, (b) according to circumstances of environment (Starck and Frick, 1958), or (c) as a signalling device towards other members of the troop. The latter is especially noted in baboons (Bopp, 1953, 1954).

Among the attitudes of social and sexual significance none is more wide-spread than the phenomenon of " presenting ". This, typically, is a reaction of females when sexually excited, and consists of displaying the perineal region before the male she wishes to entice. The tail is generally raised or diverted and there may be accompanying gestures suggestive to copulatory activity. The device is, however, also indulged in by younger animals of either sex to placate older or larger individuals who rank above them in the social hierarchy. Mature females will readily " present " to human beings in an attempt to express friendliness or to invite contact with their sexual organs. The procedure is therefore equally of social as of sexual significance.

Emotional expression, as evidenced by facial movements, has received considerable attention since Darwin's (1872) early observations on *Macaca*, *Cynopithecus* and *Papio*. Recent summaries with deeper analysis of the movements involved have been published by van Hoof (1962, 1963).

Cynomorph monkeys display, in its most effective and advanced manner, the power of grimace, a feature which led Buffon to the introduction of the name *guenon* to one of the best-known groups. Grimacing comprises a massive form of facial expression in which scalp, ears, eyelids and mouth-parts all share, and it functions basically as a form of threat-display. Its effect is enhanced in some species by crests and other adornments and by pigmentary patterning, especially in the presence of pallid patches on the upper eyelids, normally hidden, but brought into prominence when the brows are raised or the scalp drawn backwards. This patterning is best seen in mangabeys, *Cercocebus* (whence their alternative name of White-eyelid monkeys) and *Theropithecus*. Grimacing frequently involves opening of the mouth, displaying the teeth, or protrusion of the lips (*e.g.* in *Macaca nemestrina*), retraction of the ears, and is frequently accompanied by postural movements of other parts of the body.

The analysis of van Hoof indicates that each display is a compound expression consisting of a number of expressive elements ; firstly, the facial elements (including movements of jaws, lips, tongue, angles of the mouth, ears, eyes, eyelids, eyebrows and scalp) ; secondly, movements and postures of the body and its extremities ; and thirdly autonomic responses such as micturition, defaecation, pilo-erection, etc. To these may be added, in certain instances, vocal manifestations.

Four categories of major compound expressions are recognized by van Hoof, each resulting from a motivational state. The first consists of a number of expression movements in which an aggressive tendency is in conflict with a fear element urging the animal to flee. In two such states the tendency to attack is dominant ; this is associated with what van Hooff designates the " attack face " and the " aggressive threat face ". These are characterized by staring eyes, tense mouth (lips covering the teeth) with the angulus oris pulled forwards. Vocalization, if present, is low-pitched and harsh. When the flight tendency dominates, two other types of expression come into operation—the " scared threat face ", and the " crouch face ". In these the mouth is held open and the lips retracted both horizontally and vertically, leaving the teeth exposed. Vocalizations are here higher pitched and loud. Displays of all four categories are similar in all species studied.

A second category comprises four compound expressions in which a flight tendency is modified by social attraction. Here the manifestations vary considerably according to species. Many species respond to this type of motivation by lip-smacking and/or teeth-chattering. A rhythmic opening and closing of the mouth is common to both these activities. Lip-smacking is especially prevalent in Cercopithecidae, less obtrusive in Colobidae. It occurs when the element of social attraction is dominant and signifies a desire to approach a fellow or a human observer. It almost invariably accompanies the behavioural pattern known as grooming (*vide postea*, p. 169). Lip-smacking is frequently accompanied by rhythmic tongue movements, the degree of which varies with the intensity of the social motivation. On the other hand, teeth-chattering appears when the flight tendency is dominant. A modified form of this category is represented by what van Hoof terms the " grin face ". This occurs in certain species only, notably *Cynopithecus* and *Mandrillus*. In this the mouth is almost completely closed, but the lips are horizontally and vertically contracted. Usually no vocalization takes place, but it may be accompanied by lateral head-rocking and ear retractions (personal observation) ; see also Knottnerus-Meyer (1928, p. 54). Another special form of display is that found exclusively in *Macaca nemestrina*, the Pigtailed Macaque, for which reason Wilson (1937) refers to it as the " pigtail face " ; van Hoof calls it the " Flehmen face ". Here the lips are both

PLATE I

Photo: Sorby

Macaca nemestrina (Pig-tailed Monkey) ♂ pulling the " pigtail face "

protruded and pressed together. At the same time the eyebrows are raised, the back of the head is depressed between the shoulders, chin thrust forth, and the ears and scalp retracted. It may also be accompanied by postural elements affecting the body, limbs and tail. (See Plate 1.)

The third category of van Hoof is designated " pout face ". Though best seen in young chimpanzees, it also occurs in juvenile cynomorphs. It appears to be motivated by a desire for maternal care and consists of a funnelling of the lips accompanied by soft plaintive calls.

A fourth category is designated the " play face ", since it is exhibited during social play, or serves as an invitation thereto. It is characterized by widely opened mouth accompanied by staccato breathing and/or vocalization.

Not included among the above categories is the pattern noted by Darwin, among others, of expressing anger or defiance by widely opening the mouth as in yawning. It occurs markedly in baboons, but is also noted in macaques, mangabeys, guenons and langurs. It seems reasonable to assume that this is a display mechanism calculated to inform the opponent of the size and strength of the dental armament, for it is especially adopted by dominant males to enforce their authority on those lower in the social hierarchy. Bolwig (1957) disagrees with this interpretation, for he alleges that yawning in *Papio ursinus* occurs when an animal is watching or waiting for something to happen whether it be the offer of food, the approach of a female or expected attack, *i.e.* it is a displacement of activity. Yawning of a more typical nature, expressing fatigue also occurs, especially prior to sleep (Nolte, 1955) or when boredom affects a captive monkey.

The pertinent concomitant postural components of emotional expression, that are so aptly described by Martin (1841) and quoted *in extenso* by Darwin, may be alluded to. In expressing anger (possibly combined with a fear element) the facial pouting and staring eyes are accompanied by " repeated short starts as if about to spring forward, uttering at the same time inward guttural sounds ". This advancing and retarding is often carried out with the limbs somewhat spread and the body low slung, at least in *Macaca* and *Cercopithecus*; the tail also may be held rigid in a posture characteristic of the species. This pattern has been further analysed for *M. mulatta* by Altmann (1962). Some species, especially macaques, express anger or excitement by bouncing up and down, or repeatedly shaking the branches or other substrata (pattern 49 of Altmann, 1962). The fear element in these performances is expressed by involuntary defaecation—this is especially marked in Colobidae.

An elaboration of the fear response is observed in what Hunt, Landis and Jacobsen (1937) term the " startle " response. This they tested in *Macaca* and *Cercocebus* by firing a gun and recording the effects by ultra-rapid cinematography. The pattern of responses was found to resemble that previously described for Man, more particularly of the human infant. Blinking, head movements, hunching of shoulders, abduction of the brachium with pronation of forearms, flexion of elbows and fingers, forward movement of trunk, tensing of the abdomen and flexion of the knee. Occasional absence of blinking, occurrence of plantar reflexes and greater amount of bodily movement recall the reactions of the human infant. In contrast to the above, I found that during an air-raid a group of Primates, including baboons, macaques, guenons and langurs, betrayed little startle response apart from vocalization. Knottnerus-Meyer (1928) mentions a macaque falling dead from its perch on a sudden clap of thunder, while McCann (1928) reports another in the wild state which toppled off its perch on hearing a gunshot nearby.

A detailed study of the methods of communication by facial and postural expressions in the Rhesus macaque has been published by Hinde and Rowell (1962).

Preference for the use of the right or left hand rather than ambidextry has frequently been noted in Old World monkeys. Ferrier (1876) observed a Rhesus with marked preference for the use of its left hand. Grunthal (1949) on the contrary observed no such preference. Glees and Cole (1951) record several species, including *M. mulatta* and *M. nemestrina*, in which they proved a left- or right-handed dominance by discriminatory techniques. (See also Franz, 1913 ; Lashley, 1917 ; Kounin, 1938.)

FOOD AND FEEDING

For the most part cynomorph monkeys are vegetarians, subsisting on a wide variety of buds, leaves, fruit (including nuts), flowers and bark, but commonly there is some additional animal protein, obtained either from insects or other anthropods, or from birds' eggs. There is much specific differentiation in regard to food preferences, and there is an extensive literature devoted to the experimental testing of this in macaques and other laboratory animals (Maslow, 1933 ; Katz and Katz, 1936 ; Bierens de Haan and Heubel, 1938).

There is a well-marked tendency to specialization in diet, notably in the family Colobidae, where there are structural adaptations to cope with a restricted, predominantly phyllophagous, regime.

On the other hand, the baboons, in association with their more adventurous ecological excursions, are tending to adopt a more catholic diet. Though subsisting largely on grass (more particularly the underground shoots) (Hall, 1961) ; they also use their digits for digging up underground roots, tubers, ground-nuts, etc. More significant still, there have been several recent reports of baboons eating flesh—either from carcasses they have encountered casually, or on occasion, by actual predation of newborn gazelles, etc. (Dart, 1953, 1963 ; Washburn and de Vore, 1961). Hall (1963) also reports *P. ursinus* as eating marine shellfish (*Patella*), which places this species on a par with the well-known crab-eating habits of *Macaca irus*.

Cynomorph monkeys of various species become economically important, especially in parts of Africa, due to their propensity for raiding crops. This applies more particularly to the group bearing cheek-pouches. These they fill to capacity during the raid, the spoils being consumed at leisure after retreat to the neighbouring forest. In countries like Sierra Leone, where this phenomenon is of special significance, organized monkey drives are periodically carried out in areas devoted to cocoa production. Unfortunately the slaughter is indiscriminate, for, in addition to the major culprits such as the Sooty Mangabey (*Cercocebus atys*), several innocent and comparatively rare forms (*e.g. Procolobus*) are victimized (MacKenzie, 1952).

The position in India is the reverse of that in Africa, for here, in spite of the monkeys' depredations of crops and even local market stalls, the animals are regarded as sacred and not to be interfered with. On the contrary, they are pampered and offered all manner of artificial food. In many places, it is their custom to raid railway stations on the approach of trains and toll levies from the passengers. Species concerned is primarily the Sacred Langur (*Semnopithecus entellus*), though *Macaca mulatta* and *M. radiata* are also involved.

The adaptation of feeding habits to changed environment, particularly when the altered environment is due to human intervention, has been studied in the Japanese macaque (*Macaca fuscata*) by Itani (1958) who provisioned a wild troop with supplemental food (apples, wheat, sweet potatoes). At first the troop ate the two latter comestibles, but not the apples, but later got used to them and ate them. It took four months for the whole troop to become adapted to the addition of peanuts to the supplemental diet. Other items such as oranges, damsons and soy bean were accepted relatively rapidly, but the troop remained recalcitrant over more unnatural substances like boiled rice, bread, biscuits and candies, even after five-and-one-half years. Itani, after further experiment, concluded that acquisition of new food habits depended partly on discovery and partly on imitation, the latter being the more prevalent in adults, and the former in infants. Infants pass the process on to their mothers and sub-leaders ; adult females pass it on to their consorts and to other adult males. There is usually no communication between troops, with the sole exception of solitary animals that move from one group to another taking their acquired habits with them.

Feeding almost always involves manipulation of the pabulum. Typically the food is plucked or picked up manually. Before ingestion it is, if unusual, passed before the nares to ascertain its palatability. It is then inserted into the mouth. Here it may be immediately masticated and swallowed ; but in monkeys having cheek-pouches temporary storage therein is not unusual, especially where the food material is abundant or the animal is pressed for time (*e.g.* in raids upon plantations). In the Colobidae the half-masticated food is rapidly swallowed along with abundant saliva, and the primary breakdown effected in the sacculated stomach. Regurgitation occurs in both colobids and cercopithecids (in the latter into the cheek-pouches) and the bolus again swallowed; but this does not constitute rumination as not all the intake is affected, nor is there any systematic re-mastication.

Rubbing of food against the substrate or against the forearm recalls a similar propensity in *Cebus* and other Platyrrhine (Vol. IV, pp. 388, 391). It has been particularly noted in baboons by Bolwig (1957). He regards it as a sign of agitation; but it may be a means of expressing juices to permit nasal scrutiny prior to ingestion. I have myself noted it in *Miopithecus*.

Foraging for food begins usually soon after resumption of diurnal activities. Speaking of East African monkeys, other than *Papio*, Haddow (1952) says there are two principal feeding periods, early morning and late afternoon. Between these two peaks of feeding a period of minimal activity occurs in which some animals may sleep. The second period is the more prolonged and in several ways the more important of the two. Heavy rain may delay or even eliminate the morning session (Buxton, 1951), but evening feeding may occur even in heavy rain, so that the urge to feed may be stronger at this time. Feeding may continue into the short twilight. Nolte (1955) reports similar observations for *Macaca radiata* in South India.

A commonly accepted belief is that during feeding a sentinel animal locates himself in an advantageous position to give warning of approaching danger. Zuckerman (1932) could not confirm this in baboons, nor did Buxton (*loc. cit.*) or Haddow (1952) working with *Cercopithecus ascanius schmidti*. An intruder may be spotted by any member of a band engaged in feeding, irrespective of age or sex, and it appears that the first observer retreats and is shortly followed by the rest of the band. Similar reactions have been observed in *C. pygerythrus centralis*, *C. l'hoesti* and *C. mitis*.

Drinking, as in all Pithecoidea and Man, is by suction, making use of the musculature of the lips and cheeks.

Sleeping Habits

From the observations of Lumsden (1951), Buxton (1951) and Haddow (1952) on East African monkeys, it would appear that the troops retire before sunset to preferred patches of forest, sometimes even to a particular tree over periods of five-and-one-half years at least. *C. ascanius schmidti* prefers dense foliage among the smaller branches and twigs, in contrast to *Colobus abyssinicus ituricus* which rests in the highest parts of the trees, often in bare dead branches. So far, the first mentioned is the only monkey recorded as sleeping in the understorey (*vide antea*, p. 151). *Erythrocebus*, however, according to Hall (1963, personal communication) disperses for the night over an area up to 400 yards (compared with a diurnal range averaging three miles), resting in low bushes in the open. Baboons, too, may sleep individually in isolated trees. But in rocky terrain (as in Abyssinia and South Africa) they sleep on rock ledges or in clefts.

VOCALIZATION

Vocal repertoires among cynomorph catarrhines are extremely varied. They vary with the species, whilst each species has a wider range than is commonly found among platyrrhines. Andrew (1962, 1963) has attempted to systematize the recorded data and to study the phenomenon scientifically by spectrophotometry.

Till lately vocalizations have been classified into functional categories such as warning notes and threat calls, but Andrew emphasizes that calls emitted by monkeys are not given solely to warn troop companions of impending danger. He has shown the possibility of arranging the situations, evoking calls by monkeys of widely separated genera, into groups such that all the situations within a group tend to evoke the same or similar sounds.

Andrew's (1962) groupings arranged in order of a progressive intensity of associated calls are as follows :

   1. Perceiving a desired object.

   2. Encounter with a social fellow after brief separation under circumstances where no attack is feared. Such fellow may be a social equal, inferior or superior. Such encounters are subdivisible into :
     (*a*) Perception at a distance.
     (*b*) Encounter involving close bodily contact—often with mutual grooming.
     (*c*) Infant seeking nipple.

   3. (*a*) Male approaching female to attempt copulation.
     (*b*) Handled firmly in play by friendly superior, *e.g.* as in being fondled or tickled by a human.
     (*c*) Attempts to reach a desired object.

   4. (*a*) Loss of contact with other members of group.
     (*b*) Attempts to reach a desired object.

   5. (*a*) On being chased or seized by a social superior.
     (*b*) Loss of bodily contact by infant with mother.

Andrew also adds two special situations, namely (1) calls given in relatively confident threat, *e.g.* by a male defending his home range ; here the emission consists largely of noise due to violent expiration ; if a glottal sound is present, it is the type given in group 1 above. (2) Persistent calling evoked

M

by a distant strange object : it may be in the form of a variant of calls elicited under situations 2 or 3, but it may be a peculiar form of its own.

In description of vocal emissions the following definitions are offered by Andrew :

Sound is used to describe vocalization with a " tonal " structure, *i.e.* composed of a fundamental with overtones.

Noise has no tonal structure. It forms a component of vocal emissions in which energy is distributed relatively uniformly.

A *click*, or cluck, is a very narrow column of noise.

A *titter* is a bout of soft clucks.

A *purr* is a rapid series of clicks. Clicks may also merge together to form *rasps* or *crackles*.

A *grunt* has tonal structure with a low fundamental. It is a deep sound with little noise.

A *moan* is longer and has a higher fundamental.

A *wail* is higher still.

A *squeak*, which may be long or short, has a very high fundamental whose pitch may change rapidly.

A *shriek* has also a high fundamental, but so broadened that it forms a band of intense noise rather than a normal fundamental.

A *yip* is a short shriek, or a call made up of a short segment of a shriek.

Andrew has instrumentally recorded many of these vocalizations in *Cercopithecus*, *Allenopithecus*, *Macaca*, *Cercocebus* and *Papio*, but admits that the data are not yet adequate for full analysis or assessment of their causation and significance.

In *Cercopithecus* marked differences in the quality of the different calls are noted as well as in the case of their utterance. In *Papio* grunts are frequent, especially when eating (group 1 category). Group 2 calls are noted in tame *Cercopithecus neglectus* where " arr " calls are emitted at the approach of a human acquaintance whom they were seeking to groom. Infants of *C. mitis* give the " arr " call on seeking the nipple.

Other examples are best deferred for consideration under the appropriate systematic heading ; but mention may here be made of the limited data on the vocalization in Colobidae, namely Champion (1929, 1930) ; Hill and Booth (1957) and to the detailed study of vocal communication in *Macaca mulatta* by Rowell and Hinde (1962).

RECEPTIVE CAPACITIES

There seems to be no doubt, from experimental researches carried out by Bierens de Haan (1925 *a*, *b*, *c*), Katz and Katz (1937) and Cole (1952, 1953, 1963), of the primacy of the visual sense in cynomorph monkeys. Species tested have been macaques (*M. mulatta*, *M. nemestrina*) and *Cercopithecus*.

Cole, writing of *M. nemestrina* for example, stresses the acuity of vision, stating that the animal appears to derive considerable satisfaction from concentrated and minute scrutiny of small details of any object presented to it, even to such minute objects as the hairs on a human hand or forearm, minor skin blemishes, or patterns on the fabric of the observer's raiment. Rhesus monkeys and baboons lack this power of concentration, being more impatient.

Ability to appreciate two-dimensional pictures of known objects is commented on by de Haan and can be understood by anyone who has tested any cynomorph monkey with a mirror, where the common reaction is to feel with the hand at some point behind the mirror to test the substantiality of the image. With *M. nemestrina* the mirror image is reacted to by greeting it with the characteristic " pigtail face " (*vide antea*, p. 156).

Under conditions of poor illumination, Katz and Katz (1937) observed that monkeys, until adaptation has occurred, remain perfectly motionless. If food is supplied, it is not sought after, the reaction being thus in contrast to dogs, where the sense of smell is primarily operative. As adaptation occurs, the food may be sought by tactile impressions, though hesitantly, and clumsily. The authors concluded that vision is therefore the primary receptor mechanism, and found their views confirmed by observations on a nearly blind Green Monkey (*Cercopithecus sabaeus*) where the above-mentioned reactions had become stabilized. Both the sightless and the seeing monkeys appeared to depend on smell for their secondary impressions of food rather than touch, the choice with touch being within certain limits only.

Katz and Katz further studied the Purkinje phenomenon in their dark-adapted monkeys by offering achromatic food in a dish painted half red, half blue. When the food appeared to the human eye as bright spots on the red, but difficult to discriminate on the blue, the monkeys chose from the red side of the dish. When dates were used, these showed up darkly on the blue, but were obscure on the red background, and the monkeys always chose first from that side. The authors, therefore, concluded that the Purkinje phenomenon holds good for the cynomorph retina as for Man, appreciation of brightness being present under conditions of illumination not feasible for colour perception.

The problem of colour vision has already been discussed (*antea*, p. 129).

Smell and taste are both better developed than is commonly appreciated. Although from the aspect of cerebral structure cynomorph monkeys are microsmatic, it does not necessarily follow that smell is entirely obsolete. The fact is that hitherto little has been recorded of localized cutaneous scent glands in Cercopithecoidea ; there is, nevertheless, as any visitor to the monkey house in any zoological garden will appreciate, a very powerful bodily emanation from these animals which is presumably noticeable to members of their own kind. Monkey-house odours fall into the garlic-like (or alliaceous) category of Zwaardemaker (1895). They are mainly derived from Old World species which constitute the bulk of those commonly exhibited in menageries.   Nevertheless, there is considerable specific and probably some individual variation in the quality of the scent.   The functional value lies in enabling members of a troop to keep in contact, or aiding mothers to keep track of their young, or vice versa.   So far the source of the odours is elusive, apart from the specialized pectoral areas in *Mandrillus* (Hill, 1954) and *Theropithecus*. (See also *postea*, p. 222.)

Further evidence of the functional value of smell is derived from the invariable habit of passing any new food item before the nostrils prior to ingestion.   Corner (1946), referring to *Macaca nemestrina*, remarks on their sensitive discrimination between edible and poisonous fungi by olfactory testing.   After olfactory testing strange or unusual food items are usually further tested by the tongue and may be rejected by the first or only after the second gustatory sampling.

Next to vision, the auditory sense appears to be the most important receptive mechanism.   Auditory acuity is undoubtedly of a high order. Movements of the pinna are freer than in Hominoidea, indicative of the importance played by sounds of low intensity.   Evidence is also supplied by the wide range of vocal emissions used in communication between members of a troop.   Kluver (1933) by experimental methods on *Macaca irus* trained them to respond to sound stimuli of quite narrow differentials.   He also concluded that his monkeys could transpose noises and find widely differing pairs of noises equivalent.   As in many other respects, *M. nemestrina* ranks high in its attainments.   This species is trained to respond to human speech by the Malays.   Corner (1955), who used them for botanical collecting, reports that one of his monkeys knew twenty-four words of Malay and could certainly differentiate between *mari* (= come), *lari* (= run), and *chari* (= search for), and could also understand and respond to a seven-syllabled expression. Corner admits, however, that his gestures and other incidental phenomena could have aided the animal *via* its visual sense.

There is further the famous Chacma Baboon (*Papio ursinus*) who acted as a railroad pointsman at Uitenhage in South Africa.   His master had been incapacitated, but had taught the baboon the names of the levers which controlled the points.   These he operated satisfactorily for nine years (Fitzsimons, 1911, p. 38, 1919, p. 60).

Tactile discrimination is equally as important as auditory ability in aiding the cynomorph in its investigation of the environment.   This sense is ministered to by the papillary ridges of the palms and soles, and to some extent also by the fine sensibility of lips and tongue.   Cole (1952), working with *M. nemestrina*, showed the ability to discriminate by touch, without aid from vision, between a cone (with a base measurement of 4 cm. and height 5·5 cm.) and a pyramid of similar height and base lines of 4 cm.   Cole (1962) concludes that " this skill would seem to indicate a mature relationship between the sensori-motor system and the higher mental functions ".   The

Pig-tailed Macaque is, perhaps, exceptional in this degree of attainment, for Cole failed to obtain equivalent reactions with *M. mulatta*.

INSTRUMENTATION

Cynomorphs on the whole do not so readily seek the use of extracorporeal objects to assist their physiological motivity, as do the anthropoid apes or the platyrrhine *Cebus*. Kluver (1933) and Cole (1963) have tested respectively the Rhesus and Pig-tailed Macaques with L-shaped and T-shaped sticks to determine whether they will utilize them to rake in food otherwise out of reach. Scores gained are considerably below the ratings attained by *Cebus*. By contrast, in baboons, although the phenomenon is rare, Roginski (1939) has recorded its occurrence, while Bolwig (1961) has fully documented an interesting example in a female East African baboon (*P. anubis* subsp.) which, on the day of her arrival, found a stick wherewith to rake potential food towards herself. She could also, in other ways, extend her normal activities beyond the reach of her body by using other media. She could throw pebbles or bananas, albeit with poor aim, the objects being picked up by the left hand, volar aspect downwards, and then flung suddenly forward by an upward movement of the arm. Food suspended above her reach even by jumping would be attacked by throwing sticks. Later, she learned to use sticks as ladders to climb after suspended food.

Some of the activities of the Chacma of Uitenhage (*vide antea*, p. 164) seem to fall into the tool using category.

REPRODUCTIVE AND SOCIAL BEHAVIOUR

Cynomorph monkeys in a natural environment dwell in troops of varying size, sometimes up to 100 or more individuals. It follows, therefore, that members of a group stand in some sort of relationship with each other and each has its place in the group as a whole. In order to maintain cohesion within the group, powers of communication (visual and/or vocal) are available and have their specific meanings. The factors responsible for maintaining the group concept and its relationship to the environment are of supreme importance and have, in recent years, been subjected to considerable and intensive investigation in view of their importance in the evolution and dynamics of human societies.

Southwick (1963) has recently reviewed the principal participants in the development of our knowledge in an introduction to a small book edited by himself, composed of excerpts from some of the leading contributions to the subject.

As Southwick points out, prior to the present century, knowledge of the behaviour of subhuman Primates consisted almost entirely of miscellaneous anecdotes and travellers' tales—often exaggerated and dramatized or treated anthropomorphically. A certain amount of data had accrued from ancient sources anent the species regarded as sacred, *e.g.* the Hamadryas Baboon, the Sacred Langur (*Semnopithecus entellus*) and the Japanese Macaque (*Macaca fuscata*), but alongside this and, to a considerable degree, detracting from its value, there developed a welter of pseudo-scientific and mythological writing.

Not until the early 1920s did attention become focussed on the scientific importance of the social attributes of apes and monkeys when R. M. Yerkes (1929) approached the problem. Though confining his attention primarily to the chimpanzee, his aims and methods were shortly to be exploited by others interested in several cynomorph species, firstly by Zuckerman (1932), who surveyed earlier literature, studied a captive colony of Hamadryas Baboons in the London Zoo and followed this up by field work on the Chacma (*Papio ursinus*) in South Africa. Somewhat later, Carpenter (1942, 1963), following up his earlier work on the platyrrhine *Alouatta* (see Vol. V, p. 76 *et seq.*), carried out patient observations on a semi-wild population of Rhesus Macaques (*M. mulatta*) which he had liberated on the island of Cayo Santiago, off the eastern coast of Puerto Rico.

Subsequent to the Second World War there was renewed interest in and realization of the importance of work on the social and other relationships of free-ranging monkeys. In the early 1950s Japanese workers established a research centre for the study of their local macaque (*M. fuscata*), and later a journal in which a series of valuable contributions have been published by Imanishi (1957, 1960), Itani (1948, 1959), Kawai (1958, 1960), Kawamura (1958), Sugiyama (1960), Furuya (1960, 1962), and others. Meanwhile, Chance (1956) had studied certain aspects of the social behaviour of a captive colony of Rhesus monkeys at the London Zoo on the site formerly occupied by the Hamadryas Baboon colony studied by Zuckerman.

Haddow (1952), in collaboration with Buxton and others, initiated a comprehensive study of East African monkeys, more especially in connection with their relationship to the spread of yellow fever and other diseases, and a very thorough account of the habitat and field relations of *Cercopithecus ascanius schmidti* has resulted.

Indian macaques and langurs have likewise been studied in the field by Angela Nolte (1955, *a* and *b*), followed more recently by the work of Phyllis Jay (1962) and Suzanne Ripley (1963) on langurs, and by contributions on macaques from Altmann (1962) and Southwick (1963) who, with Beg, Siddiqui and Prakash, are currently following up earlier studies on *M. mulatta*, as also are Kawamura, Sugiyama, Yoshiba, Parthasarathy and Simonds on *M. radiata* as well as on Central Indian langurs. Koford (1963), too, is following up Carpenter's work on the Cayo Santiago colony of Rhesus monkeys.

Africa again comes into the picture with the establishment of the Tigoni

Primate Research Centre at Limura, Tanganyika, whence observations on three species of *Cercopithecus* have been reported upon by Cynthia Booth (1962). Zuckerman's early studies on wild baboons have recently been supplemented extensively by the work of Kummer (1957), Bolwig (1959), Hall (1962), and of Washburn and de Vore (1961 *et seq.*).

With all this recent accession of data, it is difficult adequately to summarize the present state of knowledge within a brief review; it is possible here, therefore, to emphasize only some of the basic principles, leaving details to be considered in connection with the genera and species concerned.

Virtually all cynomorph monkeys form polygynous hordes. Fundamental in the understanding of their social behaviour is the female reproductive cycle (p. 134 *antea*) and the mating behaviour in respect to the state of the sexual cycle of the adult females comprised within the group. Arising from this is the existence of a dominance hierarchy of adult males. Prominence of the mating behaviour is itself a consequence of the great duration of that part of the sexual cycle in which the females are receptive. Dominance relations in baboons (Zuckerman, 1932) and macaques (Carpenter, 1942; Chance and Mead, 1952; Chance, 1956) are conspicuously evident, influencing every aspect of behaviour.

In baboons a troop consists of a number of sub-groups which have been labelled " harems ", in each of which an adult male is dominant, forming a central figure around whom the rest of the troop arrange themselves in some form of rank order and to whom all others are, in greater or lesser degree, subservient. Imanishi (1960) objects to the use of the term " harem ", and others, such as " clan ", drawn from human societies. He introduces the term " oikia " as more precise and as giving an idea of spatial as well as social relationships within the group.

Around the dominant central male, or overlord, are commonly clustered a group of female baboons, one or more of whom is in a sexually receptive condition. Bachelor males occupy a lower rank and a more distant spatial relationship, being related peripherally to the harem of females " owned " by the overlord.

In *Macaca assamensis*, Carpenter observed groups composed of 2 adult males, 6 adult females (two carrying infants) and 2 juveniles. Another group had 4 adult males, 10 adult females (4 with infants) and 8 juveniles. In his Cayo Santiago colony of *M. mulatta*, a typical arrangement was a group containing 6 adult males, 32 adult females (25 carrying infants) and 10 juveniles—an arrangement which agrees with truly wild colonies in India. Thus in all groups of macaques females predominate in numbers (polygyny), the adult males dominate all the others, but the exclusive dominance of one male, such as occurs in baboons, is not manifested; though *M. nemestrina* may prove exceptional in this respect.

Rank order in females is proportional to their state of sexual readiness.

A dominant male keeps the most receptive female as his immediate concubine and when she becomes pregnant or passes into a non-receptive condition, she is temporarily discarded and her place taken by the next in rank.

Socially significant behaviour comprises a wide variety of modes of communication (*e.g.* threat or aggressive patterns expressing dominance ; vocal emissions, etc.) which together stabilize the group by maintaining the rank order.   Chance (1956) gives a partial catalogue of such behaviour patterns for *Macaca mulatta*, but a much more complete one is the analysis of Altmann (1962).   For the Hamadryas Baboon (*Papio hamadryas*), Kummer (1956) has made a similar analysis.

It is abundantly clear that emergence of behaviour patterns calculated to enforce the rank order are inevitable if the group's continued existence is to be maintained.   Otherwise there would be a free-for-all scramble for the receptive females with much bloodshed which, if continued, would not be biologically advantageous to the group or to the species.

Patterns of behaviour enforcing the power of the dominant male or males, or expressive of submission on the part of the females towards the males, or of one female or male to another superior in rank, can be seen in all cynomorph groupings.

According to Imanishi there are two patterns of social organization at the oikia level.   In one, each oikia occupies its own territory and is antagonistic to contiguous oikiae, though it may accept solitary intruders from them. This pattern is observed in *M. mulatta*.   The other type of organization is seen in, *e.g. Cercopithecus ascanius* (Haddow, 1952), and in *Papio ursinus* where several oikiae occupy the same general area and associate in a large troop, at any rate temporarily.

Behavioural patterns of social significance in the establishment and maintenance of the dominance hierarchy may be considered under the following main headings :

    (1) Display (including vocal manifestations)
    (2) Grooming
    (3) Presenting
    (4) Copulatory behaviour
    (5) Maternal and nursing behaviour
    (6) Interrelations between juveniles

The term *display* covers all those postures and activities used for communicating an individual's emotional status (sexual or otherwise) to other members of its group.   From the present point of view, the threat-display is the most significant as it is used by a dominant animal toward an inferior who is attempting to usurp the higher rank or secure its amenities.   By threat displays alone a dominant male keeps inferior males from his harem or even from food, until the dominant male has satisfied his own requirements. Threat is usually sufficient, but will be backed up by physical aggression should the inferior animal persist in displeasing the overlord. The nature of the display varies with the species, but involves grimacing, yawning actions, pilo-erection and other features, including vocal accompaniments.

A reverse kind of display is used in friendly approach to one of equal or higher rank. It consists of grimaces, head bobbing or other similar movements which are highly specific even within the different members of a genus (*e.g. Cercopithecus*). These are more on a par with behaviour patterns seen in birds where the display is to attract attention either of male to female or vice versa, or between members of the same sex (*e.g.* juveniles of similar age).

Grooming is a pattern of behaviour seen in its most typical form in the Cynomorpha. It is based on an innate attraction for hair or hairy objects, for the mere sight of hair seems sufficient to stimulate a monkey to a minute digital examination and search for particles of sebum. It has been termed fur-picking and sham louse picking (Ewing, 1935). In the popular mind it is misinterpreted as hunting for fleas, but as fleas and other ectoparasites are extremely rare in monkeys, the prevalence of the activity must have some other explanation. It is quite easy to determine that particulate material removed digitally consists of dried epidermal scales and/or sebum or other dried cutaneous exudate. The essence of the activity, however, is its social significance, for there is always a hierarchical relationship between the groomer and the groomee. Differences exist in the grooming pattern and its intensity and also in its frequency and in the degree to which lip-smacking or tongue movements accompany the activity. A solitary individual may groom its own coat or that of a human acquaintance, but normally two partners are involved, a dominant and an inferior, but sometimes mutual grooming parties are formed of three or four individuals who take turn and turn about in dealing with various parts of each other's coats.

Occasionally, at least in captive monkeys, grooming attains a pathological degree, the individual hairs being avulsed in an excess of vigour. I once had a solitary male Olive Baboon (*Papio anubis*) whose friendly gesture on greeting me was to groom his thigh or scrotum, pulling out a single hair which he offered me. This excessive vigour in grooming may also occur socially between cage mates, whole areas of skin being denuded in the process of time. From an example of this kind, Tinklepaugh (1931) came to the conclusion that fur plucking constitutes a method of adornment as well as a toilet procedure.

The phenomenon of grooming, especially mutual grooming, presupposes some form of rapport between the participants. This is further attested by the vocal emissions commonly accompanying it. The inference is, therefore, that grooming has social significance. Among other effects, it is included among the activities leading to mating, especially when involving a dominant male and his erstwhile partner, though by no means always necessary in the preparatory precopulatory activities. Grooming may also be indulged in immediately after copulation.

Presenting has already been discussed (*antea*, p. 155). Its social significance depends on the fact that it expresses subservience or submission. Typically it is the attitude of a female towards her overlord when desirous of attracting him sexually. In *Macaca mulatta*, Altmann (1962) defines it as essentially tantamount to the assumption of the female copulatory position. In Hamadryas baboons, Kummer (1956) has illustrated variations in the form of sexual presentation.

In a social context presenting may occur between any individual and a social superior, male or female, either as a form of appeasement or as an invitation for grooming or other form of contact. It may, for example, be adopted in the face of a threat display or overt aggression on the part of a superior. If accompanied by pelvic thrusts or other sexual gestures, it is an open invitation to copulation, but may, even so, become sublimed into a purely social approach, as I have found with *Kasi senex* and *K. johni* in making friendly gestures towards a human acquaintance.

Presenting is as frequently seen in the wild as in captivity (Haddow, 1952, p. 352).

Copulatory Behaviour.—Following on sexual presentation by the female, if the male approached is interested, mating ensues. In all cynomorph catarrhines so far observed, mounting is *a posteriore* (*more canum*). In the normal pattern, as seen in *Macaca, Papio* or *Cercopithecus*, the male approaches from behind whilst the female adopts a crouching posture. He grasps her manually round the waist, then grasps her legs below the knee with his hind feet. With accompanying pelvic thrusts the penis enters the vagina, where after a variable number of thrusts, in a fruitful coition, ejaculation occurs. Such may, however, only be consummated after a series of preliminary mountings. In the final stages the female may turn her head towards the male and often grasps one of his legs with her ipsilateral hand (Altmann's, 1962, pattern 7). After dismounting, the male usually sits down near the female and social activities (grooming, lip-smacking and/or vocal communication) are resumed.

In baboons Washburn and de Vore (1961) report that, at the beginning of their receptive period, females will mate with juvenile and less dominant males, mating with several in succession ; but later on, as the desire becomes more intense, females form temporary consort relationships with dominant adult males. Such consortships vary in duration from a few hours to a few days.

Details for *Macaca fuscata* are given by Tokuda (1962).

Copulatory patterns are modified or distorted in captive animals or in those subjected to abnormal environmental influences (Mason, 1963).

In *Cercopithecus* Cynthia Booth (1962) states that mating is not related to the female sexual cycle. In caged specimens of four species of this genus no regularity was observed in the intervals between matings. In *C. neglectus* and *C. mitis* copulation was observed with pregnant females and on one occasion with an unconscious female. Normally, however, co-operation on the part of the female is essential.

Maternal Behaviour (see especially for *Macaca mulatta*, Tinklepaugh and Hartman, 1932).—Newborn babies are characteristically carried on the mother's belly, its cheiridia grasping her fur. Moreover, in most species they remain in this relation to the mother until they are well-grown—with one notable exception, in baboons, where later on they are carried, at least part of the time, on the mother's back—as in Platyrrhini. When the mother is sitting, additional support is given to the youngster by one or both maternal arms. In this position the baby's legs sometimes release their grip and are placed upon the substrate. Support from one maternal arm may be given when she moves quickly or leaps a great distance, but ordinarily the babe is suspended without support.

Attraction of the newborn for hairy or furry objects appears to be innate and the proclivity for exploration of hair, as manifested in the grooming pattern in older animals, stems from the same source.

An interesting outcome of this infantile proclivity has resulted from the experimental investigations of Harlow (1958) and his co-workers on infants separated at birth from their mothers and reared artificially. It was found that by providing what Harlow terms surrogate mothers, a state of affection is induced for whatever the infant associates with its feeds. Surrogate mothers made up of wire or of pieces of towel stretched over a wire framework were tested. Preference is invariably for the softer, furry covering, a hairy substrate being preferred above all else.

A similar propensity exists, between lactating females, for small hairy objects, which accounts for the behaviour pattern often noted among captive animals where a mother will carry around a dead infant for days until it becomes putrid. In one instance, the corpse of a dead squirrel was offered to a female monkey that had recently produced a stillborn foetus. This was also clutched until it become putrescent. The same stimulus accounts for the numerous instances of kidnapping which have been reported in monkey colonies.

In relation to the oikia, nursing mothers seem to have a favoured place, usually staying in groups in the most protected part of the band. In macaques and baboons this is near to the overlord, and they are surrounded peripherally by the less-favoured members of the oikia. When resting, the females with babies sit together ; when the troop moves they travel in line near the centre of the procession (Imanishi, 1960 ; Washburn and de Vore, 1961 ; de Vore, 1962). In *Semnopithecus*, Phyllis Jay (1962) finds the mothers within the circle of the rest of the oikia, which includes the adult males, so that when danger threatens the mother and infant are protected by the unencumbered members of the troop. Normally, when a female langur is carrying a young infant, she avoids adult males and takes no part in mutual grooming sessions. Baboons and macaques, on the contrary, even old males, are always solicitous of the infantile members of the oikia and will tolerate from them indignities that would not be allowed from older members of the troop. A dominant male will even assist a mother in grooming her infant, whereas an adult male langur shows no interest in the newborn or small infant. He makes no effort to touch it or be near it, and if an older juvenile jostles him during its activities, he takes no notice. Maternal behaviour, too, differs somewhat in langurs from that in the Cercopithecidae. Adult females all show marked interest in the newcomer and will cluster around the proud mother from the start in an endeavour to caress the baby and if possible even to hold it. At first the mother will turn her back to the others, remaining aloof for a few hours, but gradually she allows more freedom to her associates and will even permit one of the waiting females to hold her babe for a few minutes. At the same time the female's dominance relations with the other members of her group are temporarily suspended, and she is able to retrieve her infant from any of the other members who may be holding it, irrespective of her normal status in the hierarchy in relation to them.

Duration of nursing appears to be variable. In *Macaca irus* Spiegel (1930) states that milk is secreted for eighteen months, but Haddow (1952) maintains that in *Cercopithecus ascanius schmidti* it continues in the wild for six months only. Infants of this species are capable of walking with a fair degree of muscular co-ordination within a few days of birth—the time at which the umbilical scar has healed.

An interesting correlation occurs between the contrasted appearance of the newborn compared with the adults and the social relationships between adults and infants. Most newborn cynomorphs contrast in some way with their elders. In langurs, black and white *Colobus* monkeys, and to a lesser degree macaques and baboons, the newborn differs strikingly in colour from the older animals. In other genera there may be little colour difference in the coat, but contrasts occur in the lack of pigmentation of the naked parts, size of ears and similar features. Cynthia Booth declares that in all *Cercopithecus* species she studied, the natal coat is conspicuously different from the juvenile pelage. The change begins at six to eight weeks of age and is usually concurrent with the eruption of the second milk molars.

Infants in natal coat produce strong reactions in adults of both sexes. Sight of such an infant causes marked agitation—*e.g.* if such an infant is carried by a human foster-mother—in adults of both sexes whether wild or captive. Wild monkeys will approach much closer in such circumstances than at other times and may adopt threatening gestures with vocal manifestations. The infant's colour and appearance would appear to serve the function of stimulating the adults of its kind to preserve it. Any infant left alone, dropped by its mother or otherwise separated from her, will be retrieved—sometimes even by males. A wounded female carrying a baby will push the infant away from her if she is incapacitated or about to die. Clearly this reaction will benefit the species, enabling the infant to survive if retrieved by a lactational foster-mother. As soon as the juvenile coat is assumed, the other members of the troop show no particular interest in it. Booth reports this behaviour in *Cercopithecus* and *Colobus*, while Jay mentions some similar responses in *Semnopithecus*. I have myself observed the marked agitation, particularly in adult females of *Kasi senex*, when faced with newborn infants of their kind (even of a different subspecies) carried by a human foster-mother. They attempt to seize the infant, and to fondle it—which they do in a most gentle manner if permitted. In *Macaca sinica*, handling of an infant or removal from its parents arouses considerable animosity in the whole troop, which responds with aggressive gestures and vocalizations (co-operative aggressive behaviour).

Before leaving the subject of maternal relations, the existence of paternal care of infants has also been confirmed, especially by Itani (1959), in wild ranging Japanese macaques (*Macaca fuscata*). During the delivery season, high-ranking males protect one-year or sometimes two-year-old juveniles in the same way as the mothers do. The relationship exists between a given infant and a given adult male and has a definite duration. The adult hugs the infant, walks with it, and may carry it on his loins. When sitting, he will groom it and, if danger threatens, will protect it.

Interrelations between Juveniles.—Juveniles freed from their mothers after weaning spend much of their time consorting with other members of the troop of approximately their own age. They play together and feed together. Play consists mainly of chasing one another in mock attack and retreat, thus serving to equip them for their adult rôles. For example, juvenile Bonnet monkeys (*Macaca radiata*) in India are said by Nolte (1955 *a*) to play in flocks. They learn the nature of their environment by curiosity, exploring by vision, touch, hearing and by sniffing. Altmann (1962) found little evidence of olfactory exploration in semi-wild Rhesus (*M. mulatta*), though agreeing that social contact would be associated with sniffing the consort in the oral and/or ano-genital area.

Relations with elders show little evidence of dominance or submission until puberty supervenes. Agonistic behaviour towards adults (*e.g.* tail pulling and other forms of teasing) is tolerated by the latter to a remarkable extent. This is recorded for baboons (*e.g.* by Hall), for Bonnet monkeys (by Nolte), and has been witnessed by myself in *Macaca sinica* and several species of langurs ; in the latter instance even by members of a different species or genus from that of the juvenile delinquent!

On the other hand, reprimanding youngsters who become too offensive may also occur, *e.g.* in Hamadryas baboons (*Papio hamadryas*), where adults quieten juveniles by biting a hand, forearm, or less often a foot, the severity of the reaction being a criterion of rank order (Kummer). Females of all species so far studied become petulant with persistent misbehaviour of their offspring and will reprimand by slapping, mild biting or other minatory behaviour.

Among procedures adopted in social communication are several forms of prepubertal sex play, *e.g.* mounting without sexual significance. This has been reported in *M. mulatta* by Maslow (1936), Carpenter (1942), and Altmann (1962), who interprets it as a greeting. Nolte (1955 *b*) has also reported it in *M. radiata*, whilst in baboons it has been described by Zuckerman, Hall, Washburn *et al.* Prepubertal mounting is not associated with copulation, though pelvic movements may be involved. It may be homosexual or heterosexual and, in captive groups, may occur between juveniles of different species, as, for example, between a male macaque and a male langur (personal observation). In the absence of consorts, single juveniles sublime these social trends into autoerotic behaviour ; by approaches to human contacts or digit sucking. Digit sucking (fingers, thumbs or toes) is considered by Hines (1942), and in more detail by Altmann (1962) in the Rhesus. He regards it as of no communicative significance, but a by-product of the social tendency. He illustrates digit sucking in youngsters still being carried by their mothers. (For orthodontic effects see Swindler and Sassouni, 1962.)

In solitary confinement digit sucking may occupy hours of the animal's time and frequently alternates with or is accompanied by various forms of automasochism, involving jerky limb movements, biting a hand, foot or other accessible bodily part—at least in macaques and baboons.

Sometimes older juveniles occur solitarily in the wild. These are of such age as to have become a challenge to more dominant males within their group and have been expelled therefrom. Haddow (1952) has gone into the problem of solitary monkeys, which are encountered with some frequency in several East African species. Although these have usually been interpreted as worn-out old males or younger animals driven out by powerful adults, in fact out of fifteen solitary Schmidt's monkeys (*Cercopithecus ascanius schmidti*) ten were adult males, three old males and one an adult female, all in good condition with no disability.

DISTRIBUTION

Cynomorph monkeys range over the whole of the area occupied by the Catarrhini in so far as they occur not only alongside the anthropoid apes, but also extend to all parts of the Old World (mainly the tropics) whence extant Primates have been recorded (*vide antea*, p. 50). Fossil cynomorphs too occur side by side with fossil anthropomorphs so that no additional discussion is required here.

TAXONOMY

The Cynomorpha, so named by Huxley (1871, p. 397), are today more generally known by the substitute title Cercopithecoidea, introduced by Simpson (1931, p. 271 ; 1945, p. 66). Prior to Huxley's time they constituted merely a tribe or section of the all-embracing family Simiadae. Thus I. Geoffroy referred to them as tribe 2 Cynopithecina, which he divided into two sections (not specifically named), according to whether they possessed simple or sacculated stomachs.

Gray (1870), though retaining the single Old World family Simiadae, elaborated the subdivision by recognizing an anthropoid and a quadrupedal section, each with several tribes ; thus

Family SIMIADAE

Anthropoid Section	Tribe 1	Simiina (great apes)
	Tribe 2	Hylobatina (gibbons)
Quadrupedal Section	Tribe 3	Presbytina (langurs and Colobus monkeys)
	Tribe 4	Cercopithecina (guenons, mangabeys, macaques)
	Tribe 5	Cynocephalina (baboons)

On face value this would appear to be an advanced classification foreshadowing that now adopted, but his fourth tribe, Cercopithecina, contained not only the guenons, but also mangabeys, macaques and the Gelada, while his fifth tribe, Cynocephalina, consisted solely of the baboons (then designated by the generic name *Cynocephalus*).

Mivart's (1873) classification is very similar. He still used the all-embracing family name Simiadae, but recognized within it three sub-families, (i) Simiinae (for the anthropoid apes), (ii) Semnopithecinae (equivalent to Gray's Presbytina) and (iii) Cynopithecinae (including Gray's fourth and fifth tribes).

In Flower and Lydekker's (1891) work on mammals the family Simiidae is restricted to the anthropoid apes. The title Cercopithecidae is introduced for all the cynomorphs, which are subgrouped into the same two sub-families as recognized by Mivart, but with the name Cercopithecinae (Blanford, 1888, p. 10), substituted for Cynopithecinae. A footnote (p. 724) also gives Colobinae * as an alternative to Semnopithecinae. This scheme was followed by Forbes (1894) in his monographic revision of the Primates, by Beddard (1909 *b*), and also by Elliot (1913), who, however, having adopted the generic name *Lasiopyga* for the guenons, instead of the time-honoured *Cercopithecus*,

---

* Usually quoted (*e.g.* by Simpson) as of Elliot (1913), but clearly based on Blyth's (1875) usage.

was constrained also to change the derived family and sub-family names to Lasiopygidae and Lasiopyginae. He also accepted the alternative name Colobinae as the sub-family title for the group possessing sacculated stomachs.

Pocock (1926) was the first to promote the two divisions of the Cynomorpha to full family rank, under the names Cercopithecidae and Colobidae. His action was accepted by some (*e.g.* Stiles and Nolan, 1929 ; Chasen, 1940), but by no means all subsequent authors. Current classifications, *e.g.* Simpson (1945), Ellerman and Morrison-Scott (1951), Vallois (1955) and Fiedler (1956), uphold the earlier subfamilial status.

Meantime, Rode (1937, 1938 *a*) had followed Pocock's arrangement, using, however, Semnopithecidae for the Colobidae. In a later publication (1938 *b*), however, he made a further subdivision of the Cercopithecidae (*sensu stricto*) by splitting off a family, Papionidae, to include the baboons (*Papio* and *Theropithecus*). This seemed, at the time, an unwarranted procedure, although it has been followed by Malbrant and Maclatchy (1949) and by Malbrant (1952) who change the spelling to Papioïdae.

More recent work, notably by Booth (1957 *in litt.*) (whose views were endorsed (also *in litt.*) by myself), has emphasized the contrasts between the more generalized *Cercopithecus* and its immediate allies (*Miopithecus* and *Erythrocebus*) on the one hand, and the more advanced and specialized baboons on the other. In contrast to Rode's arrangement, however, the macaques and mangabeys fall into line with the baboons rather than the guenons.

Booth's proposed classification of the Cynomorpha was therefore :

Superfamily Cynomorpha
> Family I. Cercopithecidae—simple stomach ; cheek-pouches present.
>> *Subfamily Cercopithecinae* ; Cercopithecidae with the cheek-teeth not greatly swollen at the base ; molars with never more than 4 cusps ; generally no female catamenial swelling ; Africa only.
>> *Subfamily Papioninae* ; Cercopithecidae with upper cheek-teeth greatly swollen at the base ; 5 cusps on $M_{\overline{3}}$; generally some form of catamenial swelling or at least some colour change in the sexual skin of the female.
> Family II. Colobidae—sacculated stomach ; cheek-pouches lacking (no further subdivision above generic level).

This scheme has been adopted by Sanderson (1957) in a popular work in which anglicized labels are used for the three cynomorph groups (Cercopithecoids, Cynopithecoids and Coloboids).

The only valid argument against adoption of Booth's scheme lies in the transitional status of the genus *Allenopithecus*, which Booth, like all earlier writers who treated of this genus, included alongside *Cercopithecus*. As has been described by the present writer (Hill, 1964), this monkey, although in general appearance guenon-like (it was originally described as a species of *Cercopithecus*) yet shows many features in which it approaches the macaque-mangabey-baboon assemblage—notably in body-proportions, molar characters, external ear, some details of the male genitalia and the occurrence of catamenial swelling. However, for the present, Booth's classification may conveniently be upheld, with reservations on the exact status of *Allenopithecus* and with the tentative substitution of Cynopithecinae for the subfamily containing the baboons, etc.—on the presumption that the genus *Cynopithecus* is valid; see, however, below p. 208.

N

Systematic List

INFRAORDER CATARRHINI E. Geoffroy, 1812
Superfamily CERCOPITHECOIDEA Simpson, 1931
Family I. PARAPITHECIDAE Schlosser, 1911

Genus *Parapithecus* Schlosser, 1911

1. *Parapithecus fraasi* Schlosser, 1911

(Fossil early Catarrhini *incertae sedis*)
Genus *Amphipithecus* Colbert, 1937

1. *Amphipithecus mogaungensis* Colbert, 1937

Genus *Oligopithecus* Simons, 1962

1. *Oligopithecus savagei* Simons, 1962

Genus *Apidium* Osborn, 1908

1. *Apidium phiomense* Osborn, 1908
2. *Apidium moustafai* Simons, 1962

Genus *Pondaungia* Pilgrim, 1927

1. *Pondaungia cotteri* Pilgrim, 1927

Family II. CERCOPITHECIDAE Gray, 1821 (restricted)
Subfamily Cercopithecinae Blanford, 1888 (restricted)

Genus *Cercopithecus* Linnaeus, 1758

I. Superspecies *C. mitis* Wolf, 1822

1. *C. mitis* Wolf, 1822

(a) *C. m. mitis* Wolf, 1822
(b) *C. m. boutourlinii* Giglioli, 1887
(c) *C. m. stuhlmanni* Matschie, 1893
(d) *C. m. doggetti* Pocock, 1907
(e) *C. m. maesi* Lönnberg, 1919
(f) *C. m. kandti* Matschie, 1905
(g) *C. m. schoutedeni* Schwarz, 1928
(h) *C. m. opisthostictus* Sclater, 1893

2. *C. albogularis* Sykes, 1831

(a) *C. a. albotorquatus* Pousargues, 1896
(b) *C. a. albogularis* Sykes, 1831
(c) *C. a. monoides* Geoffroy, 1841

(d) *C. a. phylax* Schwarz, 1927
(e) *C. a. kibonotensis* Lönnberg, 1910
(f) *C. a. kolbi* Neumann, 1902
(g) *C. a. moloneyi* Sclater, 1893
(h) *C. a. francescae* Thomas, 1902
(i) *C. a. nyasae* Schwarz, 1928
(j) *C. a. erythrarchus* Peters, 1852
(k) *C. a. schwarzi* Roberts, 1931
(l) *C. a. samango* Wahlberg, 1844

3. *C. nictitans* Linnaeus, 1766

(a) *C. n. nictitans* Linnaeus, 1766
(b) *C. n. martini* Waterhouse, 1841
(c) *C. n. stampflii* Jentink, 1888

II. Superspecies *C. l'hoesti* Sclater, 1898

4. *C. l'hoesti* Sclater, 1898
5. *C. preussi* Matschie, 1898

III. Superspecies *C. mona* Schreber, 1774

6. *C. campbelli* Waterhouse, 1838

(a) *C. c. campbelli* Waterhouse 1838
(b) *C. c. lowei* Thomas, 1923

7. *C. mona* Schreber, 1774
8. *C. wolfi* Meyer, 1891

(a) *C. w. wolfi* Meyer, 1891
(b) *C. w. pyrogaster* Lönnberg, 1919
(c) *C. w. elegans* Dubois et Matschie, 1912

9. *C. denti* Thomas, 1907
10. *C. pogonias* Bennett, 1833

(a) *C. p. pogonias* Bennett, 1833
(b) *C. p. grayi* Fraser, 1850
(c) *C. p. nigripes* du Chaillu, 1860
(d) *C. p. schwarzianus* Schouteden, 1946

IV. Superspecies *C. petaurista* Schreber, 1775

11. *C. petaurista* Schreber, 1775

(a) *C. p. petaurista* Schreber, 1775
(b) *C. p. büttikoferi* Jentink, 1886

12. *C. ascanius* Audebert, 1799

(a) *C. a. ascanius* Audebert, 1799
(b) *C. a. katangae* Lönnberg, 1919
(c) *C. a. whitesidei* Thomas, 1909
(d) *C. a. montanus* Lorenz, 1914
(e) *C. a. schmidti* Matschie, 1892

13. *C. erythrotis* Waterhouse, 1838
    (a) *C. e. erythrotis* Waterhouse, 1838
    (b) *C. e. camerunensis* Hayman, 1940
    (c) *C. e. sclateri* Pocock, 1904

14. *C. erythrogaster* Gray, 1866

V. Superspecies *C. cephus* Linnaeus, 1766
  15. *C. cephus* Linnaeus, 1758
    (a) *C. c. cephus* Linnaeus, 1758
    (b) *C. c. cephodes* Pocock, 1907

VI. Superspecies *C. hamlyni* Pocock, 1907
  16. *C. hamlyni* Pocock, 1907

VII. Superspecies *C. neglectus* Schlegel, 1876
  17. *C. neglectus* Schlegel, 1876

VIII. Superspecies *C. diana* Linnaeus, 1758
  18. *C. diana* Linnaeus, 1758
    (a) *C. d. diana* Linnaeus, 1758
    (b) *C. d. roloway* Schreber, 1774
    (c) *C. d. dryas* Schwarz, 1932

IX. Superspecies *C. aethiops* Linnaeus, 1758
  19. *C. aethiops* Linnaeus, 1758

aethiops group
    (a) *C. a. aethiops* Linnaeus, 1758
    (b) *C. a. hilgerti* O. Neumann, 1902
    (c) *C. a. ellenbecki* O. Neumann, 1902
    (d) *C. a. zavattarii* de Beaux, 1943

tantalus group
    (e) *C. a. tantalus* Ogilby, 1841
    (f) *C. a. marrensis* Thomas & Wroughton, 1923
    (g) *C. a. budgetti* Pocock, 1907

20. *C. pygerythrus* F. Cuvier, 1821

pygerythrus group
    (a) *C. p. centralis* O. Neumann, 1900
    (b) *C. p. arenarius* Heller, 1913
    (c) *C. p. callidus* Hollister, 1912
    (d) *C. p. johnstoni* Pocock, 1907
    (e) *C. p. excubitor* Schwarz, 1926
    (f) *C. p. nesiotes* Schwarz, 1926
    (g) *C. p. rufoviridis* I. Geoffroy, 1842
    (h) *C. p. whytei* Pocock, 1907
    (i) *C. p. cloeti* Roberts, 1931
    (j) *C. p. ngamiensis* Roberts, 1932
    (k) *C. p. marjoriae* Bradfield, 1936
    (l) *C. p. pygerythrus* F. Cuvier, 1821

cynosuros group   (m) *C. p. cynosuros* Scopoli, 1786

    21. *C. sabaeus* Linnaeus, 1766

    Superspecies *incertae sedis*

    22. *C. asnoti* Pilgrim, 1913

Genus *Miopithecus* I. Geoffroy, 1842

    1. *M. talapoin* Schreber, 1774

      (a) *M. t. talapoin* Schreber, 1774
      (b) *M. t. ansorgei* Pocock, 1907
      (c) *M. t. vleeschowersi* Poll, 1940
      (d) *M. t. pilettei* Lönnberg, 1919

Genus *Allenopithecus* Lang, 1923

    1. *A. nigroviridis* Pocock, 1907

Genus *Erythrocebus* Trouessart, 1897

    1. *E. patas* Schreber, 1775

      (a) *E. p. patas* Schreber, 1775
      (b) *E. p. villiersi* Dekeyser, 1950
      (c) *E. p. pyrronotus* Hemprich et Ehrenberg, 1829
      (d) *E. p. baumstarki* Matschie, 1905

Family I—PARAPITHECIDAE* Schlosser, 1911

A family erected by Schlosser for the reception of his genus *Parapithecus* from a study of which he came to the conclusion that, although the remains pertained to an Old World Primate, they could not be accommodated in any of the surviving families.

The family occupies a basal position in the evolution of the Catarrhini on account of its many primitive features, some of which have been regarded by Schlosser and others as annectant with the Tarsioidea, whilst others (*e.g.* Werth, 1918 ; Patterson, 1954 ; Heberer, 1956) suggest an ancestral position for the highest Primates (including the Hominoidea of Simpson, 1945, who transfers the family to that superfamily) and especially of the anthropoid apes *via Pliopithecus* and the later fossil group represented by *Oreopithecus bambolii*. Patterson (1954) expresses his views thus, " It is more likely than not that these forms (*i.e. Parapithecus* and *Pliopithecus*) arose from some anaptomorphid stock, and very possibly, that they, or rather the group they represent, were broadly ancestral to the Hominoidea and the Cercopithecoidea ".

Opinions differ with regard to the exact position of the family largely due to the morphological divergences expressed by the molars in contrast to the front teeth.

Genus *PARAPITHECUS* Schlosser, 1911 †

A new genus erected by Schlosser for the fossil Primate mandible described by him as *P. fraasi* from Oligocene strata of the Fayûm, Egypt. Type : *P. fraasi*, Schlosser, 1911.

CHARACTERS

Dental formula : $I.\frac{?}{2}$, $C.\frac{?}{1}$, $P.\frac{?}{2}$, $M.\frac{?}{3}$.

Teeth arranged in continuous closed series, *i.e.* lacking diastemata, and all approximately the same height, *i.e.* no prominence of canine beyond crowns of its neighbours.

---

* *Beitr. Paläont Geol. Österreich-ungarns*, xxiv. 58.
† *Ibid.*

Tooth rows straight but strongly convergent anteriorly (presumably also the upper teeth similarly arranged).

Incisors slightly procumbent, conical ; canine small, with conical crown ; premolars two-rooted.

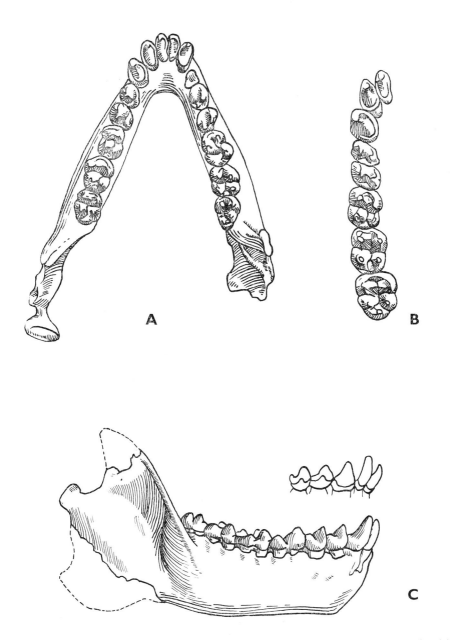

FIG. 15.—*Parapithecus fraasi* : A, mandible from above ; B, details of mandibular dentition from the occlusal aspect ; C, mandible from the right side. Based on figures by Schlosser (1911) and Werth (1918)

1. *PARAPITHECUS FRAASI* Schlosser, 1911 *

TYPE, LOCALITY AND HORIZON: Lower Oligocene beds of the Fayûm deposits, Egypt. Type and only known specimen, a well-preserved nearly complete mandible with full permanent dentition (except for right canine) in Stuttgart Museum of Natural History.

HISTORICAL

The type specimen was collected by Richard Markgraff working on behalf of Professor Eberhard Fraas of Stuttgart, during an expedition sponsored by the American Museum of Natural History of New York. Fraas deputed the work of studying the material to Max Schlosser, whose observations were later extended by Emil Werth (1918). Werth attempted to solve the problem of the systematic and phylogenetic position of *Parapithecus*. Then followed the observations of Gregory (1916, 1920) and Mollison (1924), again dealing with the systematic position and phylogenetic relationships of the genus. Recently Kälin (1960) has re-examined the original material and arrived at conclusions which necessitate some modification of earlier views.

CHARACTERS

MANDIBLE.—Size very small, the smallest of any Old World simian, comparable with that of the New World *Saimiri*. Rami converging rapidly to symphysis at an angle of 33° (Werth). Symphyseal region sloping abruptly downwards and backwards ending below $P.\overline{3}$. (Symphysis not completely co-ossified (Mollison), and marked on inner side by a distinct furrow.) Horizontal ramus shallow; two small mental foramina, one behind the other, midway between alveolar and inferior margin at level of $P.\overline{3}$. Ascending ramus stout, backwardly inclined, broad but not deep, with high recumbent coronoid process extending considerably above level of condyle, from which it is separated by a broad, shallow sigmoid notch (reminiscent of *Loris* and *Nycticebus* according to Abel, 1931). Condyle low placed, broadened transversely and widely separated from its fellow, indicating a broad cranial base, and probably therefore a globular brain-case. Angular region damaged bilaterally but sufficient remaining on one side to indicate downward and backward extension to form a broad, truncate lamina separated from inferior border of horizontal ramus and hinder border of vertical ramus by concave margins (Werth's fig. 7).

Shortening of the tooth row, and hence of the anterior part of the horizontal ramus, suggests reduction of the muzzle in the earliest Old World Primates, the tooth reduction being secondary rather than primary, *i.e.* certain elements ($P.\overline{1}$, $P.\overline{2}$) were dropped by overcrowding in the reduced

* *Loc. cit.* p. 59.

alveolar borders ; a process which accounts also for the reduction in size of the canines.

DENTITION

Dental formula : $I.\frac{?}{2}, C.\frac{?}{1}, P.\frac{?}{2}, M.\frac{?}{3}$, *i.e.* as in typical Catarrhini (Schwalbe, 1915 ; Gregory, 1916 ; Werth, 1918), though originally assessed by Schlosser somewhat doubtfully as $I.\overline{1}, C.\overline{1}, P.\overline{3}, M.\overline{3}$.[*]

Reasons given by Gregory (1916) for altering Schlosser's estimate of the dental formula are :

1. Resemblance of the second tooth of the series to $I.\overline{2}$ of *Pliopithecus* and the separation of its crown by a small cleft from the tooth identified by Gregory as the canine.

2. Comparison of the premolars with those of *Propliopithecus* and *Pliopithecus* inclines to the view that there are two and not three premolars in *Parapithecus*, although their crowns are more primitive (*i.e.* less bicuspid) than in the later types.

3. The tooth now identified as the canine (by Schlosser regarded as a premolar) is more caniniform than the anterior premolars and compares well with the canine of *Propliopithecus*.

The upper dental formula may reasonably be inferred to correspond numerically with that in the mandible, thus conforming with all other Old World monkeys recent and fossil, with the exception of *Amphipithecus* (*vide infra*, p. 191).

DIMENSIONS (in millimetres) of *Parapithecus* compared with the other early primates based on observations of Werth :

	Tarsioidea		Pithecoidea			
	Necrolemur antiquus	*Microchoerus erinaceus*	*Parapithecus fraasi*	*Propliopithecus haeckeli*	*Pliopithecus antiquus*	*Symphalangus syndactylus* (Siamang gibbon)
Mandibular tooth row, $I.\overline{1}$–$M.\overline{3}$	16	—	25	30	43	51
Molar series	8	11	12·5	15	20	24
Mandibular length from apices of $I.\overline{1}$ to condyle	28	—	36·5	—	—	86

$I.\overline{1}$, $I.\overline{2}$ slightly procumbent, with narrow crowns ; $I.\overline{2}$ much larger and twice as robust as $I.\overline{1}$ and with more conical crown.

Canine small, narrower than $I.\overline{2}$, not tusk-like, with smooth conical crown, its apex not projecting beyond level of $I.\overline{2}$ or $P.\overline{3}$, and with an incipient basal cusp posteriorly and a well-marked lingual cingulum. A single root

[*] Wrongly quoted by Gregory (1916) as $I.\overline{1}, C.\overline{2}, P.\overline{3}, M.\overline{3}$, but corrected in his 1920 publication.

which shows radiographically but a single root canal (Kälin).   P.$\overline{_3}$, P.$\overline{_4}$ two-rooted, the hinder roots somewhat medially directed, crowns incipiently bicuspid, a large buccal cusp and a low postero-medial cusp, also a low posterior cingulum.   Kälin recognizes a small tubercle intercalated between cingulum and base of principal cone disto-lingually and another on the buccal side (disto-labial ; Talonidhöcker).   These have apparently been overlooked by earlier students, though Werth noted some evidence on P.$\overline{_4}$.

M.$\overline{_1}$, M.$\overline{_2}$ with low, narrow, five-cusped crowns arranged as in the anthropomorph catarrhines, *i.e.* with protoconid, metaconid, hypoconid, entoconid and hypoconulid or mesoconid, the paraconid being absent ; trigonid basin small and talonid large.   The four principal cusps arranged in transverse pairs with metaconid to the lingual side and somewhat posterior to protoconid to which it connects by a low ridge (protolophid) ; entoconid slightly posterior to enlarged hypoconid ; hypoconulid median in position.   All cusps low, rounded, without wrinkling of enamel ; cingulum present on buccal side.   M.$\overline{_3}$ < M.$\overline{_2}$, similar, but with a narrower talonid, and, according to Kälin, a tuberculum sextum.

Probable nature of food as deduced from the dentition, especially the small size and absence of laniary specialization of canines, and the blunt non-sectorial form of premolar and molar crowns, excludes specialized carnivorous diet.   Gently sloping incisors and low cusps of cheek-teeth suggest a mixed diet possibly including fruits, insects, birds' eggs and small reptiles.

COMMENTS

Gregory (1916), whose opinion has been followed by most recent writers, placed *Parapithecus* as ancestral to the highest primates (anthropoid apes and Man) and as itself derived directly from the Eocene insectivorous lemuroids (*i.e.* those now included under Tarsioidea).   Schlosser had already suggested a connection with the Anaptomorphidae (= Microchoeridae *nobis*).   Gregory avers that such relationship may eventually be demonstrated and goes on to say : " The molars and premolars do indeed suggest derivation from a far more primitive insectivorous type, represented in *Omomys* sp. as figured by Matthew (1915, p. 449), but in this otherwise very primitive member of the Anaptomorphidae the incisors are apparently not fitted to give rise to those of *Parapithecus*.   *Anaptomorphus aemulus* has the right dental formula, 2, 1, 2, 3 (Matthew, 1915, p. 457), but in the absence of intermediate types it would be rash to regard it as ancestral to *Parapithecus*.   *Tetonius homunculus* is aberrantly specialized in many characters, and the same is true of all other known genera of the Anaptomorphidae, which as a family appear to be allied with *Tarsius* rather than with the catarrhine series."

In his later work (1922) Gregory indicates that *Parapithecus* lacks the aberrant specializations of most of the known fossil Tarsioidea which would exclude them, but not *Parapithecus*, from direct participation as ancestors of the Anthropoidea. The only feature detracting from this important position for *Parapithecus* is perhaps the too conic form of the lower molar cusps.

The form of the mandible, especially its depressed height, is a primitive feature which *Parapithecus* shares with the Hylobatidae and separates both sharply from the larger Pongidae both recent and fossil.

Returning to the difficulty of estimating the dental formula, it may be noted that Piveteau (1957, p. 167) has reverted to Schlosser's original determination, using this as argument against the primate status of *Parapithecus*—also questioned by Hürzeler (1958), who thinks there may be affinity with the Condylarthra, *e.g. Phenacodus*. Simons (1959), however, remarks that, even if Schlosser's formula were the correct one, this alone would not be inconsonant with an expected formula for an Oligocene primate of tarsioid affinities. He further adds : " It is unlikely that any final judgment as to whether the second or third tooth in the dental series of *Parapithecus* is the true canine can be reached at present. The second incisor and canine of *Callithrix* (=*Hapale*), for example, are subequal in size and have the same basic conformation. Consequently it is largely by extrapolation from the upper dentition and the dentitions of other ceboids that they can be identified in this New World primate." Simons declares such extrapolations impossible at present for *Parapithecus*, but recalls that two undoubted European Eocene Primates (*Caenopithecus*, *Protoadapis*) have a lower dental formula, $\overline{1}. \overline{1}. \overline{3}. \overline{3}.$ Moreover there is little in the cusp arrangement of the cheek-teeth of *Parapithecus* to suggest it is other than a Primate. Typical condylarths never show such reduced antemolar series, while any resemblance between certain condylarths (*e.g. Phenacodus* and *Hyopsodus*) is at most marginal.

Kälin (1960) analyses the mixture of characters of *Parapithecus* into three categories : (i) Primitive characters which, assuming we are dealing with a Primate, would place it among the most primitive of the group. These are referred to as typhophenic features ; they include the open symphysis, the extreme posterior divergence of the mandibular rami and their small depth and the identical length of $P.\overline{3}$ and $P.\overline{4}$. (ii) Apparently advanced characters foreshadowing conditions in the Hylobatidae and Pongidae, especially the bunodont structure of the molar crowns with their five cusps (with a tuberculum sextum on $M.\overline{3}$), the loss of the anterior crest on the trigonid and the increase in size (except on $M.\overline{3}$) of the talonid and its elevation to the same level of the trigonid. Kälin believes these features superficial and not susceptible to interpretation as the beginning of an orthogenetic line leading *via Propliopithecus* to the modern gibbons. (iii) Specialized features peculiar to the genus. Here are arranged the peculiar features of the anterior dentition and the identity in size and peculiarities of the two premolar crowns.

The peculiarities of the front teeth, in Kälin's view, do not permit relegation of *Parapithecus* even provisionally to the Primates. Nevertheless the resemblances of the molars to those of *Propliopithecus* seem to indicate a certain parallelism or the expression of a similar evolutionary trend. *Parapithecus* represents a unique group characterized by a combination of characters and these permit the following conclusions to be drawn :

1. The conclusion of Schlosser that *Parapithecus* is derived from an early tarsioid is untenable.

2. Specializations of the front teeth, and especially of the premolars, preclude *Parapithecus* from an ancestral position in respect of *Propliopithecus*.

3. The advanced condition of the molar crowns has surpassed the condition required for a primitive catarrhine monkey and therefore represents an evolutionary parallelism with that undergone by the higher catarrhines, *i.e.* indicates an early evolutionary divergence of two separate phyletic lines.

4. The form of the mandible presents extremely primitive characters realized also among the more primitive prosimians, but none of the characters concerned are of phyletic value permitting any direct genetic relationship therewith.

5. Taking cognizance of the parallelism in molar evolution, the hypothesis is justified to regard *Parapithecus* as representing a family of Primates evolved from the same " champ transitoire " (morphogenetisches Übergangsfeld) of evolutionary processes by which the Pongidae, Hominidae, as well as the Cercopithecidae surpassed the structural level represented by the prosimians.

PARAPITHECIDAE INCERTAE SEDIS

Reference may conveniently be made here to a frontal bone, so far unnamed, from the Oligocene of the Fayûm deposits, recently described as " an anthropoid frontal " by Simons (1959). The specimen was originally collected in 1908 by R. Markgraff and sent by him in 1909 to the American Museum of Natural History (on whose behalf he had been employed during their 1906–1907 expedition).

The frontal bone came from the upper part of the Fayûm fluvio-marine formation which is associated with remains of *Arsinoitherium*, *Metaphiomys beadnelli*, *Apidium*, *Apterodon*, *Ancodon* and *Megalohyrax* (Osborn, 1908). The frontal was recovered in loosely consolidated quartz arenite similar to that covering the other fossils. It was finally prepared by Simons for his 1959 report. The only previous published reference is apparently that of Gregory (1922, p. 289), who declared it " resembles closely the corresponding part of some of the smaller Cercopithecinae ".

In size the bone is considerably smaller than that of any recent catarrhine Primate, being little larger than that of a marmoset. Direct comparisons are therefore difficult, but sufficient evidence exists to show advance over the Eocene lemuroids and tarsioids. Primitive, however, is the midline posterior convergence of the temporal ridges thereby showing resemblance to *Notharctus*, *Hemiacodon* and *Necrolemur*, although the ridges are not as distinct as in any of these, and there is considerably greater frontal expansion anteriorly, greater in fact, than in the platyrrhines. The bone is too small to pertain to any of the other hitherto described Fayûm Primates (*e.g. Moeripithecus, Propliopithecus*), except possibly *Parapithecus* or *Apidium*.

FRONTAL BONE

Dorsal Aspect.—Marked temporal ridges course backwards and mediad from the external angular processes, converging behind at the fronto-parietal suture. Between them and the supraorbital margins is a triangular flat, slightly depressed area, showing no trace of metopic suture. A small foramen occurs on the right 4 mm. medial to the tip of the external angular process, behind the temporal crest. Numerous other smaller foramina affect the antero-dorsal part of the bone. Posteriorly the frontal ends in a short central spine, lateral to which are broad margins for articulation with the parietals comparable with the dimensions seen in *Hapale*.

Rostrum.—Naso-frontal sutures are distinct, meeting in a point 2 mm. short of the medial ends of the supraorbital ridges. The nasals therefore lacked the posterior expansions seen in some lemuroids. In the vertical plane between the sutures is the anterior edge of the nasal spine of the frontal. A fronto-maxillary suture ending above in an S-shaped curve is marked on the left anterior end of the rostrum and the position is indicative of absence of lachrymo-nasal contact seen in recent lemurs and some ceboids. Interorbital width is proportionately less than in some ceboids and suggests a foreshortened face comparable with that of *Hapale* or *Tarsius*.

The Orbital Portion.—Remaining parts of the orbital walls indicate orbits larger than those of comparable-sized ceboids, while the degree of forward direction, as judged by the plane of the supraorbital margins, was somewhat less than in *Leontideus*. At the centre the supraorbital margin is straight, but towards the rostrum and the external angular process it bends down sharply, rather as in *Notharctus*, though, to a lesser degree, it occurs in the hapalid skull. Indications therefore are against the smoothly rounded orbit such as that of *Tarsius* or *Nycticebus*. The orbit was, moreover, not sufficiently large in proportion to suggest nocturnal habits. A large foramen occurs antero-medially in the orbital roof and connects with the superior sagittal· sinus. Anterior and posterior ethmoidal canals are preserved on the right, but insufficient of the orbital plate remains to show the site of the optic foramen. Sufficient of the medial wall remains posteriorly on the right to indicate a very compressed interorbital septum. This feature separates the present form from all known Eocene primates, with the possible exceptions of *Necrolemur*, *Pseudoloris* and *Tetonius*.

On the lateral wall of the orbital aperture a deep vertical groove occurs, coursing medially at its upper end ; a suspicion of this occurs among other Primates only in some Hapalidae.

A rugose fronto-malar sutural border is present indicating complete lateral closure of the orbit, *i.e.* diagnostic at least of pithecoid rather than prosimian status.

Inner Aspect and Brain.—With the orbital plate oriented horizontally as it normally is both in platyrrhine and catarrhine monkeys, a highly vaulted frontal arc is indicated, more so than in any of these forms, with the possible exception of *Ateles*. On the antero-medial part of the anterior cranial fossa the juga cerebralia, normally found in Man and anthropoid apes, is represented merely by a gently rounded raised area. A shallow groove marks the site of the attachment of the falx cerebri—not a median ridge. The groove ends near the rostral margin of the posterior opening into the olfactory fossa. Above it two foramina communicate with the internal sinus canals.

Olfactory bulbs were evidently much reduced relative to the size of the frontal lobes, thus contrasting strongly with Eocene Primates like *Adapis* (Clark, 1945) or *Necrolemur* (Hurzeler, 1948). Moreover, instead of a single olfactory nerve each side as, for example, in *Tarsius*, there were evidently multiple fascicles ; at least three paired bundles can be made out on the endocast. No convolutions are detectible on the frontal lobe of the endocast, but they could have been obscured by dura as in *Hapale*. A Sylvian fissure is indicated by the manner of curving of the right lateral and ventral extremity of the endocast. A few blood vessels can be defined on the endocast traceable to the fronto-parietal suture.

Post-cranial Skeleton

Possibly pertaining to the same animal is a right calcaneus derived from the same horizon. In size equivalent to that of *Leontideus*, it agrees well structurally with calcanea referred to *Adapis* and *Notharctus* rather than other mammalian genera represented in the Fayûm beds.

Comment

Simons' (1962, p. 9, 1963, p. 105) latest opinion anent the above-described frontal bone is that it may pertain to *Oligopithecus* (*infra*, p. 195) as it is conformable as regards size and geological horizon ; but he admits that it may represent an otherwise unknown pithecoid Primate.

Alignment with *Apidium* or *Parapithecus* is ruled out, in spite of their suitable size, in view of the non-anthropoid features of their anterior dentitions. *Propliopithecus* and *Moeripithecus* are too large to have possessed a frontal of this size.

FOSSIL EARLY CATARRHINI INCERTAE SEDIS

Genus *AMPHIPITHECUS* Colbert, 1937 *

A fossil Primate genus from the Upper Eocene Pondaung beds of Burma and therefore even older than *Parapithecus*, from which it differs in its larger size and the retention of three premolars.   Type and only known species :

1. *AMPHIPITHECUS MOGAUNGENSIS* Colbert, 1937 *

TYPE LOCALITY AND HORIZON : Upper Eocene Pondaung beds of Burma (valley of the R. Irrawaddy and its tributaries).   Type, a part of a left mandibular ramus with P.$\overline{3}$, P.$\overline{4}$ and M.$\overline{1}$ and roots of P.$\overline{2}$ and canine.   Collected by Dr. Barnum Brown, half a mile north-west of Mogaung, now in American Museum of Natural History, New York (No. 32520).

The specimen was first diagnosed and briefly described in 1937 by Colbert, who gave a more detailed account in the following year.   He pointed out that the specimen fell into a very different category from another derived earlier from the same beds and described ten years previously by Pilgrim (1927) under the name *Pondaungia* (*vide infra*, p. 200).   The latter is doubtfully a Primate, whereas Colbert claims his *Amphipithecus* as definitely so, showing evidence indeed which seemed conclusive for its being regarded as a primitive anthropoid.

CHARACTERS

In size the fragment suggests a monkey slightly larger than the Fayûm *Propliopithecus* and therefore much in excess of *Parapithecus*.

Depth of mandibular ramus	. .	19.5 mm.
Length of M.$\overline{1}$	. . . .	6.3
Index	. . . . .	31

i.e. depth of ramus approximately thrice the length of M.$\overline{1}$.

The mandible is heavily built with a deep horizontal ramus ; symphysis short, heavy and vertically disposed, bearing posteriorly a deep pit for the genioglossus muscle,[†] its posterior border level with P.$\overline{2}$ premolar ; horizontal ramus with well-marked lingual torus ; mental foramen unusually high in position and located posteriorly well below P.$\overline{4}$.

Dimensions (in millimetres) of type fragment of *Amphipithecus mogaungensis* (rearranged from Colbert 1937 *a*) :

Mandible : depth opp. M.$\overline{1}$	19·5	M.$\overline{1}$ length	6·3
thickness opp. M.$\overline{1}$	9·0	width of trigonid	5·2
P.$\overline{3}$ length	3·8	width of talonid	5·9
width	4·2	crown height	3·6 +
crown height	4·0		
P.$\overline{4}$ length	3·6		
width	4·6		
crown height	4·0 +		

* *Amer. Mus. Novit.* No. 951.

† Sergi (1947) has justifiably criticized Colbert's identification of this structure as a genial pit, suggesting more correctly that it is a wide digastric fossa.

TABLE 10

CORRELATION OF TERTIARY HORIZONS OF BURMA

	BURMA			INDIA	3 Europe / 2 N. America / 1 Mongolia
Pleistocene	IRRAWADDY SERIES	Upper Irrawaddy	Yenangyaung fossil beds	Boulder Conglomerate / PINJOR / TATROT	3 Val d'Arno
Pliocene		Lower Irrawaddy	Red beds (*Hipparion*)	DHOK PATHAN NAGRI —CHINJI—	3 Astian / 2 {San Pedro / Blanco} / 3 Pontian / 2 Valentine
Miocene	and	FRESHWATER PEGU	Level of *Dorcatherium birmanicum*	KAMLIAL	3 Sarmatian / 2 Barstow
Oligocene			Level of *Cadurcotherium*	GAJ	3 Chattian / 2 Brule / 1 Ardyn Obo
Eocene	YAW / PONDAUNG S.S.		Pondaung Fauna		3 Priabonian / 2 Uinta / 1 Shara Murun
	Tabyn Clay / Tilin S.S. / Laungshe Sh. / Paung-gyi / Conglom.				

DENTITION

Dental formula : $I.\frac{?}{?}$, $C.\frac{?}{1}$, $P.\frac{?}{3}$, $M.\frac{?}{3}$.

Incisors are unknown, but from vertical alignment of canine could not have shown much procumbency.

Canine, judged from root, vertically implanted and well developed.   Root flattened in transverse dimension with convex buccal and flat lingual surface; its long axis oblique to dental arcade.

Premolars aligned with canine without appreciable diastema; crowns high and roots long. Crowns broad posteriorly and narrow in front, antero-posteriorly short with consequent lingual extension of the postero-lingual portion. Each bears a principal central conid from which three ridges descend, anterior, posterior and lingual. Anterior and posterior ridges are almost as high as central cusp. On lingual side between median transverse ridge and anterior corner of crown is a small anterior fovea; a posterior fossa exists between the median and posterior transverse ridges. Transverse ridges are not horizontal, but slope markedly from median to lingual borders of crown so that fovea faces upwards and lingually. Buccal cingulum present, forming a concave semicircle, upwards from base to anterior and posterior corners of crown, and connected to main cusp by a central vertical ridge.

$P._{\overline{2}}$ two-rooted, the roots being buccal and lingual in position, the buccal probably corresponding to the posterior roots of $P._{\overline{4}}$ fused to form one large transverse root. $P._{\overline{3}}$ three-rooted, the antero-lingual of $P._{\overline{4}}$ lacking. $P._{\overline{4}}$ four-rooted, two buccal and two lingual of which the anterior lingual root is very small. All premolar roots long and vertically implanted.

$M._{\overline{1}}$ axially elongated with brachyodont crown and long roots. Trigonid relatively low, barely above level of talonid, and narrower than talonid, hence protoconid and metaconid more approximated than hypoconid and ento-conid. All cusps essentially conical, but anterior pair joined by low transverse lophid; anterior and postero-transverse ridges from posterior cusps form a rim around the talonid basin. A flat facet occurs in front of metaconid and its centre bears a small pit—suggestive of a very small paraconid. Well marked buccal and lingual cingula on trigonid part of tooth and a slight cingulum on posterior border of crown. At junction of this posterior cingu-lum with talonid on buccal side is an incipient hypoconulid (? initial stage of its formation, Colbert, 1937).

COMMENTS

The systematic position of *Amphipithecus* is open to considerable doubt. It is placed here only for convenience. Considerably older than *Parapithecus* and retaining a dental formula characteristic of the New World monkeys, it may have an important place on the phylogenetic tree of the Primates; but until more extensive material is available its position remains doubtful.

Colbert (1938), in attempting to assess its affinities, points out that they lie within four main groups of Eocene mammals, namely (i) the Primates, (ii) the condylarths, (iii) the rodents, and (iv) the artiodactyls. In all these groups the molars are comparable with those of *Amphipithecus*, but the

o

premolars are directly comparable only with those among Primates. On these grounds the other orders are eliminated.

Within the Primates it is possible to eliminate the lemuroids and tarsioids, for in all these the mandible is low and elongated, whereas in *Amphipithecus* it is short, heavy and deep. There are, however, some dental resemblances between it and the Eocene lemuroid *Pelycodus*, especially in the form of $P.\overline{_4}$ and $M.\overline{_1}$, but this is very slight and indicative of considerable advance beyond the primitive prosimian stage.

Presence of three premolars suggests a possible phyletic connection with the Platyrrhini, but beyond this numerical feature there are no particular structural resemblances in the teeth. Moreover, in *Amphipithecus* the foremost premolar is small, evidently on its way to disappearance, whereas in the Platyrrhini it is large. Furthermore, the molars and the morphology of the mandibular ramus show many differences between *Amphipithecus* and the Platyrrhini.

Relationships between the present genus and the other early Burmese pithecoid *Pondaungia* are very doubtful, largely on account of the fragmentary nature of the available material. *Pondaungia* (*vide infra*, p. 200) has been classed as an early anthropomorph. The two share little in common as regards their lower molars. These are quadrate in form of their crowns in *Pondaungia* and quadricuspid, whereas in *Amphipithecus* they are elongated and five-cusped. Moreover *Pondaungia* has a primitive shallow mandible.

In certain respects *Amphipithecus* is comparable with the cercopithecoids, more especially the more advanced fossil types such as the Pliocene *Mesopithecus* (p. 52). For instance, the heavy mandible, the short symphyseal region and the form of the premolars may be cited. But the characteristic bilophodont molar crowns of the cercopithecoids rule out any direct connection here. There are scarcely any resemblances to *Apidium*, usually regarded, following Gregory, as an ancestral cynomorph. Closer still are the resemblances to the anthropomorphs ; these are numerous. Notable in this connection are the heavy mandible with its pronounced lingual torus and short symphysis and deep pit for the genio-glossus*—all features characteristic of such advanced forms as *Dryopithecus*, *Proconsul*, *Pongo* and *Gorilla*. Further likeness is the presumably parallel alignment of the two mandibular rami with resultant form of dental arcade like that of *Prolipopithecus* and contrasting with the primitive divergent rami of *Parapithecus*.

In the dentition resemblances to the pongid condition are seen in the vertically implanted canine (contrasting with the more primitive procumbent position) ; the highly developed state of the premolars, *e.g.* in the lingual extension of the postero-medial angle and the transverse lophid from the principal cusp. On the other hand, the molar of *Amphipithecus* is more primitive than that of *Parapithecus* or *Propliopithecus*, retaining a trace of

* See, however, footnote on p. 191.

paracone but not having yet developed a hypoconulid. Such type of molar is intermediate between the tribosphenic molar of *Tarsius* and the tooth of *Parapithecus*; but affinities with the Hylobatidae are also suggested (Le Gros Clark, 1959).

Genus *OLIGOPITHECUS* Simons, 1962 *

A genus established by Simons for the reception of a fossil mandible recovered from the Oligocene deposits of the Fayûm, Egypt, by the Yale Paleontological Expedition of 1961–1962.

TYPE : *Oligopithecus savagei.*

GENERIC DIAGNOSIS : Size of mandible approximately that of a *Leontideus rosalia*, and smaller therefore than the approximately contemporary *Pliopithecus haeckeli*, but larger than *Parapithecus*.

Differing further from *Parapithecus* in the presence of an undoubted large canine anterior to P.$_{\overline{3}}$; P.$_{\overline{3}}$ antero-posteriorly elongated, without metaconid (cf. *Parapithecus*), molars with paraconid ridge more extended lingually.

Differing from *Propliopithecus* in the shallower mandibular ramus, more antero-posteriorly elongated P.$_{\overline{3}}$, presence of a distinct paraconid on P.$_{\overline{4}}$ M.$_{\overline{1}}$; molars with buccal cingula less distinct and with a hypoconulid more lingually placed and not distinctly separated from entoconid.

1. *OLIGOPITHECUS SAVAGEI* Simons, 1962 *

TYPE : A left mandibular ramus with C̄—M$_{\overline{3}}$ inclusive, now in Yale Museum, but eventually to be deposited in Cairo Museum of Geology. Collected by Dr. D. E. Savage.

TYPE LOCALITY AND HORIZON : Fayûm Province, Egypt; quarry E of Yale Expedition, fossil wood zone, fluviomarine formation, Early Oligocene. Locality is about 2·3 miles north-east of quarry A (American Museum Expedition of 1907) and 8 miles west-north-west of Quasr el Sagha temple, 30 feet below top of fossil wood zone.

DIMENSIONS

Depth of mandible at M.$_{\overline{2}}$ level	9·5 mm.	
,, ,, P.$_{\overline{3}}$,,	10·2	
Dental length C—M.$_{\overline{2}}$	19·4	

For dimensions of individual teeth compared with those of *Parapithecus*, *Propliopithecus* and *Moeripithecus* Simons' original paper should be consulted.

* *Postilla*, Yale, No. **64**, 2, 5.

Although $M._{\overline{3}}$ is missing in the type, except for the anterior root, this indicates that the tooth had fully erupted. On the anterior crest of the protoconid of $P._{\overline{3}}$ is an extensive area of wear, indicative of the possession of a large upper canine.

COMMENT

Simons makes no attempt to place this new genus in a family, merely contenting himself with relegation to the infraorder Catarrhini. It is placed here alongside *Parapithecus* merely for convenience and because of its geological horizon.

Genus *APIDIUM* Osborn, 1908 [*]

A genus created by Osborn for the reception of the fossil mandibular fragment named by him *A. phiomense*. The name is a fanciful one derived from Apis the sacred bull of the ancient Egyptians.

Osborn (1908) was careful not to commit himself to an ordinal relegation of his new genus, but subsequently it was regarded as a Primate. Gregory (1920) went so far as to relate it to the basal cercopithecoid stock or to *Oreopithecus*. More recently primate affinities have again been denied, but Simons (1959, 1960, 1962) reaffirms resemblances to *Oreopithecus*, claiming these as more than mere evidence of convergence. This opinion is confirmed by the recently discovered upper dentition, where corresponding similarities are found.

At the same time, *Apidium* differs from all other known Oligocene pithecoids in respect of the more multicuspid cheek-teeth, and the shallower mandibular ramus; the canine was probably small or alternatively there may have been three premolars—a point which cannot be settled on available material.

Simons believes that differentiation of the stock from the other Fayûm primates had occurred considerably earlier than their presence together in the early Oligocene. He also expresses the opinion that in many ways *Apidium* is closest to *Parapithecus* and provisionally both may eventually need to be ranked among the Anthropoidea (? = Hominoidea) (*vide* also subsequent comments, p. 198).

[*] *Bull. Amer. Mus. Nat. Hist.* xxiv., 271.

1. *APIDIUM PHIOMENSE* Osborn, 1908

TYPE LOCALITY AND HORIZON : Upper levels of the fluviomarine beds of the Lower Oligocene Fayûm deposits, Egypt. Type, the middle portion of a left mandibular ramus containing $P.\overline{4}$ and $M.\overline{1}$—$M.\overline{3}$ (American Museum No. 13370), collected by Osborn during an American Museum expedition of 1906–1907.

CHARACTERS

The fragment indicates an animal of small size with a relatively shallow mandibular ramus ; dental characters suggest generic separation from all other mammalian fossils.

$P.\overline{4}$ with suboval crown bearing large anterior cone with anterior and posterior accessory cusps on its lingual face and with a talonid region bearing three to four accessory cuspules.

Molars brachyodont ; cuspules of crown arranged in opposite pairs ; trigonids and talonids at same level, multicuspidate, *i.e.* with numerous secondary cusps.

$M.\overline{1}$ with five main cusps and a vestigial paraconid, also with a very unusual feature, viz., a small cusp in the centre of the crown.

$M.\overline{2}$ somewhat larger than $M.\overline{1}$; similar, but paraconid entirely wanting. $M.\overline{3}$ elongate with four main cusps surrounding the central cusp and the posterior extension of the heel (hypoconulid) reinforced by a number of accessory cuspules.

2. *APIDIUM MOUSTAFAI* Simons * 1962

TYPE LOCALITY AND HORIZON : Fayûm, Egypt. Type obtained in Yale Expedition quarry G, below upper fossiliferous zone, fluviomarine formation, Early Oligocene. Type, a left mandibular ramus with $P.\overline{3}$—$M.\overline{1}$ *in situ* (no Y.C.P.E. 260).

Topotypes. Left mandibular ramus with damaged $P.\overline{3}$—$M.\overline{3}$ (No. 18007) ; Right $P.\underline{4}$—$M.\underline{3}$ (unassociated) (No. 18008) ; Right mandibular ramus with $P.\overline{3}$—$M.\overline{3}$ (No. 18009) ; Left mandibular ramus with $\overline{C}$—$M.\overline{3}$ (No. 18018) ; Left mandibular fragment with $P.\overline{4}$—$M.\overline{1}$ (No. 18042) ; Left $P.\underline{4}$?, left $M.\underline{2}$, left $M.\overline{3}$ (unassociated ; No. 18081).

CHARACTERS. Smaller than *A. phiomense* by approximately $\frac{1}{8}$.

Differing further in slighter development of lateral basal cingula and fewer accessory cuspules on $P.\overline{4}$ talonid and on $M.\overline{1}$—$\overline{3}$; postero-medial angle of $M\overline{1}$. more lingually produced.

* *Postilla*, Yale, No. **64**, p. 6.

DIMENSIONS (in millimetres):

	Type	Y.P.M. 18018	Y.P.M. 18009
Depth of mandible beneath $M._{\overline{1}}$	6·8	6·0	7·1
$P._{\overline{3}}$—$M._{\overline{3}}$ length	—	15·3	16·8
$P._{\overline{3}}$—$M._{\overline{1}}$,,	8·8	8·6	9·0
C, DC or $P._{\overline{2}}$ length	—	2·5	—
,, width	—	2·0	—
$P._{\overline{3}}$ length	2·8	2·7	2·7
,, width	2·0	2·0	1·9
$P._{\overline{4}}$ length	2·8	2·7	2·7
,, width	2·3	2·3	2·2
$M._{\overline{1}}$ length	3·7	3·5	3·6
,, width	3·0	2·8	2·7
$M._{\overline{2}}$ length	—	3·6	3·6
,, width	—	3·2	3·1
$M._{\overline{3}}$ length	—	3·6	4·0
,, width	—	3·0	2·9

No descriptions have been supplied by Simons of the upper dental elements assigned to this species.

COMMENTS

Simons considers that, on the basis of associated faunal elements, *A. moustafai* is of somewhat more ancient date than *A. phiomense*. This would entitle it, according to the practice employed by some paleontologists, to generic separation, but Simons does not approve of such action.

Newly recovered elements of the upper dentition of *Apidium* strengthen the view that this genus, together with *Oreopithecus*, may represent a third major group of the Catarrhini distinct from Cercopithecoidea, or Hominoidea (see also Simons, 1964).

GENERAL COMMENTS

Osborn made no attempt to ascribe his fossil to any particular group, pointing out that the name *Apidium* did not imply any affinity with the artiodactyls or suids. Comparisons are suggested with some species of the Upper Eocene suiforms *Cebochoerus* and *Acotherulum*, but these were much larger beasts. Evidently *Apidium* was a small omnivore or frugivore with partly cuspidate molars, but the rounded $P.\overline{4}$ contrasts strongly with the compressed form of this tooth in all Artiodactyla. Osborn regarded Primate affinities as equally uncertain because of the divergences in dental crown patterns from all then known Eocene or Oligocene primates. Osborn therefore concluded that the ordinal position of *Apidium* must remain uncertain until the anterior teeth could be made known.

Schlosser (1911) was the first to stress the primate affinities of *A. phiomense* regarding it as possibly an ancestral cercopithecoid. Gregory (1920) supported this view, which he declared to be strengthened by the undermentioned considerations :

1. Compared with the admittedly primate *Parapithecus*, there is a fundamental ground plan in $P.\overline{4}$ and the lower molars ; $P.\overline{4}$ in both being potentially more or less bicuspid and sharply differentiated from the molars, while the latter are antero-posteriorly elongate with five principal subconical cusps arranged in two opposite pairs and a hypoconulid.

2. Lower teeth in *Apidium* share with those of the later Lower Miocene *Oreopithecus* the same ground plan, but at a more primitive level, linking with a still more primitive tarsioid stage. For example $P.\overline{4}$ is incipiently bicuspid in *Apidium* and fully bicuspid in *Oreopithecus*, where the talonid and posterior cingulum are also better developed. Molars in *Apidium* retain much of the tarsioid stage of cusp formation, the talonids of $M.\overline{1}$ and $M.\overline{3}$ being notably wider than the trigonids, but, at the same time, they foreshadow the condition in *Oreopithecus* with their anterio-posterior elongation, $M.\overline{3}$ being longer than $M.\overline{2}$ and the fact that the crista obliqua carries a new cusp at its anterior extremity immediately behind the posterior slope of the talonid. Hypoconulids are prominently developed in both genera.

3. Resemblances between the molars of *Apidium* and *Cebochoerus* are, according to Schlosser, superficial and do not extend to the finer details ; moreover, their premolars are widely different.

4. " From the relatively high state of evolution attained by *Oreopithecus* in the Lower Miocene, it is to be expected that in the Lower Oligocene the *Cercopithecus* group had already begun to separate from the related anthropoid stock. *Apidium*, so far as known, appears to conform with reasonable expectations of what such a Lower Oligocene stage should be like."

5. " That ancestors or relatives of the later Cercopithecidae were present in the Lower Oligocene of Egypt is also extremely probable from the fact that the American Museum expedition in 1907 discovered there a frontal portion of a skull which resembles closely the corresponding part of some of the smaller Cercopithecidae."

Simons (1959) has recently examined the type of *Apidium phiomense* and reviewed its position. He disposes of Hürzeler's (1958) suggestion that it shows affinities to the condylarth *Phenacodus*, pointing out that the latter bears a submolariform $P.\overline{4}$, lower molars with unbroken crista obliqua and $M.\overline{2}$ lacking a separate cusp (mesoconid or centroconid) between protoconid and entoconid. The last feature is specially developed in *Apidium* and

Oreopithecus, while the only other primates having any suggestion of it are *Pliopithecus*, *Dryopithecus* and *Gigantopithecus*, in all of which it is somewhat dubious.

Apidium, despite its great temporal severance from *Oreopithecus*, shows many similarities, especially in cusp patterns, as pointed out by Gregory. In addition to the mesoconid just referred to, there is the striking increase in molar size from front to back and the marked constriction between trigonid and talonid on $M.\overline{1}$ and $M.\overline{2}$. Almost every feature on the large and complex occlusal surface of $M.\overline{3}$ can be homologized with that of *Oreopithecus*. Incurving of the antero-medial extremity of the horizontal ramus towards the symphysis about the level of the anterior edge of $P.\overline{4}$ is strongly suggestive of a reduced number of premolars.

Genus *PONDAUNGIA* Pilgrim, 1927 *

A genus erected by Pilgrim for some upper and lower jaw fragments bearing cheek-teeth collected by Dr. G. de P. Cotter from the Pondaung sandstones of Burma and of Upper Eocene age. Cotter suggested these pertained to a primitive Primate, but on account of their fragmentary nature and badly weathered condition, both he and Pilgrim, his co-worker, omitted mention of them in their publication of 1916, hoping that time would eventually result in more material being unearthed. As this did not materialize Pilgrim (1927) described them as representing a new genus and species of early Primate, possibly representing an ancestral anthropomorph. Pilgrim was by no means certain of the Primate status of these fossil fragments, but the evidence was such that he placed them there rather than in any other mammalian group.

1. *PONDAUNGIA COTTERI*, Pilgrim, 1927

TYPE LOCALITY AND HORIZON : Pondaung series, Upper Eocene, Burma. Specimen found a quarter of a mile west of Pangan, Pyaing township, Pakokku district, Burma. Type, a fragment of a left maxilla containing two molars (probably $M.\overline{1}$ and $M.\overline{2}$) and a fragment of left mandibular ramus containing $M.\overline{2}$ and $M.\overline{3}$ and fragment of right mandibular ramus bearing $M.\overline{3}$—all pertaining to the same individual.

DIAGNOSIS (as revised by Colbert, 1937)

Upper molars broader than long, quadrangular, quinquecuspid, three-rooted. Paracone and metacone separate, but protocone and hypocone connected by a ridge ; a lingual cingulum and small hypoconule present.

* *Mem. Geol. Surv. India* (N.S.), xiv. 12-15.

Lower molars with quadrangular crowns, except $M._{\overline{3}}$ which is more rounded and bears a long, narrow heel; all cusps distinct from each other, cingula lacking; $M._{\overline{3}}$ with paraconid, trigonid slightly higher in level than talonid.

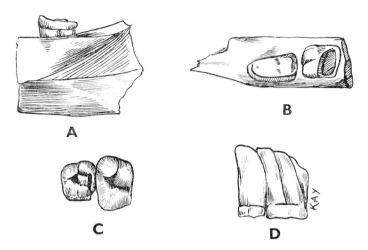

Fig. 16.—*Pondaungia cotteri.* A, right mandibular ramus, with $M._{\overline{3}}$, from the lingual aspect; B, left mandibular ramus, with $M._{\overline{2}}$ and $M._{\overline{3}}$, from the occlusal aspect; C, left $M.^{\underline{1}}$ and $M.^{\underline{2}}$ from the occlusal aspect; D, the same from the palatal aspect. All $\times \frac{3}{1}$. Redrawn from Pilgrim

CHARACTERS

No description of the maxilla is available; only the alveolar portion of bone bearing the two molars is preserved.

Two short fragments of the mandible are available; one from each horizontal ramus: (left, 21 mm. long; right, 18 mm. long). They indicate a relatively shallow mandible (12·7 mm. deep) strongly contrasting therefore in size and shape with the same parts of the fossil Pongidae described by Pilgrim in the same paper.

DENTITION

Dental formula: $I._{\overline{?}}^{?}$, $C._{\overline{?}}^{?}$, $P._{\overline{?}}^{?}$, $M.\frac{3}{3}$.

Measurements (in millimetres) of *Pondaungia cotteri*:

	$M.^{\underline{1}}$	$M.^{\underline{2}}$	$M._{\overline{2}}$	$M._{\overline{3}}$
Height	—	2·8	—	3·2
Length	5·2	5·7	6·1	7·2
Breadth	6·5	8·1 app.	5·8	5·1

Upper molars three-rooted, the two buccal roots divergent, the lingual showing a trace of division at hinder end, more so on $M.^2$ than $M.^1$; with crowns broader than long, the sides of crown sloping towards centre. Occlusal surface quadrangular with four principal cusps, but remains of original trituberculy evident, i.e. paracone and metacone distinct from each other, but protocone and hypocone forming a single ridge suggesting that hypocone developed as a bud off protocone. A hypoconule present but no protoconule. Presence of a mesostyle doubtful on account of excess weathering of the material. Traces of an internal cingulum and also an anterior cingulum, more so on $M.^2$ than $M.^1$.

Lower molars: $M._{\overline{2}}$ of type with anterior half destroyed, but crown square with presumably four main cusps. The only perfect cusp remaining is the hypoconid, the summit of the entoconid being weathered away. Weathering also prevents the certain identification of a hypoconulid, but if present it was evidently median in position and there is no indentation of the hinder margin. No cingulum preserved; it was probably lacking since the base of the crown is intact. $M._{\overline{3}}$ is much longer than broad, but tapering behind. Cingulum lacking; trigonid slightly higher than talonid; paraconid plainly present; protoconid slightly in advance of metaconid in position; entoconid and hypoconid approximately opposite each other; posteriorly a strong median hypoconulid. The six cusps enclose a broad shallow basin.

COMMENTS

The fundamental plan of the molar crowns of *Pondaungia* conforms as readily with that of the ancestral ungulate group Condylarthra as with the Primates—a not unexpected feature in view of the early geological date and the generalized structure with the possibility of fragmentary material from one group being mistaken for that of the other. The members of the contemporary bunodont artiodactyle Helohyidae (included by Simpson under Choeropotamidae) differ in showing higher cusps on the molars, while the lingual cusps of the upper molars and the buccal cusps of the upper and lower molars are crescentic, even in the Lower Eocene *Wasatchia*, which is otherwise closest in structure to *Pondaungia*. Similarly in *Cebochoerus*, where also the hypoconulid is narrower. In later suiforms the bunodonty is more established, but *pari passu* with this the molars have become extraordinarily elongated and provided with numerous accessory cusps.

Comparison of *Pondaungia* with contemporary Primates shows a general similarity in ground plan of molar structure, though there are differences in detail of cusp development and in the mode in which the cusps are formed from the primitive trituberculous upper or tuberculo-sectorial lower molar plan. There are, for example, general similarities with *Pelycodus* (Vol. I,

p. 507), but *Pondaungia* lacks the ridges connecting protoconid to metaconid and the hypoconid to the posterior wall of the trigonid. On the other hand the formation of the hypocone (or pseudohypocone) by budding from the protocone corresponds closely with the stage observed in *Notharctus*. The latter, however, possesses distinct styles rising from the buccal cingulum ; these are completely lacking in *Pondaungia*. In this last respect the resemblance is rather with the Eocene tarsioids. In *Necrolemur* and even more so in the Upper Eocene *Microchoerus*, where the quadrangular form has become almost fully established in the upper molars, a tendency to the development of small accessory cusps has resulted in a pattern not unlike that in *Pondaungia*.

With all the retained primitive features (*e.g.* the large hypoconulid on $M._{\overline{3}}$, the retained paraconid and the broad upper molars retaining evidence of the former trituberculy) *Pondaungia* approaches the Hominoidea more than any other Primate group in Pilgrim's estimation.

For instance, no parallel is to be found elsewhere as regards the lowness of the molar cusps both above and below and, in their isolation from each other, in the mandibular molars ; nor in the formation of the large basin between the cusps, especially on $M._{\overline{3}}$. The earliest forms otherwise assignable to the Hominoidea are the Lower Oligocene *Parapithecus* and *Propliopithecus*, and it is to the latter that the Burmese fossil comes closest. There is no resemblance with the characteristic bilophodont molars of the Cercopithecoidea. *Apidium* already possesses the higher cusps whereby it is claimed as possibly ancestral to the Cercopithecoids, but it differs also in the existence of the crista obliqua and the absence of the broad basin in $M._{\overline{3}}$. It does, however, resemble *Pondaungia* in the retention of the paraconid on $M._{\overline{1}}$, and in the length of the hypoconulid heel on $M._{\overline{3}}$,—both primitive features.

Possibly, therefore, in *Apidium* and *Pondaungia* we have early representatives of two divergent evolutionary lines, one leading to the cynomorph and the other to the anthropomorph groups of later Primates.

Family II—CERCOPITHECIDAE Gray, 1821* (restricted)

(SYN.: *Cynocephalina* Gray, 1825, p. 338; *Cynopithecina* Geoffroy, 1843, p. 495; *Macacidae* Owen, 1843, p. 55; *Papionidae* Blyth, 1863, p. 6; *Ascopareia* Haeckel, 1866, clx; *Cercopithecina* Gray, 1870, p. 19; *Cynopithecinae* Gill, 1872, p. 2; *Cercopithecinae* Blanford, 1888, p. 10, Forbes, 1894, Dollman, 1931, Simpson, 1945; *Cynocephalidae* Ameghino, 1889, p. 893; *Lasiopygidae* Elliot, 1911, p. 341, 1913, ii. p. 115; *Lasiopyginae* Elliot, 1913, lv; G. M. Allen, 1925, p. 306; *Cercopitheci* (in part) Winge, 1924)

DEFINITION.—Cercopithecoidea mainly distinguished by the presence of paired herniations of the buccal mucosa constituting cheek-pouches serving for the temporary storage of food, correlated with the simple sac-like character of the stomach. Manus and pes short and broad compared with those of Colobidae. Pollex variable in size, but invariably present. In all these features the Cercopithecidae contrast with the Colobidae, which lack buccal pouches but possess highly specialized sacculated stomachs. Perineum longer in female, with vulva placed inferiorly between callosities, and clitoris exposed at inferior commissura labiorum.

The family name Cercopithecidae was formerly used as synonymous with Huxley's Cynomorpha, and therefore included all the Old World monkeys (*i.e.* all Old World Primates other than Man and the anthropoid apes, which were designated Anthropomorpha). It was soon recognized that fundamental differences separated the majority of the Old World monkeys (*e.g.* the macaques, mangabeys, baboons and guenons) from the more specialized Asiatic leaf-monkeys and their African counterparts, the Colobus monkeys. Blyth (1875) gave expression to this by dividing the family into Colobidae and Cercopithecidae. Subsequent authors, *e.g.* Blanford (1888), recognized the distinction, but gave the two divisions sub-familial rank only, until Pocock (1926) reverted to Blyth's assessment. He has not, however, been universally followed. Simpson (1945), for example, though agreeing with the validity of Pocock's system, felt that the differences between the two groups were not as great as usual between mammalian families. Accordingly he has given them subfamilial status pending further discoveries. Such discoveries have since accrued in the serological, haemato-logical and cytological fields, which re-establish the familial status. Further-more, the necessity for recognition, on a lower rank, of the differences

---

* *London Med. Reposit.* xv. pt. 1, 271.

existing within the Cercopithecidae (sensu stricto) renders such familial rank obligatory.

Craniometrically Verheyen (1959) found sharp differentiation between the Colobidae and Cercopithecidae the most important being in respect of the index :

$$\frac{\text{anterior interorbital width} \times 100}{\text{glabella-prosthenion height}}$$

This worker considers the distinctions worthy of familial rather than sub-familial status.

FIG. 17.—*Macaca mulatta* ♀ adult.   Stomach from the ventral aspect for comparison with fig. 18

Chu and Giles (1957) report a pair of chromosomes with a prominent secondary constriction constantly present in the nuclei of all Cercopithecidae and not found anywhere among the Platyrrhini.   Bender and Metzler (1958) consider this might be the nucleolus organizer and may therefore exist as an undetected second arm in one of the telocentric chromosomes of *Cebus* and *Callicebus*.   Apparently telocentric chromosomes are lacking in *Papio* and *Cercocebus* in contrast to the existence of three pairs in *Cercopithecus mona*.

GEOGRAPHICAL DISTRIBUTION

The geographical range of the Cercopithecidae, as here understood, is virtually co-extensive with that of the Catarrhini as a whole (*supra*, p. 50). Like the Colobidae, they are represented both in Asia and Africa, but in both continents the range is wider than that of the Colobidae.   Furthermore, the macaques are also represented in Europe by *M. sylvana*, the Barbary Ape, whose principal range is in north-east Africa, where no other primate occurs.

In Africa the Cercopithecidae are represented by the guenons (*Cerco-pithecus*, *Miopithecus*, *Allenopithecus* and *Erythrocebus*) and also by the mangabeys (*Cercocebus*) and baboons (*Papio*, *Mandrillus* and *Theropithecus*). All of these are confined to sub-Saharan Africa, though *Papio* and *Erythroce-bus* range farther north than any of the others.

Three species of *Papio* range to the confines of the Sahara, *P. papio* in the west, *P. anubis* in the centre and *P. hamadryas* in the east. Their zones

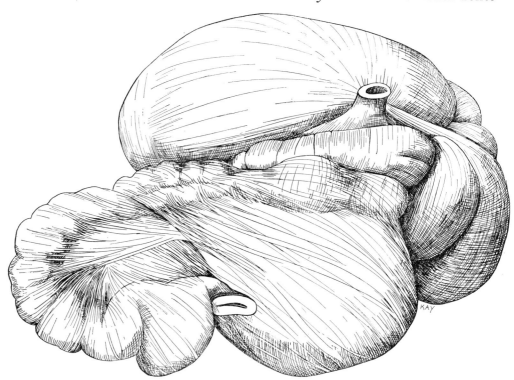

Fig. 18.—*Colobus verus* ♀ adult. Stomach from the ventral aspect for comparison
with fig. 17

of contact are not at present precisely determined, but Monod (1963, *teste* Dekeyser) gives Dabola in Guinea as the western outpost of *P. anubis*. To the west of this *P. papio* ranges northwards, passing close to Gambia between the coast and Tambacounda, thence inland in a salient as far as Tagant (south-west Mauritania) (18° N). Farther to the east the northern limit is 13° N. The northern range of *P. anubis heuglini* to the east of Chad is not precisely known, but the species occurs in the Ennedi and also in the Jebel marra in the Sudan (Setzer, 1956). Isolated populations also appear in the Aïr Massif and in the south-western part of Tibesti (*P. anubis tibestianus*, Dekeyser and Derivot, 1960) (*vide* Bigourdan, 1950, Dekeyser, 1952 and Dekeyser and Derivot, 1960). *P. hamadryas* occurs in Abyssinia alongside *Theropithecus gelada*. The former ranges from the lowlands of eastern Sudan to eastern Abyssinia (Dire Dawa), while the latter is confined to the highlands of Abyssinia mainly above 6000 feet. The precise northern limits have not been ascertained (Starck and Frick, 1958). The picture is much the same with *Erythrocebus*, which likewise occurs in the Aïr massif, though proof of its existence in Tibesti is not available. (See further *infra*, pp. 692, 699.) *Cercopithecus aethiops* is the most northerly ranging of its genus, occurring in Jebel Marra and other parts of the Sudan as well as in Abyssinia (for details see p. 543, also Strand, 1931).

Both *Papio* and *Cercopithecus* extend southwards to the Cape. The other genera have rather circumscribed areas of distribution in the rain-forest belt.

In addition to its African range, *Papio* is also locally represented in Arabia by *P. hamadryas*, but otherwise no genus except *Macaca* is common to Africa and Asia. Southern and south-eastern Asia is the home of the macaques (*Macaca*), which have the widest range of any Asiatic group of monkeys, occurring from the Indian peninsula eastwards to Japan, and being represented in most of the off-shore islands from Ceylon to Timor (*vide supra*, p. 51).

Wallace's line is further transgressed by a subgenus of macaques which inhabit the island of Celebes and some small outlying islands, along with the somewhat peculiar *Cynopithecus*, the Celebesian Black Ape.

Subfamily A—CERCOPITHECINAE Reichenbach, 1863 * (restricted)
GUENONS

(SYN.: *Cercopitheci* Linnaeus, 1758, p. 26; 1766, p. 35; Cercopithecinae Flower & Lydekker, 1891, p. 718; Blanford, 1888, p. 10; Beddard, 1909, p. 562 (restricted).)
VERNACULAR NAMES: French, *guenons* (Buffon 1767); German, *Meerkatzen* †; Dutch, *meerkatten*, Norwegian, *marekatten*.

DEFINITION.—Cercopithecidae (*s.s.*) with cheek-teeth not greatly swollen at the base of the crowns; molars never presenting more than four cusps; generally no catamenial swelling in the female (*Miopithecus* and *Allenopithecus* excepted); tail present, never prehensile, and invariably longer than head and body together; chromosomes, 54, 60, 66 or 72; placentation bidiscoidal, haemochorial; exclusively African. Genera *Cercopithecus*, *Miopithecus*, *Allenopithecus*, *Erythrocebus*.

From his craniological and craniometrical studies Verheyen (1959, 1962) deduces that *Erythrocebus* and *Allenopithecus* are subgenera of *Cercopithecus*,

---

* *Vollst. Naturgesch. Affen*, 85.

† Janson (1952) has an interesting comment on the original use of the name Meerkatze. Earliest usage is commonly credited to Hildegard of Bingen (1098–1179; *vide ante*, p. 11) but in the *Ecbasis captivi*, the earliest animal epic of the Middle Ages, dated around 940, *i.e.* over a century earlier than Hildegard, there occurs the expression *cerula catta maris*, which is clearly a translation of the German Meerkatze. Janson observes that as the word was interpreted to mean " (trans) marine cat " at this early date, considerable doubt is thrown upon the alternative derivation from the ancient Indian name *markata*.

but that *Miopithecus* is not separable from the typical subgenus *Cercopithecus*. He admits that the three recognizable subgenera are easily characterized craniologically and concludes that *Allenopithecus* is the most primitive of the group.

According to Wood Jones (1929 *b*) all African monkeys typically agree with their pongid neighbours in the undermentioned cranial specializations which do not occur elsewhere, not merely among other Primates, but even among the rest of the Mammalia (Wood Jones' type IIIB[2]) :

1. Lachrymal no longer articulating with ethmoid in orbit due to downward growth of frontal to meet maxilla.

2. Parietal fails to meet alisphenoid at the pterion due to forward process (processus frontalis) of the squamous temporal meeting frontal.

3. Mesethmoid fails to meet presphenoid in anterior cranial fossa due to bilateral superficial ingrowths from frontal.

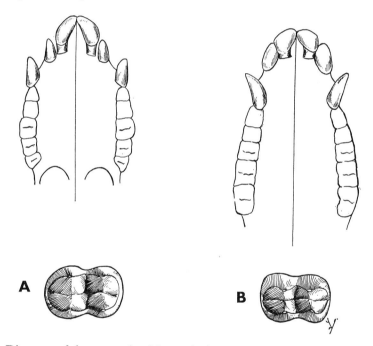

Fig. 19.—Diagrams of the upper dentition and of upper molars from the occlusal aspect of A, *Cercopithecus* and B, *Cercocebus* to show the different form of the dental arcade and the bilateral compression of the molar cusps. Based on a figure of Frechkop (1940)

These distinctions, however, particularly the arrangements at the pterion, are not absolute (see especially hereinafter under *Cercopithecus*).

The above conclusions stem from the results of Ranke (1898) who declared that the Cercopithecidae agreed in general with the chimpanzee with respect to the presence of a processus frontalis to the temporal squame. Without specifying particular genera Ranke affirmed that 72·3 per cent of crania out of 83 examined showed this condition, having found 60 crania with either bilateral or unilateral temporo-frontal union. He did, however, find the Semnopithecinae (= Colobidae) somewhat exceptional as Collins (1925) also did later ; crania in this group showing a transition towards the arrangement in the Orang-utans.

Guenons are distinguished from the mangabeys, macaques and baboons in the relationships of the occlusal surfaces of the molar crowns and, according to Frechkop (1940), these features are correlated with the elongation of the palate (*i.e.* degree of prognathism). In the short-faced guenons the molar crowns lack the bilateral compression noted in, for example, the mangabeys, where the lingual and buccal cusps of each pair are more closely approximated and the intervening crests consequently shortened. (See Frechkop's fig. 7.)

Genus *CERCOPITHECUS* Linnaeus, 1758

Typical GUENONS

(SYN. : *Cercopitheci* Linnaeus 1758, p. 26 ; 1766, p. 35 ; *Cercopithecus* Brünnich, 1771 ; Erxleben, 1777 ; Gray, 1870 ; Forbes, 1894 ; G. M. Allen, 1939 ; *Lasiopyga* Illiger, 1811 ; Elliot, 1913 ; J. A. Allen, 1925.)

DIAGNOSIS : Arboreal guenons of medium size and slender build distinguished by the absence of hypoconulid on $M.\overline{3}$ and no mesostylids on $M.\overline{1}$-$M.\overline{3}$; by the relatively small jaws and by total absence in the females of catamenial swelling. Limbs are intermediate in length and robustness between *Allenopithecus* and *Erythrocebus* ; tail very long.

STATUS OF THE GENERIC NAME *Cercopithecus*

This problem has been discussed by Palmer (1904), J. A. Allen (1925) and by Stiles and Orleman (1926) ; particularly extensively by Allen, who, nevertheless, following Elliot (1913) continued to use *Lasiopyga* Illiger for the genus.

Linnaeus (1748) placed all Primates other than Man in his all-embracing genus *Simia* without arranging them into groups. At that time he recognized sixteen species, of which ten were tailed. Brisson (1756) was the first author to subdivide *Simia* into named groups. These groups he labelled as *stirps*, of which he recognized four, two containing tailless and two tailed forms. Of the latter his stirps IV was named *Cercopithecus* and contained twenty-nine species (of which nine were described for the first time) ; it included all the long-tailed monkeys then known. As Brisson's work was published prior to 1758 his generic and subgeneric names are not available.

In the tenth edition of his *Systema* Linnaeus (1758) divided *Simia* into three subordinate groups, again on the basis of length of or absence of tail, using *Cercopitheci* (in the plural) for the long-tailed species (including some of New World provenance).

P

Stiles and Orleman have put forward convincing arguments for the availability of *Cercopithecus* Linnaeus, 1758, in spite of the fact that Palmer (*loc. cit*), had rejected plural names as valid for genera or subgenera. Stiles and Orleman, however, quote other authors, including ichthyologists and entomologists, who have adopted such Linnaean plural names, and also one mammalian generic name based on a plural form originally employed by Lichtenstein (1814).

In 1762 a second, abridged edition of Brisson's work was published by Haak. Allen argues that this is merely a reprint of the Latin portion of the original bilingual edition, *i.e.* a republication and therefore not validating Brisson's genera. Stiles and Orleman regard Brisson's (1762) *Cercopithecus* as nomenclatorially meriting consideration.

Chronologically the next citation is that of Gronovius (1763) who formally adopted Brisson's 1762 reference as a generic name. Under *Cercopithecus* he discussed two neotropical species, *midas* and *morta* and it was upon this citation that Elliot (1913) accepted *Cercopithecus* Gronovius with *midas* as type species, thereby removing the name from the Old World group, for which it had been employed by zoologists for the previous 150 years or so. This type designation by Elliot, however, remains unacceptable in view of Opinion 89 of the International Commission, which suspended Gronovius 1763 from consideration on the grounds of his inconsistent binomial usage.

This brings us to *Cercopithecus* Brünnich, 1772, which Palmer (*loc. cit.* p. 171) accepted as firmly establishing the use of the generic name of the Old World group for which it has been customarily employed. Brünnich based his genus on the " Marekatten "—a Teutonic name for the long-tailed African monkeys ; but no species were listed and hence no type-species designated, an omission which was subsequently made good by Sclater (1900) *fide* Palmer (1904, p. 172) who designated *mona* as type.

In 1777 Erxleben employed the name to include twenty-two species, some of them heterogeneous and not now accepted as related to *mona* or any others of the Meerkatzen. For example several of Erxleben's long-tailed monkeys were Asiatic and one at least was of unknown provenance. For type species *C. nictitans* (Linnaeus) 1758 was subsequently designated by Apstein (1915) presumably in an attempt to resuscitate Erxleben's *Cercopithecus* for the African monkeys after Elliot's action above referred to.

Blumenbach (1779) again used *Cercopithecus* to include two species only —both neotropical!

During the whole of the nineteenth century and the early part of the twentieth almost all zoologists employed *Cercopithecus* for the African long-tailed monkeys known to the Germans as Meerkatzen and to the French (following Buffon) as guenons. It came as a shock, therefore, when Elliot (1913) transferred this widely accepted name to a small group of tamarins, and introduced Illiger's long-forgotten *Lasiopyga* for the guenons. Opposition to this was particularly strong among European mammalogists, but Allen in America, pending a decision by the International Commission with regard to suspension of the rules in the case of the name *Cercopithecus*, preferred to follow Elliot, in spite of Palmer's advocacy of validation based on Brünnich. Stiles and Orleman, a year later than Allen, as already noted, favoured the Linnaean dating for the genus, thus avoiding the controversial matter of deciding between Gronovius' and Erxleben's application of the name.

In more recent times some authors (*e.g.* G. M. Allen, 1939; Hill and Carter, 1941) have followed Stiles and Orleman's usage (*C. diana* designated as type); a few (*e.g.* Schwarz, 1928 *c*, Rode, 1938) date *Cercopithecus* from Erxleben (with *C. mona* as type), but the most acceptable (also with *C. mona* as type) would seem to be *Cercopithecus* Brünnich (*e.g.* as employed by Simpson, 1945).

Nevertheless the International Commission on 26 July 1948 ruled that *Cercopithecus* should date from Linnaeus 1758 *Syst. Nat.* (10th ed.), i. 26 (*vide Bull. Zool. Nomencl.*, 1950. iv. 311) and therefore must now be accepted.

HISTORICAL

There can be no doubt that monkeys pertaining to the present genus were among the first, if not *the* first to become known to the ancients. It must be recalled that in the pre-Christian era, African primates were more widely dispersed than at present; there is abundant evidence of their greater northward extension in Egypt, Libya and westwards in Mauritania. Among the species so affected were guenons, including at least the species now known as the Grivet (*Cercopithecus aethiops*) and possibly examples also of *Erythrocebus*.

Ancient Egyptian monuments and literature, dating back at least to 1500 B.C., depict several kinds of monkeys. Various identifications have been attempted and several explanations given for the regard in which these animals evidently were held. They were certainly an article of trade along the Nile, but whether merely as pets, curiosities or as objects of veneration is not always clear. They were often sent as presents to distant potentates. The Grivet was engraved upon the walls of temples and tombs, *e.g.* at Gizeh, and from these depictions they have been described by many Egyptologists (*e.g.* Denon, 1802), travellers (*e.g.* Ehrenberg, 1835) and naturalists (*e.g.* Blainville), all of whom have reproduced a painting of a giraffe with a monkey riding on its neck. Other well-known figures depict the animal quadrupedally, or squatting, holding food in its hands (*vide* McDermott 1938, p. 11).

Knowledge of these monkeys spread from Egypt to Mesopotamia, where no primate is indigenous—doubtless through presents to the Babylonian king from the pharaohs (*e.g.* Amenhotep IV, 1380–1362), though probably some connection with Indian species of monkeys was also established. It is known that the Assyrian king Asurnasirpal II kept a collection of living monkeys among which African species were certain to have been included, though positive identification is uncertain.

Early spread of knowledge to the Mediterranean countries occurred probably *via* Crete, for in frescoes of the late Minoan age discovered at Cnossos are representations of a " blue monkey "—possibly one of the widespread group of greenish guenons (*Cercopithecus aethiops* subsp.). The subspecies *tantalus* has been suggested as its identity on account of white brow band depicted in the figures, but as this is a western race, the identification seems rather unlikely.

On the mainland the earliest evidence is a fragmentary figurine from Mycenae in Argolis depicting the pharaoh Amenhotep II (*c.* 1447–1420 B.C.) with a monkey on his shoulder. Similar figurines are frequently found among relics of the early Greek period at many sites, especially Rhodes, and somewhat later, Sparta, Athens, Delphi, Smyrna, Aegina, Ithaca and elsewhere.

In Greece too, the early literature abounds in references, and it is certain, from later literature, that several kinds of guenons were under reference. Greek knowledge was codified by Aristotle (384–322 B.C.) who recognized three categories of man-like animals of which the tailed forms (as distinct from apes and baboons) were κῆβos (*i.e. cepos, cephos* or *cebus*), a term clearly derived from the Arabic *keb* or *kep* and still in use along the East African seaboard. Aristotle's term is also cognate with the Hebrew koph (קוֹף), plural kophim. No positive identification of the species included under Aristotle's *Cebus* is possible, for the description could cover almost any of the smaller African monkeys and also possibly species of macaques or langurs from Asia, though not the Barbary Ape (*Macaca sylvana*) which falls into Aristotle's tailless group. Nevertheless, Aristotle's description of the animal exhibiting varying colours has led many to the assumption that he was describing the Mona monkey. The description, however, may relate to the varying colours of individual hairs—a characteristic of all the monkeys of this genus.

Aristotle's name for the long-tailed monkeys was not adopted by all subsequent authors, many of whom preferred the term κερκοπίθηκος, *i.e.* an ape (πίθηκος) bearing a tail (κέρκος)—sometimes abbreviated by certain later writers to κέρκωψ. Many antiquarian authors, *e.g.* Keller (1887), consider the σφίγξ (= sphynx) to have been a guenon and this receives support from Pliny's account of this animal. On the other hand, the *Cercopitheci* of Pliny do not conform to the guenon type, both the description and their provenance suggesting a *Colobus* monkey. Furthermore Pliny uses the name *cepi* for Ethiopian animals he regarded as rare and which were apparently not guenons—lending thus further support to the view that to him the guenons were the sphinxes.

In a thirteenth-century poem devoted to animal names *spinga* is equated with *merchazze*—clearly the Meerkatze of modern German.

Though not recognized as separate by Aristotle, the *cephus* of early writers of the Christian era (notably Strabo, Pliny and Aelian) is clearly a guenon distinct from other tailed (probably Asiatic) species.

Not much is recorded of the monkeys known to the Romans apart from the important anatomical work of Galen (A.D. 130–*c.* 200) which was based, according to medical historians, upon the Barbary ape (*Macaca sylvana*). It may be regarded as reasonably certain, however, that both Galen (a Greek) and his Roman contemporaries and precursors, were acquainted with some of the tailed species from Africa, examples of which were surely among those exhibited in Rome by Pompey. Earliest references in Latin literature according to McDermott date from Plautus (254–184 B.C.) and Ennius (239–169 B.C.). Latin authors use the name *simia* or *simius* indiscriminately for almost any Primate mammal, but more particularly as an equivalent for the Greek πίθηκος; it is derived from *simus* signifying broad-nosed or snub-nosed. Some later writers use the name *clura* meaning an ape with a tail and said to equate with *clunes triti* (*ex* Greek κλόνις = buttocks)—an allusion to the callosities in that situation. Aelian (A.D. *c.* 250) in his *De animalium natura* knew of several tailed monkeys and had a special name, πιθηκιδεύς, for their young.

During the Dark Ages following the fall of Rome, Western learning was kept alive by Arabic-speaking peoples. Among these the most renowned was Avicenna (980–1037) who described tailed monkeys under Aristotle's name *Cepos*. Doubtless returning crusaders brought monkeys home, but the species concerned remained unidentified. Guenons are not again heard of until the Italian Renaissance. Towards the end of the fifteenth century a Berber traveller and geographer, Leo Africanus, who had journeyed widely in North and Central Africa, settled in Rome, where he became a Christian. The account of his travels was published in Italian in 1550 and was for long the exclusive source of information on the Sudan and adjacent regions. He evidently knew of the Mona monkey (*Cercopithecus mona*) which he described recognizably under the name *mone*, explaining that this and its variants *mona, monina, mounina*, are the terms employed for the long-tailed monkeys in the Moorish, Spanish and Provençal tongues.

Gesner (1551), in his encyclopaedic opus, brought up to date Pliny's natural history. Although treating all monkeys under the general name *Simia*, he definitely identified guenons, albeit mixed among others that were as manifestly macaques ; *e.g.* his *cercopithecus* is figured as a tailed form and closely resembles a long-tailed macaque, although he declares it is known to the Germans as *Meerkatze* and to the English as munkai. His *cepus* (of which he cites numerous orthographical variations employed by previous authors, *e.g. caebum, cephum, cepphum, celphum*) is apparently the Mona. Among earlier writers from whom he drew his information, he quotes Diodorus Siculus, Avicenna and Albertus Magnus. The internal organs of this monkey are stated to resemble their human counterparts.

Aldrovandi, a pupil of Gesner, produced a work much resembling his master's, though it was not published until 1637. As far as monkeys are concerned, it lacked the clarity of Gesner, and much confusion has been introduced by inclusion under *Cercopithecus* of recently discovered American monkeys. He did, however, include some anatomical notes.

In the following year appeared the work of the English naturalist Edward Topsell, who quite frankly borrowed extensively from Gesner, illustrations included. His monkey (p. 5) was the same as Gesner's *cercopithecus*, and therefore a long-tailed macaque. Under the name of Martin Monkey (p. 6) he included Gesner's *cephus* which he declares to have been confused by Aristotle with the *cercopithecus*, though subsequently recognized as distinct by Strabo, Aelian and Pliny. He added that one which was brought to England had the back and flanks green and the rest whitish—a fair description of one of the green guenons of the superspecies, *Cercopithecus aethiops*.

In the intervening period between the publication of the respective works of Gesner and Topsell a number of new references appeared, some of them used by Topsell, while others served later as source-books for Buffon, whose work was published about a century after Topsell's. Among these source books were the contributions of Prosper Alpinus (1553–1617), the Fleming Clusius (1605) and the Englishman Purchas (1625). Alpinus appears to have known the Mona monkey, which he saw in Cairo. Alpinus, as well as Pietro della Valle (1665, 1), both knew also of the green-furred guenons. To these they applied the name *callithrix*, though there is some evidence to show that they were not the animals so named by the Greeks. Clusius described several African monkeys among which was an example of the greenish group of guenons to which Buffon later assigned the name Malbrouck (*Cercopithecus pygerythrus cynosuros*). Purchas (2, 955) seems to be the first to mention examples of the white-nosed group of guenons (either *C. petaurista*, *C. ascanius*, or *C. nictitans*, or possibly *C. cephus*) and these or similar animals were afterwards again mentioned in the writings of Artus (1603) and Marcgrav (1648) (*C. Angolensis alius*) (*fide* Pennant). Marcgrav is generally deemed to have described also, under its native Congolese name *exquima*, a member of the Diana group ; but there is some confusion here with his account and figures of the South American *Alouatta* (*vide infra*).

Jonstonus (1657), another imitator of Gesner, and epitomizer of Adrovandus, revised the then known species of monkeys and drew particular attention to the *Cercopithecus Meerkatze*. His description and figure indicate acquaintance with the Roloway monkey (*Cercopithecus diana roloway*), an identification dating from Latreille (1801) who, however, thought of an alternative explanation—*i.e.* a poor copy of Marcgrav's *guariba* (*vide supra*).

In the account of the travels of the itinerant Dutchman Olfert Dapper (1676) are found references to three kinds of monkeys, of which one was certainly the chimpanzee. The others were possibly guenons or mangabeys.

The first scientific attempt at a synopsis of these monkeys was that of
Ray (1693) who recognized sixteen species, of which twelve possibly pertain
to the genus *Cercopithecus*, as now restricted. His information was drawn
almost entirely from the writings of Clusius and Marcgrav, but the descriptions are not in all cases adequate for definite identification.

Further progress in knowledge of the guenons was arrested until the
latter half of the succeeding century when fresh impetus was supplied by the
establishment in Paris at the Jardin des Plantes of the Royal Menagerie
where many monkeys were exhibited.*   On their demise many of these were
dissected by Perrault (1733) who supplied the earliest anatomical studies on
Cercopithecus.   Later, when Buffon was appointed supervisor to the royal
collection (1739), they afforded him material for his great encyclopaedic work
published between 1749 and 1804 and running into many later editions.
Associated with Buffon in the description of the monkeys were especially
J. M. S. Allamand and later P. A. Latreille, while Daubenton supplied the
anatomical descriptions.   In addition to the source books already mentioned,
Buffon also relied on data culled from earlier writings of Allamand (*e.g.* for
the account of the white-nosed guenons) and of George Edwards (1758).
Guenons known to Buffon included, besides the Patas (now removed to a
separate genus) and the Talapoin (also frequently treated separately) the
following : Malbrouck (*C. cynosuros*), Mona (*C. mona*), Callitrix (*C. sabaeus*),
Mustache (*C. cephus*), and white-nose (*C. petaurista*).

Contemporary with Buffon, but having no correspondence with him,
Linnaeus was busily summarizing available knowledge and bestowing upon
all known organisms binomial scientific names.   His results will more conveniently be considered in dealing with the taxonomic history of the genus
(*infra*, pp. 389-399).

To conclude the present section, reference need be made only to the
remaining non-binomial zoologists of the period immediately following
Buffon—namely Brisson (1756) and Pennant (1781).

Brisson used in the main a binomial nomenclature, but not consistently
so ; hence his names are not acceptable to systematists.   Under *Cercopithecus*
he included a motley assemblage of monkeys both from the Old and the New
Worlds.   Among those to which the generic name may still be strictly
applied, he gives accounts only of le singe varié (= *C. mona*) and le singe vert
(*C. sabaeus*), both of which he found in Réaumur's cabinet.   The remainder
of his cercopithèques are either frankly of neotropical origin or pertain,
where positively identifiable, to the langurs, macaques or mangabeys.   He
relied rather on Clusius and Ray than on Buffon.   Pennant's list is more

---

* The precise date of the foundation of the royal menagerie in Paris is uncertain. At the time
of the accession of Louis XIII in 1610 there was already a collection of animals, including guenons,
although the foundation of the Jardin des Plantes was delayed until 1626. This was purely botanical
and remained so for over a century. In 1730 the menagerie is recorded as being in a state of neglect,
and it remained thus until 1732 on the king's appointment of Buffon as supervisor.

imposing and arranged more intelligently, although langurs and mangabeys remain intermixed with guenons. Recognizable guenons in Pennant's volume are the Palatine or Roloway (based on Allamand and Schreber), the Diana (still with some confusion with Marcgrav's *exquima*), the Green Monkey (le callitriche of Buffon), the Yellowish Monkey (possibly a variant of the preceding), the Mustache (= *C. cephus*) and the White-nosed (*C. nictitans*).

GENERAL CHARACTERS

Guenons are medium to large monkeys varying in build from slender (*e.g. C. petaurista*) to stocky (*e.g. C. neglectus*) with rounded heads, muzzles showing little prominence, especially compared with *Cercocebus* (which are approached in this respect somewhat by the *C. aethiops* group) and with the pelvic limbs slightly exceeding the pectoral. A long tail, well haired throughout, is invariably present; and the ischial callosities, though distinct are relatively small, surrounded by normal hairy skin, and in the male separated by a relatively wide area of soft integument. A sexual catamenial swelling does not occur in the female, but there may be some local tumescence of the vulva associated with mucoid discharge followed by a catamenial flow. Hands and feet of generalized character, adapted for quadrupedal arboreal progression.

The skull is small and rounded with little prominence of the face and with the teeth relatively small; molars bilophodont with the fifth cusp lacking from the hindmost lower molar.

EXTERNAL CHARACTERS

PELAGE.—Guenons are remarkable for the beauty and variety of their pelage, exceeding that of almost any other genus of Mammalia. The variations in colour are largely due to modifications in the intrinsic pigmentary pattern of individual hairs and, to some degree, in the intensity of the pigmentary deposit at various levels. Typically the dorsal pelage at least is characterized by what may be termed a pepper-and-salt effect produced by a series of alternating bands or zones of contrasting colours along the length of each individual hair-shaft—a feature met with to some degree in many wild mammals and termed by geneticists the agouti pattern. It has already been referred to in several platyrrhine genera, *e.g.* certain Hapalidae and *Saimiri*, but in none is the contrast so great as in most *Cercopitheci*, nor are the number of alternating bands so numerous. Thus alternating bands of yellow and darker orange, brown or even black produce a general mottled greenish tinge in the group of green guenons typified by *C. aethiops*.

Variations, often of an individual nature, affect the density of the pigment granules and the nature of the pigment itself resulting in the production of melanistic, erythristic, flavistic or even albinistic mutants of the general

PLATE II

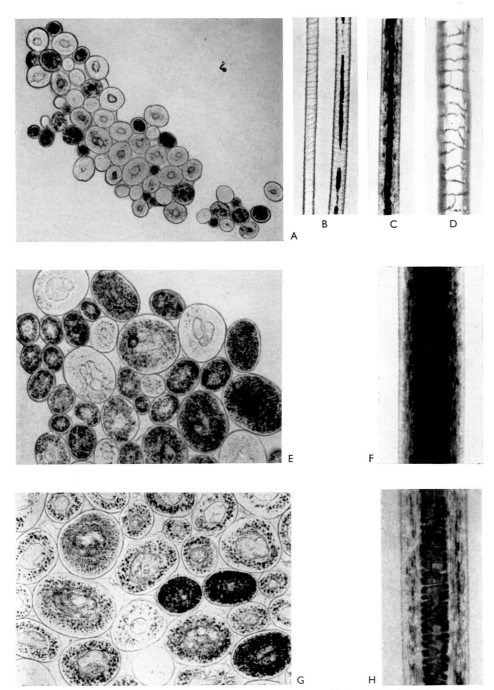

Photos: Wool Industries Research Assoc.

Photomicrographs of hair in *Cercopithecus*

Cercopithecus aethiops, foetal, mid-dorsal : A, cross-sections (× 200) ; whole mounts, B and C, fine fibres (× 200) ; D, cast of the scale pattern of a fine fibre (× 400). *Cercopithecus sabaeus* ♀ mid-dorsal : E, cross-sections (× 200); F, whole mount, coarse fibre (× 200) ; *Cercopithecus mona mona*, mid-dorsal (shoulders): G, cross-sections (× 200); H, coarse fibre, whole mount (× 200)

PLATE III

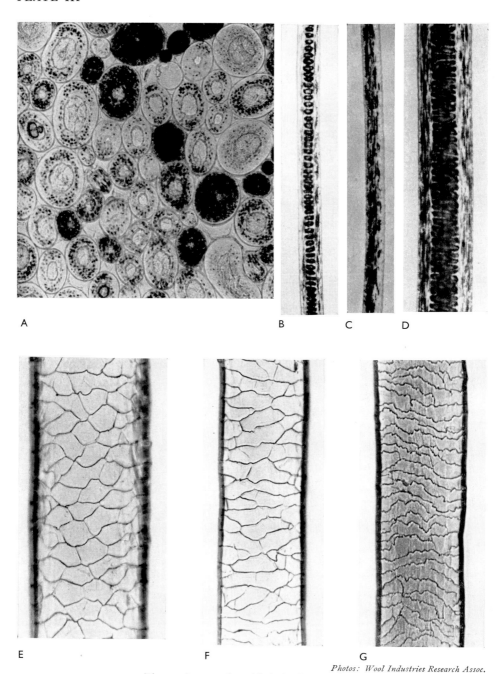

A   B   C   D

E   F   G

Photos: Wool Industries Research Assoc.

Photomicrographs of hair in *Cercopithecus*

Cercopithecus nictitans martini, mid-dorsal : Whole mounts A, cross-sections ; B and C, fine fibres ; D, coarse fibre (× 200). Below, casts of the scale patterns of coarse fibres, E, root region ; F, along the length of the fibre ; G, tip region (× 400). Kershaw Collection

PLATE IV

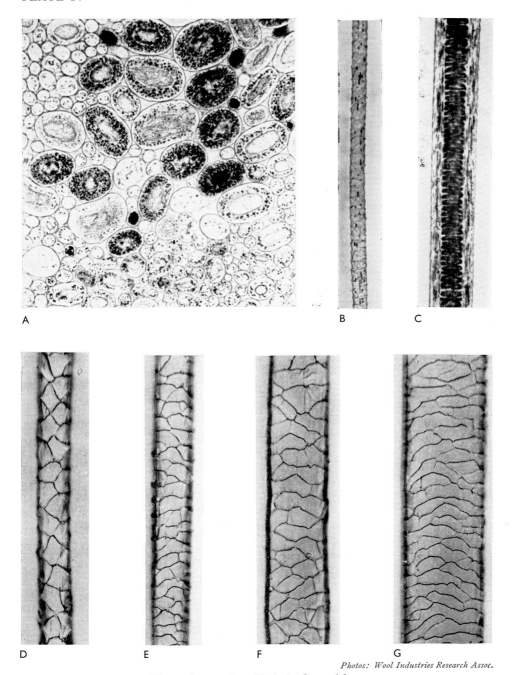

A   B   C

D   E   F   G

Photos: Wool Industries Research Assoc.

Photomicrographs of hair in *Cercopithecus*
Cercopithecus petaurista buttikoferi, mid-dorsal : A, cross-sections ; whole mounts, B, fine
fibre ; C, coarse fibre, (× 200). Below, casts of the scale patterns : D, fine fibre, root
region ; E, fine fibre along the length of the fibre ; F, coarse fibre, root region ; G,
coarse fibre, along the length of the fibre (× 400)

PLATE V

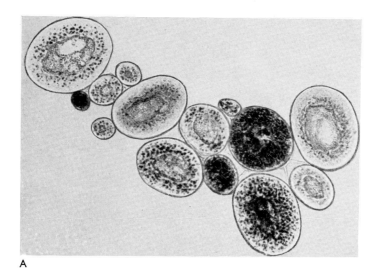

A

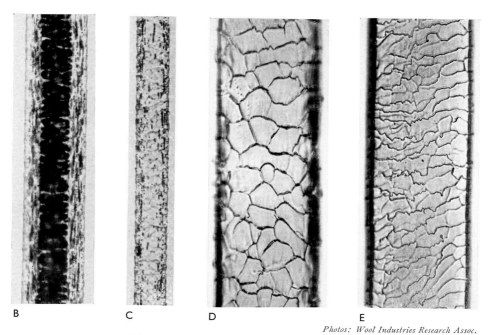

B   C   D   E

Photos: Wool Industries Research Assoc.

Photomicrographs of hair in *Cercopithecus*

Cercopithecus cephus, mid-dorsal : Whole mounts, A, cross-sections ; B, coarse fibre ; C, fibre of intermediate thickness (× 200).   Casts of the scale patterns of a coarse fibre ; D, root region and along the length of the fibre ; E, tip-region (× 400).

population. Such individuals being brought to Europe have, in the past, been described as distinct species and it has involved considerable assiduity on the part of collectors and students in more recent times to unravel the confusion resulting from over-hasty declarations of the earlier observers.

This aspect of the problem has been specially considered by Schwarz (1927). Melanin pigment is normally deposited in the hair shafts in two forms, a dark-brown large granular type (eumelanin) and a more diffused, paler (yellowish) deposit or phaeomelanin. These too are frequently mixed, especially in dark-coated animals and in the darker zones of individual hairs. In the pale zones, phaeomelanin occurs alone in varying dilution. Each type of pigment is produced and inherited independently. Black or dark-brown pigment develops ontogenetically later than phaeomelanin and therefore darkening frequently increases with age. Erythrism is the effect produced by lesser concentration of eumelanin and therefore may appear as a juvenile phenomenon, but sometimes mutants appear in which full eumelanin production is delayed or entirely arrested. Such phenomena give varying degrees of erythrism or, in the most extreme cases (when phaeomelanin alone is present), flavism. Albinism results when both forms of melanin fail to develop ; melanism when the phaeomelanin, though present, is completely masked by excessive development of eumelanin. A completely albinistic *C. cephus* was observed in the Paris menagerie (1955) and an albino *C. mona* was received in the London Zoo (October 1962). See also *infra* (p. 458).

Schwarz (*loc. cit.*) concluded that the type specimens of *C. stairsi* Sclater and *C. stairsi mossambicus* were erythristic mutants and mentions several others. In an earlier paper (Schwarz, 1910) examples of albinistic mutation had been reported in *Cercopithecus*, and to these were added (1927) a case of partial albinism in a specimen of *C. nictitans martini* and one of almost total albinism in *C. mitis*.

Even earlier, Pocock (1907), had been impressed with the interesting phenomenon in *Cercopithecus* of the frequency with which the three colours, black, red and white were interchangeable, sometimes during the lifetime of a single individual. He exemplified this by quoting *C. erythrogaster*, in which the nose-spot was believed to change from black to white during growth. Further, in *C. erythrotis sclateri* the nose-spot is white, whereas in *C. e. erythrotis* it is red ; in *C. grayi* it is yellow or reddish-yellow ; in *C. erythrogaster* the belly is red ; in *C. petaurista* it is white ; in *C. mitis mitis* a black belly is the rule, but in its Congo race (*C. m. kandti*) it is again red. Similar variations affect the hairs on the external ear, and those forming on the brow-band.

Certain areas of reddish hairs (*e.g.* the pubic region in *C. nictitans*) have been attributed by Sanderson (1940, p. 653) to staining by food, for he claims it can be removed with soap and water. This is a strange situation to be so affected by food, but other foreign substances may be responsible. The same probably applies to the reddish area at the base of the tail in the Vervet

(*C. pygerythrus*). It is true that some staining in the pubic region may be due to a local secretion from cutaneous glands since orange to brown waxy granules frequently occur, *e.g.* in *C. p. callidus*, in the groins and pubic region. On the other hand, Booth (1956), referring to colour variations in the pubic region of *C. diana*, maintains that Sanderson's hypothesis is not there applicable as the erythrism is not removable by water or organic solvents ; he therefore concluded it to be a genuine pigment.

Several species of *Cercopithecus* are remarkable for the development of facial hair. This may affect almost the whole face with the exception of the circumocular region, forming a mat of short hair—uniformly black in *C. p. pygerythrus*, but in other forms variously coloured (*e.g. C. neglectus*). In another group definite patterns are formed, notably the dense mat of contrasting white or coloured hair forming a well defined pad on the nose (*e.g.* in *C. nictitans, C. petaurista* and its relations and *C. erythrotis*). The face is also finely haired in the widespread races of *C. mitis*.

MICROSTRUCTURE OF HAIR.—This is illustrated in a number of species in Plates II-V. All show certain general characteristics, but some features in *C. aethiops* are confined to that superspecies.

Microscopic examination confirms the distribution of pigment in annular bands along the hair length. In the adult pelage there are coarse and fine hairs intermixed, with fibres of intermediate diameter in fair abundance. Coarse fibres from all species show the same type of medulla and this medulla likewise occurs in the finer hairs, but some of the finer hairs lack the medulla or show only an interrupted one. More fine hairs occur in the pelage of *C. petaurista buttikoferi* than in that of the more heavily built *C. nictitans martini* ; moreover some of these are non-medullated and the pigment is in the form of large granules arranged in short links.

Cross sectional appearances in both coarse and fine hairs are similar in shape, but there are differences in pigmentary distribution. In most cases the pigment occurs in large granules arranged in ring form, but in *C. sabaeus* the granules are smaller and more evenly distributed. All examples include some hairs with very dense pigmentation.

Cuticular scales have crenate margins near the tip, otherwise both fine and coarse hairs show the same scale pattern in all the species examined.

In a foetal *C. aethiops* only fine hairs are present, some being non-medullated, others showing an interrupted or a continuous medulla of the same type as in the adult pelage, but with the alveoli more closely attached.

HAIR TRACTS.—De Beaux (1917) has provided a very detailed account of the pilous system of a near-term foetus of the Grivet (*C. aethiops aethiops*) which agrees very closely with conditions I have recorded from a full-term foetus of *C. sabaeus* and an early postnatal *C. tantalus*. At this age the tracts are well defined as the hairy coat is not rich, depending, however, more on the fineness of the individual hairs than on sparsity of distribution or shortness.

Cercopithecus pogonias grayi ♂, Antwerp Zoo

On the supraciliary region a tract of longish though soft and wavy hairs stands out prominently, forming a fringe of quasi-vibrissae 12-18 mm. long. Over the glabella these have an upward and forward direction, but laterally they are directed upwards and laterally. Similar hairs directed outwards and a trifle backwards occur over the cheeks. On the forehead the hairs have a forward direction and in the adult these become strongly developed in many species, giving a sort of peaked-cap effect. Towards the vertex the hairs become shorter, so that, in the adult, a gentle slope is effected, gradually lowering towards the occiput. In the lanugo-bearing foetus most of the hairs on the vertex measure approximately 15 mm. long, and they shorten gradually until they measure 13-10 mm. (de Beaux). At the same time the hair slope gradually changes from the upstanding hairs posterior to those on the forehead to those on the occiput which are backwardly directed. In *C. tantalus* a group of upstanding rhinal vibrissae was observed and this persists in the adult of *C. sabaeus*.

Hairs on the face are characteristically oriented. In *C. aethiops* the short hairs on the upper limit of the interorbital region are directed upwards and medially, but at the lower limit they are directed medially and downwards (interorbital divergence ; stria glabellaris of Schwalbe). At the upper end of the nose the hairs are of the same direction as the last mentioned, but inferiorly it is possible to distinguish two groups of hairs, a medial and a lateral on the dorsum nasi. Medially the hairs continue the medial and downward trend, but laterally they are directed downwards and laterally. There is thus a line of median convergence and a line of lateral divergence. The latter tract descends forming an arcade around the upper limit of the narial opening, whereas the median tract proceeds down the internarial septum to mingle with the short hairs of the upper lip.

On the upper lip are short curved white hairs of vibrissal type but shorter than those on the supraorbital and genal regions. They are directed towards the buccal cleft. On the infraorbital region short white hairs take on a downward and lateral trend and, together with the supraorbital hairs form a complete frame around the orbit. Well developed eyelashes adorn the upper eyelids ; feebler ones affect the lower lid.

On the cheeks, apart from the vibrissal type hairs, numerous soft hairs of normal character form the basis of the whiskers (*favoris* of the French writers) so commonly found adorning this area in adults of the present genus. Their direction varies greatly even between related subspecies. In *C. sabaeus* they show an upward and backward trend towards the root of the helix, but in others they may be directed downwards or laterally and vary considerably in length, in the degree to which they hide the ears and so on.

On the chin the hairs radiate in all directions from a median centre of divergence. Anteriorly they project forwards and then proceed upwards on the lower lip, pointing towards the buccal cleft. In some species (*C. diana* and its races, *C. dryas* and in *C. neglectus*) a beard is formed in adults, varying in length and form according to species.

On the throat, posterior to the divergence centre, a median line of divergence continues back as far as the level of the nipples. The most lateral hairs on the throat take on a decidedly lateral trend and proceed to converge with those from the cheeks in augmenting the whiskers.

On the ears of *C. sabaeus* there are few or no hairs on the ascending part of the helix, but numerous short, dark hairs adorn the horizontal upper part of the helical fold. These are directed backwards and upwards. Hairs of similar direction and character occur on the scapha below the helix and on the antihelix. On the lamina they are shorter and more upwardly directed, except inferiorly where they are more horizontal. The general trend is therefore an arched one following the curve of the antihelix. On the tragus a tuft of upward and backwardly directed hairs appears. In the adults of many species the hairs on the helix and tragus are greatly developed forming prominent tufts often standing up above the elongated side whiskers. A tuft of radiating hairs stands up from the summit of the antihelix.

On the dorsal parts of the trunk and tail, hairs conform to the primitive cranio-caudal pattern. Laterally, on the flanks, they become increasingly oblique and, passing on to the belly, a median convergence is produced, which is traceable from the level of the pectoral parting (nipple level) to the umbilicus. Posterior to the umbilicus there is a reflected tract with hairs proceeding forwards and medially from the groins to the median line. In the adult, where they are longer, a median crest may thus be formed. On the perineum, dorsal to the scrotum an oblique backward and medial direction is reassumed ; and in the foetus fine lanugo hairs occur on the area destined to become the ischial callosities ; these are lost when the lanugo coat is shed post-natally.

All the hairs on the tail, both above and below proceed cranio-caudally.

On the pectoral limbs hairs are directed distally and slightly postaxiad on the brachium, both on the lateral and medial aspects—except along the anterior border, where they descend directly towards the anticubital fossa. On the forearm the hairs on the radial one-third continue the directly distal trend, but on the ulnar two-thirds they are directed somewhat postaxially, more so above, but increasingly less so below.

Dorsally this divergence is carried distally on to the dorsum of the manus. The olecranon is virtually naked.

On the thighs laterally the hairs sweep in curves more or less transverse to the axis of the limb from anterior to posterior border. On the medial side they are more distally directed, but along the anterior border of the thigh a distally directed tract is found, which continues over the knee on to the crural segment, where all the hairs have an almost purely distal trend,—a pattern which continues on to the dorsum of the foot and toes.

CUTANEOUS PIGMENTATION.—As in many other Cercopithecidae cutaneous pigment is not confined to the epidermis, but frequently also exists in specialized contractile cells (melanocytes) situated in the superficial layers

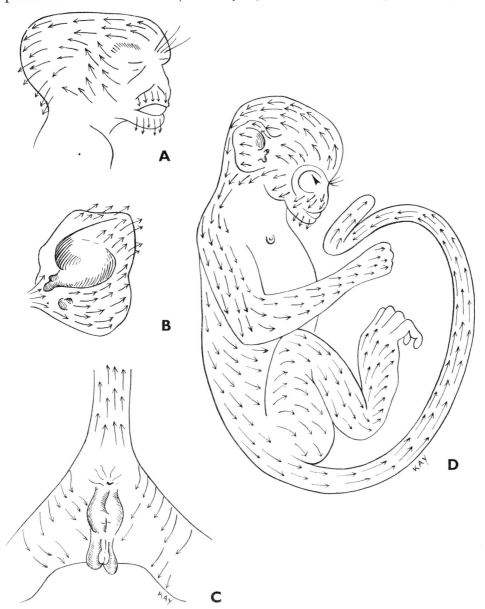

FIG. 20.—*Cercopithecus* sp. Diagrams of the hair tracts in the advanced foetus. A—C, *C. sabaeus*; D, *C. mona*

of the dermis. In this situation, the effect of the optical phenomenon termed by Tyndall " scattering ", through the semi-translucent superjacent epidermal layers, is to produce, not a black or grey tinge, but varying shades of blue or blue-green, depending on the concentration of the pigment. This is specially notable on the sparsely haired ventral regions, including the medial aspects of the limbs. In many species of *Cercopithecus* the genital area, especially the scrotum in the male, is the special site for vivid blue coloration. Remarkable subspecific differences have been described (Zuckerman and Fulton, 1934; Dandelot, 1960) in the different forms of the superspecies *C. aethiops* in respect of this pigment. Hues are modified to some extent by vascularity and haemodynamic factors.

The blue scrotal skin differs in several respects from the dull bluish effects met with elsewhere, being of a more pastel shade and a brighter tint. Oettlé (1958, 1959) has recently shown that in the Vervet (*C. pygerythrus*) the dermal melanin is not solely responsible for the blue colour of the scrotum, for in this region the superficial collagen fibres of the dermis themselves exhibit a brilliant blue reflection when viewed under the microscope by reflected light. This is regarded as a structural colour, produced by the regularity and parallel disposition of the fibres. The phenomenon is comparable with the optical interference produced by multiple thin films, although here they arise from multiple thin fibrils. The effect is not seen in the superficial dermal collagen elsewhere on the body. Presumably the layer of melanocytes in the deeper part of the dermis serves as a reflecting layer similar to the effect produced in the tapetum of the eyeball of many lower (especially nocturnal) mammals.

Whimster (1961, personal communication) has made some observations on dermal melanocytes in the scrotal and other skin of *Cercopithecus*. Areas of skin which appear black or sooty (*e.g.* the face in *C. aethiops*) owe their colour, as in dark human skin, to heavy melanin deposits in the epidermis. The same applies to the palms and soles.

Pink, red or scarlet patches, *e.g.* nipples, prepuce, etc. differ considerably from the scrotal skin in structure. For instance, the papillary layer is well developed (it is lacking in scrotal skin) and the papillae bear dilated capillaries and venules; at the same time dermal melanoblasts are lacking. Furthermore the collagen fibres show no blue fluorescence, but give a white reflex, though a few fibres may show a slight greenish reflex.

White skin, *e.g.* on the flanks of *C. aethiops*, lateral to the dull blue area, has no dermal melanoblast layer, and the superficial collagen lacks, for the most part, the greenish-blue reflex, though scattered fibres may exhibit the phenomenon.

CUTANEOUS GLANDS.—Apart from sebaceous glands associated with hair follicles and sweat-glands (which appear to be limited to specialized zones such as the palms and soles) no specialized or aggregated cutaneous glands have thus far been described for any member of this genus. That such glands are present somewhere is almost certain in view of the pronounced garlic-like odour emitted by most members of this genus. The writer has frequently noted the presence of brownish or bright orange waxy granules in the pubic and inguinal regions where the hairs are sparse or virtually lacking, especially in *C. aethiops* and its relatives. This strongly suggests the presence of hypertrophied glands of the holocrine type. In *C. ascanius* the garlic-like odour is detectable more especially on the anterior half of the body, where a yellow-brown scurfy secretion occurs at the bases of the hairs over the median pectoral region (between the acromion processes) but some is also found in the inguinal region. Modified holocrine and apocrine glands in the inguinal region of *C. pygerythrus callidus* are shown in Plate VI, the latter forming locally a stratum in the deeper part of the dermis. Sweat glands occur in palms and soles. The functions of the former have been studied experimentally in *C. aethiops* by Sakurai and Montagna (1964).

REGIONAL DETAILS

RHINAL AREA.—Fronto-nasal profile flat or slightly concave, but the external nose itself is convex and well padded. Nares are closely approximated, more so below than above, being obliquely disposed with the upper ends more patent and rounded and the lower narrow and slit-like. In the newborn they may be narrow throughout (and measure 6 mm. long ; they are separated by 7 mm. at their upper ends but by 3 mm. only below (de Beaux). The medial narial margin is slightly convex and the lateral correspondingly concave. The convexity on the medial edge takes the form of a firm lobate process often less pigmented than the rest, at the junction of upper and middle one-third of narial margin.

BUCCAL ZONE.—Rima oris not very extensive (cf. *Macaca*, *Papio*) due to relatively minor degree of prognathism. The line of the rima is virtually horizontal without the sinuous (cupid's bow) course so typical of the Hapalidae and Cebidae. Upper lip with somewhat convex profile. A frenulum is present on the mucosal side. No frenulum tethers the lower lip. The mucosa lining the vestibulum oris is herniated into the subcutaneous tissues of the cheek and neck in the form of paired pouches. These are not particularly large in the present genus compared with their size in *Macaca*, *Papio* and their relatives. In an immature ♀ *C. p. pygerythrus* of 82·5 mm. head-length, the distended pouch has a diameter of only 17 mm. Its slit-like opening (5·5 mm. long) occupies the floor of the vestibulum oris opposite the lower premolars.

OCULAR REGION.—The prominent brows form a transverse bony bar covered with integument (often exhibiting a granular surface) and forming a double arch over the two orbits, with an intervening depression in the median line. The integument may be pigmented (*e.g.* in *C. aethiops*) or not (*e.g. C. pygerythrus cynosuros*) but is adorned with long, dark vibrissal type hairs ; these also descend some distance on the interorbital region. The eyelids are thin, paler than the surrounding skin and virtually hairless, except for their margins, which are adorned with eyelashes. These are more strongly developed on the upper lid, where, *e.g.*, in *C. neglectus*, two rows are present, a finer set located behind the main series. On the lower lid only fine lashes are present. Follicles of the eyelashes are associated with sebaceous glands and the orifices of Meibomian glands are visible behind the eyelash series.

At the medial palpebral canthus a small nictitating membrane occurs ; this is flesh-coloured with a pigmented free border.

The iris varies greatly in colour according to species, but is commonly some shade of brown or olive. Coloration is also affected by age, for example, in a newborn *C. mitis stuhlmanni* the irides were bluish, darkening during early posnatal life to the adult colour.

EXTERNAL EAR.—In *Cercopithecus* the contour of the pinna is rounded, with little or no indication of the projecting angle at the postero-superior limit so well marked in members of the next subfamily. The angle is best indicated in the *C. aethiops* section of the genus ; in others it is almost indicated in the *C. aethiops* section of the genus ; in others it is almost totally lacking. In these the helix ceases abruptly at the morphological apex beyond which the posterior margin is thin and vertically elongated. Inferiorly it passes by a broadly rounded lamina into the convex lower edge of the pinna. The pinna is similar in *C. ascanius*, but no trace of morphological apex is seen in *C. mona* and its relatives, nor in *C. diana*, *C. petaurista*, *C. erythrotis*, *C. cephus*. In all these the superior part of the helix is narrower and usually extends, gradually diminishing, on to the posterior border. In *C. lowei*, however, only the forepart of the helix is preserved. In all, the crus helicis is well developed and more or less horizontally disposed. It ends in a broad base in the centre of the cymba conchae and its main portion is broad, overshadowing the inferior crus of the antihelix, though in *C. lowei* it is slender. Both tragus and anti-tragus are low, lobate elevations. A well-marked fossa intertragica occurs postero-inferior to the tragus. From the antitragus the antihelix follows the curve of the pinna upwards and then forwards to divide into its two crura, of which the inferior is the better marked, the superior being some-times, *e.g.* in *C. lowei*, almost obsolete, though the fossa triangularis is well indicated. A Darwinian tubercle is retained according to Keith (1901) in 80 per cent of ears in the present genus (see Table on p. 59 *antea*). Below the fossa antitragica the lamina may be produced into a wide flap almost simulating a lobulus and labelled as such by de Beaux in his Grivet, *e.g.* in *C. sabaeus* and *C. cephus*, though this is entirely wanting in *C. lowei*, *C. mona* and *C. diana*. The morphological apical region of the pinna is in some

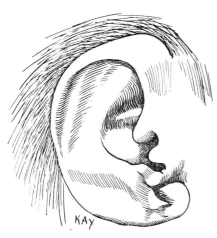

FIG. 21.—*Cercopithecus hamlyni* ♂
Right external ear

PLATE VI

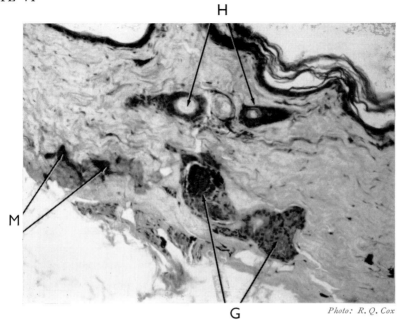

Photo: R. Q. Cox

Cercopithecus pygerythrus callidus, adult ♂. Vertical section of skin from the inguinal region to show cutaneous holocrine glands, G. Also shown are hair follicles, H, and melanophores, M. Stain haematoxylin-eosin. Magnification $\times \frac{180}{1}$

PLATE VII

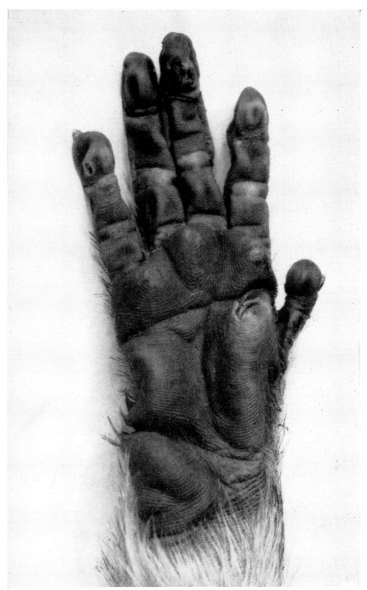

Photo: R. Q. Cox

Cercopithecus sabaeus. Photograph of manus from palmar aspect

species, *e.g. C. mona* and *C. erythrotis*, adorned with a tuft of hairs, often contrastedly coloured.

CHEIRIDIA.—Pocock (1926), after examining many specimens representative of most groups within the genus, failed to discover any characters in which the hands or feet could as a whole be distinguished from those of *Macaca*. He found minor individual variations and others between members of the different groups, but could not satisfy himself that these were constantly associated with the recognized divisions to which some authors have given subgeneric status.

In *C. diana*, according to Pocock, the palm is about one and a third times as long as the width across the palmar pad. Pads are well developed. The pollex, when aligned forwards, reaches as far distal as the middle of the palmar interdigital pads. Digital formula III > IV > II = V > I. Digit III exceeds II by the length of its distal segment ; it exceeds IV by the distal one-third of the distal segment ; V scarcely reaches the distal interphalangeal joint of IV. Interdigital webbing is shallow and basal. Pocock found the hand of *C. d. roloway* similar, but the palm slightly longer, and III definitely

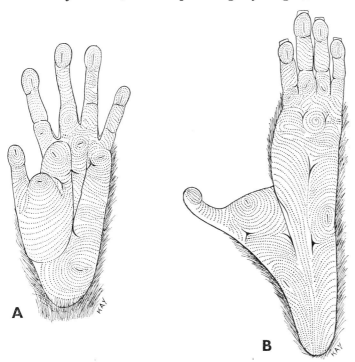

FIG. 22.—*C. campbelli lowei.* A, left manus and B, left pes × $\frac{2}{3}$

longer, but V somewhat shorter. *C. mona* too has a similar hand according to Pocock, but sometimes there is deeper interdigital webbing, especially between II and III. I have found deep webbing in *C. lowei* between III and IV, less between II and III. Dermatoglyphics are figured in an adult male

Q

C. lowei (Fig. 22). Configurations occur on all the four interdigital pads—of the concentric type around a central island ridge variously directed. Another centre formed by a transverse loop occurs on the hypothenar pad. Elsewhere on the palm the ridges run mainly in transversely disposed curves. This agrees with the findings of Midlo and Cummins (1942) who figure a number of variations on this theme, with triradii separating the principal fields. Some hands show an additional configuration on the proximal part of the thenar eminence. Similar features are described and figured by de Beaux (*loc. cit.*) in his foetal *C. aethiops*.

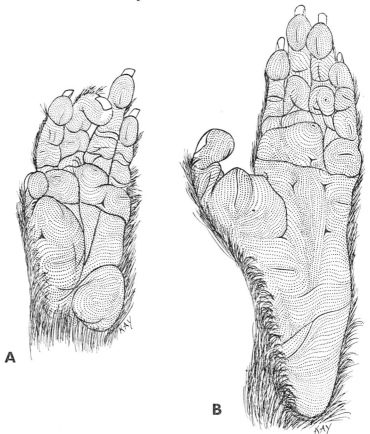

FIG. 23.—*Cercopithecus hamlyni* ♂. A, left manus and B, left pes × ¼

On the proximal phalanges transverse or oblique parallel ridges may occur, but I have found looped configurations on II and III in *C. lowei*. Transverse or oblique parallel lines only occur on the intermediate phalanges of digits II–V. On the apical digital pads the normal arched patterns around a central ridge constantly occur.

The foot in *C. diana*, according to Pocock, is three and a half times as long as the width across the interdigital pads. The hallux extends distally as far as the distal edge of the interdigital pads. Digital formula III > IV >

II > V > I. Digits II and V are shorter proportional to III and IV than in the manus. Pocock found the hallux longer and stouter in *C. d. roloway*, III longer in proportion to IV, and V proportionately shorter, only just extending beyond the distal end of the proximal phalanx of IV. Doubtless these variations are purely individual rather than indicative of adaptations to different functions. Interdigital webbing is stated to be more evident in *C. mona*. In the group which includes *C. petaurista* the sole is very long and narrow (nearly four times as long as its maximum width), but webbing is extensive, especially between II and III, and IV and V. In *C. erythrogaster* Pocock found the foot shorter and stouter, only thrice as long as the maximum width. In the *C. mitis* group and in *C. preussi* the ratio of length to width is three and a half and interdigital webbing rather deep, that between II and III in *C. mitis kandti* extending beyond the proximal interphalangeal joint of the short II. In the *C. nictitans* group the feet resemble those of *C. mitis*. In the Vervet, Pocock found the length of the sole a little over three times the maximum width, with fairly extensive interdigital webbing between II and III, but shallow between the remaining digits.

Pedal dermatoglyphics tend to be simpler than those of the hand, due to reduction in the number of interdigital configurations. However, judging from the observations of Midlo and Cummins, there is a great deal of variability in this respect, the number of distal closed fields varying from 1 to 5. When five are present one of these is located on the distal part of the hypothenar pad, proximal to the postaxial interdigital field. When a single interdigital field is present, as in the *C. lowei* here figured, this is located proximal to the interdigital cleft between III and IV as in Midlo and Cummins' fig. 405. A triradius occurs in the centre of the distal part of the sole demarcating the limits of the first interdigital pad and the fields of parallel ridges which mark the thenar and hypothenar areas.

PERINEUM AND EXTERNAL GENITALIA OF THE MALE (Pocock, 1926 ; Hill, 1958).—Members of this genus exhibit the most generalized state of male external genitalia among the Old World Primates. Although there are minor species differences, all forms agree in that the adult possesses a large, finely wrinkled, seminude, bilobed scrotum having a broad penial attachment. The small to moderately sized penis emerges from the anterior wall of the scrotum, near the root of the sac and is clothed with a short, soft, transversely folded prepuce which commonly leaves at least part of the glans penis exposed, though this is variable in degree. Often the prepuce is brightly coloured, commonly bright scarlet (*e.g.* in *C. aethiops* where it contrasts strongly with the colour of the scrotum), but in other species the prepuce and scrotum are concolorous. The reflected layer of the prepuce is carried proximally for a considerable distance beyond the corona glandis ; it has no frenulum, and consequently there is a large pars retroglandularis of the corpus penis lying freely within the preputial sheath. In prepubertal animals this arrangement does not exist, for the reflected portion of the prepuce is connected to the corpus penis, by epithelial adhesions. In still younger animals this epithelial union affects the glans also. Freeing of the prepuce from the penis is produced by splitting of the solid epithelium analogous with the canalization at puberty of the vaginal cord of the pre-pubertal female.

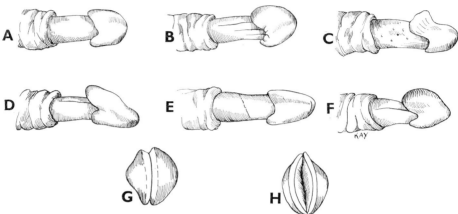

FIG. 24.—Penis of various Cercopithecinae : A, *C. ae. aethiops*. B, *C. mona*. C, *C. petaurista buttikoferi*. D, *C. albogularis kolbi*. E, *C. neglectus*. F, *Erythrocebus pyrro-notus*. G, *C. mona*, apical view. H, *C. mona*, apical view. with meatal lips everted.

The corpus penis is subcylindrical or somewhat laterally compressed with a median keel, *e.g.* in *C. albogularis kolbi* (fig. 27), on the perineal aspect ; there is also some narrowing towards the glans, providing thus a constriction or collum adjacent to the retrocoronal sulcus. The glans is provided with a markedly projecting corona expanding proximally over the collum, especially on the dorsum and somewhat less below, the sides being more or less deeply notched. The glans is acorn-shaped with some tendency to lateral compression and is incised in the median line by the urethral meatus throughout its whole dorso-ventral extent. There is little or no tendency to asymmetry so frequently seen in the next subfamily, but occasionally there may be slight over-prominence of one lip of the meatus, or the meatal slit may be a fraction off the mid line. A well-developed baculum is present. In an adult *C. neglectus* this measures 17.7 mm. long (for description *vide infra*, p. 339). Ischial callosities, according to Pocock (1926), are of the most primitive type in *Cercopithecus* in so far as, in the male, they are widely separated and the skin around them is undifferentiated. They are relatively small in size compared with the proportions attained in the next subfamily, while in shape and pigmentation they are variable. They may be rounded, elliptical or pyriform in outline or even less regular and may differ on the two sides. The dorsal edge is frequently slightly emarginate. Integument between the two callosities is normal hairy skin and this may continue dorsally to the anal prominence. Hairs springing from the surrounding skin are typically

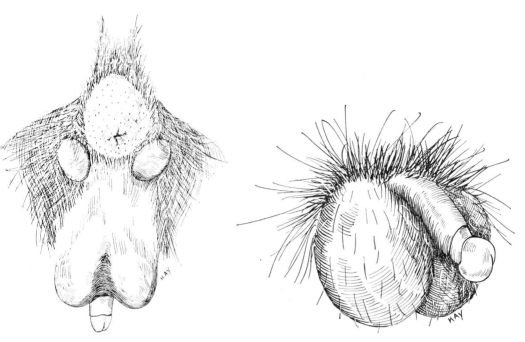

FIG. 25.—*Cercopithecus pygerythrus* ♂ genitalia etc. from behind.

FIG. 26.—*Cercopithecus aethiops* ♂ oblique view of the external genitalia

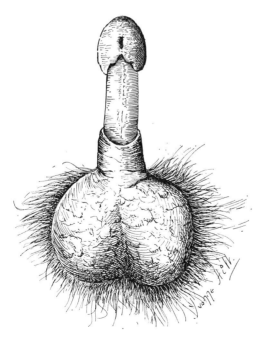

FIG. 27.—*Cercopithecus albogularis kolbi* ♂. External genitalia from the ventral aspect

long, overshadowing the margins of the callosities, and are directed centri-petally with respect thereto. Sometimes the callosities may be partially or almost wholly concealed by the overlapping hairs (hence presumably Illiger's use of his generic name *Lasiopyga* for the present genus).

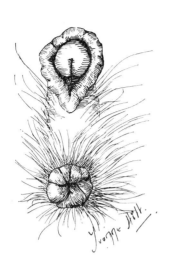

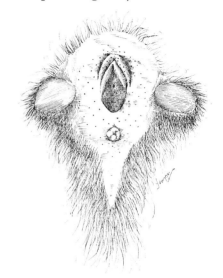

FIG. 28.—*Cercopithecus neglectus* ♀.
External genitalia

FIG. 29.—*Cercopithecus pogonias grayi*,
subadult ♀. External genitalia

PERINEUM AND EXTERNAL GENITALIA OF THE FEMALE.—The vulva in *Cercopithecus* is typically inconspicuous and situated in the integument between the ischial callosities, separated from the anal prominence by a perineal body of moderate length.

With regard to details the species of *Cercopithecus* vary little among themselves, but there are often individual differences, possibly of a physio-logical nature or indicative of the state of health of the animal, *e.g.* as regards patency of the rima or prominence of the clitoris. But *Cercopithecus* differs profoundly from *Miopithecus* in these features.

The rima is short and bordered by narrow labia minora, which are often scarcely raised above the surrounding integument. Labia majora are com-monly lacking at any rate in the adult, but small representatives sometimes persist. The clitoris is usually bright pink to scarlet and therefore contrasts with the labia. It is not usually prominent, but is markedly erectile and, under sexual excitement, is " presented " to the observer or to an interested male. Acorn-like in shape, the glans is notched on its perineal side, the notch sometimes extending to the summit. The corpus clitoridis is enclosed within a cutaneous sheath, usually pigmented, and this may terminate distally in a crenulated frill around the glans. Bright coloration is usual on the perineal area and the neighbourhood. Scattered glandular papillae may occur on prepuce, labia and perineum (*e.g.* in *C. pogonias*).

In no species of *Cercopithecus*, as here understood, is there a catamenial swelling. The most that has been observed by the writer was a slight but regular cyclical puffiness of the vulva in a female *C. albogularis erythrarchus* associated with the menstrual flow. The puffiness was restricted to the labia and did not affect any of the surrounding area. The menstrual cycle is of medium duration (31 days in *C. aethiops*, Zuckerman, 1930; Harms, 1956) and the period of menstrual flow quite short—not more than three days in *C. albogularis* (personal observation).

SKELETAL SYSTEM

SKULL

Supplying an omission of Elliot (1913), Rode (1936, 1938) enumerated the distinctions of the skull of *Cercopithecus* in which contrast is made with that of *Cercocebus*, since the only difference previously mentioned in the literature was a dental feature, namely the presence on $M._{\overline{3}}$ in *Cercocebus* of a fifth cusp posteriorly and lacking in *Cercopithecus*.

In general the adult cranium of *Cercopithecus* is smaller than that of the adult mangabey, though the difference is largely relative, due particularly to the lesser degree of prognathism and the generally more lightly built muzzle. Consequently the palate is relatively shorter and the facial angle (of Cuvier and Geoffroy) less acute (60°, Lordat, 1804). Suborbital fossae are entirely lacking in *Cercopithecus*, though strongly marked in *Cercocebus*. A further effect is that the angle formed between the orbital process of the zygoma with the temporal process is greater (70°-90°) compared with the acute angle (36°-65°) found in *Cercocebus* (conclusions based on 27 crania of *Cercopithecus*, representing 10 or 12 species; compared with 24 crania of *Cercocebus*).

The most complete account of the skull of *Cercopithecus* is that of Clara Weinbrenn (1930) based upon a series of 47 (43 ♂♂, 4 ♀♀) specimens of *C. pygerythrus*, the majority from a single area in Cape Province. Some comparative data for *C. samango* were also recorded by this author. Her conclusions are here incorporated with others deduced by the writer from examination of crania of *C. campbelli*, 11; *C. mona*, 103; *C. nictitans martini*, 87; *C. erythrotis camerunensis*, 19; *C. preussi*, 7; *C. petaurista*, 12; *C. ascanius*, 1; *C. pogonias*, 4. Single specimens of various other forms and numerous examples of undetermined species have also been examined.

In general the skull of *Cercopithecus* is of medium size with a rounded or ovoid brain-case and the face truncated and rather broad, though somewhat variable in the last respect.

Lachrymals are large, oval, with the lachrymal foramen just within the orbital rim. Forsyth Major examined 95 skulls of various species and found two extremes. In 12 he found the crista anterior entirely supported by the maxilla, which usually descends into the fossa. In 7 the opposite occurred, the fossa being entirely encircled by lachrymal, and, as the crista is generally flattened, the fossa could not categorically be described as within the orbit. In another 5 skulls this author found the crista almost exclusively supported by the lachrymal. He concluded that the extreme development of the lachrymal occurred chiefly in the species then arranged under Sclater's group of Melanochiri (= C. *mitis* and its relatives), but individual skulls of any species, age or sex, were found in all the categories.

The brain-case is somewhat flattened, elongated from before backwards and approximately parallel-sided, but with a marked post-orbital constriction, beyond which the cranium broadens rapidly to a maximum opposite the auditory meatus, thereafter describing a rounded occipital contour. The highest point of the skull cap is, in C. *pygerythrus*, according to Weinbrenn, about midway between the supraciliary ridges and the bregma. It is pronounced where a frontal ledge exists, but there may be a gradual incline to the vertex, more particularly in younger animals. Mensurational data on the curvature of the vault compared with those in *Macaca* and *Papio* are given by Duckworth (1904).

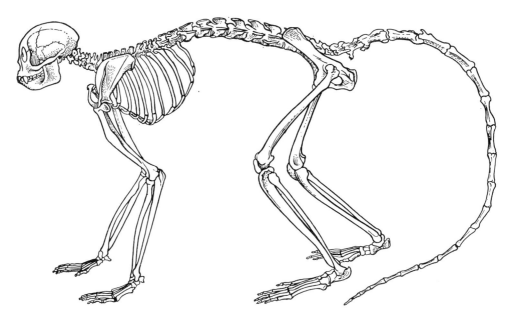

FIG. 30.—*Cercopithecus*. Skeleton (from Le Gros Clark)

Great variation occurs in cranial indices, both sexually and individually. In C. *pygerythrus* the length-breadth index is said to be brachycranial, the range varying between 90·9 and 44·4 in males and 75·0 to 61·1 for females. Cranial capacity is also very variable, the male range in C. *pygerythrus* being 70 cc. to 100 cc. and the female 66 cc. to 72 cc. Indications are that the brain increases in volume with age, even after full eruption of permanent dentition. There is some evidence that the increase involves especially the cerebellum and the temporal lobes of the cerebrum in correlation with the increase with age of basion-bregma height.

In norma verticalis the cranium is invariably phenozygous. The zygoma is very strong in adult males, but slender in the females and young males, where it is almost straight. It assumes a sinuous form with advancing age, but sometimes retains the juvenile form. It is deeper anteriorly than at its temporal end.

Temporal lines are distinctly marked, especially in males, where they sometimes meet in the sagittal plane, without, however, usually forming a

crest. A slight crest has been observed in two adult male *C. nictitans martini* out of 65 examined. Ashton and Zuckerman (1956) also mention occasional sagittal crests in males only of *C. nictitans nictitans* but give no statistical data.

Occasionally I have observed in old males and some females of *C. mona* and *C. nictitans* even when the temporal lines fail to meet, the median zone of the cranial vault between the temporal lines is raised in comparison with the level of bone covered by the temporalis muscle.

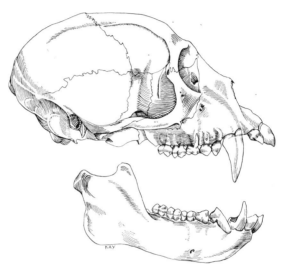

Fig. 31.—*Cercopithecus mona.* Right lateral view of the skull and mandible

The bregma is situated approximately midway between glabella and maximum occipital point, the coronal suture forming an open V, sometimes almost a transverse line, whence the relatively short sagittal (interparietal) suture proceeds to the lambda, which is situated on the upper rather than the hinder aspect of the brain-case. Sometimes, *e.g.* in examples of *C. neglectus*, the lambda lies in a transverse depression behind which the upper part of the occipital bone forms a bulge or torus, broad in the middle and narrowing laterally, where its edges merge in the lambdoid ridge descending to the mastoid area of the temporal bone. In other forms (*e.g. C. cephus*) only a linear lambdoid ridge is formed.

The sagittal suture is of varying character, being sometimes simple and almost straight throughout. Often, however, its posterior half becomes more complex with deep interpenetration of the two parietals.

The metopic suture commences to disappear very early ; it has normally ossified by the time the milk dentition has fully erupted, though signs of recent union are often visible at this age. A complete suture was observed in a *C. mona* in which the last DM had not fully erupted. Fusion occurs from the rostral end. Traces of the suture sometimes persist longer at the bregmatic end, either as a notch or as a short, usually straight suture affecting the posterior fifth or more of the frontal (see Frasetto's fig. 7). This metopic remnant is rarely in line with the sagittal suture, being either slightly to the left or right. Following are illustrative examples. In 103 skulls of *C. mona* only three showed traces of metopism, two ending to the left and one to the right of the sagittal. Among 87 skulls of *C. nictitans martini* six examples of metopism occurred :

PC 119. A wavy suture persisting on posterior two-thirds of frontal region ending to right of sagittal suture. $M.\frac{1}{1}$ erupting.

PC 437. Metopic suture persisting over one-third of its length, ending to right of sagittal. $M.\frac{2}{2}$ up.

PC 293. Similar to preceding, but aligned with sagittal. $M.\frac{2}{2}$ barely erupting.

PC 433. Female, $M\frac{2}{2}$. up. Complete metopic suture terminating to right of sagittal.

PC 284. Adult female. $M.\frac{3}{3}$ appearing. Small, very undulating S-shaped remnant near bregma, terminating to right of sagittal.

PC 200. $M.\frac{1}{1}$ appearing. Metopic suture artificially reopened by shot ; probably about posterior one-third persisted.

Among 20 skulls of *C. erythrotis* (subsp. *camerunensis* and *sclateri*) traces of metopism were found in three. A single metopic skull (posterior fourth persistent) was encountered among seven crania of *C. preussi*. Among eleven crania of *C. petaurista buttikoferi* (all juveniles) the metopic was obliterated, but three showed signs of recent fusion ; in a single *C. p. petaurista*, an adolescent with $M.\frac{2}{2}$ completely erupted, the posterior third of the metopic suture persisted as a linear feature terminating to the right of the sagittal. A more reduced trace was observed in a *C. aethiops tantalus* of similar dental age.

The parietal bone is of quadrate outline without any pronounced parietal eminence. The antero-inferior angle is acute and prolonged downwards and forwards. A parietal foramen is lacking. Occasionally accessory sutures are present. In their most advanced condition a vertical and a horizontal suture divides the bone into four and in some cases the sutures or parts of them are widened or expanded locally into adventitious fontanelles and may contain small wormian osselets. Frassetto (1903) has enumerated several such abnormal skulls represented by examples of *C. sabaeus*, *C. p. cynosuros*, *C. mona* and *C. cephus*. Parietal fontanelles have been reported by the same author in *C. mona* ; hypoasterionic fontanelle in *C. sabaeus* and episquamous fontanelle in *C. sabaeus*. Parietal wormian bones were seen in the same skull of *C. mona* which bore the parietal fontanelle.

Arrangements at the pterion have been studied by Anoutchine (1878), Ranke (1898), Frassetto (1903), Collins (1925), Hecker (1927), Ashley-Montagu (1933) and Frechkop (1954 b).

There seems to be general agreement that the pterion is very variable, as in other Catarrhini, though statements have been made that one or other type is characteristic of this or that genus, *e.g.* Sonntag (1924) makes the general assertion that in Old World monkeys the frontal articulates with the squamous temporal, thus distinguishing them from the Platyrrhini. See also Wood Jones (1929 a), Frechkop (1954) and *supra* p. 35.

Anoutchine (1878) examined a series of 38 skulls in 34 of which the pterion could be deciphered, and found 76·5 per cent exhibited a temporo-frontal contact.

Collins found the usual condition in *Cercopithecus* to be a fronto-temporal union, but noted that exceptions were frequent, particularly in *C. pygerythrus arenarius*, where he found 13 out of 17 skulls with parieto-alisphenoid contact on one or both sides. This series materially altered his averages for the genus.

Hecker (1927) found the parietal in *C. sabaeus* descending almost to the level of the cranial base, with the squamosal discoid as in *Homo*, differing, however, in the salient processus frontalis. He found a parieto-alisphenoid pterion once in five specimens, a temporal-frontal contact in two, an X-pterion once and epipteric bones once. In *C. nictitans* Hecker found the temporo-frontal type of pterion to predominate ; he met with an X-pterion once on one side only.

In *C. mona* he also found the temporo-frontal contact the more usual though often the contact was slight. Here the alisphenoid is long and narrow due to backward extension of the malar contribution. The present author has examined large series of two species, *C. mona* and *C. nictitans martini*, together with smaller series and some individuals of other forms. Results are listed in Table 11.

Odd skulls examined by Hecker included a *C. cynosuros* with temporo-frontal pterion, a *C. petaurista* with parieto-alisphenoid contact and a *C. campbelli* with a small parieto-alisphenoid contact on the left and an X-pterion on the right.

In external form the temporal bone, according to Hofmann (1926) recalls that of the Colobidae, with the mastoid portion fairly plane, the root of the zygoma extending posteriorly as a retromastoid crest. The occipital line is single and prolonged on to the mastoid, curving from above downwards behind the auditory meatus. The mastoid region anterior to this line is smooth, but the posterior part, larger and rugose, forms a muscular attachment which extends to the orifice of the facial canal. There is a pronounced

TABLE II

FORM OF PTERION IN *CERCOPITHECUS*

	No. Examined	Bilateral Temporo-frontal union	%	Bilateral Parieto-alisphenoid union	%	X-Pterion	%	Asymmetrical	%	Undecided
C. mona	104	51	50·0	41	38·0	2	2·0	10	10·0	—
C. campbelli	11	3	27·3	6	54·5	—	—	2	18·3	
C. nictitans martini	87	54	62·0	19	21·9	1	1·1	6	7·0	7
C. petaurista petaurista	1	0	—	1	—	—	—	—	—	—
C. p. buttikoferi	11	2	18·0	8	72·7	1	0·9	—	—	—
C. ascanius	2	1		1						
C. cephus	1	0		1						
C. erythrotis camerunensis	19	6	31·5	8	42·0	1	5·0	4	21·0	—
C. e. sclateri	1	—	—	1	100·0	—	—	—	—	
C. pogonias	4	4	100·0	0	—	0	—	0	—	
C. l'hoesti	1	1								
C. preussi	7	7	100·0	0	—			—		
C. pygerythrus										
C. aethiops aethiops	1	1								
C. sabaeus	1	1								
C. ae. tantalus	1	1								
C. neglectus	1	1								

post-glenoid process, compressed in the sagittal plane, broad in the coronal and somewhat concave posteriorly and convex in front.

The bony external auditory tube extends laterally, more or less in the coronal plane from the swollen inflated tympanic chamber for some 8-10 mm. There is some variation in the obliquity of the tube. In some, *e.g. C. cephus, C. erythrotis, C. ascanius*, the direction is transverse, the tubes of the two sides being aligned in the same plane. In others (*e.g. C. pogonias* and some examples of *C. erythrotis*) there is a very slight posterior trend, but more commonly (*C. nictitans, C. mona, C. petaurista, C. l'hoesti, C. preussi*) there is a pronounced backward inclination. Typically the condition is perfectly symmetrical, but occasionally, as in a cranium of *C. sabaeus* one tube is transversely aligned and its fellow shows a very slight posterior trend. Prominent styloid processes occur posteriorly in the tympanic at its junction with the auditory tube. The large round carotid foramen perforates the bulla a few millimetres anterior to the jugular foramen. More laterally, in the groove or fossa between the root of the auditory passage and the mastoid prominence, lies the small stylo-mastoid foramen.

Pneumatization of the temporal is variable, advancing with age. In adults Hofmann found it almost complete, except for the tympanic portion which is compact. In some skulls the internal table of the squamosal, at its junction with the petrosal, presents a distinct groove at the level of the tegmen tympani. Below this the bone forms the posterior wall of the antrum, around which it curves below to rejoin the outer table in alignment with the above-mentioned occipital ridge, which accordingly marks the limit between squamosal and mastoid (earlier the mastoido-squamosal fissure of the embryo).

The squamous portion presents a somewhat convex upper margin overlapping considerably the lower border of the parietal. Anteriorly this border ends typically in a processus frontalis ; either pointed or truncated according to the arrangements at the pterion. The anterior border of the squame is vertically disposed and articulates with the alisphenoid. Sometimes the squame is divided into anterior and posterior parts by a vertical or oblique accessory suture associated with a fontanelle and wormian bones. The condition is not usually bilateral in *C. sabaeus* and *C. p. cynosuros* (Frassetto, *loc. cit.*).

The internal aspect of the petrosal bears a well-defined subarcuate fossa (Straus, 1960). In the occipital bone the squamous portion above the nuchal area is of relatively small extent, broad but low. Superior curved lines are well marked as is also the median occipital crest. Lateral to the crest, the bone is deeply excavated, the hollow being separated by a vertical or oblique ridge from a more lateral plane or slightly excavated area whose inferolateral angle abuts on the mastoid portion of the temporal bone. The medial excavation is bounded below by a raised bone which forms the posterior margin of the foramen magnum. This foramen is almost a complete circle, but it is slightly wider than long, the greatest diameter being level with the posterior ends of the two condyles. Lordat declares that the horizontal level of the foramen, if projected forwards, passes through the middle of the roots of the lower incisors, whereas in *Pan* the upper incisors are level. Long axes of the condyles meet, when projected forwards, in an angle of 62°. The articular surfaces of the condyles are highly convex and are directed in the main postero-laterad. Anteriorly narrowed, they are here separated by a deep notch bordered by the thin anterior (basioccipital) margin of the foramen magnum.

The basioccipital, longer than broad, narrows somewhat anteriorly ; but, in its length-breadth relationships, it shows considerable individual variation. A median sagittal ridge on the ventral aspect is variably developed. When present it bifurcates posteriorly the two limbs joining the margin of the foramen magnum. Anteriorly the basioccipito-basisphenoidal union shows delayed ossification—considerably later than the date at which full permanent dentition is completed (Weinbrenn, confirmed by personal observations). The jugular foramen lies obliquely level with the forepart of the corresponding condyle. Its posterior border is sharp and jagged, but the temporal border is smooth.

In the sphenoid bone the most important feature concerns its relation to the mesethmoid in the cranial floor. The invariable arrangement seems to be that a broad process from the frontal on each side separates the pre-sphenoid from the mesethmoid. The two frontal components are, for a time, separated from each other by a sagittal suture. At the front end of the suture the cribriform plate lies in a narrow fusiform depression. Extending laterad from the presphenoid are the two short acutely pointed orbito-sphenoids whose concave posterior edges form the anterior limits of the middle cranial fossa. Medially they form well marked anterior clinoid processes, separated by a few millimetres only from the forwardly directed posterior clinoid pro-cesses derived from the dorsum sellae of the basisphenoid. In addition to the forwardly directed nodules, the dorsum sellae also provides postero-laterally directed blunt spicules for attachment of the anterior end of the tentorium cerebelli. Frasetto has recorded examples of persistent cranio-pharyngeal canal perforating the floor of the sella turcica (in nine specimens out of fifty-nine crania in the Turin Museum). In another (a *C. aethiops aethiops*) two apertures were observed, but these may be susceptible of other than the normal explanation for persistence. In an adult *C. nictitans* I have observed a small blind pit on the pharyngeal aspect of the bone.

The alisphenoid is of normal form; its relations at the pterion have already been discussed. Its pterygoid lamina is extremely extensive, especially antero-posteriorly. Anteriorly it is separated from the palatine by a narrow pterygo-palatine fissure. Posteriorly it extends to the foramen ovale, skirting around its medial margin to form part of the boundary of the fissure separating the petrosal from the sphenoid. The lamina is directed obliquely backwards and laterad, with a strong horizontal lower border and a thinner convex hinder border. Between it and the medial pterygoid lamina is a large interpterygoid fossa excavated both forwards and to some extent upwards.

The foramen ovale varies considerably in shape and direction, being sometimes small, round and directed downwards; otherwise larger, oval, obliquely directed forwards; sometimes even slit-like and more oblique.

In the face the nasals fuse together very early—between the date of completion of the milk dentition and the eruption of $M.\frac{1}{1}$ (at least in *C. petaurista*). At first they form short triangular scales immediately above the apertura pyriformis, but with growth they elongate extending upwards by pushing aside the nasal processes of the two maxillae. Eventually the naso-maxillary sutures are also lost. The nasal opening describes an inverted pear-shape, smoothly rounded above, narrowing to a median gutter below; widest opposite its middle

Orbits are variable in shape, rounded or squared, but usually slightly higher than broad. In *C. pygerythrus* Weinbrenn found 36 crania with megasemic indices compared with 3 mesosemic and 8 microsemic. Relative size of orbit to size of body and volume of eyeball has been considered by Schultz (1940) who reports that in an adult female guenon the size is equivalent to that of a human newborn infant. Internally capacious, their walls are highly concave everywhere. In *C. pygerythrus* according to Weinbrenn the upper orbital margin presents a distinct backward slope from medial to lateral end, but shows little evidence of a supraorbital notch. Both features are variable in other species. In *C. nictitans* conditions are much as in *C. pygerythrus*, but in quite young specimens of *C. lowei*, *C. pogonias* and *C. erythrotis* deep supraorbital notches occur. Commonly entirely lacking in *C. mona*, a slight or distinct notch occurs in approximately 2 per cent of skulls. In one anomalous cranium of this species the notch is deep and almost converted into a foramen by the hook-like lateral lip of the notch on the right side ; in the left orbit of the same skull the bony spicule guarding the notch is itself perforated by two minute foramina for branches of the nerve. The junction of medial and superior margins shows distinct tendency to angularity.

The interorbital septum is much constricted, especially in juveniles. Its minimum dimension lies about one-third the distance from its upper end. The lateral lip of the orbital opening is marked transversely at its mid-point by the fronto-malar suture. A distinct notch is frequently formed on the lateral edge of the bone at this suture (*e.g.* in *C. pygerythrus*). The maxillo-malar suture cuts the inferior orbital margin about its middle, sloping from this point downwards and laterad and somewhat backwards to the zygomatic arch.

The malar is perforated by a variable sized foramen approximately at its centre. The bone gives a large contribution to the lateral wall and floor of the orbit, forming a septum between orbit and temporal fossa. On the temporal side it is marked by a sharp bony ridge extending vertically from the fronto-malar suture or notch for a variable distance. It is absent or feebly marked in females and is never so strong or extensive as in *Cercocebus* or *Macaca*. It is very well marked in *C. erythrotis*, even in young skulls, where it may extend beyond the malar on to the frontal, parallel with the supra-orbital margin, and finally becoming confluent with the temporal line. Occasionally a second vertical ridge, rather less developed, appears posterior to and parallel with the previous one.

The zygomatic process springs from the lower lateral angle of the bone, coursing horizontally back to meet the process from the squamosal in an almost horizontal suture, the malar contribution lying below. The arch so formed is variable in thickness, but is always sufficiently bowed to be visible in norma verticalis. It is thinner in females and juveniles. Even in young skulls its root is located well above the alveolar margin.

The angle between the orbital and zygomatic processes is a right angle or less, and smoothly rounded (cf. *Cercocebus*). Premaxillae are long and narrow, broadening towards the alveolar margin. Above they extend not more than half-way along the lateral margin of the corresponding nasal (Weinbrenn gives more than three-quarters for *C. pygerythrus*). The naso-premaxillary suture is, however, early obliterated, though that between pre-maxilla and maxilla persists, cutting the alveolar margin in front of the root of the canine. Relations of the premaxillary to neighbouring bones were found by Ashley-Montagu (1933) to be variable. The naso-maxillary process is inserted between the nasal and maxilla for a distance about half-way between the base of the nasal and the fronto-maxillary suture in *C. nictitans*, *C. mitis stuhlmanni* and some individuals of *C. denti* and *C. petaurista*. In *C. sabaeus* and *C. cephus* the insertion is either slight or long. Long insertions were found by this worker in *C. diana*, *C. mona*, *C. campbelli*, *C. albogularis kolbi* and the remaining examples of *C. denti* and *C. petaurista*. The maxilla is a large bone whose nasal process ascends to meet the frontal. It may or may not surpass the fronto-nasal union. Over the root of the canine the bone forms a convexity sometimes reaching the lower orbital margin, but a triangular area bounded by the nasal, the lower medial part of the orbit and the fore-edge of the canine eminence may be flat or hollowed. Posterior to the canine, the facial aspect of the bone is smoothly concave. Infraorbital foramina perforate the upper forepart of this hollow and are variable in number and size. Two subequal foramina seems the modal arrangement, but there may be one large and one or two smaller perforations or three subequal smallish ones arranged in an oblique line. The only examples seen with more than three foramina are a *C. l'hoesti* with four perforations bilaterally, and single examples of the same in *C. nictitans martini* and *C. aethiops aethiops* and unilaterally in a *C. petaurista petaurista* cf. *Cercocebus*). Schaefer (1954) who examined six skulls (*C. sabaeus*, *C. nictitans* and others unspecified) gave four as the average number of foramina.

The malar process is stout, facing backwards and upwards. A smooth concave margin separates it below from the body of the maxilla opposite M^2.

On the palatal aspect the premaxillo-maxillary suture is indistinct, but the major part of the hard palate is formed by maxillae, with approximately the hinder one-third formed by the palatine bones. Anterior palatine foramina are very large, oblique and oval, the posterior small and rounded. There is, however, some individual variation. Weinbrenn found that in *C. pygerythrus* some incisive foramina were small and irregular, others large and definite. Variations also occurred between the two sides and in the amount of intervening bone. The whole palate is highly arched and the alveolar processes correspondingly deep, with the dentition extending almost to the end. The palate ends behind in a sharp median spine, but there are degrees in acuteness. In *C. albogularis samango* Weinbrenn found multiple spicules. The alveolar margin may be horizontal or slightly bowed downwards, but this is individually variable in degree.

Medial pterygoid plates are narrow antero-posteriorly with a concave

PLATE VIII

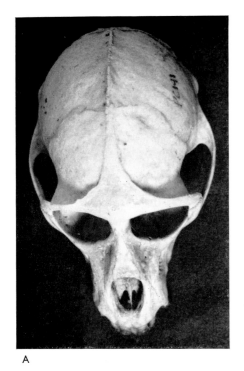

A

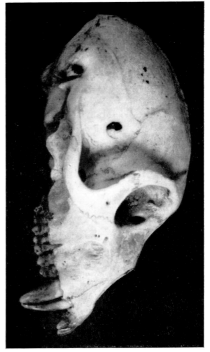

B

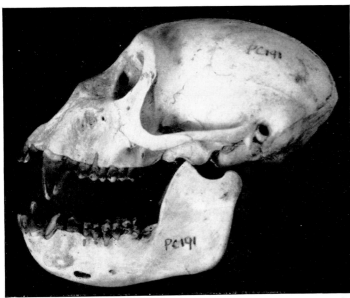

C

Photos: R. Q. Cox

Cercopithecus nictitans martini ♂. Skull in A, norma verticalis ; B, right norma lateralis ; C, left norma lateralis. Note sagittal crest in A. In B note duplication of right canine, one portion in premaxilla

PLATE IX

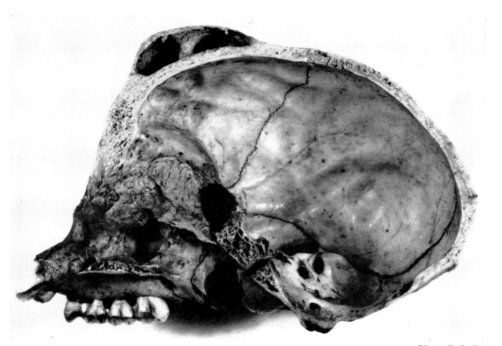

Photo: R. Q. Cox

Cercopithecus aethiops. Skull in sagittal section showing enlarged frontal sinuses

hinder edge ending below in a stout, medially directed, hamular process. Above, the root of the lamina extends backwards along the cranial base to meet the apex of the petrosal, though remaining separated by a continuation of the petro-sphenoidal suture. Anteriorly a suture separates the pterygoid from the palate bone (vertical plate). This suture passes obliquely downwards and forwards, but at the top, it turns forwards beneath the vomerine attachment to the presphenoid. Posteriorly the alae of the vomer are separated in the midline by a deep incisure, but details are individually variable, being sometimes broadly or narrowly V-shaped, otherwise by a cleft which may or may not become partly obliterated, whereon it may be ossified behind, remaining as a median slit in front.

In the nasal fossa there may be two or three turbinate bones. Inferior and middle turbinates are always present, but in some individuals at least of *C. mona*, a third, superior turbinate, occupies the uppermost part of the nose immediately lateral to and parallel with the septum. When present it is a quadrate flat thin plate with free anterior and inferior borders and a rounded antero-inferior angle. It is derived from the ethmoid. The middle turbinate, also derived from the ethmoid, is scroll-like, with an upper attached border and bluntly rounded anterior end. Beneath it, is the bony support of the bulla ethmoidalis. The inferior turbinate is a thin horizontal shelf of bone some 2·5 cm. long coursing parallel with the palatal process of the maxilla and attached some 3·5 mm. above it.

The nasal septum in the bony skull is formed solely by the vomer, as the median plate of the ethmoid (mesethmoid) is entirely occupied in forming the extensive interorbital septum. The lower edge of this meets the superior border of the vomer where the latter exhibits its dual structure. The space between the oblique antero-superior edge of the vomer and the nasals is filled in in the fresh skull by the mesethmoid cartilage.

The horizontal plate of the ethmoid is of small extent, and much depressed below the neighbouring bone. It gives a small crista galli on its cerebral surface lateral to which lie the paired olfactory foramina. There may be but one each side, in *C. mona*, leading by a canal, some 1 cm. long, into the uppermost part of the nasal fossa, where it opens in the interval between the middle turbinate and the septum or, in the event of a superior turbinal plate being present, between that and the middle turbinal. In *C. nictitans* this olfactory passage is shorter (0·8 cm.) but much wider (4 mm. at its narrowest point), more funnel-shaped, narrowing to the junction of upper two-thirds with lower one-third, thereafter widening again. Sometimes the entrance of the canal is closed by a definite but very delicate cribriform plate which is often lost in prepared crania.

The stoutly built mandible has the horizontal and vertical rami united at approximately a right angle, though tending commonly to a slightly obtuse angle, especially in juveniles. The two horizontal rami are united in

R

such fashion that the alveolar margins of the cheek teeth are approximately parallel, or with some slight posterior convergence. The anterior alveoli form an arch, convex forwards. From this the symphysis slopes downwards and backwards fairly uniformly on the external aspect, but on the lingual surface the gentle slope is abruptly interrupted, some two-thirds the way down, by the genial fossa, containing two deep narrow genial pits separated by a median spur of bone. In some specimens the pits, or one of them, penetrate through the bone, giving a median foramen on the outer face. Below the genial fossa a relatively thin simian shelf connects the two rami. Weinbrenn remarks that in *C. pygerythrus* the height of the horizontal ramus at the symphysis differs from that at the postdental level. This is caused by the slight sinuosity of the lower border, which is convex between symphysis and the molars, but concave behind the molars, where the horizontal and vertical rami meet (*vide* also Anderson, 1906). The angular region is smoothly rounded and the posterior border of the vertical ramus concavo-convex from neck to angle. The coronoid process is higher than the condylar, but broad, blunt-tipped—though varying individually—being frequently more acutely pointed, though not recurved. The sigmoid notch varies too, from broad and shallow to narrower and deeper. The stout condyle has a thick neck and is itself transversely widened, overhanging more medially than laterally. The articular area descends as a triangular field on the posterior aspect of the condyle. The posterior margin of the angular region is slightly inflected with reference to the superior part of the ramus. The lateral aspect of the ascending ramus is deeply sculptured by the masseter, especially at the base of the coronoid. On the medial aspect, the angular region is deeply excavated and ridged by the medial pterygoid muscle. The oblique opening of the inferior dental canal lies about 1 cm. below the sigmoid notch and is not provided with a lingula.

According to Straus (1962), *Cercopithecus* is unique among Old World simians (with the exception of *Nasalis*) in exhibiting a mylohyoid groove which falls into his type 2, where it is separated some slight distance from the opening of the inferior dental canal, though not to the degree categorized as type 3 (equivalent to Keith's simian type), where there is considerable separation.

The mental foramen, variable in size, even on two sides of the same jaw, lies near the lower border below the hinder lower premolar, or level with the interval between this and the first molar. Sometimes a small accessory foramen is present, or two smaller foramina may be contained within a larger oval fossa. I have seen this in *C. l'hoesti*, *C. preussi* and *C. nictitans*. In *C. nictitans* three small foramina have been observed. In a young *C. ae. tantalus* there are four small foramina on the right and six on the left in addition to the median symphysial foramen.

HYOID.—This bone has the usual form seen in Catarrhini, *i.e.*, with a large shield-shaped body, highly convex ventrally and excavated by a median laryngeal air-sac dorsally, to which are appended, by movable joints, paired bony lesser and greater cornua. The body presents a slightly convex rostral portion united at right angles to a bluntly triangular ventral element which is convex in the sagittal plane and feebly excavated at the sides. The depressed areas are separated by a broad median elevation which widens posteriorly to form the apical part of the shield. Tendons of the two sterno-hyoids are inserted on the upper part of the median ridge. The lateral

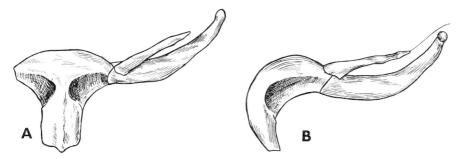

FIG. 32.—Hyoid bone in *C. cephus*.   A, ventral view and B, side view

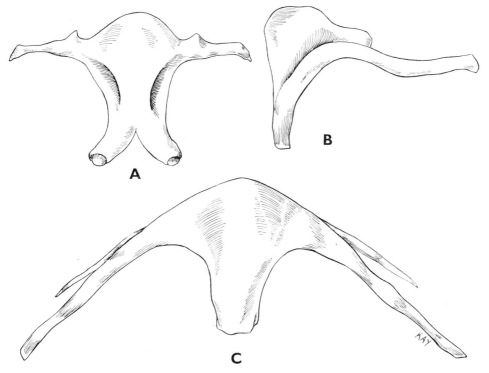

FIG. 33.—Hyoid bone in *Cercopithecus*.   A and B, ventral and left lateral aspects of hyoid of *C. l'hoesti*.   C, *C. sabaeus*, viewed from the ventral aspect and somewhat from behind (× 3)

excavations receive the thyro-hyoids. Lesser and greater cornua are attached close together at the antero-lateral angles of the body. Lesser cornua are slender rods, 13·5 mm. long in an adult male *C. cephus* receiving terminally the stylo-hyoid ligaments. Greater cornua are slightly falciform, laterally compressed bars with concave anterior and convex posterior margins. They attain a length of 17·2 mm. and narrow somewhat to their rounded cartilage-covered tips (*vide* also Flower 1870).

TABLE 12

VERTEBRAL FORMULA IN *CERCOPITHECUS*

Species	Sex	Age	C	T	L	S	Ca	Authority
C. sabaeus	♀	immat.	7	12	7	2	26	Lordat, 1804
Unspecified			7	11-13	?	2-3	?	Mivart, 1865
C. sabaeus	?		7	13	6	2	25	Flower, 1885
C. albogularis	?	—	7	12	7	3	?	pp. 78-79
C. petaurista	?	—	7	12	7	2	19 +	
C. campbelli [1]			7	12	7	2	?	Cunningham,18
C. mona [1]			7	12	7	2	?	,,
C. aethiops [2]	?	ad.	7	12	7	3	28	Shufeldt, 1914
C. ae. aethiops	?	immat.	7	12	7	3	?	,,
Average of 38 specimens of various spp.	—	—	7	12·2	6·9	3·1	26·4	Schultz and Stra 1945
C. sabaeus 4 specimens	—	—	7	12	7	3	—	Zuckerman, 193
C. mona	—	—	7	12	7	3	—	,,

[1] Estimated from Cunningham's diagrams.
[2] U.S.N. Mus. 16365.

TABLE 13

VERTEBRAL FORMULA IN *CERCOPITHECUS*
(Personal Observations)

No.	Species	Sex		C	T	L	S	Co	Ca
322/60	*C. cephus*	♂	ad.	7	13	6	2	4	20
40/61	*C. neglectus*	♂	ad.	7	12	6	2	4	23
PC 74	*C. petaurista*	♀	immat.	7	13	6	2	4	13 +
565/54	*C. l'hoesti*	♀	do.	7	12	7	3	4	25
PC 479	*C. pygerythrus*	♂	ad.	7	12	7	3	4	14 +
PC 520	*C. ascanius*	♂	ad.	7	12	6	3	4	28
—	*C. a. schmidti*	♀	ad.	7	12	7	3	4	28
97/62	*C. mona*	♀	ad. (6 yrs.)	7	12	7	3	4	20 +
737/57	*C. erythrotis sclateri*	♂	juv.	7	12	7[1]	2	5	8 +

[1] L.7 partly sacralized

Post-cranial Axial Skeleton

VERTEBRAL FORMULA.—The findings of previous observers are given in Table 12 followed by some personal observations, Table 13.

The total number of thoraco-lumbar vertebrae seems invariably 19, an assessment confirmed by Todd (1922) for *C. mona, C. aethiops, C. albogularis C. petaurista*, and one unidentified species, which therefore agree with the majority of the Cercopithecoidea.

Lordat (1804) estimated the relative length of the cervical region to total pre-sacral vertebral length as 1 to 6, with the thoracic region three-fifths and the lumbar six-thirteenths of the entire spinal length. Mivart (1865) affirmed that, with the exception of the post-sacral region, all the spinal regions bear much the same proportions to each other as in Man. Schultz (1938) included no member of the present genus in his study of the relative length of the various spinal regions.

Cervical vertebrae are arranged so that their bodies form a pronounced ventral convexity and the direction of their spinous processes is such that their apices tend to converge and form a median bony septum with the minimum of intervening fibrous and muscular tissue. Thus the neural spines of C.2-C.4 point upwards and backwards, C.5 vertically upwards and C.6 and C.7 upwards and forwards with a slight posterior recurve at the extreme tip. All the spines end in acute points and none shows evidence of bifurcation, except for some division at the root posteriorly on the axis. At the same point on the roots of the spines of the others, stunted tubercles occur. The peculiar features of the spinous process of the axis have been described and figured for *C. cynosuros* by von Eggeling (1922), whose figure of the total cervical spine, however, is artificially straightened and thus fails to show the natural curves, and true proximity of the neural spines. His descriptions of the individual neural spines are, however, accurate.

Ventral median parts of the bodies of C.2-C.5 are strongly imbricated, but the degree of overlap decreases from C.2 to C.5 and the imbricated portions become progressively broader in the same order. The median part of each centrum is raised and the raised portion flanked by depressions, deepest on C.2 and quite obliterated on C.7. Lateral to the depressed area the ventral parts of the transverse processes take an oblique direction, passing laterally, backwards and slightly ventrad, the ventral trend increasing posteriorly especially on C.6, where the ventral tubercle (costal element) expands into a broad T-shaped lamina whose summit is formed by the cross-bar of the T, the posterior limb of this being longer than the anterior. This element is completely lacking on C.7. Dorsal tubercles increase in prominence and change gradually in direction from C.2 to C.7. On C.2 they are short, blunt and barely distinct from the remainder of the transverse process. On C.3 the process is elongated, sharp tipped and recurved upwards and backwards. C.4 and C.5 have similar dorsal tubercles. Those in C.6 and C.7 are longer, stouter with rounded rather than flattened stems and are directed in the coronal plane.

Laminae of the neural arches are broadened in the sagittal plane, that of C.2 being broadest.

The atlas bears two foramina each side for the passage of vessels (vertebral artery), one above and one below the transverse process. Shufeldt remarks that they lead to a common opening just dorsal to the articular area for the occipital condyle. The neural spine is thick, directed backwards, so as to overlie the atlanto-axial membrane, and compressed transversely. The laminae are narrow medially but broaden rapidly towards the lateral mass. Posteriorly an oblique groove is formed between the lateral mass and the lamina. The ventral arch is broad laterally, narrow medially, both anterior and posterior borders being concave and thinned. Condylar areas are deeply excavated, of reniform outline, convex laterally and concave ventro-medially. Axial facets are extensive, and only slightly concave, directed postero-medially, of subtriangular outline with rounded angles.

The axis bears a relatively short odontoid process which is directed in line with the rest of the body of the vertebra ; its apex is truncated and the stem laterally compressed. The centrum is marked by a strong median ventral ridge, lateral to which the bone is excavated, except along an oblique line extending from the root of the odontoid postero-laterad to continue to the tip of the transverse process, whose direction is the same. The atlantal facet occupies the shoulder formed between this ridge and the root of the odontoid anteriorly, but separated by a notch therefrom. Laminae are broad and flat, sloping upwards and medially to form the even broader spinous process. The latter is sharp-edged, broad-tipped and bears two rough tubercles at its root posteriorly.

The seventh cervical lacks a vertebrarterial canal and the ventral element to the transverse process. Its body bears a small demi-facet for the head of the first rib near the root of the pedicle posteriorly. It shows transitional characters towards the thoracic vertebrae.

Thoracic vertebrae constitute, according to Lordat (1804) two-fifths the entire length of the spine in *C. sabaeus*. The anterior elements resemble the last cervical, while the hindmost three (two according to Shufeldt) present characters transitional towards the lumbars. Centra are, for the most part, longer sagittally, narrower transversely and deeper dorsoventrally than those of the cervicals, but the anterior two are as broad as long, while the hinder four or five become increasingly robust assuming a capstan-like shape, with the hinder surfaces more extensive than the anterior, progressively so towards the lumbar series. Pedicles are short and thick so that the laminae appear to spring almost directly from the bodies. Laminae are broad, as in the cervicals, but approach each other more at an angle. From this angle spring the spinous processes—exceedingly long on T.1-T.6. Spines of T.1 and T.2 narrow towards their tips which end in slightly expanded knobs ; on T.3 the tip is broader and more truncated and this tendency increases on T.4-T.6 where the tips are as broad as the roots, and on T.7 and T.8 even broader. All the above spines slope backwards, but to a decreasing degree posteriorly, so that the spine of T.8 is almost vertical and that of T.9 perfectly so (anticlinal vertebra). T.10 has a shorter spine narrowing towards its summit and directed slightly forwards. The remaining thoracic spines increasingly resemble those of the lumbar vertebrae. Transverse processes are large, directed in the coronal plane and typically terminate in broad expanses which bear, on their ventral aspects, the oval facets for the tubercles of the ribs ; these facets are concave and their sagittal axes longer than the transverse. They are lacking on the last two vertebrae of the series ; in these the transverse processes are short, but supplanted by sharp-pointed pleurapophyses directed obliquely backwards as in the lumbar series.

Pre-zygapophyses on the typical thoracics face dorsally and slightly laterad and are plane. Post-zygapophyses take the opposite direction. Posteriorly the post-zygapophyses become increasingly laterally directed and held between the mortice formed by the now medially directed pre-zygapophyses, which are supported and strengthened by the pleurapophyses (mammillary processes).

On the last thoracic vertebra transverse processes are abortive, but the reduction is not abrupt, being progressively apparent on the preceding. Meanwhile on the thirteenth post-cervical a costal process has appeared. This is a dorso-ventrally flattened plate with sharp anterior and posterior parallel borders, and a blunt distal border ; it is directed laterally and slightly ventrad and posteriorly. Other features in which this and, to a lesser degree, the two preceding elements resemble the lumbar vertebrae are the presence of accessory processes ; the longitudinal ridge connecting the latter with the pre-zygapophyses thereby separating the paraspinous recess from the recess above the root of the costal process ; and, finally, the increased size of the body and development thereon of a median ventral ridge.

Lumbar vertebrae contrast strongly with the typical thoracics in their robusticity. Bodies are massive, sagittally elongated with concave sides and ventral surfaces, but broadening towards their cranial and caudal extremities. Neural spines are conspicuous, forming oblong bony blades with thickened free dorsal borders, sharp concave cranial and caudal borders. They increase in height from first to last. Their posterior borders divide at their roots to become contiguous with the post-zygapophyses whose articular facets face downwards and laterad. The pre-zygapophyses of the succeeding vertebra are received into a notch formed between the post-zygapophyses and the sharp-pointed pleurapophyseal processes. Another notch separates the latter from the pedicle near its junction with the centrum. The latter notch is the intervertebral notch which transmits the spinal nerve-root. Pre-zygapophyses are provided with accessory processes and from these a distinct ridge connects with the pleurapophysis as on the last few thoracic vertebrae.

Transverse (costal) processes are large and blade-like, directed obliquely ventrad, forwards and laterally. The antero-inferior angle tends to become prolonged into a sharp point, becoming increasingly prominent in the hinder members of the series. In *C. l'hoesti* and *C. cephus* this prolongation gives the process an L-shaped form. On the ante-penultimate vertebra the stem and horizontal limbs of the L are equal in length, but on the penultimate and last lumbars the horizontal limb exceeds the basal limb. In *C. aethiops*, *C. ascanius*, *C. petaurista* and *C. neglectus*, this distinction is less evident, the costal processes being more expanded sagittally, but displaying less projection beyond the body of the vertebra. Nevertheless, even here the hind-most costal process narrows to a sharp antero-inferior projection, contrasting with the rounded postero-inferior angle. Viewed from the ventral aspect the last three lumbars with their costal processes recall the body and expanded wings of a bird in these last-mentioned species of the genus. In an example of *C. pygerythrus* a foramen penetrates the root of the costal process at its hinder margin on the right side on the ante-penultimate lumbar. In the penultimate this is represented by a notch leading to the intervertebral foramen.

The three-piece sacrum presents each side a lateral mass homologous with the costal process of the lumbar vertebrae and this is formed mainly by S.1 with a small contribution from S.2. The last two sacrals also present true transverse elements, that on S.2 lying dorsal to the costal element and sending from its posterior edge, near its root, a bony bar which joins it to the same element on S.3 thereby enclosing the middle of the three dorsal sacral foramina. Medial to this foramen and its representative on the preceding segment lies a small oblique ridge-like process, lying in alignment with the pre-zygapophysis of S.1. This last process is large, upstanding and provided with a very large articular facet on its medial face for the post-zygapophysis of the last lumbar. The transverse process of S.3 is expanded antero-laterally and postero-laterally, with a sharp concave edge between the two projections, thus giving a resemblance to the immediate post-sacral elements.

Neural spines of the sacral vertebrae are joined to form a median lamina with three projections separated by shallow depressions. The tips of the projections all usually point slightly craniad, but Speransky (1926) declares that, in his *C. aethiops*, those for S.3 resemble those of the first post-sacral in pointing backwards. Speransky gives the proportion of the post-sacral vertebrae to the remainder of the spine in *C. aethiops* as 1 : 1·8.

The first three or four post-sacral vertebrae are distinguished by features recapitulating details of the lumbar vertebrae on a smaller scale. Particularly striking are the wing-like transverse (costal) elements, which are long on the first, shortening thereafter, though becoming increasingly broad at their attached ends. Spinous processes are short, but upstanding, becoming shorter and more sloping posteriorly. Large upstanding zygapophyses are present, giving an oblong angular appearance to the neural arches. Bodies are cylindrical, capstan-shaped in the first two, which also lack ventral median ridges. The last-mentioned ridges reappear on the third and fourth. Chevron bones are present opposite the intervertebral intervals, but these are not fused with the vertebrae. The fifth post-sacral (Shufeldt says the fourth in his *C. aethiops*) differs markedly from its predecessor being more elongated with distinct short but stout pre-zygapophyses, but with the post-zygapophyses fused into a single long slender process arching backwards from the middle of the centrum. Its transverse processes form broad out-standing triangular plates. In *C. l'hoesti* this lamella is subdivided into anterior and posterior parts by a deep lateral notch at approximately the junction of its anterior and middle thirds. This is the last vertebra with a neural arch. Remaining caudals consist of elongated cylindroidal bodies. Blunt processes at the sites of the zygapophyses are present on the next three or four segments. Lateral ridges correspond to the sites of the transverse processes on the next five vertebrae. Ventral paired tubercles at the anterior extremities of the bodies of post-sacrals five to eight are associated with chevron elements which represent the pedicles only of the haemal arches. These haemal elements are directed medially and forwards. Beyond the eighth the post-sacrals become simplified though elongated ; eight to ten are subequal in length in *C. cephus*, thereafter shortening gradually sets in.

Ansell (1961) reports an anomalous condition affecting the terminal caudal segments in an adult male *C. mitis opisthostictus* obtained in Northern Rhodesia. The last thirteen caudal vertebrae deviate from the axial position in a sinuous fashion. Viewed from above there is a lateral direction to the right ; viewed from the left side the series deviates ventrad for four segments and then terminates in a dorsal convexity. Ansell considers this might be related to a semi-prehensile function such as has been recorded by Dandelot (1956) in captive examples of *C. l'hoesti*, but the appearance hardly warrants such a conclusion, as it is patently a purely individual anomaly not occurring in other specimens obtained at the same locality. Prehensility in gymnurous platyrrhines is not accompanied by bony asymmetry. The anomaly is there-fore probably of traumatic origin.

STERNUM AND RIBS.—The sternum is composed of seven bony sternebrae (in juveniles eight) with the addition of the xiphisternal cartilage. The manubrium is expanded, being almost as broad or slightly broader than long ; the remainder are rod-like.

In shape the manubrium is very variable, but whether these differences are merely individual or species differences is uncertain without more material. Thus in *C. ascanius* (two skeletons) the cranial border of the manubrium is convex, without even a median notch. In *C. mona* and *C. cephus* it is markedly concave ; in *C. neglectus* feebly concave. *C. petaurista* agrees with *C. ascanius*, while *C. l'hoesti* resembles *C. neglectus*. Other differences occur in the relative breadths of the cranial and caudal parts of the manubrium. Thus in *C. mona* the transition from the broad plate between the costal facets to the caudal stem is gradual, whereas in *C. neglectus* and *C. l'hoesti* it is abrupt, with consequent markedly concave lateral borders. In *C. ascanius* and *C. aethiops* the manubrium is more spatulate though the lateral borders are here, too, markedly concave. The ventral surface is flattened or concave, sometimes (as in *C. mitis* and *C. l'hoesti*) with a median sagittal ridge. Clavicular facets are large and oval in outline and face more dorsally than cranially or laterally. A relatively wide space separates them from the corresponding facets for the first costal cartilage. The dorsal surface is divided into a cranial part bounded by the clavicular and costal facets and by a transverse line connecting the two costal facets. This area is roughened and faces somewhat cranially. The caudal portion is smooth and plane and forms an angle with the rough cranial portion. On the other hand, no perceptible angle is formed at the manubrio-gladiolar junction.

As to the number of post-manubrial segments, earlier authors give varying figures. Thus Mivart (1865) states that in adults there are only five, with occasionally six. This exception, however, was a *C. ruber* (= *Erythrocebus patas*). Duckworth (1915) gives six ossified segments, but includes the manubrium in his enumeration. All adults examined personally have six post-manubrial segments, but in a juvenile *C. aethiops* (see Plate X) there are seven of which the penultimate is a very short rod situated between the seventh and eighth costal cartilages. With maturity it appears to fuse with the preceding segment or with the long xiphisternal ossification. All the gladiolar segments are rod-like, dorso-ventrally compressed and tending to transverse expansion at their cranial and caudal extremities. The segments do not progressively decrease in length, for the foremost is short ; this is followed by three of more or less equal size, the last two being progressively shorter. The xiphisternal segment is long and narrow ; it bears an expanded cartilagious flap at its caudal extremity.

As in all Cercopithecidae normally eight pairs of costal cartilages gain the sternum directly (compared with seven in Colobidae) ; two pairs (the ninth and tenth) end by uniting with the cartilage anterior to them, leaving the last two pairs of ribs " floating ". In all cases the first rib is short, compressed cranio-caudally, and expands towards its sternal end, where it terminates bluntly, being continued as a narrower cartilage to end on the manubrium. Lordat claimed all four non-sternal ribs to be " floating " in his *C. sabaeus*. Shafts of the other ribs vary considerably in size and in degree of antero-posterior expansion of their shafts, this being greater in males than females, and more evident in old than in juvenile examples. Even in females it is greater in the more posterior ribs (e.g. 9-11) than in the anterior segments, but in males of *C. ascanius* and *C. mitis* it is marked throughout, in contrast to males of *C. neglectus*, where the ribs are more uniformly gracile. The sigmoid twist characteristic of the costal shafts in Hominoidea is here virtually lacking. The first pair of costal cartilages approach the sternum transversely. Thereafter there tends to be an increasing degree of obliquity, although this varies considerably, possibly with the state of the thoracic contents. In an old female *C. mona* the second pair are parallel to the first, *i.e.* transverse to the sternum and the obliquity of the remainder comparatively slight, whereas in a male *C. ascanius* the elongated fusiform cartilages show considerable obliquity increasing from the second to the ninth. *C. neglectus* and *C. cephus* are similar.

The thorax as a whole is in general conical, with some tendency to lateral bowing, especially in the more posterior segments ; but the thoracic index is always less than 100, indicating a deep, narrow chest as in other cynomorphous catarrhines.

TABLE 14

THORACIC MEASUREMENTS (IN MILLIMETRES)
IN *CERCOPITHECUS*

		Max. Depth (incl. Neural Spines)	Max. Breadth	Index
PC 520	*C. ascanius ascanius* ♂	114·0	97·7	85·0
R 46/62	*C. a. schmidti* ♂	97·2	85·7	87·7
97/62	*C. mona*, ♀ old	92·5	87·5	94·7
40/61	*C. neglectus* ♂ ad.	101·0	58·0	57·5
322/60	*C. cephus* ♂ ad.	112·5	97·5	77·2
PC 74	*C. petaurista* juv.	70·0	60·0	85·5
PC 14	*C. albogularis kolbi* ♂ ad.	98·5	86·5	88·0

APPENDICULAR SKELETON

The scapula is usually described as broad in proportion to its sagittal length. Thus Duckworth (1915) gives the scapular index as 118 compared with the human index of around 65. Shufeldt (1914) too contrasts the bone in *C. griseoviridis* (= *C. aethiops aethiops*) with its human counterpart, declaring it rather to resemble that of *Callithrix* (= *Hapale*). These statements are evidently based on the examination of too few specimens, for my personal findings suggest a scapula of varying form in the different species of the genus, some, *e.g.* *C. ascanius* varying in the direction of the human scapula, others, *e.g.* *C. aethiops* and its relatives conforming to Duckworth's and Shufeldt's statements. Details may be gathered from Table 15 (see also Broca, 1878).

TABLE 15

SCAPULAR INDEX IN *CERCOPITHECUS*

	Scapular Length (Cranial to Caudal Angle)	Scapular Breadth (Glenoid to Vertebral Border)	Index
C. l'hoesti ♀	56·8	64·2	124·0
C. neglectus ♂	56·5	65·0	115 0
C. petaurista ♂ juv.	35·7	40·0	112·0
C. pygerythrus ♂	68·2	75·0	110·0
C. ascanius ascanius ♂	63·3	61·5	97·0
C. cephus ♂	65·2	60·0	92·0
C. ascanius schmidti ♂	65·2	57·0	87·5
C. mona ♀ old	48·0	56·8	85·0
C. albogularis kolbi ♂ ad.	62·0	52·5	85·0

The differences appear to be brought about by several factors, more especially by the relative sizes of the supraspinous and infraspinous fossae, the presence or absence on the axillary border of an extra flange associated with the teres major and the position of the cranial angle.

In scapulae with a low index the vertebral border is long and relatively straight, except for the portion bounding the supraspinous fossa where it is convex. In the bones with high index the whole vertebral border is convex, but the convexity increases in its cranial third bringing the superior (cranial) angle to a point midway along the cranial border. Another contrast is seen in the posterior (inferior) angle, which is acute in scapulae with low index but obtuse and rounded in those with a high index.

There is no suprascapular (coraco-scapular) notch, the cranial border taking a smooth uniform, somewhat concave course from the root of the coracoid to the " superior " angle. From this angle the vertebral border slopes towards another angle situated near to or just cranial to the root of the spinous process. This part of the vertebral border is usually emarginated. The caudal angle is provided with a suprascapular cartilage. The axillary border is double, with a fusiform depression of some depth between the two bony lips. The dorsal lip is slightly the more prominent and is continued into the edge of the flange for the teres major, but also sends a thickened ridge anterior to this. In some scapulae the lateral extremity of the teres flange is produced into a hook-like spicule (*e.g.* in *C. ascanius*, *C. pygerythrus*, *C. neglectus*). In others (*e.g. C. mona*) it ends smoothly.

The glenoid is distinctly pyriform or reniform in outline and narrower cranially than caudally, but the contrast between the two parts varies in degree. The neck is short and thick and separated from the spine by a distinct notch, sometimes converted into a foramen (*e.g.* in an example of *C. pygerythrus*).

The spinous process is well developed and extends to the vertebral border, where its two edges diverge to become continuous with the vertebral emarginations. The edge of the spine is somewhat sinuous with a caudad regression at its middle or somewhat medial thereto. The acromion is not greatly expanded, but faces forwards and slightly laterad, ending in a truncated

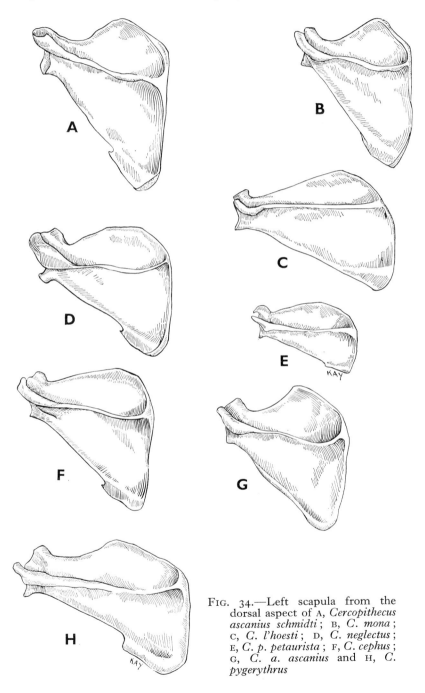

FIG. 34.—Left scapula from the dorsal aspect of A, *Cercopithecus ascanius schmidti*; B, *C. mona*; C, *C. l'hoesti*; D, *C. neglectus*; E, *C. p. petaurista*; F, *C. cephus*; G, *C. a. ascanius* and H, *C. pygerythrus*

extremity. The portion of the spine connecting the acromion to the body of the scapula is thickened. The coracoid is comprised by a short root and a distal portion set at a sharp angle to the root. The distal part is directed ventro-medially and slightly forwards, ending in a rounded tip.

The subscapular fossa is only slightly concave and marked by a depression corresponding with the attachment of the spine and another parallel with the axillary border. In an example of *C. l'hoesti* an oval foramen perforates the fossa just caudal to the junction of middle and dorsal thirds of the spinous attachment.

Presumably the variations in scapular morphology denote physiological adaptations to differing activities in the species of the genus, but field data so far are insufficient to establish such correlation—a point to be borne in mind by future field workers.

Clavicle.—The clavicle unites with the acromion at a variable angle. Lordat records an open angle of 65° compared with the more acute 45° in Man, but this discrepancy is not upheld in examples of *C. ascanius schmidti* (43°) or *C. mona* (47°).

The bone is elongated, slender, presenting the usual sigmoid curve, the medial curve not much accentuated, but the lateral well marked. The sternal end is enlarged with an oval facet for articulation with the manubrium, facing mediad and somewhat dorsad. The acromial end is much flattened cranio-caudally, forming a spatulate extremity expanding towards the tip in a dorso-ventral direction, thereby protecting the slender shoulder joint from the front and to which it conforms by becoming excavated on its posterior face. There is a distinct impression for the subclavius, while a strong deltoid ridge replaces the tubercle so named in the human bone (Duckworth).

Humerus.—Comparative mensurational data on this and other long bones of the pectoral limb have been given by Botez (1926) and Gabis (1960). Botez gives the maximum humeral length in *C. cephus* as 110·5 mm. and a radio-humeral index varying from 105·6 to 110; the same worker records a robusticity index for the humerus 25·2, *i.e.* greater than the maximum recorded for any type of *Homo*. Gabis on the contrary records the average brachial index of a group of thirty skeletons containing examples of both *Cercopithecus* and *Cercocebus* as 95, with a coefficient of variation of 4 per cent.

The humeral shaft is less straight than in Man but not so markedly curved as in *Macaca*. Not only is there a distinct torsion of the shaft, but there is a general outward bowing, as well as an angulation whereby the lower two-thirds takes a posterior direction compared with the upper one-third which is associated with the deltoideus insertion. The angularity is accentuated by the great prominence of the lateral lip of the bicipital groove. The angle formed between the upper and middle thirds of the shaft (the superior angle of deviation of Botez) is recorded as 24° which compares with 17° for *Cercocebus*, 22°-28° for *Erythrocebus* and 22° for *Macaca speciosa*.

Torsion of the humeral shaft averages about 100° compared with 161° for European man and 95° for Carnivora (Broca). Botez records 103° for *C. cephus*. Lateral to the bicipital groove the upper one-third of the shaft presents an elongated flattened surface bordered behind by a sharp crest extending distally from the base of the great tuberosity. This flattened area is played over by the deltoid muscle whose fibres insert along the sharp bordering ridges and the area of bone at the distal end of the flattened region. The posterior aspect of the upper one-third is concave transversely due to the prominence of the last-mentioned crest. Occasionally, as in *C. pygerythrus* and *C. l'hoesti*, a second smaller vertical ridge subdivides this area in its upper two-thirds. The medial lip of the bicipital groove is usually feebly developed, but sometimes forms a sharp crest overhanging medially.

The lower two-thirds of the shaft is more cylindrical, becoming flattened distally, where a further slight angle of deviation is found, whereby the axis of the bone takes a laterad trend ending in the summit of the capitellum. Botez records this inferior angle of deviation in *C. cephus* as 2° only, compared with *Cercocebus* 3°, *Macaca* 7°-10° and *Papio* 8°-9°.

The nutrient foramen is at the junction of middle and lower thirds of the shaft above the medial epicondyle.

The upper extremity presents a subglobular head whose upper limit is level with the summits of the tuberosities. The lesser tuberosity is very large, broad above and descending below to a projecting apex, which overhangs the surgical neck. It is separated by a very wide bicipital (intertubercular) groove from the great tuberosity. The latter has its summit posteriorly, while its fore portion forms the lateral limit of the bicipital groove. The posterior facet is remarkably distinct and marked by a crater-like fossa with sharp anterior and smooth posterior margins. There is no musculospiral groove, though Shufeldt reports one in *C. sabaeus*.

Differentiation of capitellum from trochlea is less marked than in Man; Duckworth suggests that flexion and extension have not been encroached upon by pronation and supination to the same degree as in the anthropomorphs—this being expected in a joint used more exclusively for quadrupedal progression. Shufeldt found the medial condyle only moderately produced in *C. aethiops*, but I find this increased in *C. neglectus* and *C. pygerythrus* though not in *C. mona*, *C. cephus*, *C. ascanius* or *C. l'hoesti*. The condyle is separated from the trochlea by a very prominent crest, which is vertically disposed on the flexor side and distally, but spirals mediad on the back of the bone, bifurcates into a rougher ridge, which spirals mediad on to the summit of the condyle, and a more acute limb which borders the articular area, keeping to the sagittal plane, and eventually turning laterally across the olecranon fossa, where it separates the articular from the non-articular intracapsular areas. A sharp vertical crest also borders the radial margin of the trochlea on the extensor aspect, but this fades on the distal surface of the bone. The lateral condyle is low and roughened, but terminates above in a well-defined supracondylar ridge, contrasting with a virtually non-existent medial supracondylar ridge.

According to Shufeldt the olecranon fossa is always perforated by a large circular foramen. This is not, however, as constant as he believed ; I find it lacking in *C. pygerythrus*, but present in *C. l'hoesti*.

Radius.—A radio-humeral index of 96 is recorded by Botez who also gives the robusticity index for the radius as 15·4.

The radius is strongly bowed in a preaxial direction (index of incurvation in *C. cephus* 16·6, Botez), whereas the ulna is relatively straight. Consequently there is a wide interosseous space recalling in outline that of *Lemur* (*vide* Botez's fig. 56). Shufeldt correctly describes the proximal one-fifth as straight and moderately compressed. The shaft gradually and moderately increases in calibre in the distal four-fifths and presents three sharp borders with the intervening surfaces of bone marked by longitudinal grooves—except the convex lateral border which is smooth and convex transversely as well as longitudinally. The distal end of the shaft broadens transversely and is compressed dorso-ventrally, the longitudinal groove of the flexor aspect expanding here into a broad shallow fossa ; in contrast the extensor groove gradually becomes shallower ending distally in a broad, flat plane.

The rounded, discoid head is set at an oblique angle with the axis of the neck, being higher medially than laterally. A foveola marks the centre of the articular area for the capitellum. The neck is long, smooth and cylindrical and forms an angle with the shaft (156° in *C. cephus*, according to Botez).

A low oblique bicipital tuberosity marks the junction of neck and shaft on the medial side. At the distal end the styloid process is well developed though short and roughened. Its dorsum is marked by a broad, shallow axial groove demarcated by raised lips. An accessory bony tubercle projects from the flexor aspect of the styloid base. Dorsally a broad, shallow depression occupies the distal end of the radius medial to the medial styloid ridge. This in turn is limited medially by another tubercle formed by the enlargement of the medial ridge descending from the shaft. The interosseous border also ends in a dorso-ventrally expanded bony thickening upon the summit of which is the facet for the head of the ulna.

Ulna.—A relatively and unusually straight bone diminishing gradually in calibre from the huge olecranon to the tiny neck at the distal end. Botez found the maximum length in *C. cephus* to be 119 mm., but in a male of this species I have found an ulna 146 mm. long (*C. neglectus* ♂ 136·8 ; *C. ascanius* ♂ 130). The robusticity index is given as 11·7 by Botez in *C. cephus*.

Greater and lesser sigmoid notches are both extensive and markedly concave. The former is bordered medially by a sharply emarginated ridge overhanging the neighbouring diaphysis, and this is continued forwards into a

prominent, somewhat preaxially directed, coronoid process. It is also continued proximally as a prominent process, but on the radial side the greater
notch is feebly separated from the lateral surface of the olecranon ; more
distally, however, a ridge is formed between it and the lesser notch. The
latter is separated from the olecranon proximally by a triangular non-
articular depression. The proximal aspect of the olecranon is very rough,
being marked by two foveae separated by a transverse bony bar, the whole
effect recalling the occlusal surface of a bunodont molar crown. Between the
proximal surface and the great sigmoid notch the olecranon is constricted.
On the flexor aspect the constriction takes the form of a transverse groove,
but medially this is separated by an axial bony bar connecting the proximal
rough surface with the deepest part of the sigmoid emargination ; this bar
forms the anterior boundary of a deeper excavation for the belly of the flexor
digitorum profundus. This depression is bordered dorsally by an acute
longitudinal ridge descending from the olecranon to the shaft, but which
soon fades in the general smoothness of the shaft. The rest of the posterior
surface of the shaft is smooth. The interosseous border is feebly marked,
except above where a prominent shelf descends for about 25 mm. from the
dorsal lip of the lesser sigmoid notch. Dorsal to this shelf is a deep longitudinal groove, which is somewhat more extensive distally.

At the lower end a ridge develops on the medial side, having an axial
trend at first but later taking a spiral course dorsally to end at the base of the
styloid process. The latter is very prominent, curved, with the concavity
facing forwards ; its apex is rounded, and smooth, but the dorsal surface
of the process is rough, and pitted. The head of the ulna is only slightly
greater in diameter than the neck, and in the main smooth.

Verneau (1903) adopted the term *platolénie* for the flattening of the ulna
that takes place at the level of the insertion of the brachialis muscle and
introduced an index denoting its degree. Botez used this in comparing
Primate ulnae, recording it as 57·2 in his *C. cephus*, compared with 70 in
Cercocebus, 69·2 in *Papio cynocephalus*, 50-53·7 in *Erythrocebus*. The ulna
is apparently more flattened in quadrupedal forms than in orthograde
Primates, and more particularly in terrestrial than in arboricolous forms.

Carpus and Manus.—The carpus resembles that of other Cercopithecidae
in possessing an os centrale (intermedium), a very large ventrally projecting
pisiform (which bears an apical epiphysis) and a small radial sesamoid
articulating with the scaphoid and trapezium. The last-mentioned develops
in the tendon of the flexor carpi radialis muscle. The unciform is larger
than the os magnum. Bardeleben (1894) recorded a small prepollex in
C. cynosuros and believed it to be present also in *C. cephus*, and *C. mona*.
The bone is situated alongside the trapezium and may be ligamentously
connected with the scaphoid.

Pelvis.—Like the thorax this is transversely narrowed, whilst the
S

innominate bones are elongated sagittally. Union at the symphysis includes both pubis and ischium.

The ilium is elongated as usual in quadrupedal forms, but the gluteal aspect is highly excavated—a feature correlated by Waterman (1929) with the faculty of upright sitting, 30 per cent of the gluteal plane being turned dorsad. Waterman gives the iliac index (length of blade × 100 divided by length of body, measured from centre of acetabulum to crown of head) as 18 in two examples of *Cercopithecus* compared with 21 in *Macaca* and *Papio hamadryas*, *i.e.* nearer to the platyrrhine condition (19 in *Cebus* and *Alouatta*). The iliac crest is almost straight and vertically disposed in the normal quadrupedal position, uniting, by rounded rectangular junctions, with the dorsal and ventral borders, which are almost parallel with one another, though the thickened dorsal border approaches the thin ventral border somewhat at its posterior end, where they fuse to form the thick " body " of the ilium. The anterior ventral spine of the ilium is, according to Benton and Gavan (1960), scarcely homologous with the anterior superior iliac spine of anthropotomy (*vide* also *supra*, p. 38).

The iliac plane faces more medially than in *Cebus* or *Macaca*, a change in direction believed by Waterman to be correlated with change in function of the gluteus medius, which has induced changes in the gluteal plane which become reflected in the iliac plane. There is no iliac fossa, the plane being uniformly flat and smooth.

As in all Old World cynomorphs there is a marked post-gluteal plane, which gives origin to the abductor caudae lateralis. Iliac tuberosities are marked on the sacral plane of the ilium and these are correlated with power of upright sitting. They face ventro-medially as in *Cebus*, but the cranio-caudal extent of the tuberosity is greater even than in *Macaca*. Moreover the iliac tuberosities are more divergent, so as to permit greater area of attachment for the erector spinae muscles on the side of the transverse processes. " These modifications favour the lateral rotation of the spine which must characterize an arboreal leaper and a swift-moving ground runner " (Waterman, p. 609).

Union with the sacrum affects two sacral segments, but the ilium advances each side considerably anterior to the sacral region to a level opposite the penultimate lumbar segment. The great sacrosciatic notch is a broad, shallow depression of the upper border of the innominate bone, cranial to the acetabulum. The latter lies just ventral to a roughened tract of the dorsal border of the ischium, homologous with the ischial spine of the human pelvis. The acetabulum much resembles in form that of man, but the floor, while very thin, is never perforated. The cotyloid notch faces downwards and somewhat backwards and is separated by a stout bony bar from the obturator foramen. In length the ischium forms 36 per cent of the length of the ilium, compared with 35 per cent in *Macaca*.

The body of the ischium posterior to the acetabulum is smooth and of prismatic form with dorsal, ventro-medial and ventro-lateral surfaces separated by smooth borders—except that between the ventro-medial and ventral-lateral, which is sharp and forms part of the circumference of the obturator foramen. Posteriorly the ischium ends in a large, expanded, greatly rugose tuberosity which is covered superficially in the fresh state by the fibro-fatty tissue subjacent to the cutaneous callosity. The ventro-lateral angle of this area is frequently produced into an apex forming a notch between itself and the body of the ischium, receiving the termination of the border separating the dorsal from the ventro-medial borders of the ischial body. Medially the tuberosity narrows to a rounded extremity whence the bone becomes continuous with that part of the ischium which is engaged in the ischio-pubic symphysis.

The pubis is a triangular dorso-ventrally flattened plate. Its cranial border unites by a rounded right angle with the body of the ilium craniad of the acetabulum. The medial or symphyseal border forms a sharp right angle with the cranial border. The postero-lateral border is thin, obliquely disposed, and forms a large share of the circumference of the obturator foramen. An ilio-pectineal line commences on the ilium posterior to the ventral part of the auricular surface. At first low and smooth, it gradually assumes a sharper character as it crosses the rectangular union between ilium and pubis. On the pubis it is extremely sharp, but expands into a roughened tubercle as it gains the pubic angle.

Union of the two innominate bones at the symphysis results in the production of a sharp keel-like ridge in the median plane heightened by the presence of cartilage. The obturator foramen varies in shape, being somewhat subcircular with a craniad extension beneath the acetabulum.

Correnti (1952) has studied radiographically the internal architecture of the pelvis of *Cercopithecus* in comparison with that of the anthropoids and Man. Systems of trabeculae are apparently correlated with method of progression and certain sacro-pubic systems are lacking in the quadrupedal *Cercopithecus*, which occur in the orthograde apes and Man, particularly a diagonal system (the systema arcuata of Cobau). Of the four recognized bundles of Correnti's ectoric system only the anterior and posterior (dorsal and ventral) can be recognized and run within the corresponding margins, one from the anterior ventral spine to the pubis, the other from the auricular area to the ischial tuber.

Femur.—In general this bone possesses a long, bowed shaft, small hemispherical head, short neck, large trochanters and normal appearances at the distal end. There are some interspecific variations in length, straightness of shaft, and in robusticity. Thus there is a great contrast between the rugged, robust strongly bowed femur of *C. pygerythrus* and the straighter more gracile yet longer femur of *C. l'hoesti*. The femur of *C. mona* is intermediate between these two extremes as regards length, robusticity and curvature of shaft ; that of *C. cephus* is long, robust, rugged, but relatively straight-shafted. *C. ascanius schmidti* again is gracile, long and relatively straight like that of *C. l'hoesti*. These differences seem to have no relation to sex and are barely likely to be purely individual ; nevertheless an adult male of *C. ascanius ascanius* shows a shorter, more robust and more curved bone than that of an adult male *C. ascanius schmidti*. In *C. aethiops* subspecies juveniles the femur appears relatively shorter and straighter shafted than in adults, whilst naturally there is less robustness in juveniles.

In length the femur exceeds the humerus by some 20 per cent, for Gabis gives the humero-femoral index as 80 with 5 per cent coefficient of variation ; this compares with 87 for the group containing *Papio* and *Theropithecus*, 90 for *Macaca* and 78 for the Colobidae. Data for robusticity are given by Schultz (1953).

The centre of the otherwise smooth, hemispherical caput femoris is marked by a deep fovea capitis of variable form, but most commonly (*e.g.* in *C. pygerythrus, C. l'hoesti* and *C. ascanius*) by an antero-posteriorly elongated fusiform depression. In *C. neglectus* it is rounded and in *C. ascanius schmidti*, subtriangular, broader anteriorly, and narrowed behind. The articular area extends towards the neck more above and behind than elsewhere ; whereas below, the articular surface projects beyond the contour of the neck producing a deep notch or groove. The collum is relatively short and antero-posteriorly compressed. Distally its anterior surface is marked by an almost horizontal ridge which continues laterad with some distal trend on to the base of the great trochanter.

The great trochanter is very large, of pyramidal form, with the apex extending well above the summit of the caput and recurved in the direction of the caput. Besides the transverse ridge anteriorly, there are various lines for muscular attachment on the lateral aspect ; but posteriorly the element is relatively smooth. A sharp postero-medial border separates the trochanter from the extremely deep trochanteric (digital) fossa. This is axially elongated, wider above and narrowing below to a fine groove, which terminates on the proximal surface of the lesser trochanter. The lateral lip of this groove is homologous with the posterior intertrochanteric line. From the posterior part of the lateral surface of the base of the greater trochanter a vertical ridge proceeds distally and eventually becomes part of the linea aspera. This is the gluteal ridge. It is variably developed but never seems to form a third trochanter.

The lesser trochanter is larger in proportion to the size of the femur, conical and projecting backwards and only slightly medially. Its apex is axially elongated, but sometimes is more pointed or bluntly rounded. In *C. l'hoesti* the process is smaller but more rugged, with vertical ridges on both anterior and posterior aspects. In all cases a fine vertical ridge descends on to the shaft distal to the lesser trochanter and posterior to the spiral line.

The spiral line (declared to be lacking in *C. aethiops* by Shufeldt) is a fine ridge commencing in the angle between neck and shaft some distance in front of the root of the lesser trochanter. Skirting the latter, it proceeds backwards and distally, parallel with the subtrochanteric line. Both lines eventually enter the linea aspera.

The femoral shaft is fundamentally cylindrical, with some tendency toward a triangular cross section due to the piling up of bone posteriorly in the linea aspera. Fairly uniform in calibre, there is a variable trend towards transverse widening in the lower third, best seen in *C. pygerythrus* and its allies, where the phenomenon affects the lower half of the shaft. The linea aspera varies in development, but is two-lipped, the lateral lip being the more prominent. The nutrient foramen lies in relation to the medial lip at the junction of the upper and middle thirds ; it is directed proximally.

The lower end of the shaft (epiphyseal aspect) is highly irregular in shape with four conical eminences at the four corners separated by four depressions for the reception of conical eminences on the epiphysis. These depressions are a deep anterior notch for the reception of the patellar part of the epiphysis, a smaller posterior (popliteal) and two lateral condylar notches.

Of the two condyles there is less discrepancy in size and position than in the human femur, the lowest points of the two being in the same plane due to a greater descent of the medial condyle. Posteriorly both condyles are prominent, separated by a deep intercondylar notch. Above, each condyle is surmounted posteriorly by a large conical sesamoid fabella. The non-articular sides of the two condyles are marked by rugged depressions for tendinous or ligamentous attachment, that on the lateral condyle, for the tendon of the popliteus, being an oblique shallow groove. Mensurational data concerning the distal femoral epiphysis, with indices of its proportions to the shaft, are recorded by Vallois (1920) for several species of this genus. Averages of the biepicondylar index (*i.e.* proportion of transverse breadth of condyles to total femoral length) are given as 68·5 for adults and 60·7 for juveniles—but the figures include data from *Erythrocebus* and several forms not properly included under *Cercopithecus*. The proportion averages somewhat higher for *Cercocebus*, but lower for *Macaca*. Similarly the index for the size of the lateral condyle in proportion to the shaft (antero-posterior diameter of condyle) averages 81·5 in adults and 78·6 for juveniles compared with 75·1 and 86·3 for adults and juveniles of *Macaca*.

Patella.—This is relatively small, ovate, transversely narrowed, but elongated sagittally. Uniformly convex and rough anteriorly, it presents a shallowly dual concave articular facet behind, with a faint median longitudinal elevation between the two concavities. There is no suprapatella.

Tibia.—Except for its greater proportionate length of shaft, this bone closely resembles its human counterpart, as reported for *C. aethiops* by Shufeldt. The crural index, wherein the tibial length is compared to that of the femur, is recorded by Gabis as 95 (with 3 per cent coefficient of variation) compared with 92 for *Macaca*, 90 for *Papio* and 100 for *Theropithecus*. The same author gives a radio-tibial index of 81 (6 per cent coefficient of variation) compared with 99 for baboons and 93 for macaques.

In *Cercopithecus* the upper third is more compressed transversely than in man, and it is more anteriorly bowed as far distally as the junction of middle and lower thirds. Some tibiae show some medial bowing as well as the antero-posterior curvature. This is marked, for example, in *C. cephus*, *C. neglectus* and *C. pygerythrus*, but virtually lacking in *C. l'hoesti*, *C. ascanius*, *C. petaurista* and *C. mona*. Vallois (1912) studied the form of the tibial shaft in transverse section with particular reference to the muscular relations. He gives the average index of the ratio between antero-posterior and transverse diameters as 65 for adults and 74·1 for juveniles, but as with his studies in the femur, he includes some material not now relegated to *Cercopithecus*. A marked rise in the index occurs in *Cercocebus* (69·5 adults, 84·4 juveniles) indicating a less flattened shaft, but in other cynomorphs except *Macaca* (also 69·3) the values are much as in *Cercopithecus*.

All three borders are rounded, the interosseous border being sometimes more sharply marked.

The upper extremity shows all the usual features, with the epiphysis giving a long tongue-shaped downward extension at the front, forming the bony basis of the cnemial tubercle. At the distal end the malleolus is very prominent, bulging medially from the shaft prior to its final distal projection. Medial and lateral malleoli project distally to the same level.

Fibula.—This is long, slender, almost cylindrical and practically straight. The distal end is bulkier than the relatively small, ovoid head. A smooth ridge descends from the neck anteriorly, curving medially to become continuous with the interosseous border. The upper third of the shaft is obliquely compressed whereby it presents two main aspects, antero-lateral and postero-medial. In the distal half the former faces entirely laterad, while the rest of the circumference becomes evenly rounded.

The distal end presents a triangular section with the base located at the inferior tibio-fibular joint, and the apex, formed by the summit of the malleolus, located laterally and posteriorly. The distal aspect of the malleolus is somewhat excavated and rugose.

TARSUS AND PEDAL SKELETON

The whole pedal segment is greatly elongated and relatively narrow compared with that of *Macaca* or *Papio*, but not so extremely as in the Colobidae. The tarsus is comprised of the usual seven bones, which have much the same relative proportions and interrelations as in the human foot. Moreover they form a double plantar arch, transverse and axial.

Talus and calcaneus are rather large with extensive articular surfaces. In the calcaneus the hinder portion is concave medially and somewhat deviated in the same direction. The area for insertion of the tendo Achillis is sharply defined by a transverse line. The anterior articular area for the navicular is concave, whereas the facet on the talus is convex. Cuboid and navicular are approximately the same size and share a mutual articulation in the centre of the tarsus. The entocuneiform is the largest and the meso-cuneiform the smallest of the three cuneiforms. On the medial aspect of the foot both navicular and entocuneiform dip down far below the other bones, thereby increasing the depth of the transverse arch.

Sesamoids are present on the plantar aspect of the metatarso-phalangeal joints as in the manus, but they are lacking from the more distal joints. There is also an ellipsoidal sesamoid in the tendon of the peronaeus longus tendon as it lies in relation with the cuboid.

Metatarsals and all phalanges, save the ungual phalanges, are strongly curved with the convexities located dorsally, but there is some slight variation in degree (*e.g.* Shufeldt found it greater in *C. sabaeus* than in *C. aethiops*). The third metatarsal is longest and has the most robust shaft.

Gabis (*loc. cit.*) gives mensurational data relative to the proportions of the pedal skeleton. A tarsal index expressing the proportion of total pedal length comprised by the tarsus is given for the arboreal group represented by *Cercopithecus* and *Cercocebus* as 32 (coefficient of variation 7 per cent) compared with 35 for baboons. An index expressing the proportionate length of metatarsal III to the total pedal length is 30 (coefficient of variation 7 per cent) compared with 32 for baboons. A similar index for the total length of the three phalanges of the third digit provides the figure 35 (with similar variation) compared with 32 for the terrestrial group of baboons. The proportionate length of the hallux to the bones of the third digit is the same in both *Cercopithecus* and *Papio* (54) in which respect they differ from *Macaca* (56), and more widely from the langurs (48). (See further Schultz, 1963).

ARTHROLOGY

TEMPORO-MANDIBULAR JOINT.—Lordat (1804) adduced several differences from the human condition, notably the plane character of the glenoid surface with only very slight elevation anteriorly. The mandibular condyle too is relatively plane (confirmed by Parsons, 1899). Mensurational data relative to the position of the joint within the skull are recorded by von Haussen (1931), but *Cercopithecus* does not materially differ in this respect from other cynomorph catarrhines.

The meniscus conforms in shape to the flatter glenoid ; it is attached behind to the post-glenoid process and in front fuses with the anterior ligament of the capsule which, when the jaw is retracted, lies horizontally and in contact with the forepart of the glenoid cavity. Fibres of the lateral part of the capsule have the same downward and backward direction as in Man (Parsons). A strong accessory ligament arising from the vaginal process of the temporal bone strengthens the capsule posteriorly ; it is attached below to the back of the neck of the condyle. The lateral aspect is also reinforced by a band arising from the root of the zygoma running downwards and backwards to attach near the preceding ligament. A medial collateral ligament occurs as in Man, in size equivalent to that of a fifth-month human foetus (Keith, 1894). Attached to the posterior border of the vertical ramus is a strong rounded stylo-mandibular ligament ; but the pterygo-mandibular ligament is not well defined according to Keith, who found, however, a well-developed pterygo-spinous ligament.

VERTEBRAL JOINTS.—Suboccipital joints have been described and figured in detail for *C. cynosuros* by Hecker (1922). The membrana tectoria resembles that of *Cercocebus*, being a wide tract of some thickness (see Vol. II, p. 17). The cruciform ligament exhibits ascending and descending branches though the former is but a fine fibrous tract ending above on the intracranial aspect of the margin of the foramen magnum. The transverse portion is a robust band connecting the two lateral masses of the atlas ; an osseous nodule the size of a lentil has been found within it at its centre, whilst a cartilaginous layer coats its ventral surface. The descending limb of the cruciform ligament, much stronger than the ascending, attaches below to the middle of the body of the axis. On the dorsum of the neck of the odontoid an articular facet for the cruciform ligament occurs forming the hinteres Zahngelenk of German anatomists.

The tip of the odontoid is connected to the occiput by a series of well-developed ligaments—a very strongly developed median occipito-odontoid ligament and two less robustly formed oblique (check) ligaments. The direction of the latter is less ascendant than in the more quadrupedal Platyrrhini, the angle formed by them being about 138°. An occipito-odontoid membrane of uniform thickness occludes the spaces between the above ligaments and the ventral border of the foramen magnum. A fibrous formation fixes the lateral borders of the check ligaments to the body of the axis and to the postero-medial aspect of the related occipital condyle ; this structure is not to be identified with the lateral leaflet of the membrana tectoria. The lateral atlanto-axial ligament (Arnold's) is well developed. Together with the lateral occipito-atlantoid ligaments it limits rotation.

VERTEBRAL LIGAMENTS.—As in other quadrupedal Primates, the vertebral ligaments differ from those of Man in their greater diffuseness and proportionally greater quantity of yellow elastic tissue in their substance (Keith).

Dorsal and ventral common ligaments are well developed but less well demarcated than in Man. Ligamenta subflava form thick masses of yellow elastic tissue connecting adjacent vertebral laminae. On the other hand the ligamentum nuchae is thin and fibrous, forming a septum between the dorsal muscles of the neck. Cervical transverse processes are connected by ligamentous bands.

COSTO-VERTEBRAL JOINTS.—These include costo-central and costo-transverse unions. The ventral costo-central ligament resembles its human counterpart and never forms a ligamentum conjugatum. The dorsal ligament is less well developed than in Man, and contains much elastic tissue especially in the anterior segments. Costo-transverse ligaments are three in number at each joint, the middle one being well developed. The posterior ligament is highly endowed with elastic fibres, especially in the hinder segments. The anterior ligament is feebler and in the hinder segments becomes an intercostal ligament.

The anterior costo-transverse ligaments are homologous with the lateral intermuscular septum of the loins, the ribs, like the costal elements of the lumbar vertebrae being ossifications within this stratum. Intercostal muscles become continuous with the anterior costo-transverse ligament in the same fashion as the internal oblique, and transversus muscles of the flanks are related to the lateral lumbar septum (Keith).

STERNO-CLAVICULAR JOINT.—The sternal facet for the clavicle faces more dorsally than in orthograde Primates, being directed forwards, laterally and dorsad. The sternal facet on the clavicle is elliptical, being greatly extended dorso-ventrally and narrow in the opposite direction. The articular area extends on to the ventral face of the sternal extremity of the bone, where it is covered by a thin portion of the capsule. The capsule is strong, but allows free movement. It is thin on the ventral side, thicker dorsally, but very strong on the cranial aspect. Behind, it is reinforced by a strong rhomboid ligament. Internally, Keith stated that the meniscus is replaced in cynomorphs by a fibrous ligament, which permits the two articular cavities to communicate. Parsons, however, found in *C. pygerythrus* a meniscus similar in all respects to that of Man, and agreeing also with his findings in *Macaca* and *Papio*.

In a large male *C. albogularis*, I found an extensive, imperforate meniscus, very thin and flat, but attached by a thicker marginal portion around the capsule. The lateral synovial cavity is more extensive than the medial and most of the movement appears to take place there.

ACROMIO-CLAVICULAR JOINT.—The plane of this joint is very oblique; in the main the facet on the clavicle faces ventrally and laterally, that on the acromion having the reverse direction. The capsule is thin and lax, but there is a complete, imperforate meniscus of oval contour, thicker at its ventral periphery, thinner dorsally and in the centre. The union is strengthened by a long coraco-clavicular ligament which is not subdivided into conoid and trapezoid elements. Keith homologized it with the human trapezoid ligament, but Parsons declared his inability to judge which of the two human ligaments it represents.

SHOULDER JOINT (Macalister, 1871 ; Bland Sutton, 1887 ; Keith, 1894 ; Parsons, 1899).—The capsule has been variously described ; in *C. albogularis* I find it thin and lax, but strengthened locally by adventitious contributions—cranially by the insertion of the tendon of pectoralis minor, and caudal to this by the more expanded insertion of the pectoralis abdominis. Deep to the latter the capsule presents the opening for emergence of the biceps tendon. Inferiorly there is the usual discontinuity associated with the emergent bursa beneath the subscapularis tendon. Beneath the pectoralis minor insertion both Keith and Parsons defined a coraco-humeral ligament strengthening the capsule, thereby refuting the assertion of Rosenfeld (1898) that the human coraco-humeral ligament is derived from fibres of pectoralis minor, whose insertion has there receded to the coracoid. I find this contribution very tenuous in *C. albogularis*, but in a newborn *C. sabaeus* it is distinct and, in part, on a more anterior position than the pectoral insertion. A single gleno-humeral ligamentous thickening of the capsule is found, corresponding to the middle one of the three ligaments described in Man. This is the usual condition in Catarrhini as described by Keith and Parsons. Parsons declares that in no subhuman Primate is the superior gleno-humeral ligament represented, and correlated this with the presence of a mesentery-like fold of synovial membrane which, in monkeys, connects the intra-articular part of the biceps tendon to the capsule, but which has been lost in Man, where the tendon lies free within the joint. The superior gleno-humeral ligament is a relic of this reflection, and not, as some earlier writers declared, a homologue of the ligamentum teres of the hip.

Macalister (1871) claims that both middle and inferior gleno-humeral ligaments are present in cynomorph catarrhines. A transverse bicipital ligament bridges the space between the summits of the two humeral tuberosities, and Keith traces the fibres to the more superficial part of the subscapularis tendon and also the minute membranous tendon of the dorso-humeralis.

Keith also found a profuse strand of fibrous tissue representing the spino-glenoid ligament attached dorsally to the root of the acromion and radiating therefrom over the capsular ligament of the shoulder.

ELBOW JOINT.—Differing little from the human elbow, there is, however, an additional oblique band of fibres superficial to the main anterior capsular ligament, passing from the medial condyle to a point just proximal to the radial tuberosity. Parsons found this in *C. pygerythrus*, but not in *Macaca* or *Papio*. The medial collateral ligament is comprised of a single band as in *Macaca*, not of three portions as in Man and *Lemur*. The brachialis tendon inserts between this and the bone. The radial collateral ligament runs downwards and backwards from the front of the radial side of the lateral condyle, its superficial fibres passing to the shaft of the radius and the deeper ones blending with the orbicular ligament of the radius. Both collateral ligaments are so arranged as to limit extension of the elbow, a point which Parson's stresses as of functional importance when the length of the forearm is considered and the great leverage it exerts. The orbicular ligament is extremely powerful. When cut and reflected a feeble quadrate ligament is exposed connecting the neck of the radius with the distal border of the lesser sigmoid notch of the ulna.

WRIST JOINT.—As in other cynomorphs there are two joint cavities only partly separated internally by a connective tissue fibrous septum. To the radial side is the radio-carpal joint, whilst medially the enlarged ulnar styloid is received into a socket formed by the cuneiform and pisiform. The articulation between cuneiform and pisiform communicates with the cavity of the wrist joint proper. The volar part of the capsular ligament is composed of fibres running in two directions : radio-carpal fibres pass disto-medially ; ulno-carpal fibres form a strong ligament on a more superficial plane, coursing disto-laterally from ulnar styloid to scaphoid. Keith found a ligament passing from the radial styloid to the same tubercle on the scaphoid.

Parsons found in *C. pygerythrus* a slight synovial projection into the forepart of the joint coresponding to the junction between the radius and the triangular fibro-cartilage above and to that between the lunate and cuneiform bones below. The triangular fibro-cartilage is present and much resembles its human counterpart. In *C. albogularis* it is free from the volar capsular ligament, permitting the synovial cavities of the inferior radio-ulnar and radio-carpal joints to communicate. Moreover the apex of the cartilage has no direct connection with the ulna.

The apex of the pisiform is connected with the styloid process of meta-carpal V by a strong pisi-metacarpal ligament. Keith affirms that in juveniles some fibres of the flexor carpi ulnaris are traceable into the ligament, but with maturity of the bone these are finally divorced from their parent tendon.

Functional anatomy of the carpal and manual joints has been studied radiographically in *C. cephus* by Schreiber (1934). The scaphoid in radio-graphs is sharply separated by a gap from radius, lunate and capitate bones. In radial deviation of the hand, its shadow moves proximally and slightly preaxially ; in ulnar deviation it moves distally and somewhat postaxially.

The os centrale is separated by a very fine cleft from the scaphoid in the resting position of the hand, but it is in close contact with the head of the capitate. A broader cleft separates it from the trapezoid. It moves proximally in radial abduction to lie wedged between the navicular, capitate and trapezoid. In ulnar abduction it shifts to a more radial and distal position. The lunate is normally separated by a gap from the radius and also from the scaphoid, but it is closely bound to the triquetrum. A radio-proximal shift occurs in radial abduction filling the gap—more marked than the corresponding move of the scaphoid. Ulnar deviation produces a proximo-postaxial shift so that the morphologically distal surface faces radio-distally.

The triquetrum presents a large shadow in radiographs with the long axis of the bone directed from a radio-proximal to an ulno-distal point. In the resting state it is separated by a distinct gap from the hamate. In radial abduction the long axis becomes more steeply inclined ; in ulnar abduction less.

Shadows of the trapezoid and trapezium are normally superposed and they do not appreciably separate during extreme hand deviation, though they remain distinct from the centrale.

The capitate moves little ; its relations in radial abduction being the same as in the resting position, except that its body presents a slight radial shift so that the morphologically preaxial aspect becomes more oblique. In ulnar abduction there is a postaxial shift of the body of the bone producing a change of direction of its distal articular surface to a more oblique (ulno-distal) position.

The hamate normally lies obliquely, with its longitudinal diameter almost vertical to the long axis of the hand. Its narrow radial margin is in contact with the basis of the capitate ; its ulno-proximal angle lying parallel with the distal aspect of the triquetrum, but separated therefrom by a distinct cleft. In radial abduction its proximal part moves but little radio-distalwards. In ulnar abduction the ulno-distal part shifts proximally, whereby the shadows of the hamate and triquetrum fuse together.

The large pisiform shadow is superposed on that of the ulnar styloid. It shifts but little during either radial or ulnar deviation of the hand, being less than the movements of the triquetrum, hence the distance between the two carpalia becomes increased in both movements.

SACRO-ILIAC JOINT.—A synovial cavity is present. The cavity is enclosed ventrally merely by transverse ligamentous fibres. Dorsal sacro-iliac ligaments are very strong, passing from the pleurapophyseal elements of the sacral vertebrae (mostly S.2 with smaller bundles from S.1 and S.3) and connected laterally to the ilium. Posteriorly these dorsal bands become continuous with the great sacro-sciatic ligament (see below) and above with the ilio-lumbar ligament.

HIP JOINT.—In the capsule the three local thickenings, ilio-femoral (Bigelow's), ischio-femoral and pubo-femoral, recognized in Man, are usually present, but less well marked.* The first mentioned is the best developed, but it lacks the Y-shaped formation of the human ligament. Parsons failed to find support for Bland Sutton's contention that Bigelow's ligament represented the divorced tendon of an aborted scansorius muscle. Internally a ligamentum teres is present, resembling the human structure, but according to Parsons not tense in any position of the joint.

---

* Keith, however, states they are more prominent than in Man.

The whole of the collum femoris is included within the capsule, and the ventral and posterior aspects of the bone are clothed with synovial membrane. Along the under surface of the neck runs Cowper's band connected by a mesentery-like structure with the capsule. It probably represents a divorced part of the ligamentum teres after confluence of the articular cartilage of the caput.

A great sacro-sciatic ligament is represented merely by a thickening in the fascia ensheathing the glutaeus maximus, passing from the tips of the transverse processes of the first three post-sacral vertebrae and blending distally with the fibro-fatty tissue underlying the ischial callosity.

KNEE JOINT.—The capsule is trilaminar : (i) a superficial lamina derived from the fascia lata, traceable over the resplendent ligamentum patellae to the tibia ; (ii) a layer continuous with the quadriceps tendon containing anteriorly the patella, and strengthened distally by the ligamentum patellae ; (iii) the synovial layer. On either side there are additional collateral ligaments of which the medial is a broad, well-defined band passing from a rounded origin on the medial femoral condyle to an attachment on the medial side of the shaft of the tibia ; it crosses the tendon of the semi-membranosus, which is ensheathed in a synovial extrusion and serves as a partial rotator of the joint rather than as a pure flexor. The lateral ligament is a more rounded cord. Both these ligaments, at their insertion, are provided with extensions of articular cartilage on the appropriate part of the corresponding tibial condyle. The distal attachment of the lateral ligament is to the upper surface of the head of the fibula as in *Macaca*, not to the lateral aspect of its neck (as in *Ateles*). Parsons found the fibres of this ligament twisted, those arising posteriorly on the femur becoming anterior and post-axial on gaining the fibula.

The posterior capsular ligament is relatively weak as it lacks the expansion from the semimembranosus. Proximally, over the femoral condyles, the capsule incorporates the sesamoids (fabellae) in the two heads of the gastro-cnemius. These are connected to the femur by the sesamo-femoral ligaments, whilst oblique sesamo-tibial ligaments connect them to the tibia. Superficial to them a fibrous lamina connects the sesamoids with the capsule, extending each side as far as the collateral ligaments and reinforced below, according to Vallois (1914), by an expansion from the sheath of the semimembranosus, and on the peroneal side by an expansion from the soleus tendon. Arc-like interfabellar fibres connect the two sesamoids and the two sesamo-femoral ligaments.

Internally the ligamentum patellae and distal part of the patella are connected to the synovial covering of the anterior cruciate ligament by a strong, fat-laden ligamentum mucosum, partly dividing the anterior part of the cavity into medial and lateral parts. There are also strong alar ligaments passing laterad from the patellar ligament, at any rate in *C. mitis*, for Vallois denies their presence in *C. sabaeus*. The two cruciate ligaments are not directly connected with each other, a synovial communication passing between them as in *Macaca*.

Vallois describes the anterior cruciate ligament as almost horizontal in position, while the posterior is nearly vertical; both are somewhat twisted. The anterior attachment of the anterior ligament spreads fanwise, but its femoral attachment is concentrated as are both attachments of the posterior ligament.

Semilunar cartilages and their connections have been discussed by Retterer (1907), Vallois (1914) and Jost (1922). All agree in that the lateral meniscus is completely circular and the medial C-shaped.

The two cornua of the lateral semilunar cartilage are connected by a broad band giving it a circular outline with a 4 mm. central opening; this is the same as in *Ateles* and *Papio*, but differs from that of *Macaca*. In other respects this structure resembles that of *Macaca* differing from that of Man in that, instead of attaching posteriorly just behind the spine of the tibia, it is continued obliquely across the back of the posterior cruciate ligament to the lateral side of the medial condyle. This connection is represented in Man by a vestigial structure—the ligament of Wrisberg. It is the menisco-femoral ligament of Vallois and Jost, who affirm that it affects the hinder one-quarter of the medial border of the meniscus. Parsons considers that the simian type of attachment is more primitive, being identical with that of ordinary quadrupedal mammals, considering the human modification— an adaption to the erect posture—which demands continual extension of the knee with consequent strain on the meniscus.

The medial semilunar cartilage resembles the human structure both in shape and attachments, being a moderately open C-shape, wider posteriorly than in front. As in other Catarrhini, it has a long anterior attachment which crosses the origin of the anterior cruciate ligament. Its posterior attachment is short and fixed in front of the posterior cruciate attachment. The two cornua are 5 mm. apart in *C. sabaeus* (Retterer).

ANKLE JOINT.—Keith and Parsons both stress the feeble development of the anterior fasciculus of the fibular collateral ligament, indeed Parsons found it entirely lacking in his Vervet (as in *Papio*). It is to be presumed that lateral movement is therefore freer than in Man. The tibial collateral ligament is markedly divided into an anterior and posterior band, and of these the former is subdivided into superficial and deep laminae. The superficial band connects with the navicular and then proceeds to the meta-tarsus (internal tibio-tarso-metatarsal ligament of Keith). The deep lamina passes to the navicular and the calcaneo-navicular ligament. The posterior band is less powerful, passing downwards and backwards to the medial surface of the talus.

During dorsi-flexion the neck of the talus approximates to the lower end of the tibia and there is correspondingly a forward extension of the articular cartilage.

The inferior tibio-fibular union resembles that of Man, but the synovial membrane is more voluminous.

In connection with the ankle some modifications of the extensor retinaculum (ligamentum cruciatum cruris) have been described by Stamm (1931). The distal part of the retinaculum is represented by the ligamentum fundiforme, which forms a pulley for the extensor digitorum longus tendon, being attached only at its fibular end to the anterior part of the upper aspect of the calcaneus. The lower fibres of the transverse ligamentous band curve laterally, dipping inwards to form a sling for the tendons of tibialis anterior and extensor hallucis longus deep to the ligamentum fundiforme. In *Cercopithecus* these fibres, forming an oblique band over the ankle-joint capsule, attach to the talus as well as to the calcaneus and have no connection with the ligamentum fundiforme (*cf. Macaca*).

PEDAL JOINTS (Förster, 1923, 1924 ; Stamm, 1931 ; Frechkop, 1937).— General interrelations of the tarsal bones are much the same as in Man, but the detailed arrangements are such that there is less evidence of the characteristic plantar arches, the whole foot being more flattened and, when supporting the body-weight, giving more extensive contact between sole and substratum. However, Förster (1924) indicates in *C. sabaeus* a trace of lateral longitudinal arch more advanced than, *e.g.* in *Lemur mongoz*, and this seems to be correlated with a more oblique groove on the calcaneus for transmission of the tendon of peronaeus longus.

The medial longitudinal arch is more pronounced and has for its keystone the talus, more particularly that portion of it which caps the sustentaculum tali. The two pillars of the arch form an angle of 125°.

TALO-CALCANEAN UNIONS.—These are two ; a joint between the body of the talus and that of calcaneus, and another between the head of the talus and the sustenaculum tali, the latter being further divided. The facet for the body of the talus is more or less quadrate, obliquely disposed with the main axis passing from behind forwards and postaxially, and the surface strongly convex in the same axis, but somewhat concave in the opposite diameter. The capsule is attached close to the edge of the articular cartilage, except posteriorly, where it extends backwards on the calcaneus some distance, the space being occupied by intracapsular fat covered with synovial membrane. Between the facet and those on the sustentaculum the capsular ligament is common to that of the joint between the head of the talus and the sustentaculum, and is extremely strong. The joint permits gliding and rotatory movements.

The other joint is a complex ball-and-socket affair wherein the rounded talar head is received into a socket formed partly by the sustantaculum, partly by the proximal concave surface of the navicular, completed inferiorly by the spring (inferior calcaneo-navicular) ligament and laterally by a triangular fibro-cartilaginous nodule occupying the angle between the medial tip of the sustentaculum and the proximo-medial angle of the navicular. The facets on the sustentaculum are two in number, a proximo-medial oval facet whose long axis is parallel with that on the body of the calcaneus and a smaller rounded disto-lateral facet. The two are separated by a non-articular interval into which the spring ligament is continued on to non-articular bone formed by the intervening part of the sustentaculum. This is supplemented below by the sustentaculo-navicular portion of Keith's tibio-tarso-metatarsal complex, which bridges the tendon of the tibialis posterior on the plantar side, forming its sheath. The ligament proceeds distally to the bases of metatarsals II, III and IV.

A dorsal talo-metatarsal ligament is a prominent feature, as in other simian feet, and as first indicated by Keith. It courses deep to the extensor digitorum brevis from the neck of the talus to the base of the third metatarsal with slight extensions to the two neighbouring metatarsals. Keith states that " when the foot is in a condition of prehension, this ligament strengthens the arch between the grasping toes and the astragalus, and it may be regarded as an accessory prehensile ligament ". Deep to it lie the shorter, but stronger and broader talo-navicular fibres, which form a strengthened part of the capsule of the talo-navicular joint.

Laterally lies the dorsal or superior calcaneo-cuboid ligament, relatively stronger than in Man, and forming part of the capsule of the calcaneo-cuboid joint. This is even stronger on the plantar side, where an inward extension occurs in an upward direction giving a virtually interosseous ligament, which occupies the hilus of the reniform articular cartilage-covered area. The plane of this cartilage on the distal end of the calcaneus is by no means flat but strongly concave transversely with the deepest part of the concavity more to the medial side. The proximal facet on the cuboid reciprocates this formation. Dorsi-flexion and plantar-flexion are therefore very limited and medial or lateral deviation virtually impossible. A certain amount of rotatory gliding is permitted in eversion and inversion of the foot around the plantar interosseous ligament, which serves as a pivot.

Articulation between cuboid and navicular occurs between the postero-medial angle of the former and the distal half of the lateral surface of the navicular. The facet on the cuboid is oval with the long axis obliquely disposed, passing from proximo-dorsal to disto-plantar in direction, with the minor axis depressed, whereby the long axis forms a scaphoid concavity. The union is effected by short, relatively thin cubo-navicular fibres dorsally, and thicker fibres on the plantar side, these latter being continuous with those of the interosseous calcaneo-cuboid ligament.

The distal aspect of the navicular presents a club-shaped outline, with the head of the club dorsally and the short handle lying obliquely on the medial side and descending towards the sole. The whole is articular cartilage covered, that on the handle being related to the ento-cuneiform, whilst poorly defined areas on the head are adapted to the meso- and ecto-cuneiforms. Inter-cuneiform and cubo-cuneiform articulations call for no special remark.

Keith describes a deep transverse tarso-metatarsal ligament which is revealed on raising the tendon of the peronaeus longus from its fibrous sheath. It runs from a tubercle on the plantar aspect of the entocuneiform to the bases of metatarsals II and III.

The joint between the entocuneiform and the base of the first metatarsal has been extensively studied by Förster (1924). The long axis of the cuneiform facet is set at an angle of 70° to the horizontal in *C. sabaeus* while the curve of the transverse tarsal arch at the level of the joint of Lisfranc forms the quadrant of a circle on the lateral side of the long axis of the joint. The angle of 70° falls between the platyrrhine value (*Ateles* = 65°) and that for the gibbons (*Hylobates moloch* = 85°). The distal cuneiform facet has no appearance of a trochlea, in fact the portion which is depressed in *Lemur* here forms an eminence. The area is subdivided into two convexities of unequal radius, a smaller, upper, more strongly curved area, and a larger, more ventral area of less pronounced curvature; they are separated by an oblique line passing from the medial side in a latero-plantar direction. The capsule of the joint is relatively lax with little strengthening by dorsal or plantar ligaments, but a more marked ligamentous bond affects the medial side. On the postaxial side a fine ligamentous band, springing from the base of metatarsal II, proceeds to unite with the plantar portion of the capsule of the joint.

DENTITION

PERMANENT DENTITION

Dental formula, as for the family.

The permanent dentition agrees in all essential particulars with that of other cercopithecoid genera (*vide antea*, p. 39) but shows less extreme sexual divergences than in *e.g. Cercocebus, Macaca* or *Papio*.

Upper incisors vary much in appearance according to age and state of wear. $I.^1$ considerably exceeding $I.^2$ in size. Senyurek (1960) observes its relatively large size in comparison with Colobidae; sometimes it exceeds $M.^1$ in robusticity. Incisors are peg-like rather than chisel-like in character, and their long axes somewhat oblique. In addition to antero-posterior obliquity the axis of $I.^1$ inclines medially so that the antero-medial tip of the crown contacts that of its neighbour, but a small triangular interdental space (larger in *C. neglectus* and *C. cephus*) separates them towards the alveolus;

T

as an anomaly the space is enlarged by complete separation of the two incisors, *e.g.* in a *C. a. moloneyi* figured by Colyer (1936). Crown markedly convex anteriorly both in transverse and supero-inferior directions. Biting surface oval to triangular, becoming more triangular with increasing attrition from exposure of dentine, leaving sharp enamel cutting edge in front. Proximal to worn edge the lingual surface is smooth, strongly convex transversely, plane from above down.

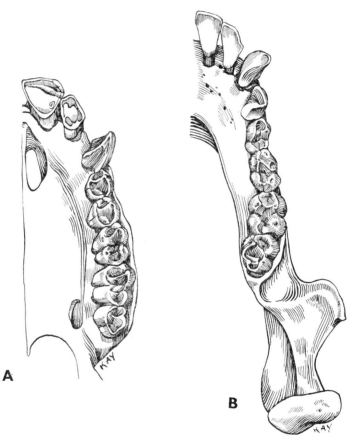

FIG. 35.—*Cercopithecus pogonias pogonias.* A, upper and B, lower dental series (× $\frac{2}{1}$)

Ockerse (1959) finds in *C. pygerythrus* the labial surface of I.^{1} quadrilateral and the lingual triangular in outline. The former is somewhat broader at the incisal edge than at the neck. From neck to cutting edge the distance averages 7 mm. in males, 6 mm. in females. The lingual surface from the incisal edge towards the enamel edge about $\frac{2}{3}$ is concave and then convex. At the cutting edge the surface is concave transversely, but at the neck convex. The mesial edge (or surface) is triangular with the apex at the cutting edge, it is convex labio-lingually and from cutting edge to neck, but less convex than the lateral (distal) surface. The distal surface is also more or less triangular, but smaller and more convex than the medial. Its enamel edge, like that on the mesial aspect, is a sharp V-shaped wedge, but its point extends a shorter distance towards the incisive border. The neck is scarcely constricted, the root single and $1\frac{1}{2}$ times the length of the crown. It is triangular in section with labial, mesial and distal aspects, the two latter bearing shallow grooves. The root apex is slightly curved laterad. The pulp cavity repeats the shape of the crown, showing two horns, mesial and distal. The tooth occludes with I.$\overline{1}$ and half of I.$\overline{2}$.

I.$\underline{2}$ relatively minute, peg-like, sloped medially and with the crown more pointed, giving a triangular appearance to the labial surface. Lingual surface strongly convex transversely. Separated by diastema from canine. Implanted on a more posterior plane than I.$\underline{1}$.

In *C. pygerythrus* Ockerse (*loc. cit.*) finds the labial and lingual surfaces of I.$\underline{2}$ with five angles. The former, rounded mesio-distally, is slightly convex from incisal edge to neck. The mesial angle is more rounded than the distal and its point somewhat lower. The incisal edge is pointed but soon wears down to a horizontal edge. The lingual surface resembles the labial, but half the surface nearer the incisal edge is concave, the rest convex. Transversely this surface is slightly convex near the incisal edge, but strongly so near the neck, where a cingulum and sulcus are formed. Mesial and distal aspects are more or less triangular. The neck is higher labially than lingually. The root is single and $1\frac{1}{2}$ times the length of the crown; oval in cross section it is curved mesially to accommodate the canine. A shallow groove marks the mesial side of the root, but there is none distally. The pulp cavity lacks cornua. The crown occludes with the lateral half of I.$\overline{2}$ by its mesial half, the distal half being opposite the short diastema between I.$\overline{2}$ and canine.

Upper canine much elongated, projecting in males thrice as far as incisors; conical with sharp apex, laterally compressed, with a deep longitudinal groove anteriorly along basal three-quarters of crown. Posterior border very sharp; axes of the two slightly divergent. A very slight diastema between it and foremost premolar. The tooth is much smaller in females.

The upper canine of *C. pygerythrus* is described by Ockerse as showing a deep longitudinal groove on the triangular labial surface dividing it into two unequal parts, a smaller mesial and larger distal. The crown is 20 mm. long in males, 15 mm. in females. The tooth is widest at the neck (5 mm. male, 4 mm. female). The enamel edge is indistinct, flat and concave towards the root. The distal aspect shows a slight lingual curve and exceeds the mesial surface in area, the width at the neck averaging 8 mm. in males, 7 mm. in females. There may or may not be a shallow groove on this surface. The labial border is rounded and the lingual sharp; enamel edge as on labial surface but horizontal or slightly concave towards root. There is no constriction at the neck. The massive root curves distally and is 25 mm. long in males, 17 mm. in females, triangular in cross section, with labial, mesial and

distal surfaces, of which the first is least extensive and bears a deep longitudinal groove from neck to apex and continuous with that on the crown.
The large pulp cavity takes the shape of crown and root.

P.$\frac{3}{}$ < P.$\frac{4}{}$; its crown bearing a single main cusp located towards the buccal
side, giving the buccal aspect a triangular outline, accentuated by enamel
ridges fore and aft, leading to a basal cingulum, which sweeps round the
medial part of the base of the crown. The mid point of the lingual cingulum
is connected by a ridge to the apex of the main cusp and sometimes, as in
C. l'hoesti, bears an incipient small nodule near its base. In C. neglectus
both ridge and nodule are lacking, there being a single large crescentic fovea
at the base of the principal cusp. Otherwise two small foveae are separated
by the ridge. Roots, three: two buccal and one lingual.

Ockerse describes the crown in C. pygerythrus as having five surfaces,
buccal, lingual, medial, distal and occlusal. In both sexes the tooth measures
4 mm. mesio-distally and the same bucco-lingually, while the crown is 4·5
mm. high. The occlusal aspect has an approximately triangular outline and
bears two cusps, buccal and lingual joined by a ridge of enamel which separates
a smaller mesial from a larger distal depression. Buccal cusp much larger
than lingual and sharp pointed. Buccal surface vaguely pentagonal, convex
mesio-distally and slightly convex from occlusal surface to neck. Lingual
surface triangular and much less extensive than buccal. From occlusal
surface to near neck it is straight, but becomes thereafter very convex to
deflect the food, making the enamel edge more distinct. Mesial surface
roughly quadrangular, with a central depression extending from occlusal
edge to angle between buccal and lingual roots; enamel edge flat and indistinct. Distal surface also quadrangular, convex bucco-lingually and from
above down; enamel edge as on mesial surface, but slightly concave towards
roots. Three-rooted, one large conical one on lingual side and two shorter
buccal roots converging towards their tips. Pulp cavity small without
cornua.

P.$\frac{4}{}$ crown intermediate in size and appearance between that of P.$\frac{3}{}$ and
that of M.$\frac{1}{}$, but often (as in C. pogonias and C. nictitans) merely an enlarged
replica of P.$\frac{3}{}$. In C. l'hoesti the occlusal surface is more quadrate than
triangular due to the expansion of the posterior fovea and elevation of its
margin postero-lingually and the tendency for the basal end of the ridge to
become elevated into an incipient cusp, the principal buccal cusp, at the same
time, being of lesser height than on P.$\frac{3}{}$. In C. neglectus a similar appearance
occurs, but the crown is more rounded circumferentially and an oblique
secondary enamel ridge divides the posterior fovea into two. In C. cephus
this secondary ridge is represented merely by a slight hummock basally.
Three-rooted.

According to Ockerse the crown of P.$\frac{4}{}$ of C. pygerythrus has the same
five surfaces as P.$\frac{3}{}$, but all are rounder and the crown slightly larger (4 mm.

mesio-distally but 5 mm. from buccal to lingual ridge in both sexes). Occlusa aspect more or less square, with 2 cusps joined by enamel ridge, separating small medial from larger distal depressions. Buccal cusp larger and longer than lingual; tips of cusps more rounded than on P.$\underline{3}$. Buccal aspect pentagonal, more convex mesio-distally than from above down; ename edge distinct, rounded, slightly convex towards root. Lingual surface triangular but of same extent as buccal, straight from above down becoming convex towards neck making enamel edge more distinct and convex towards root. Mesial aspect quadrilateral, convex bucco-lingually and slightly so from above down; enamel edge more distinct than on P.$\underline{3}$ and slightly concave towards roots. Distal surface quadrilateral, convex bucco-lingually and from above down; enamel edge distinct, slightly concave toward roots; makes contact with M.$\underline{1}$ near distal enamel edge. Neck slightly constricted. One large conical root on palatal side and two thinner buccal roots, all roots converging at their tips. Pulp cavity flat, without cornua.

Upper molar series tending to converge posteriorly—an expression of the shortened palate compared with, for example, *Erythrocebus* or *Cercocebus* (Frechkop, 1940). M.$\underline{2}$>M.$\underline{1}$>M.$\underline{3}$.

The most striking feature of the cusp pattern, as in other Cercopithecoidea, is the marked bilophodonty, *i.e.* quadritubercular molars with the anterior and posterior pairs of cusps connected by transverse ridges (crista transversa anterior et posterior). According to Remane (1951, 1960) the posterior loph is developed by loss of the oblique ridge of more typical primate molars after it has given rise to a limb connecting metacone and hypocone.

In contrast to *Cercocebus*, for example, the bases of the molars, though convex on lingual and buccal surfaces, are not greatly swollen, and in consequence the buccal and lingual cusps are not so greatly approximated.

Buccal cusps higher than lingual. A strong transverse fissure crossing the crown between anterior and posterior pairs of cusps, incising buccal and lingual margins to form notches at its extremities. In occlusion the buccal cusps bite external to the buccal cusps of the lower molars, these being received into the foveae on the upper teeth. Three-rooted.

M.$\underline{1}$ of *C. pygerythrus* is described by Ockerse as having a crown resembling the human M.$\overline{2}$. Bucco-lingual diameter 5 mm., mesio-distal 6 mm.; crown height buccally 4 mm., lingually 5 mm. (in both sexes). Occlusal aspect quadrilateral rather than diamond shaped; mesio-buccal cusp largest, the two lingual cusps subequal, disto-buccal intermediate in size between lingual and mesio-buccal. Apices of cusps in straight line mesio-distally. Surface shows three depressions, one mesial to mesial loph, one between lophs and one behind distal loph. Mesial and distal borders with small enamel ridges. Two grooves, one mesio-distal and the other bucco-lingual, the latter passing over on to middle of buccal and lingual surfaces. Buccal aspect slightly convex in both directions, enamel edge flat, indistinct, horizontal. Lingual aspect larger than buccal and more convex especially towards neck, enamel edge flat, indistinct, virtually horizontal. Mesial surface flat in both directions, enamel edge flat, indistinct concave towards roots. Distal surface very convex in both directions, larger than mesial aspect being longer from above down; enamel edge flat, indistinct, slightly convex towards roots. Roots 3, two buccal and one lingual (palatal); buccal roots subequal and flattened bucco-lingually; lingual root conical, and more robust; all roots divergent towards apices. Pulp cavity flattened, triangular in section near neck and with cornua extending towards cusps.

The M.$\underline{2}$ of *C. pygerythrus* has crown of different shape from M.$\underline{1}$, being wider bucco-lingually near buccal and lingual borders of mesial surfaces (6 mm.) compared with 5 mm. on same level of distal surface (no sexual differences in size). Mesio-distally the crown width is 6·5 mm. and the crown height 4·5 mm. on buccal side, 5 mm. on lingual side. All sides more rounded than on M.$\underline{1}$ giving crown more bulbous appearance. Occlusal surface with mesio-buccal cusp largest, the others subequal; central fovea deeper than the other two; from the latter, small fissures run bucco-lingually. A deep groove runs from mesial to distal depression and another bucco-lingually the latter passing on to buccal surface as indistinct groove and as a deeper one half-way along lingual surface. Neck slightly constricted. Roots 3; buccal roots subequal, flattened bucco-lingually; lingual root slightly larger, more robust and flattened mesio-distally dividing from the others towards palate and sometimes grooved on palatal aspect.

M.$\underline{3}$ smallest and with more rounded crown contour, due to reduction of hinder half of tooth which, however, bears small metacone and hypocone joined by a low ridge which forms the posterior margin of the occlusal surface.

M.$\underline{3}$ crown in *C. pygerythrus* resembling that of M.$\underline{2}$, but slightly smaller (bucco-lingual diameter near mesial aspect 5·5 mm., near distal aspect 4 mm.; mesio-distal diameter 5·5 mm.; crown height on buccal side 4·5 mm., on lingual 5·5 mm. without sexual difference. Occlusal aspect tapering posteriorly more than in M.$\underline{2}$; mesio-buccal cusp largest, the two distal cusps subequal and the mesio-lingual smaller than mesio-buccal, but larger than two distals.

Mesial (anterior) loph very prominent with a small depression in front from where a small fissure runs bucco-lingually, the depression is bounded mesially by a sharp enamel ridge. Central fovea very deep. A more prominent enamel ridge bounds the occlusal aspect distally. Mesio-distal groove passing half-way along distal aspect of crown, but not on to mesial aspect. Bucco-lingual groove passing half-way along buccal surface, but not at all on to lingual surface. Mesial, buccal and lingual surfaces as in M.$\underline{2}$ but distal aspect very convex in both directions with enamel edge indistinct, slightly convex towards roots. Neck constricted, giving more bulbous appearance to crown. Roots 3, the two buccal roots subequal, flattened bucco-lingually, the lingual root slightly larger, more robust and flattened in the opposite direction, divergent towards tip and often grooved on its palatal aspect. Pulp cavity very flattened, quadrangular in section near neck and with four cornua extending towards cusps.

Lower incisors smaller than uppers, with less discrepancy in size between $I_{\overline{1}}$ and $I_{\overline{2}}$; slightly proclivous. $I_{\overline{1}}$ spatulate, with sharp incisive edge, slightly convex anterior surface and subtriangular lingual surface.

In *C. pygerythrus* Ockerse finds the crown of $I_{\overline{1}}$ 9 mm. long in males, 7 mm. in females; width at incisal edge 4 mm. in males, 3 mm. in females. It occludes with $I^{\underline{1}}$ only. Labial surface vaguely quadrilateral, slightly convex longitudinally, more so transversely; enamel edge indistinct, convex towards root; angles of incisal edge slightly less than 90°. Lingual face roughly triangular, the apex at neck; flat from incisal edge for two-thirds then becoming slightly convex to neck; transversely flat at incisal edge, very convex near neck; enamel edge indistinct, convex towards root. Mesial aspect flat, triangular, with apex at cutting edge; enamel edge indistinct wedge-shaped with point towards incisal edge; distal aspect also triangular and flat longitudinally but concave labio-lingually; enamel edge indistinct and wedge-shaped as on mesial aspect. Root straight, of same length approximately as labial surface of crown, broader labio-lingually than mesio-distally, shallow grooves on mesial and distal surfaces, the latter extending beyond neck to crown. Pulp chamber lacks cornua.

$I_{\overline{2}}$ smaller with sharp antero-medial angle to crown, oblique biting edge and rounded lateral angles. In occlusion it is received into the angle between $I^{\underline{1}}$ and $I^{\underline{2}}$. A very small diastema between. $I_{\overline{2}}$ and lower canine.

In *C. pygerythrus* Ockerse states that $I_{\overline{2}}$ is the smallest of all the permanent teeth, having on the average a crown length of 8 mm. in males, 7 mm. in females, width 3 mm. in both sexes. Widest part is not at incisive edge, but about half-way between it and neck. Occludes against small part of $I^{\underline{1}}$ and the whole of $I^{\underline{2}}$; a small distance separates it from the canine.

Labial aspect roughly triangular, the base at the mesial border of the surface and the apex at the widest point on the distal border resulting in a long, narrow surface. From incisal edge to neck it is convex; mesio-distally very convex; enamel edge indistinct, convex towards root. Lingual surface also triangular, but smaller than labial; for the most part concave longitudinally, flat transversely, but near neck it is concave in both dimensions; enamel edge indistinct, convex towards root. Mesial surface flat, triangular with apex towards cutting edge; enamel edge indistinct, wedge-shaped with point upwards. Distal surface likewise triangular, smaller than mesial, slightly concave in both directions; enamel edge as on mesial aspect. Root broader labio-lingally than mesio-distally with flat mesial surface and distal surface longitudinally grooved, the groove extending on to crown; tip of root curved somewhat mesiad. Pulp cavity duplicated in root, one on labial and one on lingual side, without cornua in crown.

Lower canines smaller than upper, but provided with a distinct talonid at posterior base of crown. The talonid is sharply demarcated by an obliquely transverse groove from the main cone.

The lower canine of the Vervet according to Ockerse is smaller than the corresponding upper tooth and is therefore the second largest member of the permanent dentition. Crown length in males 14 mm., in females 11 mm.; labio-lingual width 7 mm. in males, 5 mm. in females; mesio-distal width 4 mm. in males, 3 mm. in females.

Crown conical without demarcation between labial, mesial, lingual and distal aspects. Labially triangular, convex longitudinally and more so mesio-distally; enamel edge indistinct and virtually horizontal. Lingual surface smaller, concave from tip to neck, convex transversely; the distal half of this surface occludes with the upper canine from the tip to near the neck where a prominent cingulum or cusp-like process occurs; enamel edge indistinct and horizontal. Mesially triangular, with a longitudinal groove extending from near tip to mesial surface of root; enamel edge indistinct, slightly concave towards root. Distal surface flattish longitudinally but convex mesio-distally; enamel labially prominent, horizontal. Root massive, as long as crown, curved somewhat lingually and more so distally, flattened mesio-distally but very broad labio-lingually. Flat mesial and distal sides bear longitudinal grooves, that on mesial side transgressing the neck on to crown. Pulp cavity with large apical foramen, flattened in root, expanded in crown.

P.$\overline{3}$ with usual specialization of crown met with in other cercopithecoids, but to a milder degree than in *Macaca, Cercocebus* or *Papio*. Crown transversely compressed, with a single-pointed cusp, the fore part sloping obliquely downwards and forwards, forming a shearing edge, which in occlusion bites against the posterior edge of the upper canine. Two low ridges, more vertically disposed, separated by a fovea, descend from the summit to the posterior base of the crown. Two-rooted.

Of the P.$\overline{3}$ of *C. pygerythrus*, Ockerse remarks on its likeness to that of a carnivore and opines it has a similar function in tearing rather than crushing the food. Its crown length measures 10 mm. in males, 7 mm. in females; mesio-distally the measurement is 8 mm. in the male, 6 mm. in the female, while labio-lingually the values are 4 mm. and 3 mm. The crown bears a single high labio-lingually compressed cusp. Labial aspect of crown convex in both directions, its mesial border sharp and slightly convex forming a prominent cingulum at junction with neck; distal border shorter, but sharp and slightly concave. The mesial part of the labial surface occludes with the upper canine. Enamel edge distinct, rounded but straightening at the bases of the roots. Mesio-lingual surface small, triangular, concave mesio-distally and vertically, with distinct enamel edge, rounded and concave towards roots. Disto-lingual surface smaller than preceding, but also triangular, very concave in both directions, except near neck where it becomes very convex in both directions; enamel edge distinct, rounded, horizontal. Roots two, a large anterior (mesial) and smaller posterior (distal); mesial root curves distad and with a shallow groove on its lingual face; distal root straight, with a groove on labial side. (fig. 36)

$P._{\overline{4}}<P._{\overline{3}}$ and more molariform. Two low anterior cusps, closely approximated, are connected by a lophid, in front of which is a small oval fovea. A large oval talonid basin occupies the hinder part of the crown, its margin smooth and without cusps.

The hinder premolar of *C. pygerythrus* is transitional in character between $P._{\overline{3}}$ and $M._{\overline{1}}$ but resembles the molars more closely differing, however, in its smaller size. Ockerse gives the mesio-distal measurement as 5 mm. in the male, 4·5 mm. in the female; bucco-lingual width 4 mm. in the male, 3·5 mm. in the female; crown height 5 mm. in males, 4·5 mm. in females. The crown presents 5 surfaces. Occlusal surface roughly oval, higher mesially than distally; mesial $\frac{1}{2}$ with 2 cusps, buccal and lingual connected by enamel ridge (lophid) in front of which is a small depression or pit. Behind the ridge a deeper depression which receives the lingual cusp of $P.^{\underline{4}}$ in occlusion. Distal to this depression two smaller cusps, buccal and lingual. Buccal surface rectangular, convex in both directions, with indistinct horizontal enamel edge. Lingual surface also convex in both directions, but less so in vertical dimension than on buccal side; indistinct horizontal enamel edge.

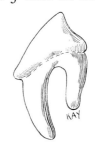

FIG. 36.—*Cercopithecus pygerythrus pygerythrus*. Left anterior lower premolar from the buccal aspect (× 3)

Mesial aspect very convex bucco-lingually, only slightly so vertically, enamel edge straight, indistinct. Distal surface smaller than mesial and highly convex in both directions, with more or less straight, indistinct enamel edge. Roots 2, mesial and distal, the former larger, both flattened bucco-lingually; a faint groove on mesial aspect of mesial root and on distal surface of distal root. Pulp cavity conforming to crown, with a single cornu under the mesio-buccal cusp.

Lower molars much resembling uppers in quadrituberculy and bilophodonty, but in origin this is different (*vide* Remane, *loc. cit.*). $M._{\overline{3}}$ occasionally shows a supplementary cuspid (protostylid) in front of the protocone as reported by Bennejeant (1935, p. 130, fig. 108) in *C. cynosuros*. A marked transverse groove separates trigonid and talonid parts of crown, incising both lingual and buccal margins, being especially deep at the buccal end (cf. Cebidae). The transverse furrow is composed of several parts. All lower molars two-rooted. Pulp cavities cynodont (Senyurek, 1953).

$M._{\overline{2}}>M._{\overline{1}}>M._{\overline{3}}$; $M._{\overline{3}}$ has the talonid reduced though typically bearing both cusps. There is a distinct tendency to reduction of the hypocone, sometimes to the point of disappearance—as normally occurs in *Miopithecus*. Schwarz (1928) has observed this reduction in *C. cephus* and *C. pygerythrus arenarius*. Reduction has also been recorded as common by Colyer (1936).

On the other hand M.$\overline{3}$ occasionally shows five tubercles (through the presence of a hypoconulid). Beddard (1909 b) recorded this in *C. mitis moloneyi* giving this as argument against the use of numerical differences in molar cusps as taxonomic indicators (*e.g.*, in separating the Talapoin generically from *Cercopithecus*).

M.$\overline{1}$ of *C. pygerythrus* is described by Ockerse as 6 mm. long mesiodistally in males, 5·5 mm. in females ; bucco-lingually 4·5 mm. in the male, 4 mm. in the female and crown-height 4·5 mm. in the male, 4 mm. in the female. The roughly rectangular occlusal aspect has the mesial border squared off and sharp and the distal rounded, anterior two cusps higher than posterior ; cusps separated by two grooves, mesio-distal and bucco-lingual, the latter transgressing half-way along the buccal surface as a deep groove. A small pit mesial to the lophid connecting the two anterior cusps, with two small fissures running respectively lingually and buccally therefrom. Centre of occlusal surface with deep depression (talonid basin) which receives protocone of M.$\underline{1}$. A distal pit occurs behind the ridge connecting the two distal cusps, with two small fissures like those of mesial pit.

Buccal surface larger than any of the others, with a deep groove on its upper half from occlusal surface. Another shallower vertical groove adorns the mesial half of the surface. The surface is convex in both directions, especially vertically ; enamel edge horizontal but indistinct. Lingual surface less convex and enamel edge as on buccal side. Mesial surface convex in both directions, distal surface even more so. Enamel edge indistinct, slightly concave towards root on mesial surface, straight on distal but higher lingually than buccally. Roots 2, long and flattened bucco-lingually ; grooves on mesial and distal sides of mesial root and frequently also on the distal root. When grooves are present there are two root canals. In the crown the pulp chamber is small, flattened from above downwards, with dome-shaped roof ending in four cornua.

M.$\overline{2}$ similar but larger, 7 mm. mesio-distally in males, 6 mm. in the female ; bucco-lingually 5·5 mm. in the male, 5 mm. in the female ; crown height, males 5 mm., females 4·5 mm. Roots tending to curve distally, mesial root grooved in front and behind, distal root grooved mesially and often also distally ; two root canals in each root.

M.$\overline{3}$ similar to M.$\overline{2}$ but smaller and with the crown tapering somewhat mesio-distally. Crown wider bucco-lingually at the mesial end of the tooth than distally (5·5 mm. in the male, 4·5 mm. in the female, compared with 4·5 mm. and 4 mm. for the distal width). Mesio-distal length 6·5 mm. in the male, 6 mm. in the female ; crown height 5 mm. in the male, 4·5 mm. in the female.

Mesio-lingual cusp higher than that of M.$\overline{2}$; both mesial and distal borders of occlusal surface rounded. Grooves on buccal surface deeper ; lingual surface marked by short continuation of bucco-lingual groove from occlusal surface ; mesial surface larger than distal ; mesial root flattened bucco-lingually and grooved front and back; distal root conical and may be slightly grooved on the front only; both roots inclined to distal curvature; pulp as in $M._{\overline{2}}$.

Variations.—Numerical variations are fairly common judged by the data of Colyer (1936). Additional maxillary incisors are recorded in *C. pygerythrus johnstoni, C. wolfi pyrogaster* and *C. grayi* (= *C. pogonias grayi*). Supernumerary premolars in the upper jaw are described in *C. ascanius whitesidei* (four premolars in the right mandible), while in a *C. pygerythrus cynosuros* a denticle is located on the buccal side of $P.^{\underline{4}}$. Various forms of additional upper and lower molars are mentioned by Colyer in *C. aethiops* subsp., *C. cephus, C. erythrotis, C. albogularis* and *C. campbelli*.

Deficiencies are listed as follows:

C. pygerythrus centralis, absence of left $I.^{\underline{1}}$.
C. pygerythrus, absence of left $P.^{\underline{3}}$.
C. ascanius whitesidei, left $DM.^{\underline{2}}$ in position but no sign of its premolar
    successor.
C. pygerythrus cynosuros, left $M._{\overline{3}}$ absent; right $M._{\overline{3}}$ malformed.
C. aethiops aethiops, left and right $M.^{\underline{3}}$ absent; another with $M.^{\underline{3}}$ and
    $M._{\overline{3}}$ lacking.
C. petaurista, $M._{\overline{3}}$ lacking.
C. nictitans (two examples), $M._{\overline{3}}$ lacking bilaterally.
C. ascanius   —   ,,   ,,

Size anomalies include asymmetry of canines (right $^{c}>$ left) in *C. nictitans nictitans*.

Supernumerary cusps on premolars are rare, but in a *C. mitis kandti* Colyer found an additional cusp on the postero-lateral border of $P.^{\underline{4}}$. On the other hand additional molar cusps may occur on the lingual surface of $M.^{\underline{1}}$, on the middle of the buccal surface of $M._{\overline{3}}$ and on the buccal surface of $M.^{\underline{3}}$. Reduction of individual teeth to a simple cone-shaped organ is reported by Colyer in two examples of *C. pogonias grayi*. (right $I.^{\underline{2}}$, left $P.^{\underline{3}}$.) Gemination of incisors was found twice by Colyer (fusion of $I._{\overline{1}}$ and $I._{\overline{2}}$ in *C. aethiops tantalus*, fusion of $DI._{\overline{2}}$ and canine in *C. albogularis kolbi*).

Colyer (pp. 223-234) also records a considerable number of individual variations in tooth position. Bateson (1894) mentions an unusual variation where the lower canines were recurved and occluded behind the upper ones (in *C. lalandii* = *C. pygerythrus*).

Size variations as affecting the molars have been recently studied in *Cercopithecus* and *Cercocebus* by Swindler *et al.* (1963) and compared with data in the literature. They found sexual dimorphism in size in all species, but these are less notable where the molars are small. It does not seem possible to decide whether an observed difference in molar size is due to sexual or specific variability. No general pattern of variability was demonstrated. If only molar dimensions are considered it would be difficult to assign a skull to a particular species, except possibly in baboons.

DECIDUOUS DENTITION

Formula : $\mathrm{DI}.\frac{2}{2}$, $\mathrm{DC}.\frac{1}{1}$, $\mathrm{DM}.\frac{2}{2} = 20$.

All deciduous teeth are smaller than their permanent successors and have more bulbous crowns, more constricted necks, and the roots, where multiple, more divergent, whilst the enamel ends abruptly at the neck.

Deciduous incisors are even more proclivous relatively than in the permanent dentition Roots larger than crowns; the crowns relatively and absolutely shorter from above down but otherwise similar in shape to their permanent successors. $\mathrm{DI}.\underline{^1} > \mathrm{DI}.\underline{^2}$. According to Ockerse in *C. pygerythrus* the crown of $\mathrm{DI}.\underline{^1}$ is wider transversely than vertically (4·5 mm. $\times$ 3·5mm.). The distal (lateral) surface is pointed; on labial aspect enamel edge is distinct, slightly convex towards root. Root long and flattened medio-distally. $\mathrm{DI}.\underline{^2}$ somewhat resembles its permanent successor except in size (crown length 3·5 mm., mesio-distally 3 mm., labio-lingually 2·5 mm.). A small cusp on distal side of neck. Enamel edge indistinct, convex towards root on labial and lingual surfaces, but concave on mesial and distal sides. Root relatively long, round and curving somewhat mesiad. Upper canine projecting well beyond incisors, but crown more pyramidal than in adult tooth, lacking the laniary character; separated from $\mathrm{DI}.\underline{^2}$ by relatively large diastema. Ockerse gives the dimensions of the upper deciduous canine of *C. pygerythrus* as 5 mm. in crown length, the same as the mesio-distal diameter; labio-lingually 3 mm. Crown flattened mesio-distally; labial aspect convex in both directions, with a small cusp on the distal surface; lingual surface with a vertical ridge grooved on either side of ridge; enamel edge fairly distinct, virtually horizontal. Root longer than crown, mesio-distally compressed, grooved on lingual surface and near apex also on labial surface. Apex of root sometimes bifid and curved distally.

Deciduous upper molars quadrituberculate, bilophodont, three-rooted (*vide* Bennejeant, 1936, p. 105). In *C. pygerythrus* Ockerse found the crown of $\mathrm{DM}.\underline{^1}$ similar to that of $\mathrm{M}.\underline{^1}$ but much smaller; crown height 3 mm.; mesio-distally 4 mm.; labio-lingually 3·5 mm. The three roots are rounded and the disto-labial root bears a groove on its mesial side. In $\mathrm{DM}.\underline{^2}$ the palatal root is largest, rounded; the others being flattened bucco-lingually. A groove on the distal aspect of the mesio-buccal root and on the mesial surface and the disto-buccal root.

Lower deciduous incisors subequal in size, but crowns shaped much as in permanent successors, $\mathrm{DI}.\overline{_2}$ narrowing to incisive margin. Lower central deciduous incisors in *C. pygerythrus* resemble the corresponding permanent teeth. Ockerse states that the distal angle of the crown is rounded. Height of crown 4 mm.; mesio-distal breadth 2·5 mm.; labio-lingual 2·5 mm. Enamel edge indistinct, convex towards root on labial and lingual aspects, but concave on mesial and distal sides. Root long, thin and slightly flattened on distal side, curving slightly mesiad at tip. Narrow diastema separating $DI._{\overline{2}}$ from canine. Ockerse states that $DI._{\overline{2}}$ differs from its permanent successor not only in its smaller size but in having a small cusp on the distal surface of the crown. A depression on the lingual surface ends in a cingulum. Crown height 4 mm.; mesio-distal diameter 2·5 mm.; labio-lingual 3 mm. Enamel edge indistinct, concave towards root on mesial and distal aspects, but convex on labial and lingual. Root long, thin, flattened labio-lingually with a vertical groove on its distal side, and with its apex inclined mesially.

Canine with shorter crown than in permanent canine, but with small talonid heel posteriorly. Ockerse describes its crown in *C. pygerythrus* as roughly triangular flattened mesio-distally; its mesial border convex and distal concave ending in a small cusp near neck. Labial aspect convex in both directions. Crown length 5 mm.; mesio-distal diameter 3·5 mm., labio-lingual 2·5 mm. Lingual surface with a small vertical ridge flanked by depressions. Enamel edge ndistinct, practically straight on labial surface, convex towards root on mesial and distal sides, concave towards root on lingual face. Root straight, flattened mesio-distally.

$DM._{\overline{1}}$ antero-posteriorly elongated, but very narrow transversely with small trigonid basin and larger talonid basin. Crista transversa anterior rather oblique, passing backwards from its buccal to lingual extremity.

In *C. pygerythrus* Ockerse finds the crown like that of the permanent hinder premolar. It is mesio-distally flattened 5·5 mm. long, and 3 mm. bucco-lingually and crown height 4 mm. The occlusal surface slopes slightly disto-mesially, bears four small cusps of which the two mesial are slightly higher than the two distal. The cusps are separated by a deep depression. An additional minute cusp lies mesiad of the mesio-buccal cusp. Enamel edge indistinct, nearly straight. Mesial root longer and rounder than distal, the latter flattened bucco-lingually.

$DM._{\overline{2}}$ larger and more closely resembling a lower molar. Crista more truly transverse. Ockerse finds the $DM._{\overline{2}}$ of *C. pygerythrus* very like a permanent $M._{\overline{1}}$ in all particulars except size.

ORDER OF ERUPTION

In the full-term *C. pygerythrus johnstoni* (C.R. 115 mm.) no teeth are visible through the gums. The earliest to erupt are $DI._{\overline{1}}$, shortly followed by $DI.^{\underline{2}}$ and then $DI._{\overline{2}}$, $DI.^{\underline{1}}$. Usually eruption of the upper canine follows, but before its lower counterpart appears the foremost deciduous molar appears in the lower jaw. The corresponding upper molar is delayed until the lower canine has appeared. The second molars are the last to erupt, the lower before the upper as in *Macaca* (see also Schultz, 1956).

Bennejeant (1936, p. 85) states that eruption of permanent teeth differs in no essential respect from that in Cebidae and that in *C. cynosuros* the sequence is the same as in *Colobus satanas* as recorded by Selenka (1899).

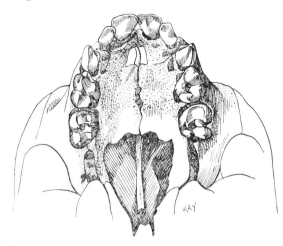

FIG. 37.—*Cercopithecus hamlyni*. Milk dentition upper jaw × 2

For both jaws the order is $M.\frac{1}{1}$, $I.\frac{1}{1}$, $I.\frac{2}{2}$, $M.\frac{2}{2}$, $P.\frac{3}{3}$, $P.\frac{4}{4}$, C., $M.\frac{3}{3}$.

Sequence of dental eruption in *Cercopithecus*, is according to Schultz (1935) identical with that in *Macaca* and *Papio*, and presumably also with *Erythrocebus* and other Cercopithecidae—although not with members of the Colobidae.

This particular type of sequence is also shared with the Hylobatidae and Pongidae, and with some minor differences, with *Cebus* and *Ateles* among the Platyrrhini.

In all these the first permanent tooth to erupt is $M.\frac{1}{1}$ followed by $I.\frac{1}{1}$ and then $I.\frac{2}{2}$. After the incisors $M.\frac{2}{2}$ appear followed in somewhat variable order by the premolars, then the canines and finally, $M.\frac{3}{3}$.

Schultz tabulates the dental picture in 100 skulls of *Cercopithecus* showing successive stages of dental eruption including some individual exceptions in both captive and wild examples. Among the latter are (i) eruption of $I.\frac{}{1}$ and $I.\frac{}{2}$ before loss of upper deciduous incisors, (ii) retention of $DM.\frac{}{1}$

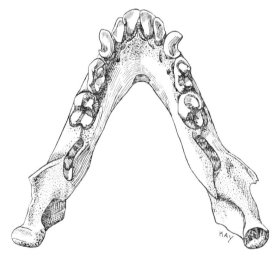

FIG. 38.—*Cercopithecus hamlyni*. Mandible with milk dentition × 2

after eruption of all other premolars, (iii) retention of $DM.\frac{1}{1}$ and $DM.\frac{2}{}$ after eruption of $P.\frac{}{3}$ and lower permanent canine, and (iv) retention of $DM.\frac{1}{}$, $\frac{2}{}$ after eruption of $P.\frac{}{3}$, $P.\frac{}{4}$ and of $M.\frac{12}{123}$.

MYOLOGY

Except for two brief papers by Dobson (1881) and Mivart (1865), the muscular system of *Cercopithecus* has not been comprehensively reported on.

There are, however, numerous references to individual muscles or muscle-groups in papers devoted to comparative myology, notably by Hänel (1932), Haughton (1864), Dzwonkowski (1935–6), Förster (1903, 1916 *a, b*, 1919), Ruge (1918), Windle (1887, 1889), and others.

Facial musculature has been fully considered in *C. sabaeus* by Hänel (1932) and there are brief references in Rex's (1887) earlier paper. Chief peculiarities relate, as in other Cercopithecidae, to the presence of the buccal pouches. These are essentially herniations of the buccal mucosa, with a

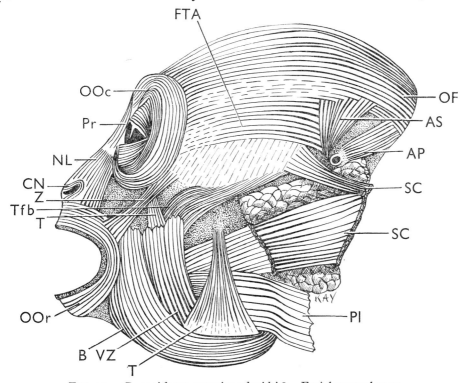

Fig. 39.—*Cercopithecus ascanius schmidti* ♀. Facial musculature

AP, auricularis posterior; *AS*, auricularis superior; *B*, buccal pouch with fibres from buccinator; *CN*, compressor naris; *FTA*, fronto-temporo-auricularis; *NL*, naso-labialis; *OF*, occipito-frontalis; *OOc*, orbicularis oculi; *OOr*, orbicularis oris; *Pl*, platysma; *Pr*, procerus; *SC*, sphincter colli profundus; *T*, triangularis; *Tfb*, tendino-fascial band; *VZ*, vertical fibres to buccal pouch from zygomaticus sheet; *Z*, Zygomaticus

covering derived from the buccinator, through the overlying fibres of the platysma colli. Fibres from the platysma proceed upwards and forwards from the neck and contribute to both superficial and deep aspects of the buccal pouch, superficial to those derived from the buccinator, but buccinator fibres are exposed here and there between the platysma fibres. Other fibres are derived from the notoplatysma, whose origin in the neck is contiguous with that of the cervical platysma. On the face these diverge somewhat from the fibres passing to the buccal pouch, proceeding towards the orbicularis oculi. In *C. ascanius schmidti* I find the picture somewhat more complex

than Hänel records for *C. sabaeus*. Here the buccal pouch receives many
vertical fibres near its neck ; these are derived from the zygomaticus sheet
and arise deep to the lower fibres of orbicularis oculi. They are also joined
by more oblique fibres derived from a tendino-fascial band over the preauricular part of the zygoma ; from this the fleshy fibres spread fanwise,
some to join the vertical part of the zygomaticus and some passing forwards
deep to the orbicularis oculi. *C. ascanius* and *C. mitis* also show a large
contribution of vertically disposed fibres derived from the triangularis. A
smaller oral branch of this muscle arises farther forwards, deep to the
orbicularis oculi, and proceeds downwards and forwards to end in the
orbicularis oris. Hänel in *C. sabaeus* indicates this as uniting with platysma
fibres which have passed over the cheek pouch before ending in the orbicularis oris, and therefore corresponding with the human risorius. Both in
C. sabaeus as well as *C. ascanius* and *C. mitis*, transverse fibres linking with
those of the opposite side cross the interramal region near the neck of the
buccal pouch.

The scalp is clothed by a system of fibres corresponding to the occipito-
frontalis of Man. Hänel refers to it under the names auriculo-occipitalis
and fronto-temporo-auricularis, and indicates a localized intervening galea
aponeurotica on the vertex in *C. sabaeus*. In *C. ascanius* and *C. mitis* the
occipital and frontal fibres are virtually continuous with little or no galea.
On the temporal region fibres are continued over the temporal fascia passing
between the ear and the lower part of the orbicularis oculi (becoming
aponeurotic, however, anteriorly). In *C. sabaeus* Hänel shows them passing
towards the upper part of the orbital region, separated by a gap from the
uppermost fibres of the sphincter colli. Around the ear are arranged radiating
fan-shaped bundles representing auricularis posterior and auricularis superior,
but the auricularis anterior is incorporated in the fronto-temporo-auricularis.

In the nasal region there is a distinct procerus, and below this a broad,
pale naso-labialis. Around the external nares are sphincter-like compressor
fibres. Lateral to the procerus is a distinct depressor supercilii, a characteristic muscle used in grimacing. Its deeper fibres constitute a distinct
transversus anguli and insert on the medial tarsal ligament.

The course of the fibres of orbicularis oculi is almost concentric, but
there is a convergence of these in the infra-angular region on to the medial
tarsal ligament. A sharp distinction occurs laterally between its fibres and
those of the zygomaticus sheet. Medially the muscular margin is not defined
from the fibres of levator labii superioris alaeque nasi.

Intrinsic auricular muscles include an auricularis proprius on the cranial
aspect of the pinna—short radiating fibres representing the vestiges of the
corrugator pinnae of the lorisoids, etc. On the lateral sculptured aspect of
the pinna are a tragicus, a trago-antitragicus and a depressor helicis (trago-
helicinus).

Deeper facial muscles include a deep lamina derived from the zygomaticus sheet consisting of several slips passing obliquely downwards and forwards from the anterior temporal region to the angle of the mouth, and a broader, more horizontal band (zygomaticus inferior of Hänel) passing from the zygomatic region to the same place. A narrow, deep band, passing obliquely from a point behind the ear downwards and backwards to the gular region, is all that is left of the sphincter colli profundus. The buccinator has the usual relations to the orbicularis oris, but laterally is grossly distorted by the development of the buccal pouch.

MUSCLES OF MASTICATION.—The temporalis is very bulky, but varies according to age and sex. It is covered by a dense temporal fascia from which some of its fleshy fibres take origin. The fascia varies in attachment and this is represented in the skull by the position of the temporal lines—occasionally gaining the vertex, though usually, even in males, falling short of this (*vide supra*, p. 233). Fleshy fibres converge on to a stout resplendent tendon which inserts on the coronoid process of the mandible and along the anterior border of the ascending ramus. Some fleshy fibres insert directly on the deep surface of the coronoid process and adjacent areas of the sigmoid notch. These are fibres derived from the intratemporal fossa and the temporal surface of the posterior wall of the orbit.

The masseter consists of superficial and deep parts, and the latter is further subdivided into anterior and posterior portions. The deep parts are visible only at the anterior edge and postero-superior angle of the superficial portion. The superficial masseter is a bulky mass, with strongly convex surface, mainly formed by resplendent aponeurotic fibres superficially, arising from the lower border of the zygomatic arch, the fibres passing downwards and somewhat backwards to insert near the lower border of the ascending ramus, as far as the angle of the mandible, by a fleshy attachment. These fibres do not transgress the lower border of the ramus. The anterior deep portion is fleshy, arising from the deep surface of the anterior half of the zygomatic arch and inserting on the lateral surface of the coronoid and adjacent parts of the ascending ramus as far as the last molar, and separated by a cleft from the posterior deep masseter. Fibres pass downwards and slightly forwards and some are visible along the anterior border of the superficial part of the muscle. The posterior deep portion arises from the deep aspect of the zygomatic arch by fleshy fibres whose direction is more obliquely downwards and forwards. The hinder fibres are exposed behind the upper part of the posterior portion of the superficial masseter, but soon pass deep thereto to end in a tendinous insertion at a somewhat higher level and behind those of the anterior deep masseter. All three parts of the muscle are supplied by the masseteric nerve derived from the same source as the mylohyoid nerve.

Of the two pterygoideus muscles the lateral is small and with a single

U

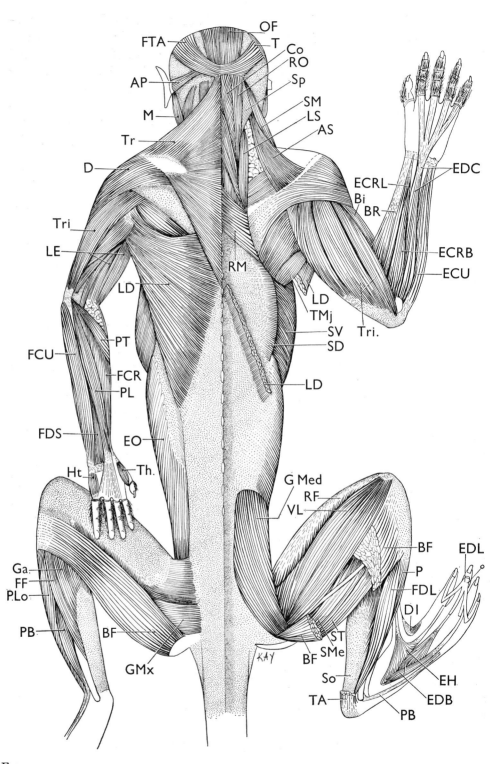

FIG. 40.

head, the medial large and bicipital. The lateral pterygoid is a short, thick, fleshy muscle which arises from the infratemporal crest and the fossa below it and also, continuously with the above, from the lateral surface of the lateral pterygoid lamina. A few tendinous fibres affect the superficial aspect antero-superiorly at the origin ; but the rest of the origin is fleshy. Fibres converge to a tendon which inserts in the usual manner. There is no head from the tuber maxillare. The main head of the medial pterygoid is the deep one, which springs from the medial surface of the lateral pterygoid lamina. The origin is mainly fleshy, but there is an extensive intramuscular aponeurotic lamina on the plane of the pterygoid plate ; this appears on the deep aspect of the muscle at several points and may be reinforced by other tendinous bundles. Fibres pass downwards and obliquely backwards to insert over most of the deep aspect of the ascending mandibular ramus peripheral to the opening of the inferior dental canal. The small superficial head arises from the lower part of the lateral aspect of the pterygoid lamina, embracing the lowest fibres of the lateral pterygoideus. They are fleshy and insert on the superficial surface of the intramuscular aponeurotic lamina. The uppermost part of the deep head is related medially to the large tensor palati, and within this lies an aponeurotic membrane continuous posteriorly with the stylo-mandibular ligament.

SUPRAHYOID MUSCLES.—The two-bellied digastric has the usual relations and arrangement. The smaller posterior belly is mainly fleshy, arising from the mastoid part of the temporal bone deep to the insertion of sterno-mastoid. Fibres converge to a short, stout, intermediate tendon, which is anchored to the hyoid bone by the bifurcation of the stylohyoideus. The larger anterior belly expands forwards to insert along the whole length of the lower border of the horizontal ramus of the mandible anterior to the insertion of the medial pterygoideus. Insertion is by fleshy fibres but there are some tendinous fibres continued along the medial margin from the intermediate tendon. The anterior bellies of the two sides, though contiguous anteriorly remain independent throughout (cf. *Macaca*). Dobson (1882) says they are connected by aponeurosis.

FIG. 40.—*Cercopithecus albogularis kolbi* adult ♂. Musculature from the dorsal aspect: superficial musculature is shown on the left and deeper muscles on the right.

AP, auricularis posterior ; *AS*, atlanto-scapularis ; *BF*, biceps femoris ; *Bi*, biceps brachii ; *BR*, brachio-radialis ; *Co*, complexus ; *D*, deltoideus ; *DI*, interosseus dorsalis I ; *ECRB*, extensor carpi radialis brevis ; *ECRL*, extensor carpi radialis longus ; *ECU*, extensor carpi ulnaris ; *EDB*, extensor digitorum brevis ; *EDC*, extensor digitorum communis ; *EDL*, extensor digitorum longus ; *EH*, extensor hallucis ; *EO*, external oblique ; *FCR*, flexor carpi radialis ; *FCU*, flexor carpi ulnaris ; *FDS*, flexor digitorum sublimis ; *FDL*, flexor digitorum longus ; *FF*, flexor fibularis ; *FTA*, fronto-temporo-auricularis ; *Ga*, gastrocnemius ; *GMed*, glutaeus medius ; *GMx*, glutaeus maximus ; *Ht*, hypothenar muscles ; *LD*, latissimus dorsi ; *LE*, latissimo-epicondyloideus ; *LS*, levator scapulae ; *M*, masseter ; *OF*, occipito-frontalis ; *P*, peronaei ; *PB*, peronaeus brevis ; *PL*, palmaris longus ; *PLo*, peronaeus longus ; *PT*, pronator radii teres ; *RF*, rectus femoris ; *RM*, rhomboideus major ; *RO*, rhomboideus occipitalis ; *SD*, serratus dorsalis ; *SM*, sterno-mastoideus ; *SMe*, semimembranosus ; *So*, soleus ; *Sp*, splenius ; *ST*, semitendinosus ; *SV*, serratus ventralis ; *T*, temporalis ; *TA*, tibialis anterior ; *Th*, thenar muscles ; *TMj*, teres major ; *Tr*, trapezius ; *Tri*, triceps ; *VL*, vestus lateralis

Stylohyoideus is well developed and fleshy, lying along the cranial border of the posterior belly of the digastric. It ends below by bifurcating into two fleshy slips which embrace the intermediate tendon of the digastric.

Mylohyoideus forms a sling for the floor of the mouth on the deep surface of the two anterior digastricus bellies. Fibres proceed obliquely forwards and upwards from the hyoid and the median raphe to end along the inner surface of the horizontal ramus a few millimetres below the line of reflection of the buccal mucosa to form the gums.

Geniohyoideus is a fleshy tract 7 mm. thick proceeding from the lower part of the mandibular symphysis to the globular rostral aspect of the hyoid body. It is completely differentiated from the genio-glossus. The latter springs by a thick tendon from a depression on the symphysis immediately above the origin of geniohyoideus. Its tendinous fibres give rise to fleshy bundles, which all proceed into the tongue without any connection to the hyoid. The majority of the fibres sweep upwards into the tongue from the upper surface of the tendon of origin; those for the hinder parts of the tongue are continued from the posterior extremity of the tendon.

Hyoglossus is well differentiated, passing from the greater hyoid cornu forwards and upwards into the hinder part of the tongue with the usual relations to lingual, hypoglossal and glosso-pharyngeal nerves. Part of its lateral surface is covered with fibres from the middle constrictor pharyngis. A styloglossus is well developed and fleshy throughout.

INFRAHYOID MUSCLES.—Sterno-hyoideus commences below as a strap-like band, but cranially becomes terete to end on the corpus hyoidei in a thick, fleshy insertion. It is in contact with its fellow medially; dorsally it is separated from the sterno-thyroideus by the lining of the laryngeal air-sac. No tendinous intersections were present in *C. albogularis*. Sterno-thyroideus is thin and strap-like throughout. The two muscles diverge as they ascend. Omo-hyoideus is normally lacking, but apparently present occasionally since Dobson (1881) reports it (without intermediate tendon) in *C. callitrichus* (= *C. sabaeus*) though Mivart (1865) found it absent in his *C. sabaeus* (= *C. aethiops aethiops*).

Thyro-hyoideus springs from the thyroid ala along an almost horizontal line which extends farther ventrally than the adjacent insertion of the corresponding sterno-thyroideus. Insertion is along the caudal border of the greater hyoid cornu.

OTHER CERVICAL MUSCLES.—The sterno-cleido-mastoideus arises by two heads, a narrow tendinous one from the manubrium and a broader, fleshy head from the medial end of the clavicle. The sterno-mastoid element unites above with the cleido-mastoid portion, whilst the cleido-occipitalis inserts close to, though not uniting with, the occipital origin of trapezius.

Scaleni (see also Tschachmachtschjan (1912), Förster (1916a)).—Scaleni are three in number, dorsal, intermediate and ventral, the scalenus dorsalis being the most extensive. Fibres arise in a continuous series from the ventral tubercles of the transverse processes of cervical vertebrae 1-6, those of scalenus dorsalis arising most cranially and inserting most caudally. The scalenus dorsalis (= S. longus) is tendinous at its origin from C.1 and C.2, but soon becomes fleshy and strap-like. Its fibres proceed to the thoracic wall and insert in two groups, separated by the emergent nerve of Bell. Those passing dorsal to the nerve and a small group of those passing ventral to it and more medially insert on the first rib. The remainder of the ventral fibres pass on in strap-like formation to end on the convexities of ribs 3, 4 and 5. The contribution to rib 3 inserts adjacent to the origin of the digitation of serratus ventralis therefrom ; the larger division passing on to the fourth and fifth ribs proceeds superficial to the neighbouring serratus digitations. The degree of interference with the serratus digitations is therefore minimal.

Scalenus ventralis (s. brevis anterior) lies ventral to the brachial plexus arising from C.3 to C.5 by fleshy fibres. These converge to insert, by mixed tendinous and fleshy attachment, to the first rib ventral to the subclavian artery but crossed by the subclavian vein. The phrenic nerve proceeds sagittally on the ventral surface of the muscle.

Scalenus medius (scalenus brevis posterior) in *C. albogularis* lies dorsal to the brachial plexus and arises by fleshy fibres as high as C.1 and as low as C.6. Tschachmachtschjan (1912) gives the origin as C.2-C.4 in four species of this genus. It is imperfectly differentiated from the preceding. It inserts dorso-lateral to the subclavian groove on the cranial surface of the first rib. Tschachmachtschjan (1912), however, indicates fibres proceeding as far as the fifth rib in *C. maxwelli* (= ?).

Prevertebral muscles include longus colli, longus capitis (rectus capitis anterior major), rectus capitis anterior minor and rectus capitis lateralis. Förster (1916) states that the longus capitis is strongly developed in *C. cynosuros* forming a fleshy belly with a short tendinous origin and insertion ; a flat intermediate tendon adorns the middle of its ventral surface. Its cervical attachments extend from C.2 to C.5.

Longus atlantis is a completely independent fleshy bundle connecting the lateral mass of the atlas with that of the axis and unconnected with the scalenus system (Förster).

POSTERIOR CERVICAL MUSCLES.—Deep to the rhomboideus stratum a large splenius forms a flat muscular sheet with fibres passing cranio-laterally from the spine to the occiput. Fibres arise from the ligamentum nuchae from as far forward as the level of C.1 and beyond the cervical region from the tips of the spines of T.1 and T.2. The lateral border of the muscle is thicker than the rest ; its fibres turn deeply and insert on the dorsal tubercles of the transverse processes of cervical vertebrae (cf. *Macaca* which lacks a splenius colli). The remainder inserts on the superior nuchal line from near the median line to the mastoid region.

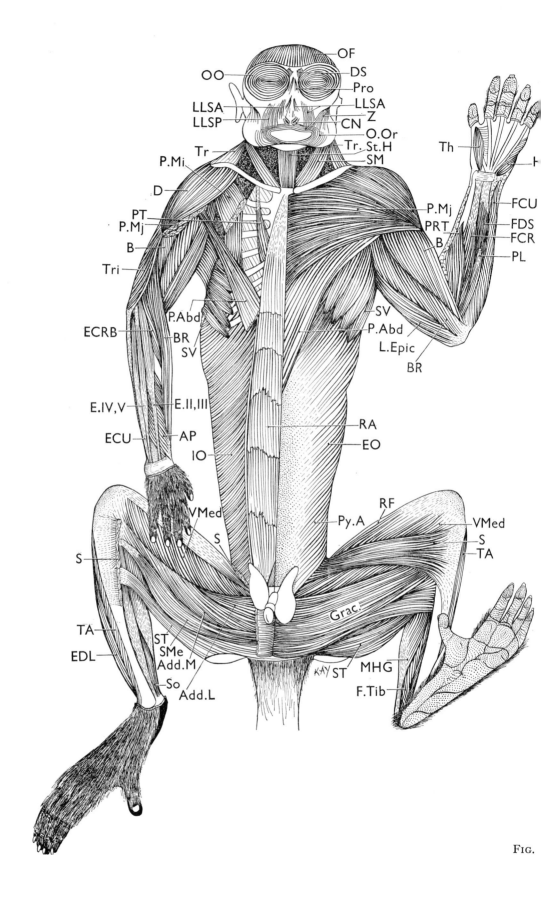

FIG.

Complexus (semispinalis capitis) lies deep to the preceding and medial to longissimus cervicis (cervicalis ascendens) and trachelo-mastoid (longissimus capitis).

The muscle consists of two fully differentiated parts, a medial more superficial and thinner stratum (biventer cervicis) and a lateral, much bulkier fleshy mass on a deeper plane (complexus proper). The first mentioned is further subdivided in a similar manner almost throughout its length into a superficial medial part divided by a fibrous intersection about its middle, and overlapping the rest of the biventer (which is not so subdivided) along its medial edge. The biventer arises by three tendinous slips from tubercles on the dorsal aspect of the thoracic vertebrae 3-5. The true complexus springs from cervical vertebrae C.3-C.7 and from the thoracic vertebrae cranial to those giving origin to the biventer. Both muscles insert between the curved nuchal lines of the occipital bone just lateral to the median crest, the biventer being nearer to or on the superior curved line, the complexus proper deeper and more lateral.

Trachelo-mastoideus springs by four slips from C.2-C.5.

Deep to the preceding is the semispinalis cervicis, arising by tendinous slips from the anterior six cervical vertebrae and inserting on the spines of the same vertebrae, ending above in an apex at the spine of the axis. Cranial to it, on the same morphological plane, are the small suboccipital muscles.

SUBOCCIPITAL MUSCLES.—These comprise the two obliqui capitis, rectus capitis posterior major (which subscribe the suboccipital triangle) and the rectus capitis posterior minor, which lies deep to and somewhat mediad of the rectus posterior major. All are thick fleshy muscles, only the obliquus superior showing a few aponeurotic fibres on its dorsal surface. The suboccipital triangle barely exists, being reduced to a mere intermuscular cleft on account of the bulky character of the surrounding muscles. All four are narrow at their origins, the fibres diverging towards their insertion. The insertion of the larger posterior rectus is linear and somewhat oblique, being overlain by the bulkier insertion of the superior oblique. Attachments are otherwise as usual and relations to the suboccipital nerve and vertebral

FIG. 41.—*Cercopithecus albogularis kolbi* adult ♂. Musculature from the ventral aspect. Superficial musculature on the left side : deeper layers on the right

Add. L, adductor longus ; *Add. M.* adductor magnus ; *AP*, abductor pollicis ; *B*, biceps ; *BR*, brachio-radialis ; *CN*, compressor naris ; *D*, deltoideus ; *DS*, depressor supercilii ; *ECRB*, extensor carpi radialis brevis ; *E II, III*, extensor proprius digiti II et III ; *E IV, V*, extensor proprius digiti IV et V ; *ECU*, extensor carpi ulnaris ; *EDL*, extensor digitorum longus ; *EO*, external oblique ; *FCR*, flexor carpi radialis ; *FCU*, flexor carpi ulnaris ; *FDS*, flexor digitorum sublimis ; *F.Tib* flexor tibialis ; *Grac*, Gracilis ; *Ht*, hypothenar muscles ; *IO*, internal oblique ; *LEpic*, latissimo-epicondyloideus ; *LLSA*, levator labii superioris alaeque nasi ; *LLSP*, levator labii superioris proprius ; *MHG*, medial head of gastrocnemius ; *OF*, occipito-frontalis ; *OO*, orbicularis oculi ; *OOr*, orbicularis oris ; *PAbd*, pectoralis abdominis ; *PL*, peronaeus longus ; *PMi*, pectoralis minor ; *PMj*, pectoralis major ; *Pro*, procerus ; *PRT*, pronator radii teres ; *PT*, pectoralis tertius ; *PyA*, pyramidalis abdominis ; *RA*, rectus abdominis ; *RF*, rectus femoris ; *S*, sartorius ; *SM*, sterno-mastoideus ; *SMe*, semimembranosus ; *So*, soleus ; *ST*, semitendinosus ; *St.H*, sterno-hyoideus ; *SV*, serratus ventralis ; *TA*, tibialis anterior ; *Th*, thenar muscles ; *Tr*, trapezius ; *Tri*, triceps ; *VMed*, vastus medialis ; *Z*, zygomaticus complex

artery typical. The insertion of the inferior oblique is very extensive, being on to the dorsal arch as well as the lateral mass of the atlas. Nerve supply to the muscles is derived from both the suboccipital and the second cervical nerve (posterior primary division).

MUSCLES OF THE PHARYNX AND PALATE.—Division of the constrictor pharyngis into superior, middle and inferior portions is indefinite, but there is a change in the direction of the fibres in passing from the cranial to the caudal part of the muscle. From the median dorsal raphe the cranial fibres pass caudo-ventrally, whereas the most caudal fibres proceed cranio-ventrad to the thyroid cartilage of the larynx. The uppermost fibres proceed successively from the raphe to the hinder border of the medial pterygoid lamina, the pterygo-mandibular raphe (which separates them from the buccinator), the posterior end of the mylohyoid line on the mandible, the side of the tongue and adjacent buccal mucosa, the lower part of the stylohyoid ligament and both cornua of the hyoid bone, finally the oblique line of the thyroid cartilage. A small triangular gap exists between the hyoidean fibres (middle constrictor) and those from the thyroid cartilage, bounded ventrally by the most dorsal fibres of the thyrohyoideus. The gap is filled by the posterior fibres of the thyrohyoid membrane and the lower part of the stylopharyngeus muscle, which passes deep to the middle constrictor fibres after entering the pharyngeal wall at the cranial border of that part of the constrictor pharyngis.

A palato-pharyngeus is present, passing from the soft palate to the pharyngeal wall under the mucous membrane forming the posterior faucial pillar. Its fibres embrace those of levator palati and course along the dorso-medial margin of the stylo-pharyngeus fibres in the pharyngeal wall inserting finally on to the dorsal border of the thyroid cartilage.

MUSCLES OF THE TRUNK.—Rectus abdominis commences as a mixed fleshy and tendinous band from the cranial border of the pubis. This origin is 20 mm. wide in an adult male *C. albogularis*. The muscle maintains this width or even somewhat increases it as it courses cranially as a strap-like fleshy band. It crosses the thoracic outlet on to the thoracic wall giving off, from its medial margin, a fleshy slip which inserts on the base of the xiphisternum. The main part of the muscle ascends as far as the fourth rib, where it gives place to an aponeurosis which inserts finally along the mid-line of the sternum and sterno-costal joints as far as the manubrium. This aponeurotic band narrows considerably as it approaches the manubrium. To its lateral border inserts a flat stratum of fleshy fibres derived from a tendinous origin on the first rib. The main rectus is subdivided by five irregularly wavy tendinous inscriptions, which are visible on both faces of the muscle. One is level with the umbilicus, one caudal thereto and the others between the umbilicus and the xiphisternum. The arrangement is essentially the same as that found by Tschachmachtschjan (1912) in *C. campbelli*, but there no slip from the first rib is referred to.

The rectus sheath is formed at the linea semilunaris by divergence of the fascia of the flank muscles. The ventral wall of the sheath is formed throughout by the fused aponeuroses of both external and internal obliques. The dorsal wall is formed by the transversus and its aponeurosis. Fleshy fibres from transversus are visible dorsal to the rectus in the cranial one-third of the sheath. A small pyramidalis lies ventral to the hindmost part of the rectus within the sheath in *C. mitis*. Tschachmachtschjan found it in only one out of four cercopithèques (in a *C. pygerythrus*). Obliquus externus arises in the usual way by fleshy digitations from the hinder nine ribs. The most cranial digitation (from rib 4) arises in relation to the scalenus insertion and in fact picks up a few fibres from the fascia covering it. No fibres are derived from the lumbo-dorsal fascia. Therefore between the last digitation and the iliac crest the muscle presents a long free fleshy border. Attachment to the iliac crest is minimal, and the caudal part of the muscle is weak. Fibres take the usual oblique course and end in an aponeurosis which joins that from the internal oblique in forming the ventral wall of the rectus sheath. The external abdominal ring is large in both sexes. It is of isosceles triangular form, but differs slightly from that in cynopithecines, for Klaatsch (1888) found the lateral pillar grooved to receive the emergent spermatic cord. Lateral to the lateral pillar the aponeurosis forms an arcus cruralis (Klaatsch's term) between the pubis and an attachment to the posterior ventral iliac spine.

Obliquus internus arises dorsally from the lumbo-dorsal aponeurosis, posteriorly from the ventral border of the ilium and from the anterior ventral spine backwards for 50 mm. or more. Anteriorly its fibres are continuous with those of the internal intercostal muscles of the posterior two or three spaces and gain connection with the hindmost three ribs near the costo-chondral junctions. The direction of the fibres is at right angles to those of the external oblique, namely ventro-craniad. Fleshy fibres terminate along a horizontal line bordering the lateral edge of the rectus sheath into which they insert. At the inguinal end the fleshy fibres proceed more medially than elsewhere and form an arch over the emergent spermatic cord (or ligamentum teres uteri). These fibres end in the conjoined tendon, which fuses with the inner pillar of the external abdominal ring, imparting thereby a valvular mechanism to the orifice of the inguinal canal.

The muscle is perforated along the mid-axillary line by the lateral branches of the hinder intercostal nerves. Transversus abdominis takes origin from the deeper layer of the lumbar aponeurosis as it emerges between quadratus lumborum and the deeper muscles of the spine. Cranially it is attached along the inner surface of the rim of the thoracic outlet, chiefly therefore to the cartilages of ribs 8-12. A mixed fibro-muscular attachment is gained to the anterior ventral iliac spine, but none to the acetabular border. Beyond the free hinder arched border of the fleshy part of the muscle the underlying fascia descends into the thigh in company with the femoral vessels. Femoral and ilio-inguinal nerves emerge between the muscle and this membrane. Direction of the fibres is mainly transverse with a slight caudal trend. Ventrally the more cranial fibres contribute to the dorsal wall of the rectus sheath and almost reach the median line. Posteriorly they are not so extensive though more so than those of internal oblique. In the inguinal region the muscle fibres form a fleshy arch and then join the conjoined tendon. They also contribute to the cremaster.

Transversus thoracis would be more suitably described under its old name triangularis sterni. Most of its fibres are more longitudinal than transverse in direction. The muscle, well developed and fleshy, is composed of six slips which narrow towards their insertions. The hindmost two are virtually transversely disposed, the others incline increasingly craniad. They insert in the cartilages of ribs 2-7.

Quadratus lumborum is a mixed tendinous and fleshy band some 1 cm. wide extending dorsally between the thoracic outlet and the iliac crest and overshadowed largely on the ventral side by the psoas complex. From its iliac attachment a few fibres of the iliacus take origin ventrally, while farther forward some psoas fibres spring from the ventral aspect of the quadratus. Fleshy fibres of the quadratus attach successively to the transverse processes of the seventh to fourth lumbar vertebrae. A further tendon springs from L.7, and its fleshy derivatives insert on the transverse processes of the anterior three lumbars and on to the medial parts of the last two ribs, passing deep to the diaphragm. Further strong tendinous accessions take origin from the tips of the transverse processes of L.3-L.1 and form the deepest (*i.e.* most dorsal) stratum of the muscle, which is thus incipiently trilaminar, as they pass through it.

The diaphragm presents vertebral, costal and sternal origins. The vertebral origin consists of the two thick, laterally compressed fibro-muscular crura, separated by the aortic hiatus, itself bounded by fibrous tissue (middle arcuate ligament) from which fleshy fibres arise independently. The right crus is stronger than the left and is mainly tendinous, with the fleshy part confined to its dorsal edge; but both crura extend to the body of L.3 which gives the main attachment. The left crus becomes fleshy anteriorly sooner than the right, its fibres spreading fanwise. The right crus divides into two bundles which surround the oesophageal opening, forming a sphincter mechanism for the tube. The left bundle interlaces with fibres from the left crus. The costal origin is by slips from the inner surfaces of the last ribs ; these interdigitate with slips of the transversus abdominis. The sternal origin is by two small slips from the dorsal aspect of the xiphisternum. A large triangular lumbo-costal hiatus, closed by fascia, occurs dorsally between vertebral and hindmost costal origins. Fleshy fibres end in the central tendon, which is a thin, membranous sheet of horseshoe-shaped outline. Costal and sternal fibres insert in the convex side of the tendon and crural fibres in the concave side. The caval opening is located at the junction of the right limb of the horseshoe with the central portion (see also Pancrazi, 1931 and Lessertisseur, 1959).

PERINEAL AND CAUDAL MUSCULATURE (*vide* Kollmann, 1894; Eggeling, 1896; Elftman, 1932).—The pelvic floor muscles show little difference in

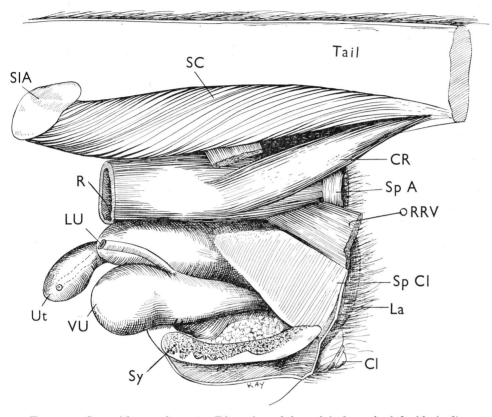

FIG. 42.—*Cercopithecus sabaeus* ♀. Dissection of the pelvis from the left side (× ¼)

Cl, clitoris; *CR*, caudo-rectalis; *La*, labium majus (left); *LU*, left ureter; *R*, rectum; *RRV*, retractor recti et vaginae; *SC*, sacro caudalis; *SpA*, sphincter ani externus; *SpCl*, sphincter cloacae; *SIA*, sacro-iliac articulation; *Sy*, symphysis pubis; *Ut*, uterus; *VU*, vesica urinaria

Cercopithecus from conditions in members of the other subfamily of Cercopithecidae, *i.e.* baboons and macaques—at least so Elftman found in *C. mona*. This is in spite of the fact that *C. mona* is essentially an arboreal climber and the baboons more terrestrial in habit. Both, in fact, frequently adopt the upright sitting posture resting upon the ischial callosities. The pelvic cavity is narrow and tubular, narrowing posteriorly somewhat and further encroached upon by the expansion of the ischial tubera and, in the male, by the large bulb of the penis with its covering muscles. This encroachment is less, however, in *Cercopithecus* than in *Papio*, *Macaca* or *Cercocebus*.

Subcutaneously surrounding the anus is a stratum of sphincteric fibres which interlace dorsally and ventrally. Dorsally they may gain connection with caudal vertebrae (caudo-analis) but Eggeling failed to find this, though Elftman mentions them. Deeper, lie fibres which, in the female, surround anal and vulvar openings (sphincter cloacae externus) but some specialized fibres omit the anus and surround vaginal and urethral openings (sphincter urogenitalis externus). A well-developed ischio-cavernosus forms a powerful mass over the bulb of the penis.

Deep to the above-mentioned superficial perineal muscles the alimentary and urogenital canals make their exit from the pelvis through a narrow cleft between lateral muscle complexes whose fibres pass obliquely from the deep aspect of the lateral pelvic walls to end on the tail. These muscle masses are divisible on each side into three parts, a ventral, lateral and dorsal. Collectively they correspond to the levator ani of human anatomy. The ventral element is the pubo-caudalis, the lateral ilio-caudalis and the dorsal sacro-caudalis (= flexor caudae longus). All to some extent serve as flexors of the basal portion of the tail, as compressors of the intervening passages and also occlude the pelvic outlet.

The division between ilio-caudalis and pubo-caudalis is marked at their pelvic origin, by the emergence of the obturator canal. The combined origins of pubo-caudalis and ilio-caudalis are linear and correspond with the pelvic brim, from the ventral margin of the sacro-iliac joint and along the ilio-pectineal line caudal to the attachment of the ilio-psoas as far as the obturator opening ; thence as pubo-caudalis the line extends ventral to the limit of the origin of the obturator internus on to the dorsal surface of the pubis as far as its symphysis and along the symphysis almost to the tuber ischii. Kollmann indicates in *C. sabaeus* a further subdivision of the pubo-caudalis into a ventral and lateral part. His division of the pelvic diaphragm is indicated in his nomenclature which is thus :

$$
\begin{aligned}
&\text{levator ani, portio dorsalis} = \text{ilio-caudalis} \\
&\left.\begin{array}{l}
\text{levator ani, portio lateralis} \\
\text{levator ani, portio ventralis}
\end{array}\right\} = \text{pubo-caudalis}
\end{aligned}
$$

Both muscles are fan-shaped, their fibres converging dorsally to form thick fleshy or mixed tendinous and fleshy insertions. Ilio-caudalis is much thicker than pubo-caudalis, becoming somewhat pyramidal as it narrows, with a concave surface dorsally adapted to the ventral aspect of sacro-caudalis (flexor caudae longus). Pubo-caudalis is a thinner sheet, but, like the preceding, thickens as its fibres converge. Caudally the sheet is continued as a strong fascia to the mid-line and corresponds to the superior layer of the urogenital diaphragm (triangular ligament of the perineum) of human anatomy. It is not as strong as in *Papio*. Insertions of the ilio- and pubo-caudalis are, for the most part, conjoined, the bundles converging dorsally and medially, with the pubo-caudalis fibres winding round the hinder part of the ilio-caudalis mass. The fibres end in a conjoined aponeurotic insertion which splits to enclose the flexors of the tail. The medial portion attaches to the median ventral line of the caudal vertebrae and to the chevron bones, contributing thus to the median ventral caudal septum. The lateral portion attaches to the caudal vertebrae (from C.3 onwards for a few segments) more laterally on a septum separating the flexors from the ischio-caudalis.

A few deep fibres of the pubo-caudalis insert on the side wall of the rectum and, in the female, adjacent parts of the vaginal wall also.

Ischio-caudalis (= coccygeus of *Homo*) is a completely separate muscle arising from the dorsal margin of the ischium, cranial to the ischial spine over a distance of 15 mm. or more. It lies on the lateral aspect of the ilio-caudalis. Its fibres converge to a tendon which inserts on the last sacral vertebra and the ventral aspect of the transverse processes of the proximal two or three caudals. In *C. mona* I found this muscle divisible into a thin cranial portion and a thicker triangular caudal part.

Deep to the ilio- and pubo-caudalis muscles a flat broad (8 mm.) band of pale fibres proceeds obliquely caudo-ventrally from the body of the first post-sacral vertebra to end on the hinder part of the rectum, anal canal, the central point of the perineum and, in the female, to the side of the vagina. In the male some fibres gain attachment also to the bulb. These constitute the caudo-analis (retractor recti et vaginae). Deep again to this is a similar band, even somewhat thicker, arising in the median plane from the front of the second chevron-bone and the ventral aspect of the second caudal vertebra. Its fibres take the opposite direction to those of caudo-rectalis passing cranially and ventrally, but in a general longitudinal direction. They merge with the muscular coat of the rectal wall. This is the caudo-rectalis ; it is composed of unstriped fibres.

Sacro-caudalis ventralis lateralis (flexor caudae longus) is a powerful fleshy mass lying longitudinally in the hollow of the sacrum separated from its fellow by a deep groove occupied by the caudal artery. Arising from the last two lumbar bodies and from the ventral aspect of the sacrum, it narrows behind and ends in a series of tendons which attach to the ventral aspect of successive caudal vertebrae and chevron bones.

Some of these tendons appear superficially on the side of the tail between the hindmost insertions of ischio-caudalis and those of ilio-caudalis. Flexor caudae brevis (sacro-caudalis ventralis medialis) is a smaller muscle partially separated off from the preceding and lying medial to its hinder portion. It arises from the ventral surface of the first two post-sacral vertebrae and ends distally in several fine tendons which attach to successive caudal vertebrae.

The tail is also supplied with extensors and abductors, there being a medial and a lateral element of each. Extensor caudae medialis is a posterior extension of the dorsal sacro-coccygeus system and therefore of the multifidus spinae. Inserting tendons are attached to the dorsal surfaces of the articular tubercles of the caudal vertebrae.

Extensor caudae lateralis is a caudal extension of the longissimus system of the back, taking origin from the roots of the transverse processes as far forward as the lumbar region, and also from the articular tubercles of the sacral and anterior post-sacral vertebrae. Inserting slips attach to the dorsal aspect of the articular tubercles of the caudal vertebrae (*i.e.* from post-sacral 4 onwards).

Abductor caudae medialis is also derived from the longissimus column. It arises from the dorsal surface of the sacro-iliac joint and adjacent parts of the sacrum and ilium. It inserts on the transverse elements of the immediate post-sacral vertebrae (coccygeals).

Abductor caudae lateralis is likewise an offshoot of the longissimus complex. Arising by aponeurosis from the dorsal border of the ilium, lateral to the preceding muscle, it lies between the latter and the origin of the glutaeus maximus. It also gains attachments to the lateral tubercles of the sacrum and of the coccygeals. Inserting tendons proceed to the lateral tubercles of the true caudals. Both abductors, acting with their fellows, serve as lateral deviators of the tail. Extensors and abductors receive their nerve supply from the dorsal primary divisions of the segmental spinal nerves.

MUSCLES OF THE PECTORAL GIRDLE AND LIMB (*vide* Mivart, 1865 ; Dobson, 1881).—Trapezius arises from the external occipital protuberance, from the ligamentum nuchae and from thoracic spines as far back as T.8.

Dobson gives the insertion in *C. sabaeus* as along the whole length of the scapular spine and the lateral extremity of the clavicle. Mivart found no clavicular insertion. Mivart mentions a levator claviculae arising solely from the tranverse process of the atlas, descending deep to the sterno-mastoid to insert on the acromion and cranial third of the scapular spine, and not at all on the clavicle ; it is covered by trapezius. As already mentioned, Mivart found no omo-hyoideus. Dobson found a double levator claviculae with a common head from the atlas and two large bellies inserting deep to the trapezius, one to the lateral third of the scapular spine and acromion, and the other to the lateral extremity of the clavicle.

Latissimus dorsi springs from the spines of the last 4, 5 or 6 thoracics, and by lumbar aponeurosis from all the lumbar spines (Ruge, 1917, 1918). No costal or scapular slips occur. About 50 mm. from the axilla both Dobson and Mivart found its tendon divided into two parts. The main more lateral portion ends in the usual way, inserting in the floor of the bicipital groove. The smaller medial portion joins the teres major and inserts therewith.

Of the rhomboidei, there is a small slip (rhomboideus capitis) springing from the tabular part of the occipital bone and inserting by distinct tendons into the medial side of the dorsal margin of the scapula, just beyond the triangular area at the root of the spinous process. On the other hand, rhomboideus major and minor are not separate, at least in *C. sabaeus* (Dobson, Mivart). Furthermore, in *C. albogularis* I found a slender muscle between the occipital band and rhomboideus minor arising from C.2 and C.3 narrowing posteriorly to an insertion on the vertebral border of the scapular opposite the root of the spinous process. Triangular spaces separate it from the other rhomboidei.

Levator scapulae is said by Dobson to be intimately blended at its insertion with the serratus. The same author found the major part of the muscle reduplicated, a portion arising from the atlas and inserting near the cranial angle of the scapula, the other from the axis inserting immediately anterior to the preceding. Two other slips from C.3 and C.5 blend at their insertions with serratus magnus. In an old male *C. albogularis* I found the muscle arising by four digitations from C.1-C.4, all of which unite to form a single bulky fleshy mass. Insertion blends as in Dobson's material with that of the serratus.

Pectoralis major, according to Mivart, lacks a clavicular head in *C. sabaeus*; it springs from the sterno-clavicular joint and the whole length of the sternum and sternal ends of the ribs. Its insertion to the lateral lip of the bicipital groove is parallel with and of the same extent as that of the deltoideus. In *C. albogularis* it is similar. Its cranial border is flush with the ventral border of the deltoideus.

Pectoralis minor is comprised of two distinct parts: the first arises from the sternum posterior to its second sternebra and adjacent parts of the costal cartilages; it is conterminous in extent with pectoralis major. The second part (pectoralis abdominis) springs solely from the aponeurosis over the rectus abdominis and external oblique. Fibres of the two converge to meet and insert on the capsule of the shoulder joint, but in *C. albogularis* I found the pectoralis abdominis giving an expansion along the lateral lip of the bicipital groove deep to the pectoralis major insertion.

Subclavius is a short but powerful muscle less transversely disposed than in Man. Its origin is mainly fleshy from the medial end of the first costal cartilage and capsule of the sterno-clavicular joint. The fleshy belly inserts on the posterior surface of the clavicle from about its middle as far as the acromio-clavicular joint.

Deltoideus is well developed. Dobson found its ventral border connected to the cranial border of pectoralis major. Some of the fibres from the scapular spine insert on the brachial fascia.

Intrinsic scapular muscles call for little remark. Both supraspinatus and infraspinatus are bulky fleshy masses, the latter compressing the teres minor into a narrow spindle-shaped band with a linear origin from the lateral half of the axillary border. Fibres of infraspinatus spring from the adjacent fascia covering the teres minor. Teres major is a large muscle with the usual relations arising from the medial third of the axillary border and from the septum between itself and subscapularis. Some of its fibres insert on the latissimus tendon.

Subscapularis is also very powerful. Commencing as a thin stratum of mixed fleshy and tendinous fibres along the vertebral border, it rapidly thickens by accretion of fleshy bundles from the scapular body and neck and from the whole length of the axillary border and from the fossa between the axillary border and the extra flange associated with teres major (p. 252 *antea*). The central portion is overlapped by the cranial and caudal parts. Fibres converge to a very stout tendon which has the usual insertion.

In the arm the biceps has two heads. The long head consists of a broad flat tendon ; the short is mixed tendinous and fleshy and united with coracobrachialis. The two bellies unite in the middle of the arm and continue as a thick fleshy mass into the antecubital fossa, where abrupt narrowing occurs to the tendon of insertion, which commences as a rounded cord on the deep surface ; a lacertus fibrosus is lacking.

Coraco-brachialis is provided with a coraco-brachialis brevis (rotator humeri of Wood). This Mivart found springing from the lateral side of the common origin of coraco-brachialis and biceps (short head), passing to insert on the humeral shaft above the teres major insertion. Dobson also found this, as well as a coraco-brachialis longus, continuing alongside the biceps, past the insertion of the coraco-brachialis medius, and ending with the biceps on the tuberosity of the radius.

In the extensor compartment the most superficial muscle is the vast latissimo-epicondyloideus (dorso-epitrochlearis). This springs from the

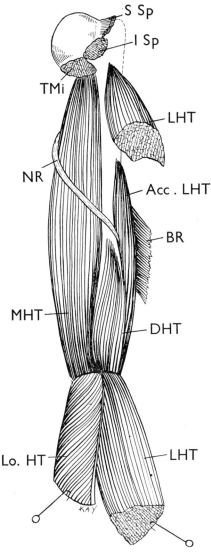

Fig. 43.—*Cercopithecus albogularis kolbi* ♂. Dissection of the brachial region from the extensor aspect (× ⅓).

Acc. LHT, accessory lateral head of triceps ; *BR*, brachio-radialis (origin) ; *DHT*, deep head of triceps (lateral part of medial head ; *ISp*, infraspinatus insertion ; *LHT*, lateral head of triceps ; *LoHT*, long head of triceps (reflected) ; *MHT*, medial head of triceps (medial part of deep head) ; *NR*, radial nerve ; *SSp*, supraspinatus insertion ; *TMi*, teres minor insertion

larger division of the latissimus dorsi, just where it becomes tendinous and, as usual, inserts on the olecranon process. The fleshy belly is broad and flat, covering the greater part of the medial and posterior surface of the arm. Distally it narrows to a tendon which forms an expansion over the olecranon on its medial side.

Brachialis is not as powerful as in *Macaca*. It is prismatic in form from compression between neighbouring muscles. Medially its origin ascends as high as the insertion of coraco-brachialis medius, laterally a little farther—as far as the deltoid insertion.

Triceps is composed of three huge fleshy bellies. The long head is attached to the inferior margin of the glenoid fossa and also for half the distance along the axillary border of the scapula. The lateral head has a restricted origin at a point on the shaft of the humerus just distal to the great tuberosity. It swells into a large fleshy mass, pyriform in section, and with the long head, with which it unites at the junction of middle and distal thirds of the brachium, forms a superficial lamina of the muscle. There is a short accessory lateral head arising by linear attachment in the distal half of the humerus adjacent to the origin of the brachio-radialis and lateral intermuscular septum. It lies on a relatively deeper plane and ends below in the common tendon attached to the olecranon. The deep stratum of the muscle is comprised by the somewhat complicated " short " or medial head. In fact, this is long and divisible into medial and lateral parts. The medial portion is the larger, arising by fleshy fibres from the whole length of the medial half of the posterior surface of the humeral shaft, *i.e.* as far proximally as the surgical neck. It broadens as it descends and presents a flattened posterior surface played upon by the long head, from which it is separated by the radial nerve, its branches and the accompanying vessels. The shorter lateral part of the muscle arises from that part of the posterior aspect of the shaft distal to the radial groove. It is more convex and is related to the principal lateral head. The radial nerve passes along its upper edge and then between it and the accessory lateral head, to which it proceeds deeply to emerge in relation to the brachio-radialis. The nerve to the deep head and to the anconeus proceeds vertically between the medial and lateral parts of the deep part of the triceps.

Of the pronator-flexor group, pronator teres lacks a deep head. The majority of its fleshy fibres derive from the septum between it and flexor carpi radialis. Its insertion is by a broad flat tendon or aponeurosis.

Flexor carpi radialis arises in common with palmaris longus. The former has the usual insertion, and the latter ends in the palmar fascia. Dobson mentions a muscular bundle on the thenar side of the insertion inserting on the palmar skin, as well as a palmaris brevis on the hypothenar side. The latter, however, springs from the pisiform and neighbouring part of the flexor retinaculum.

X

Flexor digitorum sublimis is incompletely differentiated from the radial flexor in the proximal half of the forearm. Its belly is large, fleshy with a longitudinal tendinous band in the centre. It changes to a single thick tendon of oval section at the wrist. After emerging from the carpal tunnel, it divides to supply the four ulnar digits with their perforated tendons.

Flexor carpi ulnaris is as bulky as the preceding and fleshy to the distal end of the ulna, where it abruptly narrows to its tendon, which inserts on the pisiform.

Flexor profundus presents in *C. sabaeus* (according to Mivart) four distinct bellies (i) arising from the volar aspect of the radius and adjacent interosseous membrane (ii) from the volar aspect of the ulna (iii) the main head from the medial condyle of the humerus and (iv) a very distinct head from the medial border of the ulna. The last-mentioned supplies a tendon to the fifth digit. The other three bellies give rise to a broad common tendon which divides into the perforating tendons to the four ulnar digits. From the superficial aspect of the main tendon a small tendon springs and crossing over the hand proceeds to insert on the pollex. Dobson's account is essentially similar, though three heads only are described, one being the belly which supplies the tendon to the minimus.

In *C. albogularis* I find essentially the same arrangement, but again without the fourth head described by Mivart. Moreover, I would not describe the superficial or condylar head as the main head. It is narrow and fusiform and distally joins the fleshy radial portion. Radial and ulnar heads together form the main mass of the muscle and are differentiated from each other at the proximal end only, where a deep incisure separates them.

Pronator quadratus is a thin stratum of mixed fleshy and aponeurotic fibres which take a somewhat oblique course latero-distally from ulna to radius.

On the extensor aspect, the brachio-radialis has a very broad (26 mm.) origin from the supracondylar line and lateral intermuscular septum. Commencing as a flattened band in the sagittal plane, it changes position at the elbow to a more transverse plane, coursing thus along the radial border of the forearm to its insertion at the distal end of the radius. Extensor carpi radialis longus also arises on the supracondylar line by an attachment 21 mm. long. It thickens to form a fleshy belly of triangular cross-section. It becomes tendinous just beyond the middle of the forearm and inserts on the base of the metacarpal of the index. Extensor carpi radialis brevis is incompletely differentiated from the preceding at its origin, but the two bellies become distinct though closely applied to each other. The present muscle ends in two tendons in *C. albogularis*. These are flattened and cross the radius deep to the tendon of the longer extensor, but in the same groove. They end on metacarpals II and III.

Extensor communis digitorum arises solely from the lateral humeral condyle and ends in four tendons to the four ulnar digits in the usual way. Extensor digiti minimi ends in two tendons supplying the fourth and fifth digits while the deeper extensor indicis sends tendons to the second and third digits (Mivart). Extensor carpi ulnaris arises solely from the condyle, lacking all but fascial connection with the ulna. Its belly is fusiform and ends in a stout flattened tendon at the mid-point of the forearm. Abductor pollicis longus (extensor ossis metacarpi) is a large muscle. Mivart found it ending in two tendons, one to the trapezium and one to the base of the pollicial metacarpal, as I also found in C. albogularis. Dobson's C. aethiops had a single tendon. Both Mivart and Dobson failed to find an extensor primi internodii pollicis, but Dobson found a feeble extensor secundi internodii ending in a single long tendon.

The supinator (brevis) is largely aponeurotic, at least superficially, and extremely thin. Its attachments are as usual. Nevertheless there is a bilaminar arrangement, the deeper lamina having shorter and more fleshy fibres, which extend around the radius more completely than the superficial portion. The posterior interosseous nerve lies between the two laminae. A small anconeus of triangular outline continues the deep lamina of fibres of the triceps through the space between the olecranon and the lateral humeral condyle.

In the palm Dobson found a small muscle arising from the flexor retinaculum near the insertion of flexor carpi radialis. It gave rise to a slender tendon passing superficial to the large abductor pollicis and approached the ulnar side of the branch from the flexor profundus to the thumb. It finally inserted on the base of the terminal phalanx of the pollex.

Abductor, opponens and adductor pollicis are all well developed. There is also a small flexor pollicis brevis completely hidden by the abductor. Day and Napier (1963) have studied this muscle in C. aethiops, C. mona, and C. neglectus, and confirm an earlier view, based on human dissections, that the deep head of the flexor brevis is morphologically a displaced element of the contrahentes complex and is related functionally to the more complete power of pollicial opposition. It is confined to the Catarrhini.

Abductor digiti minimi is also large, arising by two heads, one from the pisiform, the other from the flexor retinaculum in common with the short flexor. The two heads unite to form a rounded tendon, which has the usual insertion. The short flexor of the little finger is also well developed ; there is also a smaller flexor ossis metacarpi digiti minimi. Four lumbricals are associated with the flexor profundus tendons from the palmar surface of which they take origin. Besides the adductor pollicis there are contrahentes associated with the index, annularis and minimus. These have been figured adequately by Dobson and by Jouffroy and Lessertisseur (1959).

Macalister (1868) refers to a short extensor of the manual digits present in Cercopithecus as in certain platyrrhine genera (Cebus, Ateles) as well as

Macaca; and occurring as an occasional anomaly in Man (Wood, 1865; Macalister, 1867).

Palmar interossei are arranged as in Man and other Old World Primates (Macalister, 1868, Mivart, 1865). Lessertisseur (1958) has considered the comparative morphology of all the manual and pedal interossei in considerable detail.

MUSCLES OF THE PELVIC GIRDLE AND LIMB.—Tensor vaginae femoris is strongly developed, but closely joined at its origin with the gluteus medius (Mivart). The ectogluteus, as usual, is rather small and thin. Its fibres arise chiefly from the extensive gluteal aponeurosis, which is attached to the iliac crest and the dorsal and ventral borders of the ilium. A few fleshy fibres posteriorly, however, derive directly from the anterior two coccygeal vertebrae. These form a thicker band than the anterior part of the muscle, but are not well differentiated therefrom to form a separate caudo-femoralis. All the fibres insert along the gluteal line of the femur. Mesogluteus, on the contrary, is a massive fleshy structure arising from the major part of the gluteal fossa. Fibres converge to a stout tendon which attaches to the front of the great trochanter, but the more dorsal fibres proceed over the top of the trochanter and attach to its posterior surface. Mivart found the scansonius inseparable from the gluteus minimus in *C. sabaeus*. This is also the case in *C. albogularis*. The combined mass forms a fan-shaped structure, fleshy along the ventral border, but aponeurotic dorsally over its superficial aspect, arising from the hinder part of the gluteal fossa of the ilium and the body of that bone. Its fibres converge to the forepart of the great trochanter deep to the insertion of gluteus medius and for a short distance to the shaft of the femur beyond the trochanter. Pyriformis is small; it arises fleshily from the middle of the sacrum and inserts in the digital fossa of the great trochanter by tendon. In the buttock it is inseparable from gluteus minimus.

Obturator internus, with its gemelli, forms a thick fleshy mass crossing the dorsal border of the ischium anterior to the tuberosity to end on the femur. Gemelli completely obscure the obturator tendon superficially, the inferior gemellus being particularly bulky so as to obscure the quadratus femoris also. The last-mentioned is short, thick, and very obliquely disposed. Entirely fleshy, its fibres proceed downwards, forwards and somewhat mediad from the antero-inferior corner of the tuber ischii and adjacent margin of the cartilage-covered dorsal border of the corpus ischii to their insertion at the upper end of the femoral shaft. Posteriorly and somewhat laterally they are intimately related to the uppermost fibres of the adductor minimus, which is quite distinct from the pubo-femoralis part of the adductor magnus.

On the flexor side psoas parvus is completely differentiated from psoas magnus. Its fleshy belly receives fibres from the anterior four lumbar bodies. It gives place to a broad flat tendon opposite L.3, and inserts on the ilio-pectineal line and neighbouring pelvic fascia. Psoas magnus arises from transverse processes of the last thoracic and all the lumbars and, after receiving the large fleshy contribution from the iliacus, inserts by tendon on the lesser trochanter.

Sartorius has the usual broad strap-like form—about 1 cm. wide. Its origin is in common with that of tensor fasciae femoris, and its insertion on the medial aspect of the upper end of the tibia. Quadriceps femoris has the usual composition. The rectus has straight and reflected heads, the latter, however, very thin. The straight head is flat and soon swells into the fleshy belly, which is aponeurotic on its deep face. Vastus lateralis is huge, but vastus medialis of only moderate dimensions. The origin of the former extends practically the whole length of the femoral shaft, whereas vastus medialis ceases to receive fibres from about mid-shaft. Vastus intermedius is well developed, clothing the front and sides of the shaft in its distal three-quarters.

Pectineus is large, but apparently undivided, at least in *C. albogularis*. Its origin from the pubis is intimately related to the posterior attachment of the external oblique aponeurosis. Distally its insertion is in line with that of adductor longus. The latter has the usual tendinous origin concentrated on the pubic angle. The muscle becomes aponeurotic immediately before its insertion. Adductor gracilis is very broad and flat, clothing the major part of the medial surface of the thigh. It arises from the pubis parallel with the symphysis and inserts in relation to the sartorius in the usual way. Adductor brevis is a loosely woven fleshy belly lying deep to the adductor longus and separating the two divisions of the obturator nerve. It arises deep to the origins of adductor longus and the ventral part of gracilis and inserts over the same length of linea aspera as adductor longus, but dorsal thereto and by fleshy attachment. An accessory adductor on the same general plane as the preceding lies more medially, deep to pectineus. Like the adductor brevis proper, it is fleshy throughout, but its insertion is proximal to that of adductor brevis and dorsal to that of pectineus. Adductor magnus readily divides longitudinally into a pubo-femoralis and an ischio-condyloideus, the two, however, being loosely bound together. Both have coarse, loosely connected bundles of fleshy fibres throughout, the ischio-condyloideus not concentrating to a tendon. The uppermost fibres of pubo-femoralis are partially separated as an adductor minimus. This seems to have a lateral rotator action rather than adduction.

The hamstrings are an exceedingly powerful group by virtue of the extensive attachments afforded by the expansion of the margins of the tuber ischii in correlation with the presence of the callosity. Biceps is particularly affected. Though lacking a deep head, the main head, shared with the semitendinosus, is very broad and the belly retains its breadth almost to its insertion, thereby covering most of the lateral and posterior aspects of the thigh behind the vastus lateralis. Insertion is largely to the fascia cruris, with some tendinous attachment to the head of the fibula. (See Mivart, who also failed to find a deep head in *C. sabaeus*.)

Semitendinosus lies immediately posterior to the biceps arising in common therewith. Its belly has a triangular section from compression between the biceps and the adductor magnus. Nearing the knee it becomes flattened and ends in a tendon which inserts in the normal relation with the sartorius. Semimembranosus is a large fusiform belly lying deep to the semitendinosus and arising from the inferior edge of the ischial tuber behind the origin of semitendinosus. It becomes tendinous in the distal third of the thigh and the rounded tendon ends on the medial surface of the head of the tibia. A praesemimembranosus is not differentiated, but incorporated with the ischio-condyloideus.

In the leg the triceps surae comprises a gastrocnemius, a large plantaris and a rather feeble soleus. Plantaris is enclosed between the two heads of gastrocnemius, and arises somewhat proximad of the origin of the lateral head, though deriving additional fleshy fibres from the deep surface of that head. It becomes tendinous early on and the tendon flattened between the fused gastrocnemii and the soleus. Inclining medially the tendon emerges superficially to end on the medial edge of the tendo Achillis. Soleus has a limited origin on the back of the neck of the fibula. It expands into a flattened belly, partly aponeurotic and of fusiform outline. It forms the main part of the tendo Achillis. This is the same arrangement as Mivart recorded for *C. sabaeus*.

Popliteus commences as a very strong flat tendon (almost 5 mm. broad in *C. albogularis*) within the capsule of the knee joint. Immediately after emerging from the joint, it becomes fleshy, the belly having the usual flat, triangular form and its fibres inserting over the back of the upper end of the tibia, proximal to the oblique line. The nerve supply enters on its deep surface after winding round the distal border.

Deep crural flexors comprise a moderate-sized flexor tibialis, a flexor fibularis more than double the size of flexor tibialis, and buried between them, a small tibialis posterior. Flexor tibialis is more or less unipenniform, fleshy fibres springing from the back of the tibia along its medial edge distal to the oblique line. They converge to a tendon which commences as an aponeurosis on the superficial aspect of the belly. The tendon passes the ankle joint medially in relation to the tibial malleolus, the tendon of the tibialis posterior lying deep to it. Flexor fibularis arises from the back of the fibula and adjacent interosseous membrane. Its tendon also commences in a superficial aponeurosis, but this is more extensive than that of its neighbour and gives rise to a much stouter tendon. The latter passes the ankle joint near the calcaneus in its own synovial sheath. Tibialis posterior has a small bipenniform belly which ends about mid-leg in a point. From this the tendon becomes free and passes distally in relation to the tendon of flexor tibialis, but in a separate synovial sheath.

In the sole there appears to be some variation in the arrangements which

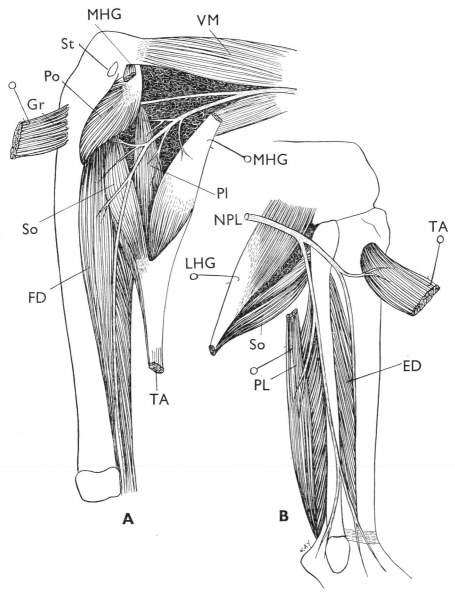

FIG. 44.—*Cercopithecus petaurista buttikoferi.* Dissections of the right pelvic limb, A, from the medial, B, from the lateral aspects

ED, extensor digitorum longus ; *FD*, flexor digitorum tibialis ; *Gr*, gracilis (insertion) ; *LHG*, lateral head of gastrocnemius ; *MHG*, medial head of gastrocnemius ; *NPL*, lateral popliteal nerve ; *PL*, peronaeus longus ; *Pl*, plantaris ; *Po*, popliteus ; *So*, soleus ; *St*, semitendinosus (insertion) ; *TA*, tibialis anterior ; *VM*, vastus medialis

may (as in Mivart's *C. sabaeus*) differ on the two sides of the same individual. In both feet of Mivart's animal the flexor tibialis tendon bifurcated, one branch proceeding to the second and the other to the fifth digit. Flexor fibularis divided into three strong tendons destined for the hallux, and for III and IV. In both feet the hallucial tendon was bent round the tendon to the second toe, becoming superficial thereto. Moreover on both sides the tendon to the little toe gave off two slender slips to join the branches of flexor fibularis supplying the third and fourth digits, and similarly a slip was given from the tendon to the second toe which on the right foot joined to the tendon serving the hallux, but which on the left foot joined with the branch of flexor tibialis serving the fifth digit. In the left foot of a *C. albogularis* dissected by the author, the same general distribution of the tendon fibres takes place, including the peculiar bending of the tendon to the hallux superficially around the smaller tendon which serves the second toe. None of the small slips was found. The two main tendons are partially fused in the centre of the sole and further masked by a superficial covering of fleshy fibres derived partly from the large accessorius and partly from a belly composed of longitudinal fibres. The origin of this belly is from the surface of the flexor tibialis tendon and commences where this tendon passes beneath the flexor retinaculum. Distally it spreads, forming a complete covering to the fused flexor tendons and continues into the bellies of the lumbricals. It might be regarded as a secondary head of the accessorius or as a proximal invasion by the lumbrical system.

Mivart found three separate lumbricals in each foot inserting on III, IV and V.

Crural extensors are covered by a firm fibrous fascia, which is attached medially to the anterior border of the tibia. Deeply it sends in intermuscular partitions separating the extensors proper from the peronaei (anterior peroneal septum) and between the latter and the flexors (posterior peroneal septum). The anterior septum is much better developed than the posterior.

The long extensors comprise a huge tibialis anterior (divided longitudinally into two apparently subequal bellies, each with its own tendon) a small fusiform extensor hallucis longus and a moderate extensor digitorum longus. Of the two parts of tibialis anterior the medial proves, on deeper scrutiny, to be much the larger, due to its greater thickness. Its fibres are derived from the lateral surface of the tibial shaft and adjacent interosseous membrane and descend obliquely to end in a stout tendon which crosses the ankle beneath a strap-like retinaculum and then proceeds to its insertion on the entocuneiform. Fibres of the lateral moiety of the tibialis anterior spring mainly from the aponeurosis covering the uppermost part of the main muscle. They become fleshy forming a flattened belly covering some of the fibres of the preceding, but mainly lying parallel thereto on the fibular side. A small round tendon emerges above the ankle and follows the main tendon, but proceeds farther to end on the base of the hallucial metatarsal. Mivart found only the distal half of the tibialis anterior subdivided, but the tendons were inserted as described here.

Extensor hallucis longus is a slender fusiform belly lying deeply between tibialis anterior and the long digital extensor, but emerging superficially between them in the distal one-third of the crus. The origin extends proximally to the junction of upper and middle thirds of the leg, the fibres being derived from the front of the fibula and partly from the interosseous membrane. Fleshy fibres are continued to a point beyond the distal edge of the retinaculum. A small tendon proceeds in its own synovial sheath and is destined solely to the hallux. Extensor digitorum longus is a mainly unipenniform structure whose fibres spring from a small part of the head of the tibia and thence along the shaft of the fibula lateral to the origin of the hallucial extensor; but a large number of fibres spring from the anterior peroneal septum. The fleshy belly is replaced by tendon at the level of the ankle joint. In the foot it is retained in position by a pulley-like sling attached to the calcaneus. Thereafter it expands into a thin triangular fibrous sheet from the distal edge of which four terminal digital slips emerge serving the four fibular toes. That to the second toe is small.

Only two peronaei are differentiated in *C. albogularis*, the peronaeus brevis being the bulkier of the two. They present otherwise no unusual features, their tendons taking the usual course to their normal destinations. In *C. sabaeus* Mivart found a peronaeus quinti digiti; a small fleshy belly springing from the middle of the lateral surface of the fibula between the two main peronaei. It ended in a long slender tendon applied closely to that of peronaeus brevis and inserted on to the extensor expansion of V.

A small extensor digitorum brevis is present on the dorsum of the foot. The belly supplying the slender elongated tendon to the hallux is well developed and widely divergent from the remaining bellies. These supply tendons to digits III, IV and V.

In the sole the superficial muscles are, as commonly, abductor hallucis, flexor digitorum brevis and abductor digiti minimi. Abductor hallucis has a limited, more or less fibrous origin from the medial tubercle on the tuber calcanei. Macalister (1868) reports this muscle in *Macaca*, but found it lacking in *Mandrillus* " and some others ". It swells into a fusiform belly whose tendon inserts on the base of the proximal phalanx. Dobson found the flexor brevis digitorum tendons for the second toe arising from a bundle of fleshy fibres connected solely with an expansion derived from the plantaris tendon and joined distally by a few fibres springing from the long flexor tendon. The other flexor brevis tendons sprang via fleshy fibres attached to the conjoined tendons of flexores tibialis and fibularis. In a second example Dobson reported no muscular connection with the long flexor tendons. In *C. albogularis* I found a normal flexor brevis arising by a single head from the tuber calcanei immediately lateral to the origin of abductor hallucis. Abductor digiti minimi comprised two strata of fibres, the deeper stratum representing Wood's muscle (flexor ossis metatarsi digiti quinti).

The contrahentes layer is well developed in the area distal to the long plantar ligament. The transverse fibres destined for the hallux (adductor hallucis tranversus, transversus pedis) are stated by Dobson to arise from the second metatarsal and by an aponeurotic attachment to the third. The other contrahentes (for digits II, IV and V) arise close together partly under cover of the adductor hallucis, that for the second toe being smaller than the others.

Plantar interossei are well developed, a pair for each digit. Their insertions are at the bases of the proximal phalanges of the respective digits. Dobson states that the most medial of the pair for the middle digit is reinforced by an additional strong muscular bundle from the navicular. Mivart found the plantar interossei arranged like those in the human hand and gives the origin as from the proximal end of the plantar surface of the third metatarsal with additional fibres from the sheath of the peronaeus longus tendon. Macalister found the preaxial interosseous of III lacking or " prolonged as a rudiment " of transversus pedis in *Cercopithecus* and *Macaca*, but there is some doubt as to whether there is some confusion here with the contrahentes layer.

SPLANCHNOLOGY

PERITONEUM

Lines of peritoneal reflection from the body wall have been figured for *Cercopithecus* by Straus (1936) (see also Vol. III, p. 38, fig. 6c) Starck, (1958), Klaatsch (1892) and van Loghem (1903).

All workers agree that *Cercopithecus* differs little in its peritoneal arrangements from those met with in other Cercopithecoidea. Resemblance is specially close to *Macaca*, whereas the Colobidae are more aberrant due to distortion by the hypertrophied stomach and displacement of the liver.

On opening the abdomen the great omentum is usually found draped over the other viscera, except for the lobes of the liver and adjacent part of the ventral wall of the stomach. The omentum depends from the greater curvature (or from a line just dorsad thereof) and varies in appearance according to the amount of fat in its subperitoneal connective tissue. This may be considerable in old captive specimens, whereas in juveniles the omentum is thin and transparent. It consists of dorsal and ventral sheets of peritoneum, each bilaminar, separated by an extension of the lesser sac (bursa omentalis). The dorsal sheet is free from the colon except for a limited adhesion at the hepatic flexure, and adjacent part of the ascending colon, though the extent of this varies somewhat and tends to increase with age, in a sinistral direction. Straus found in *C. sabaeus* extensive attachment to the transverse colon.

On raising the omentum, the coils of small intestine (jejuno-ileum) occupy the central field, with the capacious colon pursuing a horse-shoe shaped course around them. From the duodeno-jejunal flexure the coils of jejuno-ileum are slung freely in a mesenterium commune, which is continuous on the right with the mesocolon supporting the proximal (ascending) colon. This combined mesentery has a limited or pedicular attachment supported by the anterior mesenteric vessels after they have crossed the terminal duodenum. At the hepatic flexure the colon loses its mesocolon, becoming fixed to the dorsal parietes in the neighbourhood of the right kidney. To the left of this the transverse colon resumes its mesenterial attachments ; this continues as a broad sheet supporting the remainder of the gut, which is thus free to move extensively. On the rectum it gradually shortens and disappears.

The liver is supported by a series of peritoneal ligaments. Ventrally a short, delicate falciform ligament attaches it to the belly wall. Traced on to the diaphragm its two layers diverge to right and left in a relatively dorsal position to form right and left coronary ligaments of about equal extent. The left is a triangular fold which presents a free border at the margin of the left lobe. The right passes transversely and then dorsad towards the caudate lobe where it represents the vestige of the primitive mesohepar. But in some specimens it is shorter than the left coronary ligament. The post-caval vein penetrates the diaphragm at the meeting place of the falciform and right and left coronary ligaments. The liver is connected to the stomach by a relatively short lesser (gastrohepatic) omentum. This forms the ventral wall of the cranial moiety of the lesser sac, which extends forwards into the angle between the mesohepar and the left coronary ligament as a short digital recess. The left wall of this recess (recessus superior omentalis) is formed by a linear peritoneal reflection (dorsal mesogastrium) which runs sagittally caudalwards near or in the median plane. Its ventral limit is attached to the hilum of the spleen ; it therefore corresponds to the lieno-phrenic and lieno-renal ligaments of human anatomy, but here its parietal attachment is almost entirely confined to the left crus of the diaphragm and left adrenal (especially in juveniles where the latter is large). Duodenum and pancreas are entirely retroperitoneal. (See Fig. 5B, p. 71.)

The line of parietal attachment of the transverse mesocolon follows the caudal border of the pancreas. Its laminae expand on the right, leaving a wider " bare area " over the head of the pancreas and adjacent duodenum, corresponding to the area of adhesion of the colon at the hepatic flexure. To the left the mesocolic attachment curves over the medial part of the left kidney and then continues as descending mesocolon close to the median dorsal line of the body cavity. A broad but low recto-duodenal fold passes from the right side of the cranial part of the descending mesocolon, forwards and dextrad, to end on the last portion of the duodenum just oral to the duodeno-jejunal flexure. From the greater curve of the duodenum the parietal peritoneum passes loosely across to the medial border and caudal pole of the right kidney. The foramen epiploicum (Winslowi) is a narrow passage whose dorsal lining is a continuation of the above-mentioned sheet of serosa. Ventrally it is limited by the dextral edge of the lesser omentum, while cranially the posterior vena cava limits the orifice as it passes into the liver substance. Caudally and somewhat to the left the pyloro-duodenal junction limits the epiploic foramen.

ALIMENTARY SYSTEM

Lips are relatively thick, the upper being strongly convex both from above downwards and transversely. Their mucosal surfaces may or may not exhibit patches of pigment. A frenum is lacking from the lower lip, but the upper presents a median thickening scarcely raised above the level of the underlying gum ; it may consist merely of subjacent connective tissue thickening which appears as an opacity of the labio-gingival sulcus.

The vestibulum oris is remarkable for the extension of its mucosa to form the buccal pouches (bursae buccales). These are of moderate size, though Boas (1920), Hänel (1932), and Fahrenholz (1937) report them well developed. Each opens by an oblique cleft in the floor of the vestibule between the lower gum and the cheek (sulcus alveolo-buccalis inferior). In juveniles the opening is level with the lower second deciduous molar ; in adults the forepart of the opening lies level with the second lower premolar, but extends backwards over the next two teeth. Histological studies on the buccal pouch of *C. aethiops* have been published by Schneider (1958), who finds that the wall of the sac is remarkable for the large number of mucous glands, which form a stratum in the underlying connective tissue. These contrast strongly with the structure of the sac in *Macaca*, where these glands are few.

The *hard palate* is provided with an incisive papilla (better marked in juveniles) and a number of more or less symmetrically disposed transverse ridges (rugae). The incisive papilla varies in shape and structure, the details being better defined in juveniles, where a three-lobed arrangement seems the rule. In a full-term foetus of *C. pygerythrus johnstoni* there is a large median swelling of oval outline immediately behind a smaller papilla which occupies the interval between the two swellings on the gum produced by the underlying, but unerupted, central incisors. The central lobe is flanked by smaller, more rounded lateral lobes. Behind the three lobes is a transverse bar more or less continuous laterally, with the foremost pair of rugae. A juvenile *C. campbelli lowei* with erupted incisors shows the same general arrangement, but the lateral lobes are as elongated antero-posteriorly as the

PLATE X

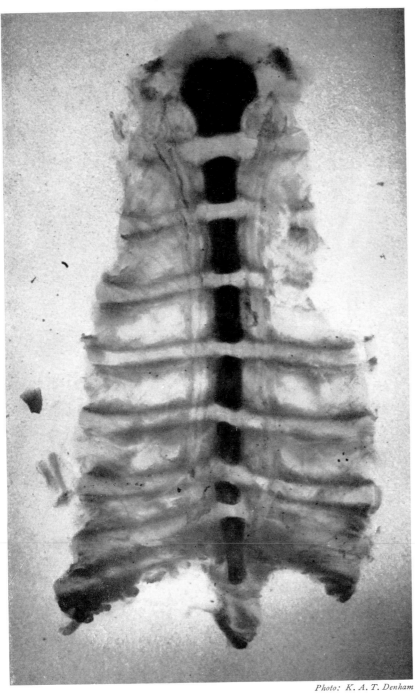

Photo: K. A. T. Denham

Cercopithecus sabaeus. Juvenile. Cleared preparation of sternum

PLATE XI

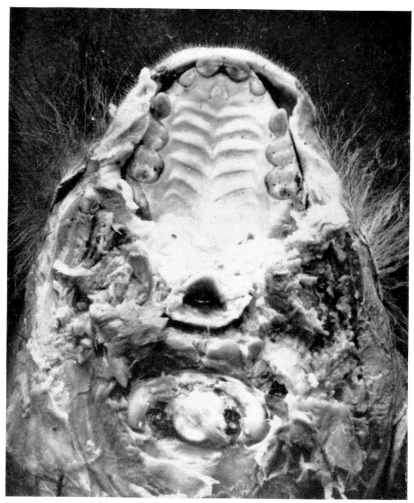

Cercopithecus campbelli. Hard palate. Sonntag collection

central one. The latter is continued both rostrally and caudally as a median sagittal bar, less elevated than the lobe itself, and well demarcated therefrom. The hinder sagittal bar forms a confluence with the foremost pair of rugae. In older examples of *C. pygerythrus* the details are effaced and the papilla has assumed the outline of an isosceles triangle with its apex at the inter-dental interval between the central incisors and its basal angles confluent with the anterior pair of rugae. In a juvenile *C. diana roloway* the papilla resembles that of *C. campbelli*.

Schultz (1949, 1958), who has studied the transverse rugae, finds them also liable to some variation. Out of thirteen *C. sabaeus* Schultz found seven bilaterally with eight ridges, three with nine and two with seven rugae. In juveniles of *C. campbelli lowei*, *C. petaurista* and *C. pogonias grayi* I found six pairs due to the absence of the pair related to the caudal end of the incisive papilla. A foetal *C. pygerythrus* shows eight pairs and a subadult only seven with a small accessory incomplete one on the right side between the two most anterior rugae. On the other hand a three-day-old infant *C. mitis stuhlmanni* presents nine pairs, the additional pairs lying anterior to the rest opposite the papilla incisiva. The rugae take the form of arches, convex rostrally ; they are thicker medially than laterally while the lateral ends trail caudally at an increasing degree at least in the last three or four ridges. The two most anterior ridges are straight and transversely directed. In some species pigmented patches occur irregularly on the hard palate, *e.g.* in *C. petaurista*, but the incisive papilla escapes this deposition.

The *tongue* is parallel-sided with a rounded to spatulate apex. The organ has been described in detail by Sonntag (1921) in *C. preussi*, *C. albogularis*, *C. mona*, *C. burnetti* (= *C. campbelli*), *C. aethiops aethiops*, *C. sabaeus*, *C. tantalus* and *C. rufoviridis*. The tongue of *C. diana* is described by Tuckerman (1890) and that of *C. petaurista* by Münch (1896) and Pocock (1907), while Schneider (1958) has added new data for *C. aethiops aethiops*.

Pigmentation of a patchy character is unusual, but is reported for *C. tantalus* by Sonntag. Apical notches and median dorsal sulci are of variable development, differing individually. The dorsum of the buccal two-thirds is covered by a uniform coat of horny papillae filiformes. Fungiform papillae occur along the lateral margins of the dorsum and especially towards the apex. Vallate papillae vary : in the *C. aethiops* group they are reduced to a double pair, but in other species they are less numerous and arranged either in a V or T formation (*e.g.* *C. preussi*, *C. mona*, also in *C. albogularis* (Owen, 1832) and *C. petaurista* (Münch, 1896)).

Foramen caecum, apical gland of Blandin and lytta are lacking. The same applies to the plicae fimbriatae in adults, but these may be present in young animals. A frenal lamella is present, its apex either entire or bifid. Lateral organs are present either as rows of oval bodies, or as flattened laminae separated by intervening sulci, but Owen found in *C. albogularis* an entire, oval, undivided lamella.

I have examined tongues of *C. cephus, C. ascanius ascanius, C. a. schmidti* and *C. erythrotis sclateri* (see fig. 45,) and find them all in essential agreement with Sonntag's descriptions.   In all, there are three vallate papillae arranged in a triangle.   Sometimes the median (posterior) papilla is larger than the others, but the reverse may be true.   In *C. a. schmidti* the right anterior papilla was double, the two papillae within a single vallum.   Fungiform papillae are arranged as described by Sonntag, only the central area

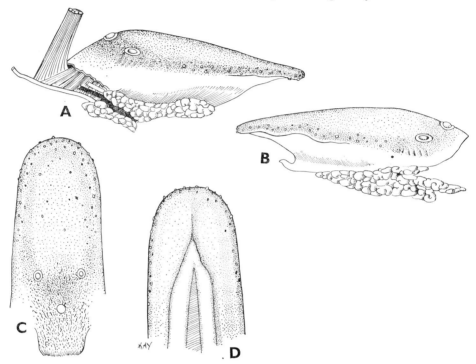

FIG. 45.—Tongue in *Cercopithecus*.   A, *C. ascanius*, right lateral aspect; B, *C. albogularis*, left lateral aspect; c, *C. ascanius*, dorsal aspect; D, the same, ventral aspect

being relatively free.   A deep median ventral sulcus failing to reach the apex, is constant.   Lateral organs consist of ten sulci with swollen anterior and posterior lips.   They may all be arranged in the same oblique direction (passing downwards and backwards), but more usually the smaller anterior sulci point downwards and forwards at an acute angle with the axes of the larger posterior four or five.   The gap between the two series lies opposite the lateral vallate papilla.   The frenal lamella may be bifid or entire.   It is connected with the body of the tongue by a frenal fold.   Plicae fimbriatae are lacking.

Salivary Glands.—Neither Huntington (1913) nor Schneider (1958) describes the salivary glands in *Cercopithecus*, though the former admits to having dissected them in *C. sabaeus, C. rufoviridis* and one referred to as

C. niger (probably an error for *Cynopithecus niger*). Presumably he found no marked differences from the other cynomorphs (*Papio, Macaca*) which he studied.

In *C. albogularis* and *C. nictitans* I find the parotid gland superficially extensive, but restricted deeply. The superficial aspect forms an oblong stratum of loosely lobulated glandular tissue covering the hinder part of the masseter and the space between the hinder border of the vertical ramus of the mandible and the auditory meatus. It is somewhat higher than broad.

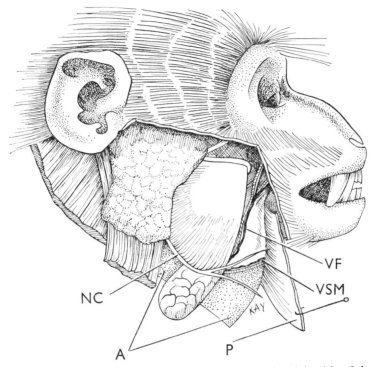

FIG. 46.—*Cercopithecus a. kibonotensis* ♀. Dissection of the right side of the face

A, laryngeal air sac ; *NC*, cervical branch of VII ; *P*, platysma (reflected forwards) ; *VF*, facial vein ; *VSM*, submandibular branch of facial vein

A few lobules overlap the zygomatic arch, but no accessory lobules occur along the duct. The latter emerges from the upper part of the anterior border of the gland which, at this point, bulges somewhat forwards. The duct courses across the masseter, parallel with the zygoma, perforating the buccinator, to open into the vestibulum oris opposite the second upper molar. The hinder border of the gland is thicker than the anterior, especially in *C. nictitans*. Large lobules project deeply to fill the gap between the mandible and the sterno-mastoid muscle extending medially to the pharyngeal wall above, while below glandular tissues are apposed directly upon the wall of the laryngeal air-sac. Anteriorly the deeper part of the gland abuts on the medial pterygoid muscle.

The submaxillary (submandibular) gland is a compact ovoid mass with some accessory lobules lying beneath the angular region of the mandible with its rostral end lying deep to the mandible. In *C. nictitans* a deep cleft divides the forepart of the gland horizontally into a smaller upper and larger lower moiety. In addition there is a completely separate lobule along the upper border of the main mass. In *C. cephus* I found bilateral asymmetry in the size of the gland, the left being more antero-posteriorly elongated than the right. Deeply the gland lies directly upon the wall of the laryngeal sac. The duct emerges from a hilum on the forepart of the deep surface of the gland. It takes the usual course to open, beside the frenum linguae (parafrenular papilla), into the buccal cavity.

The sublingual complex includes representative of greater (Bartholinian) and lesser (alveolingual or Rivinian) sublingual glands. The latter lie lateral to the greater gland, and open by several small ducts directly into the mouth by perforating the suprajacent mucosa. The Bartholinian gland opens by a single duct which runs alongside Wharton's duct to the parafrenular papilla, upon which it opens lateral and slightly caudal to the larger duct. The differentiation between the two glandular components is incomplete, being best marked posteriorly where a longitudinal cleft divides the lateral portion into upper and lower portions, between which the deeper Bartholinian gland may be seen and which may extend farther backwards. Variations in detailed arrangements are probably purely of an individual character. The nearest approach among Huntington's series to the arrangement here described is that which he depicts for *Macaca nemestrina* (his fig. 22, p. 103).

Pharynx.—The soft palate continues backwards in line with the hard palate, but is thicker and glandular. Its free caudal border is produced in the middle line into a well-defined uvula some 5 mm. long. This depends into the pharyngeal cavity to the caudal side of the epiglottis. The soft palate forms the floor of a long (16 mm.) naso-pharyngeal canal which describes a uniform curve to become continuous with the oro-pharynx. The elongated cleft-like opening of the tympanic tube is located high up near the roof of the anterior portion of the naso-pharyngeal passage. The naso-pharyngeal canal is divided into two by a median membranous septum. This is attached in front to the hinder edge of the vomer, presents a free posterior sickle-shaped border and is connected above to the roof of the canal and below to the median line of the soft palate.

From the lateral attachment of the soft palate to the pharyngeal wall two well-marked faucial pillars descend on to the sides of the oro-pharynx. The anterior proceeds downwards and forwards to end in the tongue at the junction of its buccal two-thirds and pharyngeal one-third and is supported by the palato-glossus muscle. The posterior fold passes more dorsally on to the roof of the pharynx, but fails to meet its fellow. It is supported by the palato-pharyngeus muscle. Between the two pillars on each side lies the tonsillar fossa. Within this is a vertical slit—the opening of the pocket-like tonsil, best seen in the foetus and infant. Tonsillar tissue lines the walls of the crypt, but seems to undergo atrophy with maturity. According to Hett and Butterfield (1909) the primitive tonsillar tube has become a pocket-shaped diverticulum, more or less surrounded by lymphoid tissue; but this is more in evidence on the inferior or inner lip than elsewhere (figured in *C. cephus* and *C. pygerythrus*). Hett (1929) describes the tonsil of *C. mona* as

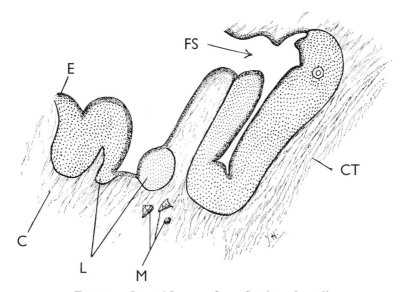

FIG. 47.—*Cercopithecus cephus*. Section of tonsil

C, capsule of tonsil; *CT*, connective tissue; *E*, epithelium; *FS*, fossa supratonsillaris; *L*, lymphoid tissue; *M*, mucous glandular tissue. (Based on Hett and Butterfield's figure 9)

flat, pocket-shaped, with the lips sometimes thickened with lymphoid tissue extending in an even layer around the pocket. A band of connective tissue separates this from the pharyngeal epithelium, but the epithelium of the main crypt is largely destroyed. Numerous solid ingrowths occur, but they form secondary crypts only rarely. An occasional concentric epithelial nodule occurs, and this may have a horny centre. Similar findings are reported in *C. pygerythrus rufoviridis*, *C. ae. tantalus* and *C. sabaeus*.

In the oro-pharynx the front wall, formed by the pharyngeal one-third of the tongue, is well provided with lymphoid tissue, while the overlying mucosa is finely wrinkled—an appearance which affects equally the area circumscribed by the vallate papillae and that aboral thereto. A short, thick median frenum connects the base of the tongue with the epiglottis. On either side of this are deep, roomy valleculae whose lining is continuous above with that of the lower part of the tonsillar recess.

In the laryngo-pharynx the ventral wall is marked by the projection of

Y

the robust, leaf-like epiglottis. This is strongly convex from side to side on its oral aspect, equally concave on its aboral side. Its free margin is thickened, especially medially, but the thickening abruptly ceases at the midline, without, however, a definite notch being produced. Its lateral margins become thinner and are continued dorsally, as aryteno-epiglottidean folds, to the arytenoids, describing a U-shaped course as they proceed. Within the concavity of the U, the swollen folds (supported by the cuneiform cartilages), connecting the arytenoids with the laryngeal aspect of the epiglottic base are revealed. Lateral to the ary-epiglottic folds lie the narrow pyriform fossae, lined with smooth mucosa. The lateral walls of the laryngo-pharynx are wrinkled transversely, due to the contraction of the middle and inferior constrictor pharyngis muscles. Dorsal to the latter on the exterior of the pharynx is a well-marked venous plexus. Fibres of the constrictor muscles gradually change their course from transverse to oblique and finally to longitudinal on the oesophagus. A smooth convex area of mucosa covering the lower part of the arytenoids and the cricoid cartilages forms the lower part of the ventral wall of the laryngo-pharynx. Aboral to this, the mucosa becomes longitudinally rugose in the oesophagus.

Oesophagus.—This is divided into cervical, thoracic and abdominal parts. The first-mentioned commences in the median line at the lower border of the cricoid, but soon diverges somewhat to the left, entering the thorax more to the left than the trachea. It returns to the median position in the centre of its thoracic extent, then again diverges to the left and ventrad before piercing the diaphragm midway between the left crus and the central tendon. It has the usual relations to aorta, thoracic duct, vena azygos major and vagus nerves. The last-mentioned form a Y-shaped junction on its dorsal wall before breaking up to form the plexus gulae.

The oesophageal mucosa is highly keratinized and thrown into about half a dozen longitudinal rugae. The epithelium is 400 μ in thickness compared with 280 μ for *Macaca* and 150 μ for *Cercocebus* (Burkl, 1958). Oesophageal glands are of mixed tubulo-alveolar type. Striped fibres occur in the transverse muscular coat in the oral five-eighths of the tube and in the longitudinal coat in the oral six-eighths only (Burkl).

The abdominal portion, 1 cm. long, turns to the left to open into the stomach at the cardia.

Stomach.—A simple pyriform sac, the stomach presents a subconical fundus, a cylindrical body and an elongated pyloric segment. Murie (1866) describes it as ovoid in *C. erythrogaster*. The angle between the axis of the fundus and body with that of the pyloric segment is approximately a right angle, so that there is not always an acute incisura angularis on the lesser curvature. On the great curvature, however, two notches, one opposite the usual site of the incisura angularis and a more aboral sulcus intermedius are sometimes recognizable, as in the stomach of *C. erythrogaster*. The cardia is situated approximately half-way between the summit of the fundus and the commencement of the pyloric canal, as found by Murie in the same species. In a *C. aethiops tantalus*, however, an acute incisura marks the lesser curvature. In *C. werneri* (= *C. sabaeus*) Vermes and Wiedholz (1930)

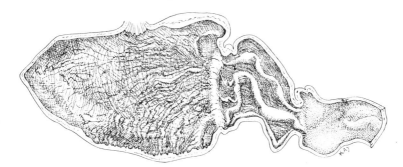

FIG. 48.—*Cercopithecus albogularis kolbi*. Ventral wall of the bisected stomach from the dorsal aspect

describe a stomach with a central contraction dividing the viscus into two balloon-like compartments connected by a narrow channel. In a *C. pygery-thrus* a similar appearance was found, but the contraction affected the greater curvature only. In *C. pogonias grayi* these workers compared the stomach to a flabby human stomach, but with the cardia more to the right than in Man, producing a more capacious fundus. Doubtless these variations are determined by the state of distension or relaxation of the viscus. Murie (1866) gives the following dimensions (mm.) :

	C. erythrogaster	C. diana	C. cephus
Transverse diameter fundus— cardia	82·55	88·9	76·2
Opposite diameter (oesophagus— curvature major)	64·5	51·8	39·1

At the cardio-oesophageal junction a sharp line of demarcation is found between the keratinized gular epithelium and the softer gastric epithelium. Its edge is crenulated in conformity with the oesophageal rugae (ora serrata). Variations here are stated not to be related to species but to be of individual character (Burkl).

The fundus and body are lined by smooth velvety mucosa with few and fine foldings. Near the cardia these present a radiating arrangement; in the body they tend to be longitudinally disposed, but the two systems interlace, producing a fine reticulated effect at the junctional region between fundus and body. A system of finer elevations (*areae gastricae*) marks the mucosa both upon and between the grosser foldings. At the junction of body and pyloric segment a thick annular contraction ring is frequently seen. Within the pyloric segment grosser longitudinal foldings of sinuous character affect the whole length of this tubular passage, where the thickness of the wall is greatly increased also by more robust muscular coats. Histology of the various mucosal regions has been reported upon by Burkl (1958), who distinguishes cardiac glands and principal glands in fundus and body respectively.

Small Intestine.—The duodenum, except for the first few millimetres, lies wholly retroperitoneally. It consists of three parts : the first lies transversely, the second longitudinally and the third, again transversely. The

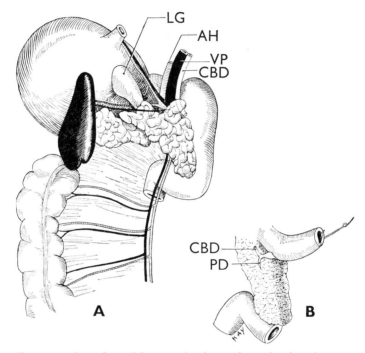

FIG. 49.—*C. cephus*. Mesogastric viscera from the dorsal aspect

AH, hepatic artery ; *CBD*, common bile duct ; *LG*, omental lymphatic gland ; *PD*, pancreatic duct ; *VP*, vena portae
Inset B shows the termination of bile and pancreatic ducts in *C. albogularis kolbi* after reflection of duodenum

second part is longest and describes a curve, convex to the right. A right-angled bend marks the junction of first and second parts, but the second and third pass into each other in an evenly rounded curve. In a *C. albogularis kolbi* ♀ and a foetal *C. pygerythrus* the second part was straight and terminated caudally in a U-shaped bend around the caudal tip of the pancreas. A sharp flexure separates duodenum and jejunum. Murie (1866) found the opening of the common bile duct in the second part of the duodenum of *C. erythrogaster* 25.5 mm. beyond the pylorus. I have confirmed this in the same species, and similar arrangements have been noted in *C. albogularis kolbi* and *C. cephus*. In all these there is an ampulla, but no papilla major, the orifice being flush with the velvety surface of the duodenal mucosa.

The remainder of the small intestine is not sharply divided into jejunum and ileum. Murie records it as of variable length (178 cm. in *C. erythrogaster*, 152 cm. in *C. diana* and 132·2 cm. in *C. cephus*).

The coils lie mainly to the left of the central part of the abdomen, slung in a free mesenterium commune, which is conterminous with the ascending mesocolon. The tube is smooth-walled and of almost uniform calibre throughout. No terminal ampulla, like that found by Machado and de Dio (1963) in so many platyrrhine monkeys, has been observed. Internally it presents no valvulae conniventes ; the mucosa is velvety in texture from the numerous villi which may vary somewhat in details in different regions of the gut. Peyer's patches are well marked, specially large and numerous in the ileum, where they may aggregate to form a so-called *tonsilla iliaca* (Muthmann, 1913). Solitary follicles are also numerous. Further histological details, including glandular appendages, are recorded by Burkl (1958).

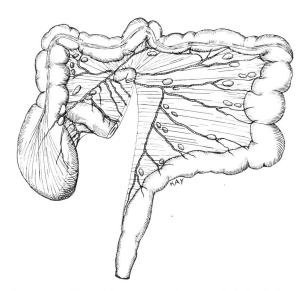

FIG. 50.—*Cercopithecus petaurista buttikoferi*, ♂ juv. Disposition of the large intestine and mesenteries

Large Intestine (van Loghem, 1903, Kostanecki, 1926, Reider, 1936, Hill and Rewell, 1948, Hill, 1958).— This is constantly divisible into colon and rectum, the former recognized by the presence of longitudinal taeniae, caused by local concentrations of the longitudinal muscle, and the correlated occurrence of sacculations (haustrae). The rectum, by contrast, exhibits a complete longitudinal muscular coat. The taeniae are three in number throughout the colon and are arranged as in the human colon, a mesocolic and two others, placed equidistant from each other. There are also, therefore, three series of sacculations. Owen (1868) mentions four taeniae in some species of *Cercopithecus*, but no later student has reported more than three.

The colon is arranged in a horseshoe-shaped curve around the periphery of the coils of the jejuno-ileum, and is anchored at the hepatic flexure due to the shortening, at this point (and to a variable degree therefrom in both directions), of the mesocolon. Hereby the colon becomes subdivisible into (i) a short ascending colon, having a short mesocolon, (ii) a long, loop-like, dependent (sometimes, as in specimens I have examined of *C. ascanius*, ansiform) but more frequently forming a simple festoon as in Man, and (iii) an extremely elongated descending or distal colon which, like the preceding, bears a wide mesocolon, which is here of sufficient width to permit some irregular coiling of this part of the tube. The most aboral coils correspond to the pelvic colon of anthropotomy, but do not differ morphologically from the descending colon in so far as no tendency is shown to reduction in the number of taeniae.

The ileo-colic junction is in general situated at the level of the iliac crest (van Loghem), but it may lie more anteriorly in the newborn—as van Loghem found—since the final migration has not at that stage been completed and the caecal apex only has gained the level of the crista iliaca. I have confirmed van Loghem's findings in neonatal stages of *C. aethiops*, but find the complete descent of the caecum has already occurred in juveniles of *C. ae. tantalus* of 240 mm. crown-rump length. On the other hand, in adults of *C. erythrotis sclateri* and *C. diana*, the neonatal position was retained.

The caecum agrees closely with that of *Papio* rather than that of *Erythrocebus* (Hill and Rewell) being slightly asymmetrically curved. Reider (1936) also found, in two specimens, a close similarity to *Papio*. The sac is divisible into two parts by a marked annular constriction, a basal, sacculated portion and an apical smooth-walled region of somewhat conical form. On the former the taeniae coli are continued from the ascending colon. These merge at the constricted zone to give a complete longitudinal muscular coat on the apical region. Considerable variations in shape accrue from the varying degrees of contraction or dilatation of the muscular tissue. These account for the descriptions of appendices or pseudo-appendical formations so frequent in the earlier literature (*e.g.* Broca, 1869, in *C. ae. aethiops*; Weinberg, 1906; Neuville, 1922, in *C. ascanius*). In the completely relaxed state the caecum presents the form of a simple bag with its rounded or conical fundus directed either straight backwards or more usually tilted somewhat to the left. Limited contraction reveals the bipartite nature of the organ by emphasizing the constriction between apical and basal segments and by manifestation of the sacculated structure of the basal segment. Further contraction affects mainly the longitudinal fibres, whereby the taeniae of the basal sac further emphasize the haustra, whilst at the same time the apical segment is shortened and also constricted by contraction of its circular fibres. This produces the extreme form, like that figured by Wood Jones (1929 *b*) in *C. tantalus*, which has been misinterpreted as a vermiform appendix, despite Hervé's (1882) denial of Broca's interpretation. Cf. *C. erythrogaster* (Murie, 1866). Intrinsic contractibility of the caecal musculature is apparently controlled by ganglionic tissue in its walls (Gluckmann, 1946).

The medial wall of the caecum is connected to the anti-mesenteric wall of the terminal ileum by a triangular fold of peritoneum (mesotyphlon). This receives a branch of the dorsal caecal artery via a dorsal ileo-caecal fold and a smaller one from the ventral caecal artery. The dorsal fold forms a pocket between itself and the mesotyphlon. Within the mesotyphlon the artery branches into several caecal branches and a recurrent ileal branch. The ventral wall of the caecum is supplied by a slightly larger caecal artery, but the arterial asymmetry is much less than in other cercopithecoid genera. This is attested by the fact that both caecal arteries provide branches to the mesotyphlon and their contributions to the supply of the apical region is almost equal, at any rate in *C. mona* (see fig. 51) (see also Förster, 1918; Kostanecki, 1926).

INTESTINAL MEASUREMENTS (in millimetres) in *Cercopithecus spp.*:

	Duodenum	Jejuno-ileum	Intestinum crassum	Caecum	Authority
C. albogularis ad.	—	166·0	61·0	5	van Loghem
C. sp. neonatus	—	76·0	29·0	1	
C. erythrogaster	—	178·0	57·25	—	
C. diana	—	152·0	55·9	—	Murie
C. cephus	—	132·2	53·3	—	

The ascending colon is relatively short and, with the caecum entirely enclosed in peritoneum, free from the parietes as far as the hepatic flexure, which is firmly attached to the dorsal abdominal wall neighbouring the right kidney and duodenum. Three taeniae, one mesocolic, one ventral and one dorsal are continued on to the basal caecal sac and aborally beyond the hepatic flexure on to the transverse colon. There is no sharply defined splenic flexure, the descending and transverse colons being freely continuous in view of the continuity of their mesocola. The descending colon is thrown into numerous loops which depend ventrally and may overlie some of the small intestinal coils from the left. At the level of the left iliac crest the descending colon

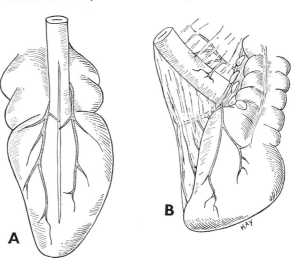

FIG. 51.—*Cercopithecus mona*, ♀ adult. Caecum from A, medial and B, dorsal aspects

passes into the sigmoid or pelvic colon whose loops may also project towards the umbilicus and mask some of the other intestinal loops. In the neonatus van Loghem found the sigmoid coils specially well developed and occupying all available space in the pelvis major and surpassing the intercristal plane. In the neonatal *C. aethiops* I found the pelvic colon forming a single cranially directed loop occupying the pelvis minor and major dorsal to the caudal coils of the small intestine. On the other hand, in juveniles of *C. tantalus* and *C. petaurista buttikoferi*, the descending mesocolon narrows considerably towards the pelvis and the pelvic colon is merely a straight, uncoiled continuation of the descending colon.

The radix mesocoli follows the cranial border of the pancreas and then at the left turns caudally to follow a sagittal course just to the left of the median line.

Aborally the taeniae become fainter on the pelvic colon, so that there is no sharp demarcation between colon and rectum in most instances. The rectum may be taken as that part of the gut beyond the level of cessation of the mesentery. In *Cercopithecus*, according to Lubosch and Schaller (1928), a ventral concentration of longitudinal muscular fibres affects the rectum, otherwise the tube is as in *Papio*, *Macaca* and *Presbytis*, showing an ampulla and lateral sacs. Peritoneum covers the ventral wall of the gut as far caudad as the plane of the cranial border of the obturator foramen (in an adult ♀ *C. erythrotis sclateri*).

A dorsal kink occurs at the junction of rectum and anal canal. The latter some 6-8 mm. long is provided with a strong external sphincter of striated muscle and a weaker internal sphincter lying deep to it. The internal sphincter is continuous with the muscular coat of the rectum. The lining of the anal canal is in some cases, e.g. *C. mitis stuhlmanni*, clearly demarcated into cutaneous, intermediate and mucous zones, the first deeply pigmented, the intermediate slightly so and the mucous unpigmented. The cutaneous zone ends cranially in a crenated margin from which ridges of columns extend inwards towards the mucous zone. In other cases, *e.g. C. ascanius schmidti*, the intermediate zone is not clearly recognizable, being unpigmented, whilst the deeply pigmented cutaneous zone ends abruptly in a crenated margin. Age possibly influences the details somewhat, these being better marked in foetal and neonatal stages, where, in spite of the lack of pigment, anal columns are well differentiated in the intermediate zone and terminate above in an annular, shelf-like structure comprised by a series of anal valves. Beyond these again lie the anal sinuses, which intervene between the aboral ends of the columns of the mucous zone. Histological details in *C. aethiops* have been described by Ortmann (1958) and myological relations by Kollmann (1894).

Liver (Ruge, 1906 ; Lipp, 1958).—The liver of *Cercopithecus* stands at a relatively primitive stage as regards its situs and lobation compared with the more advanced conditions seen in *Papio* or the specialized arrangements found in the Colobidae. Ruge compared it with the liver of *Ateles* among the Platyrrhini, although the extreme degree of development of the caudate lobe in the latter is not attained in *Cercopithecus*.

In its general form the right half greatly exceeds the left in bulk and, moreover, extends to a greater degree dorsally. The division into these two main parts is demarcated by the lines of attachment of the falciform ligament, of the ligamentum venae umbilicalis and ligamentum hepato-gastro-oesophagicum (lesser omentum). There are four main lobes separated by deep fissures, which incise the organ almost to its dorsal border. These are left and right lateral, a central lobe (subdivided merely by the ligamentous attachments) and the caudate-Spigelian complex. The oesophageal notch is of variable depth, being shallower in *C. mitis* and other large species, deeper in *C. cephus*, and quite acute in *C. preussi*, where the main axes of the right and left halves run sagitally, so that the organ, in cranial view, describes a U-shaped contour. This is less marked in *C. cephus*, as is shown in Ruge's figure, and still less so in *C. cynosuros*, and *C. albogularis* (two examples examined).

The central lobe is largest : it lies more to the right side than the left. It is subdivided into larger right and smaller left parts by the line of attachment of the falciform ligament and, on the visceral aspect, for a short distance only by the umbilical incisure. Laterally it overlaps the left and right lobes superficially. Its visceral aspect, on the right bears the deep fossa for the gall-bladder. To the left of the umbilical notch a smaller incisure sometimes separates off a small paraumbilical lobule, *e.g.* in *C. cephus* (see Ruge's figure). A larger one was observed in *C. preussi*, while in *C. albogularis* a shallow incision cuts across from the gall-bladder fossa to the umbilical fissure, separating a quadrate paraumbilical lobule.

The left lobe, cranio-caudally compressed, is provided with a large processus triangularis which projects caudally and medially on the visceral aspect from its medial border. The cranial border may be somewhat subdivided by short incisures, as I found in *C. preussi*. The right lobe is wedge-shaped, with the base dorsally and apex ventrally. Its caudal border may be sinous or indented, while near the ventral end the visceral aspect is marked by a sinuous fissure (fissura interlobaris dextra) partly dividing the lobe into central and lateral portions. In *C. cephus* Ruge also defined a fissura praecaudalis incising the visceral aspect of the right lobe from its medial border, but failing to gain the lateral margin. This is not present on my example of *C. cephus*, nor on the livers of *C. albogularis kolbi* or *C. preussi*.

The Spigelian complex is somewhat variable. Essentially it consists of a flat, oblong area, longer sagittally than transversely, on the dorsal part of the right half of the central lobe, facing somewhat medially (lobus dorsalis of Ruge). It is not, or but little raised from the general surface of the liver, but is defined by well-marked incisures on the two longer sides and along its caudal border. The porta hepatis forms the boundary along the medial and caudal borders, and the line of the mesohepar (with the postcaval buried in the subjacent liver substance) along the lateral border. In *C. preussi* and *C. cephus* the oblong is converted into a parallelogram by obliquity of its long axis, and the same is incipient in *C. albogularis*. Appendages to the lobus dorsalis are (i) papillary process, (ii) caval lobule and (iii) caudate lobe or process, of which the last is the most constant, though variable in development. In *C. cephus* the caudate is a large leaf-shaped extension of the right caudal angle of the lobus dorsalis, its apex gaining the lateral liver margin, and its visceral aspect excavated by the renal impression. In the same species the caval lobule is a mere lappet applied to the left wall of the vein, prior to its entry into the liver substance, while the papillary process is barely represented, being merely the postero-medial angle of the lobus, which is separated by a shallow concavity from the root of the caudate process. In *C. preussi* the papillary process is not definable, but the caval lobule is more elongated sagittally and passes farther ventrad on the left wall of the vein. The caudate is smaller, formed merely by an extension postero-laterally of the main lobus dorsalis. The liver of *C. albogularis kolbi* is somewhat intermediate in all the above features.

The gall-bladder is an elongated pyriform sac occupying a deep fossa on the visceral aspect of the right part of the central lobe. The depression has sharply defined margins and gains the free margin of the liver. The gall-bladder varies in shape being for the most part simple and straight, but in a young *C. cynosuros* I found it somewhat tortuous. The cystic duct is joined by ducts from the liver lobes to form the common bile duct. The latter takes the usual course from the porta hepatis via the lesser omentum and dorsal to the first part of the duodenum to the ampulla, where it is joined by the pancreatic duct, the two entering the duodenum by a common orifice some 10 mm. beyond the pylorus.

Pancreas.—This occupies the same general position and shows the same peritoneal relationships as in Man. It is, however, variable in shape. It consists of two main portions, a horizontal and a sagittal, the former homologous with the " body " of the human organ, and the latter with the " head ". The horizontal portion ends abruptly, without narrowing to form a " tail " at the splenic hilum, and a few millimetres of this are sometimes free, being clothed by peritoneum on both aspects. The rest of the gland is, however, constantly retroperitoneal. The sagittal portion is more variable, depending upon the disposition of the duodenum which lies in contact with it to the right, grooving its dextral aspect. In a *C. albogularis* I found this part as long as the horizontal part and almost as thick, but in *C. cephus* both parts were shorter and thicker. In *C. erythrogaster*, the organ was more like the human pancreas, though lacking an uncinate process.

The uncinate process seems invariably lacking, resulting in greater exposure of the anterior mesenteric vessels as they proceed between the pancreas and third part of the duodenum. On the other hand, an omental lobule or lappet is commonly present on the cranial border in relation to the portal vein and hepatic artery as they enter the lesser omentum.

RESPIRATORY TRACT

Larynx.—Apart from some scattered remarks by Negus (1949) on the larynx of *C. aethiops* and of a " Mozambique guenon ", little seems to have been published on the organ in this genus.

The hyoid has already been considered (*supra*, p. 242).

There are considerable variations according to age and sex, all the cartilages being smaller in females. The following account is based mainly upon the adult male.

The thyroid cartilage is comprised of two approximately oblong alae, broader dorso-ventrally than high. Their union is produced cranially into a beak-like process, sometimes slightly notched in the median line. Over this the emergent air-sac passes. The superior cornu, short and stout, makes contact with the tip of the greater hyoid cornu : it is separated by a shallow

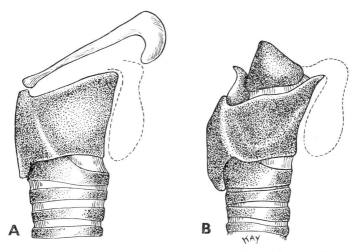

FIG. 52.—Skeleton of the larynx from the right side in A, *Cercopithecus neglectus*; B, *C. mitis stuhlmanni.* In A the hyoid is shown. The dotted outlines indicate the median air-sacs

notch from the remainder of the cranial border. The dorsal border curves mediad towards its caudal end, the transverse diameter being less here than cranially.

The inferior cornu, much longer than the superior, is equally robust and overlaps the cricoid almost to the caudal margin of the latter, to which it is bound not only by a capsular ligament medially, but also by adventitious ligamentous bands dorsally.

The epiglottic cartilage is " floating ", having no direct skeletal connection with the thyroid. The region where the ligamentous connection exists in Man is interrupted by the passage of the air-sac. The cartilage is moored laterally merely by connective tissue within the aryteno-epiglottidean fold.

In form the epiglottic cartilage is tent-shaped, consisting of two alae sloping laterally from their cranio-median union. The cartilage therefore presents three borders, two caudo-lateral and one cranial (or superior) normally facing somewhat dorsad.

The cricoid has the usual form. On its dorsal expanded portion a strong median sagittal keel separates the areas for the crico-arytenoideus muscles of the two sides. A shorter median ventral ridge similarly separates the areas for the two crico-thyroid muscles.

The slender arytenoid cartilages rest upon the forepart of the thick cranial border of the dorsal part of the cricoid. They present the usual processes, of which the apical is very slender and not capped by a separate cartilage of Santorini. On the other hand, a well-developed cartilage of Wrisberg appears in the dorsal part of the aryteno-epiglottidean fold. Dorsally the arytenoids are deeply excavated by the massive interarytenoideus muscle.

The oval aditus laryngis of *C. aethiops* has been figured by Starck (1960) whose photograph agrees in all but minor details with personal findings in *C. mitis stuhlmanni*, *C. albogularis*, *C. neglectus*, *C. erythrotis sclateri* and *C. ascanius ascanius*. Ventrally the opening is guarded by the curved contour of the epiglottis, thick-edged in front, thinning at the sides. Dorsally are the prominent sausage-shaped tubercles (*noduli corniculati*) formed by the thickened mucosa over the apices of the two arytenoids, and separated by a median incisure (*incisura interarytenoidea*). These are elliptical and curved, convex towards the laryngeal cavity, concave on the pharyngeal aspect, and also obliquely disposed. Between the latter and the dorsal end of the ary-epiglottic folds is a well-marked tubercle (*nodulus cuneiformis*) formed each side by the cuneiform cartilage. In the species that I examined these tubercles lay somewhat more deeply than in Starck's *C. aethiops*, bulging inwards and overshadowed by the ary-epiglottic fold.

The vestibule of the larynx is chiefly remarkable for the median ventral opening of the median air-sac. This is located at the base of the epiglottis. An oval or rounded opening (6 mm. wide in *C. ascanius*), it leads ventrad into a thin-walled diverticulum of the laryngeal mucosa, which occupies the concave dorsal aspect of the corpus hyoidei and protrudes thence into a variably developed caudal extension beneath the sterno-hyoid muscles. Negus depicts it in *C. sabaeus* as a small outgrowth not transgressing the hyoid excavation, but in all the examples I have examined it is more extensive. In *C. erythrotis sclateri* the transgression is minimal, the sac ending in blunt lateral cornua connected by a transverse portion overlying the thyro-hyoid membrane. In *C. ascanius* the organ is larger, proceeding caudally as a simple median sac some 15 mm. between the infrahyoid muscles and the thyroid cartilage. In males of *C. mitis stuhlmanni*, and females of *C. albogularis* and *C. neglectus*, the sac is even larger and bilobed, with processes extending cranio-laterally deep to the angular region of the mandible, as well as caudo-laterally beneath the sterno-mastoids.

The vestibule is limited caudally by the vestibular folds. These are prominent, elastic folds of mucosa with sharp free edges medially and attached each side along the wall of the larynx level with the cranial border of the thyroid cartilage. Ventrally their attachment coincides with paired tubercles on the beak-like process mentioned above. Adjacent to these and for the ventral third of their length, the folds are thick and fleshy, but the dorsal two-thirds is thin and membranous. Dorsally each fold ends on the vocal process of the corresponding arytenoid adjacent to the attachment of the vocal fold. The folds are directed somewhat caudally, *i.e.* towards the laryngeal ventricle, which thus ascends on their deep aspect. Beyond this general extension there is no accessory lateral saccule corresponding to the paired outgrowths found in Hominoidea. The vocal fold is co-extensive with the ventricular but less sharply defined, *i.e.* the reverse of the condition in *Homo*. This is due to the massive muscular development in the lateral wall of the subglottic chamber (*cavum laryngis inferior*) which renders the vocal fold thick and fleshy throughout. The fold is directed towards the aditus, so that a narrow fusiform gap is left between its free edge and that of the vestibular fold. The wall of the subglottic chamber is smooth and unmarked, sloping gradually caudally and somewhat laterad from the thyroid to the cricoid and subcricoid regions of the passage.

The trachea is a wide cylindrical tube with the cartilages deficient dorsally. In a female *C. cephus* thirteen cartilaginous rings support the cervical and fifteen the thoracic portion. Bifurcation occurs as far caudally as the sixth thoracic vertebra, so that an unduly long thoracic trachea is present. The main bronchi are relatively short and diverge at a rather acute though variable angle (65° in *C. petaurista*, 85° in *C. ascanius*). The left bronchus divides into two main bronchi. One to the basal lobe is a continuation of the primary bronchus. The other supplies apical and middle lobes, the bronchus to the latter branching off from the ventral aspect of the undivided cranial division of the primary bronchus. On the right a large eparterial bronchus supplies the apical lobe. The primary bronchus then continues into the basal lobe giving off first a bronchus to the middle lobe ventro-laterally. The main stem then bifurcates within the basal lobe, but first gives off a dorsal branch to the dorsal thick border of the lobe, and opposite this a ventral branch which is the sole supply of the azygos lobe. Thereafter the divided main stem supplies minor dorsal and ventral tertiary bronchi.

Histologically the bronchi of *C. albogularis* have been studied by Hayek (1960) who found cartilage fragments in the bronchial walls peripherally as far as the alveolar ducts of the bronchioli. Between this cartilage-laden lamina and the muscularis a rich vascular network is present. The muscular tissue in the bronchiolar walls is strongly developed. In the epithelium goblet-cells are numerous, whilst alveolo-tubular (muco-serous) glands occur in the submucosa.

Lungs.—In all species examined (*C. aethiops* several forms ; *C. cephus, C. mona, C. albogularis, C. petaurista, C. ascanius, C. nictitans*) the left lung is three-lobed and the right four-lobed. The general arrangement has been figured by Duckworth (1915, figs. 91, 92). On the left the three lobes correspond in a general way with the three lobes of the human right lung ; in the right these are supplemented by a fourth, infracardiac or azygos lobe (lobus impar). Apical lobes present the usual conical form, with rounded summit ; the fissure between apical and basal lobes commences dorsally at the same level on both sides, sloping ventrally and caudally to end at the junction of ventral and caudal borders or slightly dorsad thereof on the caudal border (*vide* Narath, 1901). The middle lobe is sandwiched between apical and basal lobes, but fails to reach the dorsal margin, though approaching this more closely on right than left. On the left the middle lobe may not be as fully differentiated from the apical lobe as on the right, though more so on both sides than in *Macaca* or *Erythrocebus*. Usually it shares on the left a common root with the apical lobes, whereas on the right it is completely separate.

The lobus impar presents no unusual peculiarity.

Pleura.—According to Ruge (1892) the level of reflection of parietal pleura from vertebral to diaphragmatic surfaces extends caudally to a variable extent, but commonly beyond the last thoracic vertebra by the extent of one or even two vertebral bodies, as is commonly the case with species bearing greater numbers of thoracic vertebrae than the Hominoidea.

The retrosternal line of reflection (Ruge, Tanja, 1891) from the level of the second or third costal cartilage as far as the xiphoid in the costo-mediastinal sinus is almost in the median line, the left and right sacs being contiguous (see also Hayek, 1960). In *C. mona* from the xiphoid the line of reflection follows the eighth rib laterally along the diaphragmatic attachment and thence to the dorsal line of reflection crossing all the more posterior ribs in turn, crossing the tenth rib in the mid-axillary line.

URINARY TRACT

The two kidneys vary in size, absolute weights for the organs in *C. aethiops matschei* (=*ellenbecki*) being recorded by Frick (1957) as varying between 15 and 28·5 gms., while the ratio to gross body-weight ranges between 2·76 and 6·29.

In form the kidneys are of the long, narrow type (in an adult ♀ *C. cephus* 36 mm. long, 16 mm. broad and 12 mm. dorso-ventrally). They lie relatively close together, their medial margins separated only by the width of the great vessels. The right is located somewhat craniad of the left, more so in the foetus than in the juvenile. The cranial pole is relatively pointed, the caudal broader and more rounded. The dorsal aspect is relatively flat and the ventral facetted by neighbouring viscera. Medial margins are relatively straight and the hilum a little indented, facing somewhat dorsad. The adrenal is in contact bilaterally with the corresponding kidney at the cranial pole and along the medial margin.

Among eight kidneys examined by Straus (1934, 1958) five showed medullae of his type C (a single primary pyramid with undivided apex), two had type A pyramids (single pyramid ending in a flattened or concave shelf or ledge), while a single medulla bore a type D pyramid which resembles type C but with the papilla subdivided apically into two or more false papillae. I have encountered type C pyramids in *C. petaurista*, *C. ascanius*, *C. cephus* and *C. preussi*, and type D in *C. campbelli*. Columns of Bertin proceed medially from cortex into medulla and, in coronal sections, give a spurious suggestion of multiple pyramids.

Ureters commence in a dorso-ventrally flattened pelvis of triangular outline which branches into two (cranial and caudal) major calyces within the kidney. The abdominal part of the tube is thick-walled, and about 1 mm. in external diameter. The lining is longitudinally folded, the folds diverging radially on entering the renal pelvis. The duct takes the usual course retroperitoneally along the psoas muscles to open into the dorsal or dorso-lateral aspect of the urinary bladder near its neck some 14 mm. apart from each other.

Urinary Bladder.—This is a pyriform sac of which the fundus, comprising the cranial half of the collapsed organ, is located cranial to the anterior border of the pubic bone. Approximately the same part of the organ is clothed with peritoneum. There is no mesocyst, and the urachus leaves no remnant in adults.

Internally the lining is relatively smooth, and shows little difference in the area of the trigone. This is formed by the part of the bladder wall circumscribed by the ureteric openings and the internal urethral meatus. The former are very close together (not more than 5 mm.) on account of the lengthy (9 mm.) oblique intramural course of the ureters. Their openings are very oblique, with slightly raised lips, giving a valvular character. No raised inter-ureteric bar is indicated, but the lateral borders of the trigone are indicated by veins running in the submucosa.

Urethra.—In the male this is divisible into prostatic, membranous, bulbar and penile sections. In *C. ascanius* it is recognized by its bluish colour, due to engorgement of the surrounding veins and erectile tissue. The prostatic portion, 14 mm. long, passes entirely ventral to the prostate, lying in a groove on the gland. The membranous portion (12 mm. long) is thick-walled, being surrounded in its distal portion by a compressor or sphincter muscle. Dorsally it is related to the bulbo-urethral glands. The bulbar section, 12 mm. long, is surrounded by a large mass of erectile tissue, and this in turn is clothed with a thick layer of striped muscle (bulbo-cavernosus). A short section of the duct intervenes between the end of the bulbo-cavernosus and the ischio-cavernosi. Within these the urethra is continued distally as a cylindrical structure embedded in the erectile tissue of the corpus spongiosum. This occupies a deep groove on the perineal aspect of the corpus cavernosum penis and carries the urethra into the glans, to open in the floor of the meatal cleft as described under external characters. The total length of the penile urethra (excluding the bulbar portion) in an adult *C. a. ascanius* is 64 mm., of which 6 mm. occupies the glans, 58 mm. the corpus spongiosum. The keeled portion of the pars intrapreputialis corporis penis is formed by the corpus spongiosum and occupies the retroglandic 16 mm. of the tube.

Internally the prostatic urethra presents a well-marked low, smooth-topped conical elevation, the verumontanum, which bears the utriculus masculinius and openings of the ejaculatory ducts. It is flanked by deep grooves into which open the ducts from the prostate.

REPRODUCTIVE SYSTEM

MALE GENITAL ORGANS.—Testes are fully scrotal in adults, but varying degrees of parapenial or postpenial positions occur according to age and even emotion—due to the retractibility endowed by the powerful cremaster muscles.

The testes are relatively smaller than in macaques and baboons. In a well-nourished adult male *C. ascanius ascanius* of body-weight 5356 gms. the testes (with epididymides) weighed 3 gms., giving a ratio of 1/1785 (=0·036 per cent), compared with an average of 0·668 for 12 *Macaca irus* recorded by Schultz (1938). Testes, with epididymis, measured 20 mm. from pole to pole, 15 mm. dorso-ventrally and 10 mm. transversely. Testis alone measured 16·5 mm. between its poles. The gonad lies in a saccus vaginalis of some considerable extent ; it remains open as far as the external abdominal ring. Attachment by a mesentery-like fold is to the dorsal wall of the sac, extending caudally to the cauda epididymidis, where a firm fibrous connection to the fundus of the sac is attained.

The epididymis is somewhat triangular in section, presenting a broad, flattened dorso-lateral surface, and a shorter, more rounded dorso-medial surface. The ventral surface is applied to the testis, there being no sinus epididymidis. There is little enlargement at caput or cauda, the latter being slightly the larger of the two, and, with the adjoining convoluted portion of the ductus deferens, more readily separable from the corpus testis than the rest of the epididymis. The axis of the epididymis pursues a some-what sinuous course, the caput lying rather more laterad than the cauda.

The epididymis is slightly lobulated from the convolutions of its duct system and yellowish in colour in contrast to the opaque white of the tunica albuginea of the testis.

The ductus deferens commences on the medial side of the cauda epididymidis and ascends along the medial border of the corpus, becoming detached about midway along the corpus.

Hydatids of Morgagni have been recorded by Zuckerman and Krohn (1937) in *C. sabaeus*.

The ductus deferens takes the usual course, firstly within the mesepididymis and then in the mesentery shared with the spermatic vessels within

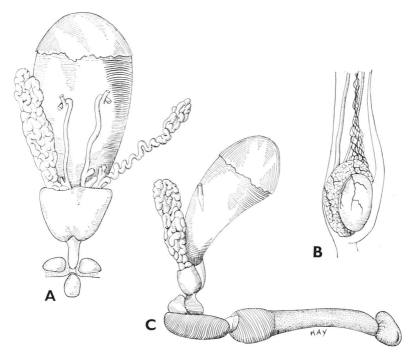

FIG. 53.—*C. ascanius ascanius*. Internal genitalia. A, from the dorsal aspect ; B, left testis from the medial side ; C, from the right lateral aspect

the spermatic cord ; thereafter in the inguinal canal and pelvis. The duct unites with that from the seminal vesicle to form the ejaculatory duct at the neck of the bladder near the cranial edge of the prostate, passing through the last-named gland to open on either side of the utriculus masculinus on the colliculus seminalis (verumontanum) within the prostatic urethra. The first part (some 15 mm.) of the ductus deferens is convoluted, the coils being closely packed. There is no distinct ampulla where the ductus joins the duct of the seminal vesicle, but a ventro-lateral diverticulum, 4 mm. long, is present at this site.

Seminal vesicles vary in size according to age and reproductive condition.

z

In fully mature males they attain a length of 30 mm., width 6 mm. and dorso-ventral diameter of 8 mm. Each consists mainly of a single unbranched highly convoluted tube, its coils close packed into a compact fusiform mass and held together by connective tissue—containing vessels—including a rich venous plexus. The apex of the gland is not formed by the end of the tube, the latter being folded over among other coils. At the attached end, however, is a small mass of coils constituted by an accessory tube folded into the angle formed by the main mass—the ductus deferens and the base of the prostate—and largely hidden by the raised dorsal margin of the latter. The

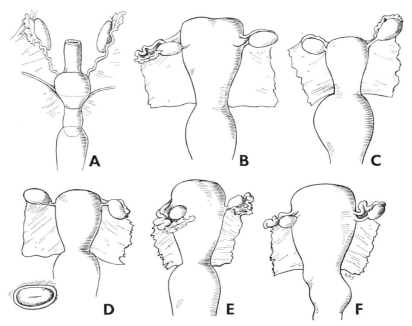

Fig. 54.—*Cercopithecus* spp. Series of uteri and appendages viewed from the dorsal aspect. All ×¼. A, *C. preussi*; B, *C. cephus*; C, *C. nictitans martini* (juvenile); D, *C. diana*; E, *C. albogularis kolbi*; F, *C. mitis stuhlmanni*. Inset of D shows the cervix from the vaginal aspect.

duct of the seminal vesicle is wide and smooth, with a different texture from the secreting coils.

The prostate is a firm mass forming a three-sided pyramid. In the adult *C. ascanius* it measures 14 mm. transversely, 13 mm. cranio-caudally and 8 mm. dorso-ventrally. The dorsal aspect is flat, the two ventro-lateral surfaces convex, with the ventral aspect grooved by the prostatic urethra. The base is concave, due to the uprising of the proximal margin of the dorsal surface, the concavity being occupied by the roots of the seminal vesicles and adjacent structures. The apex is rounded (*vide* fig. 53). The utriculus in *C. mona*, according to Zuckerman and Parkes (1935), resembles that of *Macaca*, with an exceptionally well-marked fibrous capsule separating it from the prostatic tissue and from the ejaculatory ducts. Glandular offshoots from the T-shaped lumen are more conspicuous than in *Macaca*. In *C. pygerythrus* the glands are branched and tubular, while the histological structure of the utriculus is markedly " uterine " in appearance.

Bulbo-urethral glands are well developed, of compressed pyramidal form, resting upon the dorsal aspect of the bulbus urethrae with their apices directed peripherally. Each is, in *C. ascanius*, 8 mm. long, 6 mm. wide across the base and 3·5 mm. in the opposite dimension. The duct perforates the dense fascia overlying the bulb to open into the lateral wall of the bulbar section of the urethra.

Within the glans penis a well-developed baculum is invariably present. In *C. neglectus* the bone is 18 mm. long, laterally compressed, with a fusiform apex separated by a constricted region from the more rounded proximal end. In *C. mitis stuhlmanni* a baculum of 11·5 mm. was found but in *C. mona* the bone attained 23·7 mm. Pohl (1928) figures the baculum in *C. mona, C. cephus* and *C. neglectus*.

FEMALE GENITAL ORGANS.—The ovary varies in shape from ovoid to globular, but occasionally, as in a *C. preussi* examined, it is prismatic. In size, variations occur according to age, the organ being relatively larger in young animals (see table 16). At no stage is the ovary as large

TABLE 16

DIMENSIONS (IN MILLIMETRES) OF FEMALE GENITALIA
IN *CERCOPITHECUS*

Species	Age and Reproductive Condition where known	Ovary		Uterus				Vagina
		Length	Breadth	Total Length	Length of Cervix	Breadth	Dorso-ventrally	Length
. erythrotis sclateri	Immature	10·0	6·5	19	10·0	9·0	4	35
. preussi	+6 years ; nonparous	11·5	6·0	19	9·0	17·0	6	27
. diana	Subadult	9·0	7·0	28	17·0	15·0	9	—
. sabaeus	,,	8·5	5·0	24	12·0	14·0	5	33
. nictitans martini	Prepubertal	10·0	6·0	31	17·0	12·0	10	45
. cephus	+13 years ; nonparous	8·0	6·0	45	15·0	23·0	14	—
. albogularis kolbi	adult ; primiparous	8·0	6·0	43	21·0	20·0	17	33
. mitis stuhlmanni	adult ; multiparous	8·0	7·0	44	25·0	26·0	13	44
. neglectus	adult ; nonparous	20·0	9·0	31	15·0	12·0	6	45
. ascanius schmidti	adult	12·5	6·5	32	13·5	13·5	12	40

proportionately as in cebid genera. All the specimens examined have been smooth-surfaced. The ovary is attached to the dorsal aspect of the broad ligament by an extremely short mesovarium. It is overshadowed cranially by a hood-like fold derived from the anterior mesosalpinx, and this is connected laterally to the ovarian fimbria of the uterine tube. The organ tends towards a sagittal orientation, its cranial pole being drawn forwards by the long ovario-pelvic ligament. The caudal pole is connected to the side of the uterus by a short, stout outstanding utero-ovarian ligament.

In table 16 are given dimensions of the ovary and parts of the genital tract in a representative series of cercopithèques.

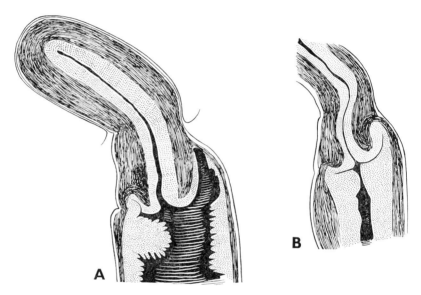

Fig. 55.—Median sagittal sections of the uterus in
A, *Cercopithecus nictitans martini*, subadult ; B, *C. mitis stuhlmanni*, adult

Uterine Tube.—This is thick-walled, highly convoluted and terminates laterally in an elliptical infundibulum provided with numerous fimbriae, of which two, the uterine and ovarian, are greatly elongated. The tube is also provided with an anterior mesosalpinx which expands to form a hood over the anterior border of the ovary. At its uterine end the tube narrows considerably to an isthmus before penetrating the uterine wall. The intramural portion measures 6 mm. long in a multiparous *C. albogularis kolbi*.

The *uterus* is a median pyriform thick-walled structure sometimes asymmetrically placed, either tilted or twisted to one side, or anteverted and antiflexed, or both. The fundus is commonly globular, smoothly rounded, without trace of median notch ; but in a *C. cephus* it was flat-topped with rectangular lateral angles. The cavity of the corpus uteri has a triangular form, with dorsal and ventral walls. The cylindrical cervix forms a large and massive proportion of the total organ, even in the adult, but especially so in prepubertal animals (see table 16). But it lacks internally the specializations seen in the uterus of *Macaca*, the cervical canal being a simple fusiform passage, narrowed at its ends (internal and external os). In the juvenile the canal is occluded by epithelium which breaks down only at puberty. The caudal end of the cervix is telescoped into the vaginal lumen as in Man, producing a shallow ventral and deep dorsal fornix. The external os is a transverse slit, with the dorsal lip thicker than the ventral.

Vagina.—This is thick-walled and muscular, the muscular layer being continuous at the fornices with that in the cervix. The caudal end widens to a funnel-like vestibule into the ventral wall, which the urethra opens upon a small elevation (caruncle). The lining is highly keratinized, but varies in appearance with age and phases of the sexual cycle. In a prepubertal *C. nictitans* the lining is beset with closely aggregated conical horny papillae, which are specially well developed, adjacent to the fornices. One patch, neighbouring the ventral fornix, is specially raised to form a kind of cushion. On the contrary, in older animals the horny papillae are less evident and more flat-topped, with a tendency to be arranged in longitudinal columns. In *C. sabaeus* Zuckerman (1938) found the vaginal canal imperforate before puberty, but in quite juvenile examples of *C. petaurista* I found a canalized vagina.

Mammary Glands.—In a juvenile *C. mona* the nipple is located at the hinder part of the third intercostal space adjacent to the costa-chondral junction of the fourth rib. Zuckerman (1932) examined a series of mammary glands of *C. sabaeus* in different functional stages, comparing their condition with that of the ovaries. Apparently size alone is no criterion of functional state, which can be judged only by the degree of expansion of the secretory alveoli. Body-weight moreover is not a good criterion of reproductive maturity. In a specimen apparently lactating up to a short time before death the glandular tissue measured 50 by 64 mm. On the other hand, in a slightly expanded gland from a presumed nullipara a diameter of 73×79 mm. was recorded.

Ductless Glands

Spleen.—Daubenton (1764) described the spleen of *C. sabaeus* as almost pointed dorsally and very broad ventrally, imparting a triangular form to the viscus. Retterer and Neuville (1916) state that in *Cercopithecus* the organ resembles that of *Macaca*, being distinctly pyramidal; its ventral border is notched in the middle and the renal facet 1 cm. wide. The hilum lies at the junction of gastric and renal facets. Krogh (1936) illustrates three spleens of *C. cephus* showing a strongly incurved dorsal margin and a caudal beak-like process; the breadth almost equals the length. I have found a notched inferior pole. In an adult ♀ *C. erythrogaster* the spleen is a compressed pyramid. Its triangular parietal aspect has a dorsal border 28 mm. long; ventral 34 mm. (slightly notched at cranial pole); caudal border 24·5 mm.

Hypophysis.—This has been studied by Köhne (1944) and Hanström (1948, 1952, 1958). A collar round the infundibulum formed by pars tuberalis is recorded in *C. cephus*. In the same species the pars intermedia covers only the rostral (or rostral and ventral) aspects of the processus infundibuli. The hypophyseal cleft may or may not persist (Köhne). In *C. sabaeus* and *C. pygerythrus cynosuros* Hanström found the pars tuberalis weakly developed and not forming a collar around the pituitary stalk. Pars intermedia is normal in arrangement and does not extend to the dorsal surface of the processus infundibuli. It is intimately fused in front with the pars distalis, with remnants of the cleft transformed into Rathke's cysts. These are occupied by azan blue staining, colloid containing cells, which have migrated from both pars distalis and pars intermedia. In a wild-caught Malbrouck, Hanström found no zona tuberalis and a pars intermedia of peculiar shape, forming caudally a double fold surrounding more than half the ventral aspect of the processus infundibuli, only the dorsal aspect being free. Local invasions of intermedia cells into the processus are reported.

Thyroid.—Usually cosisting of two separate lateral lobes. Connection by an isthmus is rare and may be merely by a ligamentous strand or two such bands. In a *C. petaurista* the right gland was bifurcated caudally. Forsyth (1910) found several variations in nature and position of these isthmic structures in *C. aethiops* and its relatives (summarized by Pischinger, 1937 and Bargmann, 1958). Accessory thyroid bodies have been noted by Forsyth (1910).

Parathyroids.—Forsyth (1908) found in three examples of *Cercopithecus sabaeus* individual differences in numbers and locations of parathyroids. In one a single parathyroid was found embedded in the thyroid; another had eight parathyroids, two on the right, three on the left and three in the adjacent connective tissues, together with an accessory thyroid. A third had three accessory thyroids, one on the right, two on the left, one of the latter associated with a parathyroid.

Thymus.—In a juvenile *C. petaurista buttikoferi* (body-length 218 mm.) the thymus is a yellowish, lobulated mass, 25 mm. long, lying deep to the manubrium sterni and extending caudally over the pericardium as far as the fourth costal cartilage on the left, rather less on the right. On the right, however, a few cervical lobules, slightly more independent than the rest, project craniad, dorsal to the sterno-clavicular joint.

Adrenals.—Those of an adult male *C. aethiops* have been figured by Bachmann (1958) based upon a preparation by Starck, but no specific description is provided.

Meckel (1806) gave the earliest description of the glands in a *C. mona*, where he found them to be small in comparison with kidney and body as a whole, being very flat (2·1 mm. thick) with rounded contours. This is certainly the case with adults, where the left gland has a triangular outline with rounded apex, while the right is more elongated cranio-caudally and presents a more acute apex, partly hidden by the vena cava. Both glands are dorso-ventrally flattened and present wrinkled surfaces. In the foetus and newborn and for some considerable time postnatally the glands are relatively much larger. Thus, in a newborn *C. aethiops* (crown-rump 167 mm.; wt. 230 g.) with left kidney length of 15 mm., the base of the corresponding adrenal is 10 mm. broad; furthermore the gland is not as flat as in the adult, presenting a bloated appearance and a smooth surface. Moreover, it is highly vascular, with numerous arteries entering the cortex from the aorta and from the renal artery, while the single large emergent vein drains from the ventral hilum into the adjacent renal vein. Similar findings were confirmed in a foetal *C. mona* of 113 mm. CR length (renal length 14 mm.; adrenal breadth 8 mm.).

In an adult female *C. albogularis kolbi* the cortex is thicker ventrally than dorsally. Zona glomerulosa is composed of short columns of small, darkly staining cells continued deeply into the broader columns of the zona fasciculata. A narrow zona reticularis is present. Medulla reaches the surface over a limited area at the hilum along the wall of the emergent vein. In *C. sabaeus* Kohno (1925, quoted by Bourne, 1949) found, in some parts of the zona glomerulosa, small cavities lined by a single cell layer and occupied in life by serum. There is no cortico-medullary band of connective tissue. Medullary cells are small and many are binucleate; some have their nuclei almost completely filled with an enormous nucleolus.

ANGEIOLOGY

HEART AND PERICARDIUM

The fibrous pericardium is a broad, fusiform bag which has no direct relation to the diaphragm, being merely tethered thereto by the long intra-thoracic part of the postcaval vein and by bilaminar folds of pleura derived from the two pleural sacs, including those associated with the infracardiac lobe of the right lung. Ventrally it is tethered by a mesentery-like structure resulting from the mid-sternal apposition of the right and left pleurae (*antea*, p. 90). Both diaphragmatic and sterno-costal aspects of the heart are therefore ensheathed by fibrous pericardium. The pericardium narrows cranially and fuses over the great vessels to become part of the anterior mediastinum. Phrenic nerves course along its surface each side beneath the pleural covering.

Serous pericardium clothes the greater part of the cardiac surface and the inner surface of the fibrous pericardium. The two are continuous (*a*) along a mesentery-like fold connecting the perforations caused by the anterior and posterior caval veins ; this includes, caudal to the anterior caval opening, the mouths of the two right pulmonary veins from which a short serous attachment extends leftwards to enclose the two left pulmonary veins. Thereby a short, shallow oblique pericardial sinus is outlined, opening caudally. (b) Cranial to the afore-mentioned transverse fold is a narrow transverse sinus separating the venous reflection from the arterial. The arterial reflection (arterial mesocardium) encloses the ascending aorta and the pulmonary artery as far as its bifurcation. The ventral wall of the transverse sinus is a broad bilaminar fold of serous pericardium with connective tissue between the two layers. It connects the venous and arterial mesocardia. From the ventral surface a frenal fold bridges the angle between parietal and visceral layers of serous pericardium at the interval between anterior vena cava and aortic trunk.

Data relating to size relations of the heart in *Cercopithecus* have been published by Frick (1957, 1960).

In accordance with the narrow, elongated form of the thorax, the heart itself is a narrow, elongated oval in shape. The apex is not conspicuous or acute, but is directed somewhat to the left, the long axis of the heart making an angle of only 20° with the median sagittal plane. The apex lies opposite the anterior part of the fifth left intercostal space about 1 cm. from the median line.

The heart presents dorsal and ventral aspects which unite at the right and left borders. Both aspects are convex, the dorsal only slightly, the ventral strongly. The borders are both rounded, but the so-called margo acutus less sharply indicated than the margo obtusus. The ventral aspect is composed almost entirely of right ventricle, with about a quarter by right atrium, at the base. A narrow strip of left ventricle occupies the apex ventrally, but narrows further cranially, leaving the ventral surface entirely about half-way along the left margin. The dorsal aspect is formed by left ventricle and root of aorta, with a lappet of left atrium to the right of the aorta basally. The right surface (or base) is a quadrangular area formed by the atrial chambers and a small part of the rounded base of the left ventricle.

Myocardial structure and arrangement in *Cercopithecus* have been studied intensively by Marit (1960). Three fundamental strata of fibres are recognized in the ventricular walls, a deep system of longitudinal fibres derived from the fibres of the tubular stage of the embryonic heart, a middle zone of more or less annular fibres and a thin superficial layer developed independently of the two preceding. These include the vortex fibres at the apex, continued basally into an elongated S-arrangement. They appear to penetrate and become continuous with fibres of the deep system. A hiatus appears at the apex of the right ventricle where superficial fibres are absent and the middle layer is covered only by epicardium. The superficial layer is thicker over the pulmonary infundibulum and over the dorsal aspect of the ventricles. Some fibres (parieto-septal) enter the septum.

The middle stratum is derived from the circular fibres of the embryonic heart-tube. Three main bundles are distinguishable, left and right parietal and parieto-septal. The deep, or longitudinal layer, comprises many bundles of which the chief are (a) infundibular—a thin structure situated at the junction of the infundibulum and the right ventricle proper, and the only bundle which extends from the right atrio-ventricular ring to the pulmonary ring without a relay at the apex—a primitive feature; (b) bundle of the " bandelette ansiform "—connects the apex with the pulmonary ring; (c) and (d) fascicles of the right dorsal and ventral papillary muscles; (e) fascicle of the aortic ring (occupying the deeper layers anteriorly of the left ventricular wall); (f) and (g) bundles of the left dorsal and ventral papillary muscles.

For further details of the courses and relations of these bundles, Marit's work should be consulted.

Fibres of the conducting system have been referred to by Bortolami and Callegari (1957). They found no Purkinje cells. The well-differentiated Tawara's node agreed in position and structure with that in *Semnopithecus entellus*. It lies on the postero-inferior part of the interatrial septum immediately above the dorsal point of insertion of the aortic cusp of the mitral valve. In section it has the form of an isosceles triangle with the apex ventrad and the base dorsad. From its apex the crus commune proceeds into the thickness of the interventricular septum, but undergoes further increment immediately prior to its bifurcation. The two branches course subendocardially directly towards the cardiac apex.

Internally the right atrium exhibits the usual structural formations, a well-defined fossa ovalis medially with its cranial margin more outstanding than the rest; a large Eustachian valve at the dorso-lateral side of the postcaval opening. The free margin of this valve is prolonged medially and bifurcates to enclose a cleft-like depression into which opens the coronary sinus ventro-caudal to the fossa ovalis. The dorsal lip of the cleft is thicker than the ventral, which is a low, delicate membrane. The oval atrioventricular opening lies ventrally; cranial to this, a semilunar passage leads into the capacious atrial appendage. A broad, low crista terminalis is well defined, but musculi pectinati are weakly developed. In the heart of a juvenile female *C. campbelli* a long (4 mm.) thin columna carnea connected the roof of the atrium with the medial (septal) wall commencing near the ventral edge of the opening of the anterior vena cava and ending near the dorsal end of the atrio-ventricular opening. Presumably this consists of conducting tissue associated with the sino-atrial node or connecting this with the atrio-ventricular node. A short distance from its origin this strand gives off a slender retaining tendon which attaches to the septal wall ventral to the insertion of the parent column.

In the right ventricle of the same heart four papillary muscles were found, a single ventral and three on the septal wall. Of these the most dorsal has two roots, one on the lateral wall and the other septal, uniting in an inverted Y-formation, supplying chordeae to the lateral and septal cusps of the tricuspid valve. The central septal muscle (m. papillaris proprius septalis) is longer, matching the ventral or parietal pillar, the two together supplying chordeae to the ventral cusp. The third and most ventral (m. papillaris subarterialis) arises high up on the septal wall and is very short, soon breaking up into chordeae supplying the ventral and septal cusps of the tricuspid valve.

The ventral and central septal cusps are both elongated, slender columns. No moderator band was found. The arrangement is probably an individual one, as Frick (1960) found considerable variation in the papillary muscles among all cynomorphs, particularly baboons. Cusps of the pulmonary valve are arranged one ventrally and two dorsally.

The left heart shows little out of the ordinary. The ventricle has two short, thick papillary muscles, dorsal and ventral, each supplying chordeae to both cusps of the mitral valve. The aortic cusps are arranged two ventrally and one dorsally. The left atrium is for the most part smooth walled. Its appendage is roomy and demarcated by the thick base of the ventricle, covered by smooth endocardium, from the atrio-ventricular opening. Four pulmonary veins, two from each side, open separately into the body of the atrium.

CORONARY VESSELS

The left coronary artery, a short, wide stem, gives from its root the ventral interventricular artery and a dorsally directed atrial vessel which, in the deep atrio-ventricular sulcus, divides into branches to the ventral and lateral walls of the left atrial appendage. The parent stem thereafter bifurcates into circumflex and left marginal arteries. This corresponds to Chase and de Garis' (1939) second, less usual, category for *Macaca* (*vide antea* p. 91).

The right coronary gives off first a large ramus infundibularis, then a branch to the ventral surface of the right ventricle. The trunk continues thereafter deeply in the auriculo-ventricular groove, supplying a large right marginal branch and then gains the crux. Here it gives cranially an atrial branch, a branch to the interventricular septum and a descending interventricular, the circumflex not gaining the crux.

Aorta and Branches.—As found by Keith (1895), the usual pattern of branching from the arch in *Cercopithecus* corresponds to his type B, *i.e.* two branches (innominate and left subclavian) with the former dividing into right common carotid and brachiocephalic (which bifurcates to give right subclavian and right common carotid). The origin of the left subclavian, however, is very close to that of the innominate and maybe from the angle between the arch and the root of the innominate (type A), *e.g.* in *C. petaurista buttikoferi* and as Keith found in some examples of *Presbytis*.

The common carotids take a straight unbranched course as far as the neck of the mandible. Here the internal carotid continues the main trunk after a bend medially. At the point of bifurcation all the main branches derived from the external carotid appear at once, so that virtually no external carotid exists. This, at any rate, is the condition encountered in *C. neglectus* and *C. mona*. What would nor-mally comprise the external caro-tid is a T-shaped bifurcation of which the anterior (or ventral) limb forms a common trunk from which derive the superior thyroid, facial and lingual arteries. The dorsal or posterior limb forms a trunk which proceeds obliquely backwards and provides the pos-terior auricular, superficial tempo-ral and internal maxillary arteries.

The superior thyroid takes at once a recurrent course and, after supplying branches along both margins of the gland, continues obliquely caudo-medially to end in supplying the laryngeal air sac and infrahyoid muscles, accom-

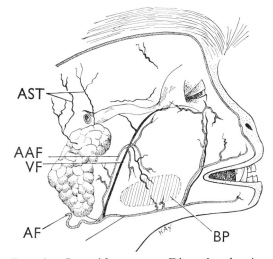

Fig. 56.—*Cercopithecus mona*. Dissection showing branches of the facial artery

AF, facial artery ; *AAF*, ascending branch of facial artery ; *AST*, superficial temporal arteries ; *BP*, location of neck of buccal pouch ; *VF*, facial vein

panying the descendens hypoglossi. The facial is a large vessel with a circuitous course. Descending at first medial to the inner pterygoid muscle, it becomes involved among the lobules of the submandibular salivary gland, supplying a large branch to its hilum. Emerging therefrom, it skirts round the border of the mandible, dividing there into an ascending and a submandibular branch. These two embrace the neck of the buccal pouch, the former giving branches to its lateral wall and the latter supplying long twigs to its medial wall. From the submandibular division a stem ascends obliquely to the angle of the mouth, where it divides into a superior labial and an angular branch, the latter being directed towards the medial palpebral canthus. The lower lip and chin are supplied by rami from the submandibular. The ascending terminal branch of the facial proceeds along the anterior border of the masseter, accompanying the facial vein. Its target is the lateral palpebral canthus, but anastomotic twigs unite it with the terminal rami of the other division within the lower eyelid. Communica-tions are also established with the infraorbital artery. Twigs are given dorsally to the parotid and masseter. This, judged from Tokarski's (1931, 1935–36) conclusions, is an advanced pattern of distribution of the facial artery—and is doubtless to be correlated with the advanced degree of differentiation of the facial musculature.

The lingual emerges deeply from a common stem with the facial and takes the usual course.

The posterior auricular proceeds through the substance of the parotid gland, to which it gives two large vertical descending branches and a number of smaller twigs. Thereafter it proceeds beneath the ear to the postauricular region supplying scalp and external ear. The superficial temporal proceeds through the same gland immediately in front of the ear, ending superficially over the temporal fascia and adjacent scalp. There is no conspicuous transverse facial branch. The internal maxillary turns medially deep to the neck of the mandible between the lateral and medial pterygoid muscles. It gives deep auricular and tympanic twigs, branches to both pterygoids and to the masseter, a large inferior dental (accompanying the corresponding nerve) and several deep temporal rami, some within and some deep to the temporalis muscle. The middle meningeal is also derived from the internal maxillary, after which the parent vessel may pass through an alar (alisphenoid) canal before proceeding into the orbit to become the infraorbital artery (as I found in *C. mona*). The internal carotid takes the usual course into the cranium and, after supplying hypophyseal branches, gives off the large ophthalmic artery, which accompanies the optic nerve on its deep side, into the orbit, where it divides into frontal and supraorbital arteries. A large lachrymal branch is given off laterally and from this slender ciliary branches accompany the long ciliary nerves. It also supplies the lateral rectus, but gives no recurrent meningeal branch. The other main branch which crosses over the optic nerve to gain the medial side of the orbit supplies the superior rectus, ethmoidal and medial ciliary vessels, and finally provides frontal, nasal and palpebral twigs.

Cerebral branches and circle of Willis are arranged as in other Cerco-pithecoidea (*antea*, p. 93).

Subclavian arteries take the usual course in relation to the scalenus muscles, the ventral muscle serving to divide the artery into three parts. First branch is the vertebral, which emerges at the medial border of the scalenus ventralis. Almost opposite, on the concave side, arises a short common stem which bifurcates into suprascapular and internal mammary arteries. The former provides the ascending cervical as it crosses the scalenus then proceeds parallel with the clavicle to the suprascapular notch after giving a series of radiating superficial branches over the shoulder and deltoid region and also a superficial cervical branch on the trapezius.

The internal mammary is a large vessel which provides ventral intercostal arteries and terminates by dividing into musculo-phrenic and anterior epigastric arteries. It also gives off a slender comes nervi phrenici. From the angle between the above-mentioned common trunk and the main subclavian there arises a very slender inferior thyroid artery and also the superior intercostal. The latter supplies the first intercostal space only. The former

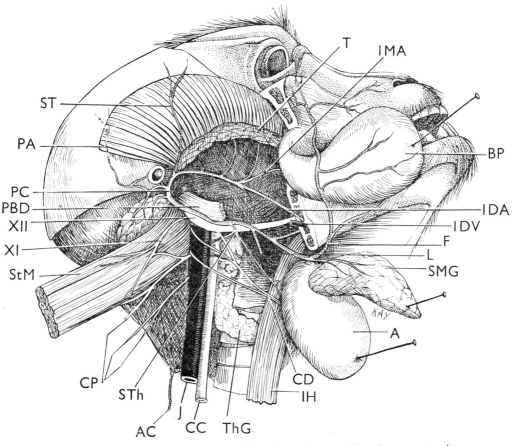

FIG. 57.—*Cercopithecus mona.* Deep dissection of pterygoid region, etc., to show arrangement of the branches of the carotid artery

A, air sac ; *AC,* ascending cervical artery ; *BP,* buccal pouch ; *CC,* common carotid ; *CD,* cervicalis descendens ; *CP,* cervical plexus ; *F,* facial artery ; *IDA,* inferior dental artery ; *IDV,* inferior dental vein ; *IH,* infrahyoid muscles ; *IMA,* internal maxillary artery ; *J,* internal jugular vein ; *L,* lingual artery ; *PA,* posterior auricular artery ; *PBD,* posterior belly of digastric ; *PC,* posterior branch of external carotid artery ; *SMG,* submandibular gland ; *ST,* superficial temporal artery ; *STh,* superior thyroid artery ; *StM,* sterno-mastoideus ; *T,* cut edge of temporal muscle ; *ThG,* thyroid gland

consists mainly of the inferior laryngeal, which accompanies the recurrent laryngeal nerve, but it also provides a transverse branch which passes deep to the common carotid and the trachea. From the main stem arise also tracheal and oesophageal twigs and some terminal glandular filaments which anastomose with those from the superior thyroid. This artery may arise from the common carotid as, *e.g.* in a *C. mona* I examined—an arrangement previously recorded by Theile (1852) in *Macaca sylvana*. An a. transversus colli seems to be lacking.

The axillary artery continues the subclavian. It is closely related to the brachial plexus, lying on the ventral face of C.7 and C.8. A branch is given off dorsally into the angle of junction between these two nerves. Manners-Smith (1912) found in *C. sabaeus* the lateral thoracic as the first branch from the axillary; this supplies branches to the pectoral muscles and then courses along the chest wall. A little below this is a branch to the subscapularis. At the caudal border of the last muscle a short trunk is given from which are derived the anterior humeral circumflex (double in most of its course), posterior humeral circumflex and subscapular arteries. The posterior circumflex is distributed as in Man; the a. subscapularis provides a large circumflex scapular branch, which passes into the triangular space and proceeds between teres major and teres minor to be distributed over the caudal part of the infraspinous fossa. In a *C. mona* there was an acromio-thoracic branch supplying the area over the shoulder joint. The lateral thoracic was as described by Manners-Smith, with very large pectoral branches. The anterior humeral circumflex arose independently, distal to the common origin of the posterior circumflex and subscapular.

The brachial artery in *C. sabaeus*, according to Manners-Smith, gives off a brachialis superficialis just beyond the middle of the brachium; this passes immediately over the median nerve. More proximally, the brachialis gives a branch which divides into brachialis profunda and an a. collateralis ulnaris superior. The former follows the radial nerve and is used up in supplying the triceps. The latter follows the ulnar nerve, but sends a branch to the triceps. A muscular branch from brachialis supplies the biceps. Inferior ulnar collateral is also derived from the brachial. I found a precisely similar arrangement in *C. mona*, except that here the large inferior ulnar collateral was derived from the brachialis superficialis, which afterwards passed to the flexor aspect of the forearm. In a *C. sabaeus*, Müller (1904) found the brachialis superficialis and brachialis profunda formed at the beginning of the arm by bifurcation of the axillary. The former ran superficial to the median nerve and after providing an a. antebrachii superficialis volaris and a. radialis recurrens, proceeded in the radial groove accompanying the distal part of the musculo-cutaneous nerve. The deep brachial continued deeply to the antecubital fossa, where it furnished firstly the ulnar artery, then the dorsal interosseous, dividing finally into a short comes nervi mediani and a volar interosseous.

In the forearm the brachialis, in *C. sabaeus*, according to Manners-Smith, gives the dorsal ulnar recurrent, ulnar, and two interosseous arteries, volar and dorsal separately. A large comes nervi mediani is furnished by the volar interosseous. Other branches of volar and dorsal interossei are as in Man. The superficial volar arch is formed of approximately equal contributions from radial and ulnar arteries. The arch provides a digital vessel to the ulnar side of the pollex, and others to the clefts between III and IV, and IV and V.

Brachialis superficialis meanwhile gives a branch to the front of the medial epicondyle, then continues as the radial—a condition also present in *C. mona*. After supplying muscular branches, the radialis divides distal to the middle of the forearm into dorsal and volar terminal stems. The volar runs as superficial volar to the hand to share in formation of the superficial palmar arch. The dorsal branch proceeds beneath the extensor tendons of the thumb, gives a slender dorsalis pollicis, a dorsalis indicis and a ramus carpeus dorsalis. Rami perforantes are provided for the first two inter-metacarpal spaces, and a finer one for the third space. There is also an a. metacarpea dorsalis for the second space.

A deep palmar arch is present, but very fine, providing aa. metacarpeae volares to the third and fourth spaces. In *C. mona* no deep palmar arch is formed, the deep branch of the ulnar ending in radiating rami at the wrist. One of these contributes to a powerful volar carpal arch derived mainly from the radial. The superficial arch also was incomplete; most of the digits being supplied from the superficial volar branch of the radial, the superficial branch of the ulnar being taken up mainly in supplying the hypothenar muscles.

The thoracic aorta begins at the level of the third thoracic vertebra. Intercostal arteries are furnished to the spaces between the ribs from the second onwards. These arise in a longitudinal series somewhat to the right of the median dorsal line of the aorta, each pair from a common stem. Adjacent to the origin of the common stem of the second pair arise the two bronchial arteries, one cranial and one caudal to the related common inter-costal. The thoracic aorta also supplies oesophageal branches from its ventral wall.

The abdominal aorta has the coeliac axis as its first visceral branch. This arises ventrally immediately the aorta has passed the diaphragm and may, as in *C. aethiops*, incorporate the anterior mesenteric. Alternatively the latter may spring from the angle between the origin of the coeliac and the aorta, as I found in a *C. diana roloway*. The coeliac branches in the usual way into left gastric, hepatic and splenic arteries. The first-mentioned supplies the lesser curvature of the stomach. In *C. albogularis* it gains the lesser curvature half-way along its length, then bifurcates, sending one branch to the cardia and one to the pylorus. The hepatic gives the gastroduodenal artery and a pyloric branch before proceeding to the liver within the lesser omentum. The splenic courses along the cranial border of the pancreas, supplying small glandular branches, then enters the spleen. Immediately before doing so, it furnishes gastric branches to the fundus.

The anterior mesenteric crosses the duodenum to enter the mesentery.

After providing the posterior pancreatico-duodenal in the concavity of the duodenum, it is directed towards the ileo-caecal region, giving off rami intestini tenuis on the left and a right colic branch on the right. The main vessel is continued as the ileo-colic which, after providing anastomotic arches with the most distal ramus intestini tenuis, and with the right colic, bifurcates into dorsal and ventral caecal arteries of almost equal proportions. The dorsal artery provides a recurrent ileal vessel, which supplies the anti-mesenteric border of the terminal ileum.

From the sides of the aorta lateral to the origins of the coeliac and anterior mesenteric arteries small twigs are delivered to the adrenals. These per-forate the coeliac ganglion to reach their destination. On the left, one of these supplies the inferior phrenic artery, which ascends on the left pillar of the diaphragm to reach the cupola. A separate right inferior phrenic arises directly from the aorta.

Paired renals arise a little caudal to the anterior mesenteric, the right slightly craniad of the left. Each supplies adrenal branches, while the left also gives the spermatic (or ovarian). The right spermatic springs directly from the aorta. A ureteric twig arises when the parent vessel reaches the renal hilum.

The posterior mesenteric arises from the ventral wall of the aorta some distance behind the renals. It courses backwards and to the left in the descending mesocolon, giving off half a dozen colic branches and then con-tinuing as the anterior haemorrhoidal (or rectal) artery. The colic branches bifurcate before reaching the gut, sending twigs to either side of the gut wall. Only the most cranial colic branch forms a loop with branches from the right colic in *C. petaurista* and *C. erythrotis*, but in *C. mona* all the branches are linked by loops.

Like the intercostals the segmental lumbar arteries arise in a series, but somewhat to the left of the median dorsal wall of the aorta. Each bifurcates into left and right lumbar, the right vessels proceeding dorsal to the post-caval vein to gain the appropriate intervertebral foramen.

The aortic bifurcation occurs at the hinder border of the last lumbar vertebra. The two common iliacs diverge at an angle of 40°. Each gives off an ilio-lumbar artery immediately after its origin, and after a course of some 10-15 mm. divides into internal and external iliac. The internal iliac provides a dorsal (gluteal) and ventral group of branches, the latter including vesical, uterine, obturator and pudendal arteries. According to Popowsky (1889) the gluteal runs dorsally, and enters the buttock cranial to the pyri-formis, ending by supplying the gluteal muscles. The obturator in *C. mona* arises from a long common stem which also provides the medial femoral circumflex. The latter accompanies the external iliac vessels, entering the thigh with them. Manners-Smith reports a similar origin in *C. diana*. The obturator proceeds more dorsally and enters the thigh through the obturator canal, ending in the adductor muscles. In a *C. nictitans* Popowsky found the uterine artery on the left side arising from the obturator.

In a female *C. mona* two sets of vesical arteries are present, the anterior, corresponding to the human superior vesical, is connected with the obliterated hypogastric. The caudal set is directed towards the neck of the bladder and is continued as the uterine artery. This anastomoses in the broad ligament with the corresponding ovarian artery.

The internal pudendal takes the same course as in Man, gaining the perineum via the buttock. Before leaving the pelvis it supplies the middle haemorrhoidal vessels, the posterior (inferior) ones branching from the perineal portion of the vessel. Other branches are a transverse perineal, bulbo-urethral and dorsalis penis (or clitoridis). Popowsky describes cross anastomoses between the two dorsalis penis arteries.

A sciatic artery has not been described for this genus.

The external iliac enters the thigh in the usual way after providing an inferior epigastric to the ventral abdominal wall. An external pudendal has been described by Popowsky as arising from the epigastric in *C. nictitans*. A similar vessel has been found by me from the first part of the femoral in *C. mona*. A deep circumflex iliac is the last branch from the external iliac.

From the first part of the femoral in *C. sabaeus* a common trunk gives rise to superficial epigastric and superficial circumflex iliac twigs. Manners-Smith mentions, in *C. sabaeus*, a small twig which enters the psoas magnus accompanying the femoral nerve. Next is given off deeply the lateral femoral circumflex. Bluntschli (1906) failed to find this, its area of distribution being replaced by branches of the profunda femoris. Popowsky, however, found it in *C. nictitans* and *C. sabaeus* arising independently from the femoral, while Manners Smith reported the same for *C. diana*. The vessel divides into ascending and transverse branches. Close to the origin of the lateral circumflex is that of the profunda femoris. This gives a descending branch corresponding to the ramus descendens of the human lateral circumflex; also numerous muscular branches to the adductors and a fine twig which anastomoses with the medial circumflex. The profunda ends as an arteria perforans—apparently the only perforating branch of this vessel—but a branch from the lower part of the femoral itself perforates the distal half of the adductor magnus.

At the knee, the femoral divides into aa. poplitea and saphena, the former being a continuation of the main vessel after its passage through the opening in the adductor magnus to the popliteal fossa. The saphena divides at the middle of the tibia into a superficial (dorsalis hallucis) and deep divisions (dorsalis pedis). The superficial division crosses the tibialis anterior and is distributed to the medial side of the hallux and the first interosseous space, sending also a communicating branch to the plantar arcade. This division also gives an a. malleolaris anterior medialis.

2 A

The deep division proceeds deep to the tibialis anterior and is continued distally as the dorsalis pedis, giving branches as in Man. It provides an a. malleolaris anterior lateralis, a. tarsea lateralis, and an a. arcuata, the latter (sometimes the former) vascularizing the third and fourth interosseous spaces. In *C. sabaeus* Manners-Smith found a communicating vessel connecting the superficial and deep divisions of the a. saphena in the foot. From this, branches are given to first and second interosseous spaces. Macdonald Brown (1881) in *C. campbelli* and Manners-Smith in *C. diana* found a perforating vessel from the dorsalis pedis in the second intermetatarsal interval communicating with the sole.

The popliteal is a large artery which recedes but little within the fossa, forming instead a gentle curve across the knee. In *C. sabaeus* it furnishes a single deep branch which divides into superior lateral articular, an a. genu media and an inferior medial articular, from which an intra-articular branch penetrates the joint-capsule posteriorly. The inferior lateral articular is derived from the superior lateral. A similar arrangement has been confirmed in *C. petaurista*. At the lower end of the fossa, between the gastrocnemii, the popliteal artery divides into anterior and posterior tibial arteries, of which the latter is the larger.

About 32 mm. beyond its origin the posterior tibial provides a large a. peronaea, leaving the parent vessel much reduced, coursing along the medial edge of the gastrocnemius to the ankle, where it divides into medial and lateral plantar arteries, after supplying some medial calcaneal twigs. The peroneal artery gains the lower third of the leg and is used up in supplying muscles. In *C. sabaeus*, Manners-Smith also reports a rudimentary posterior tibial derived from the a. saphena, ending in the back of the lower end of the tibia. In *C. diana*, the posterior tibial is entirely derived from the saphena, the poplitea providing only an a. peronaea and an anterior tibial artery.

In *C. petaurista* I found another branch of the posterior tibial coursing along the medial border of tibialis posterior. It ends on the medial malleolus in a number of branches, one of which turns laterad deep to the muscle and ends by anastomosing with the main posterior tibial before the latter divides into its terminal plantar branches.

Whereas in *Erythrocebus* the lateral plantar is absent, both plantar arteries are present in *Cercopithecus*, as in *Macaca* and *Semnopithecus*, but whereas in the latter the medial plantar is the larger, I find them subequal, or the lateral, at least proximally, slightly the larger of the two in *C. petaurista*. The medial plantar gives fine branches to the digital clefts, but no plantar arch appears to be formed, the principal supply of the toes coming from the dorsum, reaching the sole via the perforating vessel of the second interosseous interval. The lateral plantar in *C. petaurista*, after supplying a medial calcaneal branch, proceeds deep to the abductor hallucis, providing muscular branches to the short plantar muscles and then gradually dwindling in size without contributing to an arcade.

The anterior tibial artery in *C. petaurista* proceeds through the interosseous membrane between tibia and fibula and enters the anterior compartment, where it meets the anterior tibial nerve, with which it descends to ankle. It supplies muscular branches to the extensor group and is not traceable past the ankle.

In the venous system no special peculiarities have been noted. The azygos vein is large and drains the intercostal spaces (all except the first) from both sides.

In the lymphatic system the lymphatic glands and nodes are distributed as in Man, but the groups contain smaller numbers of relatively larger glands. In some places, such as at the iliac bifurcation, a single large gland occurs each side. An epicondylar gland occurs at the elbow and a large popliteal node at the knee. In *C. erythrogaster* a huge flattened gland occurs at the cranial border of the pancreas adjacent to the left gastric artery. Glands and nodes are widely distributed in relation to the mesenteric vessels.

NEUROLOGY

CENTRAL NERVOUS SYSTEM

BRAIN.—The brain weight of *C. mona* is given as 55·5 gms. by Ziehen (1899) who also repeats earlier records thus: *C. albogularis* ♀, fresh, 55·7 g. ($\frac{1}{32}$ of body-weight); *C. p. cynosuros* ♀, 70·5 g. ($\frac{1}{31}$ body-weight); *C. sabaeus*, 47, 51, 42 g. compared with *M. talapoin* 39 g. ($\frac{1}{19}$ body-weight) and *Erythrocebus patas*, 52 g. The fissuration of the cerebral hemispheres has been recorded by Elliot-Smith (1902) in *C. diana* (2 specimens), *C. petaurista* (3), *C. aethiops* (2), *C. pygerythrus* (1), *C. sabaeus* (1), *C. cynosuros* (2), *C. nictitans* (1), and *C. campbelli* (1). Connolly (1950) reports on *C. sabaeus* (4) and *C cephus* (1). I have examined brains of *C. albogularis* (1), *C. neglectus* (1), *C. mona* (1), *C. cephus* (1), *C. petaurista* (1), *C. sabaeus* (2), *C. pygerythrus* (1), *C. ae. tantalus* (1), and *C. cynosuros* (3). Some remarks and figures of the hemisphere of *C. sabaeus*, are also given in Parker's (1896) monumental memoir.

Not much difference has been recorded between the fissural pattern in *Cercopithecus* and that in *Cercocebus* and *Macaca*, the chief distinctions being due to the smaller size. A certain amount of asymmetry seems normal; thus in a brain of *C. sabaeus* I found the right hemisphere more projecting anteriorly and the left more so behind. There may also be fissural asymmetries, *e.g.* Elliot Smith mentions a brain of a Vervet (*C. pygerythrus*), in which the Sylvian and parallel fissures fail to meet on the left hemisphere, but do so on the right—which is the normal condition. The opposite arrangement is reported by Connolly in his *C. cephus*.

On the lateral aspect the frontal lobe is demarcated from the parietal by a

deep sulcus centralis, which is invariably bowed forwards, turning towards
the Sylvian below. It incises the superior border, though I found it failing
to do so in both hemispheres of a *C. ae. tantalus*. Connolly found the fissures
poorly marked on the frontal lobe, but in all my specimens, with the exception of the *C. ae. tantalus*, there is a well-developed inferior precentral,
curved, with the concavity forwards (in *C. mona* and *C. neglectus*) or S-
shaped (as in *C. pygerythrus*, and one example of *C. cynosuros*). Sometimes
a triradiate arrangement develops (as in *C. sabaeus* and *C. albogularis*) by

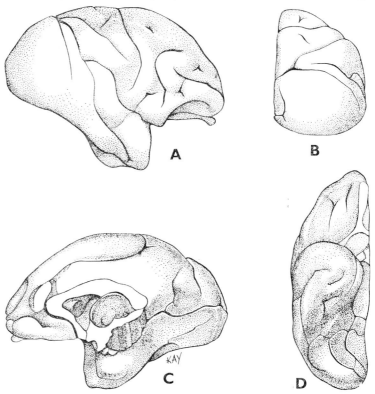

FIG. 58.—*Cercopithecus mona*. Four views of brain (× ⅔). A, right cerebral hemisphere from
the lateral aspect ; B, the same from the occipital aspect ; C, the same from the medial
aspect ; D, the same from below

fusion with the horizontally disposed transverse frontal sulcus. A short
posterior ramus has been noted in *C. albogularis*. A sulcus rectus may also
be present below the transverse frontal. The area of cortex between the
upper ends of the central and precentral sulci may be marked by a dimple,
sometimes expanded into a small triradius (*e.g.* in *C. mona* and *C. neglectus*)
or even into a short horizontal sulcus (*e.g.* in *C. albogularis* and *C. petaurista*).
Connolly refers to short anterior and posterior subcentral sulci in one of his
examples of *C. sabaeus*. I have seen the former as a mere dimple in *C. albogularis*, but well developed in *C. mona*. The latter has been noted in *C.
tantalus*.

Half-way between the central sulcus and the occipital pole the superior margin is incised by a deep parieto-occipital fissure. This has a very short limb on the superior surface of the hemisphere, then bifurcates into an arch-like formation which embraces the upper end of the united Sylvian and parallel sulci, the anterior limb (intraparietal sulcus) passing on to the parietal lobe and the posterior to the occipital. In *C. cephus* I found the

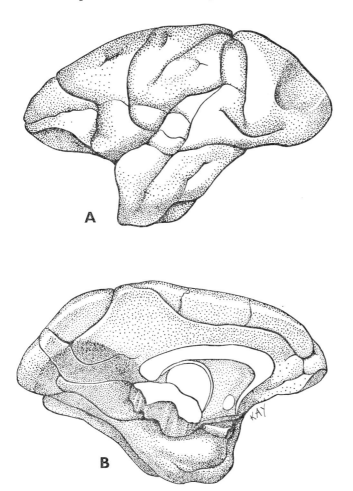

FIG. 59.—*Cercopithecus ascanius schmidti* ♂. Brain A, left hemisphere from the lateral aspect ; B, left hemisphere from the medial aspect (×¼)

posterior limb gradually approaching and joining the parallel fissure below the union of the latter with the Sylvian, and in a *C. cynosuros* the tip of the united fissures turned backwards to join the parieto-occipital.

Connolly, describing the hemisphere of a *C. sabaeus*, relates that the sulcus, without meeting the Sylvian, ends in a fork resulting from superficial union of a small sulcus dorsal to the end of the Sylvian. The extended parallel sulcus, judged from Brodmann's figure 90, forms the anterior limit of the dorsally prolonged area 19. According to Shellshear (1927) the portion of the parallel bordering areas 21 and 22 is homologous with the post Sylvian of lower mammals.

The occipital lobe is practically unmarked laterally, but is delimited below by a deep transverse sulcus (inferior occipital) curving upwards from the inferior margin to end just short of the parallel sulcus. Below this the occipito-temporal just gains the lateral surface in most hemispheres, greatly so in *C. albogularis*. Almost invariably the occipital lobe is marked near its superior margin by a sagittal sulcus. This may be confined to the medial surface, but is more often pushed dorsally and then laterally by expansion of the calcarine area. Its posterior end turns medially and is then found to be a continuation of the retrocalcarine sulcus. The latter is elongated and very deep. It continues obliquely forwards and downwards as far as the sulcus cinguli, and is joined half-way along its length by the medial portion of the parieto-occipital.

The temporal lobe may show, besides the parallel sulcus, indications of a second temporal sulcus behind the parallel.

On the inferior surface there is a long collateral sulcus and, medial to its anterior third, a well-marked rhinal fissure. In *C. diana* the collateral may consist of two or three interrupted parts, the hindmost meeting the calcarine (Elliot Smith). The calloso-marginal turns upwards posteriorly, where it may bifurcate (*e.g.* in *C. mona*) without cutting the superior margin. It fails to meet the parieto-occipital. In *C. cephus* Connolly describes a long oblique sulcus extending from below the parieto-occipital towards the angle on the calloso-marginal. On the orbital aspect of the frontal lobe is a simple sagittally disposed or slightly oblique orbital sulcus. Often there are two sulci, but they are never connected by a transverse element. The lateral (fronto-orbital) sulcus may develop a lateral branch, as described for *C. sabaeus* by Connolly.

SPINAL CORD.—In a *C. sabaeus* with a maximum cerebral hemisphere length of 60 mm. the spinal cord measured 220 mm. long. Cervical and lumbar enlargements are well marked, the former extending over segments C.3-T.2, and the latter from L.2 to L.5. Posterior to the latter the cord gradually lessens in diameter to the filum terminale without the abrupt change between conus medullaris and filum characteristic of the human cord. The linea splendens is well marked, but ligamenta denticulata are reduced to mere threads of arachno-pia.

In the upper cervical cord the posterior column is sharply demarcated by a fissure (and septum) from the lateral column. Median dorsal and ventral fissures are also well marked. The dorsal grey horn is feebly marked, being narrow and pointed, but the ventral horns are broad and festooned at their edges.

PERIPHERAL NERVOUS SYSTEM

Little need be added to the account given for the Cynomorpha in general (pp. 110-125). Reference has already been made there to Winckler's observations on the third, fourth, fifth and sixth cranial nerves and the ciliary ganglion. These have been confirmed by the present writer in *Cercopithecus mona*. Lacroix's (1926) dissections of the lachrymal nerve have also been alluded to. Ashton and Oxnard (1958) found the zygomatic nerve entering the infraorbital canal independently of its parent stem, the infraorbital nerve, from which it has already separated in the pterygo-palatine fossa. Coursing laterally on the orbital floor, it divides into zygomatico-temporal and zygomatico-facial branches, the former supplying skin over the temporal region and the latter becoming cutaneous near the lateral palpebral

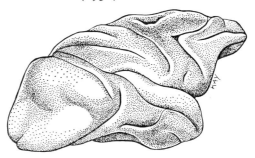

FIG. 60.—*Cercopithecus albogularis*. Right hemisphere from the lateral aspect (× ⅔).

canthus. Posterior superior dental nerves also separate in the pterygo-palatine fossa. They enter canals in the posterior surface of the maxilla. They innervate the cheek-teeth. Canines and incisors are innervated by the anterior superior dental nerves which diverge from the infraorbital nerve whilst in the infraorbital groove. In the infraorbital groove the infraorbital nerve splits into nasal and labial divisions. The nasal division may emerge through a single infraorbital foramen, but in two out of three *Cercopithecus* examined by Ashton and Oxnard the medial branch of the canal was duplicated and the nasal division of the nerve emerged in two parts. The central aperture of the infraorbital canal is occupied by one branch of the labial division of the nerve. The rest of this division occupies a lateral opening which commences in the lateral wall of the infraorbital canal. On the face, fibres of the lateral division make connections with the facial nerve. Bowden *et al.* (1960) also showed that the facial nerve receives communications from the medial part of the labial division in *C. aethiops tantalus*. Likewise in the lower jaw the mandibular branch of VII communicates with mental and labial branches from the inferior dental branch of V.

The two vagi, in their thoracic course, unite on the dorsal wall of the oesophagus, posterior to the level of crossing of the azygos vein. They continue into the abdomen as a single trunk, dividing again at the cardia.

In the suboccipital region I found the dorsal branches from the first three cervical nerve roots distributed in *C. albogularis* exactly as in Man. The great occipital is derived mainly from C.2, of which it forms the medial branch.

The small lateral branch, after supplying a twig to the obliquus inferior, ends in the splenius and trachelo-mastoid muscles. The suboccipital nerve is used up in supplying the muscles bounding the suboccipital triangle.

The cervical plexus is arranged and distributed as described by Huntington (1897) (see also *antea*, p. 110). The descendens hypoglossi and descendens cervicis do not form an ansa but merely merge and become incorporated in the same sheath. Extensive descending cutaneous branches proceed over the clavicle and especially over the deltoid region.

The brachial plexus also conforms to the normal cynomorph pattern.

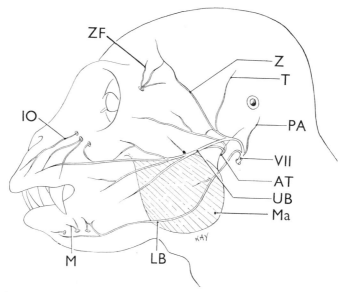

FIG. 61.—*Cercopithecus aethiops tantalus.* Nerves of the left side of the face (redrawn and modified from Bowden *et al.*, 1960)

AT, auriculo-temporal nerve; *IO*, infraorbital nerves; *LB*, lower buccal division of VII; *M*, mental nerves; *Ma*, masseter muscle; *PA*, posterior auricular nerve; *T*, temporal branch; *UB*, upper buccal division of VII; *Z*, zygomatic branch of VII; *ZF*, zygomatico-facial nerve

Harris (1939) examined it in *C. petaurista* and *C. pygerythrus*. Chief variations occur in respect of contributions from Th.2. Harris found it contributing to the plexus by sending a branch to Th.1 in *C. pygerythrus*, but this was definitely lacking in *C. petaurista*. My findings in *C. mona* indicate nonconformity with the usual pattern of peripheral distribution. The median, formed by union of medial and lateral heads, does not incorporate the musculo-cutaneous, which is a large and completely separate nerve derived from the lateral cord of the plexus. It supplies a large twig to the coraco-brachialis previous to entering that muscle. The median does, however, form a common pathway with the greater part, but not all of the ulnar. The latter consists of two parts (*a*) a larger, travelling with the median as far as the distal part of the antecubital fossa, and (*b*) a smaller portion derived from the posterior cord in common with the radial. This part runs with the radial for about 25 mm. then takes the course normally occupied by the ulnar nerve in Man, winding around the medial condyle, through the common flexor origin into the antecubital fossa. In the antecubital fossa, plexus formation occurs. The secondary ulnar having meantime divided, each division receives a contribution from the median, the principal one going to the larger, more radial portion of the divided ulnar, but a smaller one passing to the postaxial division. The latter follows the ulnar artery and becomes much attenuated, ending as the dorsal branch. The larger division, now combined with the contributions from the median, becomes the palmar branch. This branches into deep and superficial divisions at the wrist, and the latter forms further communications with the median in the palm. The ulnar contributes to the supply of the lateral two digits both dorsally and on the volar side (see also Kosinski, 1927).

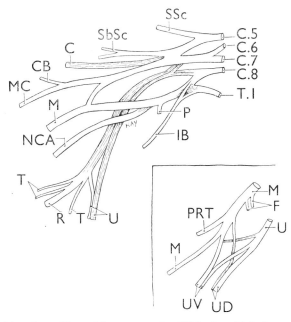

Fig. 62.—*Cercopithecus mona* ♀. Right brachial plexus (Inset shows arrangement at elbow)

C, circumflex nerve ; *CB*, nerve to coraco-brachialis ; *F*, nerves to flexors of forearm ; *IB*, intercosto-branchial nerve ; *M*, median nerve ; *MC*, musculo-cutaneous nerve ; *NCA*, nervus cutaneus antebrachii medialis ; *P*, pectoral nerve ; *PRT*, nerve to pronator radii teres ; *R*, radial nerve ; *SbSc*, subscapular nerve ; *SSc*, suprascapular nerve ; *T*, nerves to triceps brachii ; *U*, ulnar nerve ; *UD*, dorsal branch of ulnar nerve ; *UV*, volar branch of ulnar nerve

The intercosto-brachial nerve is derived from C.8 and T.1. No contribution was found from T.2.

In *C. petaurista* seven lumbar nerves are present, but only the last five enter into plexus formation, the first and second running independent courses, the first as the ilio-hypogastric and the second as ilio-inguinal.

The third lumbar gives the genito-femoral and a large contribution which joins another from L.4 to form the lateral femoral cutaneous. The femoral nerve derives from L.3, L.4 and L.5, and the obturator from L.4 and L.5. The remainder of L.5 unites with L.6 and L.7 to form the lumbo-sacral cord.

In *C. sabaeus* Zuckerman (1938) found the great sciatic nerve derived from L.5-7 and S.1.

The internal pudendal nerve runs with the sciatic into the buttock, then breaks away to follow the usual course in the lateral wall of the ischio-rectal fossa. In a female *C. sabaeus*, I found it giving branches to the levator ani, and sacro-analis muscles, thereafter dividing into two, a cranial division which enters the pubo-rectalis and pubo-coccygeus and a caudal division which runs ventrad to become the dorsal nerve of the clitoris, after supplying cutaneous branches to the labia pudendi.

The great sciatic divides in the distal part of the thigh into medial and lateral popliteal nerves. The medial nerve, much the larger in *C. petaurista*, arches across the popliteal space and passes between the gastrocnemii,

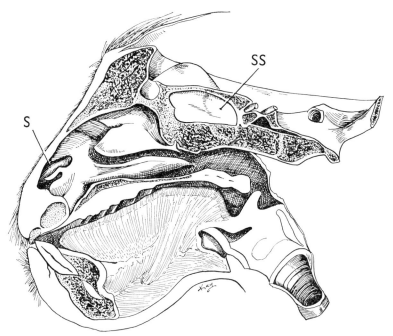

FIG. 63.—*Cercopithecus pygerythrus cynosuros*. Sagittal section of the head to show details of the lateral wall of the right nasal fossa

S, supranarial organ ; *SS*, sphenoidal sinus

supplying large branches to both heads and also to soleus and plantaris. Thereafter it courses down the leg between the long digital flexors, proceeds under the flexor retinaculum and divides into medial and lateral plantar nerves.

The external popliteal or common peroneal nerve gives off a cutaneous branch (sural nerve) then passes from the fossa across the lateral aspect of the lateral head of the gastrocnemius, under cover of the biceps insertion. At the neck of the fibula, it divides into musculo-cutaneous and anterior tibial nerves. The former enters the peronaeus longus, gives off a large muscular branch to the peronaei, then proceeds as the cutaneous division. This gives a dorsal branch, which crosses the extensor retinaculum laterally and ends on the skin of the ankle and lateral border of the heel region. The main nerve then divides into medial and lateral terminal branches. The former proceeds to the medial edge of the foot and hallux, the other supplies digital branches to the lateral three-and-a-half toes (see also Winckler (1934), who followed the nerve in *C. mona*).

The anterior tibial supplies a large branch to the tibialis anterior, then courses distally between the extensor digitorum longus and extensor hallucis to the ankle. It supplies both muscles. At the ankle it divides, supplying all the bellies of extensor digitorum brevis. The cutaneous supply has been worked out by Winckler (1936, *vide* also *antea*, p. 121).

SENSE ORGANS

Schultz (1940) gives the absolute size of the eyeball in *C. sabaeus* as 3·89 cc. Relative size of eyeball in the adult male is recorded as 0·09 (in comparison with body-weight), with a relative orbital capacity of 0·20. Size of globe in relation to orbital capacity in a female *C. sabaeus*, 44·7, and a male *C. pygerythrus rubella* (= *C.p. callidus*), 42·3.

For other data see above pp. 47 and 128.

NOSE.—The presence of a special feature associated with the vestibulum nasi has already been discussed (*antea*, p. 125). There are some variations in the present genus in regard to this structure. In *C. cynosuros* there is little more than a groove leading upwards for 10-12 mm. on the rostral part of the nasal roof. In *C. albogularis* and *C. mona* the groove is guarded below by a lobate structure of cartilaginous consistence. This almost converts the groove into a tunnel. The lobate body is produced forwards so as to over-hang and assist in forming the margin of the hinder (upper) portion of the external naris. In *C. petaurista* an intermediate condition between that in *C. cynosuros* and that in *C. mona* is manifested. Here the upper margin of the groove is highly developed, possibly in correlation with the superficial thickening associated with the nose-pad. The lower marginal fold, though larger than in *C. cynosuros*, is less developed than in *C. mona*. In *C. neglectus* the arrangement is also intermediate, though more advanced than in *C. petaurista*. Here the lobate lower margin appears as an infolding of the dorsal edge of the narial opening (Hill, 1965).

Conchae are two in number, a long, narrow inferior, and a tongue-shaped upper (= middle turbinate), the superior being usually absent. A small elevation, dorsal to the free anterior end of the middle turbinate, occurs, however, in *C. mona*. The tongue-shaped structure is attached posteriorly and free elsewhere. The maxillary antrum is typically the only accessory sinus, but Aubert (1929) describes a frontal sinus in *C. sabaeus* (*vide antea*, p. 127; also Plate IX). Aubert also interprets a small excavation in the body of the sphenoid as a rudimentary sinus.

BEHAVIOURAL CHARACTERS

HABITAT : ECOLOGY

The guenons form a large and evolutionarily labile group which has succeeded in occupying a varied range of environments within the African tropics, and extending southwards even beyond the tropical belt. Consequently there has been a considerable amount of adaptation to these varied biotopes and a parallel degree of speciation and subspeciation therein.

Though these monkeys are fundamentally quadrupedal, arboreal and diurnal in their activities, one widespread group has diverged sufficiently to constitute a superspecies (*C. aethiops*) more or less completely adapted to life in the savannah. Of the truly forest forms, a wide variation in habitat occurs in relation to the microclimates exhibited within the tropical rain forest (see above, pp. 148 *et seq.*). The forest floor, however, is not colonized by guenons of this genus, but is the only niche not occupied by them. On the contrary, each of the horizontal strata in the forest canopy is occupied by more than one species.

Writing of *C. ascanius schmidti* in Uganda, Haddow (1952) states that within the seven main vegetational assemblages (with their seven main subtypes) recognized for Uganda by Eggeling and Dale (1947), this monkey regularly occurs in only a few of them, namely lowland rain forest, upland rain forest and ground water forest (with its two main sub-types, riverine forest and swamp forest). It is absent from savannah and from various types of grassland, where patchy bush thicket forms the nearest approach to forest conditions. Though never found far from tall trees, it seems that quite small localized patches of high-canopy forest are adequate for its survival, in an otherwise unfavourable biotope. Usually survival in such circumstances involves the raiding of native plantations.

Swamp forest in Uganda is usually confined to small belts within or in contiguity with large blocks of lowland rain forest. Here *C. ascanius schmidti* is prevalent, but in the few larger blocks this monkey, though present, is not abundant, the dominant species being *C. mitis doggetti* and a mangabey (*Cercocebus albigena johnstoni*).

In rain forest the distribution may be uneven, *C. a. schmidti* being most prevalent in tangled areas of secondary growth and in colonizing forest round the edges. It is scarce in ancient high-canopy forest of the interior, where *Colobus abyssinicus ituricus* is a dominant inhabitant.

In the eastern Congo a related form *C. a. montanus* replaces the typical Red-tailed Guenon. This inhabits highland rain forest at about 5000 feet altitude, though descending in places as low as 3000 feet.

Bands of *Cercopithecus* monkeys may associate with monkeys of other genera, or bands of one species with those of another. Thus Haddow reports that members of the genera *Cercopithecus*, *Cercocebus* and *Colobus* may, on occasion, be found together, but baboons (*Papio*), though inhabiting the same general area and feeding there, do not mix with the other monkeys. The associations of smaller monkeys are generally diurnal, the bands becoming segregated at nightfall, when each group withdraws to its own sleeping quarters. Sometimes a single member of a foreign species may move and feed with a band of *Cercopithecus*. Allen and Loveridge (1942), for example, mention a single female mangabey (*C. albigena johnstoni*) in a band of Red-tails (*C. ascanius schmidti*), while in another locality a single male *C. ascanius* associated with a female *C. mitis stuhlmanni*. Allen *et al.* (1936) mention two Red-tails in a band of *C. mitis stuhlmanni*. Haddow quotes Buxton (personal communication), who observed an association between *C. a. schmidti* and *C. neglectus* and gives personal records in Uganda of association between Red-tails and *C. pygerythrus centralis*, *C. mitis stuhlmanni*, *C. m. doggetti*, *C. denti*, and with *Cercocebus albigena johnstoni*, *Colobus abyssinicus ituricus*, *C. badius tephrosceles* and *C. badius ellioti*; and in Kenya of associations between Red-tails and other races of *C. mitis*, and with *Colobus abyssinicus matschiei*. In Kaimosi forest, mixed bands of *C. mitis* and *C. ascanius* are the rule rather than the exception.

In most of Kenya, according to Booth (1962), *C. mitis* competes with the local forms of the savannah monkeys (*C. aethiops* superspecies). Into drier forests *C. mitis* extends from lusher forests, while *C. aethiops* extends from the drier scrub vegetational zone. In such localities *C. mitis* is relatively stunted, whereas *C. aethiops* attains a larger size than in its typical savannah habitat. Sometimes the troops are mixed, but this is not usual, and Booth records fighting between bands of Sykes' monkeys (*C. albogularis*) and an invading group of *C. aethiops*, albeit the latter were not expelled; in fact finally the two groups moved, fed and played together, though the *aethiops* individuals kept together. Booth in Kenya also observed temporary associations between *C. mitis* and *Colobus abyssinicus*; and no fighting occurred between them.

In Kenya, Booth found *C. mitis stuhlmanni* and *C. albogularis* separated geographically by the Rift Valley, the former to the west and the latter to the east, both extending in altitudinal range up to 10,000 feet, the examples from the higher zones having shaggier coats. To the east Sykes' monkey extends down to sea level, to the west *C. mitis* ranges down to 3000 feet.

COMPOSITION AND BEHAVIOUR OF BANDS

Here again more is known concerning *C. ascanius schmidti*, from the exhaustive work of Haddow (1952), than any other form.

In the first place, the continual struggle for dominance among the males of a band, so characteristic of baboon assemblages, is not particularly obvious with guenons, or is at least difficult to establish on field observations. Accordingly Haddow feels that *Cercopithecus* aligns itself with gibbons and howlermonkeys where the dominance gradient (of Carpenter 1942) shows a very low slope. Thus the threat-display (which varies in character among the different species of the genus) is used against intruders, whether human or animal, but rarely between members of a troop, at any rate in its complete form (with vocal accompaniment) nor in defying a member of another simian species. Haddow never encountered the full display between one Red-tail and another in the field, and only very rarely with captive specimens.

The only social activity between members of a band observed by Buxton (1951) or Haddow was mutual grooming. The various dominance and minatory gestures (*e.g.* presenting) so commonly observed in baboons, are not encountered in *Cercopithecus ascanius*. In captivity, however, besides grooming, presenting, both towards humans and other monkeys, has been observed by the present writer in *C. sabaeus*, *C. albogularis*, *C. a. erythrarchus* and *C. cephus*. Haddow correlates the absence of such overt signs in *Cercopithecus* with the total lack of sexual swelling or other external manifestations of sexual receptivity on the part of the females. Confirmation of the reticent behaviour of guenons in connection with their sexual activities is found in the observations of Luck (1959) on *C. pygerythrus*, Booth (1957) on West African forms and Booth (1962) on East African species of this genus.

Regarding numbers of individuals in a troop, earlier writers give large figures. Buxton believed that very large bands, such as those recorded for *C. pygerythrus centralis* and *C. l'hoesti*, occur in species which favour open country or a partly terrestrial existence. Also, it would appear that very large troops are formed where raiding of native plantations has become a habit, as recorded by Pitman (1929) who mentions bands of 200 individuals and Haddow (1952) who noted bands of 40-50 individuals of *C. ascanius schmidti*. Such bands seem to be formed under the stimulus of some particular food supply (*e.g.* fruiting *Ficus* sp. and *Mildbraediodendron*).

Such large bands are, however, not typical. From studies on the nightresting habits of *Cercopithecus* monkeys in Uganda, Lumsden (1951) and later both Buxton and Haddow have arrived at the conclusion that the small family unit of 4-5 or even 3-4 animals (with a single adult male) is the basic association. Such small groups sleep together. In the daytime, however, two or more such units feed and travel together, breaking up again towards evening. Lumsden found daytime bands of approximately ten animals due to fusion of smaller units. Larger bands, over ten in number, occur in *C. p. centralis* (Buxton) and *C. p. johnstoni* (Haddow) and these may remain together at night. There is therefore some difference related to type of habitat preferred. Another feature that emerges from the detailed studies of Haddow and his associates is that, even in the daytime, the members in a troop do not remain constant either in number or constitution. Bands exceeding ten in number are most frequently observed at certain times of day, notably around the early-morning feeding session (9.00 hrs.) and again around 14.00-16.00 hrs. At other times the troops are smaller, as if there is some segregation of the component parties during the resting and travelling periods. Buxton found the smallest parties before sunset, presumably after the break up, prior to movement to the sleeping quarters, though Haddow records larger groupings at this time.

It should be noted that large counts in a single large tree at nightfall do not mean that all belong to the same association. A large tree may harbour several unit formations, and they may even belong to more than one species.

Explanation of the diurnal variation in troop size relates to the frequent occurrence of solitary animals. These have commonly been assumed to be old or impotent males which have been expelled from their band, but Haddow and his colleagues have shown this not always to be so. Solitaries may be of either sex, and, if males, are not necessarily aged or impotent. Solitaries form a remarkably constant fraction of the total population at all times of the day. Their presence is not associated with any special activity-phase of the population, and they have been encountered feeding, travelling, resting and even asleep. Solitary examples are recorded of nine different forms of *Cercopithecus* by Haddow, while Sclater (1900) in South Africa had even at that early date reported adult males of *C. pygerythrus* in their prime as occurring solitarily, whereas old males with worn dentition were usually members of a troop. This phenomenon of adult virile males occurring alone is strongly suggestive of a temporary phase, and that temporary peaceful exchanges of males within troops may occur, for there is no recorded evidence of expulsion by fighting, either by direct observation or by reports of battle scars on monkeys of this genus.

The presence of a potential master male in a band is, however, suggested by one facet of behaviour in *C. ascanius schmidti*, seen only when the group is alarmed. In such circumstances the whole band may retreat *en masse*, but, if the retreat is rapid, frequently a single animal emits a repeated alarm call, which serves presumably as a signal to the retreating band. The animal, probably a male, may stay a considerable distance from the rest, keeping up his call until the threatened danger has passed.

ENEMIES

Guenons live in fear of relatively few predators. Their chief enemy is Man—not so much as a predator, but as despoiler of their environment, which is so changed by cultivation, cattle rearing and other activities, that, unless adaptable to such changes, the forest forms cannot survive. In these circumstances the monkeys may take to raiding crops and then suffer destruction by firearms, trapping, etc., either by local inhabitants or in officially organized monkey drives, such as have occurred in recent years in Sierra Leone. In some places (*e.g.* Liberia), monkeys are trapped for food, in others for the sake of their fur for ornamental or ritual use. Haddow records the use of skins of *C. mitis stuhlmanni* and *C. l'hoesti* for these purposes.

Next to Man, the most frequent predator is the Crowned Eagle (*Stephano-aëtus coronatus*) which is widely distributed in Africa and is blamed by both Haddow and C. Booth for attacking monkeys. Allen and Loveridge (1942) recovered remains of *C. mitis moloneyi* from the gut of one of these eagles. Chapin (1925, 1932) has also reported *Cercopithecus* remains, generally of young animals, in the gut of this eagle. The eagles' method of attack is to swoop down and grab the monkey by the head in its talons, then drop it from a height, leaving it to die from its wounds before picking it up to devour it.

Leopards are often quoted as enemies of monkeys and this is certainly the case with baboons and other terrestrial forms, but they can hardly be responsible for many deaths among arboreal species, though *C. mitis moloneyi* has been recorded as a victim by Allen and Loveridge.

A more likely predator of arboreal guenons is the Python (*P. sebae*), a large serpent which has a preference for damper localities, swamps, etc. It lies in wait for prey coming to drink. Here its victims include *C. pygerythrus centralis*, which sometimes feeds in papyrus swamps (St. Clair Thompson, quoted by Haddow) and *C. mitis doggetti*, which has similar habits according to Schouteden (1947). *C. neglectus* too, is often found near water in the Congo.

DAILY CYCLE OF ACTIVITY

Detailed studies of diurnal and nocturnal behaviour of *C. ascanius schmidti* have been made by Buxton and quoted by Haddow, who adds material of his own.

During the morning there are two main peaks of activity, the first reaching its maximum after sunrise and the second at 08.00 to 09.00 hrs. The first is the major feeding session. The second corresponds to the period when the largest aggregations of individuals occur. The afternoon also shows two peaks of activity, one between 15.00 and 16.00 hrs (where the second period of large aggregations appears)—associated with active feeding, but this becomes even more intense later, after the bands have broken up. Buxton surmises that, during the period of larger aggregations, interchange of individuals between the component units takes place. This prevents the formation of close inbreeding units. In the event of the formation of very large bands like those referred to above, due to the presence of some specially favoured food supply (*e.g.* native plantations) feeding may not follow the regular diurnal pattern, the overwhelming stimulus of the food supply serving to break down or throw into abeyance the normal social structure. Such aggregations may in fact involve bands of several species.

Regarding the question of territory in *Cercopithecus* monkeys, Buxton found that the small troops of Red-tails he studied in an isolated patch of forest had no territories or regular daily routes. Haddow, however, though in general agreement, considered that territoriality definitely occurs where large groups in more extensive forests are concerned. He writes, " Thus in a large forest it can be stated with confidence that a given area of perhaps half a square mile will contain a particular band of Red-tails, perhaps thirty to fifty in all. On any given day these will be found divided into smaller groups, but under ordinary circumstances these groups will be limited to the particular area concerned. Under certain stimuli, notably that of a fruiting tree they will coalesce, and all the Red-tails of that particular area will be found banded together temporarily. While the evidence is not conclusive, it is thought that when such very large aggregations do occur they consist of monkeys from a particular area, which may have fairly definite boundaries. Thus on one occasion when a very large band of Red-tails was found in a fruiting fig, another band of about ten was observed within about a quarter of a mile, feeding quietly on leaves. At that distance even a casual human observer could not fail to note the continuous overhead passage of hornbills and other birds to the tree in question, and the noise made by the feeding birds was clearly audible. In other words, the band concerned must have been perfectly well aware of what was going on, though they were making no effort to join the numerous Red-tails already feeding in the fig.

" With regard to daily routes the writer feels that in one respect Buxton's results are misleading. Thus the forest area he studied was a very small one, representing only about the total area over which a given band would range while feeding in a large forest. Past experience has shown that where monkeys travel to feed, entering a particular area in the morning and leaving it in the afternoon, the routes followed may be very well fixed. Thus where a road or small river occurs it will be crossed very regularly by the branches of a particular tree, and usually within about the same hour. When it is necessary to collect specimens, the most effective way is not to go in search of the monkeys but to wait at some such point until they cross. Once within the feeding-area, of course, the band probably splits up to a considerable degree."

A seasonal shift of feeding ground is suggested by certain observations of Lumsden in Uganda, but apparently the distances involved are short. Haddow agrees that such shifts occur, but the new territory may overlap the old ones sufficiently to permit the conclusion that the same troop will be found in the same general area daily throughout the year. Some species centred in one area for resting purposes will make long foraging journeys daily, especially to plantations. Haddow mentions two bands of *C. l'hoesti* in the Ruwenzori foothills, which descended 2000 feet every morning from mountain forest to feed in plantations, returning to the forest by midday. In the afternoon the journey was repeated and the return to high forest was completed by dusk. Long journeys are also regularly made by bands of *C. mitis stuhlmanni* and *C. pygerythrus centralis*.

SLEEPING HABITS

All species of guenon have preferred sleeping areas which remain in use for long periods; in many instances individual trees are constantly resorted to (Haddow *et al.* 1947 *a* & *b*). Further details have accrued from the work of Lumsden (1951) on *C. ascanius schmidti* and Buxton (1951). In contrast with *Colobus abyssinicus*, which prefers the highest parts of a tree (even in bare dead branches), *C. a. schmidti* sleeps among smaller lower branches and twigs. According to Buxton it prefers dense foliage, especially among the lower branches of large trees, or in the upper branches of under-storey trees. The Red-tail seems to be the only species so far known to utilize the understorey for nocturnal use. The Red-tail does not share its sleeping quarters with other species. Sleeping parties include 4-5 individuals in the Semliki forest (Lumsden) but, in Uganda, Buxton found only 3-4 individuals. At sunset a small band may even split up into pairs or individual monkeys. Large trees may harbour larger bands, but these usually divide into the smaller units before settling down for the night.

Sleeping trees are usually entered before dark and left before sunrise, but feeding may continue till dusk and be resumed before sunrise before the groups leave the sleeping quarters, but there is no evidence of any East African monkey being active during the night, though evidence of some nocturnal activity has been presented by Allen (1925) for *C. hamlyni* in the Congo forest. Under certain abnormal conditions on Buvuma Island in Lake Victoria, where the Red-tails have been much persecuted, nocturnal raiding of plantations has been reported (Pitman (1942)), while Haddow mentions nocturnal activity in moonlight among captive groups of *C. pygerythrus centralis* in large open-air runs at Entebbe, Uganda.

FOOD AND FEEDING

A very detailed study of the food substances ingested by the Red-tailed Guenon (*C. ascanius schmidti*) is incorporated in Haddow's study. This is based upon examination of stomach contents (which, due to the thorough mastication employed, gives only vague information) and of the contents of mouth and cheek-pouches of animals shot while feeding. Analysis reveals that the food may be classified into eight main categories—leaves of trees, other leaves, green shoots, flowers and fruits of trees, other wild fruits, products of cultivated crops and miscellanea such as gummy exudates and ants. Of leaves, those of *Markhamia platycalyx, Cyanometra alexandri* and various *Ficus* species make up the bulk of the diet. The flowers of *Markhamia* are highly favoured, upwards of one pound of which have been recovered from stomachs of Red-tails. Fruits form the major part of Haddow's list and include those of *Markhamia, Cyanometra* (eaten unripe), various *Ficus* species, *Rauvolfia vomitoria* and other apocynaceous fruits, *Phoenix reclinata* (date palm), *Elaeis* (oil-palm) and numerous unidentified hard and soft fruits, berries and seeds. Of the cultivated crops raided maize, banana, pineapple, sweet potato, passion-fruit, pumpkin, finger millet, cassava and beans are mentioned.

Cassava and sweet potatoes are exhumed by the monkeys. On the other hand, although captive guenons relish pawpaw (*Carica papaya*) and yams (*Colocasia, Xanthosoma*) these are not commonly included in the raiding by wild guenons ; the same applies to citrus fruits.

An interesting observation is that ingestion of the fruit of the oil-palm by monkeys results in a bright yellow staining of the serum and omental fat (Haddow ; who quotes Bugher as authority for the same phenomenon in Man). No remains of birds or birds' eggs have been reported in stomach contents, though Pitman (1938) cites two records of solitary Red-tails causing wanton slaughter of domestic fowl. Insects are freely ingested by captive guenons, but there is little evidence of this occurring in the wild, with the sole exception of the eating of ants of the genus *Crematogaster*, which possess a powerful sting. Possibly this indicates an addiction to " anting " such as has previously been recorded in *Cebus* (*vide* Vol. IV, p. 387), but the quantities involved (over 1000 insects forming a thick layer lining the stomach) suggests that some dietetic need is supplied also. Captive individuals have reputedly taken to strange forms of animal food, *e.g.* Buckland's (1859) account of the capture and ingestion of mice by his pet Vervet.

Drinking is not known to occur in the wild state in *C. ascanius* in Uganda, and, provided adequate water intake is insured in the solids, no drinking occurs even in captivity. In more arid environments, however, such as South Africa, several writers have confirmed that the Vervet (*C. pygerythrus*) drinks regularly.

As already mentioned, there are two principal feeding sessions during the day, the first in the early morning, the second longer one in the late afternoon or evening. Between these the monkeys are relatively inactive and may even sleep. The morning session lasts until 10.00 hrs. Feeding is resumed after midday, continuing till sunset or even later, but there are no East African records of nocturnal feeding, except for a single report of Pitman (1942) of Red-tails acquiring the habit after being subjected to human molestation. The rhythm is retained in captive specimens (Lumsden, 1951 ; also personal experience with *C. cephus* and various races of *C. mitis*).

Alteration may be effected by the weather, for there is evidence that heavy morning rain may delay the first feeding session or reduce it, whereon additional time is spent on feeding in the afternoon or evening, even if heavy rain is then falling.

Some modification of the normal rhythm also occurs at seasons when certain trees are in fruit. The fruits ripen and they last perhaps not more than three or four days. During such periods large numbers of monkeys, squirrels and birds may all be found gorging themselves, eager to ingest as much as possible while the supply lasts, and active feeding may be more or less continuous except for a shortened midday siesta. Abeyance of the normal rhythm also occurs at times when cultivated crops are in a suitable state to induce raiding. Monkeys disturbed whilst raiding have been observed to stuff their cheek-pouches to capacity before retreating.

Posting of a sentinel whose function is to warn members of a feeding band of impending danger does not appear to occur in guenons. This is on a par with the low dominance gradient exhibited in their social structure. Such sentinels have, however, been suggested by earlier writers, especially with reference to the Vervet in South Africa (Boulenger, 1936).

MOTILE ACTIVITIES

In quadrupedal progression the limbs are advanced alternately in the usual way. Specific differences exist both as to general activity and to postures and body carriage. The members of the *C. aethiops* superspecies and the smaller spot-nosed monkeys (*C. petaurista*, *C. ascanius* and their allies) and *C. diana*, are highly excitable with rapid darting, often jerky, motions, which are in great contrast with the more sedate and deliberate behaviour of the *C. mitis* formenkreis or *C. neglectus*. *C. mitis* adopts a characteristic trotting gait quite different from the leaping and darting movements of *C. ascanius* or *C. mona*. According to Sanderson (1957), whose observations relate to West African forms, translocation through an arboreal environment differs from the type adopted by most monkeys. Instead of jumping from branch to branch, guenons dash through the foliage along the most direct available path, leaping thence into the air to land in a vertical posture due to the effect of the relatively heavy weight of the tail. Having landed on the face of the dense mass of foliage of the next tree, they grasp this with all four extremities. Righting themselves on the first available branch, they then proceed as before through the tree. In this fashion the rate of progress equals that of a man running along a path on the forest floor. Sometimes slips are made and an individual will crash to the ground, or even into water, where a stream passes through the forest. Sanderson cites a group of Mona monkeys (*C. mona*) which thus in panic fell into a stream, but all recovered themselves by swimming to the shore, using a dog-like paddle stroke.

PLATE XII

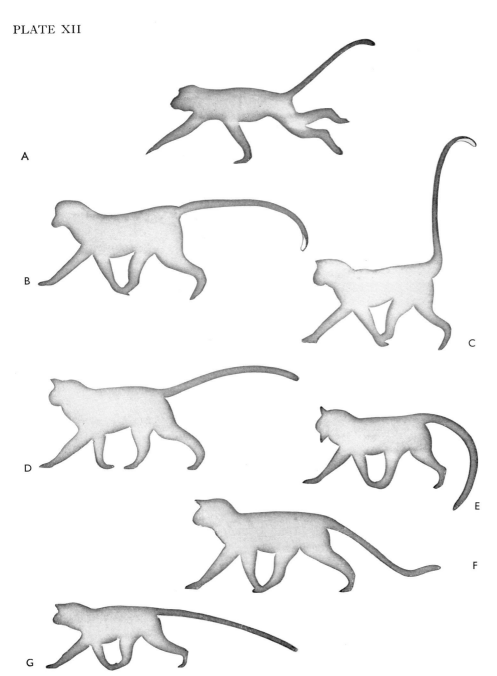

Cercopithecus spp. Series of silhouettes to indicate postures in quadrupedal progression.
A, *C. sabaeus* ; B, *C. aethiops* running in branches ; C, the same running in grass ;
D, *C. mitis* ; E, *C. neglectus* ; F, *C. l'hoesti* ; G, *C. ascanius schmidti*
A, Based on Dekeyser ; B and C based on Starck and Frick ; D–G based on Haddow

Species differ, notably in tail carriage, during quadrupedal progression. In *C. ascanius schmidti* and *C. denti* the tail is carried extended in line with the back, drooping however, towards the tip, giving the silhouette a mouse-like appearance. Standing still or feeding, the organ is carried in a drooping curve or sometimes merely loosely dependent. In *C. pygerythrus centralis* the tail is also carried low, but its relatively shorter length and sparser hair gives it a slimmer appearance. The tip is frequently markedly decurved.

The heavily furred *C. mitis* assemblage again contrast in carrying the tail high in a slight curve, concave downwards, and the terminal part at a higher level than the body line. The heavily furred tip produces a clubbed appearance in the field. *C. diana* carries the tail held vertically upwards with the tip above turned slightly back.

In *C. neglectus* the tail is carried in either a drooping arch or hanging straight down with a slight terminal curve. *C. l'hoesti* resembles *C. mitis*, but the tail is less heavily furred near the tip. It is carried in a very characteristic way both when the animal is stationary and when moving. Proximally it exhibits a downward curve, but near the tip it bends upwards often in a sinuous fashion, a feature that has been regarded as an incipient form of prehensility (Dandelot, 1956). The same sinuous terminal portion is observed in *C. hamlyni*. Two individuals sitting together on the same perch, with dependent tails, will generally interlace the terminal portion with that of the companion. This seems to be a steadying device. It is specially well marked in juveniles who intertwine their tails with their mother's. The phenomenon probably occurs in many cercopithèques.

All guenons exhibit display posturings, but these vary greatly according to species. In general they consist of facing the adversary or whoever the display is intended to impress, crouching the forepart of the body, with the arms wide apart, followed by bobbing movements of the head. Head movements, however, seem calculated to make the most of the contrasted patterns marking the face. Thus in the white-nosed *C. petaurista* up and down bobbings are utilized, whereas in *C. cephus* the head is jerked from side to side, thereby obtaining greater effect from the pale transverse facial stripe. These displays are usually accompanied by intrinsic facial movements, affecting especially the mouth and lips, and also by vocal chatter—again varying enormously with the species. As already noted (*antea*, p. 155) the powers of grimace reach a high level in *Cercopithecus*, a circumstance to which the name guenon (French, "one who grimaces") is due, having been given by Buffon (1766).

Yawning is especially apparent in *C. aethiops* and its relatives and also in *C. mitis stuhlmanni* (see Plate XIII) and *C. diana*, but absent or less marked in the smaller species such as *C. petaurista*, *C. ascanius* and *C. cephus*.

Movements of the eyebrows are less marked in most guenons than in mangabeys, macaques or baboons, but Bolwig (1959) noted similar movements in Vervets (*C. pygerythrus*) to that observed in baboons—lowering of eye-brows, raising the head, and ears bent forwards, preceding an attack. But this threat pattern is often mixed with a fear element, as van Hoof (1963) also found. When this element is in evidence, pilo-erection of the hairs on the nape and shoulders is marked. The flight response is indicated by lowering of the head, raising of the brows and pressing back of the ears.

Bolwig criticizes Worner's (1940) conclusions, based on cinematographic evidence, that emotional expression in monkeys is determined by the rhythm of their facial and other movements. These convey to other monkeys the idea of anger or friendliness. Bolwig's criticism is that in any given cir-cumstance the responses expressed are a delicate balance between the aggressive and fear-reactions, swaying now to one side now to the other—as is also implicit in van Hooff's analysis.

VOICE

Considerable variations in vocal utterances differentiate the species of the genus. Haddow states that in general the calls of the various species of *Cercopithecus* are readily distinguished from those of *Cercocebus* and *Colobus*, and with practice the field worker can learn to differentiate between one species of *Cercopithecus* and another.

Both *Cercocebus* and *Colobus* are characterized by their utterance of croaking and chuckling sounds, and Haddow correlates this with the pos-session of a " croaking sac ". This, presumably, refers to the laryngeal air sac, which, in spite of Haddow's denial, is also present in *Cercopithecus*, although not so extensively developed as in the other two genera under reference.

In general, *Cercopithecus* monkeys emit grunts and low croaks, but harsher sounds without musical notes are characteristic of the various forms of *C. aethiops* (sensu lato). Thus Haddow refers to the harsh, grating note of *C. p. centralis* which thereby is readily distinguished from all other East African guenons. Yelling is a term that has been used to describe the vocal manifestations of *C. diana*, whilst *C. mona* is described as " rowdy " by Sanderson. These contrast with the bird-like twitterings of *C. pogonias* (Sanderson) and *C. ascanius schmidti* (Haddow). In the last-mentioned the twitterings are interspersed with faint, high-pitched whistles, and are heard whenever a band is disturbed or alarmed. After dispersal a different sound is heard—a periodic sharp call rendered *kyuh!* or *keeyuh!* (with a short *u* sound) given by the male, and repeated at intervals, serving probably as a signal for reassembly of a dispersed band.

A warning or threatening call, used by *C. ascanius schmidti* when defying a human or canine intruder and accompanied by a threat display, is described by Haddow as a sharp, loud chirp rendered phonetically as *tchip!*, and another very short, low-pitched, throaty purr, rendered *chrrt!* These calls are also produced in captive examples when handled.

The male *C. cephus* emits a characteristic warning note, a sharp, staccato rhythmically repeated bark. I never heard this from a female I kept for many years, her voice being limited to the short soft croaks and chuckles.

In West Africa the calls of *C. mona* and *C. campbelli* are, though inter-distinguishable, closely related. *C. petaurista* is more distinct, but with musical overtones (Booth, in Hill and Booth, 1957). *C. mitis* is a sedate undemonstrative animal, little given to vocalization, its emissions being limited to grunts and croaks. The same applies to *C. neglectus*.

Andrew (1963) has analysed the vocal emissions of a number of *Cercopithecus* species, finding marked differences in quality of the calls, and the ease with which they are elicited. Lowest intensity patterns of vocalization comprise rapidly repeated narrow columns of noise (*arr* and *ha* calls) given during approach of a friendly superior from whom food or grooming is anticipated. They are emitted by infants seeking the nipple. Andrew also records grunts and more prolonged *moos*—due to a broadening of the *arr* element with increased glottic tension. Grunts are employed during grooming or when approaching a social equal. Very soft grunts were emitted in these circumstances by *C. neglectus*. In this species too, a loud *moo* beginning with strong resonance of 0·8 kc/s is abruptly replaced by three centring at 0·4, 1·2 and 2·2 kc/s.

TOILET

The pelage is cleaned principally during mutual or social grooming, the fur being combed by the fingers with repeated manual strokes, the hairs being pushed aside and particles of sebum and extraneous matter removed with fingers, often assisted with the lips or teeth. In self-grooming the same occurs, but naturally is limited to certain parts of the body only. Other parts, *e.g.* the crown, nape and back, are subjected to rapid scratching with the fingers or toes according to convenience. Repeated scratching occurs also in situations of fear or stress in which no toilet function is served, *e.g.* one hand being used to scratch the other and then reversed.

Licking is never employed in cleaning the fur—with the sole exception of the mother cleaning her infant.

RECEPTIVE CAPACITIES

Visual powers are remarkably keen and presumably (by analogy with *Cercocebus*) colour vision has been attained, an inference which is supported by the multicoloured pelage of so many of the species of the genus. The question has been specially studied by Dahl (1907).

Ohtsuka (1937) has carried out experimental work on the visual capacity in respect of multiple choice situations.

The auditory capacities have not been experimentally explored in this genus, but doubtless they are considerable and, in co-operation with the visual sense, enable the animal to adapt admirably to its environment.

Olfaction is usually regarded as feeble, but there can be no doubt that it serves an important purpose in testing the suitability of food materials. Strange or unusual foods offered to captive guenons are invariably placed before the nares prior to ingestion, and may, indeed, be discarded after this preliminary olfactory sampling. Possibly the supranarial organ (*antea*, p. 363) is involved in this preliminary testing.

Further evidence that olfaction occupies an important place in the life of guenons lies in the pronounced body odour of garlic-like quality that characterizes all members of the genus.

Gustation is equally important, but so far studies have related solely to the individual variations in the capacity to taste pheno-thio-carbamide, and the genetic implications attaching thereto (Chiarelli, 1960, 1963). The proportion of tasters to non-tasters in *Cercopithecus* is 90 to 10 per cent (cf. *Erythrocebus*, where only 60 per cent are tasters).

REPRODUCTIVE BEHAVIOUR

COPULATION.—As before mentioned (pp. 137 and 171), guenons are remarkably reticent in their sexual behaviour, contrasting markedly with *Cercocebus*, *Macaca* and *Papio*.

Haddow (1952) concluded that mating " must occur in the sleeping trees, or at least after dark ". A. H. Booth (1957 *in litt.*) confirms that nocturnal copulation is the rule in West African species, and Luck (1959) referred to the reticence of *C. pygerythrus* in its sexual behaviour. Cynthia Booth (1962), however, claims that this reputation is not altogether deserved as far as East African guenons are concerned, for she has observed mating in both wild and captive specimens, admitting, nevertheless, that it is much more difficult to observe than in *Cercocebus*, *Papio* or *Macaca*. Little or nothing of the female sexual cycle is visible to the unaided eye, and even tame animals are shy, breaking off attempts at copulation when they suspect an observer within 20 yards ; a conclusion I arrived at after keeping examples of several races of *C. albogularis*, *C. cephus* and *C. sabaeus*. The only matings observed were between a male and female *C. albogularis kolbi*, diurnally and followed by successful pregnancy. Cynthia Booth also claims diurnal copulation in *C. mitis stuhlmanni* and *C. albogularis*, and reports the activity also in *C. aethiops* subsp. and *C. neglectus* between 7.30 a.m. and 12 noon, also between 5 and 6 p.m.—but so far never in the intervening period.

Mating in the wild takes place, according to C. Booth, on a branch of a tree, never on the ground, though she admits the latter is feasible when the animals are not subject to disturbances. In captivity it has been observed on the floor of the cages, but not in the less tame specimens ; otherwise it occurs on the shelves or branches near the top of the cage. This, too, confirms my own experience.

There is no prelude to mating. Usually the male examines the female's genital area rather cursorily, sometimes pushing her tail aside with one hand. Visual and possible olfactory inspection are not always followed by immediate copulation. The female usually displays no interest, while Booth claims she does not adopt any special posture. On the other hand, presenting was the only marked external evidence of sexual receptivity in my female *C. albogularis erythrarchus*, for whom, unfortunately, I had no suitable available male.

When the male has decided to accomplish mating, he puts a hand on the female's hips and proceeds without further courtship, adopting the usual posture (*antea*, p. 137). The female stands squarely on all four limbs and she supports the entire weight of the male, who is invariably heavier than herself. The male does not place his hands on the female's back, but grasps the fur around her waist. His feet grip the female's calves just below the slightly flexed knees, the hallux medially and the other toes laterally. The male's knees are flexed and located lateral to the female's thighs; her tail extends back between his legs, never raised over her back. Unless disturbed, insemination is completed in a single coitus.

No regularity in copulation has been observed in caged animals in Kenya. Copulation has been observed after pregnancy has supervened in both *C. neglectus* and *C. mitis* (Booth, 1962).

Copulation recurs very soon after parturition, especially if the infant is removed for hand rearing, one week after in *C. mitis*, but the female was unresponsive and hurt, so that the mating was unsuccessful. In a *C. aethiops*, coitus occurred satisfactorily only five days after parturition. Copulation does not apparently occur with females carrying infants, but a wild shot lactating female *C. albogularis* has been reported as in early pregnancy.

Breeding appears to be continuous throughout the year, *i.e.* there is no convincing evidence of a limited breeding season. Fitzsimons (1919) recorded Vervets (*C. pygerythrus*) in South Africa carrying young babies in December and January, but Stevenson Hamilton (1947) declares the young are born at irregular times during the warm season (*i.e.* November till February). In the tropics, however, these seasonal differences do not occur, therefore neither Haddow (*loc. cit.*) nor Booth (1962) found evidence of seasonal births in the species studied by them in East Africa. Haddow found pregnancies in every month except November and December, but the total sample included very few females from these two months. His records, for wild *Cercopithecus*, on breaking down, read as follows :

January–April	17%
May–August	27%
September–December	25%

Haddow goes into greater detail in his records of *C. ascanius schmidti* and deduces evidence that early pregnancies occur during the early part of the year, advanced pregnancies in the later months, as follows:

Period	Percentage Early Pregnancy	Percentage Late Pregnancy	Percentage Carrying Infants
January–April	19	—	31
May–August	4	36	—
September–December	—	9	18

Samples are admittedly small, but Haddow concludes that, for this species in Uganda, the evidence suggests at least a preferential breeding season.

Booth maintains that, provided data are collected over a wide and varied area (*e.g.* the whole of Kenya for *C. mitis*), breeding can and does occur throughout the year. But if attention is paid only to a restricted area, and if this be one where the food supply seasonally fluctuates, there tends to be a concentration of births at one time of the year. This is reflected not only in the occurrence of females in advanced pregnancy, or females carrying infants, but also in troop composition (*i.e.* proportions of infants, juveniles of first year or of one year older—factors which can be determined by field observation). Caged animals, with an unlimited food supply the year round, breed throughout the year. If a baby is removed the mother will produce another seven months later.

GESTATION.—Rode (1937) quotes Sclater * without giving the reference, that the gestation period is about seven months, while Jennison (1927) gives 213 days. Haddow thinks this is too long and suggests a figure nearer to six months, as in many other cynomorph genera ; but he produces no exact data in support of this. Zuckerman (1953) gives 210 days based on statements by Asdell (1946) and Kenneth (1947).

A single young is normally produced but twins have occasionally been met with, *e.g.* in *C. pygerythrus* (Fitzsimons, 1919). The placenta is bidiscoidal.

A tubal pregnancy in *C. aethiops* has been reported by Lapin and Yakoleva (1957).

PARTURITION.—This has been observed only in captive animals. Cynthia Booth (1962) notes that parturition may occur either by day or night. The mother sits as near the top of the cage as possible on a shelf or branch.

* Probably W. Sclater (1900), *The Mammals of South Africa*, referring to *C. pygerythrus* or *C. albogularis samango*.

She assumes a squatting posture with the tail dependent over the edge of the substrate, both during labour and at the time of the expulsion. As the foetus emerges she passes a hand over the perineum to aid in extraction. When emergence is complete, she draws the infant forwards bimanually and up to her ventral surface.

The placenta is normally eaten, but if part of it drops, this is not retrieved. Between spells of ingestion of the membranes, the mother cleans up the baby by licking. She also licks her own hands to clean them.

Takeshita (1962) has given a complete account, with detailed protocols of parturition in *C. mona* that took place in the Japan Monkey Centre, Inuyama, Aichi. Labour continued for 1 hour 2 minutes—first stage, 4 minutes; second stage, 3 minutes; third stage, 55 minutes. The parent spent the time sitting on a perch or lying on the cage floor; she did not move very much apart from exerting manual pressure on her dilated abdomen. At 3.5 p.m. she rose on the perch and began to defaecate and urinate in rapid succession, followed by the expression of a large quantity of mucus from the vulva. Foetal movements (or labour pains) caused her to lie down. During the first stage of delivery she alternately sat down and stood up, grasping the perch or wires of the cage. During a phase of manual compression of the abdomen the foetal head was delivered and, on the head being fully expelled, the mother grasped it in both hands and gave manual traction. The mother's coat, at this stage, was wet with greasy sweat. The traction resulted in the emergence of the rest of the foetus, at which moment the foetus uttered a low cry, *ki*. It was pulled upwards by the parent and clasped in her arms. Twenty minutes later the placenta and membranes were expelled and eaten by the mother.

The neonatus weighed *c.* 300 gms. compared with the maternal weight of 4000 gms.

Until recent years few guenons have been bred successfully in captivity —possibly due to lack of privacy. But with more modern methods of housing and care, more success has been attained. The species so far bred in captivity so far as known are listed in Table 17.

In spite of the chromosomal divergence, hybridization between *Cercopithecus* species and monkeys of three other genera has been reported. *C. sabaeus* ♂ has crossed with a female Rhesus macaque (*M. mulatta*) in the London Zoo (Zuckerman, 1931–33). In Pretoria *C. pygerythrus* ♀ has been successfully fertilized by a male Toque monkey (*M. sinica*), producing a male offspring and also by a male *M. irus* (Gunning, 1910; Przibram, 1910). A stillborn young was produced by a female White-collared Mangabey (*Cercocebus t. torquatus*) which had been sired by a *Cercopithecus mitis* (Montagu, 1950). *Allenopithecus* is fertile with *Cercopithecus* in so far as in the Naples Zoo a ♂ *Allenopithecus* produced a normal male offspring with a female *C. aethiops* (Chiarelli, 1961).

TABLE 17

BREEDING OF *CERCOPITHECUS* SPP. IN CAPTIVITY

Species Bred	Where Bred	Date	Reference and Remarks
C. mitis mitis	Antwerp	1961	
	Colombo	1951	
	Liberec, Czecho-slovakia	1959	
	Lisbon	1951	
C. m. stuhl-manni	London Zoo	18 Sept. 1949	Several others born later
C. albogularis subsp.	Berlin	1961	
	Memphis, Tenn.	1961	
	Zürich	1961	
	Zürich Zoo	1962	Ann. Rept., 1962
C. a. kolbi	Privately in Colombo	1938	By the author
C. a. samango	East London, S.A.	1961	
C. l'hoesti	Blijdorp Zoo	1959, 1960	I.Z.N.
	Antwerp Zoo	1961	Gijzen, 1962
	Berlin	1961	
	Copenhagen	1961	
	Helsinki	1961	
	Paris	1961	
C. mona	Calcutta	1961	
	Caracas	1961	
	Dallas, Tex.	1959, 1960, 1961	
	Oklahoma	1959, 1960	
	Paris	1960	
	Wassenaar	1960	
C. campbelli	Baltimore, Md.	1961	
C. petaurista	Baltimore, Md.	1961	
	Dublin	1961	
C. cephus	Jerez, Spain	1960	
	Paris	1961	
	Washington	1961	
	Zürich Zoo	1962	Ann. Rept., 1962
C. hamlyni	Blijdorp Zoo	1959, 1960	I.Z.N. Appelman
	Amsterdam	1960, 1961	
	Paris	1961	
C. neglectus	London Zoo	24 Nov. 1960	(hand-reared)
	Baltimore, Md.	1960	
	Dallas, Tex.	1961	
	Paignton	1961	
	San Diego, Calif.	1959, 1961	
	Vienna	1961	
	Washington	1959, 1961	
C. diana	Berlin	1961	
	Birmingham, Ala.	1960, 1961	
	Colombo	1960, 1961	
	Copenhagen	1961	
	Paris	1961	
	Seattle, Wash.	1961	
	Privately in U.S.	1963	Hand raised to maturity, Brandt, 1964

Species Bred	Where Bred	Date	Reference and Remarks
C. aethiops		1960, 1961	Numerous other records from zoos in England, U.S.A, Holland, Germany, South Africa, Egypt, Japan, Finland, Israel, etc. Wuppertal, 1956 (see I.Z.Yb. 1960, 1961)
C. pygerythrus	London Zoo	8 June 1849 11 July 1850 31 Mar. 1853 18 Mar. 1855 23 Mar. 1855 11 June 1893	Zuckerman, 1953
C. sabaeus	London Zoo	31 Jan. 1835 22 Feb. 1890 13 July 1873	} Zuckerman, 1953
	Paris	3 generations	Saint-Denys, 1881
	Saarbrücken	7 Oct. 1952	Moog, 1957

Interspecific hybrids (females) are known between *C. hamlyni* ♂ and *C. l'hoesti* ♀, *C. mona* ♂ and *C. neglectus* ♀ (New York, *teste* Crandal, Chiarelli, 1961) and *C. aethiops* and *C. mona* (Benzien, 1959). In the Zürich Zoo I observed in 1960 a female *C. cephus* carrying an infant which it was inferred had been sired by a *C. mona* as she had no mate of her own species.

In the Antwerp Zoo crossing has occurred between a male *Cercopithecus mona* and a female *C. mitis doggetti*. The male offspring is described in detail by Gijzen (1963), who also mentions, on the authority of Jacobi, the birth of a series of hybrid young of a female *C. albogularis* sired by a male *C. mona*.

MATERNAL CARE

The infant is carried on the ventral aspect of the mother's body supported by one or both of her hands. When sitting with knees drawn up, one hand or both may be used. When walking, running or leaping, one hand alone supports the baby, but the latter is capable of clinging to the mother's fur without additional assistance in the event of the mother's need to use all four limbs in locomotion.

The infant seeks the nipple and suckles instinctively, and frequently both nipples are suckled simultaneously, at any rate in *C. aethiops* and its allies (Sclater, 1893 c; Booth, 1962).

Females jealously guard their young and will not allow other monkeys to hold them. They show no interest in dead babies. A stillborn baby is only carelessly cleaned and is soon abandoned. Movement of the neonatus evidently serves as a stimulus for the normal maternal reactions. Artificial movements induced in a stillborn infant immediately galvanize the mother into activity, causing her to lick the baby and attempt to nurse it. She ceases these activities when the movement stops. Infants dying during the first few weeks are similarly abandoned. Weakly infants may be abandoned in captivity even before death.

A remarkable feature of the newborn of all species of *Cercopithecus* is the conspicuous divergence in pelage from that of the juvenile and adult. Infants in the postnatal coat evoke a strong reaction in adults of both sexes. The sight of such an infant, when carried by a human observer, produces great excitement, even in a troop of wild monkeys. Males adopt aggressive attitudes, emit vocal threats and approach much closer than they would dare in ordinary circumstances. The reactions would seem to stem from an instinctive desire to rescue the infant. The same reactions occur if an infant is left untended accidentally or otherwise. If a mother is shot and her infant falls uninjured, it will be retrieved by other members of the band irrespective of sex. No such reactions ensue in the case of older infants that have lost the natal coat —a change which begins at 6-8 weeks old with the appearance of new hairs on the brows, but which is not completed until the young are about 3-4 months old—concurrently with the eruption of the second deciduous molars (Booth, 1962).

Infants in natal coat are capable of producing most or all of the vocal emissions characteristic of their kind, but the vocalizations are apparently not or only secondarily effective in inducing the same reaction in adults as the sight of the natal pelage.

Pelage of juveniles, after the change from the natal coat, differs little from that of the adult in most species, but *C. neglectus* is exceptional in that the juvenile coat resembles the natal coat more than the adult pelage. In juveniles of *C. pygerythrus callidus* the scrotum is a dull blue, changing to bright turquoise in the adult; presumably the same degree of difference applies to other forms of the *C. aethiops* superspecies.

DEVELOPMENT OF THE YOUNG

In the earliest postnatal stage the behaviour of the young is purely instinctive. Only after some weeks, according to Booth (1962) and Gijzen (1962), does it begin to take notice of extraneous objects and to distinguish between its own mother (or foster mother) and other creatures. The recognition is based on visual receptivity. Animals reared by a human foster mother recognize the person by its normal appearance, and if this is altered by change of raiment or adornment, recognition fails to occur. Alteration of smell, however, by change of scent makes no difference.

When old enough to sample food, the infant watches and learns from its mother. Similarly a hand-reared baby copies its foster parent in the matter of what is eatable and what is not.

Vocalization conforms to an inborn pattern characteristic of the species. The neonatus is at once capable of manifesting its voice, and, if forced away from the mother for foster rearing, the voice is retained unmodified and no new vocal range is acquired from other species, though such calls may be recognized according to their true significance. This may serve a purpose in nature where several species inhabit the same forest, *e.g.* A. H. Booth (1957) records that the alarm call of *C. mona* is recognized and acted upon by *Procolobus verus*.

Although the sound production is inborn, their applications are learned by experience. Thus, C. Booth found that alarm calls, and the reactions to alarm calls, are inborn, but the circumstances in which they are appropriate are learned. Examples are given by Booth derived from observations on an orphaned female *C. mitis stuhlmanni* hand-reared from the postnatal period. No appreciation of danger was recorded as long as the foster-parent was with her ; but some months later, when placed with several young *C. aethiops*, she recognized their alarm call and ran for cover, without realizing to what the alarm call had been due.

LONGEVITY

For the most part species of the present genus are hardy in captivity and, provided they surmount the initial difficulties, survive for many years. Potential length of life in the genus exceeds 20 years, and may extend beyond 30 years. Available data are listed in Table 18. Latest information is culled from Jones' (1962) valuable compilation.

PARASITOLOGY AND PATHOLOGY

Pathogenic protozoan parasites affecting *Cercopithecus* monkeys include many that are common to other Old World monkeys, notably *Entamoeba* (first recorded for the genus by Macfie, 1915), *Trypanosoma* and *Balantidium*. *Trypanosomiasis* has been blamed upon the species named *T. simiae* which, like *T. gambiensi*, is carried by the tsetse fly from natural hosts such as wart-hog and the domestic pig. Experimentally *T. rhodesiense* has been trans-mitted to Green monkeys (*C. sabaeus*) with subsequent cardiac damage (Regendanz and Hoeppli, 1929).

Blood protozoans include *Hepatocystes kochi* (Garnham, 1948 ; Haddow, 1952), the most common malarial parasite in African monkeys, but apparently not *Plasmodium gonderi*, which though confined to African monkeys is specially common in *Cercocebus*, but not so far recovered from guenons. A spirochaetal infection (*Spirochaeta harveyi*) has been reported in *C. pygerythrus centralis* (Garnham, 1947), and *C. petaurista* (Macfie, 1915) (in the latter an

TABLE 18

LONGEVITY OF *CERCOPITHECUS*

Species	Duration of Life Yrs.	Mths.	Place	Authority
C. mitis mitis	15	11	London Zoo	Flower, 1931
C. m. stuhlmanni	16		London Zoo	Smith, 1958
	12	11	Philadelphia	Jones, 1962
C. m. kandti	9		London Zoo	
	10	3	Rotterdam	
C. albogularis albogularis	12	7	Washington	Jones, 1962
C. a. kolbi	4		London Zoo	Smith, 1958
	10		San Diego Zoo	Smith, 1958
	11	1	Philadelphia	Jones, 1962
C. a. erythrarchus	14	6	Philadelphia	Jones, 1962
C. a. moloneyi		7	Philadelphia	Jones, 1962
C. a. samango	1	3	Washington	Jones, 1962
C. nictitans nictitans	12	10	London	Jones, 1962
C. n. signatus	6		London	Jones, 1962
C. n. martini	12	10	London	Jones, 1962
C. l'hoesti	9		London Zoo	Smith, 1958
	12	7	New York	Jones, 1962
C. preussi	19	4	Washington	Jones, 1962
C. mona	16		Washington Zoo	Baker, 1927
	22	5	Rotterdam Zoo	Flower, 1931
	22	3	Philadelphia	
	17		Rotterdam Zoo	Flower, 1931
	15		San Diego Zoo	
	8		London Zoo	Smith, 1958
C. campbelli	11	5	New York	Jones, 1962
C. c. lowei	4	6	London	Jones, 1962
C. wolfi	10	3	London	Jones, 1962
C. pogonias pogonias	1	8	London	Jones, 1962
C. p. grayi	3	5	London	Jones, 1962
C. petaurista petaurista	20	10	Washington	Jones, 1962
	10		San Diego	Smith, 1958
	10		London	Jones, 1962
C. p. buttikoferi	15	11	San Diego	Smith, 1958
C. ascanius ascanius	12	7	New York	Jones, 1962
C. a. schmidti	16	3	London	Jones, 1962
C. erythrogaster	12	7	Paris	Jones, 1962
C. erythrotis erythrotis	14	2	New York	Jones, 1962
C. e. sclateri	6		London	Jones, 1962
C. cephus	13		London	Smith, 1958
	13	2	Washington	Jones, 1962
C. hamlyni	12	7	New York	Jones, 1962
C. neglectus	20	7	Washington	Jones, 1962
	10		San Diego Zoo	Smith, 1958
	9		London Zoo	Smith, 1958
C. diana	19		Chicago Zoo Park	Rabb, 1958
C. d. roloway	30	8 *	Washington	Jones, 1962
C. aethiops aethiops	24		Gizeh	Flower, 1931
	17	7	Gizeh	Flower, 1931
C. ae. hilgerti	9	2	London	Jones, 1962
C. ae. tantalus	11		London	Smith, 1958
	10	4	London	Jones, 1962
C. p. pygerythrus	22	10	Washington	Jones, 1962
C. p. cynosuros	6	1	London	Jones, 1962
C. p. johnstoni	4	4	Berlin	Jones, 1962
C. sabaeus	22	10	Washington	Jones, 1962

* Still alive, 1.2.64.

intestinal infection found incidentally in a monkey dying of amoebic dysentery).

Helminths are numerous—usually in the intestine—the most important being the strongylid *Oesophagostomum apiostomum*, which attaches to and imbeds itself in the intestinal wall. It is a frequent cause of illness and death in newly imported guenons. Schistosomiasis (due to *S. mansoni*) has been produced experimentally in *C. sabaeus* (Meisenhelder and Thompson, 1963). Filariasis is a natural disease in guenons. Microfilariae have been recorded from the subarachnoid spaces (Peruzzi, 1927) as well as in the blood. Leger (1922) described a new species of Microfilaria from *C. buttikoferi.*

Arthropod parasites include ticks, mites and lice. Hoogstraal (1956) found ticks frequently in laboratory Grivets (*C. aethiops*) kept in the Sudan, but wild animals of the same species, and of *C. mitis stuhlmanni* were tick-free.

Mites recorded include that causing ordinary scabies (Philippe, 1948), but more important is pulmonary acariasis caused by *Pneumonyssus duttoni*, which appears to be specific for the genus *Cercopithecus* (most simian respiratory acariasis is due to *P. simicola*). *P. duttoni* differs from *P. simicola* in its preference for the trachea and larger bronchi. It has been recovered from *C. nictitans* and *C. ascanius* (Paulicki and Hilgendorf, 1869 ; Paulicki, 1872 ; Newstead and Todd, 1906 ; see also Ruch, 1959 ; and references there cited).

Three species of lice of the genus *Pedicinus* are reported from guenons, *P. obtusus* is the commonest, having been found on wild Vervets (*C. pygerythrus*) in the Transvaal (Ferris) and from zoo specimens of *C. diana, C. aethiops, C. mona* and *C. ascanius* (Hopkins, 1949). *P. erythrogaster* has also been recovered from the two last mentioned, while *P. patas*, originally described from *Erythrocebus patas*, has been received from wild examples of *C. albogularis kibonotensis* and *C. a. kolbi* in Kenya. Luck (1957) has drawn attention to an unnamed transparent louse as common on laboratory Grivets (*C. aethiops*) but it produces no untoward effects.

Bacterial infections of importance in guenons are dysentery, due to Shigella, tuberculosis and pseudo-tuberculosis. Cruickshank and Bray (1950) give an account of an epizootic of shigellosis due to *S. flexneri. C. aethiops* were among the victims after a latent period.

Guenons, in contrast to Talapoins, are very susceptible to tuberculosis. Both the human and bovine strains of the responsible organism have been implicated (*vide* Ruch, p. 204) and the avian type has also been found once in *C. aethiops* (Urbain, 1949). Lesions show the usual distribution and dissemination.

Spontaneous pseudo-tuberculosis (due to *Pasteurella pseudotuberculosis*) has been isolated from *C. sabaeus* by Saenz (1930), while two of the same species are reported by Urbain (1942) as dying of the disease in the Paris menagerie.

2 C

Septicaemia resulting from infection with *Staphylococcus pyogenes* has been reported by Gourlay (1960) as fatal in Vervets (*C. pygerythrus*) in Uganda.

Among cardio-vascular conditions Haddow (1952) reports hypertension and an aberrant renal artery in a wild example of *C. ascanius schmidti* and *C. albogularis kibonotensis*. Hypertension was associated with gross cardiac hypertrophy and dilatation, hydronephrosis and splenomegaly, but there were no gross abnormalities in the larger vessels, though the smaller ones were prominent and tortuous. There was a high temperature (104·4° F.).

Splenic lesions are of some frequency, even in wild guenons, according to Haddow. He mentions perisplenitis as relatively common, but its relation to protozoan blood infections is not known. Splenomegaly, of course, frequently occurs in the case of such infections, especially of *Hepatocystes*. An intense dark pigmentation of the spleen, giving the organ a deep slaty or inky-black appearance has been recorded without apparent disease elsewhere. Histologically the splenic pulp is crowded with large and small granules of black pigment, much like that seen in human malaria. *H. kochi* does not produce so dark a pigment, so this factor has been ruled out of the aetiology. The condition has been noted in *C. pygerythrus centralis*, *C. mitis doggetti*, *C. albogularis kibonotensis* and *C. ascanius schmidti* in Uganda.

A condition termed locally " salami spleen " is described in detail by Haddow (1952) as occurring frequently in *C. pygerythrus*, *C. mitis stuhlmanni*, *C. albogularis kibonotensis* and *C. ascanius schmidti*, as well as other genera (*Cercocebus*, *Papio*). No causal factor is known, but there are resemblances to human lymphadenoma. The early stage shows accumulation of multinucleate giant cells around the Malpighian bodies, with a mild fibroblastic reaction, recalling the "foreign body reaction". Later, larger masses of firm tissue develop forming pink areas macroscopically in the fresh specimen. These are commonest on or near the surface, but may be distributed throughout the pulp. They vary in number from one or two to very large numbers differing in size from a pinhead to a coffee-bean. Microscopically the tissue is composed of reticular cells with some eosinophils. In extreme cases the whole splenic pulp may be replaced by the reticular tissue and the organ shrinks and may be distorted from contraction of the dense fibrous masses developing in the abnormal areas, thereby causing further strangulation of any remaining normal pulp.

Metabolic and deficiency disease occur as in other Old World Primates. Diabetes has been recorded in captive examples of *C. mona* and *C. mitis* (Hill, 1957). Vitamin C deficiency resulting in scurvy within 3-4 months has been described in laboratory Vervets fed solely on maize. Treatment with ascorbic acid led to recovery (Follis, 1957). Osteomalacia from rickets has also been frequently seen ; it affects only the long bones (Pick, 1943).

Of neurological conditions calling for remark are subacute combined degeneration and encephalomyocarditis. The first is a demyelinating disease responsible for the condition formerly known as cage paralysis. In this, loss of use of the pelvic limbs occurs ; they become flaccid and the animal drags itself around using its forelimbs for support. Both a cerebral and a spinal type is known, the latter being the commoner, and specially prevalent in guenons. Hamerton (1937, 1938) gave a full account in a Stairs' monkey (*C. albogularis erythrarchus*) and found the condition amenable to treatment with liver extract intramuscularly (2 c.c. campolon once a week).

Encephalomyocarditis in which both brain and heart are affected has been described by Dick (1948) in *C. pygerythrus centralis* and also in laboratory *Macaca* in Uganda. It is of viral origin (Mengo virus ; E.M.C. virus), sometimes producing neurological and at other times cardiac symptons (see also Ruch, pp. 357 and 408).

Paralyses also occur where origin has yet to be identified. Among these, Luck (1957) has reported a slowly progressive paralytic condition in young Vervets in South Africa. Affected individuals become tame and docile, without loss of appetite or activity, in fact appetite was above normal, with salivation and oedema of eyelids and lips. Clumsiness of hand movements was the first neurologic sign, followed by frank ataxia, and sometimes nystagmus. The disease ended in coma and death. A dietary factor would seem to be responsible.

Neoplasia has occurred in irradiated Green Monkeys (*C. sabaeus*) which produced, after five years, osteosarcomata near the sites of radium implantations in the bone marrow (Petrov *et al.*, 1951). Experimental inoculation of emulsions of subcutaneous tumour material resulted in infection in *C. aethiops tantalus*, but not in *Erythrocebus* or *Cercocebus* (Bearcroft and Jamieson, 1958). I know of no case of spontaneous neoplasia in *Cercopithecus* unless we include Hamerton's (1942) examples of lymphocytosis (in *C. sabaeus*) and lymphatic leukaemia (in *C. albogularis erythrarchus*).

Diseases associated with reproduction include a case of eclampsia in *C. mitis stuhlmanni* (Hill, 1953) and septicaemia from a retained placenta in *C. diana* (Ratcliffe, 1942).

Developmental deficiencies have been encountered in a few guenons as follows : hydrocephalus in a 10-month-old *C. aethiops*—Fox, 1941 ; hernia (internal) in *C. mona* (death from strangulation)—Scott, 1927 ; renal agenesia in a wild *C. ascanius schmidti*—Haddow, 1952 ; hare lip in *C. cephus*—Russell, 1938.

GEOGRAPHICAL DISTRIBUTION

Guenons are confined to Africa south of the Sahara. They occupy all suitable ecological situations within that area and have undergone extreme

FIG. 64.—Sketch map of eastern Africa indicating the Rift Valley System
(Modified and extended from Spinage, 1962)

speciation and subspeciation in relation to the multifarious environments encompassed. Hereby a number of clines can be recognized, especially in passing from west to east across the continent, and also, at least in the eastern half, in passing from north to south. The extreme northern limit of distribution of guenons (and indeed of any cynomorph except for baboons) does not, according to Rode (1938) transgress a line drawn from St. Louis de Senegal, passing via Chad to Khartoum and thence to the Red Sea coast. Southwards guenons occur in suitable terrain to the extreme southern limit of the continent. Madagascar, of course, has no pithecoid primates, but the coastal islands, such as Pemba and Zanzibar on the east, and Fernando Po on the West, are within the range of *Cercopithecus*. Examples of *C. sabaeus* inhabiting the Cape Verde Islands are suspected of having been introduced from the mainland. This same species has been successfully introduced into Barbados and St. Kitts in the Lesser Antilles, whilst on the latter island and on Grenada *C. mona* is also established (Hollister, 1912).

TAXONOMY

Following the practice of the ancients, the name *Cercopithecus* was first scientifically employed by Brisson (1756) to signify all the long-tailed monkeys embraced under the wider generic title *Simia*. Linnaeus (1758), in attempting to subdivide *Simia* into three subordinate groups, using the development of the tail as criterion, adopted *Cercopitheci* (in the plural) for the long-tailed forms, including some platyrrhines.

In the ordinary binomial sense Erxleben (1777) was the first to use the name for all the then known species of long-tailed monkeys of the Old World. He included twenty-two species of which the following seven are all that remain of his original list : *diana, mona, sabaea, nictitans, petaurista, cephus* and *roloway*. Restriction to the African groups to which the generic name is now unanimously applied dates from Martin (1841).

With the progress of knowledge the genus has become more and more restricted in meaning by gradual dismemberment. Nevertheless, the process, though scarcely concluded today, still leaves the genus the largest in the order.

Illiger (1811) changed the generic name to *Lasiopyga* (with *nictitans* as type) and started the dismemberment by proposing the name *Colobus* for the African species known as the Guereza.

In the following year E. Geoffroy Saint-Hilaire (1812) split off *Cercocebus* (for the mangabeys), *Pygathrix* (for the Douc), and *Nasalis* (for the Proboscis monkey). Eschscholtz (1821) separated under *Presbytis* the remaining langurs known at that time.

In 1842 I. Geoffroy removed the Talapoin to a separate genus *Miopithecus*, on rather slender evidence which has not been universally accepted, since many later authors, including most contemporary writers, retain the species within *Cercopithecus*.

Of earlier reviewers of the order, Reichenbach (1862) stands out for his subdivision of the Catarrhini. He included all the *Meerkatzen* under his " family " Cercopithecinae (Schwanzaffen) alongside *Colobus*, *Semnopithecus* and *Nasalis*. His *Meerkatzen*, however, included, besides *Cercopithecus* proper, the genera *Meiopithecus* (*sic*), *Cercocebus* and *Lasiopyga* (the last to include the Douc).

Reichenbach recognized four subdivisions or subgenera of the still larger genus *Cercopithecus*. They may be tabulated thus :

> (a) *Petaurista* (Schaukelaffen) for :
>   *cephus, melanogenys, ludio, petaurista, histrio, ascanius, nictitans.*
> (b) *Diademia* (Diademaffe) for :
>   *roloway, diana, leucampyx, pluto.*
> (c) *Mona* for :
>   *mona, campbelli, pogonias, erxlebenii, nigripes, burnetti, labiatus, martini, erythrarchus, erythrotis, albogularis, monoides.*
> (d) *Callithrix* for :
>   (α) greenish or yellowish forms : *werneri, rufoviridis, lalandii, sabaeus, callitrichus, griseoviridis, pygerythrus, cynosurus,*
>   (β) red-brown or brown forms : *tephrops, ochraceus, flavidus, patas, ruber, poliophaeus, circumcinctus, pyrrhonotus.*

This scheme shows a curious mixture of broad critical acumen with uncritical observation of detail. The composition of the *Mona* subgenus, for example, strongly foreshadows recent assessments, but at the same time includes the quite divergent *C. erythrotis* alongside forms (such as *albogularis* and *erythrarchus*) now known to be allied to his *Diademia*. Similar criticism could be levelled against his very heterogeneous *Callithrix*, with its justifiably allied greenish forms set against the reddish series now separated as *Erythrocebus*. Among the latter, too, Reichenbach assigns specific names to individual variants, and even accepts as distinct species names from the literature which are pure synonyms.

Following the reviews of Martin (1841), I. Geoffroy (1843), Wagner (1855), Gray (1870) and Schlegel (1876), the next serious revision of the genus was that of Sclater (1893 *a*), who had to accommodate many newly described species. Excluding *Cercocebus* and *Myopithecus* (*sic*), Sclater divided the genus into six sections to which he gave Latin names, publishing also keys to the identification of the species in each group. His scheme reads thus :

> Section A. RHINOSTICTI (with a distinct nose-spot, white, blue or red : 9 species) : *petaurista, buttikoferi, martini, ludio, melanogenys, schmidti, nictitans, erythrotis, cephus.*
> Section B. CHLORONOTI (green monkeys ; 6 species) : *cynosurus, griseoviridis, callitrichus, lalandii, pygerythrus, erythrarchus.*

Section C. ERYTHRONOTI (above rufous ; beneath white : 2 species only: *patas, pyrrhonotus.*

Section D. MELANOCHIRI (arms, hands and feet black; 9 species) : *mona, albigularis, campbelli, samango, moloneyi, stairsi, erythrogaster, neglectus, leucampyx.*

Section E. AURICULATI (ears with long tufts ; 3 species) : *erxlebeni, pogonias, nigripes.*

Section F. BARBATI (with long, pointed, white beard ; 2 species) : *diana, brazzae.*

In an appendix, Sclater listed an additional fifteen species which he had not then personally seen and which, therefore, he was unable to assign definitely to any of his six sections. These were *C. boutourlinii* Giglioli, *C. flavidus* Peters, *C. grayi* Fraser, *C. labiatus* I. Geoffroy, *C. monoides* I. Geoffroy, *C. palatinus* Wagner, *C. picturatus* Santos, *C. signatus* Jentink, *C. stampflii* Jentink, *C. ochraceus* Peters, *C. rufoviridis* I. Geoffroy, *C. tantalus* Ogilby, *C. temmincki* Ogilby, *C. werneri* I. Geoffroy and *C. wolfi* Meyer.

In a later contribution in the same year (1893 b), after visiting the Florence Museum, where he examined the type of *C. boutourlinii*, he was able to prove to himself its distinctness from *C. albogularis* and to assign it to his melanochirine section of the genus. In the same contribution he published additional notes on *C. brazzae* and *C. stairsi*. A still later addition (Sclater, 1893 c) was the original description of *C. opisthostictus* stated to be allied to *C. samango* and therefore likewise assigned to the Melanochiri.

Sclater's work was to some extent supplemented by that of Matschie (1893), while Forbes (1894) adopted Sclater's scheme *in toto*, but for fourteen years thereafter no attempt was made—apart from Trouessart's (1897–9) *

---

* Trouessart's classification excludes *Miopithecus*, but introduced subgeneric titles and his arrangement is as follows :

Subfamily Cercopithecinae

Genus *Cercopithecus* Erxleben

    A. *Rhinostictus* Sclater, 1893 (= *Petaurista* Rchnb, 1863, *nec* Desmarest, 1825).
        petaurista, buttikoferi, erythrogaster, signatus, erythrotis, martini, nictitans, ludio, schmidti, melanogenys, stampflii, cephus.

    B. *Cercopithecus* proprement dit (= *Callithrix* Rchnb, 1863, *Chlorocebus* Gray, 1870, *Chloronoti* Sclater, 1893).
        cynosurus, sabaeus, callitrichus, werneri, pygerythrus, tantalus.

    C. *Erythrocebus* nobis (= *Chlorocebus* in part Gray, 1870, *C. erythronoti* Sclater, 1893).
        patas, pyrrhonotus, ochraceus, rufoviridis.

    D. *Mona* Rchnb, 1863 (= *Mona* + *Diademia* Rchnb, *C. melanochiri* Sclater, 1893).
        mona, albogularis, albotorquatus, boutourlinii, campbelli, samango, labiatus, opisthostictus, stairsi, moloneyi, neglectus, leucampyx, stuhlmanni.

    E. *Otopithecus* nobis, 1896 (= *C. auriculati* Sclater, 1893).
        grayi, pogonias, nigripes, wolfi.

    F. *Diana* Lesson, 1840 (= *C. barbati* Sclater, 1893).
        diana, roloway, brazzae.

In a later contribution Trouessart (1904–5, p. 10 *et seq.*) :

  (i) added *fantiensis* as a race of *petaurista*.

  (ii) recognized *ascanius* as a species with *histrio, melanogenys, picturatus* and *schmidti* as synonyms.

  (iii) added *preussi* to subgenus *Mona* alongside *albogularis* and also the following : *kolbi, omensis, centralis, francescae* and *l'hoesti*.

  (iv) reduced *erxlebeni* and *nigripes* to rank of subspecies of *pogonias*.

  (v) added *ignitus* to *Diana*.

exclusion of Sclater's *Cercopitheci erythronoti* to a new subgenus *Erythrocebus*—to interpolate the many new forms added to the literature since Sclater's fundamental revision.

An entirely new revision was produced by Pocock (1907) who was well acquainted with most of the species in the living state by virtue of his official position as Superintendent of the Zoological Society's menagerie, as well as being familiar with museum material.

Pocock divided the genus into thirteen groups which, however, included one, first described by himself as *C. nigroviridis*, which is now regarded as generically distinct. Another of Pocock's groups was that including Sclater's red-backed section which had been made into the genus *Erythrocebus* by Trouessart, but which Pocock did not, at that time adopt, although later (1925) he urged its acceptance.

Pocock's classification may be schematized thus :

A. *Diana* group (*Pogonocebus* Trt., 1906)
    1. *C. diana*
    2. *C. roloway*
B. *Neglectus* group (*C. barbati* Sclater, in part ; *Pogonocebus* Trt., in part)
    1. *C. neglectus* (with *brazziformis* as subspecies)
C. *Leucampyx* group (*Diademia* Rchnb, 1862)
    1. *C. leucampyx* (with subspecies *leucampyx, stuhlmanni, carruthersi, doggetti, nigrigenis, pluto, boutourlinii, opisthostictus* and *kandti*)
D. *Nictitans* group
    1. *C. nictitans*
    2. *C. martini*
E. *Albogularis* group
    1. *C. albogularis* (with *beirensis, rufilatus* and *albotorquatus* as subspecies)
    2. *C. kolbi* (with subsp. *hindei*)
    3. *C. moloneyi*
    4. *C. stairsi* (with subsp. *mossambicus*)
    5. *C. rufotinctus*
    6. *C. francescae*
    7. *C. preussi*
    8. *C. labiatus*
F. *Mona* group
    1. *C. mona*
    2. *C. campbelli*
    3. *C. burnetti*
    4. *C. denti*
    5. *C. wolfi*
    6. *C. grayi* (with *nigripes* as subspecies)
    7. *C. pogonias*
G. *L'hoesti* group
    1. *C. l'hoesti* (with *thomasi* as subspecies)
H. *Erythrogaster* group
    1. *C. erythrogaster*

I. *Petaurista group*
1. *C. petaurista* (with *buttikoferi* as subspecies)
2. *C. ascanius* (with *schmidti* as subspecies)
3. *C. signatus*

J. *Cephus* group
1. *C. cephus*
2. *C. erythrotis*
3. *C. sclateri*

K. *Aethiops* group
1. *C. sabaeus*
2. *C. aethiops* (with *ellenbecki* and *hilgerti* as subspecies)
3. *C. matschiei*
4. *C. djamdjamensis*
5. *C. tantalus* (with *budgetti* as subspecies)
6. *C. cynosuros*
7. *C. pygerythrus* (with *rufoviridis*, *whytei*, *johnstoni* and *centralis* as subspecies)
8. *C. nigroviridis*

L. *Talapoin* group
1. *C. talapoin* (with *ansorgei* as subspecies)

M. *Patas* group
1. *C. patas* (with *pyrrhonotus* as subspecies)

Notable improvements in Pocock's scheme are the recognition of the apartness of *C. nictitans*, *C. petaurista*, *C. ascanius* and *C. cephus*, and the association of the first-mentioned alongside his *leucampyx* section—albeit interpolated between the *leucampyx* and *albogularis* section. *C. neglectus* is justifiably divorced from the *diana* group, but the *Mona* section seems to have been taken over wholesale from earlier reviewers, after divesting it of *albogularis* and its congeners. In this, Pocock was less astute than Sclater and Trouessart, who both appreciated the distinctness of *pogonias* and its allies. However, Pocock correctly assessed the position of *wolfi*, which had been wrongly aligned with *pogonias* by Trouessart. The reason for Pocock's allocation of *erythrotis* and *sclateri* to his *cephus* group rather than with the *petaurista* group where it would seem to pertain is obscure. All the revisers seem to be in agreement as regards the composition of the group of green-backed guenons. Pocock's discovery of the new species, which he named *nigroviridis*, is important and its allocation to the *aethiops* group seemed justifiable as far as the available evidence permitted.

In Elliot's (1913) monograph the arrangement propounded by Pocock is largely followed, but the generic name *Lasiopyga* is resuscitated and subgeneric names (without definitions) are utilized for Pocock's groupings. Only eight subgenera are, however, recognized, since the *talapoin* and *patas* groups are given separate generic rank, and so also is *hamlyni*, which is separated under a new genus *Rhinostigma*—on quite indefensible grounds. This leaves the following subgenera of *Lasiopyga*, listed in the order in which Elliot treated them :

Subgenus 1. *Allochrocebus* (for *l'hoesti* and *insolita*)
     ,,   2. *Rhinostictus* (equivalent to Pocock's *petaurista* group)
     ,,   3. *Melanocebus* (equivalent to Pocock's *leucampyx* and *nictitans* groups combined)
     ,,   4. *Neocebus* * (equivalent to Pocock's *cephus* group with addition of two new forms, *cephodes* and *inobservata*)
     ,,   5. *Chlorocebus* (equivalent to Pocock's *aethiops* group with the following new additions : *griseisticta, alexandri, rubella, callida, lutea* and *silacea*)
     ,,   6. *Mona* (equivalent to Pocock's *mona* group with additional new forms, *pallida* and *petronellae*)
     ,,   7. *Insignicebus* (equivalent to Pocock's *albogularis* group with some new additions : *nubila, kinobotensis* [*sic*], *insularis, thomasi, insignis*)
     ,,   8. *Pogonocebus* (a reversion to Sclater's and Trouessart's conception, *i.e.* including *neglectus, brazzae* as well as *diana* and *roloway*)

Elliot, by accident or design, thus confirms Pocock's recognition of the relatively greater affinity of *nictitans* and *martini* with the *leucampyx* section than with the smaller spot-nosed species, but his retrograde step in reuniting *neglectus* with *diana* and *roloway* is unfortunate. Furthermore his general sequence shows little appreciation of the interrelationships of the recognized groups.

In 1925 Allen, studying the Primates of the Congo, minutely reviewed the taxonomic history of the genus, giving a critical appraisal of the relative merits of Pocock's and Elliot's schemes. His treatment follows the lines of Elliot's arrangement and nomenclature even to the recognition of Elliot's *Rhinostigma* whereof he makes the extraordinary statement that " *R. hamlyni* appears to me to be closely related to the *Lophocebus* section of *Cercocebus*. Elliot first recognized it as a mangabey and not a guenon, as supposed to be by Pocock, its first describer."

The serious error anent *C. hamlyni*, originated by Elliot, was pointed out by Pocock and rectified in 1925, where it was shown that Elliot in his description of *hamlyni* had combined characters based on a skin of the animal with cranial characters derived from a skull of a *Cercocebus* under the impression that it belonged to the skin. Pocock's paper appeared too late to prevent Allen (*loc. cit.*) from adopting *Rhinostigma*.

In a series of valuable papers Schwarz (1926 *a*, 1928 *a* and *b*) contributed meticulously careful observations on the systematics of *Cercopithecus*. His first two publications dealt in detail with the *aethiops* and *mona* groups ; the third is a résumé of his views on the whole genus. Schwarz recognized ten sections within the genus, of which one contained only the Talapoin. He thus reduced Pocock's groups by three by lumping together the *albogularis* group with the *leucampyx* group, recombining all the white-nosed forms as

---

* Elliot also (2, p. 224) uses this same name for a subgenus of macaques, thus invalidating its subsequent (*tom. cit.* p. 319) adoption for subdivision of *Cercopithecus*.

well as *C. erythrogaster* under a single species *C. nictitans* and by eliminating *C. nigroviridis* (which had been relegated by Lang, 1923, to a new genus, *Allenopithecus*).

In spite of his extremely careful analysis Schwarz's conception of the species within the genus is, as in other genera, whose revision he undertook, often too broad. Moreover, in spite of results derived from field work by later students he persisted to the end of his life in his views. Schwarz worked on the basis that, regardless of differing morphological, genetic and evolutionary values, all forms which approximately replace one another geographically " gehören alle noch einer Art (Formenkreis) an.", *i.e.* constitute a single species.

But Schwarz did not always abide by his own fundamental concepts in, for example, his acceptance of *petaurista* and *ascanius* and their allies as subspecies of *C. nictitans*. These do not even replace each other geographically, quite apart from their morphological and other distinctions. Both Schouteden (1947) and Haddow (1952) expressed dissatisfaction with this arrangement. The same criticism applies to Schwarz's treatment of *pogonias* and its variants as races of *C. mona*. Morphological distinctions were, however, recognized by Schwarz merely as indicating " sections " within a Formenkreis, hence his (1928 *b*) division of his *C. mona* as follows :

C. mona
  (a) *mona* section : for *campbelli, lowei* and *mona*
  (b) *pogonias* section : for *pogonias, grayi* and *nigripes*
  (c) *wolfi* section : for *wolfi, pyrogaster, elegans* and *denti.*

Most subsequent writers have slavishly accepted Schwarz's views without cavil. Raven and Hill (1942) in reviewing the status of *C. hamlyni* had occasion to examine museum material of the whole genus and recognized tentatively the following subdivisions within the genus :

1. *Diana* group : for *C. diana diana, C. d. roloway* and *C. dryas* (this last having been described as new by Schwarz in 1932).
2. *Neglectus* group : for *C. neglectus* only.
3. *Aethiops* group : a single species with races as of Schwarz, 1928.
4. *Cephus* group : for *C. c. cephus, C. c. erythrotis, C. p. petaurista, C. p. buttikoferi, C. a. ascanius, C. a. katangae, C. a. montanus, C. a. schmidti, C. a. cirrhorhinus, C. a. whitesidei.*
   C. erythrogaster } stated to be of questionable status, possibly races of *C. signatus* } *petaurista.*
   C. mona (with races as of Schwarz, 1928 *a*, but with *C. pogonias*, with *grayi* and *nigripes*, possibly specifically distinct).
   C. talapoin (with *ansorgei* as subspecies).
5. *Nictitans* group : for *C. n. nictitans* and *C. n. martini.*
6. *L'hoesti* group : for *C. l'hoesti l'hoesti* and *C. l'h. preussi.*
7. *Mitis* group : renaming of *leucampyx* group with content as of Schwarz 1928 *c*.
8. *Hamlyni* group : for *C. hamlyni.*

Raven and Hill conclude that " conceivably, more material will modify this grouping, but we have seen nothing indicative of intergradation between the species here listed ". In many respects their scheme is an improvement, especially inasmuch as the *petaurista* and *nictitans* are re-separated. Chief criticism is to be levelled against the incorporation of *petaurista* within an extremely heterogeneous *cephus* group ; with *C. erythrotis* reduced to the rank of a subspecies of *cephus* ; with the incorporation of the whole of Schwarz's *mona* group therein and—most indefensible of all—of *talapoin* also. Many subsequent writers have adopted Raven and Hill's modifications of Schwarz's scheme, but not apparently the only warrantable one—severance from each other of Greater and Lesser White-nosed monkeys.

Recent studies, which have resulted in a clearer picture of the relationships of many of the species of this genus, include the field work of Booth (1955, 1956) and Tappen (1960 a) ; the introduction of Mayr's (1942) concept of superspecies as applied to the *aethiops* Formenkreis by Dandelot (1959) ; and the work on chromosomes by various students (*vide antea*, pp. 131-134).

In the sequel the superspecies concept has been extended to all the principal " groups " of Pocock, with slight modifications and adjustments to meet more recent knowledge, and the species have been arranged according to a descending scale of chromosome numbers, in so far as these are available, on the assumption that diminution in number has occurred during evolution and therefore that the species with higher numbers are the more primitive. Subjoined is therefore the scheme adopted, followed by a key to distinguish the superspecies tentatively recognized.

Genus *Cercopithecus* Linnaeus, 1758

    I. Superspecies *C. mitis* Wolf, 1822

1. *C. mitis* Wolf, 1822	Diadem Monkey
(a) *C. m. mitis* Wolf, 1822	Pluto Monkey
(b) *C. m. boutourlinii* Giglioli, 1887	Boutourlini's Guenon
(c) *C. m. stuhlmanni* Matschie, 1893	Stuhlmann's Monkey
(d) *C. m. doggetti* Pocock, 1907	Doggett's Guenon
(e) *C. m. maesi* Lönnberg, 1919	
(f) *C. m. kandti* Matschie, 1905	Congo Red Monkey
(g) *C. m. schoutedeni* Schwarz, 1928	
(h) *C. m. opisthostictus* Sclater, 1893	Rump-spotted Guenon
2. *C. albogularis* Sykes, 1831	White-throated Guenon
(a) *C. a. albotorquatus* Pousargues, 1896	Pousargues White-throated Guenon
(b) *C. a. albogularis* Sykes, 1831	Sykes' Monkey
(c) *C. a. monoides* Geoffroy, 1841	Maritime White-throated Guenon
(d) *C. a. phylax* Schwarz, 1927	
(e) *C. a. kibonotensis* Lönnberg, 1910	Kilimanjaro Blue Monkey
(f) *C. a. kolbi* Neumann, 1902	Kolb's Guenon

(g) *C. a. moloneyi* Sclater, 1893   Moloney's Guenon

(h) *C. a. francescae* Thomas, 1902

(i) *C. a. nyasae* Schwarz, 1928   Nyasa White-throated Guenon

(j) *C. a. erythrarchus* Peters, 1852   Stairs' Guenon

(k) *C. a. schwarzi* Roberts, 1931

(l) *C. a. samango* Wahlberg, 1844   Samango Monkey or White-lipped Guenon

3. *C. nictitans* Linnaeus, 1766   Greater White-nosed Monkey

(a) *C. n. nictitans* Linnaeus, 1766   Hocheur Guenon

(b) *C. n. martini* Waterhouse, 1841   Martin's Guenon

(c) *C. n. stampflii* Jentink, 1888   Stampfli's Guenon

II. Superspecies *C. l'hoesti* Sclater, 1898   Mountain Guenons

4. *C. l'hoesti* Sclater, 1898   L'Hoest's Monkey

5. *C. preussi* Matschie, 1898   Preuss's or Cross's Monkey

III. Superspecies *C. mona* Schreber, 1774

6. *C. campbelli* Waterhouse, 1838

(a) *C. c. campbelli* Waterhouse, 1838   Campbell's Monkey ; Burnett's Monkey

(b) *C. c. lowei* Thomas, 1923   Lowe's Monkey

7. *C. mona* Schreber, 1774   Mona Monkey

8. *C. wolfi* Meyer, 1891

(a) *C. w. wolfi* Meyer, 1891   Wolf's Monkey

(b) *C. w. pyrogaster* Lönnberg, 1919   Fire-bellied Guenon

(c) *C. w. elegans* Dubois et Matschie, 1912

9. *C. denti* Thomas, 1907   Dent's Guenon

10. *C. pogonias* Bennett, 1833   Crowned Guenons

(a) *C. p. pogonias* Bennett, 1833   Crowned Guenon : Golden-bellied Guenon

(b) *C. p. grayi* Fraser, 1850   Gray's or Erxleben's Guenon

(c) *C. p. nigripes* du Chaillu, 1860   Black-footed Guenon

(d) *C. p. schwarzianus* Schouteden, 1946

IV. Superspecies *C. petaurista* Schreber, 1775

11. *C. petaurista* Schreber, 1775   Lesser White-nosed Monkey

(a) *C. p. petaurista* Schreber, 1775

(b) *C. p. buttikoferi* Jentink, 1886   Büttikofer's Monkey

12. *C. ascanius* Audebert, 1799   Black-cheeked White-nosed Monkey

(a) *C. a. ascanius* Audebert, 1799   Black-cheeked White-nosed Monkey

(b) *C. a. katangae* Lönnberg, 1919   Katanga Black-cheeked White-nosed Monkey

(c) *C. a. whitesidei* Thomas, 1909	Whiteside's Guenon ; Yellow-nosed Monkey
(d) *C. a. montanus* Lorenz, 1914	Montane Red-tailed Guenon
(e) *C. a. schmidti* Matschie, 1892	Schmidt's Monkey
13. *C. erythrotis* Waterhouse, 1838	Red-eared Nose-spotted Guenon
(a) *C. e. erythrotis* Waterhouse, 1838	
(b) *C. e. camerunensis* Hayman, 1940	
(c) *C. e. sclateri* Pocock, 1904	Sclater's White-nosed Monkey
14. *C. erythrogaster* Gray, 1866	Red-bellied Guenon

V. Superspecies *C. cephus* Linnaeus, 1766 — Moustached Guenons

15. *C. cephus* Linnaeus, 1758 — Moustached Monkey
(a) *C. c. cephus* Linnaeus, 1758 — Red-tailed Moustached Monkey

(b) *C. c. cephodes* Pocock, 1907 — Grey-tailed Moustached Monkey

VI. Superspecies *C. hamlyni* Pocock, 1907

16. *C. hamlyni* Pocock, 1907 — Owl-faced Guenon; Hamlyn's Monkey

VII. Superspecies *C. neglectus* Schlegel, 1876 — Chestnut-browed Guenons

17. *C. neglectus* Schlegel, 1876 — Schlegel's Guenon ; de Brazza's Monkey

VIII. Superspecies *C. diana* Linnaeus, 1758

18. *C. diana* Linnaeus, 1758 — Diana Monkey
(a) *C. d. diana* Linnaeus, 1758
(b) *C. d. roloway* Schreber, 1774 — Roloway Monkey
(c) *C. d. dryas* Schwarz, 1932 — Dryas Guenon

IX. Superspecies *C. aethiops* Linnaeus, 1758 — Savannah Monkeys

19. *C. aethiops* Linnaeus, 1758 — Grivets

aethiops group
(a) *C. a. aethiops* Linnaeus, 1758
(b) *C. a. hilgerti* O. Neumann, 1902
(c) *C. a. ellenbecki* O. Neumann, 1902
(d) *C. a. zavattarii* de Beaux, 1943

tantalus group
(e) *C. a. tantalus* Ogilby, 1841 — Tantalus
(f) *C. a. marrensis* Thomas and Wroughton, 1923
(g) *C. a. budgetti* Pocock, 1907

20. *C. pygerythrus* F. Cuvier, 1821   Vervets

pygerythrus group
- (a) *C. p. centralis* O. Neumann, 1900   Black-faced Vervet
- (b) *C. p. arenarius* Heller, 1913
- (c) *C. p. callidus* Hollister, 1912   Naivasha Vervet
- (d) *C. p. johnstoni* Pocock, 1907   East African Vervet ; Yellow Monkey
- (e) *C. p. excubitor* Schwarz, 1926
- (f) *C. p. nesiotes* Schwarz, 1926
- (g) *C. p. rufoviridis* I. Geoffroy, 1842   Reddish-green Guenon
- (h) *C. p. whytei* Pocock, 1907
- (i) *C. p. cloeti* Roberts, 1931
- (j) *C. p. ngamiensis* Roberts, 1932   Okavango Vervet
- (k) *C. p. marjoriae* Bradfield, 1936
- (l) *C. p. pygerythrus* F. Cuvier, 1821   Black-chinned Vervet

cynosuros group
- (m) *C. p. cynosuros* Scopoli, 1786   Malbrouck Monkey

21. *C. sabaeus* Linnaeus, 1766   Green Monkey

Superspecies *incertae sedis*

22. *C. asnoti* Pilgrim, 1913

The position of *C. l'hoesti* is somewhat doubtful. It has usually been placed near to the White-throated Guenons, but its chromosome number, stated to be 72, is the highest in the genus. This needs confirmation. The question of the separation of *C. albogularis* from *C. mitis* is discussed below.

KEY TO THE SUPERSPECIES OF THE GENUS *CERCOPITHECUS*

I. Prevailing colour light greenish or greyish   .   .   *C. aethiops*

II. Prevailing colour not greenish
- (A) Limbs distal to elbows and knees wholly black
  - (*a*) Belly blackish ; whiskers white   . . . *C. l'hoesti*
  - (*b*) Belly whitish ; whiskers dark   . . . *C. mitis*
- (B) Limbs distal to elbows and knees not wholly black
  - (*a*) Face black
    - (α) With a white brow band and a long white beard . *C. diana*
    - (β) With chestnut brow band and short white beard *C. neglectus*
  - (*b*) Face with muzzle flesh-coloured   . . . *C. mona*
  - (*c*) Face with white nose-spot or other pattern
    - (α) Nose spot cordate, white, yellow or red . *C. petaurista*
    - (β) Nose spot oval, white   . . . *C. nictitans*
    - (γ) A transverse pale blue stripe on lip ; whiskers yellow   . . . . . *C. cephus*
    - (δ) A median vertical white streak on nose . *C. hamlyni*

As regards cranial distinctions between these subdivisions of the genus, little has been published, due doubtless to the inadequacy of the material.

The general consensus appears to be that apart from individual, sexual and age variations there is no hard and fast cranial differentiation. Raven and Hill (1942) found *hamlyni* to differ craniologically from other guenons and maintain further that the " species—groups " can be characterized cranially to allow the identification of the majority of the skulls without skins or mismatched, at least as regards the group, but that species within a group cannot be separated satisfactorily except on external characters. As regards size, Raven and Hill arrange crania in three categories, large, medium and small. The last includes only the Talapoin. Largest crania occur in *C. mitis*, *C. nictitans*, *C. l'hoesti*, *C. hamlyni*, *C. diana*, *C. neglectus* and *C. aethiops*. Skulls of the undermentioned are considerably smaller : *C. petaurista*, *C. ascanius*, *C. cephus*, *C. mona* and *C. pogonias*. Quite apart from size, I found it quite simple to differentiate skulls of *C. nictitans martini* and *C. mona* in a large series of each collected in the Cameroons. Verheyen (1962), using craniological (including craniometric) features, finds *Erythrocebus* and *Allenopithecus* readily separable from *Cercopithecus* s.s., but the same does not apply to *C. talapoin* except as regards size. This author would not commit himself to craniological subdivision of *Cercopithecus* s.s.

Apropos of craniological variability, the work of Ashton and Zuckerman (1950–51) on the effect of geographical isolation on the skulls of Green Monkeys (*C. sabaeus*) introduced into the West Indies is of major importance.

I. Superspecies *CERCOPITHECUS MITIS* Wolf, 1822 *

(SYN. : Genus *Diademia* Reichenbach, 1862 ; *Cercopitheci melanochiri* of Sclater, 1893, and Forbes, 1894 ; *Leucampyx + Albogularis* and *Nictitans* groups of Pocock, 1907 ; subgenera *Melanocebus + Insignicebus* of Elliot, 1913 ; *Leucampyx* group of Schwarz, 1928)

All members of this group are characterized by the form of the head, especially in the smooth backward and downwardly directed adpressed whiskers, which form a neat, smooth, ovoid pad, composed of annulated hairs, each side of the head ; a beard is lacking and the face of triangular outline rather well haired except around the eyes. A contrasted white hairy patch on the nose occurs in one species (*C. nictitans*). In all forms too, the limbs are predominantly black, but this may be variably relieved by grey speckling, at any rate on the hind-limbs proximally. Hands and feet entirely black. Under parts predominantly black or grey. Typically the lumbo-sacral area is more brightly coloured than the rest of the dorsum (cf. superspecies *C. mona*).

Compared with members of other groups, the members of this superspecies are of relatively large size and, in demeanour, staid and aloof. A considerable discrepancy in size occurs between the sexes.

* *Abbildungen und Beschreibungen merkwürdiger naturgeschichtlicher Gegenstände*, ii. 145, pl. 34.

PLATE XIII

Photo: P. Street

Cercopithecus mitis stuhlmanni, adult ♂ in London Zoo.   In threatening attitude

PLATE XIV

Photo: Sorby

Cercopithecus albogularis kolbi, adult ♂, in Chester Zoo

Diploid chromosome number 72 (Chiarelli, 1962 *a*).

As here understood this superspecies comprises the monkeys formerly regarded as three distinct species, *C. mitis*, *C. albogularis* and *C. nictitans*, with their variants. In recent years, following Schwarz (1928 *c*), *C. albogularis* has been united with *C. mitis*, but according to C. Booth (1962) working in East Africa, *C. mitis*, as listed in Allen's (1939) check list, comprises two clearly distinct forms, known by local residents respectively as Blue Monkey and Sykes' Monkey. The former is the local representative of *mitis* proper, the latter is the local race of *C. albogularis*, but pending a review of the scientific status and nomenclature of the group, it was found more convenient to discuss them under their English names. The need for this arose when it was found that the ranges of the two forms are separated by the Great Rift Valley: Sykes' Monkeys are restricted to the east of the valley and Blue Monkeys to the west. This natural barrier prevents intermingling of the two forms, hence their divergence—but whether this divergence is sufficient to warrant more than sub-specific status is a moot point. As the two replace each other geographically, they are of subspecific rank only—if Schwarz's estimate of what constitutes a species is accepted. Pocock (1907), as already shown (p. 392), recognized all three species as representatives of separate " groups ". Elliot even regarded *leucampyx* and *albogularis* as types of distinct subgenera. But Schwarz (*loc. cit.*) has shown that *mitis* and *albogularis* are connected by transitional forms. For example, in the Katanga and Bangweolo regions, there is a grey-headed " *leucampyx* " (*C. m. opisthostictus*) ; while Boutourlini's Monkey (*C. m. boutourlinii*) of southern Abyssinia and the white-throated *C. albotorquatus* of the Juba river are described as perfectly intermediate between Stuhlmann's Monkey (= Blue Monkey—a typical " *leucampyx* ") and *C. kolbi*, a well-defined variant of the eastern Sykes' monkey.

On the other hand recent field studies have produced no evidence of intergrading between *C. m. opisthostictus* and *C. albogularis moloneyi* where their ranges are separated by a few miles (see below, p. 414).

RANGE

The *mitis* group is represented in forested areas of West Africa by *C. nictitans* whilst *C. mitis* and *C. albogularis* are predominantly eastern in range, where they extend from southern Abyssinia (*C. m. boutourlinii*) to the eastern part of Cape Province, South Africa (*C. samango*). *C. mitis* also has one western form—the nominate race from Angola.

A general review of the superspecies, with plotting of the localities whence the various recognizable forms have been collected, leads to the conclusion that there exist three north–south clines. Two of these are very well marked and range respectively east and west of the Great Rift Valley

2 D

without, so far as can be determined, intermingling. These are (i) the *albogularis* cline to the east, between the Rift Valley and the coast, with an extensive latitudinal range from Somalia (*albotorquatus*) to the Cape (*samango*), and (ii) the *mitis* cline to the west, with a broad spectrum of forms extending from Abyssinia (*boutourlinii*) to Rhodesia (*opisthostictus*).

A third West African (Guinea) cline includes the geographical races of *C. nictitans* which may link up in the east with the *mitis* cline.

1. *CERCOPITHECUS MITIS* (Wolf, 1822 *)

Diademed Guenon

(SYN. : *Cercopithecus diana* (le diane femelle) F. Cuvier, 1824, pl. xvi, *nec* Linnaeus, 1758 ; *Simia leucampyx* Fischer, 1829, p. 20 ; *C. diadematus* I. Geoffroy, 1834 ; *Cercopithecus leucampyx* Sclater, 1893, Forbes, 1894, Pocock, 1907, and most modern authors, including Schwarz, 1928. *Lasiopyga leucampyx* Elliot, 1913)

VERNACULAR NAMES : French, *cercopithèque à diadème, singe argenté* ; German, *Diademaffe. Grossbartige Meerkatze, Sanfte Meerkatze* (Wolf, 1822).

TYPE LOCALITY : " Guinea "—(probably = Angola). Original description taken from a captive specimen in a travelling menagerie (in Nürnberg) ; it is illustrated in colour. The type of both Fischer's *leucampyx* and Geoffroy's *diadematus* was based on F. Cuvier's *diane femelle*—a living specimen in the Paris menagerie whose portrait in colour forms Plate 14 of Cuvier's work.

NOMENCLATURE : Earlier authors have usually treated the Diademed Guenon under Fischer's name *leucampyx*, but Schwarz (1933) first pointed out that the earlier name *mitis* was used in 1822 in a little known work by Johann Wolf, whose description applies without doubt to the Angolan race of the species.

CHARACTERS

PELAGE : ADULT MALE.—It is difficult to give an over-all picture of *C. mitis* in view of the remarkable variations found in different geographical regions—beyond the remarks made under the superspecies.

From *C. nictitans* it differs in lacking the contrasted nasal patch, the face being blackish-slaty blue and relatively well clothed with short hairs which vary in colour on different parts of the face without, however, forming any definite circumscribed pattern.

From the *albogularis* series the more typical forms of *mitis* differ in being dark-headed and with the back either black, ticked with whitish, greenish or even reddish ; the *albogularis* forms always showing some red on the lower back and with the head markedly paler than the back. In true *mitis* the throat is never sharply contrasted white, though chin and throat may be whitish or grey, paler than the rest of the under parts.

Ears are provided with well developed hairy tufts, almost always white.

* *Abbildungen und Beschreibungen merkwürdiger naturgeschichtlicher Gegenstände*, ii. 145, pl. 34.

There is no black supraorbital band or dark stripe on cheek or temple, but often a paler, speckled brow band (as in Cuvier's type) contrasting with the black crown.

Cheeks clothed with adpressed annulated hairs, usually speckled grey and black, contrasting with black crown and nape; occasionally they are themselves black.

Arms black, the black often continuous over shoulders with opposite side. Forearms black laterally, dark, but not black medially, the two shades intergrading along margins. Legs black on lateral sides, sometimes speckled on thighs, medially dark grey.

ADULT FEMALE.—Differs from the male only in smaller size.

JUVENILE.—See under subspecies.

ECOLOGY AND ETHOLOGY

C. mitis is primarily a forest species and is recorded from forests from approximately 3000 feet up to montane forests at 10,000 feet, and also occurs in adjacent savanna and in wooded savanna (e.g. in the Katanga region) containing gallery forests. West of about 25° E. it is sparsely scattered and records are few. None extend west of the Ubangi—except for the isolated C. m. mitis which is confined to north-western Angola.

According to Schouteden (1947), C. mitis is confined in the Congo area to deep equatorial forests, gallery forests and savanna woodland. One form shows a preference for high bamboo forests, while another frequents swamp forests and may even descend into treeless papyrus swamp to feed.

Haddow gives the diet of the Uganda representative of the species as fruits, leaves and shoots. They are not there implicated as raiders of cultivated crops, but according to Booth, in Kenya, they raid maize, potatoes and legumes.

Cynthia Booth (1962) records seeing mixed groups of the Blue Monkey (C. mitis stuhlmanni) with a C. pygerythrus subsp. Its ecological range extends into drier forests where it overlaps the territory of the local Vervet, although more typically it prefers wetter forests, where it resides in company with Colobus abyssinicus, with which it forms temporary associations.

Their method of eating maize is to peel back the husk in human fashion; potatoes are cleaned by rubbing back and forth between the palms of the hands.

Fighting does not occur between C. mitis and Colobus, but does occur between individuals of C. mitis; males, that have borne old scars, are reported as having been shot.

In temperament, individuals of C. mitis, and indeed of the whole Formenkreis are, by cercopithecine standards, rather stolid and aloof. They are more sedate and less demonstrative than members of, for example, the petaurista or ascanius assemblages.

DISTRIBUTION (MAP 2)

Except for the typical race which is confined, so far as known, to a limited area of West Africa in north-western Angola, *C. mitis* is a central and eastern species ranging from Central Abyssinia southwards to Katanga and neighbouring parts of Northern Rhodesia. It is for the most part restricted to forests west of the Great Rift Valley, at least in Kenya.

(a) *C. mitis mitis* Wolf, 1822,* Angolan Diademed Monkey, Pluto Monkey

> (*Syn.*: *Simia leucampyx* Fischer, 1829, p. 20 ; *C. diadematus* I. Geoffroy, 1834, p. 51 ; *C. dilophos* Ogilby, 1838, p. 343 (based on Cuvier's *diane femelle*) ; Temminck, 1853, p. 36 ; *C. pluto* Gray, 1848, p. 56 ; *C. samango* Peters, 1865, p. 400 ; *C. leucampyx nigrigenis* Pocock, 1907, p. 692)

> *Vernacular names* : French, *cercopithèque diadème*.

> *Type locality* : See under species. Type of *leucampyx* : none preserved. Type of *dilophos*—the *diane femelle* of F. Cuvier (based on an animal in the Paris menagerie). Type locality of *pluto*, Angola. Type in British Museum (No. 50.7.9.2),† *ex* Zoological Gardens. Type locality of *nigrigenis*, West Africa. Type ♀, a menagerie animal from the London Zoo, exhibited as *C. leucampyx* on Sclater's authority ; now in British Museum.

> PELAGE : ADULT MALE.—Face slaty-blue, with nose, lips and chin covered with short, white hairs. A conspicuous bow-shaped brow-band, white tinged with yellow. Crown, nape, shoulders, arms, legs and tail black ; chest and belly dark grey. Back, sacral region and thighs sharply differentiated from shoulders by grey effect produced by alternate black and white annulations on individual hairs. Cheek below eye-ear line covered with grey, speckled hairs, this pattern extending posteriorly on to sides of neck. In the type specimen of *C. pluto* Gray, there is a black patch on the preauricular region, but the rest of the cheek is speckled black and grey. The brow band is not sharply demarcated behind from the crown which also is not completely black, some speckling being found as far as the nape. In Pocock's *nigrigenis* the whole cheek-patch is black.

> For the above reasons Pocock, although admitting that *pluto* had latterly been synonymized with *leucampyx* (=*mitis*), felt that *pluto* should be resuscitated, chiefly on the grounds that the brow band lacks the definition of that in typical *mitis* and in his *nigrigenis*, thereby approaching *C. boutourlinii*. He described the animal with a completely black cheek-patch as a new subspecies (*C. m. nigrigenis*).

> My examination of the type of *pluto* revealed also that the lips are black like the face, but sparsely covered with white hairs. Otherwise it resembles the type of *nigrigenis*.

> There can be little doubt, however, that these features are within the normal range of variation of a single race and it is, to say the least, unlikely that more than one race occurs in the limited area of West Africa where *C. mitis* is distributed.

> ADULT FEMALE.—Differing from the male only in smaller size.

> JUVENILE.—In his description of the *diane femelle*, Cuvier noted pelage changes that had occurred during its sojourn in the Paris menagerie. When it arrived its

---

* *Loc. cit.*

† It lacks the skull. Ticket reads " apparently not a synonym of *moloneyi* " in Schwarz's handwriting. For discussion of synonymization of *pluto* with *leucampyx* (=*mitis*) see Lydekker (1902).

head, neck, shoulders, arms, forearms, hands, chest, belly and tail were uniformly black, with slightly less intensity on the under parts and greater part of the tail. Back and sides were speckled black and white, and the " favoris " black and yellow, and there was some yellowish also in the white brow band. Some white hairs on chin but not tending to form a beard (a point made by Cuvier in conformity with his belief that he was dealing with a female of *C. diana*).

Face described by Cuvier as violaceous, with the bluish element predominating over the cheek-bones, and a reddish element around the eyes and on the muzzle.

DIMENSIONS * (in millimetres) :

Locality	Number	Sex	Head and Body	Tail	Foot
Benguela (?)	Leiden Mus. 2572	♀	*c.* 520	*c.* 740	121
Angola	,, 2600	♀			
,,	,, 2504	♀			
,,	,, 2585	♂			
,,	Brit. Mus. 50.7.9.2	♂			Type of *pluto*

SKULL.—Cranial Dimensions † (in millimetres) :

Locality	Number	Sex	Maximum Cranial Length	Basal Length	Biparietal	Basion-bregma Height	Least Frontal Breadth	Bimastoid	Bizygomatic	Palatal Length	Breadth Rostrum behind Canine
Benguela (?)	Leiden Mus. 2572	♀	100·9	68·7	56·4	45·2	40·4	57	65·9	38·5	26·1
Angola	,,	♀	100·9	69·2	56·4	46·7	41·1	55·6	64·2	34·4	25·8
,,	,,	♀	99·4	68·9	57·5	48·3	40·8	59·1	68·4	33·1	26·1
,,	,,	♂	109·3	83·4	59·4	51·2	48·1	60·1	74·2	39·4	29·8
,,	Brit. Mus. Type of *pluto*	♂	102·7	72·6	—	47·8	44·1	58	69·4	34·4	29·2

DISTRIBUTION.—The only form of *C. mitis* inhabiting West Africa, where it is confined to an area south of the Congo in Angola. Specimens in zoos and museums have usually been recorded as from Benguela, which is, in all probability, merely their port of departure from the country, *e.g.* two presented to the London Zoo by Messrs. de Camara and Barnes, 9 October 1927 (*Proc. Zool. Soc.*, 1928, p. 265). Definite locality records in the literature are Sansamanda, Pango Andongo district (Peters, 1865) ; Columbo and Loanda (Bocage, 1889) ; and Dondo (Elliot, 1913). All these are in north-western Angola. A report of one from the Manyema district just north of the Congo mouth is dubious (Schouteden, 1947).

The range inland is unknown, so that whether or not it meets and intergrades with any of the eastern races of *mitis* is uncertain.

* From Hill and Carter (1941).　　† From Hill and Carter (1941).

(b) *C. mitis boutourlinii* Giglioli, 1887,* Boutourlini's Guenon

(*Syn.*: *C. albigularis* Giglioli, 1888, *nec.* Sykes; *C. omensis* Thomas, 1900, p. 801)

Vernacular names: None recorded.

Type locality: Kaffa, Southern Abyssinia. Type ♀ collected by Dr. Traversi; in Florence Museum. Topotype adult in British Museum (from Charada forest, Kaffa, alt. 600 feet) collected by W. N. Macmillan. Type locality of *C. omensis*: Mursu, Omo river, which flows southwards into Lake Rudolf. Type a juvenile in British Museum. Pocock considered this form to be obviously more nearly related to *leucampyx* (=*mitis*) than to *albogularis*, with which Giglioli, Sclater and Forbes compared it—a mistake which probably misled Thomas into describing the type of *C. omensis* as a new form.

PELAGE: ADULT MALE.—Face slaty blue, paler round eyes and muzzle, the latter covered with white hairs. Ears almost nude, with a hairy pencil on concave surface. Frontal diadem not sharply differentiated from crown, anterior hairs darker than in *stuhlmanni*. Crown and nape blackish but speckled with yellowish grey. No black patch on preauricular region.

Shoulders black, with some grey speckling, at least in midline. Rest of back and flanks speckled greyish-yellow; tail speckled at base only, the rest black. Body hairs long and rough.

Belly uniformly black, without annulations.

Lips, chin and throat with white hairs, " a smudge of black defining the white of the lips ". (Description based on the topotype in the British Museum.)

ADULT FEMALE.—According to Sclater, smaller and showing less annulation of hairs on head and back.

JUVENILE.—Hair over shoulders long, silky, contrasting with the harsh fur of the adult. Over shoulders, upper arms and legs the hairs are grey-based with darker distal parts—not, however, annulated. No frontal diadem present; ear tufts white; throat dirty white. Tail black, save for the last 50 mm. beneath, which is white, contrasting sharply with the black dorsum and sides (*ex* type of *C. omensis* in British Museum).

DIMENSIONS of topotype adult.—Head and body, 600 mm.; tail, 700 mm.; foot, 145 mm.; ear, 30 mm.

SKULL.—CRANIAL DIMENSIONS (in millimetres) of topotype: Maximum cranial length, 116·4; Occipito-nasal length, 95·6; Bizygomatic, 75·6; Maximum cranial breadth, 58·3; Least frontal, 41·4; Palatal length, 81·9; Upper cheek-teeth, 46·4; Mandibular length, 78·2; Lower cheek-teeth, 32·9.

DISTRIBUTION.—The most northerly ranging form of *C. mitis* in the east. Ranges over central and southern Abyssinia. Recorded from Djimma, a province in central Abyssinia, south of Gojjam and from the type locality Kaffa, a province to the south of Shoa. The Charada forest in Kaffa, altitude 600 feet, is the source of a specimen in the British Museum. The range extends along the Omo river, which flows southwards into Lake Rudolf. At Mursu on the Omo, 40 miles north of Lake Rudolf, the type juvenile described by Thomas as *C. omensis* was collected. Starck and Frick state that this race occurs in the Gojjam Province and according to de Beaux its northern range extends as far as Lake Tana. Starck and Frick give the total latitudinal range as between 5° and 11° N.

* *Zool. Anz.*, X, 510.

Note.—Skins of Boutourlini's Guenon are marketed openly in Djimma and Djibat (Starck and Frick).

(c) *C. mitis stuhlmanni* Matschie, 1893,* Stuhlmann's Monkey

(*Syn.* : *C. otoleucus* Sclater, 1902, p. 237 ; *C. neumanni* Matschie, 1905 ; *C. carruthersi* Pocock, 1907, p. 691 ; *C. princeps* Elliot, 1909, p. 304 ; *Lasiopyga leucampax* (sic) *mauae* Heller, 1913, p. 7 ; *C. schubotzi* Lönnberg, 1917, p. 36 ; *C. elgonis* Lönnberg, 1919.)

Vernacular name : Blue Monkey, of English-speaking inhabitants of East Africa.

Type locality : North of Kinyawanga, north-west of Lake Albert, Congo. Moreau *et al.* (1946) corrected this to " North of Kinyawanga, near Beni, Semliki Valley ", pointing out that Kinyawanga is not to the north-west of Lake Albert, but many miles south of it. It is in the Semliki Valley, west of the river at altitude 950 metres on Stuhlmann's route between Lesse and the old station at Beni. Ituri, cited in the original account 29° 35′ E., 0° 25′ N. is a misprint for Itiri. Type in Berlin Museum. Type locality of *otoleucus*, Latuka mountains (now called Imatong mountains) 100 miles east of Upper Nile in northern Uganda ; type lived in London Zoo 1.3.1902 till 29.1.1911, now in British Museum, collected by Major Delmé Radcliffe. Type locality of *carruthersi* : Ruwenzori east, 10,000 feet (= Mabuku valley). Type in British Museum (No. 6.7.1.1), collected by D. Carruthers. No skull. Type locality of *princeps* : Fort Portal, Mpanga forest, Toro, Uganda. Type skin and skull in British Museum (No. 7.4.6.6), collected by R. E. Dent. Sex not stated, but evidently male (Allen, 1925). Type locality of *mauae* : Summit of Mau escarpment, between Londiani and Sirgoit, Kenya. Type in U.S. National Museum. Type locality of *schubotzi* : Mawambi, Ituri river, Congo. Type, adult male, in Berlin Museum (Nos. 33607, 33608) collected by Dr. H. Schubotz. Type locality of *elgonis* : Mt. Elgon, Kenya. Based on three adults—all in Tervuren Museum. Type locality of *neumanni* : Kwa Kitoto, North Kavirondo, Tanganyika. Moreau *et al.* (1946) maintain that all the Kavirondo country is in Kenya and the site of Kitoto's or Kwa Kitoto is in the Nyando Valley near Muhoroni, 30 miles east of Kisumu. Type in Berlin Museum (*fide* Elliot).

Pelage : Adult Male.—Face deep slaty-blue, paler round the eyes and on muzzle. Dorsum nasi clothed with downwardly directed black hairs, a few of which, at the root of the nose, show a single white annulus, the rest being uniformly black. The black tract ends abruptly below, the rostral part of the nose being clothed with short, soft, downy white hairs which show a lateral trend, except towards the narial margins where they are more downwardly directed. Lips with longer white hairs of bristly character, downwardly directed on upper lip, diverging radially from a median point on lower lip, and continuing on to chin and throat.

Frontal diadem indistinctly outlined, the hairs directed forwards and upwards, black with alternating annuli of light yellow. Laterally these hairs are continued on to the cheek-pads and over the maxillae, where they end abruptly in front along a line passing from the nasal bridge to the angle of the gape.

Ears dusky, with heavily developed tufts of white hairs. (Pocock says they were pinkish white in *otoleucus* when alive.) Crown and nape jet black ; same colour continued on to shoulders and arms. Rest of body above and sides speckled grey and black. Thighs similar, not sharply demarcated from sacral area, but lower legs black. Tail, like back, becoming wholly black towards tip.

* *Sb. Ges. naturf. Fr., Berlin,* p. 225. Named in honour of Franz Stuhlmann, a companion of Emin Pasha on his expedition to Lake Victoria in 1890.

Belly black, speckled like the back but less thickly—continuing on to medial side of thighs. Chin and throat whitish, but a dark transverse band on chest crossing the paler tract.

All the forms listed in the synonymy are within the normal range of variation of the subspecies.

ADULT FEMALE.—Similar to the male in all save size.

JUVENILE.—Newborn ♂ animals weigh 402 gm. (placenta 80 gm.). At birth the face is barely pigmented, and only on the muzzle, which has the same distribution and colour of hairs as in the adult. The frontal diadem is merely represented by a band of stiff, forwardly-directed black hairs. The unpigmented body is uniformly covered with short, soft, downy hairs uniformly black. Palms and soles only very slightly dusky ; nails brownish-grey. Callosities unpigmented. Prepuce pigmented slightly, but scrotal and perineal areas not so. Testes prepenial. Iris bluish.

VARIATIONS.—These have been very fully considered by Allen (1925, p. 394 *et seq.*)

DIMENSIONS of a male born in London Zoo, 2 July 1950, died 1955 (parents from Uganda) : weight, 4449.4 gm. ; crown-rump length, 510 mm. ; tail, 490 mm. ; head length (muzzle-occiput), 120 mm. ; foot, 165 mm. Ear : physiognomic length, 47 mm. ; morphological length, 38 mm. Of a newborn male : crown-rump length, 202 mm. ; tail, 231 mm. ; foot, 72 mm. Ear : physiognomic length, 29 mm. ; morphological length, 26·5 mm. ; physiognomic breadth, 23 mm. ; morphological breadth, 16 mm.

SKULL.—Cranial dimensions of adults (in millimetres) :

	Locality	Number	Sex	Max. Cranial Length	Condylo-basal Length	Biparietal	Bizygomatic	Least Frontal	Bimastoid	Mandibular Length	Upper Cheek-teeth	Lower Cheek-teeth
U.S. Nat. Mus. From Heller	Kakumega	182386	♂	109	97·1		70·8	43·7	57	78·3	27·2	34·2
	Lukosa R.	182361	♂	112·5	90·4		72	43·7	60·3	76·3	27·3	33·5
	,,	182378	♀	114	93·1		78·3	45·8	63·7	81·8	27·1	33·3
	,,	182370	♂	97·8	78·3		64·4	39·9	54·1	69·3	24·7	30·7
	Mau escarpment	173002	♂	121·5	99·2	76·8		40·7	62·4	88·1	27·5	35·1 [1]
	Mount Elgon			100		58	67·5				26·5	30 [2]
	Mabuka Valley Ruwenzori dist.			94		52·5	62	41		62·3	26	30·5 [3]

[1] Type of *mauae*.   [2] Type of *elgonis*.   [3] Type of *carruthersi*.

DISTRIBUTION AND ECOLOGY.—Western Kenya : Mau escarpment (Heller, 1913), Mount Elgon. Uganda : Latuka Mountains ; Kipia, Imatong mountains ; Char, Didinga mountains (Setzer, 1956) ; Ruwenzori east ; Mpanga forest. Congo : Rutschuru, gallery forest (Poll, 1939), Ituri river.

Schouteden (1947) states the range extends from the Uelle in Aruwimi to Lake Albert, southwards to Lake Edward and north-western Tanganyika. He gives numerous Congolese localities.

In 1954 Schwarz claimed that the range of *neumanni* falls within that of *stuhlmanni* and therefore regarded it as merely within the range of variation of the latter. He gave the southern limit of the range as Mbulu, 60 miles south of Ngorongoro on the western rim of the Rift Valley, and only a short distance short of the westernmost location for *C. albogularis kibonotensis*. Specimens from Mbulu collected by L. Heck were on exhibit for several years in the Berlin Zoo.

Stott (1960) says the southern limit is usually given as a line extending from Lake George to Masaka in Uganda, the only races of *C. mitis* to the south thereof being *C. m. doggetti* and *C. m. kandti*; but in October 1958 he and C. J. Selsor encountered several troops of *C. m. stuhlmanni* south of the above mentioned line, (*a*) at the northern end of the Kayonsa forest (alt. 6000 feet approx.), a single animal was feeding in a low tree alongside the Luhiza road, about 55 miles north of Kisoro, Kigezi district; (*b*) about 15 miles nearer Kisoro on the same road, another troop was encountered at altitude 7000 feet, feeding on bamboo shoots; (*c*) another 4 miles to the south, still another troop was seen. Therefore three distinct races of *mitis* are recorded from the Kayonsa forest, but their ecological preferences seem to differ; *C. m. stuhlmanni* occurs in montane broad-leafed forests and adjacent bamboo groves; *C. m. doggetti* in stands of papyrus in the marshy valley bottoms, and *C. m. kandti* in montane bamboo forests.

According to Booth (1962), the range of the Blue Monkey is separated in Kenya from that of Sykes' Monkey (*C. albogularis*) by the Rift Valley, the former residing west of the valley in forests up to 10,000 feet altitude; lower altitudes in Western Kenya are 3000 feet.

The eastern limit is also given as the western rim of the Rift Valley by Schwarz (1954) who affirms that *neumanni* is to be synonymized with *stuhlmanni*, because its type locality falls within the distributional area of the latter.

This race is said by Schwarz to be common in now isolated strips of mountain forest throughout Uganda and western Kenya, also in the larger Mabira and Kakamega forests and on the Mau plateau.

Schwarz saw three living juveniles in the Khartoum Zoo. These had come from the Latuka mountains (now called Imatong mountains) about 100 miles south-east of Juba, and close to Torit in the territory inhabited by the Latuka tribe (now in the Equatoria province of Sudan).

(d) *C. mitis doggetti* Pocock,[*] 1907, Silver Guenon; Doggett's Guenon; Ankole Blue Monkey

> (*Syn.*: *C. doggetti* Pocock, 1907, p. 691; *C. sibatoi* Lorenz, 1913, p. 439)
>
> *Vernacular names*: French, *singe argenté, singe de marais à longs poils*; Flemish, *zilvermeerkat*; German, *Silbermeerkatze*.
>
> *Type locality*: South-west Ankole, between Lakes Victoria and Albert Edward. Moreau *et al.* (1946) have restricted this to " between Lake Karenge and Burumba, north of Kagera river, South-west Ankole, Uganda ". Holotype female in British Museum. Collected by W. G. Doggett. Type locality of *sibatoi*: Sibatwa Mountain forest, 2000 m. north-west of Lake Tanganyika in Congo territory.
>
> Distinguished by the rufous speckling at the base of the tail and extension of the speckled area towards the tip of the organ, and by the yellower tinge of the back compared with the sides, which are definitely grey; also in the grey under parts.

PELAGE.—Crown, including area around ears, nape, also interscapular region, jet black. Brow-band and whiskers olive-grey ticked with black. Speckling with greenish grey commencing between the shoulders and affecting median area of rest

---

[*] *Proc. zool. Soc. Lond.* 1907, ii. 691.

of dorsum, the flanks similar but greyer ; sacral area with reddish-brown tinge, speckled. Tail almost black distally, the rest greyish both above and below, speckled only at the base. Arms and hands jet black on lateral surface, medially ashy grey. Leg from hip blackish-grey, speckled ; feet black ; legs medially ashy grey. Abdomen ashy-grey. A dark line across clavicular region. Middle of throat white, narrower than in type of *C. omensis*.

In the type skin the black pileum is very soft and resplendent. The face and forehead are heavily speckled ; under parts are pale silvery grey, which colour extends on to the medial surfaces of both fore and hind limbs. The black areas of the arms and hands are soft in texture like the crown.

Dimensions (in millimetres) of adult female : head and body, 487 ; tail, 65·5 (? imperfect) (*ex* Pocock).

Skull.—Cranial dimensions (in millimetres) of an adult female from Baraka, Congo, assigned by Lönnberg (1919) to *C. leucampyx sibatoi* : maximum cranial length, 103 ; condylo-basal length, 81 ; maximum cranial breadth, 55 ; bizygomatic, 65·4 ; least frontal, 42·2 ; upper cheek-teeth, 27·5 ; lower cheek-teeth, 33·6.

Cranial dimensions of type female (personal measurements) : maximum cranial length, 92 mm. ; biparietal breadth, 54 mm. ; bizygomatic, 60 mm. ; least frontal, 41 mm. ; biorbital, 51 mm. ; palatal length, 33 mm.

Distribution.—Range extends both sides of the chain of lakes between Lake Albert and the northern end of Lake Tanganyika, being especially prevalent between Lake Kivu and Lake Tanganyika.

Uganda : Katera, Mangira forest, Masaka (British Museum), Masaka district, near Lake Victoria, Lake Bunyoni, near Kabale, Kigezi (Chicago Museum).

Schouteden (1947) gives the following localities for its occurrence in the Congo. Kivu district : Sibatwa, near Baraka (type locality of *sibatoi*), Muja (Poll, 1939). Ruanda-Urundi : Usumbura, Ngozi, Kabira river ; Kigali, Muhinga, Rugege forest in Ruanda and Kibungu in the Kagera valley. Schwarz (1954) adds : Usambura, north end of Lake Tanganyika ; highland forest near Balmanati. There is therefore some overlap in the territories of *C. m. doggetti* with *C. m. stuhlmanni*, but apparently the bands do not mix and interbreed, for there is a difference in ecological preference, *C. m. doggetti* occurring in marshes and papyrus swamps. It feeds on papyrus stems, being specially fond of the tender, white, submerged portion.

Sometimes consorts with *Colobus* bands (Pitman in St. Leger, 1929).

(e) *C. mitis maesi* Lönnberg, 1919 *

(*Syn.* : *C. leucampyx maesi* Lönnberg, *loc. cit.*)
Vernacular names : None recorded.
Type locality : Kutu, Fini river, Lake Leopold II district, Congo. Type a young specimen (No. 2645 in the Congo Museum, Tervuren, collected by Dr. Maes).

Pelage.—Interorbital region black haired ; lower nose and upper lip white-haired ; brow band narrow, speckled, containing many long uniformly black forwardly directed hairs. Crown, nape, interscapular region and arms and hands black. Back and flanks dark grey, speckled. Sacral region, hind-limbs, including feet, black, the legs sparsely speckled with pale annulations on a few hairs. Posterior aspect of thighs wholly black.

Root of tail beneath and long hairs around anal area dark reddish brown. Rest

* *Rev. zool. bot. Afr.* viii. 133.

of tail grey, speckled with light putty colour, or partly brownish tips to hairs, but becoming wholly black terminally.

Under parts, except throat, sooty grey; throat white. A whitish, or very pale area is shown on the fore part of the cheek-patch in adults figured by Schouteden (1947).

DIMENSIONS.—No data available.

SKULL.—No data available.

DISTRIBUTION.—Confined, so far as known, to the Central Congo. Schouteden gives the following localities for material in the Tervuren Museum: Lake Leopold II district: Kutu; Tschuopa district: between Irebu and Ikingo, Ilimgampangu, near Moma, Bamania; Congo-Ubangi district: Bomana, Budjala; Sankuru district: Pania Mutombo, Lusambo.

(f) *C. mitis kandti* Matschie, 1905,* Congo Red Monkey

(*Syn.*: *Cercopithecus kandti* Matschie, 1905; *C. insignis* Elliot, 1909, p. 274; *Lasiopyga insignis* Elliot, 1913, p. 372)

Vernacular names: In Kivu, *nyengi*; Bahunda, *chabira*; Asongomeno, *ngeye*; Otetele, *nge* (Freehkop, 1953); French, *singe doré, cercopithèque du Kivu*; Flemish, *goudaap, goudmeerkat*; German, *Goldmeerkat*.

Type locality: Near Lake Kivu. Types in Berlin Museum, collected by Dr. Kandt. Type locality of *insignis*, Congo forest. Described from an animal living in the Antwerp Zoo, its skin is now in the Tervuren Museum.

Distinguished from other races of *C. mitis* by the large extent of red in the pelage, especially in the rusty under surface and of the area around the base of the tail.

PELAGE.—Pelage long, dense. Frontal band, cheeks and sides of neck, also hinder part of shoulders speckled olive grey and black, each hair with 2-4 very narrow grey-brown zones. Crown and nape jet black. Back from behind shoulders to sacral region speckled greyish green with reddish-yellow bases to individual hairs. A large extent of rusty red on buttocks both above and below tail-root and also at sides of tail. Tail rusty at base, the red gradually diminishing distally and becoming more speckled with black, the black increasing gradually until almost complete at tip. Arms jet black laterally; legs blackish but speckled. Under parts, including medial aspects of base of fore and whole of hind limbs, rusty and unspeckled.

The amount and shade of the red in the pelage is individually variable, even among skins from the same locality (Lönnberg), but the half-grown juvenile is already like the adult in this respect. The type of Elliot's *insignis* had not yet developed speckling on the lower back.

A specimen exhibited in the Tring Museum has shoulders and upper arms black; rest of back and flanks golden. There is a distinct pale collar between cheeks and shoulders, very sharply demarcated from the black of the latter, but less so from the cheek-patch.

DIMENSIONS of cotypes (in millimetres):

Head and body	65	Tail	—
,, ,,	64	,,	79
,, ,,	57	,,	—

SKULL.—No data available.

DISTRIBUTION.—Kivu district of the Congo.

* *Sb. Ges. naturf. Fr., Berlin*, p. 264.

Schwarz (1928 *a*) gives the undermentioned localities for skins in the Tervuren Museum : 4 miles north of Kesinyi, Lake Kivu ; Nya Muzinga, Karissimbi volcano ; Mutura, between Karissimbi and Lake Kivu ; Lulenga, Mikeno volcano ; Burunga, Mikeno volcano ; Ruanda ; Kabare, south-west of Lake Kivu. Poll (1939) adds Rugari, region of volcanoes.

C. m. kandti appears to be a mountain dwelling form and is sharply demarcated in pelage from its neighbours. Its ecological preference is bamboo forest, the bamboo shoots forming one of its principal food items.

(g) *C. mitis schoutedeni* Schwarz, 1928 *

(*Syn.* : *C. leucampyx schoutedeni* Schwarz, 1928)
Vernacular names : None recorded.
Type locality : Kwidjwi island in Lake Kivu. Type adult ♂ in Berlin Museum, No. 33553, collected by Duke Adolf Friedrich of Mecklenburg.

CHARACTERS.—Very similar to *C. m. kandti*, with the same long, thick pelage and with similar whitish hairs around the muzzle, but quite lacking the reddish tinge characteristic of *kandti*.

Males with back greyish olive, thighs blackish mouse-grey ; under parts deep mouse grey (Ridgway's colour scheme).

Females with back deep greyish olive, thighs dark mouse-grey ; under parts light greyish-olive.

Tail in both sexes as in *kandti*, but without yellowish tint ; speckled silver grey.

No yellowish tinge in frontal diadem or on cheeks. No reddish or brownish tinge on rump or medial sides of thighs.

The light unbanded portions of individual hairs affect not more than one-third of the base, compared with almost one-half in *kandti* and one-quarter in *doggetti*.

DIMENSIONS (in millimetres) of type adult ♂ : head and body, 630 ; tail, 790.

SKULL.—Cranial dimensions (in millimetres) of type male : maximum cranial length, 121 ; basal length, 88·4 ; bizygomatic, 79 ; palatal length, 45·6 ; upper dentition, C – M³, 41·4 ; mandibular length, 87·6 ; lower dentition, P – M₃̄, 37·7 (Schwarz).

DISTRIBUTION.—In addition to the islands in Lake Kivu, *C. m. schoutedeni* is recorded from Bobandana, north-west of the lake ; from Burunga, at the foot of Mount Mikeno ; and from Ruhengera in Ruanda.

(h) *C. mitis opisthostictus* Sclater, 1894,† Rump-spotted Guenon

(*Syn.* : *C. opisthostictus* Sclater, *loc. cit.*, Forbes, 1894, p. 72, Pocock, 1907, p. 694)
Vernacular names : In Katanga, *mbele* (*fide* Freehkop, 1954). Kivu, *nkima* ; Asongomeno and Otetele, *nfunga* (Frechkop, 1953). Flemish, *blauweaap* ; French, *singe bleu*.
Type locality : East shore of Lake Mweru, Northern Rhodesia ; two cotypes (unsexed) in British Museum (nos. 92.2.6.2 and 94.3.8.22)—two flat skins collected by Sir Alfred Sharpe, Vice-consul in southern Nyasaland. The skins had been used as native adornments.

Schwarz (1928, p. 653) designated one of the two original skins as lectotype, but the number given in error is 94.3.3.22.

* *Rev. zool. Bot. Afr.* xvi. 22.　　　　† *Proc. zool. Soc. Lond.* 1893, p. 725.

In Sclater's original description it is suggested that this monkey is related to *C. albogularis samango*, its neighbour to the south, but differs in the blackish under parts, in the wholly black upper back, and in the two small rufous areas on each side of the tail.

Original diagnosis : Suprâ pallide cinereo et nigro confertim annellatus, capite obscuriore ; cervice postica, humeris cum manibus et pedibus extus et cauda (nisi ad basin) nigris ; plaga parva ad latus dorsi postici utrinque castanea ; subtus nigrescens. Long. corp. 24 poll., caudae 25 poll.

PELAGE : ADULT MALE.—Recalls *C. nictitans* in general appearance. Upper lip white-haired, lower lip, chin and throat white. Grey speckling predominating in frontal diadem, but black predominant on rest of crown and nape, the two pale annuli on each hair being narrower than the intervening black bands. Cheeks and sides of neck like frontal band. Interscapular region blackish, the grey annuli very narrow. Rest of back, flanks and root of tail speckled, the hairs showing 4 or 5 grey annuli totalling more than the intervening black bands. Under parts from cranial end of chest to pubic region, jet black. Legs from hip to foot black laterally, grey medially, but darker than grey of back.

Tail greyish in basal one-third, distal two-thirds jet black. A reddish-brown spot on each side near tail root, not constantly present (Schouteden ; Ansell, 1960).

ADULT FEMALE.—Not so black beneath as the male, but there is also some geographical variation according to Ansell, who states that males from the Mwinilunga and Kabompo districts tend to have blacker limbs than those of the same sex from farther east. Moreover, in north-western Northern Rhodesia the tails are darker, the distal two-thirds entirely black rather than grizzled.

JUVENILE.—Ansell (1960) records a nearly full term foetus from west of the Kasanka Game reserve as fully haired, darker on the sides and under parts than the neonatus. A male neonatus of about one week old from the same locality is described as paler, but in both specimens the crown is wholly black, without speckling while their tails are also identical.

DIMENSIONS (in millimetres) : Head and body (crown-rump), 525 ; tail, 700.

SKULL.—Cranial dimensions : No data available.

DISTRIBUTION.—Katanga (around headwaters of the River Congo) and neighbouring parts of Northern Rhodesia, west of the southern half of Lake Tanganyika as far west as the Lubilash river. Northern range extends to near Albertville (Schwarz, 1954).

Ansell (1960) gives numerous localities in Northern Rhodesia whence this race has been obtained, notably Lufubu river, Lusenga plain, Munwa, Luera and Lwimbe streams ; Ntambos area, just west of Kasanka Game Reserve, also in the north-west part of the Reserve ; Kabompo and Mwinilunga districts ; West Lunga river. He also records it as occurring in the Kasempa district as far south as 13° 15′ S. on the East Lunga river and in mushitu patches in the Chingola district. Lancaster (1953) is authority for its occurrence in the Ndola and Mkushi districts, but no records of its presence in the Balovali district are known, and in any event there is little, if any, suitable habitat there.

In Katanga, Schouteden (1947) records the undermentioned localities : Lualaba district : Kando, Dilolo, Kanzenze ; Upper Katanga district : Lukafu, Kitalanga, Kundelungu, Kilwa, Lukonzolwa, near Elisabethstad and Luishwishi.

Ansell (1960) believes it probable that the Kabombo and Mwinilunga districts may yield intergrades between *opisthostictus* and the nominate race. Both these localities are admittedly near the Angolan frontier, but nevertheless a considerable area intervenes between them and the known localities whence *mitis* has been procured.

There is no evidence of intergrading with *C. albogularis moloneyi*, although the two populations are recorded from localities only a few miles apart in the Kasanka Game reserve of Northern Rhodesia. Schwarz (1954) also remarked on the narrow zone separating these two monkeys in the Northern Province of Northern Rhodesia, although the monkey here treated as *moloneyi* was regarded by Schwarz as *monoides*.

2. *CERCOPITHECUS ALBOGULARIS* (Sykes, 1831 *)

White-throated Guenon

(SYN. : *Semnopithecus* ? *albogularis* Sykes, 1831, p. 106 ; *Cercopithecus albigularis* Sykes, 1832, p. 18 ; *Lasiopyga albigularis* Elliot, 1913, p. 363 ; *C. monoides* Is. Geoffroy, 1841, p. 558 ; *C. rufilatus* Pocock, 1907, p. 702)

VERNACULAR NAMES : Kiswahili, *kima* or *nchima* (see also under subspecies) ; French, *cercopithèque à collier blanc* ; Italian, *cercopiteco a gola bianca* ; German, *Weisskehl Meerkatze.*

TYPE LOCALITY : Fixed by Schwarz (1927) as Zanzibar. The type male was a menagerie specimen presented by Major Sykes to the London Zoo. It had been procured in Bombay, but was assumed to have come from Madagascar. Sykes provisionally referred it to *Semnopithecus*, considering it might be intermediate between the Oriental and African long-tailed monkeys. The following year, after the death of the type specimen, Sykes was able to confirm its essential resemblances to *Cercopithecus*. At the same time Owen (1832) gave a résumé of his dissection of the animal. Type skin and skull now in British Museum (No. 55.12.24.13).

Type locality of *monoides* unknown ; based on an old female menagerie specimen presented alive by the Princesse de Beauveau, 22 October 1838. Lectotype, chosen by Schwarz (1928 *c*, p. 656) from Rufiji river, 8° S. Tanganyika. Type in Paris Museum (skull in department of comparative anatomy).

Type locality of *rufilatus* ; Rufiji river 8° S. (south of Zanzibar). No type designated by Pocock. Lectotype subadult male in British Museum (No. 78.12.26.1). Collected by Capt. Wharton, designated by Schwarz (1928 *c*, p. 656).

GENERAL REMARKS

For reasons stated under *C. mitis*, the white-throated forms of the *mitis* Formenkreis are here treated as a separate species. Although there is no definite evidence of either geographical or ecological overlap, they are in fact sharply isolated geographically, so that gene flow is thereby prevented. Pocock and his contemporaries, although admitting their close affiliation with the *leucampyx* (*i.e. mitis*) group, treated them as a distinct group, with *C. nictitans* sandwiched between, and even Schwarz (1928 *c*, p. 652) admitted that the forms he regarded as subspecies of *C. leucampyx* were susceptible of arrangement into two series corresponding to Elliot's subgenera *Melanocebus* and *Insignicebus* ; he maintained, however, that intermediate forms exist

* *Proc. zool. Soc. Lond.* 1831, p. 106.

between the black-headed, green-backed *leucampyx* series and the pale-headed and red-backed *albogularis* type, *e.g.* the Katangan *opisthostictus* and the Juba river form referred by him to *albotorquatus*.

PELAGE : ADULT MALE.—All the forms of the *albogularis* series agree in lacking the wholly black crown found in *C. mitis* (s.s.). All are, moreover, white-throated, the white often contrasting sharply with the dark of the nape and tending to encroach upon it, forming a collar of greater or lesser extent. This reaches its maximum in *C. a. kolbi*, where the median dark dorsal band is reduced to a very narrow streak, the white patches being then visible from the dorsal aspect of the animal.

Pocock separated his *albogularis* assemblage mainly on the lesser degree of black pigmentation in the pelage ; the head, including the cheek-patches, being uniformly coloured, *i.e.* without distinct frontal diadem. These areas, together with the nape and shoulders, speckled yellowish grey and black, the lighter tinge predominating, the head commonly a shade darker than the rest, more rarely with a reddish tinge, or with localized reddish patches. Lumbar and sacral areas of back always more brightly coloured by increase in the quantity of yellow or reddish annulations in the individual hairs. The brighter area may be restricted to near the median line or spread laterally on to the flanks. Under parts are never black but may be grey or more usually whitish, the throat, at least pure white.

ADULT FEMALE.—Resembling male, but considerably smaller in size.

JUVENILE.—See under subspecies.

SKULL

Resembling that of *C. mitis*. A detailed account of the skull of *C. a. labiatus* (= *samango*) based on two crania (one ♂, one ♀) is given by Weinbrenn (1930) who made comparison with *C. pygerythrus*. The skull is narrower, the cranium less rounded and capacious and the face less elongated and prominent than in *C. pygerythrus*. The least frontal diameter is less. Temporal lines are well developed, more pronounced anteriorly than in *C. pygerythrus*, though less so posteriorly. The frontal inclines abruptly above the orbits, reaching its highest point about the middle of the bone.

Zygoma stouter in the malar than the squamosal portion, with anterior border linear and posterior curved (Weinbrenn). Auditory bullae thick-walled with tapering anterior ends and roughened surfaces ; external auditory meatus large ; postglenoid tubercle large, sharper and more elongated than in *C. pygerythrus*. Foramen magnum diamond-shaped with length and breadth subequal. Condyles on antero-lateral margin of foramen, separated by a wide, shallow notch anteriorly.

Premaxillae smaller, shorter and palate broader than in *C. pygerythrus*, but palatines forming smaller proportion of palate. Degree of palatal convexity variable, but in general less than in *C. pygerythrus* ; hinder palatal margin serrated instead of showing a single median palatal spine (? individual variation). Nasals less uniform in shape. Medial orbital margin vertical, lacking the backward inclination seen in *C. pygerythrus* ; openings rounded, less angular, but with well defined supraorbital notch.

Vertical ramus of mandible stouter than in *C. pygerythrus* and less inclined with respect to horizontal ramus. Sigmoid notch more symmetrical, the coronoid more acute and mental foramen more anteriorly situated.

DISTRIBUTION AND ECOLOGY (MAP 2)

White-throated guenons are restricted to Africa east of the Rift Valley ranging over the whole area, in suitable forests, between the Rift Valley and the coast. The latitudinal range extends from north of the Juba river as far south as the eastern half of Cape Province. From the coastal plain and neighbouring islands, the altitudinal range extends on elevated land to forests at 9000 feet or more.

REPRODUCTION

White-throated guenons (usually exhibited in zoological collections as Sykes' monkeys) have rarely been bred, but this has occurred in the West Berlin Zoo (1961, *fide International Zoo News*, 8, No. 4).

For data concerning wild examples see under *C. a. monoides* (*infra*, p. 419).

(a) *C. albogularis albotorquatus* Pousargues, 1896,* Pousargues' White-throated Guenon
(*Syn.* : *C. rufotinctus* Pocock, 1907, p. 706 ; *Lasiopyga albitorquata* (*sic*) Elliot, 1913, p. 360 ; *C.* (*Insignicebus*) *albogularis zammaranoi* de Beaux, 1924, p 248 ; *C. mitis albotorquatus* Schwarz, 1928, p. 654 ; *C. mitis zammaranoi* Starck and Frick, 1958, p. 57)
Vernacular names : None recorded.
Type locality : Unknown. Type an incomplete skin of an immature male (*fide* Rode) in Paris Museum from a menagerie animal originally presented in 1855 by M. Pottier-Prouhon (it died 5/V/1887). It appears to have reached the adult state but its canines were feeble. Skull in skin. Type locality of *rufotinctus* : " East Africa, ? Mombasa ". Type a living female, presented to the London Zoo by J. W. W. Pigott, 20 September 1895. Skin now in British Museum (No. 8.5.7.1). Later (1927) said by Schwarz to represent the form from the forests on the lower Juba. Type locality of *zammaranoi* Bidi Scionde, lower Juba, Somaliland. Type, adult male and two paratypes (♂ ♀) in Milan Museum. (All flat skins with skulls of the two males.)
Original diagnosis : *C. c. albogulari* (*Sykes*) *affinis; vertice, temporibus, collo superiore medio, dorso, lateribusque concoloribus, nigro et fulvo variegatis; pilis superciliaribus erectis; artubus externe nigricanis, posticus pallidioribus; regione anali caudae basi femorunque parti posteriore rufis; caudâ mediâ nigrocanâ; reliqua?; manibusque*

* *Bull. Mus. Hist. Nat. Paris*, 56.

PLATE XV

Photo: E. Kirkland

Cercopithecus albogularis kolbi, adult ♀, in Chester Zoo

PLATE XVI

Photo: W. Ted Roth

Cercopithecus l'hoesti ♂. National Zoological Park, Washington D.C.

nigris; gula, genis, pectore, colloque fere toto quasi torquato, nitidissime albis; corpore subtus artubusque interne canescentibus; palpebrâ superiore carneâ; facie reliquâ mentoque obscure caeruleis.

Almost complete wide white collar; top of head and temporal region same colour as back, typically no olive green anywhere. Under parts white, with suggestion of bluish-grey instead of the blackish ticked white of Sykes' monkey. Cheek-hairs relatively shorter than in *albogularis*, leaving ears completely free.

PELAGE: ADULT MALE (based on type of *zammaranoi*).—Short hairs on nose, lips and ears white; crown no darker than cheeks or shoulders, but nape has less yellow speckling than shoulders. Chin, throat and front of neck white, the transition from the white to the dark dorsum on the neck gradual. Transition from dark dorsum to light underparts on flanks also gradual. All hairs, except the completely white or completely black ones, are annulated alternately with black and yellow, the latter here reaching its maximum intensity on the lumbo-sacral area, where a general old gold effect is produced. Individual hairs in the distal two-thirds show four bands of Naples yellow alternating with three almost black zones, of equal extent. Length of hairs over nape and posterior half of trunk over 70 mm.

Forearm, hand and pedal digits black, also distal half of tail, but dorsum of foot, like upper arms, almost black. Hips and thighs deep neutral grey and concolorous with ventral aspect of trunk, but a spot on the knee almost black. Root of tail resembling lower back, but basal one-third iron grey and no lighter beneath than dorsally. Inguinal region light olive grey.

The type of *rufotinctus* has practically the whole lumbar and sacral areas reddish. There is also a red frontal band and a reddish suffusion over the whole crown. Shoulders and arms jet black; lateral aspect of thighs grizzled. Schwarz considered this an erythristic mutant of the form described later by de Beaux (1924) as *zammaranoi* (a note to this effect in Schwarz's handwriting is appended to the label on the type skin). This is also affirmed in his paper of 1927 (p. 153) where *rufotinctus* is stated to agree with *zammaranoi* in the dark shoulders and arms and the deep mouse-grey thighs, and also in the upward extension of the white throat.

Schwarz maintained therefore that *rufotinctus* and *zammaranoi* are the local representations of Sykes' monkey in the gallery forests of the lower Juba river from whence specimens now in the Frankfurt and Berlin Museums have been obtained. Later (1928) Schwarz added both these names to the synonymy of *albotorquatus*, the type of which he had in the interim seen in the Paris Museum. He found this an immature animal and like *rufotinctus*, somewhat abnormal, affected by erythrysm and partial albinism. Rufous tinge strongly marked on sacral area.

Apparently *zammaranoi* represents the normal phase of this race; a very detailed account of the type and paratypes is given by de Beaux, together with comparisons with other races of *albogularis*. By Starck and Frick (1958) it is treated as an eastern variant of *C. m. boutourlinii*.

Three living examples from Somaliland were on exhibit in the Paris menagerie (Jardin des Plantes) in 1960 and had been there for three years. Rather small in size, they presented a completely olive-green back without trace of rufous tint. The white collar was smaller than in the type of *albotorquatus* and the under parts ashy grey (Dandelot *in litt.*).

DIMENSIONS.—Length, head and body of type 580 mm.; tail 420 mm. (incomplete) (Elliot gives total length, 1447·8 mm.; tail, 939·8 mm.; foot, 139·7 mm.).

2 E

SKULL.—Cranial measurements (in millimetres) :

	♂ Type of zammaranoi	♂ Paratype of zammaranoi
Maximum cranial length	96	95
Condylo-basal length	71·8	—
Least frontal	38	39
Bizygomatic	66	69
Median length of nasals	15	20
Upper cheek-teeth	23	22

DISTRIBUTION.—See Map 2.

(b) *C. albogularis albogularis* Sykes, 1831,[*] Sykes' Monkey : Zanzibar White-throated Guenon

(*Syn.* ; *Semnopithecus* ? *albogularis* Sykes, 1831 ; *Cercopithecus albigularis* Sykes, 1832, p. 18 ; *Lasiopyga albigularis* Elliot, 1913, p. 363.)

Vernacular name : Kiswahili, *kima*.

Type locality : Zanzibar (see under species).

A coloured plate is in Fraser (1849), *Zoologia typica*, Plate II.

CHARACTERS.—Smaller than the mainland races.

PELAGE: ADULT MALE.—Differing from the mainland races (especially *monoides*) in the colouration of several areas. Crown, nape and shoulders, lighter in colour, more greyish, the ashy-grey tinge dominant, but speckled lightly with creamy white, the darker annulations being slaty grey ; arms dark iron grey, darkening to sooty on the forearms and hands ; legs lighter, more greyish and more heavily speckled than arms. Lumbo-sacral area more or less reddish yellow, the russet increasing towards the root of the tail.

Under parts distinctly lighter than in *monoides*, ashy grey, with the medial aspect of the arms and even more on the thighs, whitish.

The throat and collar are pure white in both island and mainland races.

Ear tuft small, white, but varying in size with age ; large animals have more complete tufting, the hairs covering most of the ear instead of being limited to a fringe along the superior border.

ADULT FEMALE.—Like the male, but smaller.

JUVENILE.—Distinguished by bright reddish tufts at the base of the tail and adjacent to callosities, as in females and juveniles of *C. a. nyasae*.

DIMENSIONS.—No data available.

DISTRIBUTION.—As now understood, the nominate race is restricted to the island of Zanzibar.

Dandelot (1962), after examining the types of *albogularis*, *monoides* and *rufilatus*, came to the conclusion that all three were representatives of the nominate race. Subsequently (unpublished ; seen in typescript), he has rectified certain errors in his earlier paper after examining a fresh series of skins from Zanzibar in the British Museum. Apparently his earlier knowledge of the insular form was based on a skin from Mafia which was identical with skins from the coastal districts of Tanganyika. The newer material from Zanzibar indicates that the island race differs consistently in size and colour from the mainland coastal races, so that the subspecific name *monoides* must be retained for the latter.

[*] *Proc. Zool. Soc. Lond.*, 1831, p. 106.

(c) *C. albogularis monoides* I. Geoffroy, 1841,* Maritime White-throated Monkey

(*Syn.*: *C. albogularis rufilatus* Pocock, 1907, p. 702; *Lasiopyga a. maritima* Heller, 1913, p. 8; *L. a. kima* Heller, 1913, p. 9)

Vernacular names: Kiswahili, *kima*; Kitaita, *ngima*; Kipokomo, *chima*.

Type locality: Unknown. Type a menagerie animal originally received in the Paris menagerie as an adult on 22 October 1838 from the Princesse de Beauveau. Figured in *Arch. Mus. Paris*, ii, pl. 31. Lectotype chosen by Schwarz, Rufiji river 80° S, Tanganyika. Type locality of *rufilatus*, Rufiji river. Original description mentions two specimens in the British Museum (Nos. 78.12.26.1–2) both presented by Capt. Wharton, and a third ticketed " Kima, from coast up to 9000 feet ", collected by Carlisle Fraser (No. 97.2.14.4). Pocock also refers to a specimen from Zanzibar which evidently pertains to the nominate race and which he describes (as would be expected) as less brightly coloured than the mainland examples. Type locality of *maritima*, Mazeras, British East Africa (=Kenya). Type, female, in U.S. National Museum, (No. 182272). Collected by E. Heller, Rainey African Expedition, 17 December 1911. Type locality of *kima*, Mount Mbololo, Taita Hills, Kenya. Type in U.S. National Museum (No. 182242). Collected by E. Heller, Rainey African Expedition, 6 November 1911. Both localities fall within the known range of *C. a. monoides* although Schwarz placed them in the synonymy of *C. a. kibonotensis*.

PELAGE : ADULT MALE.—Larger and more darkly coloured than the nominate race.

Crown, cheeks, nape and shoulders distinctly olive tinged, the yellowish olive predominating over the grey. Arms dark slaty grey, speckled, darkening distally to uniformly black on forearms and hands. Legs dark iron grey, sharply demarcated from the brightly coloured lumbo-sacral area, darkening on the shanks ; feet black. Lumbo-sacral area much as in typical *albogularis*, but inclining more frequently to reddish, and changing gradually on hinder thoracic region to the olive anterior tinge.

Under parts uniformly dark slaty grey, including the flexor aspects of the limbs, only the chin and throat being white, the extent of which, however, is identical in the two races.

Tail proximally above like the sacral area for a few inches, changing gradually to black. Below slightly rufous basally then greyish, finally changing to black in the distal two-thirds.

Ear-tufts white, as in *albogularis*.

VARIATIONS.—The type of *maritima*, a female, differs scarcely from the above description. Its conspicuous white ear-tufts contrast with the dark crown and cheeks. The white collar is not particularly extensive dorsally. The brighter coloured upper parts are extensive, inclining to a greenish-sandy or golden tinge affecting the whole dorsum behind the shoulders, with the spinal area more deeply tinged, especially over the anterior part of the coloured area. There is a considerable reddish area at the root of the tail below, and a golden tinge over the basal 25 mm. dorsally. The dorsum of the foot is lightly speckled, but the hands, like the forearms are wholly black.

Main difference is in the under parts, which are creamy white, with a greyish wash confined to the pectoral region—in this it resembles *albogularis* rather than *monoides*.

---

* *Arch. Mus. Hist. nat. Paris* (1), ii. 558, Pl. *xxxi.*

In the type of *kima*, on the other hand, the under parts are darkly speckled from the chest posteriorly, except around the perineum, which is uniformly grey and without red subcaudal tufts. There are radiating white circumanal hairs extending ventrad between the callosities. Ear tufts dirty white.

DIMENSIONS (in millimetres):

Locality	Sex	Head and Body	Tail	Foot	Ear	
Mazeras	♀ ad.	420	675	125	31	Type of *maritima*
Mt. Mbololo	♂ ad.	510	725	150	38	,, *kima*
,,	♂	595	660	150	40	} Allen *et al.* (1936)
,,	♀	470	670	120	37	

SKULL.—Cranial dimensions (in millimetres):

Number	Locality	Sex	Max. Cranial Length	Condylo-basal	Biparietal	Least Frontal	Bimastoid	Bizygomatic	Palatal Length	Upper Cheek-teeth	Mandibular Length	Lower Cheek-teeth
	Kenya	♂ ad.	126	—	62	44·7		80·8	46·8	29·5	87	37·8
Brit. Mus. 78.12.261 [1]	Rufiji river	♂	79		47·5	35·6		56·5	31	24	54·5	38
182241 [2]	Mt. Mbololo	♂	104·5	82		45·4	57·4	68·7		25·2	73·3	32
182242 [2]	,,	♂	113·5	93·8		44·2	57·9	76·2		27·7	83·8	35·5
182248 [2]	,,	♂	109·4	87·9		44	56·5	76·6		27	78·3	32·9
182243 [2]	,,	♀	97·8	74·3		42·5	55	66·3		23·5	67·2	27·7
182249 [2]	,,	♀	95·7	72·6		41	53·1	63		24·4	63·3	27·7
182250 [2]	Mt. Umengo	♂	108	87·3		44·1	58·3	76·7		26·2	78·7	32·2
182254 [2]	,,	♀	93·3	74·8		40·3	52·7	63·7		24·8	67	29
182272 [3]	Mazeras	♀	95·6	72·6		42·1	54·5	62·2	37	25·1	64·4	28·1

(U.S. National Mus. — numbers 182241–182272)

[1] Type of *rufilatus*.　　　[2] *kima*.　　　[3] Type of *maritima*.

DISTRIBUTION.—Coastal forests of south-eastern Kenya and eastern Tanganyika inland, in suitable areas, to the foot of Mt. Kenya and Mt. Kilimanjaro ; also the coastal islands of Mafia and Tumatu. Probably meeting and intergrading in the north with *C. a. albotorquatus* somewhere between the Juba and Tana rivers. To the south the range crosses the Rufiji river and probably meets that of *C. a. moloneyi* or *C. a. francescae*.

The Rufiji area was designed by Schwarz as the type locality. He increased the known range by personal observations in his paper of 1954. He observed captive specimens taken in the Uluguru mountains, and examined skins from the Udzungwe (=Uchungwe) mountains. To this race he also attributed specimens in the Kaffrarian Museum collected in Northern Rhodesia by D. G. Lancaster from Mufinga

(= Muchinga) mountains, Isoka district, alt. 5000–7000 feet, Sunzu, Saisi Valley, 31° 30′ E., 9° S. and Kalambo river, Abercorn district, 31° E., 8° 30′ S. Isoka is the southernmost limit of this form, which is replaced on the plateau along Lake Nyasa, farther east, by *C. a. moloneyi*, while just west of Isoka *C. mitis opisthostictus* occurs (for discussion see Ansell, 1960).

Heller (1913) reporting on the monkeys he identified as *Lasiopyga albogularis kima* found them confined to the forests of the extreme summits of the Taita Hills where, even then, their environment was suffering severe encroachment at the hands of the Waitaita tribes, who, incidentally also eat them. The same remarks apply in general to the lighter animals Heller separated as *L. a. maritima*, which live in the forests of the coastal hills.

Allen *et al.* record these monkeys as common on the summit of Mt. Mbololo and as being less wary than the other forest animals encountered (squirrels, blue duikers, hyrax) suggesting that they were no longer hunted by the Waitaita for food. They were not noisy, apart from an occasional piping whistle from a young animal and more rarely a deep grunt from an old male.

(d) *C. albogularis phylax* Schwarz, 1927 *

> (Syn: *C. leucampyx phylax* Schwarz, 1927, *loc. cit.*)
> *Vernacular names*: none recorded
> *Type locality*: Patta Island, Witu group, off coast of Kenya. Type an old female in the Berlin Museum (No. 35422) collected 21 March 1903 by A. Voeltzkow.

CHARACTERS.—A small dark insular race allied to *C. a. kolbi*, which it resembles more closely than it does *C. a. albogularis*.

PELAGE.—Frontal band, crown, upper part of cheeks and shoulder region dark olive, similar to, but somewhat more brownish than light brownish olive of Ridgway. Ear-tuft short, white.

Dorsum of body dark reddish brown, the lighter annulations of the hairs ochraceous tawny, giving a general impression, due to the black speckling, of cinnamon brown. The back is brightest posteriorly and gradually merges anteriorly into the colour of the shoulders—never as grey as in *kolbi*. The usual russet tuft at the root of the tail below, projects laterally and even slightly overlaps the dorsum ; it becomes more intensely coloured around the anal region and extends someway on to the medial surface of the thighs.

Upper arms black laterally, liberally speckled with greenish white on the shoulders, less so on the hands. Thighs dark mouse grey, lightly washed with greenish to beyond the knees. Feet black, the hairs with narrow greenish bands.

Tail basally above like the back, followed by a region of greenish grey, and the distal half black. Beneath mouse-grey, lightly speckled.

Under parts white, lightly speckled with mouse grey ; but inguinal region and greater part of medial surface of thighs whitish.

Throat, and pectoral region, up to a line connecting the axillae, creamy white. From the throat the white extends around the sides of the neck as in *kolbi*, leaving only a median dorsal sagittal band of 4 cm. breadth free of white, and on all sides sharply demarcated from the dark dorsal colour.

DIMENSIONS of type female ; head and body, 490 mm. ; tail, 480 mm.

SKULL.—Striking features are the short, broad rostrum and the antero-posteriorly shortened basioccipital.

Cranial dimensions (in millimetres) of the type ♀ : maximum cranial length, 91·9 ;

---

* *Sb. naturf. Fr., Berlin* 1926, p. 32.

basal length, 59·5 ; biparietal, 50·9 ; bizygomatic, 56·1 ; palatal length, 28·1 ; upper cheek-teeth, including canine, 28·8 ; lower cheek-teeth, excluding canine, 27·7.

DISTRIBUTION.—Known only from the type locality : Patta Island, Kenya coast.

(e) *C. albogularis kibonotensis* Lönnberg, 1908,* Kilimanjaro Blue Monkey

(*Syn.* : *C. albogularis kibonotensis* Lönnberg, 1908, p. 3 ; *C. leucampyx kibonotensis* Schwarz, 1928, p. 25.)

Vernacular name : Swahili, *kima.*

Type locality : Kibongoto, 19 miles north-west of Moshi, south-west foothills of Mt. Kilimanjaro, northern Tanganyika. Type presumably in Stockholm Museum. Kibongoto is a village (3° 12′ S. ; 37° 07′ E.) 19 miles north-west of Moshi and is shown on early maps as " Kibonoto " (Swynnerton, 1945).

CHARACTERS.—Closely related to *C. a. monoides*, whose territory it meets. Elliot doubted whether it was even subspecifically distinct from *albogularis*, but Schwarz, a confirmed lumper, retained it.

PELAGE : ADULT MALE.—Much like *C. a. kolbi*, but with more reddish element in the dorsal pelage.

Crown, nape and shoulders black, the hairs annulated with yellow, or reddish yellow, but on hinder part of neck annuli are paler, more whitish than in typical *albogularis*. Shoulders and fore-limbs wholly black, except medial aspect of upper arm, which is greyish ; forearms intensely black without speckling. Hind-limbs black, speckled ashy grey. At root of tail and around callosities numerous red hairs, but less developed than in female.

Lumbar and sacral areas rich golden to reddish in general tone, this hue extending laterally to flanks.

Chin and throat white, the white of the throat passing round the sides into a broad speckled iron-grey field, separated from its fellow by a broad black median dorsal tract which is only lightly speckled with yellow or reddish yellow. Rest of under parts grey.

ADULT FEMALE.—Resembling male, but reddish tract around base of tail and ischio-pubic region better developed.

JUVENILE.—Resembling that of *C. a. kolbi.*

DIMENSIONS (in millimetres).—No measurements given in original account. Following recorded from an immature male, measured in the flesh : Head and body, 367 ; head length, 86 ; hand, 70 ; foot, 111 ; ear : morphological length, 18 ; morphological breadth, 19 ; physiognomic length, 28 ; physiognomic breadth, 21.

SKULL.—Cranial measurements (in millimetres) of a male from Taveta (U.S. Nat. Mus., No. 34661) : maximum cranial length, 103·4 ; condylo-basal length, 67·7 ; least frontal, 41·5 ; bizygomatic, 67·7 ; bimastoid, 57·6 ; upper cheek-teeth, 24·8 ; mandibular length, 72·2 ; lower cheek-teeth, 30·1 (Hollister, 1924).

DISTRIBUTION.—Given by Swynnerton and Hayman (1951) as Kilimanjaro and Mt. Meru and the valleys of rivers flowing off them ; Usa ; Gonja ; Pare Mountains ; Usambara Mountains ; Magroto Hill ; Mkulumuzi river ; and coastal forest near Tanga and Pangani.

Schwarz (1928) records examples in the Tervueren Museum from the Tsavo, Zuwani and Lumi rivers, all collected by Bayer.

In 1954 Schwarz personally saw a troop on the Ngorongoro-Arusha road at Mto wa Mbu (= mosquito creek) in rain forest within the Rift Valley, north of Lake Manyara. This is the most westerly point so far recorded for this form. He also mentions it in the coastal area (along Sanya creek, a tributary of the Pangani river,

* *Wiss. Ergeb. schwed. zool. Exped. Kilimandjaro,* ii. Mammalia, p. 3.

south of Moshi). The status of the animals recorded from the coastal plain is somewhat confused. According to Schwarz's earlier estimate of the range of typical
albogularis, with which he synonymized Pocock's *rufilatus* from the Rufiji river
(where he also fixed the type locality of *monoides*), this would also encompass the
localities (Tanga, Pangani) in the coastal plain adjacent to Zanzibar (whence examples
of *kibonotensis* are recorded by Swynnerton and Hayman) as well as the type localities
of Heller's *maritima* and *kima*, which Schwarz himself added to the synonymy of
kibonotensis. In view of the very slight differences between the present race and
monoides, either it must be suppressed and reduced to the synonymy of *monoides*, or
the name must be restricted to montane forms from Kilimanjaro, Mt. Meru, and other
adjacent highlands of similar altitude—except where otherwise occupied by the
much more distinct *C. a. kolbi*.

Lönnberg, in his original description gives field notes by Sjöstedt which affirm
it to be very common in dense rain forest, living in bands of varying numbers in
trees and on the farms. Captured specimens remained wild and kept their angry
disposition. They are trapped on the farms in weighted baskets placed on the ground.

(f) *C. albogularis kolbi* Neumann, 1902,* Mount Kenya White-collared Guenon ;
Kolb's Monkey

(*Syn.*: *C. kolbi hindei* Pocock, 1907, p. 703 ; *C. nubilus* Dollman 1910, p. 202,
Kollmann, 1919, pl. I.)

Vernacular name : Swahili, *kima*.

Type locality : Kedong escarpment, east side of Mt. Kenya ; corrected to The
Escarpment, 70 miles south-west of the mountain (Moreau *et al.*, 1946). Type in
Berlin Museum. Topotype collected by C. S. Belton in British Museum (no. 0.1.3.1).
Type locality of *nubilus* " Nairobi forest " Kenya. Type ♀ in British Museum
(no. 0.2.1.4) collected by H. J. Mackinder, 14 July 1899. Type locality of *hindei*,
Tutha, Kenya, altitude 8000 feet. Type ♂ in British Museum (no. 3.5.25.1) collected
by Dr. S. L. Hinde, December 1902.

CHARACTERS.—The largest form of the genus. A heavy, stockily built race of
albogularis, with shorter, more robust appendages.

A coloured plate labelled *C. kolbi nubilus* is given in Kollmann (1919, *Voyage de
Babault*, pl. 1).

PELAGE : ADULT MALE.—Coat long, dense. Markedly distinct from typical
albogularis in its brighter, more contrasting colour pattern, and particularly in the
extension of the white collar almost to the mid dorsal line, a very narrow dark stripe
alone separating the white of the two sides. Below, the white extends to the acromion
and front of the shoulders, giving the appearance from the dorsal side as of epaulettes.

Ear tufts longer, white to greyish. Iris dark amber.

Scrotum iron grey ; prepuce slaty blue.

Pocock's *hindei* is described as differing in a more distinct coating with white
or greyish hairs on the nose and upper lip, and in the reddish-yellow tinge rather
than greyish yellow on the cheeks ; ear tufts distinctly yellowish and banded, collar
less white and less sharply defined ; lumbar and sacral areas brownish red to rusty,
which extend to base of tail both above and below and thence around the callosities.
Under parts uniformly ashy grey.

Schwarz affirms, and, having examined both types, I am in full agreement with
him, that this description of *hindei* and likewise that of *nubilus* (with the coloured plate)
fall within the range of individual variation of *kolbi*.

* *Proc. zool. Soc. Lond.* ii. 144.

ADULT FEMALE.—Exactly like the male except for considerably smaller size. Rima pudendi 12 mm. ; no labia ; perineal skin light violet ; callosities black, with dorso-medial margin pink.

NEWBORN.—Face unpigmented ; cheeks hairless ; no brow fringe present. Crown black ; upper back black without speckling ; lumbar and sacral regions speckled. Tail relatively short, black. Under parts white, the collar extending to the acromion.

Greyish cheek-hairs appear at four days at which time slight pigmentation of the face has also commenced, eyelids remaining palish. A long upstanding yellow-ticked brow fringe has also developed.

(Based on a male born in the author's private menagerie in 1938).

VARIATIONS.—A fully adult female (No. 317971) in the U.S. National Museum said to be from Arabuka forest, Kenya (collected by R. Alison, 24 July 1948) is atypical of the other ten specimens of *kolbi* in the collection and agrees perfectly with the female of *C. a. erythrarchus*. Its ear-tufts are poorly developed and the collar is not extensive dorsally ; lumbo-sacral area almost uniformly red gold, speckled only anteriorly and diminishing gradually until completely lacking on the rump and base of tail above. Considerable quantity of rusty hairs on perineum and root of tail below, and the whole of the under parts silvery white, unspeckled. Major part of tail paler than in *kolbi*.

This suggests a mistake in locality as there is no question on geographical grounds of possible intergradation between *kolbi* and *erythrarchus*.

DIMENSIONS (in millimetres) :

Number	Locality	Sex	Wt. gms.	Head and Body	Wt. gms.	Tail	Foot	Ear	
PC.14	Mount Kenya	ad. ♂	6349	451	95				Measured in the flesh Coll. by C. Schultz
PC.16	,,	ad. ♀	4535						
	Kedong escarpment			580		790	110		Measured as skin by Elliot
	" Nairobi forest "	♀		620		650	121	27	Type of *nubilus*
	Tutha	subad. ♂		560		690	120		Type of *hindei*
PC.50	Mount Kenya	ad. ♀		537		599	155	32	
PC.9		♂ Infant 4 days		197	72	252	70	29	
U.S. Nat. Mus. 163939	Mt. Kenya, 9000 ft.	♂		275		330	96	25	Collected by Mearns
,, 163938	,,	♀		310		340	101	26	,,
,, 162844	L. Naivasha, Aberdare Mts., 8000 ft.	♀		535		610	152		

SKULL.—Cranial dimensions (in millimetres) :

Number	Locality	Sex	Max. Cranial Length	Condylo-basal Length	Biparietal	Least Frontal	Bimastoid	Bizygomatic	Palatal Length	Upper Cheek-teeth	Mandibular Length	Lower Cheek-teeth
162844	Naivasha	♀	102·4	80·3		41	56·7	73·1		26·8	72·4	3·04 [1]
164526	Kijabe	♀	95·8	76·8		42·5	52·2	61·3		25·5	67·2	29·2 [1]
182185	Aberdare Mountains	♂	115.4	90·9	61	41	62·7	79·4	48	28·4	81·3	34·2 [1]
182186	,,	♀	97·7	73·4		41·6	55·4	66·1		25·1	65·6	28·7 [1]
164832	Nyeri	♀	97·6	75·3		41·7	54	65·2		25·5	—	— [1]
317970	Mt. Kenya	♂	111		57	42·5	59	73	46	29	75	35
317970	Mt. Kenya	♂	115·2		55·3	42·1		76·2	43·1	27·2	83·6	33·3 [2]

(Left margin: rows 162844–317970 bracketed as "U.S. Nat. Mus."; last row "B.M.")

[1] Mainly from Hollister.   [2] From Elliot.

DISTRIBUTION.—Kenya Highlands. Apparently confined to forests on the eastern slope of Mt. Kenya at altitudes around 8000–9000 feet. The British Museum has examples from Mt. Kenya, Roromo, Tutha and another from the Zoological Society ticketed " Uganda " erroneously.

The U.S. National Museum has a good series, all from Kenya. Localities other than Mt. Kenya include Kijabe, Aberdare Mountains and Nyeri. Mt. Kenya material was collected at 9000 feet. Nanyuki forest is the source of several specimens in the writer's possession. Ticket on U.S. National Museum 162844 states " bamboo forest, 8000 feet".

(g) *C. albogularis moloneyi* Sclater, 1893,* Moloney's Monkey.

(*Syn.* : *Cercopithecus moloneyi* Forbes, 1894, p. 74 ; Pocock, 1907, p. 704 ; *Lasiopyga moloneyi* Elliot, 1913, p. 368 ; *C. leucampyx moloneyi* Schwarz, 1928, p. 654)

Vernacular names : none recorded.

Type locality : Nkonde district near Karonga, on north-west shore of Lake Nyasa. Type collected by Sir J. A. Moloney, who obtained it from Mr. A. Whyte of the African Lakes Company, Karonga (April 1892). Type not in British Museum ; never registered there, so presumed lost.

PELAGE.—Crown blackish, speckled with yellow, the cheeks much lighter, strongly contrasted with the crown, speckled with greyish yellow ; brow-band with considerable intermixture of white hairs. Ear tufts whitish, occasionally red. Interscapular area speckled with greyish yellow. Lower back and lumbar and sacral regions rich chestnut brown contrasting with speckled grey on flanks and thighs. Arms entirely black, except for medial surface of brachial region, which is greyish, in some cases speckled. From the brachium the black extends proximad as a streak along front of shoulder. Crural segments of hind limbs grey, speckled. Hands and feet black. Chin, throat, dirty greyish white ; under surface of body darker grey, more or less speckled. Tail

* *Proc. zool. Soc. Lond.* 1893, p. 252.

black but showing some speckling towards base and some reddish hairs above its root, but not at sides or beneath in males. A considerable number of red hairs in this situation in females.

NEWBORN.—Ansell (1960) describes the natal coat as lacking distinct annulations, although rufosity of the back is already evident. An irregular streak of black between and behind shoulders. Ear tufts yellowish. Crown wholly black; cheeks light grey.

DIMENSIONS.—Much like *C. samango*, but larger (Forbes).

DISTRIBUTION AND ECOLOGY.—Northern shores of Lake Nyasa. Ansell (*in litt.* 1963) confirms its presence in the riparian or gallery forest of the steep ravines of the Muchinga escarpment, Serenje district. In one locus at least the range extends to the valley floor below the Muchingas, where there is suitable riparian forest, so that the dry valley floor (*Brachystegia* woodland along the foot of the escarpment and the mainly mopane woodland to the Luangwa river) forms the barrier to its westward range, not the escarpment as such. Berry (1965, in press) recalls that Pitman (1934, p. 380) drew attention to the possible existence of a red-backed monkey in the Luangwa valley, believing it to be a representative of *C. ascanius*, but Ansell (1960) showed this to relate to the Blue monkey (*C. albogularis moloneyi*). Berry confirmed this and collected an immature female at the Mchemadzi river (now in the British Museum, no. 64.1279). Berry also observed these monkeys on the west bank of the Luangwa, opposite the Mtipwazi confluence and on the opposite bank a mile or so below the confluence.

There is some evidence (Ansell, 1960) that, to the south, intergrading occurs between *moloneyi* and *erythrarchus*. A specimen from the eastern part of the Lusaka district had whitish hairs in the ears, prominent red ischial hairs, but these did not extend over the base of the tail; yellow dorsal speckling intermediate between *moloneyi* and *erythrarchus*—richer and deeper than in the latter, but not as chestnut or reddish as in typical *moloneyi*. It agrees with *moloneyi* in the contrast between crown and cheeks, which is not the case in *erythrarchus*.

Other material obtained later from the same locality proved to be typical of *moloneyi*, so that the intermediate animal is evidently an individual abberation inclining towards *erythrarchus* (Ansell, 1963 *in litt.*). Later (1964) Ansell confirms these remarks and notes that, while preferring dense woodland gorges, the Blue monkey may venture on occasion into less heavily wooded country when trees are in leaf and water plentiful. The presence of *Khaya nyasica* is regarded as a good indicator of likely sleeping places. Food, in this area, judged from contents of cheek-pouches, comprised dried fruits of *Feretia aeruginescens*.

The above mentioned Luano Valley female was at the time of collection (27 November 1960) carrying an infant of approximately 3–4 weeks old, indicating parturition in early November (Ansell, *in litt.* 1961).

Ellerman *et al.* (1953) give the range of *moloneyi* as extending into Northern Rhodesia and south-western Tanganyika. This form does not intergrade with *C. mitis opisthostictus* (*fide* Ansell, 1960, see also above, p. 413).

(h) *C. albogularis francescae* Thomas 1902 *

    Vernacular names: none recorded.

    Type locality: Near Mount Waller plateau, west side of Lake Nyasa. Type in British Museum (No. 2.7.24.1), collected by Rev. James Anderson and presented by Mrs. H. R. Hill. A native-made skin lacking face, hands and feet.

          * *Ann. Mag. nat. Hist.* (7), x. 243.

CHARACTERS.—Similar to *monoides*, but smaller. Schwarz (1928) added *francescae* to the synonymy of *moloneyi* of which he regarded it as representing the juvenile pelage. Ansell (1960) has recently, however, produced evidence that *francescae* is a valid race, indeed a very distinct one.

Chiefly distinguished from *albogularis* and its relatives by the red ear-tufts and the reduction in yellow element in body pelage ; in this it contrasts strongly with its nearest geographical neighbour *moloneyi*, which is particularly strongly coloured on the back.

According to Ansell the present form is readily distinguished from *moloneyi* by its much darker colour, especially on the flanks and hind-limbs ; furthermore there is less contrast between the crown and cheek areas of the pelage.

Ansell also shows that Schwarz was mistaken in regarding the colour differences of the type skin of *francescae* as evidence of juvenility, for one of the newly collected specimens (K.M. 11545) is younger than the type, but already in post-natal pelage indistinguishable from that of adults.

Further confirmation of the validity of *francescae* is brought forward by Ansell (*in litt.* 1961) in so far as an adult male (No. 11338)—the only one so far known—agrees with the above description in the red ear-tufts and general body colour, which, if anything, is even darker (which would be expected if, *e.g.*, *opisthostictus* is any guide). In fact *francescae* is the darkest of all races of *albogularis* except *C. a. samango* (*infra*, p. 432).

JUVENILE.—Lacks the pale tips to the individual hairs found in adults ; rump less brightly rufous with a more greenish tinge, due to lighter subapical annulations.

Schwarz says this agrees with a young skin collected by Dr. Fülleborn at Ufipa, now in the Berlin Museum, from a locus east of the southern end of Lake Tanganyika.

DIMENSIONS.—Approximate dimensions of type skin, measured by Thomas ; head and body, 450 mm. ; tail 620 mm.

DISTRIBUTION AND ECOLOGY.—Rain forests along western shore of Lake Nyasa from Mt. Waller southwards to Nchisi mountain. Ansell (1960) records material from Nkata Bay, Nchisi mountain, Kota-kota and Chintechi. These are the only known records apart from the type locality. The specimen from Chintechi was originally identified by Roberts (1948, p. 63) as *C. nyasae* Schwarz, presumably on geographical grounds. Further material from 8 miles south south-west of Nkata bay is referred to by Ansell *et al.* (1962).

Ansell (1961, *in litt.*) correlates the dark pelage with the very high rainfall in the area of distribution along the west shore of Lake Nyasa.

(i) *C. albogularis nyasae* Schwarz, 1928,* Nyasa White-throated Guenon

(*Syn.* : *C. leucampyx nyasae* Schwarz, 1928, p. 656)
Vernacular names : none recorded.
Type locality : Fort Lister, Mlanje, Southern Nyasaland, 3500 feet. Type, old ♂, in British Museum (no. 94.1.25.1), collected by A. Whyte, 16 July 1893.

PELAGE.—Very similar to *C. erythrarchus* from Beira and the northern Transvaal, and somewhat transitional between it and the more northern *C. a. monoides*. Differing from *erythrarchus* by its darker back and thighs and in the stronger rufous tinge, which, however, is not so marked as in *monoides*. The rusty patch at the root of the tail dorsally, so marked in *erythrarchus* is, in *nyasae*, found only in the juvenile, where it is distinctly darker. From *albogularis* it differs in the paler under parts

* *Ann. Mag. nat. Hist.* (10), i. 656, footnote.

and in the distinctly greyer dorsal pelage. The whitish throat area does not extend to the sides of the neck and is sometimes tinged (especially in juveniles) with brownish. The medial surface of the thigh may also present a yellowish tinge.

DIMENSIONS (in millimetres).—An adult male from Fort Lister, Mlanje, head and body, 470 ; tail, 830 ; foot, 150 (ex Elliot).

SKULL.—Cranial dimensions (in millimetres) of type ♂: maximum cranial length, 118·6 ; biparietal, 60·6 ; least frontal, 44·2 ; bizygomatic, 81·4 ; biorbital, 67·2 ; palatal length, 50 ; upper cheek-teeth, 29 ; mandibular length, 83 ; lower cheek-teeth, 34·8.

DISTRIBUTION.—Original description is based on eight examples in the British and Paris Museums from the undermentioned localities : Fort Johnston (Lake Nyasa) ; Manzi (east shore of Lake Chilwa), Mt. Chiradzulu, Fort Lister (Mt. Mlanje) Chirinda forest. " Région des lacs " (Collected by Foa). This race, therefore, appears to be centred on the southern end of Lake Nyasa and the area between it and Lake Chilwa (=Lake Shirwa) east of the Shire rift (Ansell, 1960).

(j) *C. albogularis erythrarchus* Peters, 1852,* Mozambique Monkey ; Beira Monkey ; Stairs' Monkey

(*Syn.* : *C. stairsi* Sclater, 1893, pp. 252, 443 ; *C. mossambicus* Pocock, 1907, p. 705 ; *C. albigularis beirensis* Pocock, 1907, p. 701, *C. mitis stevensoni* Roberts, 1948, p. 63)

Vernacular names : In Mossambique : *nscho'go* (Inhambane) ; *coro* (Quelimane) ; *nimbo* (in Beira). In Nyasaland : *nchima* (Ansell *et al.* 1962).

Type locality : Inhambane, Portuguese East Africa, south of the River Zambezi. Type in Berlin Museum (a juvenile) (No. 16059). Peters (von der Decken's *Reise* III, p. 3) mentions an adult male collected by von der Decken at the foot of Buraberge, Chinde. Type locality of *stairsi*, Chinde, Zambezi delta, based on an erythristic mutant (a juvenile female) living in the London Zoo, presented by Mr. Hillier to Dr. Moloney of Lt. Stairs' expedition, now in British Museum (No. 93.11.16.1). Type locality of *mossambicus*, Mozambique. Based on an adult ♂ erythristic menagerie specimen, in British Museum (No. 8.5.7.2). Type locality of *beirensis*, Beira, south-east Africa. Type ♂ in British Museum. Type locality of *stevensoni*, Mount Selinda, Melsetter district, eastern Southern Rhodesia.

Material examined : types of *stairsi, mossambicus* and *beirensis*. A living female from Beira in captivity ; a skin in Edinburgh University Museum and one from Vumba Mts. collected by J. J. C. Mallinson.

PELAGE : ADULT MALE.—A relatively pale race of *albogularis*, its dorsal pelage being in general a speckled light grey with tendency to olive green. The ochraceous suffusion seen in *albogularis* and *kibonotensis* is also lacking.

A narrow line of black brow hairs forwardly and upwardly directed. Ear-tufts yellowish white. Crown, cheeks, nape and interscapular region somewhat darker than lower back, individual hairs black with yellow annulations. Lower back and flanks paler, silvery with olive-green speckling increasing posteriorly and on basal portion of tail. Tail otherwise black and almost devoid of speckling. Red is reduced normally to a conspicuous patch near the root of the tail and the adjacent sacral region. Legs pale greyish ; forearms, hands and feet black ; under parts white.

Iris, chestnut, yellower than in *C. a. kolbi.*

* *Reise Mossambique, Säugethiere,* i, pl. i, P. I. (Reichenbach gives a reference *Mitt. Ges. naturf. Fr., Berlin,* 16 July 1850.)

ADULT FEMALE.—Not distinguishable from male in pelage. One kept alive for 5 years by the writer.

During the sexual season the labia pudendi became swollen and pigmented, the clitoris prominent and unpigmented, purplish-pink. The summit of the labial swelling projected 5 mm. beyond the surface level of the callosities. Labia were too tense to permit separation for inspection of vestibule. Rima extending to within 12 mm. of anal margin. Anus raised, with puckered margin within a naked field of reddish flesh-colour. Callosities dark brownish-black concealed by long hairs of ischial region.

VARIATIONS.—Chiefly depend on tendency to increased erythrism. The type of *stairsi* is pale olive green dorsally with much pale rusty red posteriorly, most conspicuous around the root of the tail and the circumanal region, but also spreading to the medial surface of the thighs and along a narrow line on the back of the thighs.

Red also appears on the crown and there are two bright rusty-red patches above the ears corresponding to the anterior portion of the dark parieto-occipital band of *C. petaurista*. The normal speckling is obsolete except for a small area of the interscapular region. Under parts nearly white.

The type of *mossambicus* is very similar, but is a somewhat older animal, which accounts for the differences noted by Pocock—*i.e.* reduced rufosity of back and head and the less well defined ear-marks ; arms and thighs pale grey, hands and feet blackish ; under parts as in type of *stairsi*. Erythrism most complete on hindmost part of back, traces extending forwards in the midline to thoracic region. The type of *beirensis* differs in no way from normal *erythrarchus*. The type skin proves that the scrotum was pendulous. Proximal 50 mm. of tail red changing to speckled pelage like sacral region, thereafter abruptly to uniform black.

DIMENSIONS (in millimetres) :

Locality	Sex	Head and Body	Tail	Foot	
Mt. Selinda	♂	—	—	—	Type of *stevensoni*
Zambezi delta	♂	—	—	—	*ex* Elliot " *stairsi* "
Beira	♂	561	601	172 (?)	*ex* Elliot " *beirensis* "

SKULL.—Cranial dimensions (in millimetres) :

Locality	Sex	Max. Cranial Length	Least Frontal	Bizygomatic	Upper Cheek-teeth	Mandibular Length	Lower Cheek-teeth	
Mt. Selina	♂	121·5	45	78·5	29·2	85	37	Type of *stevensoni*
,,	♀	110·5	42·7	69	27	74·7	31	*ex* Roberts
,,	♀	106	44	69	26·5	70·7	30·5	,,
Zambezi delta	♂	114·5	43·2	77·5	26	85	33·5	*ex* Elliot " *stairsi* "
Beira	♂	117·6	44	75·7	26·6	79·8	31·7	*ex* Elliot " *beirensis* "
Vumba	♀	95	41·5	64·5	25·5	65	28·5	*ex* Roberts

DISTRIBUTION AND ECOLOGY.—East Africa south of the Zambezi river and in the forests of its delta. Peters (1852) stated that this monkey abounded on the plain inland of Inhambane near Cape Corrientes, and less frequently around Quelimane north of the Zambezi delta. Kirk (1864, *Proc. zool. Soc.* p. 649) also reported it from Quelimane and again from Luabo, south of the Zambezi delta.

Darkish monkeys are recorded as having been sighted by B. L. Mitchell (in Ansell *et al.* 1962) on the Mwanza river, Chikwawa; Lengwe; and Tangadzi which, on geographical grounds might perhaps belong to *erythrarchus*, which is stated to occur in Southern Rhodesia and the Gorongoza area of Portuguese East Africa.

Ansell (1960) mentions a female collected at Vumba in Southern Rhodesia.

Ellerman and Morrison-Scott (1953) give the western range of *erythrarchus* to Gorongoza and Umtali in Southern Rhodesia.

Mitchell noted the distinctive voice of these monkeys.

The following observations made in the Vumba mountains above Umtali and supposedly relating to "Samango monkeys", I owe to Mr. J. J. C. Mallinson. Aside from the geographical locality, the identity of these monkeys with *erythrarchus* is confirmed by a very fine adult male skin collected and given to me by Mr. Mallinson.

"The main concentration of the Samango monkeys at the moment, appears to be in the forest slopes on either side of the Castle Beacon, although there are some troops behind the Leopards Rock Hotel. The vegetation is true forest round the castle beacon, and it is almost impossible for the sun to filter through to the ground.

"When dawn breaks at about 5 a.m., the Vumba mountains are usually covered with 'guti', a heavy, cool, damp mist, and the Samangos commence their daily infiltration down through the forest, descending from 750-1000 feet during the course of the day, retracing their tracks in the late afternoon. The largest troop I saw was only seven to eight strong, sticking to the uppermost branches of the trees, making little noise in their progress through the forest, although the occasional dislodgement of rotten branches revealed their whereabouts.

"In one clearing for telegraph poles running through the forest, the gap was too wide for the Samangos to negotiate, so they had to come down from their usual strictly arboreal life, in order to continue their journey. They made one path through the long grass before gaining the safety of the other side, and unless you were searching the area for this path, you could easily miss it. I placed a trail of bananas and hens' eggs leading up to a large wire trap on this path, and a trail of eggs and bananas immediately after the trap. One particular troop of seven strong, ate all the eggs and bananas leading up to the trap, and the fruit after it. However, their suspicion was accentuated by the fact that even a banana one-quarter in the trap and three-quarters out, was not taken, despite their obvious enjoyment of the other fruit.

"The enclosed Samango skin, was shot by a Lt.-Col. H. G. Seward, when this male, completely on his own, was found robbing Col. Seward's chicken eggs. His property is approximately 750 feet down the mountain from Castle Beacon, and the Samangos usually put in their appearance mid-morning and also rob his fruit trees of apples. They are also known to eat wild figs and grenadillers.

"In the Vumba Mountains, the small troops of Samangos seem to keep to the upper regions of the slopes, and the very much larger troops of Vervet Monkeys, inhabit the not quite so dense regions. However, in places they do overlap. Although the Samango is not often seen unless one is really out looking for them, they are extremely inquisitive, and will often sit surveying you from the protection of dense foliage with obvious interest."

Ansell (1960) refers to four topotypes (2 ♂♂, 2 ♀♀) of Robert's *stevensoni*. The locus is so close to the known range of *erythrarchus* and the differences described are so slight (quantity of reddish hairs in ischial region) as to be well within the range of individual variation. I have no hesitation therefore in reducing *stevensoni* to the synonymy of *erythrarchus*.

(k) *C. albogularis schwarzi* Roberts, 1931*

(*Syn.* : *C. leucampyx schwarzi* Roberts, 1931.)
Vernacular names : None recorded.
Type locality : Mariepskop, Pilgrim's Rest district, eastern Transvaal. Type adult male in Transvaal Museum (No. 4484), collected by G. van Dam, 20 November 1925. Two topotypes and seven other specimens referred to in original description.

PELAGE : ADULT MALE.—Face blackish on naked areas, but lips and chin with greyish-white hairs.

General colour speckled olive greenish above, the superficial colouring of the hairs annulated alternately black and yellow, darker on the head, yellower on the lumbo-sacral region, greyer along the flanks, but all dorsal hairs show a broad basal band of white merging distally into grey. On the crown the bases of the hairs are either white or grey followed by a broad darker, almost black, band.

Cheeks like flanks, but sides of neck paler, the whitish throat area extending upwards in a linear fashion as high as the ear level. Ears strongly demarcated from surrounding darker areas by buffy white tufts.

Arms and hands black, with some light whitish speckling on the forearms, and more heavy speckling on the shoulders.

Hind-limbs blackish and grey, darkening at the knees and calcaneal region ; toes and dorsum of foot black, but base of foot speckled with white, merging proximally into colour of thighs.

Tail uniformly black in distal two-thirds, but basal one-third ticked with yellowish bands on individual hairs increasing proximally, but darker above than below. The dark dorsal area is broader than in *samango*, but some individual variations are recorded.

Under parts greyish. Throat white, becoming greyish white on chest due to development of blackish banding on hairs ; middle of belly darker due to increase in black-banded hairs, extending down from the flanks. Flanks with long hairs greyish-white at base, thereafter banded alternately black and buffy, giving a general greyer effect than on back. From the chest a band of whitish hairs extends on medial sides of arms to elbows, and thence less distinctly as a thin line to the wrists.

Long hairs on scrotal area and base of tail below uniformly buffy with darker bases.

DIMENSIONS of type male (in millimetres) : Length of head and body, 530 ; tail, 711 ; foot, 146 ; ear, 39 (measured in the flesh).

SKULL.—Cranial dimensions of type male (in millimetres) : Maximum cranial length, 113 ; basilar length, 84 ; condylo-incisive length, 97 ; biparietal, 59·5 ; least frontal breadth, 43·5 ; bimastoid, 63 ; bizygomatic, 75·5 ; palatal length, 43·5 ; upper cheek-teeth, 27 ; mandibular length, 82 ; lower cheek-teeth, 34·2.

DISTRIBUTION.—This race appears to be related closely to *C. samango* its nearest neighbour to the south. It probably occupies all suitable areas north of the Vaal river and is separated by the Limpopo from the territory of *C. a. erythrarchus*.

* *Ann. Transv. Mus.* xiv. 222

Besides the type locality, Roberts mentions specimens from Leydsdorp and Woodbush to the north of the Olifants river.

(1) *C. albogularis samango* Wahlberg, 1844,* White-lipped Guenon ; Samango Monkey

(*Syn.* : *Cercopithecus labiatus* I. Geoffroy, 1842,† *nomen nudum* ; *C. samango* Wahlberg, *loc. cit.* ; Sclater, 1894, p. 251 ; *C. chimango* Temminck, 1853 ; *Lasiopyga labiata* Elliot, 1913, p. 375 ; *Cercopithecus leucampyx labiatus* Schwarz, 1928, p. 657.)

Vernacular names : Afrikaans, *samangoaap* ; Amaxosa, *insimango* ; French, *cercopithèque aux lèvres blanches*.

Type locality : Inland of Port Natal (=Durban), Natal. Type in Stockholm Museum. Cotype male (No. ?) in British Museum. Type locality of *labiatus* (South) Africa. Type an immature male from the Paris menagerie (1840), now in Paris Museum (No. 283, gallery No. 152). A stuffed exhibition specimen, with skull inside ; said by Rode (1938) to be in fair condition. This monkey is usually known as *C. labiatus* or *C. mitis labiatus*, but Geoffroy's original reference gives no description beyond it being white-lipped monkey.

PELAGE : ADULT MALE.—Pelage long, thick, darkly coloured—the darkest race of *albogularis*. Differing from *C. a. schwarzi* in the greater extent of buff ticking on the base of the tail which affects the basal 200–250 mm. compared with only 100–155 mm. in *schwarzi*. The colour affects the sides as well as the under surface, leaving but a narrow dark dorsal band.

Face black with white hairs. Ears pigmented, with tufts short, dirty white. Crown almost black, with minimum speckling with buff. Upper parts of body black speckled with yellowish-grey, the lower back and flanks not more brightly coloured than the fore parts. Tail dark along median dorsal line, but in basal one-third nearly white beneath and along sides, the pale band exceeding in width the dark dorsal band and sharply defined therefrom. Distal part of tail wholly black. Usually no reddish hairs at base of tail or on ischial area, which is clothed with white hairs, but Pocock mentions a menagerie specimen with slight reddish tinge in the grey hairs lateral to the callosities.

Pectoral limbs jet black from above elbow distally ; pelvic limb smoky grey, speckled with yellow, not sharply differentiated from dark of body.

Under parts from chin to pubes whitish ashy grey and unspeckled. No pale half-collar around neck. Paler hairs extending over medial surface of thighs.

Callosities, palms and soles black. Nails black.

DIMENSIONS (in millimetres).—Type of *labiatus* ♂: length head and body, 558·8 ; tail, 658·8 ; foot, 127.

SKULL.—See p.

DISTRIBUTION AND ECOLOGY.—The southernmost representative of *albogularis*, ranging from Zululand to the eastern part of Cape Province.

The Samango monkey inhabits wooded gorges and kloofs and the denser forests of the eastern part of South Africa. It is not common in Cape Province or the eastern parts of Natal, but common in the forests of Zululand and Pondoland (Fitzsimons, 1919).

Does not, in the wild state, associate with the Vervet (*C. pygerythrus*) and when

* In Sundevall, *Ofvers. Vetensk. Akad. Forh. Stockh.* i. 160.
† *C.R. Acad. Sci. Paris*, xv. 1083 ; *Dict. univ. Hist. nat.* iii. 302 (1843).

PLATE XVII

Photo: A. Gijzen

Cercopithecus l'hoesti with young born 6/4/61. Photographed 8/4/61

PLATE XVIII

Photo: A. Gijzen

Cercopithecus l'hoesti with young born 19/4/61 and 14/11/62. Photographed 29/1/63

the two meet, they are at enmity. They differ markedly in temperament; the Samango agreeing with other races of *albogularis* in its staid, self-possessed character and deliberate movements.

Samango skins are used as ornaments by the Zulus.

3. *CERCOPITHECUS NICTITANS* (Linnaeus, 1766 *)

Greater White-nosed Guenon or **Putty-nosed Monkey; Hocheur Monkey.**

(SYN. : *Simia nictitans* Linnaeus, 1766 ; *S. nitctitans* (sic) Shaw, 1800, p. 45 ; *C. nictitans* Erxleben, 1777. *La guenon à nez blanc proéminent*, 7 ; *Le hocheur* Buffon, 1789 p. 58 Suppl. ; *Lasiopyga nictitans* Illiger, 1811, p. 68 ; Elliot, 1913, p. 316)

VERNACULAR NAME : See under subspecies.

TYPE LOCALITY : " Guinea ". For localities of synonymous forms see under subspecies.

CHARACTERS (See fig. 65 c, p. 451)

Much like the members of the *mitis* and *albogularis* groups in respect of size, shape and general colouration, but with the hairs on the nose forming a well defined large white or yellowish pad, sharply differentiated from the darker surrounding areas of nose and lips, the contours of the pad oval higher than broad, with a strongly convex upper border. In the shape of the nose-pad *C. nictitans* sharply contrasts with that in the superspecies *C. petaurista*, which also differs in the presence of a black brow fringe and a black stripe crossing the temple between eye and ear.

Cheek-pad shaped as in *C. mitis*, with the hairs directed as in that species, and uniformly speckled green and black, *i.e.* without the black cheek-strip found in some species of the *petaurista* Formenkreis. Ears without definite fringe or tuft. Crown and nape darker than back, the latter blackish, speckled with grey, showing little if any yellow tinge. Tail blackish above and below. Fore-limbs black throughout. Under parts greyish black, somewhat grizzled, but throat, and sometimes chest, whitish.

In the skull Schwarz (1928 *c*) found that the nasals are characteristically broad and flat, a feature doubtless correlated with the presence of the nose-pad in so far as it also occurs in *C. petaurista*, thus providing one of the reasons for Schwarz's aggregation of all the forms as races of a single species *C. nictitans*. But, as Booth (1956) has pointed out, apart from the nose spot and a preference for a high proportion of leaves in the diet, *C. nictitans* and *C. petaurista* have little in common. Moreover, as Booth (1956) has also shown, geographical ranges of the forms of *nictitans* overlap with those of representatives of the *petaurista* Formenkreis. For example, the range of *C. n. stampflii* is wholly included within that of *C. petaurista*, whilst in

---

* *Syst. Nat.* i. 40.

2 F

Nigeria the range of *C. erythrogaster*, a number of the *petaurista* assemblage, is wholly within that of *C. n. martini*. There can, therefore, be no question of the conspecificity of *nictitans* and *petaurista*.

DISTRIBUTION AND ECOLOGY (Map 3)

C. nictitans is a West African representative of the *C. mitis* superspecific assemblage and, like its eastern congeners, is a forest dwelling species. A more or less continuous population extends from Liberia eastwards to the Bandama river in the Ivory Coast. Another population occurs in Nigeria extending inland, in isolated forest patches, as far as 9° N. (Rosevear, 1953). Continuous with the latter group, representing a third subspecies, the range extends southwards along the coastal tract to the Ogowe river (1° S.) and, inland, according to Sanderson (1940), to about 15° E. Cabrera (1929) gives Cette Cama on the Gabon coast as the southern limit (2° S.), but Schwarz (1954) extends the range as far as Landanon, Cabinda (Angola) (5° S.) on the evidence of a specimen in the Brussels Museum.

Fernando Po is occupied by a population of *C. n. martini*. Inland the extension of the range in the Congo basin occurs in the gallery forests along the Ubangi, as far as 8° N., which extension is probably continuous with the Cameroon population, where, according to Jeannin (1936), this monkey is very common. The last-named author mentions it as far as 7° N. 14° E. in a climatic zone he refers to as " almost Sudanian ". In the former Belgian Congo it extends southwards to 2° N. and eastwards to about 26° E. (Schouteden, 1947). The southern limit is the Congo river and its tributary, the Itimbiri. There is a possibility that the ranges of *C. nictitans* and *C. mitis stuhlmanni* meet in the Congo forests, but this has not been definitely determined.

North of the former Belgian territory the nominate race is mentioned by Malbrant (1952), on the authority of Blancou, as occurring only in the extreme south of the French controlled Chad area—a little south of N'délé, within the drainage basin of Lake Chad, which is probably its extreme northward extent. In the Ubangi territory south of this, it is stated to be common.

In the former French Equatorial Africa, Malbrant and Maclatchy (1949) state that *C. nictitans* occupies both high secondary forest and lower strata of brush. Bands are relatively localized and do not encroach on each others' territories. In the secondary forest, they subsist on fruits and shoots, but ants were recovered from the stomach in one individual. This monkey rarely comes to the ground even to get from one group of trees to another, but solitary examples near native settlements will on occasion steal chickens, but take them back to the trees for eating.

According to Booth (1956), the western form, *C. n. stampflii*, is confined to primary forest and indeed to its upper layers only, whereas *C. n. martini* in Nigeria is found at all levels in primary forest, in secondary forest as well as in brush country. These two races are separated by a 400-mile gap (Dahomey Gap).

As regards behaviour, this monkey is noted for its peculiar attitudinizings, especially its effective display pattern of wagging the head, resulting in the French name *hocheur* (from *hochement*, wagging the head).

In a male *C. n. martini* in the Washington Zoo, head jerking was confined to up and down movements, contrasting markedly with the side-to-side jerking observed in *C. cephus*. The display is evidently calculated to emphasize the nose-spot. The French name has also been translated to mean " vaulting monkey ", which indicates another specific behavioural pattern observed frequently in captive animals. An adult male of the nominate race recently observed in the St. Louis Zoo drew attention to itself by repeated backward somersaults, landing each time on all four feet with the tail arched over the back.

According to Malbrant and Maclatchy, the male emits several cries, especially a raucous, gutteral *ho-ho*, at other times a more nasal loud *hohon hohon*, which seems to be an alarm note in so far as it is followed by immobility on the part of other members of the band. It occurs especially when the troop is threatened by the Crowned Hawk-eagle (*Stephanoaëtus coronatus*). Both males and females give also an alarm note which is described as a short, metallic whistle.

Food plants in the Gabon and French Congo include seeds and fruit of secondary forest species, such as *Irvingia gabonensis*, *Pachylobus buttneri*, *Pycnanthus kombo*, probably also of *Dialium pachyphyllum*, the drupes of *Elaeis* and shoots of the Umbrella tree (*Musanga cecropioides*).

KEY TO THE SUBSPECIES OF *C. NICTITANS*

(A) Under parts from chest backwards including under-arms dark grey ; no red hairs on ischio-pubic region . . . . *nictitans*

(B) Under parts, except hinder part of abdomen, white

    (*a*) Pale area of throat separated by dark grey band from that of chest ; considerable quantity of reddish hairs on ischio-pubic region . . . . . . *martini*

    (*b*) Pale area of throat, chest and arms uninterruptedly white ; no red hairs on ischio-pubic region . . *stampflii*

Jentink's *C. signatus* has been regarded by some (*e.g.* Booth, 1956) as a subspecific form of *C. nictitans*. Based on a specimen formerly living in the

Rotterdam Zoo, its exact provenance is unknown. It clearly belongs to a spot-nosed species, and the nasal spot is intermediate in outline between that typical for *C. nictitans* and that occurring in *C. petaurista*. Pocock considered it more closely allied to *C. ascanius* ; he also attributed a specimen from Fernando Po to this form. Schwarz's (1954) latest pronouncement, after re-examination of the type skin, is that *signatus* should be reduced to the synonymy of *C. erythrogaster* (*vide* below, p. 499).

(a) *C. nictitans nictitans* Linnaeus, 1766,* Greater White-nosed Monkey ; Hocheur

(*Syn.* : *Lasiopyga nictitans* Illiger, 1811, p. 68, Elliot, 1913, p. 316 ; *C. nictitans laglaizi* Pocock, 1907, p. 698 ; *C. sticticeps* Elliot, 1909, p. 263)

Vernacular names : Bulu, *avembe* (Perret & Aellen 1956) ; Spanish Guinea, *avem* (Bates) ; Bapounou, Eschira and Eveira, *ilobo* ; Pahouin, *avem* ; Shake and Bakota, *yemba* ; Balali, *n'senngui* ; Gabon, *n'douba* (fide Aschemeier) ; Bakouélé, *kouyé* ; M'boko, *koye* ; Avandji and Adouman, *liwembé, louembé* ; Zande, *bissa* ; Bassa, *mbinda* ; Ndzimu, *kô* ; Ewondo, *osok* ; Mbute, *nduhu* ; Baya, *tong* ; French, *le hocheur, blanc-nez, pain à cacheter* ; German, *Weissnasenmeerkatze*.

Type locality : " Guinea ". Type locality of *laglaizi*, Gabon. Type ♂ in British Museum. Type locality of *sticticeps* N'dongo-leti, upper Ubangi river. Type (unsexed) in British Museum, collected during Alexander-Goslin Expedition.

PELAGE : ADULT MALE.—Differing from *C. n. martini*, its neighbour to the north, in having the chest and medial surface of brachial region dark and in lacking red hairs on the ischio-pubic region and base of tail.

Face, except for upper eyelids and nose-spot, blackish ; upper eyelids flesh-coloured.

Cheek-pads clothed with hairs alternately annulated black and yellow.

Crown, back, base of tail and lateral aspect of thighs dark grey, the hairs annulated black and light yellowish-grey. Lateral aspect of upper arms, and both aspects of forearms and of crural segments, together with hands and feet black. Terminal part of tail also black.

Chin and throat light grey ; rest of under parts dark grey, including chest, medial side of arms and thighs. No reddish hairs on ischio-pubic region or base of tail.

The type of *laglaizi* closely resembles *C. mitis stuhlmanni*, except for the white nose-spot. Arms and forearms, and the whole of tail black, thighs and legs grey with a paler medial streak on former.

In the type of *sticticeps*, the upper parts are duskier than in *martini*, again resembling *stuhlmanni*, but with more light speckling on the head. Nose spot dirty white ; under parts black.

JUVENILE.—A female young in natal coat (U.S. Nat. Mus., No. 220079) from Moeri, Fernan Vaz, collected by C. R. Aschemeier, has crown and shoulders black, with a paler patch on the nape and posterior to shoulders. The lumbo-sacral area is feebly speckled with grey. Tail, arms and legs black throughout. A few white hairs on nose patch and some speckling on the frontal diadem.

DIMENSIONS.—Weight, 5–7 kg. : Length head and body, 550–700 mm. ; tail, 950–1000 mm. (Malbrant).

Schouteden gives head and body, 600 mm. ; tail, 950 mm.

* *Syst. Nat.* i. 40.

Dimensions (in millimetres) of C. nictitans:

Number	Locality	Sex	Head and Body	Tail	Foot	Ear	Weight in kg.	
U.S. Nat. Mus. 220072	Moeri Fernan Vaz	♂	594	1029	167			Collectors' measurements
,, 220362	N'tyonga	♂	516	848	146			
,, 218473	,,	♂	405	678	125			
	Sindara	♂	560	890	145		5500	
	Kango	♂	620	950	155		6000	
	,,	♂	530	960	165		5500	
	Booué	♂	645	880	150		7500	Malbrant and Maclatchy, 1949
	,,	♂	630	895	155		6800	
	,,	♂	656	977	161		7800	
	,,	♂	595	914	150		6700	
	,,	♂	590	930	161		6100	
	,,	♀	533	757	130		4100	
	,,	♂	630	753	147		7100	
	Makokou	♀	475	750	130		3900	
	,,	♂	587	885	142		5500	
	,,	♂	615	916	153		6600	

SKULL.—Cranial dimensions (in millimetres) (from Verheyen, 1962):

		Prosthion-inion	Glabella-inion	Biparietal	Least Frontal	Basion-bregma	Bizygomatic	Palatal Length	Mandibular Length
Average	♂♂	113·6	79·8	58	43·1	50·2	72·8	37·9	69·3
Minimum	♂♂	110·5	75·5	55·5	41·5	48	68·5	36	63
Maximum	♂♂	117·5	84	60·5	46	52	77	40	72
Average	♀♀	100	74·8	55·2	41·8	47	64·2	32·1	59·7
Minimum	♀♀	93·5	71	54·5	40·5	46	61·5	28·5	54·5
Maximum	♀♀	103	77·5	56·5	43	48·5	66·5	35·5	63

Other cranial measurements (including indices) are given by Verheyen.

DISTRIBUTION AND ECOLOGY.—The most southern race of *C. nictitans*, inhabiting forested areas of the South Cameroons—Gabon area, extending northwards to the Donga river. Inland the range includes all of the Congo and Ubangi areas of the distribution of the species. Southwards the range is now known to extend as far as Landana in Cabinda (Angola).

In the Congo the following localities are mentioned by Schouteden as having provided material in the Tervuren Museum. Congo-Ubangi district : Libenge, Lisala (Motima river), Bumba/Lisala, Budjala, Ebambi, Bonjia, Bosobolo and Zongo. Uelle district : Djamba (Itimbiri river), Buta, Ibembo. Jeannin (1936) declares the animal to be common in the Cameroons. Malbrant (1952) says the same concerning the formerly French controlled Ubangi territory, whence the range extends northwards to just south of N'délé in the drainage basin of Lake Chad.

In southern Cameroon, Mertens (1929) found material from the undermentioned : Assobam forest ; Yukaduma ; Besom, north-east of Yukaduma ; Bange forest ; Mpeum and also from Duma in Ubangi (Frankfurt Museum).

Perret and Aellen (1956) give the following localities for *C. n. nictitans* : Wangan, Moneko, Nkut and Ngani, all in Cameroon.

A large series (7 male, 4 female) from the Gabon, collected by Aschemeier of the Collins-Garner expedition, is in the U.S. National Museum ; all are from the region around Fernan Vaz, the Rembo N'kami (Agouma, Moeri, Ntyonga, Ogogga) and Lake Anenghue.

(b) *C. nictitans martini* Waterhouse, 1838,* Martin's White-nosed Monkey ; Ludio Monkey

Syn. : ? *C. temmincki* Ogilby, 1845 ; *C. ludio* Gray, 1849, p. 8 ; *C. insolitus* Elliot, 1909, p. 258 ; *Lasiopyga insolita* Elliot, 1913, p. 298.

Vernacular name : French, *le hocheur de Martin.*

Type locality : " Fernando Po " on label of type specimen. Type ♀, a menagerie animal which lived in the London Zoo from 19 February 1884 till 6 April 1894, now in British Museum (No. 9.11.13.2). Type of *ludio*, skin and skull in British Museum (No. 49.1.12.37 and 49.1.12.41 =skull), purchased from " Heiftse ". Type locality of *insolitus* Northern Nigeria (Dr. Baikie). Type, a juvenile, unsexed, skin in British Museum (No. 62.7.17.3).

PELAGE : ADULT MALE.—Face, except eyelids and nose, slaty blue-grey, paler on the free margin of upper lip and whole of lower lip and chin. Eyelids, above and below, flesh-coloured, which colour also affects the lip margins. Bridge of nose with short black hairs converging to form median crest, sharply defined below from white pad over rostral part of nose and internarial septum. Lips with a few short white hairs and sparser, longer, black vibrissal hairs.

Forehead with forwardly directed hairs which become increasingly oblique posteriorly, finally merging with backwardly directed hairs of crown. In colour these are black, heavily annulated with yellow, the yellow ticking gradually diminishing posteriorly until completely lacking on back of crown.

---

* *Proc. zool. Soc. Lond.*, p. 58.

Laterally also completely black hairs separate the yellow-ticked frontal hairs from the less heavily speckled cheeks. Black hairs continue over the whole preauricular area. Ears without tufts, but provided with sparse short yellowish hairs, especially on the helix and scapha. Ears only feebly pigmented.

Cheek-pad moderately yellow speckled anteriorly, the speckling diminishing behind and below (above description based on an entire preserved head of an adult female).

Back, from shoulder to rump, black, fairly heavily speckled with yellowish grey, the latter hue predominating over the black. Tail in basal one-quarter like the rump, but some reddish hairs beneath at base continuous with considerable quantity of rusty red hairs on ischio-pubic area; distal three-quarters black. Arms laterally black; legs darker than back, but speckled; hands and feet black.

Throat and chest dirty greyish-white, the pale area of throat separated from that on chest by a narrow transverse, faintly blackish, band. Pale area of chest extending laterally on to medial surface of arms and posteriorly to end of sternum. Belly smoky grey, finely speckled, becoming paler posteriorly and on medial surface of thighs. Callosities black.

In the type skin of Gray's *ludio*, yellow speckling is confined to the front half of the crown. Under parts are grey on throat, white on chest and medial surface of upper arms, greying again on hinder chest and abdomen, but whiter again on medial aspect of thighs, darkening to dark grey on the crural segment. Ear-tufts absent. Possibly an individual variant of *martini*.

ADULT FEMALE.—Smaller than male. Rima pudendi, 17·5 mm.; glans clitoridis purple; perineal skin black, with a few white hairs around anus. Circumanal skin with pustules.

JUVENILE.—Speckling on forehead ochraceous rather than yellow; only a few red hairs around base of tail, nose patch yellowish white (based on Hayman's 1940 description from the type skin of Elliot's *insolitus*, the exact locality of provenance of which is unknown).

Hayman states that none of Dr. Baikie's specimens is definitely localized, there being no particulars on the labels, and it is consequently surprising to find Pocock (1907, p. 699) stating that the specimen was labelled " Delta of the Niger " and Elliot (1909, p. 258) giving the locality of the same skin as Northern Nigeria.

DIMENSIONS (wts. in gm : linear in millimetres):

Locality	Number	Sex	Weight	Head and Body (CR)	Head Length muzzle-occiput	Tail	Hand	Foot	Ear Morphological Length	Morphological Breadth	Physiognomic Length	Physiognomic Breadth
Cameroons	PC.506	♀ ad.	2380	430	97	560	99	132·5	28·3	27·5	34·2	24
Cameroons	59/62	♀ ad.	2750	430	107	620	72·5	129·3	26·5	29·7	35·5	25·4

Collector G. M. Durrell.

CRANIAL MEASUREMENTS (in millimetres) British Cameroons. Collector Dr. W. E. Kershaw.

Number	Sex	Max. Cranial Length	Biparietal	Least Frontal	Basion-bregma	Bizygomatic	Bimastoid	Palatal Length	Upper Cheek-teeth	Mandibular Length	Lower Cheek-teeth
PC.198 [1]	old ♂	110	60	45	52	73	61	46	28	83	28·5
PC.199 [1]	♂	110	59·5	44	53	74	60	46	26	75	35
PC.204 [1]	♂	112	59	45	54	73	61	43	28	75	35
PC.218 [1]	♀	102	57	41	50	67	60	42·5	25·5	71·5	31
Colls. No. 444 [1]	♂	108	60	43	53·5	69	61	43	25	72	32
PC.88 [1]	♂	114	59·5	42	55	73	63	48	26	81	32·5
PC.112 [1]	♂	114·5	60	45	56	73	62	47	26·5	75	34
PC.110 [1]	♀	94	55·5	41	49	61	54	32	24·5	60·5	28
PC.207 [2]	♀	99	58	44	50	63	56	40	25	61	30

[1] Permanent dentition complete.   [2] M$\frac{3}{3}$ not fully erupted.

DISTRIBUTION AND ECOLOGY.—Fernando Po and adjacent mainland from about the Nyong river (Cameroons) westwards to the Dahomey faunal gap. Here there is a complete break in the forest and the savanna extends all the way to the coast. The gap has been artificially enlarged on the Nigerian side by human agency, thus preventing the mingling of *martini* with *stampflii*.

Hayman (1940) states that the range of *martini* to the north and west is not yet clearly defined, but the range includes the Niger delta and the forested part of the Cross river. Hayman mentions a young specimen from Nko, Obubra division of southern Nigeria, which agrees with the type of Elliot's *insolitus*.

On the other hand specimens in the British Museum from Bambarang, Donga river, Northern Nigeria in the Benue basin, are more like typical *nictitans* in appearance than *martini*, lacking both the whitish chest and under arms as well as the pubic rufescence of *martini*.

Sanderson (1940) collected 5 ♂♂, 7 ♀♀ and two unsexed skins in his expedition to the Cameroons ; his material was from the following localities : Mamfe, Eshobi, Victoria, Tinta, Makumunu, Badchama, Mainyu Bridge, Mt. Kpani, and N'ko (300–3000 feet altitudinal range).

Sanderson states that in the Cameroons these monkeys keep to the high deciduous forest trees from which they seem never to descend, but they also occupy isolated patches of mountain forest in mountain grass north of the forest fringe. In one locality (N'ko) they descend to feed on native farms, entering secondary and tertiary growth. In Mamfe, Sanderson recorded *C. n. martini* as breeding in January.

Monard's (1938) reference to a white-nosed monkey in Portuguese Guinea suspected as being *C. nictitans* evidently relates to a race of *C. petaurista*.

(c) *C. nictitans stampflii* Jentink, 1888,* Stampfli's Guenon

(*Syn.* : *C. stampflii* Jentink, *loc. cit.*)
Vernacular name : French, *le hocheur de Stampfli*.
Type locality : Pessi country, Liberia. Type in Leyden Museum, collected by Büttikofer and Stampfli.

Schwarz (1928), following Elliot (1913), maintained that *C. stampflii* was indistinguishable from *C. martini*. Sanderson (1940) considered it distinct from other white-nosed monkeys, but Schwarz (1954), after re-examination of the type, reaffirmed his earlier opinion. He argued that the only white-nosed monkeys in Liberia are representatives of *C. petaurista buttikoferi*, and concluded that the type specimen must have been mislabelled and probably collected at the coast, whence it had been brought on board ship from Nigeria.

Booth (1956, 1957 *in litt.*) also recognized *stampflii* as a true " putty-nose " and found its range overlapped that of the two " spot-noses ", *C. petaurista petaurista* and *C. p. buttikoferi*, besides differing from them morphologically, and ecologically.

Recently Kuhn has collected material from the type locality and other parts of Liberia that confirms the presence there of a race of *nictitans* which differs both from *martini* and the nominate race.

PELAGE : ADULT MALE.—Stated in original description to differ from typical *nictitans* in having throat, chest and medial sides of arms as far as the elbow whitish. Jentink made no reference to any red hairs on the ischio-pubic area or tail.

Nose-spot white, broad below, pointed above ; spot on lower lip black ; crown, nape, back, limbs laterally and distal part of tail black ; speckled with rufous. Yellow occurs on the forehead, cheeks, back and flanks and on the basal part of the tail giving a general rufous-green tinge.

Chin, throat, breast and medial aspect of arms to elbows, also anterior part of belly, white.

Booth (1956), although admitting there is no absolutely constant morphological difference from *martini*, states that none of the four specimens of *stampflii* collected by himself had any trace of red, and that local hunters assert that it does not occur.

In spite of the alleged differences from *martini*, both Pocock and Schwarz add *stampflii* to the synonymy of *martini*, the latter without discussion.

Although separated from the area of typical distribution of *stampflii* by the Dahomey gap, Hayman (in Sanderson 1940) tentatively refers some half-dozen Nigerian skins from west of the Cross river to this race (three wild-killed specimens, one from Jebba, one from Nassawara, and a large specimen of Dr. Baikie's collection without locality (B.M., No. 65.4.27.1), and three menagerie specimens (one " Benin ", one " S. Nigeria " and one " Lagos ")). All six agree with each other and differ from *martini* and *nictitans* in having whitish chests and under arms to elbows, and in lacking red ischio-pubic hairs—apart from a few red hairs on the prepuce in the Lagos skin. Some Fernando Po skins in the British Museum also agree in respect of the lack of red ischio-pubic hairs.

Sanderson (1940) affirms that presence or absence of red hairs in the pubic area or base of tail is of little systematic import due to their individual variability and to the fact that the colour can often be washed out with soap and water. He regards it as due to staining with urine or faeces after ingestion of certain specific food substances. He declares that certain leaves from forest trees, when crushed, provide a reddish juice, which he considers sufficient to colour the faeces and thence the subcaudal

* *Notes Leyden Museum*, x. 10.

hairs. This may apply to certain cases, but certainly not all. Staining may also be induced by secretions from cutaneous glands in the inguinal region.

DIMENSIONS.—Head and body, 641·3 mm. ; tail, 976·9 mm. (Forbes).

DISTRIBUTION AND ECOLOGY.—Typically from Liberia, but now known to extend eastwards into the Ivory Coast at least to Daloa and possibly therefore to the Bandama river. In the eastern Ivory Coast, Gold Coast and Dahomey no monkeys of this species are found. The nearest population is 400 miles off in Nigeria, where certain specimens are said to conform to the present subspecies (see Hayman's remarks above); but for the most part Nigeria is the home of *C. n. martini*.

Booth (1956) declares that in the Ivory Coast, *stampflii* is confined to primary forest, and, like *C. diana*, occupies the uppermost strata thereof. In contrast, *C. martini*, in Nigeria, occurs at all forest levels and also in secondary forest and farm bush.

II. Superspecies *CERCOPITHECUS L'HOESTI* Sclater, 1898 *

Mountain Guenons

(SYN. : *L'hoesti* group of Pocock, 1907, p. 714; subgenus *Allochrocebus* Elliot, 1913, p. 297)

This group is introduced at this point for two reasons, (1) the general colour pattern of the pelage recalls that of the previous superspecies, a feature which led Sclater (1898) to assign it to his section " *d* ", Melanochiri, where he considered it affined to *C. albogularis* rather than any other member of that group. Pocock also noted the similarity in coat colour and pattern to *C. albogularis* making *l'hoesti* the representative of a group by itself ; (2) the diploid chromosome number is given as 72 by Chu and Bender, *i.e.*, as in *C. mitis*, although Chiarelli's revised estimate is only 60, as in the *aethiops* and *neglectus* groups.

The independent discovery of the form now known as *preussi* by Matschie and Forbes led the former to the view that the new species was a variant of the *albogularis* section of the genus, and to this group Pocock (1907, p. 700) assigned it, an action in which he was followed by Elliot (1913).

Schwarz (1928 *c*) first placed *l'hoesti* and *preussi* together as subspecies in one group. Raven and Hill (1942) accepted this.

Hayman (in Sanderson, 1940), meantime had confirmed the relationship of *preussi* with *albogularis* and suggested that *l'hoesti* is a specialized offshoot from the same stock.

CHARACTERS

Schwarz correctly maintained that the *l'hoesti* group, as understood here, is a natural group, characterized by features in the condition of the pelage, markings, and also cranial anatomy.

* *Proc. zool. Soc. Lond.*, 1898, p. 586, Pl. XLVIII.

Pelage long, dense and soft, the long dorsal hairs extending a considerable distance along the tail and being especially marked below the root of the tail ; the nose hairy, but without a defined nose spot ; with pale infraorbital marks on face ; tail silvery grey ; under parts blackish, but the throat patch white or yellowish, forming a prominent ruff laterally, the direction of the hairs upwards and lateral, the pale area extending in the direction of the sternum.

Further resemblance to the *mitis* Formenkreis is seen in the fact that the brighter colours on the back are restricted to the lumbo-sacral area, contrasting thus with the *mona* assemblage.

Cranial distinctions include the great extension of the horizontal part of the palatine bone, and the conspicuously high cusps on the molars. Verheyen (1962) notes further that *l'hoesti* agrees with *C. mona* in having a conspicuously developed frontal boss, sometimes extremely so ; and remarks on the relatively wide occlusal surface of the molars (as in *C. hamlyni* and contrasting therein to *C. aethiops* and *C. neglectus*).

Hayman believes the cranial features alleged by Schwarz to be peculiar to the present group are not confined to them.

DISTRIBUTION AND ECOLOGY

Both species of the *l'hoesti* group inhabit mountain forests in western and central Africa. They form a remarkable instance of discontinuous distribution. This type of range, in the form of isolated pockets on the higher montane areas, is paralleled in other groups of mammals, but whether this is indicative of parallel evolution or the case of relic survival from an earlier continuous range is at present undetermined.

According to Sanderson (1957), these montane guenons are leaf and berry eaters, and they frequent moss-festooned dense woodland.

4. *CERCOPITHECUS L'HOESTI* (Sclater, 1898 *)†

L'Hoest's Monkey

(SYN. : *C. thomasi* Matschie, 1905, p. 262 ; *C. insolitus* Elliot, 1909,‡ p. 258 ; *Lasiopyga insolita* Elliot, 1913, p. 298 ; *L. thomasi* Elliot, 1913, p. 370 ; *C. thomasi rutschuricus* Lorenz, 1915, p. 172)

VERNACULAR NAMES : Batoro (Uganda), *enkende* (*fide* Haddow) ; German, *Vollbartmeerkatze* ; French, *cercopithèque de l'Hoest, cercopithèque à barbe en collier*.

TYPE LOCALITY : " Congoland ", restricted by Pocock to Chepo or Tschepo (=Tschopo river near Stanleyville, Uelle district). Type living ♀ in the London Zoo, received from Antwerp Zoo. Type now in British Museum (No. 8.5.7.4). Type locality of *insolitus* " Northern Nigeria ", type juvenile in British Museum, collected by Dr.

---

* *Proc. zool. Soc. Lond.*, p. 586, Pl. XLVIII.

† Named in honour of François l'Hoest, Director of the Antwerp Zoo (1888–1904).

‡ *Ann. Mag. nat. Hist.* (8), iv. 258.

Baikie. Type locality of *thomasi*, east shore of Lake Kivu, between Lakes Albert Edward and Tanganyika. Type in Berlin Museum. Type locality of *rutschuricus* mountains east of Rutschuru plains, eastern Congo. Type in Vienna Museum.

ORIGINAL DESCRIPTION : Size as *C. albogularis*. Above, back ferruginous brown with narrow transverse black lines ; head black with slight whitish freckles ; sides of face and neck covered with elongated ruff-like hairs, white ; throat white ; belly cinereous ; all four limbs dark cinereous, above blackish.

Pocock noted the resemblance of *C. l'hoesti* to his *leucampyx* section, especially to the southern race, *opisthostictus*, which it recalls in the blackness of the shoulders, legs, abdomen, and, to a lesser degree, the head. In the brighter tinge of the lumbar and sacral areas it resembles the *albogularis* section of the *C. mitis* superspecies. It is distinguished by the pure white colour and longish hairs of the cheeks, in the upward sweep of which it resembles the *aethiops* series more than any other. Pocock thought the direction of the whiskers, the white throat and the thick covering of black hair on the nose pointed to an affinity with *C. erythrogaster*, next to which he placed it in his survey.

CHARACTERS

PELAGE : ADULT MALE.—Face black, the nose thickly clothed with black hairs, the lips more sparsely so ; suborbital region clothed with short hairs, some black, some white, the posterior ones lengthening and tending to join the whiskers. Whiskers white, long, directed upward and backward, forming a thick fringe between face and ear, the latter partly concealed thereby, and continuing backwards beyond ear.

Posterior half of interramal region and throat densely clothed with white hairs continuous laterally with whiskers, and extending caudally in a narrowing median field on to chest as far as the intermammary region.

Crown black, but its central area, like the nape and sides of neck, interscapular region and flanks heavily speckled with greyish white. Beginning in the middle of the interscapular region and gradually expanding posteriorly over the costal and lumbo-sacral areas is a band in which the hairs are speckled black and orange red, the latter colour replacing the greyish white of the surrounding areas.

Tail for the greater part grey, speckled with black, but the black increasing distally until at the tip the hairs are wholly black. About 100 mm. of the base beneath also entirely black.

Shoulder, arm, forearm, hand, hip and whole hind-limb jet black, both laterally and medially.

Apart from the median pectoral white streak, the under parts are clothed with black hairs with a tinge of brown from the infraclavicular region to the area around the anus.

The cinereous belly described in the type by Sclater is probably the result of fading induced by captivity.

ADULT FEMALE.—Similar to the male, but smaller. The type of Matschie's *thomasi* differs only in having the dorsal orange red somewhat deeper in tone (chestnut red) in the more distinct greyish-white infraorbital band and in the slightly greater extent of the white pectoral tract posteriorly, reaching the middle of the sternum. These are plainly individual variations.

JUVENILE.—The newborn is uniformly brown, without pattern (Gijzen, 1962). A very young male from Gamangui, collected 10 February 1910, is described by Allen (1925) as 695 mm. in total length (maximum cranial length 80 mm.) and differing only slightly in pattern and colour from the adult. Three others of nearly the same size had almost acquired the adult colour pattern, but show evidence of immaturity in the texture and length of the pelage and the lack or slight development of a grey band on the flanks.

DIMENSIONS (in millimetres) :

	Sex	Head and Body	Tail	Foot	Ear	
Average of 2 measured in the flesh	♂♂	Max. 575	755	172	42	
		Min. 545	700	172	—	From Allen (1925)
Average of 5	♀♀	Max. 515	550	140	—	
		Min. 460	480	130	—	
		700	800			Schouteden

SKULL.—Cranial dimensions (in millimetres) :

	C. *l'hoesti* No. 565/54 ad.	Average of 2 ♂♂	Max.	Min.	Average of 5 ♀♀	Max.	Min.
Max. cranial length	105	106·7	107	106·4	96·8	98·9	94
Glabella-occiput	76	—	—	—	—	—	—
Condyle-basal length	77	90·3	91·2	89·5	71·4	74·5	68·6
Biparietal	55	—	—	—	—	—	—
Occipito-nasal length	—	98·9	99·7	98·1	82·9	84·4	82·9
Least frontal	39·5	44·9	45·1	44·8	42·4	43	40·9
Bimastoid	54·2	63·3	64·2	62·5	56·3	57·3	55·2
Basion-bregma	47	—	—	—	—	—	—
Bizygomatic	66	76·1	77·8	74·5	62·9	65·6	61·4
Biorbital	58	—	—	—	—	—	—
Palatal length	37	—	—	—	—	—	—
Upper cheek-teeth	27	19·2	19·4	19·1	18·4	19	17·5
Mandibular length	68	—	—	—	—	—	—
Lower cheek-teeth	30	—	—	—	—	—	—

Distribution, Ecology and Ethology (Map 4)

Confined to montane forest in the eastern Congo, south of the Uelle river, the southern limit of the range being approximately 4° S. Westwards the species is not known west of the Lualaba. To the east, the range includes Ruanda and Urundi, and parts of western Uganda.

Examples are recorded by Allen (1925) and Schouteden (1947) from the following localities : Uelle district ; Gamangui and Babeyru ; Kibali-Ituri district : Mawambi ; Stanleyville district : Tschoppo Falls (collected by Wehns—in Tervueren Museum—specimen referred to by Matschie (1905))), Angumu. Kivu district : between Masisi and Lake Kivu ; Rushayu, Lake Kivu ; Masisi ; Burunga ; Rutschuru ; N. Lubero ; Mugombe ; Shangugu ; Ruanda Urundi : Rugombo (near Usumbura) ; Ruhengeri ; gallery forest near Kibira ; Ngozi, bamboo forest ; Bugoie ; Uganda : Batoro country (*fide* Haddow, 1952, p. 304).

C. l'hoesti is thus very restricted in geographical range, but makes up for this in its great adaptability to different micro-climates within its territory, since it inhabits both high altitude forests and those in the valleys of the rivers descending to the Congo and to the lakes, especially Lake Kivu. It has been recorded from both gallery forest and bamboo forest, and is known also to assume, on occasion, a terrestrial existence, feeding on the forest floor. It has been suggested (Tappen, 1960), that of the factors limiting its distribution the food or foods of the undergrowth may be important. Shantz and Marbut (1923) have indicated that in montane forests in Africa a greater variety of vegetation clothes the forest floor than in lowland forests.

Dandelot (1956) records in captive specimens a semi-prehensile character of the tail, and I have myself confirmed this—although the same occurs in other guenons, *e.g. C. hamlyni*. Dandelot himself, in fact, quotes I. Geoffroy in his original account of *C. monoïdes* (= *C. albogularis*) as noting the capacity of rolling the tip of the tail round external objects. The tail is often intertwined with that of cage companions, or presumably, in the wild, around trailing or other creeping plants. Infants steady themselves by intertwining their tails around that of the parent. Dandelot figures the tail carriage in quadrupedal stance with the distal proximal half held horizontally in line with the back, the part then curving vertically upwards with the tip turned abruptly downwards in a hook. L'Hoest's monkey has been successfully bred and reared in the Antwerp Zoo. Agatha Gijzen (1962) reports abdominal swelling in the pregnant female, but the birth which occurred on 6 April 1961 remained unobserved, as it occurred in the sleeping box. The newborn was held firmly to the mother's ventral surface and her temperament became fierce. The infant at first lacked all resemblance to its parents, being uniformly brownish and without the elongated whiskers, but gradually changed this for the adult pattern. In a few weeks it was able to climb, jump and gambol by itself. Photographs of mother and infant at the age of 13 days and at 6 months are reproduced in Plates XVII and XVIII.

5. *CERCOPITHECUS PREUSSI* (Matschie, 1898 *)
Preuss's Monkey; Cross's Monkey

(SYN. : *C. crossi* Forbes, 1905, p. 630 ; *C. p. insularis* Thomas, 1910, p. 191, *Lasiopyga preussi* and *L. p. insularis* Elliot, 1913, p. 370)

TYPE LOCALITY : Victoria and Cameroon mountain, West Africa. Original description based on four specimens collected by Dr. Preuss and deposited in the Berlin Museum. Type locality of *crossi*, Cameroons ; type a living subadult ♂ imported by Cross, the Liverpool dealer. Type locality a *insularis*, N. Bantabiri, Fernando Po, alt. 1806 M. Type ♀ in British Museum (No. 4.1.7.5), collected by E. Seimund.

Originally described as an " Abart " of *C. albogularis*, with which section of the genus it was included by both Pocock and Elliot—presumably simply because of its white throat.

Forbes (1905) likewise compared his *C. crossi* with one of the *albogularis* group, placing it near *C. a. moloneyi*.

ORIGINAL DESCRIPTION : " sine fasciâ frontali albidâ ; pectore et abdomine atro-schistaceis, vix griseo-undulatis, corpus lateribus cervice, vertice griseo et nigro undulatis, dorso castaneo".

Schwarz separated *preussi* from the *albogularis* group (which he combined with his *leucampyx* (=*mitis* section) and united it with *l'hoesti*, making it, on insufficient grounds, a subspecies thereof. Hayman (in Sanderson 1940) made a fresh comparison and concluded that *preussi* aligned itself much more readily with *albogularis* than with *l'hoesti*, though the latter, with its unspeckled cheeks and strongly developed, backwardly and upwardly directed white whiskers might be regarded as a specialized off-shoot of the *albogularis* stock. Cranial characters alleged by Schwarz to unite *l'hoesti* and *preussi* are not confined to these two. There is thus less essential difference between *preussi* and *albogularis* than between *C. mona* and *C. pogonias* which Schwarz regarded as races of one species.

CHARACTERS

PELAGE : ADULT MALE.—In general colour and pattern *C. preussi* much resembles *C. l'hoesti*, differing mainly in the greyer cheeks, which are strongly speckled with dark grey banding of the individual hairs. The living animal, however, differs more than descriptions of the coat pattern would suggest, lacking the benign facial expression of *C. l'hoesti* ; and approaching the fiercer mien characteristic of the *C. aethiops* group,—a point well brought out in Sanderson's (1940) excellent coloured plate.

Face slaty grey, paler on the eyelids and infraorbital region, the nose with short, densely planted black hairs forming an upstanding median crest on the interorbital region, and with a convergent downward trend on the rostral area of the nose. Lips with scattered grey and white hairs, with the

* *Sb. naturf. Fr., Berlin*, p. 76.

darker hairs becoming longer and more evident on the lateral part of the upper lip, finally merging with the whiskers. Ears slaty, with a few short black hairs best developed on lamina.

Whiskers elongated, outstanding, but scarcely concealing ears ; the hairs with their basal three-quarters dark grey to black and the apical one-quarter alternately annulated white and black. No yellow annuli anywhere on head.

Crown, neck, shoulders and flanks blackish, speckled with grey, the hairs with basal one-half uniformly grey and distal half banded alternately black and white. Dorsum of body from interscapular region to root of tail, speckled, chestnut brown, with the reddish annuli narrower than the black zones. The brightly tinged area has the same form as in *l'hoesti*, narrow anteriorly and broadening regularly posteriorly ; it includes the basal part of the tail, but the major part of the tail is grey, speckled, like the flanks, slightly darker only along the median dorsal line. The terminal one-third is entirely black above and below.

Upper arms like shoulders, but darker anteriorly also darkening distally, the forearms black with only light speckling, the wrists and hands wholly black.

Thighs black laterally, but speckled along the front, passing gradually proximally into darker tinge of flanks ; the lateral and posterior black areas of thighs are continued into the wholly black shanks, ankles and dorsum of foot.

Under parts dark smoky grey, sometimes with trace of speckling, but throat and chin white, the lighter hairs passing up to the lower limit of the ear, where they mingle with the grey speckled whiskers. Callosities brownish black ; Forbes (1905) describes them as purplish sooty grey.

Iris very dark red (Sanderson).

ADULT FEMALE.—Similar to the male, but smaller. Perineal skin bluish grey with some purple suffusion dorsal to the callosities ; callosities brownish black ; clitoris pink. Area between callosities and rima pudendi with short, black hairs directed ventro-medially, converging to a tuft on ventral commissura labiorum.

JUVENILE.—Neonatus unknown, but presumably like that of *C. l'hoesti*. The juvenile female which constitutes the type of Thomas's *C. p. insularis* differs in nought save its size from mainland adults. Schwarz (1928 *c*) declares them to be merely individual differences ; the long shaggy pelage is undoubtedly a feature of immaturity.

DIMENSIONS (in millimetres) :

Number	Locality	Sex	Head and Body	Tail	Foot	Ear	
Berlin Mus.	Buea, Cameroon		505	535	—	—	Cotype
PC.463	Br. Cameroons	♀	450	616	129	28	
B.M. No. 4.7.1.6	Fernando Po	♀	262	315	91	21	Type of *insularis*

PLATE XIX

Photo: E. P. Walker

Cercopithecus preussi, adult ♂. A living specimen in the National Zoological Park,
Washington D.C.

PLATE XX

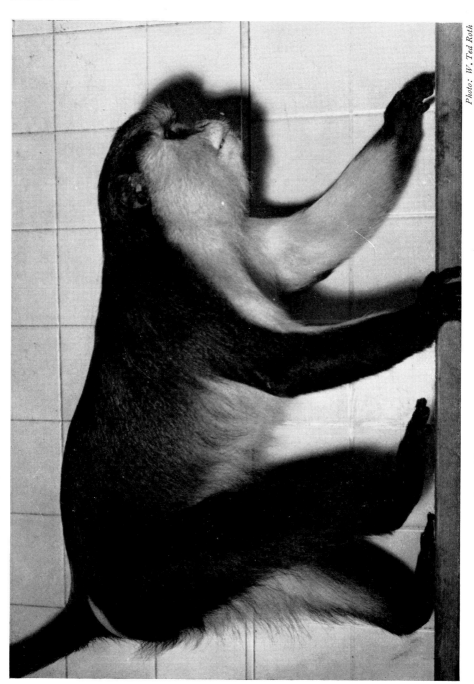

Photo: W. Ted Roth

Cercopithecus mona, adult ♂. Note the white rump area

Additional measurements of PC.463 are : head length (muzzle-occiput), 102 ; hand, 112 ; ear, morphological length, 28 ; morphological breadth 28 ; physiognomic length, 41 ; physiognomic breadth 31 ; intermammillary distance, 14 ; rima pudendi, 15 ; distance between callosities, 13.

SKULL.—Cranial measurements (in millimetres) :

	Buea, Cameroon, Berlin Mus.	Fernando Po B.M. ♀	Cameroon [1]						
			P.C.						
			409	276	411	275	278	102	408
			♂	♀	Subad.	♀ ad.	♀ ad.	juv.	♂ ad.
Max. cranial length	97	94	97·2	87·4	93·3	95·3	96·9	81·6	108
Occipito-nasal length	83	—	74·2	68·8	70	73·5	72·9	65·7	71
Max. cranial breadth	—	51·5	55	55·5	55·8	57·8	54·5	51	57·5
Least frontal	40	37	41·5	42·4	41	45·6	42	39·3	45
Bimastoid	—	—	56·4	50·4	54	55·4	53·2	47·2	61
Bizygomatic	64	48·5	69·6	56	59·7	66	59·6	50·6	73
Palatal length	—	23	41	32·5	33·4	36	35·2	27	46
Upper cheek-teeth	23	15·4	26	22·2	21·6	24·5	26	17	25·5
Mandibular length	64	38·8	—	53·4	54·4	62·5	60·5	42·5	71
Lower cheek-teeth	27 Type	15·8 Type of insularis	—	24	23·9	29·3	29·6	16·2	31·5

[1] Collector W. E. Kershaw.

Matschie (1898) noted a difference from *C. albogularis* in the zygoma of *C. preussi* in so far as, in his material, the zygomatic process of the temporal undergoes attenuation before meeting the temporal process of the malar, whereby its lower margin rises up. In *C. albogularis* the lower margins of the two processes are in alignment. I do not find this condition constant, as it affects approximately only 50 per cent of the skulls examined.

DISTRIBUTION, ECOLOGY AND ETHOLOGY (MAP 4)

The range of *C. preussi* is remarkably restricted and discontinuous. It is confined to high elevation forests in Cameroon and Fernando Po. Sanderson (1940) states that in Cameroon it is restricted to the northern face of the ridge dividing Assumbo from Mamfe, but is also found in isolated patches of mountain forest and mountain grassland to the north. Not even gunfire would compel the small bands to pass over to the southern face of the mountains. Matschie gives Mount Cameroon as a site of occupation, based on Dr. Preuss's field notes. The British Museum has an immature ♀ from

2 G

North Bantabiri, (1800 m.)   Fernando Po, collected by Seimund, and also two native prepared skins from the island (Thomas, 1904).

Sanderson reports native evidence of an unusual behavioural pattern for this monkey.   Remarkable hanging nests of spherical form, with a circular entrance, usually located among dense branches at the forest edge, almost overhanging the grass, are allegedly the homes of the monkeys, and from which they can be dislodged only with great difficulty.

III. Superspecies *CERCOPITHECUS MONA* Schreber, 1774 [*]

(SYN.: *Mona* Reichenbach, 1863; *Cercopitheci melanochiri* (in part) + *Cercopitheci auriculati* of Sclater, 1893, p. 250 and 253, and Forbes, 1894; *Mona* + *Otopithecus* Trouessart, 1897; *Mona* group of Pocock, 1907; subgenus *Mona* of Elliot, 1913)
VERNACULAR NAMES : See under species.

DEFINITION.—Large, robust, big-headed guenons with a pear-shaped facial outline, with eyes deeply insunk, longish, dense cheek whiskers and a very long, thin tail (Reichenbach).   Pallid medial aspect of fore-limbs strongly and sharply contrasted with the dark lateral aspect, especially along the radial border.   Dark crown sharply separated by a black preauricular bar from the paler cheeks.   A pale frontal band generally present, sometimes extending more or less faintly towards vertex.   Face slaty blue, with the exception of median area of lips which is flesh-coloured.   Lumbo-sacral area darker than remainder of back, which is either redder or greyer (*i.e.* the reverse of *C. mitis* and *C. l'hoesti* groups).

Diploid chromosome number, 66.

COMMENTS

Pocock's *mona* group comprised seven species, namely : *mona, campbelli, burnetti, denti, wolfi, grayi* (with subspecies *nigripes*) and *pogonias*.

Schwarz (1928 *a, c*) treated all the forms relegated to this group as races of a single species, *C. mona*.

Nevertheless Schwarz recognized, on morphological grounds, three subordinate groups within his polytypic species, namely (*a*) *mona* section (for *campbelli, lowei* and *mona*) : (*b*) *pogonias* section (for *pogonias, grayi* and *nigripes*) and (*c*) *wolfi* section (for *wolfi, pyrogaster, elegans* and *denti*).

The first to disapprove of Schwarz's treatment of this group was Rode (1937) who treated *C. mona* and *C. pogonias* as distinct species, purely on morphological grounds.   In 1940 Sanderson showed that one form of *C. pogonias* occurred in the same locality as *C. mona*, thus establishing a basis for discarding Schwarz's view of its being a race of *C. mona*.   This overlapping of the territories of *C. mona* and *C. pogonias* was confirmed by the localities of their occurrence in Schouteden's (1944) monumental work on

[*] *Säugetiere*, i. 97.

the Congo mammals. Finally, Booth (1955) maintained that almost the entire range of *C. pogonias* is occupied by *C. mona*, and also produced evidence that *C. campbelli* is a distinct species from *C. mona*.

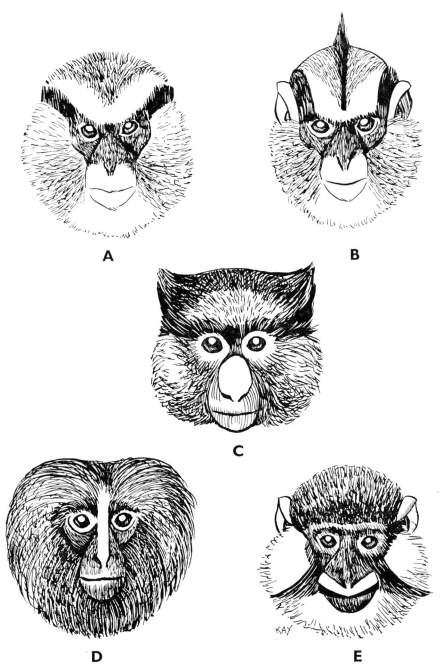

FIG. 65.—Facial appearance of various species of *Cercopithecus*. A, *C. mona*; B, *C. pogonias*; C, *C. nictitans*; D, *C. hamlyni*; E, *C. cephus*. (Based on sketches by P. Dandelot)

A summary of the development of the systematics of this group of monkeys is tabulated herewith, as given by Booth, whose arrangement is given in the last column and is the one accepted here :

TABLE 19

NOMENCLATURE AND STATUS OF MONKEYS OF THE SUPERSPECIES *C. MONA*

Describer's Name	Sclater, 1893 *a*	Pocock, 1907	Elliot, 1913	Schwarz, 1928 *b*	Rode, 1937	Booth, 1955
mona Schreber, 1774	*mona*	*mona*	*mona*	*m. mona*	*m. mona*	*mona*
campbelli Waterhouse, 1838	*campbelli*	*campbelli*	*campbelli*	*m. campbelli*	*m. campbelli*	*c. campbelli*
burnetti Gray, 1842	*campbelli*	—	*burnetti*	*m. campbelli*	*m. campbelli*	*c. campbelli*
c. lowei Thomas, 1923	—	*burnetti*	*burnetti*	*m. lowei*	*m. campbelli*	*c. lowei*
denti Thomas, 1907	—	*denti*	*denti*	*m. denti*	*m. denti*	*denti*
wolfi Meyer, 1891	*wolfi*	*wolfi*	*wolfi*	*m. wolfi*	*m. wolfi*	*w. wolfi*
elegans Dubois & Matschie, 1912	—	—	—	*m. elegans*	—	*w. elegans*
pyrogaster Lönnberg, 1919	—	—	—	*m. pyrogaster*	—	*w. pyrogaster*
pogonias Bennett, 1833	*pogonias*	*pogonias*	*p. pogonias*	*m. pogonias*	*pogonias*	*p. pogonias*
nigripes du Chaillu, 1860	*nigripes*	*g. nigripes*	*p. nigripes*	*m. nigripes*	*pogonias*	*p. nigripes*
grayi Fraser, 1850	—	*g. grayi*	*g. grayi*	*m. grayi*	*pogonias*	*p. grayi*
erxlebenii Dallbet & Pucheran, 1856	*erxlebenii*	*g. grayi*	*g. grayi*	*m. grayi*	*pogonias*	*p. grayi*
pallidus Elliot, 1909	—	—	*g. pallidus*	*m. grayi*	*pogonias*	*p. grayi*
petronellae Buttikofer, 1911	—	—	*petronellae*	*m. grayi*	—	*p. grayi*
m. schwarzi Schouteden, 1944	—	—	—	—	—	*p. schwarzi-anus*

DISTRIBUTION

The superspecies inhabits forested areas of west and central Africa from the Guinea coast to the Great Rift Valley. In West Africa populations of *C. c. campbelli* are not completely separated from *C. c. lowei* by the Dahomey faunal gap, but in coastal areas opposite the Bight of Biafra, *C. mona* and *C. pogonias* occur together. *C. mona* also invades the territory of *C. c. lowei*. The range of the *pogonias* section continues along the forested coastal area as far as the mouths of the Congo. In the Congo basin occur the various forms of *C. wolfi*, while to the north, following the Ubangi and its tributaries *C. denti* occurs, extending eastwards to the western rim of the Rift Valley and northwards as far as M'Bres in Ubangi-Chari territory. Details are given under specific and subspecific headings.

All members of the group are highly arboreal acrobats with more lively temperaments than members of the *C. mitis* superspecies, though not as volatile as the Lesser Spot-nosed Monkeys (*C. petaurista* and *C. ascanius*). They move about in relatively large troops and are reputedly very rowdy. They move chiefly in the upper canopy, upwards of 80 feet above ground, but spend the night in the middle storey.

Dietetically they are mixed feeders, taking many kinds of leaves and fruits supplemented by insects and other animal food, notably tree-snails (Sanderson, 1957). Booth (1955, 1956, 1960), however, believes the whole of the Mona group to be almost entirely frugivorous.

6. *CERCOPITHECUS CAMPBELLI* (Waterhouse, 1838 *)

(SYN.: Includes *C. burnetti* Gray, 1842 †; *C. mona*, var. *monella* Gray, 1870, p. 22; *Lasiopyga campbelli* Elliot, 1913, p. 352)

VERNACULAR NAME: French, *la mone de Campbell*.

TYPE LOCALITY: Mandingo country, Sierra Leone. Type skin in British Museum (No. 55.12.24.408), " *ex* Zoo ", lacking hands and feet. Type locality of *burnetti*, Fernando Po. Type (unsexed) in British Museum (No. 44.11.2.3), collected by R. N. Thomas. Type locality of *monella* " Senegal ". Type in British Museum.

CHARACTERS

PELAGE: ADULT MALE.—Face bluish, paler around the eyes, and with the lips pink.

Frontal band broad, distinct, whitish or yellow, with the hindmost hairs tending to present a rusty-red tinge. Cheeks light coloured, but the hairs, as in *C. mona*, indistinctly annulated. Ears tufted with annulated or uniformly yellow hairs.

Crown black with some yellow speckling. The yellow increases in amount on the nape, shoulders and upper back, which is of a general golden green. Lower back very dark grey, with little speckling—continuing on to basal portion of tail. No white areas on the buttocks. Arms and legs laterally grey darkening to almost jet black on forearms and dorsum of feet. Throat, under parts and medial surfaces of limbs white, sharply demarcated along the borders from the darker extensor surfaces.

DIMENSIONS.—See under subspecies.

DISTRIBUTION, ECOLOGY AND ETHOLOGY (MAP 5)

Ranges in rain forested areas of the Guinea coast from Senegal more or less continuously eastwards to the Volta river, bridging the Dahomey

---

* *Proc. zool. Soc. Lond.*, 61.   † *Ann. Mag. nat. Hist.*, (1) x, 256.

gap. Inland the bands congregate along the forested fringes of the main rivers as far as the edge of the savanna.

All the Mona group of the present superspecies have a preference for the middle and lower strata of the high rain forest, living entirely upon wild fruits and leaves. They occur normally in troops of about a dozen, but during their daytime activities bands join up, re-segregating again at dusk. Fusion of bands occurs more readily when adjacent to cultivation.

Ecologically, according to Booth (1955), in areas where there is no overlap between *C. campbelli* and *C. mona*, the two are approximately equivalent, but where overlap occurs between *C. c. lowei* and *C. mona* they differ slightly, the latter being more addicted to river-banks where *C. c. lowei* is less common, in fact Booth only encountered *C. c. lowei* once (on the right bank of the Volta). At 200 yards from the rivers both forms occur, and bands of the two may unite temporarily.

Booth interprets his field observations as evidence of recent invasion by *C. mona* of the territory of *C. c. lowei* and attributes its success to the fact that much of the forest in Togoland is, in fact, riverain and that monkeys in that area would have a preference, if only a psychological one, for that type of forest. There is no evidence whatever either from skins or living animals of any interbreeding in the area of overlap.

Active and vocal when undisturbed; when alarmed they give tongue to calls which warn other more stolid and less observant forest creatures. Their vocabulary is wider than that of any other west African monkey. Even the bark of the male, usually a constant specific attribute, is variable, having been phoneticized as *wa-hu, we-hu, wo-hu* or plainly *wë*. There are more intimate emissions of a highly musical quality and also a booming call likened to a ship's siren. This has been attributed to the Giant Forest Squirrel (*Protoxerus stangeri*) but, according to Booth (1960), it is produced by *C. mona*. Booth (1955) states that the voices of *C. mona* and *C. campbelli* differ distinctly, that of *C. mona* being invariably harsher and less musical. He avers that the musical call *úiù* of *C. c. lowei* is frequently uttered and serves to hold the troop together. The corresponding call of *C. mona* is identifiable, but said to recall the creaking of an iron hinge. The barks of males uttered in the early morning and late evening are similar in the two species, but whereas the troop leaders of *C. c. lowei* utter the same bark when leading a retreat, it is then a disyllabic *úahà* whereas that of *C. mona* is a monosyllabic *úe*. The *wa-hu* call of the male *C. c. campbelli* has been heard in captivity (St. Louis Zoo, 1964).

(a) *C. campbelli campbelli* Waterhouse, 1838,* Campbell's Guenon

    For synonymy, see under species.
    Vernacular names: French, *singe des palétuviers, singe mone de Campbell.*
    Type locality: Mandingo country, Sierra Leone. Type a menagerie animal,

---

    * *Proc. zool. Soc. Lond.*, 1838, p. 61.

ex London Zoo, received from Major H. D. Campbell, now in British Museum (No. 55.12.24.408).

PELAGE : ADULT MALE.—Frontal diadem broad, especially at the sides, whitish or silvery, with the hindmost hairs tinged with russet. Cheeks grey, with yellow annulations and slight speckling with black, the black being gradually lost towards the throat and neck, where a more uniform greyish-white tinge prevails.

Ear-tufts speckled yellow and black.

Crown black, speckled with yellow, rather more liberally than in *C. mona* and differing from *C. c. lowei* in having more black-speckling. Shoulders similar, less rusty in tinge than in *C. mona*, the general effect being olive green. Speckling diminishing behind shoulders and on upper arms, which resemble the lumbo-sacral area in showing a more uniform greyish-black coloration ; lateral aspect of thighs similar. No white spot at base of thigh.

Tail at base blackish above and below, concolorous with lumbo-sacral field, thereafter becoming speckled above and grey beneath, but terminal portion entirely black.

Throat, greyish-white ; remainder of under parts and medial aspects of limbs white.

Differences claimed for *C. burnetti* are attributable to immaturity and captivity. The type skin, which has a defective tail, is more yellow on the forehead, and the diadem less sharply defined posteriorly ; cheeks and sides of neck olive grey, speckled and contrasting strongly with the white throat ; ear-tuft reddish yellow contrasting markedly with colour of crown and nape. Lumbo-sacral area darker than in typical adult skins of *C. campbelli*. Under parts also darker than in typical *campbelli*.

DIMENSIONS (in millimetres) :

Number	Locality	Sex	Head and Body	Tail	Foot	Ear
PC.2	Liberia	♀ immat.	364	—	105·2	25·2
PC.530	Sierra Leone	♂ juv.	255	391	82	22·8

DISTRIBUTION.—Coastal rain-forests from the Casamance in Senegal, to the Cavally river in Liberia, the last mentioned river separating its area of distribution from that of *C. c. lowei*. The most eastward recorded locality for *C. c. campbelli* is Fort Binger on the Cavally river. There is thus no overlap between the two races (*cf. C. mona* and *C. c. lowei*, infra p. 457). Precise range inland undetermined. Dekeyser and Villiers (1947) report extension of the range northwards beyond the Casamance in the region of Bignona, but state examples from there proved somewhat atypical.

Exact localities from whence *C. c. campbelli* has been obtained are given by Schwarz : French Guinea : Conakry (Paris Museum) ; Sierra Leone : Makera (Rokelle river) ; Tasso Island : Buyabuya (Little Scarcies river) (British Museum) ; Liberia : Mount Barclay, Bavia (St. Paul's river) (Leiden Museum). The U.S. National Museum has one skin from Liberia collected near the Firestone Estate, Harbel, about 70 miles west of Monrovia. Ivory Coast : Upper Cavally near Fort Binger (Berlin Museum). Monard (1938) lists examples from Enchelé and Cacheu in Portuguese Guinea (coastal area).

(b) *C. campbelli lowei* Thomas, 1923,* Lowe's Guenon

Vernacular name : none recorded.

Type locality : Bandama, Ivory Coast.   Type adult ♂ in British Museum (No. 23.2.3.2), collected by W. P. Lowe, 4 January 1923.

PELAGE : ADULT MALE.—Face as in *C. c. campbelli*. Some longish black downwardly directed hairs on dorsum nasi, and long ones on cheeks anterior to whiskers. Hairs on unpigmented part of face, white.

Frontal band with no white zone or only a very narrow one anteriorly, the remainder bright yellow or yellow green, tinged with yellow ochre.   Cheeks dark grey, individual hairs speckled black and yellow, the yellow more prevalent anteriorly bordering the face.   Ear-tuft with considerable amount of yellow, due to broad yellow annuli alternating with short black bands on individual hairs.

Crown more heavily speckled with yellow than in *C. c. campbelli* or *C. mona*. Nape, interscapular region and anterior part of back greenish golden (brighter and more ochreous than orange citrine of Ridgway).   Lower back and lateral surfaces of limbs dark grey, darker than in *C. c. campbelli*, the arms almost black, thighs dusky neutral grey, due to light grey flecks on individual hairs.

Tail dark grey above, paler below.

Under parts and medial aspects of limbs white, sharply demarcated on the borders of limbs from the darker dorsal colour, but merging gradually on the flanks (*cf. C. wolfi*).

Schwarz (1928b) considered that it was this form which Pocock, and following him Elliot, treated as *C. burnetti*.

ADULT FEMALE.—Resembling the male, but smaller.

VARIATIONS.—A subadult male (CCL.10) shows a small white brow band, less distinct than in *C. c. campbelli*, though much more so than is usual in *C. c. lowei* ; it is confined to the middle of the forehead. CCL.11, a subadult female ; has sacral area and thighs speckled only little less than the brighter anterior portion of the back. (Booth, 1955.)

DIMENSIONS (in millimetres) of adult male (No. PC.512) measured in the flesh : Crown-rump length, 500 ; head length, 98·8 ; tail, 500+ ; hand, 92 ; foot, 123·5 ; ear, morphological length, 30 ; morphological breadth, 22 ; physiognomic height, 34·2 ; physiognomic breadth, 31·4 ; weight, 3·5 kg.

Dimensions of type specimen ♂ ; head and body, 546 ; tail, 771 ; foot, 147 ; ear, 28.

SKULL.—Cranial dimensions : No records available.

DISTRIBUTION AND ECOLOGY.—Coastal rain forests from the Cavally river in the west to the Volta in the east.

Besides the type locality Schwarz refers to material in the British Museum from Beoumi, Ivory Coast, while the Paris Museum has further Ivory Coast specimens collected by Chevalier and Moskovitz, besides others from the Upper Niger (collected by Mme Pobéguin) and upper Senegal (collected by Dr. Bouet).   Booth (1956) collected *C. c. lowei* in the Ivory Coast at Guiglo.   From Ghana this form was first collected by Pel at Boutry ; another, collected by Major C. M. Ingoldby, was seen alive by Schwarz in the London Zoo.

In Ghana, Booth (1956 *a*, *b*) affirms that representatives of the *mona* group are found throughout the high forest zone in both primary and secondary forest, as well as in forest outliers and fringing forest at least as far north as Bamboi, though tending

* *Ann. Mag. nat. Hist.* (9), xi. 608.

to become sparse and local in that area.   *C. c. lowei* is limited to the area south and west of the Volta-Black Volta, while *C. mona* occurs to the east thereof.   Along the Afram river, however, and penetrating westwards as far as Kwahu, *C. mona* overlaps the territory of *C. c. lowei*.   In the area of overlap a slight ecological difference occurs, *C. mona* preferring the riverside forest, while *C. c. lowei* prefers the deeper forest back from the rivers, though mixed parties are recorded as feeding together when the fruit of particular trees is in abundance.

Based on an examination of stomach contents, Booth claims that the present animal is almost entirely frugivorous.   They spend the night in the middle storey and rarely ascend the tall emergents.

Booth's Guiglo material proved somewhat atypical and may integrate, interbreeding with the nominate race, since the locality is less than 40 miles from the Cavally river.

7. *CERCOPITHECUS MONA* (Schreber, 1774 [*])

Mona Monkey

(SYN. : *Monne* Leo Africanus, 1550, p. 342 ; *Monichus* Prosper Alpinus 1735, I, p. 242 ; *La mone* Buffon, 1767 ; *Sima mona* Schreber, 1774, p. 97 ; varied monkey Pennant, 1781, p. 195 ; *Cercopithecus mona* Erxleben and most subsequent authors, except Elliot (1913) who used *Lasiopyga*.

VERNACULAR NAMES : M'boko, *mammbe*; Balali, *n'semgui*; French, *la mone* ; German, *Monameerkatze*.

TYPE LOCALITY : " Barbary ".   No type specimen in existence.

CHARACTERS

PELAGE : ADULT MALE.—Characterized especially by the distinct dark temporal band extending between eyes and ears ; by the rusty tinge of the upper back and by the rounded or oval white spot on the buttocks, each side the root of the tail.   The last feature is unique in the genus, though it may represent the beginning or remnant of the white femoral stripe occurring in *C. diana* and *C. neglectus*.

Frontal diadem with a fringe of black hairs followed by a distinct broad white band, broader laterally than medially, but not extending to ears. Ear-tufts dense, long, the hairs with alternate yellow and black annulations. Crown and nape speckled yellowish green ; cheeks light greyish, the hairs terminally annulated yellow and black.

Shoulders, upper back and sides of body speckled rusty red to chestnut, hairs with light grey bases, becoming paler distally, the distal half bright reddish, with black annulations near the tip in some of the hairs only.   The brighter tinge extends almost to the sacral region.   Tail almost black above, grey beneath in the proximal half.

Arms laterally black to wrist ; thighs blackish, sparsely and weakly speckled ; shanks similar, but paling along anterior border.   Hands black, but feet showing some speckling.

[*] *Säugetiere*, i. 97.

The white coxal patch varies in size and in shape from rounded to oval. When oval, the long axis lies obliquely, passing downwards and backwards from the ilium to the ischium.

Chin, throat, chest, belly and medial aspects of limbs clothed with white hairs, with sharp line of demarcation from darker areas, except along flanks, where the change is more gradual. Skin of belly sky blue with a greenish element, but nipples pale pink, with a blue areola lacking the greenish element and therefore sharply contrasted with the surrounding skin.

Ears blue-black, darker than in *C. c. lowei*, but preauricular skin blue ; lips and nasal septum pink ; bridge of nose dark grey, upper eyelid similar, but lower paler, more slaty ; skin of cheeks blue. Throat, chest and abdomen greenish blue ; medial sides of pectoral limbs similar, but hinder abdomen and medial sides of legs pure blue without the greenish element.

Glans penis pink ; prepuce very pale blue ; scrotum similar, but a shade deeper, especially at the sides, where a dusky tinge appears. Perineum blue green.

Callosities dark grey, paler towards the borders. Palms and soles black. Iris dull cinnamon.

ADULT FEMALE.—Resembling the male, but somewhat smaller.

VARIATIONS occur in the depth of rufescent tinge on the back and in its extent. The median dorsal line posteriorly may lack or show deficient reddish speckling especially posteriorly, but on the other hand the whole back and flanks may be rusty.

Albinism has been recorded. There was a complete albino in the London Zoo in October 1962.

A skin, without hands or feet, from St. Kitts, West Indies, where the species has been introduced (U.S. Nat. Mus., No. 13236, collected by F. A. Ober), lacks the white hip-patches and is generally of a duller colour than the African animal. The crown is heavily speckled with light grey ; shoulders and thoracic region very pale, due to heavy grey speckling, darkening gradually over lumbo-sacral area which exhibits only feeble cinnamon speckling. Legs like back, but even darker. Arms and hands black.

DIMENSIONS (in millimetres) :

Number	Sex	Crown Rump Length	Head Length	Tail	Hand	Foot	Ear Morphological Length	Ear Morphological Breadth	Ear Physiognomic Length	Ear Physiognomic Breadth
PC.513	♂ ad.	555	119·4		94·3	136·7	33·8	24·5	33	26
PC.24	♂ juv.	231		355		80	33	—	28	—

Weight of PC.513—4·63 Kg. Weight of PC.24—400 gm.

Booth (1960) gives average weight of males 8–12 lb.; females 6–9 lb. Takeshita (1962) gives average weight of males 5 kg.; females about 4 kg.

SKULL.—Cranial measurements (in millimetres):

Number	Sex	Max. Cranial Length	Biparietal	Least Frontal	Basion-bregma	Bizygomatic	Bimastoid	Palatal Length	Upper Cheek-teeth	Mandibular Length	Lower Cheek-teeth
PC.166	♂	111	54·4	42·3	47·5	70	57	44·5	25	72	31·1
PC.186	♂	113·2	59·1	46·5	52	73·2	66·5	49·3	26·5	75	32·6
PC.150	♂	103	59	43·4	50	73·1	61	41	25·2	68·7	30
P.C.160	♂	103·7	56·5	45·6	49·7	71	59·5	40·5	25	68·5	30
PC.132	♂ old	104·9	56·2	43·5	52·8	70·5	58·3	46	25	74·5	30·5
PC.164	♂	104·5	56·1	45·7	49·6	72	58	45·7	23·5	78·5	33·8
PC.364	♂	98·8	56·3	42·6	55	71·1	58·1	40·3	24·9	71	31·6[1]
PC.155	♂	102	56	42·5	48·2	68·5	60	39·4	24·2	65·1	29·2
PC.176	♂ immat.	93·2	56·3	44·6	48·6	64·8	56·4	35	19·8	58·5	23
97/62	♀	88·6	55	43·6	51·2	61	54·5	36·7	23·5	58·5	26·6
PC.162	♀	92·5	53·6	40·8	47	60·7	54	37·5	23·9	59	28·2
PC.161	♀	88·2	51·2	42·2	45·2	58·7	49·3	33	22·5	56	26·2
PC.340	♀ old	94	54	42·6	48·7	63·5	53·2	38·6	22·4	58·6	24·8

All from British Cameroons: Collector W. E. Kershaw.   [1] M³ not erupted.

DISTRIBUTION, ECOLOGY AND ETHOLOGY (Map 5)

Forested areas in the coastal tract of West Africa from Kwahu state in Ghana at least to Edea on the Sanaga river, Cameroons (Booth 1956). Sanderson (1940), who collected 18 males and 14 females from various localities in the Mamfe division of the Cameroons, states, on the evidence of a skin in the Powell-Cotton collection in the British Museum, that the range extends southwards beyond the Sanaga river at one point as far as the Ongui creek in southern Cameroon, whilst Schwarz takes it as far as the Nyong river. Perret and Aellen (1956) claim that it even crosses the Nyong as far as Longji, the southern limit being probably Kienké or Lobé. They definitely found it at Lolodorf.

In the west the range overlaps that of *C. campbelli lowei*, a little beyond the Afram river, a right bank tributary of the Volta. Animals from both sides of the Volta are identical, and there is no evidence of intergrading with *C. campbelli*. The true *C. mona* therefore is a monotypic species—unless evidence accrues to prove that the form from Togoland is sufficiently and constantly distinct to merit subspecific status. (Schwarz found a Togo skin to be more brightly coloured than skins from Mount Cameroon and southern Nigeria, besides showing other minor distinctions.)

Inland, Schwarz produced evidence for the presence of *C. mona* in the montane forests in the area of the Benue river.

Following are localities from whence specimens have been obtained or recorded: Togoland: Bismarckburg, Ho, Misahöhe, Sokode or Basari (Berlin Museum); Dahomey: Djonajo (Paris Museum); Nigeria: Iju waterworks (near Lagos); Jebba (Niger), Oban, Owerri, Makana (all in British Museum); Cameroon, Mt. Cameroon (British Museum, collector Crossley); Victoria (Berlin Museum), Isongo, Bibundi (Wiesbaden Museum), Tate river, Gonda (Donga river), Tabati (British Museum), Mamfe (Cross river), Yabassi, Baoho, Manska (between Bafum and Bum), Ako, Nama (Donga river), Nsot, Kentu (Berlin Museum), Edea, Longji, Lolodorf (both south of the Nyong river), (Perret and Aellen, 1956).

West Indies: introduced and established on St. Kitts and Grenada, Lesser Antilles (Hollister, 1912, Miller and Kellog, 1955).

Mona monkeys are among the commonest in their area of distribution, where they appear equally at home in the middle and lower storeys of the rain-forest. They feed almost entirely on wild fruits. They are also among the commonest species of the genus exhibited in menageries, where they thrive well and have occasionally been known to reproduce (*vide antea*, p. 380).

Monas travel in large bands, probably due to the temporary fusion of smaller units. They are active and noisy. Sanderson endows them with a hysterical temperament in comparison with other guenons. He reports them as sometimes misjudging their distances during flight, resulting in numerous falls to the ground, or even into water when crossing a stream. These falls seldom result in severe accidents as the victims soon recover, and scamper up the nearest climbing plants to rejoin their band. When they fall into water, they swim to the bank and then adopt the same procedure.

In the area of overlap between the ranges of *C. mona* and *C. campbelli lowei* the two show slightly different ecological preferences (*vide antea*, p. 454).

8. *CERCOPITHECUS WOLFI* A. B. Meyer, 1891 *

Wolf's Guenon

(SYN.: *Lasiopyga wolfi* Elliot, 1913, p. 351, Allen, 1925, p. 404; *C. mona wolfi* Schwarz, 1928 *b*, p. 1313, and subsequent writers except Booth, 1956.)
VERNACULAR NAMES: None recorded.

* *Notes Leyden Museum*, xiii. 63.

TYPE LOCALITY : " Central West Africa ". Original description based on an adult, but not aged, ♀ animal living in the Dresden Zoo from 1887 till 1891, procured by Dr. L. Wolf. Type now stuffed (skull separate) in Dresden Museum.

CHARACTERS

PELAGE short ; without sagittal hairy crest on crown ; with well-developed pointed ear-tufts, a markedly outstanding white frontal diadem ; tail with terminal tuft of elongated hairs.

Booth (1956) in elevating *C. wolfi* to separate specific rank gives the following significant morphological distinctions between it and *C. mona*.

(1) The brow-band is always well marked and extends laterally to a point above the ears, whereas in *C. mona* it fades over the temples considerably anterior to the ears, and moreover tends to blend gradually posteriorly with the colour of the crown. (2) There is a sharp line of demarcation between the pigmented and non-pigmented fields of the pelage covering respectively the dorsal and ventral surfaces. In *C. mona* (except on the arms) they merge gradually. (3) The colour of the thighs is sharply divided from that of the sacral region—a feature not encountered in *C. mona*, *C. campbelli* or *C. denti*. (4) White areas on the hip region are lacking.

DIMENSIONS.—See under subspecies.

DISTRIBUTION (Map 5)

The whole of the forested area on the left bank of the Congo river and its tributaries. Geographically widely separated by unsuitable terrain from the territory of *C. mona*. Presumably this separation is of ancient date, so that the two forms have undergone a considerable period of independent evolutionary divergence.

(a) *C. wolfi wolfi* A. B. Meyer, 1891,* Wolf's Guenon

> (*Syn.* : see under species)
> *Vernacular names* : French, *la mone de Meyer*.
> *Type locality* : Congo. Based on a menagerie specimen living in the Dresden Zoo from 1887 till 1891. Collected by Dr. Ludwig Wolf in Central West Africa. Colour plates are given by Meyer (1894) and Dollman (1931).
> PELAGE : ADULT MALE.—Face bluish, with reddish pink around the eyes and a dull orange flesh-coloured unpigmented muzzle. Iris red brown.
> Frontal diadem upraised, prominent, composed of yellowish-white hairs, bordered anteriorly by a line of black hairs, and extending laterally along the temporal region and over the ears. The pale band broader laterally than in the median line and posteriorly more sharply defined from the dark crown than in *C. mona*.
> Crown brownish grey ; a dark, almost black bar, below the extended frontal diadem, between eyes and ears. Ear fringe well developed, forming a pointed tuft, golden yellow to red brown.
> Cheeks with long hairs, citron yellow vermiculated with brown and produced laterally into tiny yellowish-white whiskers.

---

* *Notes Leyden Mus.* xiii. 63-64 ; *Proc. zool. Soc. Lond.*, 1894, p. 83.

General colour of dorsal surface of body dark slate grey, passing to blue grey laterally, individual hairs with 2-3 pale rings alternating with black and tipped with black. From the nape posteriorly the hairs of the median line form an olive-yellowish dorsal stripe 40 mm. broad, tapering to a point towards the tail; the colour becomes more vivid on the crown and more brownish yellow towards the tail. On the lateral areas the pale annuli of the hairs are pearl grey; but on the basal half of the tail above they become ashy grey with black tips. On the under surface of the basal half of the tail the annuli are whitish. Terminal third of tail black.

On the flanks, below the blue-grey area, the elongated hairs are orange yellow, forming a well marked lateral stripe between the darkly pigmented area and the whiter under parts.

Shoulders and upper arms laterally black, speckled with pearly grey, the forearms deep glossy black, separated from the white flexor surface by a narrow line of ochre, which runs distally as a stripe to the flexor side of the wrists. Hairs on dorsum of hands, feet and digits black.

Thighs laterally bright red brown, sharply demarcated from the blue grey of the sacro-iliac area. This colour passes into orange towards the white medial surfaces, the difference being due to the presence of a basal ash-grey zone in the red-brown hairs, replaced by white in the orange area. Shanks tawny, washed with Chinese orange (Ridgway).

Chin, sides of neck, medial aspect of arms, breast, belly and medial aspect of legs white, the hairs on the belly with faint orange-yellow tips.

VARIATIONS.—According to Lönnberg (1919) these are not great, affecting chiefly the intensity of the orange flank stripe which may be only faintly yellow. The tan of the hind-limbs also varies slightly in intensity.

DIMENSIONS.—Meyer (1894) gives for the type female the following: Body length, 46 cm.; tail, c. 60 cm.; height at shoulder, c. 32 cm.; height at hip, c. 35 cm.

An adult male from Mosembe, south-west of Nouvelle Anvers, measured in the field is recorded by Allen (1925) as having head and body, 283 mm.; tail vertebra, 732 mm.; foot, 142 mm. An adult male (PC.558) received in the flesh had the following dimensions, in millimetres:—crown-rump length, 470; tail 715; head length (muzzle to occiput) 101; hand length 105; foot 146; ear, morphological length 22; morphological breadth 23·7; physiognomic length 30; physiognomic breadth 22.

SKULL.—Described by Meyer (loc. cit) as having a straight facial profile (from root of nose to prosthion), only the base of the nasal opening being slightly elevated. Angle of face with line of forehead 30°. Apertura pyriformis elongated (7 × 16 mm.). Orbits round, projecting at medial upper angle.

CRANIAL DIMENSIONS (in millimetres):

Locality	Sex	Max. Cranial Length	Glabella-inion	Basion-gnathion	Biparietal	Basion-bregma	Least Frontal	Bizygomatic	Upper Cheek-teeth	Mandibular length	Lower cheek teeth
Unknown (type)	♀	94	70·4	64·2	42·2	43·9	42·2	61·2	22·4		
Mosembe	♂	93·6	82·4					64·2	28·2		
Zoo (PC. 558)	♂ ad.	93·6	75·4	68·8	57	49	45·9	66·1	23·5	56·8	29·3

Meyer also records the undermentioned skeletal dimensions of the type female : length of vertebral column, *c.* 290 mm. ; caudal vertebrae, *c.* 540 mm. ; length of os innominatum, 106 mm. ; breadth of same, 61 mm. ; humerus, 116 mm. ; radius, 135 mm. ; ulna, 125 mm. ; manus, 96 mm. ; femur, 145 mm. ; tibia, 150 mm. ; fibula, 143 mm. ; pes, 140 mm.

DISTRIBUTION.—Left bank of the Congo between the Kasai and Lomami rivers. Most recorded specimens have been from the Lake Leopold II area, including a large series collected by Dr. Maes. Lake Leopold II district : Inongo, Kutu, Mpe, Bokoro, Tolo, Oshwe, Bolobo, Kunungu, Bumbuli, Dwa, Mongama ; Tshuapa district : Eala, Ikengo, Bikoro, Tondu, Lukolela, Befale, Mondombe, Irebu, Inkongo ; Congo-Ubangi district : Bumba ; Stanleyville district : Elisabetha, Stanleyville (left bank ?) ; Sankuru district : Tshombaka, Lodja, Komi ; all the above in the Tervueren Museum as listed by Schouteden.

In addition, Elliot (1913) mentions one from Batempas on the Sankuru, and Allen (1925) refers to one collected in July 1909 by the American Congo expedition from Mosembe, to the south-west of Nouvelle-Anvers, about 250 miles from the Lake Leopold II area. The only specimen living in the London Zoo was one mentioned by Pocock (1907) as deposited in August 1904 by Lord Rothschild, who had received it from the dealer, J. D. Hamlyn, on whose testimony it had been captured by natives and received by Hamlyn in Brazzaville. This is presumably the same animal whose stuffed skin is now on exhibit at the Tring Museum.

(b) *C. wolfi pyrogaster* Lönnberg, 1919,* Fire-bellied Guenon

> *Vernacular name* : *bundi* (Schouteden, *teste* Goethals).
>
> *Type locality* : Atene, Kwango, Congo. According to Moreau *et al.* (1946), Atene is in the Kwango district about 5° 30′ S., 19° 20′ E., east of the upper Kuila river and about midway between the Kasai and Kwango rivers. Type, adult female (skin and skull), in Tervueren Museum, collected by Charliers.

PELAGE : ADULT.—Frontal diadem comparatively narrow, basally with mixed whitish and black hairs ; behind, the light hairs change to light buff. Brow band continued laterally on sides of crown as a broad buff stripe as far as ears, the buff hairs with narrow black tips and whitish subapical rings. Below the lateral strip a broad black band (some hairs with subapical light rings) passing between eye and ear.

Ear-tufts well developed, brick red.

Nose with sparse black hairs ; upper lip with greyish white hairs. Cheeks clothed with longish, downward and backwardly directed whiskers. Above, the hairs are basally buff, distally alternately ringed black and pale buff, but below the whiskers are more brightly coloured, inclining to rust red.

Crown, nape, neck, scapular region and lateral aspects of arms, also hands, black, the individual hairs with dark grey bases and the distal parts of many of them annulated yellowish white and black alternately.

Longest hairs on back 60 mm. or slightly less. Median line of back from inter-scapular region onwards to sacral region chestnut, much as in *C. w. wolfi*, due to the subapical annuli attaining a rusty-red tinge.

Lateral to the chestnut dorsal area the back is the same colour as the scapular area and postero-laterally is, as in *C. w. wolfi*, sharply demarcated from the bright colour of the thighs.

* *Rev. zool. Afr.* vii. 137.

Lateral aspect of hind-limbs rusty red, becoming somewhat duller on dorsum of foot, the long hairs on the posterior aspect of thighs with some blackish annuli.

Tail above in proximal half speckled greyish brown, much paler brownish grey below, becoming increasingly black towards the middle and the distal half completely black above and below.

Chin, light buff; throat rather darker; remainder of under parts bright rusty red (more yellow according to Schwarz), which extends also to medial aspects of limbs, reaching its greatest intensity on the anterior and medial aspects of the hind-limbs.

DIMENSIONS.—Lönnberg merely mentions that the tanned skin of the type measures 98 cm. long of which 55 cm. are made up of tail.

SKULL.—The type skull is much damaged, lacking most of the brain case. Lönnberg gives the length of the upper cheek-teeth as 21·3 mm. and the lower 23·6 mm.

DISTRIBUTION.—Confined to the area between the Kasai and Kwango rivers, Congo.

Exact localities of recorded specimens have been given by Schwarz (1927, 1928) and Schouteden (1947). These are: Kwango District: Atene, Kasongo Lunda, Franz-Josef waterfall; Kasai district: Luebo, Kabumbaie, Macaco, Belenge, Zapo Kalamba, near Luebo, Upper Tschuapa river. All the material is in the Tervueren Museum.

(c) *C. wolfi elegans* Dubois & Matschie, 1912 *

(*Syn.*: *C.* (*Otopithecus*) *elegans* Dubois and Matschie, 1912, p. 440; *C. mona elegans* Schwarz, 1928, p. 1316; Schouteden, 1947, p. 61; *C. wolfi elegans* Booth 1955, p. 442)

Vernacular names: None recorded.

Type locality: Probably Lower Lomani river.

Based on two specimens in the Tervueren Museum. Schwarz fixed No. 346, an adult male, as holotype.

PELAGE: ADULT MALE.—Differing from *C. w. wolfi* and *C. denti* in the whiter cheeks, the greater extent of the black temporal band and in the grey hind-limbs, and the complete suppression of red pigment. Resembling *C. w. wolfi* in the great distribution of black pigment, and in the sharp line of demarcation along the flanks between the dorsal pigmented and ventral unpigmented zones.

Crown as in *C. w. wolfi*, but without any reddish tint; ear-tufts white, with the longest hairs alone showing a slight yellowish tone. Back as in *C. w. wolfi*.

Thighs laterally light grey with only very light speckling with greenish yellow, the individual hairs, in contrast with those of *C. w. wolfi*, with broad black annuli and tips.

Under parts creamy white, without any reddish tinge.

DISTRIBUTION.—Confined to the area between the Lomami river and the left bank of the Congo. Extent of range to the south unknown.

This race is known at present solely from five specimens, the two para-types, believed to be from the Lower Lomami, and three others in the Berlin Museum collected by Grauer, at Kibombo, Kasongo district, left bank of the Upper Congo.

---

* *Rev. zool. Afr.* i. 440, tex. fig. 4.

PLATE XXI

Photo: E. Kirkland

Cercopithecus mona, adult, in Chester Zoo

PLATE XXII

Photo: W. C. Osman Hill

Cercopithecus campbelli lowei, adult ♂

9. *CERCOPITHECUS DENTI* (Thomas, 1907 *)

Dent's Guenon

(SYN. : *C.* (*Otopithecus*) *denti liebrechtsi* Dubois & Matschie, 1912, p. 439 ; *C. mona denti* Schwarz, 1928 ; Malbrant, 1952)

VERNACULAR NAME : French, *la mone de Dent*.

TYPE LOCALITY : Ituri forest, Congo, between Mawambi and Avakubi, altitude 3000 feet. Type adult ♂ in British Museum (No. 7.1.2.1.1, original No. 184), collected by R. E. Dent. (Colour plate in original description).† Type locality of *liebrechtsi*, Stanley Falls, Congo.

CHARACTERS

PELAGE : ADULT MALE.—Allied to *mona*, but differing from all other members of the superspecies in the complete absence of darkening on the lower back and hind limbs, and also in the sharply contrasted white belly.

Crown and nape olive grey ; a light whitish or slightly yellow frontal band present, but not conspicuous. Back dark grizzled chestnut brown (near burnt amber of Ridgway) : rump not darker, but passing gradually into paler tone of hips and thighs. Under parts from chin to pubes, also medial surfaces of limbs to wrists and ankles, creamy white, sharply defined from dark upper parts, not only on limbs (as in *mona* and *campbelli*), but also on the flanks where the white rises half way up the sides of the body and is visible above the thighs when the animal is sitting (personal observation of a pair in St. Louis Zoo).

Ears with short yellowish tufts rising from their concave surfaces. Lateral surfaces of forearms black from elbows. Hind-limbs, including ankles, grizzled, yellowish olive, lighter than back peripherally. Metatarsal region and toes black. Tail blackish above at base, becoming dull greyish white for two-thirds of its length, darkening again towards tip ; inferiorly dirty white in proximal two-thirds, leaving only a narrow dark median dorsal tract—not sharply demarcated ; tip with a well defined tuft.

ADULT FEMALE.—Similar to the male, but smaller.

JUVENILE.—Two skins in immature pelage are described by Allen (1925). The youngest, in natal coat (♂ from Medje, length 515 mm., maximum cranial length, 63·5 mm. D_1^1 and DM^1 alone erupted), shows the same general pattern as in the adult, but the pelage differs in texture, being short, very soft and, on the under parts, very sparse. Frontal diadem well developed, composed of stiff hairs, mixed buffy grey and black, bordered anteriorly by row of entirely black hairs, followed by broad grey band, the hairs of which are black tipped. Crown wholly black, but the hidden bases of hairs grey ; nape greyish black ; remainder of dorsal surface mixed black and pale

* *Abst. Proc. zool. Soc. Lond.*, 1907, p. 1. (22 January 1907.)
† *Proc. zool. Soc. Lond.*, 1907, 2, Pl. I.

2 H

rufous, the hairs with pale grey bases, a subapical rufous zone and black tips. Lateral surface of forelimbs blackish, rather thinly haired ; but hind-limbs clothed with long hairs which are grey basally and superficially finely grizzled with pale rufous and blackish. Tail, as in adult, but somewhat less strongly coloured, the lower surface white, faintly tinged in the proximal half with yellow. Under parts and medial surfaces of limbs almost bare, except on hinder abdomen, the golden skin being clothed with soft white hairs.

An older specimen (♀ from Akenge, with total length 583 mm., maximum cranial length 63·5 mm. and milk dentition complete except that DM 2/2 is not fully erupted), is more heavily furred than the preceding. Coarser hair has developed on the crown and sides of the head, of same colour and texture as in adult, but shorter. Remainder of dorsal surface mixed black and rufous, the pelage short and thick. Under parts thinly haired, the hairs soft and white. Arms thickly clothed laterally, forearms and hands intensely black ; hind limbs and tail as in adult.

Half-grown animals resemble the adults ; the white ear-tufts are present. In some specimens rufous speckling has developed over the back.

DIMENSIONS of type ♂ (measured in the flesh).—Head and body, 501 mm. ; tail, 850 mm. ; foot, 155 mm. ; ear, 40 mm. ; Malbrant (1952) gives total length averaging between 110–140 cm., of which the tail accounts for 70–90 cm. Weight 3–6 kg. Allen (1925) gives average body dimensions (minima and maxima in brackets) of 13 females (in millimetres), thus : head and body, 402 (330–460) ; tail vertebrae, 676 (530–770) ; foot, 127 (120–135) ; ear, 34 (32–37).

SKULL

Cranial measurements of type male : maximum cranial length, 105 mm. ; basal length, 75 mm. ; cranial breadth, 55 mm. ; upper cheek-teeth, 23 mm.

Average cranial dimensions of 35 adults are given by Allen (*loc. cit.*) (in millimetres) :

	Maximum Cranial Length			Condylo-basal Length			Occipito-nasal Length			Least Frontal		
Sex	Av.	Min.	Max.	Av.	Min.	Max.	Av.	Min.	Max.	Av.	Min.	Max.
22 ♂♂	100·2	90·7	109·2	78·2	69·4	83	84	78·5	90·7	43	40·6	45·4
13 ♀♀	89·2	84	94·8	67·2	63·8	73	78·6	74·2	82·7	42·1	40·8	44·4

	Bimastoid			Bizygomatic			Biorbital			Upper Cheek-teeth		
Sex	Av.	Min.	Max.	Av.	Min.	Max.	Av.	Min.	Max.	Av.	Min.	Max.
22 ♂♂	58·5	54·2	62·5	68·3	59	71·5	56·2	50·5	64	30·4	28·5	36·4
13 ♀♀	53·2	50·9	55·2	60·1	54	63·7	50·6	48·4	52·5	26·9	26	28·4

Distribution (Map 5)

Forests along the Ubangi river and its tributaries (especially the Uelle river) as far east as the western rim of the Rift Valley. Not extending westwards beyond the point where the Ubangi takes a sharp turn southwards. North of the Ubangi the species has been recorded as far north as M'Brés on the road to N'delé (Malbrant, 1952).

Schwarz examined material from the following localities : Uelle : Upper Uelle (British Museum), Angu (Frankfurt Museum), Buta, Koteli (Rubi river), Arebi (south of Kibali) (all in Tervueren Museum) ; Ituri : between Mawambi and Avakubi (type) ; Mawambi : Djamba (upper Itimbiri river) (Tervueren Museum) ; Semliki : " probably Beni " (British Museum) ; Upper Congo : Kabambaré (south of Luama river) ; Stanley Falls (type of *liebrechtsi*) (Tervueren Museum) ; Tanganyika, Baraka (N.W. Tanganyika) ; Monogambi (Kivu) (Tervueren Museum).

Additional localities, based on material in the Tervueren Museum, are listed by Allen (1925) and by Schouteden (1947).

Southwards to the east of the main Congo stream the range, according to Schouteden's distribution map, reaches almost to the Luaba.

According to Haddow (1945), *C. denti* is common in the Bwamba country, western Uganda, this probably being its eastern limit. The most easterly localities previously recorded are those of J. A. Allen (1925) and G. M. Allen (1939), both of whom refer to the Mawamba–Avakubi area, 100–150 miles west of the Semliki.

Ecology

Haddow *et al.* (1951) affirm *C. denti* to be mainly arboreal, but descending to the ground occasionally. Usually confined to secondary forest growth (Haddow, 1952), it is less frequently observed on forest fringes than deeper in the forest. In the Congo forest, it is seldom seen from the road, but here it occurs in both primary and secondary growth.

A specimen obtained by Haddow (1947) in the Bwamba forest, Uganda, had stomach contents composed almost entirely of leaves and shoots, with practically no fruit—possibly due to season.

10. *CERCOPITHECUS POGONIAS* (Bennett, 1833 *)

Crowned Guenon

(SYN. : *Lasiopyga pogonias* Elliott, 1913, p. 354 ; *Cercopithecus mona pogonias* Schwarz, 1928, p. 657)

VERNACULAR NAMES : Baksueli, *pid* or *pindi* ; Bakota, *koundi* ; Adouma, *pindi* ; Pahouin,

* *Proc. zool. Soc. Lond.*, 1833, p. 67.

essouna ; Bapoundu, *poundi* ; Eshira, *poundi* ; Bulu, *esuma* ; French, *cerco-pithèque pogonias.*

TYPE LOCALITY : Fernando Po.   Type in British Museum (No. 42.11.4.14) collected by Mrs. Thomson (Niger Expedition).

Bennett, in his original description, justly remarked that, in colour, the present species differs from every known monkey.   It is, in fact, in its typical form, probably the most brightly coloured of the family, if not of the whole order.

ORIGINAL DIAGNOSIS : *Cerc. nigrescens, albo punctulatus ; dorso medio, prymnâ, cauda supernè et ad apicem, fasciâque temporali nigris ; fronte, scelidibusque externé flavidis, nigro punctulatis ; mystacibus longissimis, albido-flavescentibus ; corpore caudâque subtus, artibusque internè, flavido-rufis.*

Long. corporis cum capite 17 ; caudae 24 une.

This species, with its very marked local subspecific variants, forms a well-defined group characterized by (i) the median sagittal crest on the crown, composed of long caudally directed hairs, (ii) greenish dorsal and (iii) golden ventral surfaces.   It not only differs from *C. mona* and its allies in respect of these features, but also in voice.   Furthermore it overlaps them in distribution.   Therefore the contention of Schwarz (1928 *b*) and some subsequent authors, that *pogonias* is merely a race of *mona*, cannot be upheld.   This was first pointed out by Bourdelle and Matthias (1928) whose opinion was followed by Rode (1937) and Sanderson (1940) and then confirmed by Booth (1955) and by Perret and Aellen (1956).

DISTRIBUTION, ECOLOGY AND ETHOLOGY (Map 6)

Fernando Po and adjacent mainland (Cameroons) southwards to the mouth of the Congo and eastwards across the Ubangi river to the edge of the Stanleyville district.   In the north of the range the species occurs side by side with *C. mona.*

C. pogonias favours the tops of the highest trees in the rain forest and in the Cameroons, at least, only in elevated territory.   It lives in large bands of up to fifty individuals or more and, where it occurs, is quite common.

According to Malbrant and Maclatchy (1949), *C. p. nigripes* forms mixed foraging bands with *C. n. nictitans* and *C. cephus* whose tastes concur in the matter of seeds and fruits.   All are addicted to raiding plantations, but are shy of approaching human habitations, though a solitary *C. pogonias* once approached a camp to feed in an umbrella tree (*Musanga cecropioides*).

Dietetically a mixed regimen is favoured, and, although vegetable substances form the bulk, insect food is often acceptable.   Sanderson (1940) found the stomach of one wild shot specimen distended with insect remains.

The voice is characteristic, recalling that of bird rather than mammal. Sanderson likens the call to that of the European Lapwing (*Vanellus vanellus*), *i.e. pee-wit.*

By Malbrant and Maclatchy, one cry is described as a dull bleat so characteristic that the sound identifies the animal even when it is not visible. A musical bird-like voice is also referred to by Russell (1938) in describing a captive juvenile female of *C. p. nigripes* kept at Lambaréné.

Cercopithecus pogonias pogonias ♂ ♀ and young, Cincinnati Zoo

The same specimen is further described by Mrs. Russell as affectionate, intelligent, high-spirited and tractable.   She followed her mistress everywhere and instead of showing a preference for high trees, as did examples of *C. mona* and *C. cephus*, preferred low bushes and swamps, finding a great attraction in water anywhere along the banks of the Ogowe river.   Sometimes she would swim across large stretches of water.

This species bred for the first time in captivity in the Cincinnati Zoo (Schrier, 1965).   See Colour Plate facing p. 468.

(a) *C. pogonias pogonias* Bennett, 1833,[*] Crowned guenon ; Golden-bellied Guenon

    (*Syn.* : *C. mona pogonias* Schwarz, 1928, p. 657)

    Vernacular names : See under species.

    Type locality : Fernando Po.   Type (unsexed) in British Museum (No. 42.11.4.14) received from Mrs. Thomson.

    PELAGE : ADULT MALE.—Face black, but paler around the muzzle, which is clothed with short yellowish hairs. A narrow line of black hairs on brows. From the supraorbital region three sagittally directed black bands proceed to the crown, one a narrow median band, composed of long upstanding hairs, which form a crest, and a pair of broad temporal bands proceeding to the preauricular region. Between the three bands are paler areas of shorter hairs of general olive-green tint, due to alternate banding of individual hairs with black and Naples yellow, the latter predominating. Some of the hairs, especially anteriorly, are wholly Naples yellow or that tint with black tips only.   No lateral white or yellowish white stripe above the temporal band.

    Remainder of crown, nape, shoulders and arms laterally, also the sides of the body, speckled yellow and black, giving a general yellowish-grey tinge to preserved skins, but stated by Sanderson (1940) to appear vivid green in the wild animal. Hands black. From the mid-thoracic region to the root of the tail a broad black band of silky hairs, blending gradually in front with the speckled hairs on the shoulders, but sharply defined laterally from those on the sides of the body.   The black band widens gradually posteriorly and is continued on to dorsum of tail.

    Tail mainly black above, darker in proximal third, but usually faintly speckled in middle part, inclining again to pure black in distal third. Below, near the root, yellowish, speckled with black, sometimes with a reddish tinge ; black increasing distally, the terminal third wholly black.

    Ear-tufts yellow ; cheeks light yellow ticked with black and bordered in front by some wholly black hairs.

    Thighs laterally similar to lateral parts of back, but lighter due to more heavy speckling with yellow. Distally more black hairs appear giving a darker tinge to the shank ; feet black with many yellow hairs inter-mixed.

    Under parts, including medial aspects of limbs vivid golden yellow.

    Iris reddish brown (Sanderson, 1940).

    (Description based mainly on four skins from Cameroons collected by W. E. Kershaw and one other (♀) from the same area collected by C. S. Webb and examined alive in the London Zoo, where it died 13th June 1950. Comparison made with type skin in British Museum.)

    ADULT FEMALE.—Resembling the male in colour and pattern. The pink vulva is

* *Loc. cit.*

bounded ventrally by a horseshoe-shaped fold representing a commissura labiorum majorum. This, together with the surrounding perineal skin, including all the area between the callosities and around the anus, together with a well-defined naked triangular field on the under surface of the base of the tail is slaty blue in colour and marked by scattered opaque white glandular papillae. Callosities smoky grey.

JUVENILE.—Natal pelage unknown. Juveniles past the natal coat resemble the adults in all particulars of colour and pattern.

VARIATIONS.—There is some individual variation in the crown pattern due to varying development of the median black stripe. This may be virtually lacking, especially anteriorly, in which event the pale yellow supraocular marks fuse to form a diadem. The absence of black does not detract from the crest formation.

DIMENSIONS.—Weight of juvenile female 1431·25 gms.

Linear dimensions (in millimetres) :

Number	Locality	Sex	Head and Body	Tail	Foot	Ear	
PC.226	Br. Cameroons (Mungo river c. 9 m. N. of Kumba)	♀ juv.	363·9	?	110	28·6	Measured in the flesh Coll. C. S. Webb
PC.223	Br. Cameroons	♂	517	686	—	—	Measured on flat skin
PC.224	,,	♂	559	735	—	—	
PC.225	,,	♀	460	655			Coll. W. E. Kershaw
PC.101	,,	♀	454	678	—	—	

SKULL.—Cranial dimensions (in millimetres) :

Number	Locality	Sex	Max. Cranial Length	Glabella-orpisthion	Biparietal	Least Frontal	Bimastoid	Bizygomatic	Palatal Length	Upper Cheek-teeth	Mandibular Length	Lower Cheek-teeth
PC.226	British Cameroons	♀	77·8	68·7	53·4	40	48·8	50	27	18·8	42	19 $M_{\frac{1}{1}}$ up
PC.223	,,	♂	86	71·1	52·4	41·8	52·3	58·8	36·4	24	56·1	28
PC.224	,,	♂	96·5	75·2	55·1	44·6	57·4	66	39·8	16·5	64·1	31·3 [1]
PC.225	,,	♀	82·2	68·6	50	40	49·3	60	32	21·7	51	25

[1] Congenital absence of $M^{\underline{3}}$.

Skulls show wide individual variations, noticeably in the nasal bones, which are prominent in the males, more flattened and spade-like in females. Variations also affect the supraorbital notches, which may be deep or shallow and variably overhung by the thickening of the supraorbital margin. More often than not a long spur guards the notch laterally, and this may be perforated by a foramen. Infraorbital foramina 3–4 each side.

Mental foramen near lower border of ramus beneath $P_{\overline{4}}$.

DISTRIBUTION.—Fernando Po and adjacent mainland in the south-western part of the Cameroons ; usually found only at high elevations. Southern limit appears to be the Sanaga river.

Schwarz (1928 *b*) mentions material in the Berlin Museum from Basho ; and in the Wiesbaden Museum from Isongo and Bibundi. He questioned the validity of the Fernando Po record considering the type to have been purchased on the mainland.

Sanderson (1940) collected two, a male from Bashauo and an unsexed skin from Atulo (750–1400 ft.), both now in the British Museum. He recorded the animal as very numerous in high deciduous forest around Bashauo, in the foothills of the northern escarpment.

(b) *C. pogonias grayi* Fraser, 1850,* Gray's Guenon ; Erxleben's Guenon

(*Syn.* : *C. erxlebenii* Dahlbett & Pucheran, 1856,† p. 96 ; *C. pogonias pallidus* Elliot, 1909, p. 261 ; *C. petronellae* Buttikofer, 1911, p. 1 ; *Lasiopyga grayi pallida* Elliot, 1933, p. 356 ; *L. petronellae* Elliot, 1913, p. 358 ; *C. pogonias grayi* Booth, 1955 ; Perret & Aellen, 1956)

Vernacular names : Fang, *shumé* (Bates) ; M'boko, *mammbi* (Malbrant & Maclatchy) ; French, *mone de Gray*.

Type locality : Unknown. Based on a female which lived for several years in Lord Derby's collection at Knowsley. It died in 1836 and its skin was deposited in the Liverpool Museum. Type locality of *C. erxlebenii* " West Africa ". Based on a young female which died in the Paris menagerie. Type locality of *pallidus* Gabon. Type, old female, in British Museum (No. 80.6.7.2) collected by L. Laglaize. Type locality of *petronellae*, Upper Congo. Type in Leiden Museum ; paratype in Tervueren Museum (No. 3482).

Original diagnosis of *C. erxlebenii* : *Subparvus, cati dom. magnit. ; olivaceo, fulvo, ferrugineo, griseo nigrique variegatus ; subtus et artuum lateribus internis luteus fundo albido ; caudae parte basale infra olivaceo et nigro varia ; vittis capitis tribus, intermedia cristam efficiente ; regione lumbosacrali, caudae parte supera et toto apice, artubusque antices externe nigris ; manibus omnibus facie que frescis, ore carneo.*

PELAGE : ADULT MALE.—Face and ears said to be flesh coloured (Forbes, 1894). Crown with well-marked median sagittal crest composed of black hairs ; separated by broad lateral yellow tracts from the broad black temporal bands which extend back above and beyond the ears almost to the occiput. Ear-tufts rusty yellow to orange.

Cheeks covered with bushy whiskers, completely yellow.

Entire back and lateral and anterior aspects of thighs dark chestnut brown, without any median black stripe, the hairs alternately annulated rusty yellow and black.

Fore-limbs laterally black from shoulders to dorsum of hands and digits ; shanks laterally black, speckled with yellow ; dorsum of foot black with a little speckling.

Tail above black, beneath black in proximal two-thirds, terminally black throughout. Some white hairs around the anus.

Under parts from chin to pubes, also medial aspects of limbs, bright golden yellow to orange.

COMMENT.—The type of *C. pallidus* is a typical *C. p. grayi*, except for the paler tinge of the underparts. Like *petronellae*, it represents an individual variation

* *Cat. Knowsley Collection*, p. 8.   † *Rev. Mag. Zool.*, 1856, p. 96.

caused by reduction of melanin in the general pigmentary picture of the pelage (*cf.* Schwarz, 1928 *b*, p. 1311).

DIMENSIONS (in millimetres).—Head and body, 500–550 ; tail, 600–750 (Malbrant and Maclatchy).

SKULL :

Number	Locality	Sex	Max. Cranial Length	Biparietal	Least Frontal	Bizygomatic	Biorbital	Palatal Length	Upper Tooth Row	Mandibular Length	Lower Tooth Row
B.M. No. 80.6.7.2	Gabon	♀ old	85	51	37	56	46·8		22	55	24·4 [1]
U.S. Nat. Mus. No. 256311	Unknown ex Zoo	♀	76	50	41	48	46	25	13	39	14 $M\frac{1}{1}$ up

[1] Type of *C. pallidus.*

DISTRIBUTION.—West Africa, from the Sanaga river in Cameroon to the Gabon. On the coast the Nyong river seems to be the southern limit of its range. Inland the range follows the Ja river into the northern part of the Congo basin. Eastwards, ranging to the Ubangi and along the north bank of the Congo as far as the Stanleyville area. Schouteden (1947) lists the undermentioned localities for the Congo-Ubangi district : N. Lisala, Mombwa river, near Bosomboda, Budjala and Bosobolo.

From the former French Congo (Moyen–Congo, Ubangi), specimens have been collected between Mbera Nyoko and Bakota or Singa (Labaye river) ; Upper Ubangi ; Bangui ; Upper Ogowe, Safo (Mayumbe forest) ; Pelle (upper Logone river) ; Bere river. Malbrant and Maclatchy state that in this area *C. p. grayi* is confined to forested parts in the east and north-east of Moyen-Congo (Sangha, Likouala—Mossaka, Likouala aux Herbes, Alima). It is not uncommon in the Etoumbi-Ewo region.

From South Cameroon : Lolodorf, Bipindi, Yaunde, Akoafim (all in Berlin Museum), Efulen (British Museum). Bök, Bamba district, Mabambu, Nginda, Molundu (Frankfurt Museum, Mertens, 1929).

From South-eastern Cameroon : Dume district : Godje (Dendeng) (Berlin Museum) ; Odjimo ; Bange forest ; Lomie (Frankfurt Museum).

(c) *C. pogonias nigripes* du Chaillu, 1860,* Black-footed Guenon

(*Syn.* : *C. erxlebenii* var. *nigripes* Gray, 1870, p. 23 ; *C. pogonias* Schlegel, 1876, p. 82 ; *Lasiopyga pogonias nigripes* Elliot, 1913, p. 354 ; *C. grayi nigripes* Pocock, 1907, p. 713)

Vernacular names : In Gabon, *ponday* (du Chaillu), *m'poondi* (Russell) ; Eschira and Bapouno, *poundi* ; Bakota, *poundi* ; Pahouin, *essouma* ; Saké, *poundo* ; Bakouélé, *pid, pindi* ; Lingomo, *m'pinda* ; Adouma, *poundi* (Malbrant & Maclatchy, 1949) ; French, *mone à pieds noirs.*

Type locality : Ofoubour river, Gabon, in montane forest. Type, an adolescent female skin and skull in the British Museum (No. 61.7.29.16).

PELAGE : ADULT MALE.—General colour of back iron grey to greyish olive ; hairs of flanks with yellowish-white annuli and black tips, and on the nape, shoulders

* *Proc. Boston Soc. nat. Hist.* vii. 360.

and back with reddish annuli ; hinder back, also lateral surfaces of fore-limbs and the feet, wholly black ; thighs cinereous grey, ringed and tipped with whitish.

Face black, or bluish flesh-colour, also naked, but cheeks hairy, yellowish rufous. Nose black throughout its length.

Forehead with horseshoe-shaped area of yellowish white extending back to level of ears, the intervening areas black, as in *grayi*. Ear pencil yellowish rufous.

Tail in basal half above blackish, speckled with yellowish rufous ; distal half above and below, black ; under surface of basal half and area around anus rufous chestnut. Nails dark horn colour.

Scrotum blue (shade unstated).

FEMALE.—Like the male, but under parts paler in colour.

VARIATIONS.—The broad black dorsal band varies in extent. It may be lacking over the sacral region and loins. The depth of colour on the under parts is also subject to considerable individual variation. Colour of the naked facial skin varies also from bluish black to bluish flesh colour, the latter being a feature of juveniles.

DIMENSIONS.—Weight in kilos ; others in millimetres :

Number	Locality	Sex	Weight	Head and Body	Tail	Hand	Foot	
	Kango	♂	4·5 kg.	540	795	85	140	Malbrant and Maclatchy
	,,	♂	4·7 kg.	570	780	95	140	
U.S. Nat. Mus. 220358	Ofoubour R. Fernan Vaz	♂		505	759		148	(paratype)
U.S. Nat. Mus. 220359	Rembo N'Kami	♂ juv.		344	488		86	
U.S. Nat. Mus. 220357	R. Nyambi	♂		510	871		142	

SKULL.—Cranial measurements (in millimetres) :

Number	Sex	Max. Cranial Length	Glabella-max. Occiput	Biparietal	Least Frontal	Bimastoid	Basion-bregma	Bizygomatic	Biorbital	Palatal Length	Upper Cheek-teeth	Mandibular Length	Lower Cheek-teeth
U.S. Nat. Mus. 220082	♂	88	71	53	42	55·5	46	61	51	33	22	54	26
,, 220357	♂	97	77	57	45	59	52	70	59	38	23	64	27
,, 220355	♀	78	65·5	51	38	51	42	54	44	29	13	44	14 M^{2-3}_{2-3}
Brit. Mus. No. 61.7.29.16 (type)	♀	—	—	52	41	—		60	50	31	22	54·5	26·5

DISTRIBUTION.—Forested areas of the Gabon and western parts of Moyen-Congo. The range encompasses the banks of the Ogowe river and its tributaries.

Besides skins ticketed merely " Gaboon ", Schwarz examined material from

Uompokosa (Lake Ogemwe, Ogowe river) and from " Kamerun " in the Berlin Museum, while in the Paris Museum there is one from Cette Cama.

The U.S. National Museum possesses a fine series collected by C. R. Aschemeier, mostly around Fernan Vaz, *e.g.* Agouma, Rembo Nkami, Mpiria, Nyongo, Anguanamo and along the R. Ngoumi, a tributary of the Ogowe.

(d) *C. pogonias schwarzianus* Schouteden, 1946 *

(*Syn.*: *C. mona schwarzi* Schouteden, 1944 *a*, p. 196 ; *C. m. schwarzianus* Schouteden, 1946, new name for *C. m. schwarzi* preoccupied by *C. mitis schwarzi* Roberts, 1931, p. 222 ; *C. pogonias schwarzianus* Booth, 1955, p. 442)

Vernacular names : None recorded.

Type locality : Maduda, Mayumbe, Belgian Congo. Type in Tervueren Museum. Originally brought alive by M. Vingerhoet to Belgium.

PELAGE.—Known only from the type specimen, which resembles *grayi*, but differs in its darker upper parts, which are washed with yellowish red ; in its grey thighs and in the whitish under parts, which are only lightly tinged with yellow. Ear-tufts orange red. Arms and hands black with greyish digits.

Possibly merely an individual variation.

DISTRIBUTION.—Known only from the type locality near the mouth of the Congo. Malbrant and Maclatchy consider that it may occur in the extreme south-west of the equatorial region of the former French territory. Apparently around Mayumbe there is a small " peninsula " of forest just north of the mouths of the Congo.

IV. Superspecies *CERCOPITHECUS PETAURISTA* Schreber, 1775 †

Lesser White-nosed or Spot-nosed Guenons

(SYN. : *Petaurista* Reichenbach, 1863 ; *Rhinostictus* Trouessart, 1897, Elliot, 1913 ; *Cercopitheci rhinosticti* Sclater, 1893 (p. 243) in part ; *Petaurista* + *Erythrogaster* groups of Pocock 1907, p. 717)

DIAGNOSIS

Smaller-sized slender guenons with general colour dark green speckled with black, with a cordate or triangular pale patch of closely adpressed hair on the nose, varying in colour and differing in shape from that in *C. nictitans*. Face otherwise slate blue to blackish except lips, which are paler blue or purplish pink. A distinct brow band of forwardly directed black hairs continued laterally as a temporal band separating the crown area from the cheeks and extending back to ear-level and in some forms beyond. Inter-orbital region with a median vertical tract of black hairs expanding below on nose and confluent with the cordate nose-patch.

Under parts from chin to pubes white or greyish white, occasionally, as in some examples of *C. erythrogaster*, reddish. Hair on throat and sides of neck projected forwards forming with the whiskers a girdle or ruff.

* *De zoogdierden van Belgisch Congo en van Ruanda-Urundi*, ii, Pl. 553.
† *Säugetiere*, i. 103, Pl. XIX B.

Tail typically bicoloured, the dorsal and ventral areas sharply defined along the sides.

Scrotum pale blue.

Diploid chromosome number, 66.

DISTRIBUTION, ECOLOGY AND ETHOLOGY

This widely dispersed group is represented by a number of forms in the West African rain-forest belt from Portuguese Guinea southwards to north-western Angola, with a special aggregation of species in the region adjoining the Bight of Biafra. Eastwards there is a broad extension in the Congo basin and thence into Uganda.

Thanks to the work of Haddow (1952) and his co-workers our knowledge of the ecology, food preferences and other behavioural features, as based upon the most easterly representative of the group (*C. ascanius schmidti*), is fairly extensive and has been liberally consulted in documenting the ecology of the whole genus (*antea*, pp. 364-378).

All members of this superspecies are extremely active, ebullient, rest-less animals of volatile temperament. They display great curiosity and imitativeness, and in all these features contrast strongly with the forms of *C. nictitans*.

The display pattern is calculated to emphasize the nose-spot, consisting of rapid up and down head-bobbing, with the fore part of the body in a crouched posture, the arms widely spread. It may be accompanied by opening the mouth and vocal chirrups of staccato character.

The tail is normally carried horizontally with the terminal third drooping so that its tip is held just clear of the substrate.

In progression the movements are characteristically leaping and darting, whereby a rapid translation through the trees is effected. This again con-trasts markedly with the trotting gait of *e.g. C. mitis* and its allies, resembling rather that of the *C. mona* assemblage. Haddow has compared the move-ments of *C. ascanius schmidti* particularly to those of *C. denti*.

Booth (1960) states that in the wild the spot-nosed monkeys are fairly silent, though having a wide potential vocal range. The bark of the male is the most frequently used, a deep resonant *ke-urr*. The voice of *C. ascanius* is a flute-like trill, but a low growl, *grrr*, is also emitted.

In West Africa the Lesser White-nosed Monkey is one of the commonest diurnal mammals. It subsists on fruit and leaves and frequents the lower strata of the forest canopy. On account of its catholic food preferences, it can survive in quite small islets of forest which would be insufficient to support troops of Monas of equal numbers. In West Africa, at any rate, its field of activity is admirably suited to secondary forest growth and the range here and there extends into the Guinea savannah.

TAXONOMY

As already explained (p. 395) Schwarz (1928 *c*) included all the members of this Formenkreis as subspecies of *C. nictitans*, but recent work has shown this position untenable.

Following Booth (1956 *a*) the superspecies is here treated as comprising the three species, *petaurista*, *ascanius* and *erythrogaster*, with a fourth, *C. erythrotis*, added. These are all treated as specifically distinct for the simple reason they do not represent a graded series or cline. Far from being intermediate between *C. petaurista* and *C. ascanius*, *C. erythrogaster* stands apart in having a red (or sometimes grey) lower chest and belly. The situation is further obscured by the fact that unexpectedly there is a resemblance in coat pattern between the widely separated *C. petaurista* and *C. erythrotis sclateri*, but more properly documented material of all these forms is needed before their true interrelations can be precisely determined. The territory of *C. erythrotis*, moreover, overlaps considerably that of *C. erythrogaster*.

11. *CERCOPITHECUS PETAURISTA* (Schreber, 1775 *)

Lesser White-nosed Monkey

(SYN.: *Le blanc-nez* Allamand (in Buffon), 1766 also Buffon 1789, suppl., vii, p. 67 ; *Simia petaurista* Schreber, 1775, p. 103 ; Audebert, 1799, p. 23 ; *S. albinasus* Reichenbach, 1863 ; *C. fantiensis* Matschie 1893, p. 64 ; *C. buttikoferi pygrius* Thomas, 1923, p. 607 ; *C. nictitans petaurista* Schwarz, 1928, p. 660. Rode, 1937, p. 91)

VERNACULAR NAMES : None recorded

TYPE LOCALITY : " Guinea ". No type specimen in existence. Type locality of *fantiensis*, Fanti, Rio Boutry, Gold Coast. Type male infant in Berlin Museum (No. 2963). Type locality of *pygrius* Bandama, Ivory Coast. Type a male, collected by Willoughby Lowe, in British Museum (No. 23.2.3.1).

Monkeys of this, or a related species, have been known under the general name of " white-noses " for centuries. They were doubtless striking elements of the local fauna to the earliest voyagers to West Africa. Possibly the earliest certain references are those of de Bry (1603), and of Samuel Purchas (1625, *Purchas's Pilgrims*, ii. 955). Definitely applicable to the Lesser White-nose are the references of Artus (1746–1747) and Allamand and Buffon (1766) who give a description and figure under the title *Blanc-nez*.

CHARACTERS

PELAGE : ADULT MALE.—Face bluish, paler around the muzzle, which is purplish pink. Except around the eyes, the colour of the skin is masked by hairy growths. Ears bluish, untufted, hidden.

* *Säugetiere*, i 103. Pl XIX B

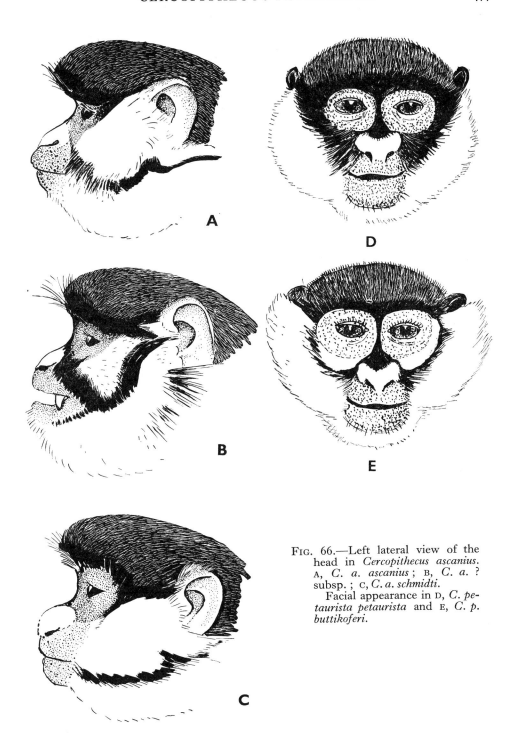

Fig. 66.—Left lateral view of the head in *Cercopithecus ascanius*. A, *C. a. ascanius* ; B, *C. a.* ? subsp. ; C, *C. a. schmidti.*

Facial appearance in D, *C. petaurista petaurista* and E, *C. p. buttikoferi.*

A transverse line of black hairs along the forehead forming a brow band of some depth, the foremost hairs of which are longer than the rest and projected forwards. Laterally the band is continued as a longitudinal temporal stripe as far as the ears and, in the nominate race, beyond as a thin parieto-occipital stripe which may meet its fellow on the back of the head.

Median line of nose above with black hairs continued downwards from the frontal band. Black hairs also clothe the anterior part of the whiskers, sweeping forwards to the angle of the mouth and as far as the lateral borders of the pale nose-spot. Nose spot broad, cordate, with the notch superiorly, and apex below, opaque white.

Below the black temporal stripe a white bar affects the preauricular region ; it runs obliquely backwards and downwards from a point some distance behind the lateral palpebral canthus to beneath the ear. Beneath this again is another black streak, passing in the same direction from the black cheek-hairs to the side of the neck.

Throat white, the ruff running upwards on to the cheek, considerably above the angle of the mouth, as high as the level of the inferior limit of the ear ; these hairs are directed obliquely upwards and backwards, a direction which also affects the black hairs of the anterior part of the cheek.

Crown, between the black areas, nape, shoulders, back and lateral aspects of the limbs dark greenish in general hue due to alternate annulations of black and yellow on individual hairs, sometimes with ochraceous-rufous bands on back.

Forearms wholly black laterally, some of the hairs merely tipped with yellow ; hands and feet black.

Tail above speckled throughout ; below greyish white.

Under parts and medial aspects of limbs white-haired on bluish skin, which shows through in most places.

ADULT FEMALE.—Differing from the male only in size.

VARIATIONS.—Much confusion has arisen in the past from the description of pale mutants as distinct races or species. Thus, Elliot (1913, 2, p. 300) refers to the fact that Schreber's original figure depicts a very darkly coloured animal, almost black, speckled with yellowish, a fact which he claims later workers have overlooked with the result that a supposedly different animal, hailing from the Gold Coast, has borne the name *petaurista*. Matschie (1893) named the lighter animal *C. fantiensis*. Elliot further claims that " Guinea " specimens in the Berlin Museum prove the differences between the two alleged forms.

Schwarz (1928 c, p. 660) maintained that the type of *fantiensis* is a baby and, except for characters of youth, does not differ from ordinary *petaurista*. Pointing out that Matschie had compared this skin with another (dark) juvenile, Schwarz nevertheless concluded that both were examples of typical *petaurista*.

The type of Thomas's *pygrius*, although described as a subspecies of *buttikoferi*, also represents the pale phase of typical *petaurista*. It has a very attenuated parieto-occipital band, hence, presumably its relegation to *buttikoferi* which always lacks this band. Schwarz found one almost exactly like it in the Leiden Museum. This came from the Gold Coast. Another in the Paris Museum from Aniasué, Ivory Coast, is perfectly typical of *petaurista*. Hayman (1936) also found among material from the Gold Coast examples indistinguishable from the type of *pygrius*.

DISTRIBUTION (Map 7)

The West African Lesser White-nosed Monkey is restricted to the Guinea rain-forest belt from Portuguese Guinea to Togoland. Two races are recognized, a northern (typically from Liberia) known as *C. p. buttikoferi* and the nominate race from the Ivory Coast, Ghana and Togoland. The two presumably meet somewhere in the Ivory Coast, but the exact boundary between the two races has not yet been defined. Booth (1956 *b*) believes it to follow approximately the Sassandra and Nzo rivers. The eastward range is limited by the Dahomey faunal break.

(a) *C. petaurista petaurista* Schreber, 1775.* Lesser White-nosed Monkey

      Syn. : See under species.
      Vernacular names : None recorded.
      Type locality : See under species.

      CHARACTERS.—As described for the species. Differing from *C. p. buttikoferi* chiefly in the constant presence of a black parieto-occipital band as a backward extension of the temporal band. It may or may not meet its fellow on the occipital region. As first pointed out by Pocock (1907), the nominate race also differs in lacking the pale infraorbital patches.

      DIMENSIONS.—Weights in kilos ; No. PC.68, ♂ subadult, 2·0 ; No. PC.69, ♀ juvenile, 0·9 ; No. PC.70, ? subadult, 1·4 ; No. PC.73, ♀ juvenile, 1·5 ; No. PC. 560, ♀ adult, 2·44.
      Linear in millimetres :

Number	Locality	Sex	Head and Body	Tail	Foot	Ear	
P.C.500	Gold Coast	♀	435	625	121	35	Measured in the flesh
P.C.68	,,	♂	352	578	111	27·7	*Ex* Edinburgh Zoo
PC.69	,,	♀	393	657	100·3	29·1	,,
PC.74	,,	♀	346	385	100	—	,,
Berlin Mus.	" Guinea "	?	440	570	—	—	*Ex* Elliot

* *Säugetiere*, i. 103, Pl. XIX B.

SKULL.—No measurements available.

DISTRIBUTION.—Confined to rain-forest tracts in the Gold Coast and adjacent parts of Togoland and of the Ivory Coast. The western limit appears to follow the line of the Sassandra river and its tributary, the Nzo. Exact localities given in the literature include Sekondi, Rio Boutry, Krobo Mountain (where it is said by Booth, 1956, to be abundant), the Shai Hills, Goaso, Mampong and Ejura, Gold Coast (Hayman, 1936).

According to Booth (1956) this race freely enters forest outliers, fringing forest and coastal scrub, being essentially a dweller in thickets. It occupies high forest mainly where a fallen emergent has created a gap in the canopy, permitting daylight to penetrate to ground level and subsequent growth of dense under-brush. It also affects swampy areas where emergents are scarce. It sleeps in the middle and lower storeys of the canopy.

(b) *C. petaurista buttikoferi* Jentink, 1886,* Büttikofer's Monkey

Syn.: *C. albinasus* Reichenbach, 1863.
Vernacular name: None recorded.
Type locality: Sofore Place, St. Paul's river, Liberia. Types collected in July 1880 by Büttikofer and Sala—in the Leiden Museum.

Original description based upon a series of eight specimens, in the Leiden Museum, adults and young of both sexes collected in Liberia by Messrs. Büttikofer and Sala. These were compared with a series of seven specimens of typical *petaurista*, adults and juveniles of both sexes, all from the Gold Coast. Two cotypes (Nos. 91.11.3 and 91.11.3.3($\female$)) in British Museum.

PELAGE.—Differing from typical *petaurista*, which it closely resembles in size and colour, in the complete absence of the black band across the vertex connecting the two ears.

Another feature in which this race departs from the nominate form is the presence of pale semilunar markings infraorbitally. These are typically formed by a tract of yellow hairs, sharply demarcated below and laterally by the black hairs of the anterior part of the whiskers.

No cranial or other skeletal differences mentioned in the original description, the numbers of vertebrae and ribs being reported the same in both races.

DIMENSIONS (in millimetres):

Number	Locality	Sex	Weight	Head and Body	Tail	Foot	Ear
110/50	Sierra Leone	$\female$ juv.	527	280	430	87·8	22·7
PC.52	,,	$\female$ juv.		235	403	81·2	23·6
		$\female$ inf.		213	345	72·8	25·2

* *Notes Leyden Museum*, viii. 56.

PLATE XXIII

Photo: E. Kirkland

Cercopithecus ascanius schmidti, adult, in Chester Zoo

PLATE XXIV

Cercopithecus ascanius schmidti, juvenile, Cologne Zoo

SKULL.—Cranial dimensions (in millimetres) :

Number	Locality	Sex	Max. Cranial Length	Glabella-opisthion	Biparietal	Least Frontal	Basion-bregma Ht.	Bimastoid	Bizygomatic	Biorbital	Palatal Length	Upper Cheek-teeth	Mandibular Length	Lower Cheek-teeth
	Sierra Leone	♂ ad.	88·6	66·7	51·4	40	40·6	50·2	55·3	46·7	34·6	21·2	47·5	23·7 [1]
	,,		81	63·7	48	38·4	43·6	45·5	51·2	46	31·5	16·5	45·3	19 [1]
	,,	juv.	70	61·7	50	36·8	39·6	45·5	43	36·9	21·3	12·7	32·3	10 [2]
	,,		73·8	61	49·5	36·4	38·5	45·3	46·4	40·2	24·6	13·9	39·5	15·8 [2]
	,,		76	63·7	50	39·1	42·7	45	46·8	41·5	24·7	15	38·2	16 [2]
	,,		75·2	65	51·7	39·4	41·5	47·6	48	40	24·4	14	39·5	16 [2]
	,,		70	58·5	46·5	36·8	38·8	44·8	43·7	38·8	24·7	12·7	35·6	15·5 [2]
	,,		64	60·2	48·2	36·7	41·3	42·6	45·1	40·5	18·6	13·2	34·3	14·5 [2]
	,,		69·5	62·5	51	36	40	45	43	35·7	21·8	8·4	34	8·8 [3]
	,,		72·2	64	51	38·5	40·6	47·5	43·3	38·5	23	9·3	32·5	9·6 [3]
	,,		71	61	49·1	39	39·8	45	43·5	39·5	20	9·7	33	11 [3]
PC.524	,,		67·5	58·4	46·5	37·1	—	39·4	37·7	37·7	19·5	9·3	29·3	9·9 [3]

[1] All permanent molars erupted except $M^{\underline{3}}$.   [2] All milk dentition + $M^{\underline{1}}_{\overline{1}}$.   [3] Complete milk dentition.

DISTRIBUTION.—West African rain forest westwards from the line of the Sassandra-Nzo rivers at least as far as Portuguese Guinea, including the islands of the Bissagos Archipelago.

This race is very common in Sierra Leone, and formerly also in Liberia, but in the latter country its haunts have been eliminated by cultivation and large numbers have been destroyed for food. The U.S. National Museum has two skins, without other data, collected near Harbel on the Firestone Estate. Tervuren Museum has two from the environs of Tappi, Liberia, collected 1962 by Hemmelheber.

Booth (1956 b) found between Guiglo and Tai, just west of the Nzo in the Ivory Coast examples of both buttikoferii and petaurista, and also intermediates, and declares that the only significant differences between the two races there lies in the presence or absence of the parieto-occipital black bar.

In Sierra Leone it occurs in the coastal scrub. Although I was not successful in observing them, I was informed that they were seen daily in the compounds of dwellings adjacent to the airport at Lungi, and also in the forest reserves inland from and to the east of Freetown.

Dekeyser (1955) is the authority for the occurrence of the species on the island of Bubaque in the Bissagos Archipelago, and in the former French Guinea. Presumably the present race is involved. This is the monkey tentatively identified by Monard (1938) as C. nictitans.

2 I

12. *CERCOPITHECUS ASCANIUS* (Audebert, 1799 *)

Black-cheeked White-nosed Monkey

(SYN. : *Simia ascanius* Audebert, 1799, p. 21 ; *Cercopithecus melanogenys* Gray, 1845, p. 212, 1849, p. 212 ; *C. histrio* Reichenbach, 1863, p. 106 ; *C. picturatus* Santos, 1886, p. 95 ; *C. nictitans ascanius* Schwarz, 1928 *a*, p. 28)

VERNACULAR NAMES : French, *l'ascagne* ; Italian, *l' ascagno.*

TYPE LOCALITY : Unknown, probably Angola. Type in Paris Museum. Type locality of *melanogenys* " Africa ". Type skull in British Museum. Type locality of *histrio*, unknown. Type locality of *picturatus*, West Africa (Ambriz, coast of northern Angola). Type ♂ adult in Lisbon Museum (No. 72a), presented by J. A. de Sousa. The type has been redescribed by Schwarz, 1935.

Distinguished at once, according to Pocock (1907), from *C. petaurista* by the colour and arrangement of the hair on the cheek. Typically a black browband extends laterally from the forehead and thence, broader, backwards to the ear, but never crossing the back of the head. Beneath the black cheek-band the preauricular hairs are arranged radially in a whorl ; they are yellowish in colour. Beneath these again a second, narrower black tract extends from beneath the ear, where it is narrowest and palest, forward to the sides of the face between the angle of the gape and the lateral palpebral canthus.

The nose spot is typically white and of cordate outline, as in *C. petaurista.*

ORIGINAL DIAGNOSIS.—*S. ascanius, caudata, barbata, facie subcoerulea, naso albo.*

CHARACTERS

PELAGE.—Face bluish (cf. blackish in *nictitans*). For other features see under subspecies.

DISTRIBUTION (Map 7)

Heavy forested area from Angola, via the Congo basin to Uganda. Numerous names have been given to supposed races of this species, but most are based on minor individual variations. Besides the nominate race from Angola, probably there are not more than four others and even these may, with further study on a wider range of material, be reduced to synonymy.

(a) *C. ascanius ascanius* Audebert, 1799, Black-cheeked White-nosed Monkey

(Syn. : See under species)
Vernacular names : None recorded.
Type locality : Unknown, probably Angola. Type in Paris Museum.

PELAGE : ADULT MALE.—Face bright bluish with violet tinge. Ears small, flesh-coloured, almost nude, but a thick reddish pencil present in type of *picturatus*. Moustache black ; cheek-stripe very broad (30 mm.) ; only a small triangle infra-

---

* *Hist. nat. singes*, fam. iv, sect. II, fig. XIII.

orbitally paler, the hairs showing pale tips. A yellowish whorl below ears. Nose-patch white. Crown somewhat paler than back, without parieto-occipital band; black grizzled with cartridge buff (Hill and Carter, 1941).

Dorsal surface of body black, speckled with orange rufous, the under fur olive brown, giving a general greenish hue, slightly tinged with reddish brown. Lateral aspect of pectoral limbs black. Thighs like the back, becoming iron grey distally and on shanks scarcely speckled; dorsum of pes similar. Under parts white or whitish, clearest on throat and chest, duller on medial aspects of limbs. Tail above like back basally, whitish below, becoming more reddish distally above and below, the dorsal and ventral colours not sharply defined on sides (cf. *whitesidei*).

ADULT FEMALE.—Like the male, but smaller.

JUVENILE.—Unknown.

VARIATIONS.—A very fine large male (PC.520) received in the flesh from Chessington Zoo on 11 April 1961, probably pertains here, though somewhat aberrant in several respects. Areas around eyes and mouth bluish, with only a few downwardly directed black hairs on upper lip. Nose-spot large, white, bounded by black hairs which form the anterior limit of a very broad maxillary band which runs at first transversely and then sweeps upwards to meet the lateral extension of the supraorbital band, the fused bands proceeding thence to the ear. In the angle is a triangular yellow patch which extends downwards lateral to the orbit to meet the transverse part of the maxillary band. The preauricular area is white, slightly tinged with yellow, and some of the hairs have black tips. Below, this patch is joined by the up-sweeping white ruff continued up from the interramal area and throat, whilst behind the uppermost part of the white area are some long backwardly directed black whiskers sweeping past the lower edge of the ear. The longest of these black hairs are above; below they become progressively shorter and more obliquely directed (fig. 66 A–C).

Ears bluish with a few white hairs only.

Tail markedly bicoloured with sharp line of demarcation between dorsal and ventral pattern; above black, speckled with yellow, below whitish, but towards the tip the dorsal area becomes solid black and gradually encroaches along the sides so that the terminal fringe is black above and below.

Perineum and scrotum peripherally Eton blue, darkening centrally due to epidermal melanin, producing a colour approximating to indulin blue, and in spots nearly black. Prepuce dark slaty. Penis, both corpus and glans dark blue grey. Iris, Rood's brown.

Body odour musky rather than garlic-like, chiefly emanating from the inguinal region.

Pocock (1907) remarks on the variability of the black pattern on the cheeks. The above described specimen approaches, in the extent of the black areas, the type of Gray's *melanogenys* where, according to Pocock, the whole area between the eye and the angle of the mouth is black, but in a young specimen then living in the London Zoo, a small patch of yellow-speckled hair interrupted the black below and lateral to the orbit, similar to the above described specimen, only smaller. That the yellow infraorbital patch is not a juvenile feature is proved by its conspicuousness and great extent in the above described adult male. As Pocock surmised, it is possible that more than one race is involved.

DIMENSIONS.—The only data available relate to the above atypical male. Head and body, 500 mm.; tail, 690 mm.; head length (muzzle-occiput), 111 mm.; hand, 90 mm.) foot, 128·5 mm.; ear, morphological length, 31 mm.; morphological breadth, 25·4 mm.; physiognomic height, 36·5 mm.; physiognomic breadth,

28·7 mm. Intermammillary, 44 mm. Weight, 5·36 kg., *i.e.* very large for any member of the present superspecies.

Skull.—Cranial dimensions (in millimetres) :

Number	Locality	Sex	Max. Cranial Length	Glabella-occiput	Condylo-basal Length	Biparietal	Least Frontal	Bimastoid	Bizygomatic	Biorbital	Palatal Length	Upper Cheek-teeth	Mandibular Length	Lower Cheek-teeth
PC.520	Chessington Zoo	ad. ♂	99	71	73	51	39	54·7	65	56	40	25	64·5	30
B.M.[1] 43.5.27.3	Unknown	juv.	78			50·5	39		50	43	24·5		40	

[1] Type of *melanogenys*

Distribution.—Tropical West African rain forest south of the mouths of the Congo from the Angolan coast inland as far as the Kasai river.

The Vernay Angola Expedition collected a single specimen at Vila Arriaga, 180 km. east of Mossamedes (Hill and Carter, 1941). The species had been previously recorded from Encoge (Monteiro, 1860) and Bembe (Sclater, 1860). Additionally we have the type locality of *C. picturatus*, viz., Ambriz (=Ambrizete) on the coast of northern Angola. Barros Machado (1957) reports it common in the forest north of Lunda.

In the former Belgian territory Schouteden (1946) gives the following localities, whence *C. a. ascanius* has been collected : Lower Congo district : Monolitle, Thijssville, Leopoldville, Kidada, Bangu, Mukimbungu ; Lake Leopold III district : Kwamouth, Kabandele, left bank of Beneden-Kwango, Masia, Luswe, Tua, Lekana, Mpa, Erebo ; Kasai district : Basongo ; Kwango district : Kasongo Lunda, Atene, Franz-Joseph Falls, Bayaka, Djuna, Idiofa.

(b) *C. ascanius katangae* Lönnberg, 1919,* Katanga Black-cheeked White-nosed Monkey

Type locality : Kinda, Katanga. Type in Tervuren Museum. Eleven topotypes referred to in original account, all agreeing with each other and showing constant differences from typical *ascanius*.

Characters.—Nose spot whitish, but frequently with faint maize-yellow tinge on its upper half. In one female the upper third of the spot is yellowish buff, the rest faintly tinted.

Black frontal band lacking, the maximum development being a black spot behind the eyes, but interorbital median black streak well developed, encroaching in some specimens on the pale nasal spot, as a triangular black area.

The lower black cheek band commencing as a very broad area lateral to the nose-spot, narrowing abruptly and fading away behind the ear ; it is formed by the black tips of the longer lower whiskers, which bear a subapical yellow ring, being otherwise white to the base.

Hairs of crown banded with yellow, sometimes a pale yellowish buff ; elsewhere on upper surface the speckling is with brownish terra-cotta, giving a more rufous tinge to the back.

Upper arms and thighs like back, but forearms almost black, with minimal speckling ; lower legs blackish grey, lightly speckled with yellow. Hands black ; feet blackish grey.

* *Rev. zool. Afr.* vii. 122.

Tail above coloured like back, proximally, changing to black distally without any maroon intermediate section. Below proximally white, changing in the middle part to fawn ; terminally black. Along the lateral demarcation line a vivid red line occurs and in a few specimens the lower surface is blood red inside the black tip.

A single skin labelled " Kassai " in the U.S. National Museum (No. 101479, collected by S. P. Verner) has the tail above, in its proximal half like the back, thereafter the dark area narrows to a median dorsal stripe, the sides becoming ochraceous rufous ; below it is dirty whitish grey in the basal half, not very sharply demarcated from the dorsal pattern.

SKULL.—Cranial dimensions (in millimetres) :

Locality	Sex	Max. Cranial Length	Condylo-basal Length	Basal Length	Biparietal	Least Frontal	Bizygomatic	Biorbital	Palatal Length	Upper Cheek-teeth
Kinda, Katanga	♂	98	74·8	65·5	58·7	44·5	65	55	35·5	23·7
,,	♀	96·2	72	62·5	55	41·5	63·8	53·5	35·5	22

DISTRIBUTION.—Originally from Kinda, west of the upper Lualaba in Katanga. Kinda lies in fact on the west bank of the Lupweshi river, a tributary of the Lualaba. This form therefore probably occupies the area between the upper Lualaba and the upper Kasai. Schwarz (1928 *a*, p. 32) extended the range, by his attribution to this race, of specimens in the Tervueren Museum from the following localities : Kabambaie, Dumbi, Belengi, Makumbi and N'Gombe, all on the upper Kasai ; Luebo on the lower Lulua, Kamaiembi, between Luebo and Djoko-Punda ; Luluaborg ; Sandoa on the upper Lulua and Kongoslo on the upper Lualaba. As the last mentioned locality proves, *katangae* ranges right up to the Congo in the east and in the north-east meets the territory of *whitesidei*.

(c) *C. ascanius whitesidei* Thomas, 1909,* Whiteside's Guenon ; Yellow-nosed Monkey

(Syn.: *C. (Rhinostictus) a. omissus* Matschie, 1913, p. 68 ; *C. (Rhinostictus) a. cirrhorhinus* Matschie, 1913, p. 70 ; *C. (Rhinostictus) a. kassaicus* Matschie, 1913, p. 74 ; *C. (Rhinostictus) a. pelorhinus* Matschie, 1913, p. 76)

Vernacular names : None recorded.

Type locality : Nsoli, Ikau, Upper Lulonga river, Central Congo, about 1° N. 22° E. Type ♂ adult in British Museum (No. 11.10.19.1), collected by Rev. R. M. Whiteside, 15 July 1909. Type locality of *omissus* unknown. Brought by caravan coming from Manyema (q.v. under *schmidti*). Type an immature female in Berlin Museum. Type locality of *cirrhorhinus*, Stanley Falls area ; probably from lower Lomani river. Six specimens referred to in original description. Type locality of *kassaicus*, Pogge Falls, north bank of the Kasai. Based on subadult female animal imported alive into Berlin Zoo. Now in Berlin Museum (No. 13384), collected by Frobenius. Type locality of *pelorhinus* uncertain. Type an adult female. Skin bought at Yambuya, Congo (Duke Adolf-Friedrich of Mecklenburg's expedition).

CHARACTERS.—Differing from typical *ascanius* in the lesser development of the inferior band on the cheek and in the buff or yellowish tinge of the nose-patch.

* *Ann. Mag. nat. Hist.* (8), iv. 542.

Agreeing with *ascanius* in the red ear-tuft. Tail tricoloured, and therefore intermediate between the grey-tailed and the fully red-tailed sections of the species.

PELAGE : ADULT MALE.—General colour of upper parts warm tawny olive, individual hairs alternately zoned black and ochraceous. Under parts creamy white, sharply demarcated from dorsum. Nasal spot described as pinkish buff in original account, but more often yellow (*e.g.* in a living specimen seen in the Dublin Zoo, 1956).

Auricular hairs orange rufous. Face with sparse black hairs on lips and chin.

Well-defined black frontal line passing laterally to base of ear. An inconspicuous temporal whorl present, its hairs creamy white ; hairs below this tipped with black, giving the relatively poorly marked inferior cheek-bar, none of the hairs being black to their bases.

Forearms both sides blackish grey from elbows distally, the dark colour encircling the wrist ; medial aspect of upper arms white. Thighs laterally like back as far as knee, thereafter becoming slaty greyish ; medially white to ankles. Feet black slightly speckled with buff.

Tail dorsally and proximally like back, becoming darker distally, then rufous, but ending in black tip ; beneath white proximally then reddish at mid length and finally black. Dorsal and ventral colours sharply demarcated on sides, as in *petaurista*, but line of separation marked by red in middle section, the red increasing distally at the expense of the white, which is gradually lost.

DIMENSIONS of type (measured in the flesh by collector).—Head and body, 530 mm. ; tail, 880 mm. ; foot, 120 mm. For other measurements see Allen (1925, p. 406).

SKULL.—Cranial dimensions (in millimetres) : Maximum cranial length, 98 ; Basal length, 70 ; Maximum cranial breadth, 52 ; Upper cheek-teeth, 22.

Of type adult male (personal measurements) : Maximum cranial length, 90 ; biparietal, 50·5 ; least frontal, 39·2 ; bizygomatic, 64·5 ; biorbital, 52·3 ; palatal length, 35 ; upper cheek-teeth, 21 ; mandibular length, 62·1 ; lower cheek-teeth, 28·2.

For more extensive data see Allen (*loc. cit.*).

VARIATIONS.—Allen (1925, p. 405 *et seq.*) discusses this form at length under the headings *Lasiopyga ascanius cirrhorhinus* and *L. a. pelorhinus*, giving among the synonyms of the former, *omissus, sassae, enkamer, montana, ituriensis* and *rutschuricus*, but without mention of Thomas's *whitesidei*. There was evidently in his mind a good deal of confusion with *schmidti*, much of which was later cleared up by Schwarz (1928 *c*), although the promised detailed treatment of the group by Schwarz never materialized.

Allen noted a wide range of colour variation in his material, which comprised 39 specimens attributed to *cirrhorhinus* and 5 imperfect native prepared skins assigned to *pelorhinus*.

Allen quotes Lönnberg's (1917, 1919) remarks on the variations met with in skins of the *ascanius* group from the same locality, based on twelve specimens from the Rutschuru district and 25 from the Ituri forest. Respecting the Rutschuru series, he mentions variations in the colour of the crown, ears, limbs and tail. Ear hairs are said to be white or whitish, but in others pale reddish ochre hairs occur, with some showing intermediate colours. Tail colours are equally variable, hence Lönnberg refers to the difficulty of basing a subspecies on so variable a structure ; in consequence he considered *montana, ituriensis* and *sassae* as not differing sufficiently from *enkamer* to be accorded recognition.

Allen's own series from Akenge, north of Bafwaboli, showed, in comparison with other mammals, including *Colobus*, little individual variation, yet this is of the same order as in Lönnberg's series. General colour varies according to the width of the ochraceous annulations on the individual hairs. White under parts vary little, except that some have a grey-washed appearance due to grey-tipped hairs among the white. The crown usually is much lighter than the rest of the upper parts, and sharply defined in front by the black brow-band. Sometimes a feeble parieto-occipital band is detectable. The whole nape is predominantly black in some skins; in others it is no darker than the rest of the upper pelage.

Some variation was noted by Allen in the shape, size and colour of the nose spot, which ranges from clear white, through pale yellow to a slightly brownish tint, though the collector, Lang, maintained that the yellowish and brownish tints were the result of subsequent alteration as all the specimens observed in the field by himself and Chapin had white nose-spots. It is, however, difficult to imagine how such precise differences could be determined in the dull light of heavy forest in moving animals. Moreover, as noted above, a yellow nose-spot was present on the living specimen observed in the Dublin Zoo.

The black interorbital streak is even more variable, yet has been used as a diagnostic character. It may be broad based and usually extends upwards as a narrow streak to meet the frontal band. This it may fail to do, or there may be but a single line of hairs connecting the black triangle bordering the pale nose patch with the frontal band.

The upper temporal black band is commonly broad and heavy, composed of long, black, bristly hairs. They meet the frontal band anteriorly, but they are often narrowed almost to obsolescence medially.

The inferior lateral black band is more irregular in extent, being sometimes double the width of the minimal size. In some it extends anteriorly as far as the eyes as a narrow line of short, black hairs; in others it virtually ends at a point below the anterior base of the ear. It is formed in part by black-tipped cheek-hairs.

Whiskers vary in length and fullness and in amount of black tipping of individual hairs and hence in general colour, which varies from pure white to light greyish.

The chin is clothed generally with short black bristly hairs, but these may be inconspicuous or lacking.

Greatest individual variation occurs in the colour of the tail, especially in respect of the extent of the proximal grey area inferiorly, the length of the terminal black portion and the extent and tone of the dorsal red or lateral red line. The inferior grey zone varies from 100 to 200 mm. in length, *i.e.* from one-eighth to one-quarter the total tail length. A similar range of variations affects the black terminal area, which varies from 30 to 150 mm. of the length. The red tone varies according to the amount of black mixture in the dorsal pelage, so that a range from almost black to bright red is found.

The tail of the single skin in the U.S. National Museum (No. 61698, collected by J. H. Camp, ticketed ? Upper Congo) has the proximal third above black with orange speckling; this changes gradually distally to bright chestnut, brighter on the sides than along the median dorsal line. The distal third is black above and below, while the proximal half beneath is white, sharply demarcated along the sides from the dorsal hue. The rufous section along the sides is paler and occupies the middle third.

Sexual variation is no greater than the range of individual variation; but the usual marked sexual difference in size occurs, males averaging one-sixth larger than females (Allen).

As regards age variations, the adult pattern and texture of pelage is already attained in infants with full milk dentition.

Cranial variations are slight and follow the normal pattern met with in other species of the genus. These include varying stages of ossification in individuals of the same dental age. This applies to sutural unions and such matters as the degree of development of the temporal ridges.

DISTRIBUTION.—Forests of the central and north-eastern Congo extending on both banks of the Congo river, (a) on the right bank between the Kasai, and the Lomami, north of the area occupied by *C. a. katangae*, and (b) on the left bank from Bumba eastwards over the Stanleyville area.

Besides the type locality (Lulonga river) Schwarz (1928 a) records numerous other localities based on a very large series examined by himself in the Tervuren Museum, and Schouteden (1947) adds further localities based on a total of 175 specimens assigned to *C. a. whitesidei*.

Lake Leopold II district: Inongo, Bumbuli, Kutu, Mpe, Luakere, Bokoro, Oshwe, Tolo, Kunungu, Dwa, Bolobo, Mongana, Mongende, Kala, Tendem, Gomo; Tschuapa district: Eala, Ikengo, Tondu, Bikoro (Lake Tumba), Lukolela, Mondombe, Tschuapa, Lokolenge, Bamania; Congo-Ubangi district: Bumba; Stanleyville district: Stanleyville environs, Loleka, Elisabetha; Manyema district: Kindu. Material from the Bumba district; Duma, Libenge (both Ubangi district), from Badingoua and Nana (Upper Shari) and Angu (Uelle) is referred by Mertens (1929) to *C. a. schmidti*, but presumably pertains to *whitesidei*.

The assignment of Matschie's *kassaicus*, from Pogge Falls, to this race, rather than to the nominate race or to *C. a. katangae*, is due to Schwarz. The locality is on the right bank of the lower Kasai, so that the river evidently forms the barrier between the ranges of *ascanius* and *whitesidei*. The type was a young female brought alive to the Berlin Zoo by Frobenius. Schwarz states that it is a dark example of *whitesidei*, with a rusty nose-spot.

(d) *C. ascanius montanus* Lorenz, 1914,* Montane Red-tailed Guenon

(*Syn.*: *Lasiopyga schmidti montana* Lorenz, 1914, p. 356; *C. nictitans montanus* Schwarz, 1928, p. 661)

According to Schouteden, *rutschuricus* is a synonym of *montanus*, although Schwarz held this to be a synonym of *schmidti* (q.v.).

Type locality: Wabembe, north-western shore of Lake Tanganyika.

Moreau *et al.* (1945) correct this to read " west of north end of Lake Tanganyika ". Type, adult male, skin and skull; 4 topotypes mentioned in original account, all collected by Grauer, now in Vienna Museum.

CHARACTERS.—Schwarz considered this a very distinct form, the darkest of the red-tailed group of *C. ascanius*, but Haddow (1952) expresses doubts as to its validity in so far as its characters merge with those of individual variants of *schmidti*; moreover, the total range of *schmidti* encompasses that of *montanus*.

PELAGE.—Long and dense. Frontal band almost entirely black; considerable black tipping on the hairs of the whiskers—additional to those of the black cheek stripes. The upper (temporal) black stripe very broad, ending above the ears in a distinct parieto-occipital stripe, which converges to meet its fellow on the occiput, as in *C. p. petaurista*. A definite black chin spot. Nose spot white.

* *Anz. Akad. Wiss. Wien, math-nat. Kl.* 51, 357.

Dorsal aspect of body with characteristically deep brown toning, with very dark, minimally speckled extremities, and the grey, instead of white, under parts, except on the throat and upper chest, where a light yellowish tone is developed.

Tail beneath at root dark mouse grey scarcely differing from the upper surface ; distally very deep red.

DISTRIBUTION.—Montane forests in the area between the Lualaba river and Lake Tanganyika.

Material in the Tervueren Museum is listed by Schouteden from the under mentioned localities, all in the Kivu district :

80 km. west of Ubemba (=Wabembe), Fizi, Batembo district, west of Kalehe, Bwahi, Ibanda, Dalemwa, Shabunda (and also, on the assumption that *rutschuricus* is a synonym), mountains east of Rutschuru, and Mutwanga, western Ruwenzori.

Schwarz (1954) gives evidence (*fide* B. W. Savory, local district commissioner) of the occurrence of *C. a. montanus* on the east side of Lake Tanganyika, his informant having personally seen it 40 miles north of Kigoma, near the lake, and in the Kangosi mountains, 75 miles north of Kigoma.

(e) *C. ascanius schmidti* Matschie, 1892,* Schmidt's Monkey ; Uganda Red-tailed Guenon.

(*Syn.* : *C. sassae* Matschie, 1913, p. 72 ; *C. kaimosae* Heller, 1913, p. 10 ; *C. schmidti mpangae* Matschie, 1913, p. 67 ; *C. schmidti enkamer* Matschie, 1913, p. 37 ; *C. schmidti ituriensis* Lorenz, 1914, p. 357 ; *C. schmidti rutschuricus* Lorenz, 1917, p. 228 ; *C. ascanius orientalis* Lönnberg, 1919, p. 125)

Vernacular names : In Uganda : Laburaburi (Kuamba), *tebe* (Haddow, 1952) ; Lubwizi, *nkunga* (Haddow, 1952) ; Lunyoro—Lutoro, *enkunga* (Haddow, 1952) ; Lukiga, Lunyuruanda, *enkunga, enkima, sukende* (Haddow, 1952) ; Lukonjo, *engande* (Haddow, 1952) ; Luganda, *nakabugo* (Haddow, 1952) ; Lusoga, *enkembo* (Haddow, 1952). In Kenya : Luragoli, *enhondo* (Allen *et al.*, 1936) ; Lutereki, *ikhondo* (Allen *et al.*, 1936). English-speaking inhabitants of East Africa—*Red-tail monkey* ; French speaking inhabitants of East Africa—*hocheur, pain à cacheter.*

Type locality : Manyema country. No type locality specified in original description, but this is given as the origin of Schmidt's specimen, stated in a later paper (1913) to have been purchased at Mpapua from a caravan en route from the Manyema country eastwards when Schmidt was aiming to meet Emin Pasha and Stanley. A second locality is given near Mengo (=Kampala) Uganda. Matschie (1913) refers to a male adult (No. A.5564) and a female adult (No. A.5569) in the Berlin Museum. Type locality of *kaimosae*. Upper Lukosa river, near Kaimosi, Kenya. Both collected by Stuhlmann from near Mengo, in the Murchison Bay area. On p. 68 he definitely states that the male No. A.5564 collected 4 January 1891, between Mengo and " Mjongo " is the type—and this was accepted as such by Schwarz (1928 *a*, p. 36). Moreau *et al.* failed to locate Mjongo on any map, but from Stuhlmann's account of his journey (1894) the locality of the type is " between Mengo (=Kampala) and the shores of Murchison Bay, Uganda ". Type locality of *mpangae*. Mpanga forest, eastern base of Mt. Ruwenzori, Uganda. Based on juvenile specimens in Berlin Museum, (No. 33201) collected by Grauer. Type locality of *sassae*. Sassa, west of Lake Albert Edward. Moreau *et al.* consider this to be the Ishasha river

* *Zool. Anz.* 161. Named after Dr. Rochus Schmidt, who brought the first specimen alive to Berlin.

which forms the boundary between Uganda and the Congo, and is south-east, not south-west of the Lake. Type, adult female, in Powell-Cotton Museum, Quex Park, Birchington, Kent. (*fide* Schwarz). Type locality of *enkamer*. Chima Kilima, north of Mawambi, upper Ituri river. Type, an adult male, skin and skull. Three paratypes mentioned from adjacent localities, Pemba and between Mawambi and Beni, Ituri forest. All collected by Powell Cotton. Type locality of *ituriensis*. Ituri forest, Ukaika, near Beni, and Mawambi. Four skins mentioned, none designated as holotype. Later (1917) referred by Lorenz to *enkamer*, Matschie 1913. Type locality of *rutschuricus*. Mountains on east border of Rutschuru plains. Based on a single adult male, skin and skull. Name preoccupied by *C. thomasi rutschuricus* Lorenz, 1915. Type locality of *orientalis*. Camp Simba, Zuwani river, Kenya. Camp Simba is Swahili for Lion Camp, and therefore may be anywhere. Moreau *et al.* devote a couple of pages in an attempt to thrash out the problem without much success. Apparently the type specimen was collected by Dr. Beyer, and from comparison with other known sites where this collector obtained his material, the Zuwani river is not the place of origin of Lönnberg's type. Schwarz maintains that the race does not range so far eastwards. He considered it belonged to the Rift Valley.

PELAGE: ADULT MALE.—Much like typically *ascanius* in general facial pattern, but differing in that the hairs of the cheeks beneath the upper black (temporal) stripe are greyish yellow and weakly black-tipped, and in possessing marked white ear-tufts, and a predominantly red tail.

In some specimens the yellow is confined to the area immediately above the lower transverse stripe, continuing backwards beyond the level of the ear. Cheek-hairs lack the whorl-like arrangement seen in the nominate race.

Naked parts of face bluish around eyes and below the white nose-spot, but lips and chin bright pink.

Iris between buckthorn brown and Dresden brown.

General colour of upper parts lighter than in *C. a. montanus*, but with much individual variation, producing intermediates between this and the forms of *white-sidei*, occupying the area between the Congo and Ubangi. The type of *mpangae*, for example, is extremely dark, and would seem to represent what Schwarz terms a biophaenotype (an environmental variant associated with dense rain forest) rather than a biogenotype (see especially the discussion by Schwarz, 1928a, pp. 34-36).

Speckling of individual hairs of dorsal surfaces averaging between tawny ochraceous and ochraceous rufous, but on crown and nape a lighter tinge, olive yellow, is responsible for the pale annulations.

Lateral aspect of upper arms like back, but darkening on forearms and hands due to diminished light speckling, the hands almost black, except for light speckling on central part of dorsum. Thighs to knees like back, with long hairs. Beyond knees the limbs are greyer, and the foot like the hand but more heavily speckled with olive.

Tail beneath proximally iron grey, never white, above for the first few centimetres like the back, becoming thereafter gradually red brown, without speckling, the intensity increasing towards the tip, which is never black. Beneath, the distal two-thirds are likewise red brown, with tendency towards golden reflections in certain angles of illumination at apex.

Under parts, including throat, mouse grey, the basal part of the individual hairs dark grey, becoming gradually paler in the distal two-thirds.

Scrotum pale blue (ethyl-blue) changing to purplish on prepuce ; glans penis pigmented, dark slate grey.

Body odour garlic like, emanating chiefly from the anterior region. In fresh material a yellow-brown scurfy secretion accumulates around the bases of the hairs over the mid-pectoral region between the two acromion processes, and more abundantly in the inguinal region.

ADULT FEMALE.—Resembles the male in pelage. Differs only in smaller size. Margins of rima pudendi and glans clitoridis pigmented, but corpus clitoridis and parts within the rima pink. Clitoris, 8·2 mm. long in an adult ; rima, 20 mm. long ; distance from dorsal commissure to anus, 13 mm.

JUVENILE.—Two lactant females in natal coat (U.S. National Museum, Nos. 184894, 184193) collected by Heller at Kaimosi have the body uniformly dark grey, darker, almost black on the crown and along the spine, but a transverse band across the shoulders is paler ; cheeks light grey without the black horizontal stripe in one, but present in the other. Tail with sparse yellow speckling, but no reddish tinge whatsoever. Under parts covered with light grey fluff.

A somewhat older animal, male (No. 1822373) from Kisumu, Lukosa river has soft pelage, with the adult pattern already evident.

VARIATIONS.—Schwarz (1928 a, p. 126) mentions an albino from Uelle that he considers must pertain to this race. It is almost completely white, with some dusky tinge on the crown, especially along the brow band, and on the fore limbs. The red of the tail is represented by a buffy tinge.

DIMENSIONS.—Body-weight has been minutely considered by Haddow (1952). He submits the following data (in lbs.) :

	Males	Females
Mean	9·2 ±0·3	6·4 ±0·2
Median	9·0	6·8
Maximum	14·0	8·5
Minimum	7·0	4·0

Haddow (*loc. cit.*) also recorded in millimetres five body dimensions in 100 wild specimens.

	Average of 38 Males	Average of 37 Females
Total length	1271 ±10	1078 ±16
Length head and body	475 ± 5	408 ± 4
Length of tail vertebrae	792 ±32	670 ± 9
Length of foot	142 ± 1	124 ± 2
Morphological length of ear	33 ± 0·7	30 ± 0·5

For other details, including comparison with Allen's data on Congo specimens, Haddow's paper should be consulted.

SKULL.—Cranial dimensions (in millimetres) (Haddow's data) :

	Average of 21 Adult Males	Average of 16 Adult Females
Maximum cranial length	97·0 ±0·5	88·0 ±0·8
Condylo-basal length	73·2 ±0·5	64·9 ±0·6
Occipito-nasal length	85·6 ±0·4	77·8 ±0·6
Biparietal	52·4 ±0·5	51·2 ±0·5
Bimastoid	56·6 ±0·4	52·3 ±0·7
Least frontal	41·8 ±0·4	39·6 ±0·5
Biorbital	54·6 ±0·5	49·3 ±0·4
Bizygomatic	65·5 ±0·4	58·4 ±0·6
Upper cheek-teeth	29·3 ±0·6	26·3 ±0·3

Haddow's figures (based on specimens from Uganda) differ not more than 0·1 mm. from those of Allen, based on Congo material. Haddow also makes comparisons with Rode's data.

Measurements from an adult male not available from Haddow's table are : mandibular length, 56·8 mm. ; lower cheek-teeth, 24·7 mm. ; cranial measurements of adult ♂ R.46/62 from Uganda : maximum cranial length, 96 mm. ; glabella-occiput, 72 mm. ; condylo-basal length, 70·5 mm. ; biparietal, 52·5 mm. ; least frontal, 40·5 mm. ; bimastoid, 53 mm. ; byzygomatic, 65 mm. ; biorbital, 51 mm. ; palatal length, 35 mm. ; upper cheek-teeth, 23 mm. ; mandibular length, 58 mm. ; lower cheek-teeth, 28 mm.

DISTRIBUTION.—Extreme north-eastern Congo, southern Uganda and extreme western Kenya.

To the west the range of *C. a. schmidti* evidently meets that of, and presumably intergradation occurs with, *C. a. whitesidei*. Consequently many examples from this area have been assigned by different students to real or supposed races other than *schmidti*, *e.g.* Allen (1925), who had at his disposal thirty-nine examples from the north-eastern Congo (Faradje, Rungu, Akinge, Niapu, Medje, Gamengui, Bafwabaka, Avakubi, Bafwasende, Kamunionge, Lubilo, Munye Katoto, Bafwaboli and Stanley-ville), treated them as *C. a. cirrhorhinus*, which is now generally regarded as a synonym of *C. a. whitesidei*. Another five specimens from Ukatureka, an island in the Middle Congo, he treated as *C. a. pelorhinus*, also now synonymized with *white-sidei*. His reasons for doing so were not based on the characters of the nose-spot, which was lacking in the admittedly imperfect skins. He agreed that they matched in colour the material from the Akenge-Medje-Avakubi-Stanleyville area in all except the ear-tufts and tail, the latter showing a greater amount of white inferiorly at the base.

Other Congo localities are listed by Schouteden. The Congo distribution em-braces the districts of Congo-Ubangi (in part); Uelle; Kibale-Ituri, Kivu, Stanley-ville and Maniema, but does not, as Haddow claims, extend as far west as the confluence of the Ubangi with the Congo as this western strip of territory is the home of *C. a. whitesidei*. It does, however, include the whole area east of the Lualaba as far south as the Lukuga river (which flows from Lake Tanganyika into the Lualaba, except again for areas occupied by *C. a. montanus*, which Haddow is inclined to include under *schmidti*).

The range in Uganda has been closely studied by Haddow (1952, p. 306), who states that, in that country, the range is limited to the north by the rivers draining from Mount Elgon to Lake Salisbury, by the swamps connecting the latter with Lake Kioga, by the lake itself and by the Victoria Nile, flowing from Lake Kioga to the northern end of Lake Albert. The southern limit is the Kagera river. At one point the river sweeps southward into Tanganyika and *C. a. schmidti* here enters that country, where it occupies the Nyakabadzi (Minzira) forest. The U.S. National Museum has specimens from Nabea, Lukosa river, Budongo forest, and Kakemya forest.

In western Kenya the race is recorded from the Kaimosi forest in Kavirondo and the Zuwani river. From the former the animal has been collected by Heller (1913), by G. M. Allen *et al.* (1936), who also mentions it on Mount Elgon in company with a band of *C. mitis stuhlmanni*, by Garnham *et al.* (1946), and by Haddow. Pitman (1931) recorded it from Kapsabet, a little east of the Kaimosi forest.

REPRODUCTION.—Allen *et al.* (1936) record an early pregnancy in a wild female shot on 3 March, and two others were at the same date carrying infants of different sizes, both males of 185 mm. head and body length, the other 195 mm.

13. *CERCOPITHECUS ERYTHROTIS* (Waterhouse, 1838 *)

Red-eared Nose-spotted Guenon

(SYN. : *Lasiopyga erythrotis* Elliot 1913, p. 324 ; *Cercopithecus cephus erythrotis* Schwarz 1928, p. 662. Includes *C. sclateri* Pocock, 1904, p. 18)

VERNACULAR NAME : German, *Rotohr Meerkatze*.

TYPE LOCALITY : Fernando Po. Type, a flat skin, without face or skull, in British Museum (No. 55.12.24.410), collected by G. Knapp.

Originally described by Waterhouse from a skin presented to the Zoological Society's Museum by George Knapp, who had received it from Fernando Po. Although considering it a distinct species, Waterhouse regarded it as related to *C. cephus*, an opinion which Pocock (1907) shared, in opposition to Pousargues (1896), who classified it with his *ascanius* section of the Rhinosticti, from which group *cephus* was excluded. Recent studies have shown the great variations in this Formenkreis resulting in the recognition of several subspecies, some of which link typical *erythrotis* with *ascanius* rather than with *cephus*, confirming Pousargues' view to be correct.

ORIGINAL DIAGNOSIS.—*Cercopithecus griseus ; pilis corporis suprâ flavo nigroque annulatis ; gula genisque albis ; rachiis nigrescentibus ; cauda splendide rufa, linea nigrescente per partem superiorem excurrente, apice nigrescente ; regione anali, auribus rufis. Longitudini capitis corporis 17 unc. Longitudini caudae 23 unc.*

* *Proc. zool. Soc. Lond.* 1838, p. 59 (also *loc. cit.* 1841, p. 71).

CHARACTERS

A small nose-spotted guenon, recalling *C. petaurista*, but distinguished by the bright red hairs adorning the concave aspect of the external ear, the brilliant red tail and the bright red hairs of the perineal region. In a second skin received from Fernando Po, Waterhouse (1841) recorded a red patch on the nose as a " transverse red mark, crossing the nose ". The nose spot, though red in the nominate race and in *C. e. camerunensis* is typically white in *C. e. sclateri*, but both these races agree in having the pale area of the whiskers between the black temporal and preauricular bars yellow.

In the male the relatively naked skin of the belly and medial surfaces of thighs is pale lilac. The scrotum and a broad median tract between it and the base of the tail is clothed with bright orange-red hairs. The glans penis is pink, with a meatal cleft 5·5 mm. long in a total glandic height of 9·4 mm. It is of the usual cercopithecine form. The prepuce is not pigmented.

In the female the vulva is blue (light Windsor blue), and occupies the space between the chocolate coloured callosities. The area dorsal to this beneath the tail and around the anus is virtually nude and rosy pink, slightly browner near the anal margin and on the perineal body. The naked area extends as an isosceles triangular area on to the base of the tail, whereas in the male the tail is hairy almost to its root (based on an example of *C. e. sclateri*).

DISTRIBUTION (Map 7)

Fernando Po and the adjacent mainland, where the species is patchily distributed in the area from just west of the Niger eastwards possibly as far as the Sanaga river. In the whole of this area no representative of either *C. petaurista* or *C. ascanius* occurs, therefore *C. erythrotis* may be regarded as the local evolutionary product of the *petaurista* basic stock.

(a) *C. erythrotis erythrotis* Waterhouse, 1838 *　Fernando Po Red-eared Guenon

　　(*Syn.* : See under species)
　　Type locality : Fernando Po. Type, an unsexed flat skin in British Museum (No. 55.12.24.410) collected by G. Knapp.
　　Hayman (1940) in investigating the material collected by Sanderson in the Cameroons had occasion to make a full comparison of all available specimens from Fernando Po, with those from the mainland. These had, following Schwarz's (1928 c) pronouncement, been regarded as uniform. Hayman concluded that continental specimens were constantly larger than those from the type locality. It was also found that insular skins possessed noticeably longer, softer and denser fur than those from the mainland (except for one of the latter). Comparison of dates of capture indicated all the island skins to have been collected during February and March, and that, among the mainland series, only the soft-furred specimen from

---

* *Loc. cit.*

the Southern Cameroons was collected at this season. Cameroon pelts collected in May and October all have short, thin fur. This suggests a seasonal change in coat, but the phenomenon needs confirmation.

CHARACTERS.—Face almost naked with circumorbital region bluish, becoming pink on the eyelids ; muzzle region pink with a few short black hairs. Nose spot triangular with the apex above and the basal angles extending laterally towards cheeks, typically brick red to orange ; chin white. A black supraorbital bar extends laterally as a temporal bar to ear. Beneath the latter, elongated cheek hairs form a broad white streak, slightly tinged with yellow ; beneath this again another black streak extends from the basal angle of the nose patch across the cheek to a point below the ear, in a similar way to *C. ascanius*. Hairs of this inferior band have yellow annuli. Below the inferior black band the dirty whitish hairs form a sort of ruff continued across the throat as in *C. petaurista*. Ears pink with bright red hairy tufts.

General colour of crown, nape, dorsum of body, flanks and extensor aspects of limbs almost black, speckled heavily with yellowish grey or golden yellow, individual hairs being alternately annulated black and gold.

Tail bright red, except for a narrow darker median dorsal line ; perineal and circumanal hairs bright red. Remainder of under parts greyish white.

DIMENSIONS (in millimetres) :

	Locality	Sex	Head and Body	Tail	Foot	Ear	
B.M.	Fernando Po	♂ ad.	452	578	93	33	Hayman 1940
B.M.	,,	♀ ad.	329	572	112	30	

SKULL.—Cranial measurements (in millimetres) :

Locality	Sex	Maximum Cranial Length	Condylo-basal Length	Biparietal	Least Frontal	Bizygomatic	C – M³
Fernando Po	♂ ad.	94 approx.		28	38·5	58	29
,,	♀ ad.	89·5	64·5	28·8	39	59	26·8

DISTRIBUTION.—Confined to the island of Fernando Po, where it inhabits forests on the upper mountain slopes. The British Museum has material from Bubi Town, 500 m., and Bantabiri, 1800 m. (Thomas, 1904). Mertens (1929) mentions specimens in the Frankfurt Museum collected at O-Wassa at 1000 m. and 2000 m.

(b) *C. erythrotis camerunensis* Hayman, 1940.* Cameroon Red-eared Guenon

   (*Syn.*: *C. e. erythrotis* Waterhouse, 1838 ; *C. cephus erythrotis* Schwarz, 1928, p.662)
   Type locality : Badchama, northern Mamfe Division, British Cameroons. Type a subadult ♂ collected by I. T. Sanderson, 28 April 1933, in British Museum (No. 39.317). Coloured plate in Sanderson (1940).
   On discovering that the mainland representatives of *C. erythrotis* differed at least in size from specimens from the type locality, Hayman (1940) suggested the name *camerunensis* as a suitable subspecific name. The form from Benin described by

   * *Trans. zool. Soc. Lond.* xxiv. 649.

Pocock (1904) from a menagerie specimen had been transferred by Schwarz to the synonymy of *erythrotis*. Hayman, however, confirmed the validity of *sclateri* as a distinct subspecies of *erythrotis* on material in the British Museum, thus rendering this name unavailable for the Cameroon animal. The following account is based on material (five skins and skulls) collected by W. E. Kershaw in the Mamfe division, Cameroons, and on fresh cadavera from menagerie sources known to have been collected in the Cameroons.

PELAGE.—Face naked, around the eyes blue ; muzzle pink ; nose spot as in typical *erythrotis*, bright orange-red. Ear-tufts red. A thin black supraorbital line expanding laterad into broad temporal band. Beneath the latter the elongated cheek whiskers end in a pointed tuft, bright yellowish in colour, and bordered below by a narrower inferior black bar. Throat and chin with greyish-white ruff, similar in hue to the under parts.

Crown, nape, shoulders, back, flanks and lateral surfaces of limbs of a generally dark green tinge, due to alternate black and yellow bandings of individual hairs, but distal parts of forearms, with hands, black ; feet also black. The dark tinge of the back is continued broadly on to the dorsum of the proximal third of the tail, thereafter narrowing to a median dorsal stripe, the rest of the organ above and below being bright coppery red.

Under parts greyish white, except for the red perineal hairs. The individual hairs uniformly coloured, *i.e.* without speckling.

VARIATIONS.—In an adult female originally in Chester Zoo, the whole of the pectoral limb from the shoulder and the whole pelvic limb from the hip is dark grey (blackish-slate of Ridgway), and without speckling save for a few yellow tickings at the base of the thigh and some sparse whitish annulations on the centre of the dorsum of the foot. The tip of the tail is darker than the major portion, becoming almost black. Throat and upper chest paler (yellowish white) than the rest of the under parts. The medial aspect of the arm is even darker and increases in depth distally towards the wrist ; the colour of the extensor and flexor aspects are not sharply demarcated. On the hind limb the medial aspect of the thigh is olive grey ; darkening occurs some distance beyond the knee, increasing further towards the ankle.

JUVENILE.—A young male of 200 mm. crown-rump length already shows the full adult pattern, but ear-tufts are lacking, being represented merely by a few short gingery hairs on the concave aspect of the pinna. The red perineal area is well developed as is also the red nose patch. Chin and throat are pure white.

DIMENSIONS (in millimetres) :

Number	Locality	Sex	Head and Body	Tail	Foot	Ear	
	Mamfe	♂	537	725	134	24	From Hayman 1940
	,,	♂	549	770	136	29	
	,,	♂ subad.	402	770	126	28	
	Zoo	♀	403	645	126	32	
PC.478 [1]	Chester Zoo	♀	400	620	112	30·5	
PC.466 [2]	London Zoo	♂ juv.	200	235	61	27	

[1] Weight, 1·983 kg.　　　　[2] Weight, 318 gm.

PLATE XXV

Courtesy W. Windecker

Cercopithecus ascanius schmidti, juvenile, in Cologne Zoo

PLATE XXVI

Photo: R. Golding

Cercopithecus erythrogaster, adult ♂

Number	Locality	Sex	Max. Cranial Length	Condylo-basal	Glabella- m.o.p.	Biparietal	Least Frontal	Bimastoid	Basion- bregma	Bizygomatic	Palatal Length	Upper Cheek- teeth	C – M³	Mandibular Length	Lower Cheek- teeth
British Mus.	Mamfe	♂	113	90	—	34	44·6	—	—	73·2	—	—	32·4	—	—
,,	,,	♂ (Type)	97	—	—	54·3	44·7	—	—	63·1	40	23·2	—	60	28
,,	,,	♂ subad.	103	74	—	33·3	46	—	—	64	—	—	30	—	—
,,	Zoo	♀	94·8	72·6	—	29·8	42	—	—	57·5	—	—	28·5	—	—
PC.398	Mamfe	♀	89	62	69	54	40	54	48	58	33	22	26	54	23
PC.399	,,	♂	96	71	72	54	41	56	46	64	39	22	28	71	32
PC.274	,,	♂	103	73	77	57	43	57	46	66	40	25	31	65	34
PC.412	,,	♂	99	—	73	54	39	58	—	66	40	23	30	69	30
PC.270	,,	♀	86	66	68	56	45·5	55·5	47	60	31	21	27	54	26
PC.105	,,	♀	91	66	71	54	41	54	49	60	34	25	29	61	27
PC.413	,,	♂	93	—	64	52	38	55	—	63	35	22	29	65	28
PC.271	,,	♀	97	74	73	54	43	57	49	65	39	22	29	62	27·5
PC.273	,,	♀	94	65·5	70	53	40	54	49	58	35	24	29	56	25
PC.221	,,	♀	96·5	73	75	58·5	44	57	51	63	36	24	29	58	30·5
PC.414	,,	♂	103·5	73	75	56	43	61	52	71	43	24	32	—	—
PC.400	,,	♀	97	—	72	53	43	56	—	64	33	22	29	64	26
PC.222	Kumba	♂	100	75	72	56	44	58	50	67	38	24	32	68	31 No M₃

(Rows PC.398–PC.222 bracketed:) [1]

[1] Collected by W. E. Kershaw.

DENTAL ANOMALY.—In a female skull from a menagerie specimen (PC.478), small supernumerary incisors are present bilaterally between 1^1 and 1^2.

DISTRIBUTION.—Northern Cameroons ; exact range unknown. Sanderson (1940) collected specimens at Mamfe, Eshobi, Badchama and Makumunu (450-2200 feet). Kershaw collected in the same general area and also farther south at Kumba, altitude 1000 feet.

The habitat, according to Sanderson, is the tops of high deciduous trees and isolated patches of mountain forest 10 miles north of the fringe of the main forest.

(c) *C. erythrotis sclateri* Pocock, 1904,* Sclater's White-nosed Monkey

(*Syn.* : *C. sclateri* Pocock, 1904, p. 433, 1907, p. 725 ; *Lasiopyga sclateri* Elliot, 1913, p. 323, *C. cephus erythrotis* Schwarz, 1928, p. 662)

Type locality : Benin, West Africa ; Type, juvenile male, a menagerie animal described during life in London Zoo, where it was received 12 July 1902 from Mrs. Pickering Phipps. It died 11 August 1902 and the skin was forwarded to the British Museum (No. 17.10, 15.1).

* *Proc. zool. Soc. Lond.* 1904, pp. 433-436. *Abstr. Proc. zool. Soc.*, 1904, No. 5, p. 18.

2 K

Coloured plate in Sanderson (1940).

For many years this form was known only from the type specimen. Schwarz (1928) placed it in the synonymy of *erythrotis*, considering it merely an individual variation. A second skin and skull of an adult male was received in the British Museum in 1935, having been collected the previous year in the Okigwi division of the Owerri province, S. Nigeria. Its importance was overlooked, but in 1940 Hayman perceived its nature when making comparisons for the purpose of identifying the specimens brought from the Cameroons by Sanderson. The Owerri specimen confirmed that Nigerian examples of *C. erythrotis* agreed with Pocock's account, and the type skin of *sclateri*, but differed in several important respects from the Cameroon representative of *C. erythrotis*.

No further specimens were forthcoming until after the second World War, but in 1945 the London Zoo received a second living specimen from Obubra, Nigeria, and since that date several others have been on exhibit in zoological collections (London, Chester, New York and Birmingham, Alabama) as well as in private ownership.

PELAGE : ADULT MALE.—Face around eyes blue, muzzle pink, nose-spot stated to be white (Hayman), but the type is described by Pocock (1904) as having the central part white and the extreme margin and apex tinged with pale red ; ear-tufts whitish. The black temporal bar is continued back past the ears. Above the ears it broadens so as almost to unite in the mid line of the nape with its fellow ; thence they continue posteriorly on the sides of the nape, almost parallel to each other for 25 mm. or more, finally bifurcating, the lateral branch being the longer, both branches finally narrowing before ending on the side of the neck. Crown well marked off by the black lines and brighter in colour than any other part, except the cheeks, the long hairs of which are yellowish with black annulations and tips.

Whiskers yellow, bounded below by a sinuous black bar. Nape, shoulders and back, of general dark green tinge, if anything greener than in typical *erythrotis*, and with a tendency to a brownish or reddish suffusion over the lumbo-sacral area (due to alternate banding of hairs with black and coppery yellow).

Lateral aspect of arm speckled yellow and black, darkening to almost black at wrist and hand, also along the posterior border as far proximad as elbow. Leg laterally also speckled yellow and black as far as dorsum of foot, but duller than sacral region, the tints of the two areas blending imperceptibly.

Tail morocco red above, becoming yellower distally and then greyish black, the terminal hairs wholly black ; below red in basal half, passing into ashy grey distally ; laterally a sharp line of demarcation between dorsal and ventral tints. Some rusty red hairs on perineum and scrotum. Throat and chest between neutral grey and carbon grey ; abdomen dusky olive grey, the hairs annulated. Iris rich chestnut brown.

VARIATIONS.—In two specimens examined in the flesh, the black frontal band is separated from the naked part of the face by a narrow band of maize yellow continuous laterally around the orbital area with the yellow whiskers. In a third the black frontal band is entirely lacking, the maize yellow being continued, with minimal black speckling as far as the bregma. In this animal the yellow of the whiskers is not continuous with that on the forehead, but separated by the broad black temporal band. The whiskers have black-tipped yellow hairs with an incipient intermediate horizontal black bar, and a feebly developed inferior black bar continued into the whiskers a short distance only from the black maxillary area. The inferior black cheek bar varies greatly in its breadth and backward extent.

Variations occur also in colour of nose spot and ear-tufts. According to Hayman, the Owerri skin (an adult male) has the greater part of the nose missing, but what remains of the nose patch is white, and the ear-tufts are also whitish. It is also white in the type skin. In two of my fresh specimens the centre only of the nose patch is white and its periphery brownish in one (female) and pinkish buff in another, the latter being the specimen with the extensive yellow forehead. A third, older female, from Obubra, Nigeria, has the nose brick red throughout, as in *camerunensis*. This last animal also has red ear-tufts, whereas in the other two they are white. The crown pattern posteriorly in all is as described by Hayman. Some variation also affects the naked facial skin. In the Obubra female the circumorbital area in life was lilac, but in another female (locality unknown) only the periphery of the area was Delft blue, the eyelids and area immediately adjacent being pale brownish-drab.

DIMENSIONS (in millimetres and grams) :

Number	Locality	Sex	Head and Body	Tail	Foot	Ear	Inter-mammilary	Weight
	Obubra	♀ ad.	440	390	120	30	25	—
305/51	Unknown (Zoo)	♀ juv.	330·2	560	106	31	—	1459·5
—	,,	♀ juv.	375	—	110·8	26·7	18·5	—
Brit. Mus. 17.10.15.1	Benin	♂ imm.	363	613	—	—	—	—[1]

[1] Pocock's measurements taken on a dried skin.

SKULL.—Cranial dimensions (in millimetres) :

Number	Locality	Sex	Max. Cranial Length	Condylo-basal	Glabella-occiput	Biparietal	Least Frontal	Bimastoid	Bizygomatic	Biorbital	Palatal Length	Upper Cheek-teeth	C – M³	Mandibular Length	Lower Cheek-teeth
	Benin	♂ imm.	93·6	68	—	—	42·5	—	59	—	—	—	—	—	—
	Owerri	♂ ad.	98·5	74·5	—	—	41·6	—	63	—	—	—	30·3	—	—
737/51	Zoo	♂ juv.	80	50	65·2	49·2	38	42·8	49	42·8	24·3	15	—	43	15·3[1]

[1] (Dental measures $DM\frac{4}{1}$ – $M\frac{4}{1}$.)

DISTRIBUTION.—Southern Nigeria, west of the Cross river, especially the Niger delta. The specimen from Obubra possibly pertains to *camerunensis*, though the town lies to the west of the Cross river, and this suspicion is confirmed by its wholly red nose patch and ear-tufts.

14. *CERCOPITHECUS ERYTHROGASTER* Gray, 1866 *

Red-bellied Guenon; Jentink's Guenon

(SYN. : *C. signatus* Jentink, 1886, p. 55 ; *Erythrogaster* group of Pocock, 1907, p. 715 ; *Lasiopyga erythrogaster* Elliot, 1913, p. 301 ; *C. nictitans erythrogaster* Schwarz, 1928 c, p. 660 ; *C. nictitans signatus* Schwarz, 1928 c, p. 661)

* *Proc. zool. Soc. Lond.* 1866, p. 169, Pl. XVI.

VERNACULAR NAMES : None recorded.

TYPE LOCALITY : ? Lagos (*fide* Pousargues). Type, a young female, in British Museum (No. 66.8.6.15), previously in the London Zoo. Type locality of *signatus*, West Africa " perhaps from Banana, Congo ". Type, female, in Leiden Museum.

Gray's original description was based on a juvenile female specimen which Pocock contends shows no trace of the white nose-patch found, as shown afterwards, in " some adults ". Sclater (1893) also knew only the young animal and classified it along with his melanochirine section of the genus. Matschie (1893), however, pointed out the affinity with the spot-nosed group, and this view was corroborated by Pousargues (1897), who declared categorically that the nasal field is completely naked in the young animal and covered with white hairs in individual adults. Pocock (1907) published a photograph of a living specimen. The type skin, as shown by Sclater and later by Pocock, has the nasal field adorned with short black hairs bearing whitish bases. The face is now so damaged in the type skin as to be almost useless to determine this point, but sufficient remains to confirm that the animal is very closely affined to the *petaurista* group. This is still further supported by the characters of the rest of the pelage, which closely resembles that of *C. p. buttikoferi*, except for the continuous erythrism of the ventral surface.

Re-examination in 1949 of the type-skin of Jentink's *C. signatus* convinced Schwarz (1954) that this form should be reduced to the synonymy of *C. erythrogaster*. A subadult female, it closely resembles the type of *erythrogaster*, agreeing in the general colouration of the pelage, in the white chin and throat and in the shape and colour of the nasal patch, which is pale and intermediate in outline between that of *C. nictitans martini* and that of *C. petaurista*. It likewise agrees in the absence of a cheek-band, the upper cheek-hairs being speckled green, with an orbito-auricular black band above continued back beyond the ear. There are, however, some differences, namely (i) in the ventral colouration, which is neither rusty nor plumbeous, showing only a faint reddish tint (*i.e.* intermediate between the two colour mutants now known to occur in *erythrogaster*), and (ii) in the absence of black on the vertex. Schwarz considered the possibility that these differences may be purely individual or even the result of captivity.

CHARACTERS

Size as in *C. petaurista*.

PELAGE : ADULT MALE.—Skin of face around eyes bluish grey ; lips and chin pinkish grey. Nose-patch with white based black hairs, which, at least in some individuals, turn completely white, or are replaced by new white hairs.

Crown speckled golden green and surrounded by a continuous black line formed by the frontal band continued laterally as a very broad temporal band and thence as a narrower parieto-occipital stripe, meeting its fellow on the back of the head, as in *C. p. petaurista* and *C. erythrotis sclateri*. Beneath the temporal stripe a greyish-speckled patch bordering the cheek and beneath this a smaller black patch near the angle of the mouth continued backwards and upwards in an arch in the direction of the ear. Below this the cheeks and throat are clothed with longish silky white whiskers.

Entire dorsal surface of body uniformly blackish, speckled with yellow, somewhat lighter than on the crown. Lateral aspect of fore-limbs with slighter speckling, almost black, darkening further distally to the completely black hands. Thighs laterally blackish grey, but speckled ; feet black. Tail above like the back ; below greyish white, with a sharp line of demarcation along its sides.

Under parts, except for throat, sparsely covered typically with rusty-reddish hairs, but medial aspects of arms and legs dirty white. (Pocock gives blackish grey for arms and greyish white for legs.) Some individuals, however, have entirely greyish under parts. Both red-bellied and grey-bellied examples occur within the same troop. The rusty colour is a true pigmentary effect and not due to extraneous staining of otherwise grey hairs (Sanderson, 1957, p. 113).

ADULT FEMALE.—Unknown, except for the type specimen of *C. signatus* which in colour of under parts is intermediate between the red- and grey-bellied males. An adult female (mounted) in the Tring Museum, originating in the London Zoo, is ticketed Jentink's monkey. It evidently pertains here, though showing individual peculiarities. Large for a member of the *petaurista* assemblage, it displays a distinct triangular, dull white nose-patch, with the usual bluish circumocular areas and flesh-coloured muzzle. A broad, black orbito-temporal bar ceases at the ear, but there are black oblique moustachial streaks passing from the base of the nose-patch each side towards the angle of the mouth. A median crest of short, black hairs on the interorbital region extends below into a black triangle above the pale nose patch and is continuous laterally with the black maxillary area. A strong superciliary tract of outstanding black hairs (longest hairs 33 mm.), borders the crown anteriorly. Crown and upper parts clothed with golden hairs annulated with black. Cheeks yellowish-white speckled with black. Fore-arms and hind limbs almost uniformly grey with faint speckling only on the legs. Under parts dirty white, darkening slightly on the abdomen and medial aspects of thighs. Tail imperfect.

JUVENILE.—Nose covered with short black hairs, sometimes with white bases. Normally these are replaced or become bleached to white ; in some individuals, however, the black hairs persist in the adult, as in the example figured by Pocock.

VARIATIONS.—Apart from the dichromatism of the under parts and the variations in colour of the nose patch, there is little individual variation. A second specimen from captivity in the British Museum (No. 15.6.12.1), a male, is described by Schwarz (1927) as much like the type, but paler throughout, having a general greenish-yellow hue, with the crown citrine, demarcated posteriorly by an even broader parieto-occipital black stripe. Chest and belly are pale brownish grey (paler than hair-brown of Ridgway), but as sharply contrasted from the white throat as in the type. Another example, also a male, in the Tring Museum agrees with the grey bellied Lagos specimen, but resembles the type in having a red belly.

Schwarz later (1928 c, p. 660) reports three further red-bellied specimens (two in the Paris and one in Berlin Museum, none with locality, and therefore presumably from captivity).

DIMENSIONS.—Of type juvenile : head and body 380 mm. ; tail 345 mm. ; foot, 100 mm. Of adult female (Tring Museum) measured on the stuffed skin : crown-rump 410 mm. ; foot 115 mm. : head length (muzzle-occiput) 94 mm.

SKULL.—Cranial dimensions of type female (immature) : maximum cranial length 80 mm. ; biparietal, 47 mm. ; least frontal, 37 mm. ; bizygomatic, 50 mm. ; biorbital, 45 mm. ; upper cheek-teeth, 20 mm. ; mandibular length, 47 mm. ; lower cheek-teeth, 22·6 mm.

DISTRIBUTION (Map 8)

Not definitely known, apart from " West Africa ". The localities Lagos and Banana evidently refer merely to ports of shipment to Europe, since all the known examples that have been referred to *erythrogaster* have reached the museums from menageries. Although he failed to obtain fresh specimens, Sanderson (1940) gives the range as between the Dahomey gap on the west and the Niger on the east where, according to his map (p. 646), its range overlaps that of *C. erythrotis sclateri*.

V. Superspecies *CERCOPITHECUS CEPHUS* Linnaeus, 1766 *

Moustached Guenons

(SYN. ; *Cercopitheci rhinosticti* of Sclater, 1893, p. 243 (in part) ; *Rhinostictus* Trouessart, 1897 (in part) ; *Cephus* group of Pocock, 1907, p. 721 ; subgenus *Neocebus* Elliot, 1913 † in part.)

GENERAL COMMENTS

Moustached guenons stand apart from all other members of the genus, notably by virtue of the very distinct pale blue transverse crescentic facial

---

* *Syst. Nat.* (10th ed.), i. 27.
† Elliot also uses *Neocebus* for a subgenus of Macaques, earlier in the same volume.

stripe which adorns the upper lip below the nares, narrowing to a pointed cornu each side on the cheek. This is a contrasted pigmentary effect, the affected area being sharply defined from the darker bluish epidermal pigmentation of the remainder of the face.

There can be no confusion between this feature and the nose patch of the *petaurista* assemblage or of *nictitans*, where the contrasted marking is due to a patch of hair.

It is therefore strange that so many earlier writers, beginning with Reichenbach and Sclater (who included *C. cephus* among his *Rhinosticti*), should have lumped *cephus* with the nose-spotted guenons.

Elliot erected the subgenus *Neocebus*, to include *cephus* (with some supposed varieties), *C. erythrotis* and *C. e. sclateri;* He diagnosed the group merely as having the " tail red or mostly red ; nose spot usually present ".

The animal is named " moustached monkey " not solely on account of the blue stripe, but equally on account of the presence below it of a true labial moustache comprised of short black hairs adorning the lower part of the upper lip. These are not vibrissal hairs, but a distinct tract of true contour hairs.

In the presence of a black frontal line, expanding laterally in a temporal bar, and the uniform speckling of the head, back and sides of the body, *C. cephus* resembles the more typical members of the *petaurista* group, while the existence of an inferior black cheek-band aligns it with *C. ascanius* and *C. erythrotis*. It further agrees with the last mentioned in the mass of yellow whiskers between the two lateral black bars.

Differing from all members of the *petaurista* Formenkreis in the absence of the black frontal band and in the fact that throat, chest, belly and medial aspects of the limbs (at least proximally) are dark ashy grey instead of white or greyish white.

Diploid chromosome number, 66 (Chiarelli, 1964).

DISTRIBUTION, ECOLOGY AND ETHOLOGY

Moustached monkeys are among the commonest species in the gallery forests of the general area of Lower Guinea and the Congo. Sometimes it is rarer, and in certain isolated forests lacking the Oil Palm (*Elaeïs*), it may be absent, this food plant appearing essential to its survival.

Although highly arboreal, *C. cephus* differs in its mode of existence in several respects from its congeners, especially in its adaptation to subsist on the pulp of the oil palm nut. It therefore occurs in places where the oil palm has long been cultivated and is less frequent in high forest where the palm is lacking or sparse. Other items of diet consist of the terminal buds and the seeds of the Umbrella tree (*Musanga*) and various products (fruit and seeds) of secondary forest, especially *Pachylobus buttneri*, *Irvingia gabonensis*, and *Pycnanthus kombo*.

Elaeïs assures abundance of food supply at practically all seasons, so that the bands of *C. cephus* are relatively more sedentary than those of, *e.g.* *C. pogonias*, which inhabit the same areas. This does not apply, however, to those bands which populate the high forest, where they behave in the same manner as the bands of *C. n. nictitans*, which share the habitat with *C. cephus*.

Russell (1938) mentions an addiction to marine shellfish in a captive specimen brought to England from the Gabon. These would be caught by ransacking through masses of seaweed and paddling in rock pools.

C. cephus is an agile monkey of similar temperament to *C. petaurista*. Amicable in disposition, they make excellent pets, being friendly to humans and full of curiosity. According to Sanderson (1957) their curiosity is akin to that of the Capuchins, as they display great patience in examining and dismantling human artifacts. The same authority remarks upon their fascination for pills of all kinds, and those he kept displayed great diligence in obtaining them by smashing bottles. On one occasion a monkey ingested several dozen hypnotic capsules without ill effect !

In the wild their curiosity accounts for their frequently being found on the edge of the forest or along forest tracts where timber is being felled.

Their extreme agility in the wild is commented upon by Malbrant and Maclatchy, who remark upon their sure-footedness in rapid flight through their arboreal habitat, leaping up to 20 metres without mishap in passing from one group of trees to another. They appear to use regular routes through the branches, each animal following the next along the same path.

The display pattern is characteristic. It is accompanied by jerky body attitudinizations with head movements chiefly from side to side, thus producing the most effect from the facial mystacial stripe. This contrasts with the up and down bobbing of the head in *e.g.*, *C. petaurista* and its allies.

A curious, apparently self-rewarding activity, akin to display but carried out by solitary individuals, consists of seizing in one hand a length of twig or straw then pressing one end of it against the chest or flank, the body being curved over to the opposite side. I have seen this in captive animals of both sexes.

The male emits a characteristic warning note, a sharp, staccato rhythmically repeated bark. I have heard this in captivity. In the wild, Malbrant and Maclatchy designate it (in French) as *hohon*. It is not used by the female, whose voices are quiet clicking notes rendered by the above-mentioned authors as *ke-ke*. Malbrant and Maclatchy also mention a note rendered *caraon* similar to that emitted by *Cercocebus torquatus* and another, *niak niak*—sometimes transformed to *niou*—all used by the male in certain circumstances.

A guttural *ke-ke-ke* and an acute whistle, signifying fear, are used by both sexes. The bands are sometimes escorted by hornbills (*Tropicranus albo-*

cristatus cassini) which are furtive, silent birds that appear to obtain advantage from the numerous seeds and other vegetable products, also insects, disturbed by the monkeys in their transit—a mild case of harmonious symbiosis.

Details of methods of capture by the natives are recorded by Malbrant and Maclatchy (p. 44).

15. *CERCOPITHECUS CEPHUS* Linnaeus, 1758 *

Moustached Monkey

(SYN. : *Simia cephus* Linnaeus, 1758, p. 27 ; *C. cephus* Lesson, 1840, p. 77 and most subsequent authors ; *C. buccalis* Le Conte, 1857, p. 10 ; *C. c. cephodes* Pocock, 1907, p. 724 ; *C. inobservatus* Elliot, 1910, p. 81 ; *Lasiopyga cephus, L. cephodes* and *L. inobservata* Elliot, 1913 ; *C. pulcher* Lorenz, 1915, p. 171 ; *C. c. cephus* Schwarz, 1928 *c*, p. 662)

VERNACULAR NAMES : Bulu, *ossok* (*fide* Perret and Aellen 1956) ; French, *le moustac* ; German, *Schnurrbartaffe, Blaumaul.* See also under subspecies.

TYPE LOCALITY : " America " (=Guinea). Linnaeus' original account was based on Marcgrav. Type locality of *buccalis*, Gabon. Type no longer in Philadelphia where Le Conte's other types are found. Type locality of *cephodes*, Gabon. Type female, in British Museum (No. 80.6.7.3) collected by Laglaize. Type locality of *inobservatus*, West Africa. Type, an unsexed skin, in British Museum (No. 47.3.1.6) collected by W. D. Bartlett. Type locality of *pulcher*, Cameroons. Type locality of *gabonensis*, Gabon. Type collected by P. B. du Chaillu.

CHARACTERS

PELAGE : ADULT MALE.—Face bluish slate grey to violet, relieved by a crescentic horizontal sky-blue to bluish-white stripe on the upper lip immediately below the nares, extending obliquely laterad from the mid-line and ending in a point. Beneath the latter a moustache of black hairs near the border of the upper lip, continuous laterally with the inferior black cheek-bar ; labial margins pink. A few black or blackish hairs on chin. Nose-patch lacking, the nose being naked or feebly pubescent. Ear-tufts short, yellow or yellowish white. Ears blackish peripherally, shading to hyacinth blue in concavity ; whiskers bushy, directed obliquely downwards and backwards, bright chrome yellow, those near the ear lightly annulated with black. Beneath the yellow patch heavier black annulation occurs, the black predominating towards the maxillae.

Forehead with a thin line of prominent black hairs. Crown, nape and upper and lateral surfaces of body of a general greenish-brown hue, some-what lighter on the crown, especially anteriorly, where the pale annuli are greener, whereas on the body they are darker, almost rusty red (rouge acajou of French writers).

Limbs speckled on extensor aspects, but the darker bands predominate giving them a generally darker hue than the body ; hands and feet black.

---

* *Syst. Nat.* (10th ed.), i. 27.

Tail variable in colour according to subspecies (*vide infra*). Under parts, except for some white hairs on the interramal region, ashy grey, unspeckled. Callosities black. Naked and seminude areas in groin and on scrotum sky-blue, darkening to cobalt blue on prepuce and intrapreputial part of corpus penis. Glans pigmented brownish black.

ADULT FEMALE.—Like the male in colour, but smaller. Naked perineal and circumanal skin purple, except the margins of the rima pudendi, which are pink as is also the glans clitoridis.

JUVENILE.—According to Pucheran (1857) and Pousargues (1897), the nose of the young is clothed with a diamond-shaped patch of hairs, but Pocock failed to confirm this on his material. In an otherwise hairless foetus (CR.90 mm.) a line of black superciliary vibrissae and a tuft of mystacial hairs is well erupted, but the nose quite nude.

VARIATIONS.—In July 1955 I saw in the menagerie of the Jardin des Plantes, Paris, an albino which I attribute to this species. Dandelot considered this to be an example of *C. mona*, but its behaviour alone convinced me of its identity, for in this it conformed exactly to that of a female which I had in my own collection in Colombo for many years. Its attitudinizing was typical, especially its side-to-side head movements and its frequent examination of the dorsum of its own hand, followed by self-grooming. The albino had an unpigmented face, but normally coloured eyes; the pelage was dirty white, inclining to yellowish, but the tip of the tail was black.

DIMENSIONS.—See under subspecies.

DISTRIBUTION (MAP 8)

West Africa, south and east of the Sanaga river. The southern limit appears to be the right bank of the Congo. Inland, *C. cephus* is distributed throughout the Cameroons, Rio Muni, Gabon, Cabinda and the Ubangi-Shari country. In the Congo it is restricted to the lower Congo, but the precise limits inland are undefined. Exact localities are given under the subspecies.

Variation in the colouration of the tail among moustached monkeys was first noted by Pousargues (1896) who considered it merely individual. He found that out of a series of ten skins in the Paris Museum all but three had red tails. The three without red on the tail were all females and came from Doumé (? = Ngounie), a tributary of the Ogowé, and from Mayumba on the coast of southern Gabon. The other seven red-tailed animals included an adult male from Samkitta (Ogowé), an adult female, an immature male and an unsexed juvenile from San Benito, another adult male from the Ogowé and two adult males from the Mayumbe forest.

In reviewing Pousargues' work, Pocock (1907) came to the conclusion that, on the basis of the Paris material, combined with that from the Rio Benito in the British Museum (all of which have red tails), the difference in tail colouration is not attributable to age or sex, in spite of the emphasis made by Pousargues that all the specimens lacking red on the tails were females. Among the British Museum series a young adult male from Gabon (No. 80.6.7.3, collected by Laglaize) also lacks the red on the tail.

Pocock continues "Pousargues did not admit that any systematic importance was to be attributed to the absence of red in the tail. But his series of skins does not establish the fact that the two forms occur together in the same locality. If that were the case, I think one would be compelled to assume, from the available evidence, that *C. cephus* is dimorphic with respect to the colour of the tail." Pending the confirmation of this conclusion Pocock decided that the grey-tailed form should be nominally recognised, and since Linnaeus had the red-tailed form in mind when describing his *Simia cephus*, the name *cephodes* was applied by Pocock to the aberrant animals.

(a) *C. cephus cephus* Linnaeus, 1758,* Red-tailed Moustached Monkey

(*Syn.* : *C. buccalis* Leconte, 1857, p. 10)

Vernacular names : Bapounou, *issiemba* ; Eschira, *moussouki* ; Bulu, *ozok* ; Bakota, *peka* ; Bakouelé, *pindi* ; Pahouin, *oussouk* ; M'boko, *koueri* ; Balali, *n'sima* ; Sake, *soukou* ; French, *moustac à queue rousse* ; German, *Rothschwanzschnurrbartaffe.*

Type locality : As for the species.

PELAGE.—Distinguished from *cephodes* only in the fact that the greater part of the tail is bright coppery red ; its under side near the base alone is dark grey, but the extent of the grey varies individually.

DIMENSIONS (in millimetres) :

Number	Locality	Sex	Head and Body	Tail	Hand	Foot	Ear, Morphological Length	Ear, Morphological Breadth	Ear, Physiognomic Length	Ear, Physiognomic Breadth
322/60	Zoo	♂ ad.	520	700	91	144·3	27·8	24·5	36·5	30
						Measured in the flesh				
U.S. Nat. Mus. 84532	Benito R.	♀	380	670	—	110	Collector's measurements			
	Makokou	♂	555	765	95	138	Malbrant and Maclatchy			
	Kango	♂	575	805	90	140				
	Booué	♂	575	840	89	140				
B.M.	Benito R.	♂	580	780	—	—	Pocock			
,,	,,	♀	475	670	—	—				
,,		♀	490	720	—	—				
,,	,,	♀	495	690	—	—				

Average weight 4-5 kg. (Malbrant and Maclatchy, 1949).

* *Loc. cit.*

SKULL.—Cranial dimensions (in millimetres) :

Number	Locality	Sex	Max. Cranial Length	Glabella-occiput	Condylo-basal Length	Biparietal	Least Frontal	Bimastoid	Basion-bregma	Bizygomatic	Biorbital	Palatal Length	Upper Cheek-teeth	Mandibular Length	Lower Cheek-teeth
322/60	Zoo	♂ ad.	105	72	78	55·5	44	63	49	70	58·2	41	25·2	69	30
Amer. Mus. 52569	Zambi	♂ imm.	—	—	73·5	—	42·7	56·7	—	62·3	51·2	—	—	—	—¹
U.S. Nat. Mus. 84532	Benito R.	♀	87	67·5	—	51·5	38	53	41	59	50	34	21	55	24·5

¹ M^3 not up.

DISTRIBUTION.—The whole range of the species with the exception of an area in south-western Gabon, where the grey-tailed form occurs.

Exact localities whence red-tailed specimens have been collected are : Rio Benito and San Benito (British, Paris and U.S. National Museums), Rio Como, Gabon (British Museum); Makokou, Kango and Booué (all in the former French Equatorial Africa, (*teste* Malbrant and Maclatchy), and the following localities on the right bank of the Lower Congo, as listed by Schouteden : Banana, Rosa island, Malela, Moanda, Matiba, Kimongo, Kimaleley, Sanga Ngomo, Kitandi, Kudiboma, Temro, Matadi, Luali, Kisala, Tsehela, Makaia, Ntete, Kakongo, Ganda Sundi and Lukula. There is also a record in Allen (1925) from Sambi, 30 miles inland from the mouth of the Congo.

Perret and Aellen (1956) record *C. c. cephus* from the following localities in Cameroon : Foulassi, Alangan, Moneko, Nkut, Libamba, all near Tangmelima (upper Dja river).

(b) *C. cephus cephodes* Pocock, 1907,* Grey-tailed Moustached monkey

(*Syn.* : *C. c. gabonensis* Maclatchy and Malbrant, 1947, p. 254)

Type locality : Gabon. Type male subadult in British Museum (No. 80.6.7.3) collected by Laglaize. Type locality of *gabonensis* : No type designated in original description, which refers, however, to three specimens (*a.i.j.*) in the Paris Museum discussed by Pousargues (1897) collected at Doumé-ogooué and Nayumbe. The first-mentioned, specimen, *a*, from Doumé-ogooué is here designated as lectotype.

PELAGE.—Similar to typical *cephus*, except for the tail, which is described as brown olive above, tinged with rufous, below greyish yellow. Describing the type, Schwarz (1928 *c*, p. 662) states that the tail is unusually covered with black, the red being reduced accordingly, but he claims that the whole does not surpass the range of individual variation in *cephus*, for he declares that normally-coloured skins have been examined " from the same general region ".

Pocock, however, mentions living examples in the London Zoo, one at least of which was obtained by Hamlyn from the forest between Loango and the Gabon. Another, also from captivity, was less yellowish red on the back than the type, and had greyer limbs and tail. In both these skins the face is naked, whereas in the type the nose and lips are greyish pubescent.

In 1947 Maclatchy and Malbrant re-described the grey-tailed form of *cephus* as " new " under the subspecific name *gabonensis*, pointing out that specimens from a certain region of the Gabon were uniformly of this type.

* *Ann. Mag. nat. Hist.* (7), x ; also *Proc. zool. Soc. Lond.* 1908, p. 160, Pl. X, fig. 3.

A large series of 37 skins (20 male, 17 female) in the U.S. National Museum, Washington, all collected by Dr. C. R. Aschemeier in the general area inland from Fernan Vaz, bears out the contention of Maclatchy and Malbrant. There can be no question of the differences being seasonal, since the Aschemeier collection includes skins obtained in January, March, April, May, June, July, August, October, November and December.

DIMENSIONS.—Collector's measurements (in millimetres) :

U.S. Nat. Mus. No.	Locality	Sex	Head and Body	Tail	Foot
220334	Ntyonga	♂	509	834	135
220373	Anenghue	♂	499	811	157
220337	Anguanamo	♂	539	909	158
220343	,,	♂	398	633	134
220328	Ntyonga	♂	553	990	155.
220329	,,	♂	486	722	136
220808	Mperi	♂	535	778	151
218840	Ntyonga	♂	525	803	168
218836	Omoué	♂	347	513	102
218472	Ashania	♂	555	808	149
219062	Ntyonga	♂	446	647	139
220076	,,	♂	422	565	126
218843	Rembo Kotou	♀	446	683	134
218838	Ntyonga	♀	435	657	130
218837	,,	♀	502	795	138
220073	,,	♀	494	780	127
218839	,,	♀	465	671	122 pregnant (Nov. 1917)
220341	,,	♀	462	763	130
220333	,,	♀	503	733	131
220340	,,	♀	473	603	131
220339	,,	♀	343	492	99
220336	,,	♀	480	699	126
220335	,,	♀	468	679	125
220085	,,	♀	469	712	124
220331	,,	♀	477	628	130

SKULL.—Cranial dimensions (in millimetres) :

U.S. Nat. Mus. No.	Locality	Sex	Max. Cranial Length	Glabella-occiput	Biparietal	Least Frontal	Bimastoid	Basion-bregma	Bizygomatic	Biorbital	Palatal Length	Upper Cheek-teeth	Mandibular Length	Lower Cheek-teeth
220337	Anguanamo	old ♂	109	79	57	44·2	61	50	73	61	39	22	69	28
220373	Anenghue	♂	98·5	72	54	43	57	50	66	54	37	24	64	29
220336	Ntyonga	old ♀	92	71	50·5	40	54	44	60	52	32	22	58	22
220335	,,	♀	93	70	51	40	53	42·5	58	50	37	22	58	24

DISTRIBUTION.—Restricted to an area of the Gabon and adjacent Moyen Congo, circumscribed by a line commencing in the north at the coast, at about Port Gentil, passing firstly eastwards to the confluence of the M'Boumi with the Ogowé river, skirting Booué, on the north bank of the Ogowé, then north of Latourville to Francesville, then obliquely towards the south as far as a point north of Mouyondzi (which place is excluded from the range), finally turning westwards towards the coast just north of the mouth of the Kouilou-Niari river system, following the limits of the western forest belt. The inland limit of the range of *cephodes* is formed by the plateau.

Specific localities, for example, of *C. c. cephodes*, are listed in the above tables of dimensions. The material collected in the Gabon by du Chaillu, which formed the basis of Leconte's description of *C. buccalis* evidently was obtained outside the area inhabited by *cephodes* as it is definitely stated to be red-tailed. This explorer is known to have collected along the Ogowé, but also explored the Rio Como and the Crystal Mountains in the north. Thus *C. buccalis* becomes a synonym of *C. cephus cephus*.

VI. Superspecies *CERCOPITHECUS HAMLYNI* Pocock, 1907 *

(SYN. : Genus *Rhinostigma* Elliot, 1913 †)

Comprised solely by the remarkably distinct species *C. hamlyni*, which has no close affinities with any other member of the genus.

16. *CERCOPITHECUS HAMLYNI* Pocock, 1907 *

Owl-faced Guenon; Hamlyn's Monkey

(SYN. : *Rhinostigma hamlyni* Elliot, 1913, p. 273 ; *Cercopithecus leucampyx aurora* Thomas & Wroughton, 1910, *Trans. zool. Soc. Lond.* xix. 485)

* *Ann. Mag. nat. Hist.* (7), x ; also *Proc. zool. Soc. Lond.* 1908, p. 160, Pl. X, fig. 3.
† *Review of the Primates*, ii. 273.

VERNACULAR NAMES : French, *cercopithèque d'Hamlyn*, *cercopithèque à tête de hibou* ; German, *Eulenkopfaffe, Hamlyn Meerkatze*.

Allen (1925) states that the term Owl Monkey is a translation of the native name, based on its alleged nocturnal habits.

TYPE LOCALITY : Ituri forest, Congo. Type immature ♂ in British Museum (No. 1939, 1099) originally a menagerie specimen exhibited in the London Zoo from 5 November 1907 until 23 November 1907, where it was deposited by Lord Rothschild, who obtained it from Hamlyn, on whose testimony it came from the Congo.

This species was originally described from an immature male in captivity ; it was redescribed by Thomas (1910) as *C. leucampyx aurora* from a native-made skin lacking face, hands and feet. Elliot made it the type of a new genus *Rhinostigma*, basing the diagnosis thereof on the external characters of *C. hamlyni* combined with cranial and dental characters derived from a skull of an immature *Cercocebus* and erroneously allocating the latter to the type skin. Pocock (1925) rectified this error, although his paper appeared too late to prevent Allen (1925) from adopting Elliot's name and arriving at the conclusion, on the basis of the deciduous dentition, that *Rhinostigma* was affined to the *Lophocebus* section of *Cercocebus* !

Subsequent arrival of living specimens in the Antwerp and other European zoos, and of skins and skulls in the Tervueren Museum (Schouteden, 1934), led to the rectification of these errors. For other historical data, see Raven and Hill (1942).

CHARACTERS

PELAGE : ADULT MALE.—Distinguished primarily by the shape and site of the white nose-patch, which forms a narrow sagittal streak, extending from the glabella to the internarial septum. Somewhat narrower above than below, its frontal end, at least in the adult, is truncated, but its inferior end forms a triangular internarial patch with the apex below at the junction with the base of the upper lip. All hairs on this mesial nasal tract are directed downwards. The general effect on the otherwise dark plum-coloured face (somewhat browner on the muzzle) has led to a comparison with the face of a barn owl, but, as Pocock (1925) remarked, the nose-patch is no more eccentric than that of *C. nictitans* or *C. petaurista*.

Skin underlying nasal white tract unpigmented. Irides deep rose red (brick red of Ridgway).

Another unique feature is the arrangement of the hair on the head. There is no demarcation of the hairs of the crown from those forming the whiskers, the whole head pelage forming a smooth compact hood over crown, cheeks and throat ; the ears are completely hidden, but a nude area occurs behind them.

In general colour the pelage is a rather dull greenish olive, speckled heavily with black; individual hairs, some 50 mm. long, are buffy whitish at the root, becoming greyer (pearl grey) distally, the terminal half being annulated with four wide black bands alternating with Naples yellow, the tip also being sometimes of the lighter tint, sometimes black. Of the three yellow bands, the proximal is broadest and the distal narrowest.

In the type skin the green tinge predominates on the back posterior to the shoulders, the head (including cheeks) and neck being more definitely speckled. On the sacral region, root of tail and proximal part of thighs the green is replaced by clear grey. Grey extends also for two-thirds the length of the tail, both above and below, gradually replaced distally by black; distal one-third wholly black.

Fore-limbs proximally like the shoulders laterally, becoming blacker distally on forearms and hands, and on the medial surface; hind limbs jet black medially, but laterally only from the knee onwards.

A thin line of long stiff black vibrissae along the brows; those in the centre pale basally. Behind this in an adult male examined in the flesh is a narrow Naples-yellow band anterior to the darker portion of the scalp. Ear, between seal brown and chocolate.

Under parts from chin backwards to pubes, jet black, the black hairy tract narrowing on the abdomen. Some short white hairs on scrotum and perineum.

Nails black, elongated; nipples pink, surrounded by ill-defined whitish zone. Callosities confluent, blackish brown, sometimes incompletely pigmented, the dorsal portions then appearing pink. Naked skin of perineum root of tail, circumanal area and medial aspects of thighs bright greenish sky blue, becoming more slaty on the area above the callosities, and definitely slate grey on the distal part of the prepuce. Glans penis and intrapreputial part of corpus penis flesh-coloured. Glans of the usual form for *Cercopithecus*, with a marked lateral notch on the corona glandis. Scrotum malachite green.

ADULT FEMALE.—An immature female described by Allen (1925) showed a conspicuous nasal stripe; the dark grey and black head had the hairs strongly vermiculated with yellowish, the yellow being predominant supraorbitally, as described above for the adult male; chin black, throat grey, only lightly speckled. Body colour dorsally as in the male, brighter than on the head. Tail in proximal five-sixths, especially near the root, with hairs tipped silvery grey, as on thighs, but the tip darker. Limbs, including hands and feet, black, the forearm and leg, however, with slight yellow speckling. Under parts from chest to abdomen black with minimal yellow speckling. Female genitalia, etc., so far unknown.

JUVENILE.—The neonatus contrasts strongly with the adult and is without facial pattern. The pelage appears uniformly pale from the only published photograph available (*International Zoo News*, vi, p. 162, 1959).

PLATE XXVII

Photo: W. Ted Roth

Cercopithecus cephus ♀, fostering a young *C. nictitans*

PLATE XXVIII

Courtesy A. C. V. van Bemmel

Cercopithecus hamlyni ♀, with newborn young in Rotterdam Zoo

Van Bemmel (*in litt.*, 1964) informs me that the newborn is uniformly golden yellow with a pallid face, which gradually darkens, except for the median nasal stripe. A four-months-old female born in the Rotterdam Zoo and now preserved in the Leiden Museum (No. 16825) is in juvenile coat, the pelage being soft and silky. It differs in colour both from the neonatal and the adult pelage and may be described as follows :

Forehead and forepart of crown with long erect hairs (20 mm.), those of back even longer (30 mm.), but close-fitting. The general colour is brighter than in the adult from the greater prominence of the yellow bands, especially on the hinder region of the back and on the hind-limbs, where the yellow increases peripherally towards the ankles, the dorsum of the feet being almost pure golden yellow. This also occurs on the arms beyond the deltoid region, the postaxial border of the forearms, the dorsum of the hands being almost pure greenish yellow, with minimal black speckling. A few short black hairs on the digits. Nails horn-coloured, darkening peripherally.

Individual hairs on mid-back are mouse grey in the proximal half, the distal half bearing three yellow annuli alternating with black annuli, the tips also being black.

The tail, both above and below, is predominantly greenish yellow, but becomes darker in the distal half above, the yellow diminishing gradually and virtually disappearing in the distal 25 mm., which is greyish black.

Face bordered by soft black hairs, increasing in quantity over the maxilla, where they constitute the anterior part of the whiskers. Black hairs also occur on the nose (which still shows no white vertical stripe), and around the mouth opening. Remainder of whiskers bright yellow with some black speckling. Throat, sides of neck and forepart of chest clothed with long pure golden yellow hairs. On the hinder chest the hairs have dark grey bases and yellow tips, the grey increasing and the yellow diminishing on the belly. Medial aspect of arms silvery white ; of thighs light golden. Medial aspect of crural segment dark grey with minimal yellow speckling. No sharp line of demarcation on flanks between dorsal and ventral pelage, but on sides of neck and on upper arms distal to deltoid region and along preaxial border of forearm the transition is abrupt.

Face (except for hairs), ears, palms and soles unpigmented.

In the juvenile coat, judging from Schouteden's photographs, the frontal band is proportionately wider than in the adults and the cheeks, moreover, are contrastedly paler than the crown.

VARIATIONS.—-These occur in the amount of yellow speckling on the upper parts. In the type of *aurora* the yellow is more predominant than usual, but becomes replaced by grey on the tail. Thomas and Hinton (1910) in their original account, compared it to *leucampyx* and *albogularis*, but the imperfection of the type precludes any positive statement as to its affinities with other species of the genus.

2 L

DIMENSIONS (in millimetres) :

Number	Locality	Sex	Head and Body	Head Length (muzzle-occiput)	Tail	Hand	Foot	Ear Physiognomic Length
PC.555	*ex* San Diego Zoo	♂ old	551	119	570	103·4	148	43·5
Brit. Mus. 1939 1099	*ex* London Zoo	♂ immat.	500	—	550	—	—	(type)
Amer. Mus. 52463	Congo	♀ immat.	280	—	420	—	110	35 (Allen)

SKULL.—To rectify the error committed by Elliot, Pocock borrowed from Lord Rothschild the skull taken from the type skin. He found the last molar unerupted but embedded in the bone ; it had no fifth cusp, proving therefore its affinities were not, as Elliot and Allen supposed, with *Cercocebus*. Pocock found no resemblance between the skull and the photograph published in Elliot's *Review* (ii, Pl. XXX), which evidently pertains to another monkey, probably the type of *Cercocebus hamlyni* (= *C. aterrimus*).

The skull of *C. hamlyni*, although belonging to the larger type, has a relatively short muzzle, in which it contrasts greatly with *Cercocebus*. Both cranially and externally, Raven and Hill (1942), considered *C. hamlyni* to show resemblance to *C. mitis*.

Schwarz (1928 c) adduces resemblances to *C. l'hoesti* in the shape of the palate bone and in the high cusps of the cheek-teeth (as well as in some external features, *e.g.* hairy nose, silvery tail). But Schwarz's contention has not been borne out by material available since he wrote this.

Raven and Hill (1942), from a study of the adult skull, maintain that *C. hamlyni* is distinct cranially from all the other members of the genus. The brain-case is described as shorter and more rounded ; the nasal profile is straight (admittedly some skulls of *C. mitis* show this feature) ; pterygoid fossae are deeper and more extensive. Both upper and lower incisors are slenderer. The principal cusps of the molars are high and connected by sharp lophs, showing resemblance to the condition in Colobidae, though less extreme. The cusps are located near the margins (cf. *Cercocebus*). The foremost upper premolar is subequal with its neighbour instead of being smaller as in most other species, and both are relatively large. The talon in $P_{\overline{3}}$ is larger than usual. The mandible is weaker in structure with less depth at the level of $M_{\overline{3}}$.

Compared with *C. diana*, whose skull it resembles in size, the rostrum is slenderer and the post-orbital constriction deeper, the frontal is less elevated above the brow and the cheek-teeth larger.

Compared with the average of 15 skulls of *C. neglectus*, the skull of *hamlyni* is somewhat smaller, the rostrum narrower, less rugose ; the teeth on the whole smaller and the brow-ridges less pronounced ; also the temporal ridges are less robust, the nasals longer and less anteriorly expanded, while the brain case is more elevated.

The brain-case is larger than the average skull of *C. aethiops*, being broader and shorter.

Comparisons with other species (*C. mitis*, *C. nictitans*, *C. l'hoesti*, *C. mona*, *C. ascanius* and *C. cephus*) are given in Raven and Hill's paper.

SKULL.—Cranial dimensions (in millimetres) :

Number	Locality	Sex	Max. Cranial Length	Glabella-occiput	Biparietal	Least Frontal	Bimastoid	Basion-bregma	Bizygomatic	Biorbital	Palatal Length	Upper Cheek-teeth	Mandibular Length	Lower Cheek-teeth
Amer. Mus. 86948	Mt. Karisimbi	♂ ad.	109·5	72·8	—	42·3	60·9	51·7	73·5	—	37·7	Raven and Hill (1942)		
Amer. Mus. 90028	Mt. Kahusi	♂ ad.	112	74	—	41	63	48·3	74	—	36·9			
B.M., 1939 1099	Ituri forest (Type)	♂ juv.	91	—	50·5	42·3	—	—	59	55·2	35	24	54	28·5 (personal measure-ments)
Amer. Mus. 52463	Congo	♀ juv.	775	—	—	—	—	—	—	—	*ex* Allen (1928)			
Leiden Mus. 16825	Zoo	♀ 6 mo.	67	58	47·2	37·5	39	38	40	38	—	10	30	10·2 DM$\frac{2}{2}$ erupting

DISTRIBUTION AND ECOLOGY (Map 9)

C. hamlyni is confined to heavy forest in a small area of the eastern Congo basin. Its exact range has not been delineated. Localities whence specimens in the Tervueren Museum have been procured are listed by Schouteden (1947) thus : Stanleyville district, Topoke ; Kibole-Ituri district, Epulu ; Kivu district, north-west of Lake Kivu, also near Shabunda ; Ruanda-Urundi, between Ruhengiri and Rwankeri. Schouteden also reproduces photographs of a young specimen from the upper Kiloboze, near Kamituga, and in the letter accompanying the photographs the animal is stated to occur in great numbers at Urega.

Raven and Hill (1942), referring to material in the American Museum mention two, one found mummified in forest near the summit of Mount Karisimba (14,800 ft.) by J. P. Chapin, and another collected by Raven in forest near Mount Kahasi (= Kahuzi) west of the southern end of Lake Kivu.

Field notes on the last mentioned indicate that the animal, apparently solitary, was shot in a large forest tree, one of a small group of such trees nearly surrounded by bamboo forest. Nearer Mount Kahusi more bamboo forest, and also grassland and mountain forest was encountered.

Supposedly nocturnal habits (Allen, 1925, legend to pl. lxxxix) need further investigation.

In captivity the tail is used in the same way as Dandelot (1956) has described for *C. l'hoesti.*

REPRODUCTION

Nothing of this is known in the wild state, but young have, in recent years, been born in captivity in several European zoos—the earliest being in 1959 at Rotterdam (van Bemmel *et al.*, 1960), followed by Amsterdam, West Berlin and Paris. At the Blijdorp Zoo, Rotterdam, two births occurred in successive years. In the successful birth the infant was born on 27 September 1959 and survived four months. Two abortive births preceded the successful one.

VII. Superspecies *CERCOPITHECUS NEGLECTUS* Schlegel, 1876 *

Chestnut-browed Guenons

(SYN.: *Cercopitheci barbati* Sclater, 1893 (in part); *Pogonocebus* Troussart, 1897 (in part) and of Elliot, 1913; *Neglectus* group of Pocock, 1907)

This, like the last, includes but a single species, viz.:

17. *CERCOPITHECUS NEGLECTUS* Schlegel, 1876 *

Schlegel's Guenon; de Brazza's Monkey †

(SYN.: *C. leucocampyx* (*sic*) Gray, 1870, p. 22; *errore* for *leucampyx* Fischer, 1829; *C. brazzae* M. Edwards, 1886, p. 15; Sclater, 1893, p. 255; *C. brazziformis* Pocock, 1907, p. 686; *C. ezrae* Pocock, 1908, p. 10; *Lasiopyga neglecta* Elliot, 1913, p. 376; *C. uellensis* Lönnberg, 1919, p. 130; *Lasiopyga brazzae uellensis* Allen, 1925, p. 380)

VERNACULAR NAMES: In Cameroons, *avut, fum* (Bates, 1905). Perret and Aellen (1956) give the Bulu names, *avout, foum* and *foung*; M'boko and Bakota, *pounnga*; Shaké, *pfoumwa*; Bakouélé, *pouhon*; Pahouin makina, *pfong*; Pahouin mazouna, *foung* (Malbrant & Maclatchy); French, *cercopithèque de Brazza*; German, *Brazza-meerkatze.*

TYPE LOCALITY: Probably Niam Niam in Mongbottu country. Type, a native-made flat skin, in British Museum, collected by Consul Petherick, who obtained it on the White Nile, where the species does not naturally occur (see Schwarz 1928*c*, p. 659). Type locality of *brazzae*, French Congo. Lectotype in Paris Museum (cat. gen. No.

---

* *Mus. Hist. nat. Pays-bas.* vii. 70.

† Named in honour of Savorgnan de Brazza, an Italian (naturalized French) explorer who travelled along the Ogowé and Congo rivers (1870–1895).

1886–115) (chosen by Schwarz, *loc. cit.*). Type locality of *ezrae*, unknown " probably Upper Congo ". Based on an immature animal in the London Zoo, skin now in British Museum (No. 9.7.19.2). Schwarz (1928 *c*, p. 659) reports seeing five examples at the same stage, two at Antwerp, two at Berlin and one at Frankfurt. Development of the black markings were followed over a period of two years. Type locality of *brazziformis*. Said to be French Congo. Type skin is that of a monkey identified when living by Sclater (1896, p. 780) as *C. brazzae*. It was purchased for the London Zoo from Antwerp Zoo and may therefore have come from Belgian territory. Skin not found at British Museum. Type locality of *uelensis*, Poko, Uele district, Congo Belge. Type, an unsexed adult in Tervueren Museum, collected by Dr. Christy.

The presence of a white beard and thigh-stripe induced Sclater (1893, p. 255) to place *C. brazzae* among his *Cercopitheci barbati* alongside *C. diana* and *C. roloway*. He did not then realize that *C. brazzae* was the same as *C. neglectus*, which he had placed (p. 253) among his *C. melanochiri*, next to *C. leucampyx* to which, moreover, Gray (1870) had erroneously referred it. The confusion is doubtless due to the incomplete and modified condition of the type skin, which, as Schwarz noted, had been smoked in the process of preparation. Elliot (1913) affirmed also that head and feet were lacking, which would account for certain omissions by Gray. However, my personal notes on the type make no reference to this fact, so Elliot may have had some other skin in mind. My notes merely state " resembles any other Brazza Monkey ".

Sclater (1893, p. 443) in redescribing and figuring *C. brazzae* had meantime arrived at the conclusion that it was a close ally of *C. neglectus* and that it was even possible they were the same species.

Gray originally described the skin as having " fur grey brown, minutely grey-grizzled, under side of body black ; crown, outside of limbs, and all but base of tail black ; front edge of thighs and a band across the haunches whitish. White Nile." In spite of the marked differences from other forms, he places it, as already noted, under *leucampyx*. Schlegel (1876, p. 70) noted the apartness and, although he did not see the skin, endowed it with the name *C. neglectus*. Later material from the French Congo sent to the Paris Museum by de Brazza was described as a new species by Milne Edwards under the name *C. brazzae*. This presented further distinctions not hitherto appreciated, notably the upstanding reddish frontal diadem composed of short erect hairs, bordered posteriorly by a broad black band extending laterally and posteriorly to the ear, and in front by a narrower black supra-orbital stripe over each eye.

Pocock (1907, p. 684) first recognized the apartness of *C. neglectus* from the Diana group and assigned it to a group by itself. His views have been universally adopted by later writers (except Elliot, who retained it with *diana* in his subgenus *Pogonocebus*).

CHARACTERS

PELAGE : ADULT MALE.—A stockily built animal by guenon standards, with robust limbs and tail.

Face, except eyelids, hairy. Upper eyelid brownish flesh-colour ; lower eyelid and circumorbital region slaty grey. Muzzle, including inferior part of nose, flesh-colour, sometimes with a bluish tinge. Bridge of nose with short, close-fitting black hairs diverging from the glabella, those above directed upwards, those below downwards and medially. Hairs on un-pigmented part of face, including lower part of nose, internarial septum, upper lip, lower lip and chin, silvery white, lengthening on the chin to form a short, spade-shaped beard, which is continued on the interramal region with hairs up to 65 mm. long. Maxillary region from infraorbital margin to angle of mouth clothed with long, closely adpressed hairs forming a mat like that in *C. mitis*, with individual hairs alternately banded with black and Naples yellow, the latter predominating. These occupy the whole side of the face and extend back beyond the ears, the lower parts of which they obscure. Ears lightly pigmented, without hairy tufts, but with scattered white hairs, mostly confined to the antihelix.

Forehead with a thin brow-band of black hairs, interrupted over the glabella ; above this a broad fiery-red upstanding frontal diadem which tapers laterally to a point situated midway between eye and ear each side. Beyond this again a sharply-defined jet-black transverse or coronal band, narrowest in the middle and broadening laterally to extend, as a temporal band as far as the ear, immediately above the cheek patch.

Remainder of crown, also neck, dorsal surface and sides of body light yellowish grey, speckled with black. Individual hairs have light grey bases, for approximately one-third the total length and thereafter alternately banded with light yellow and black (five black rings, including a black tip).

Tail basally for about 50 mm. like the back, remainder jet black above and below.

Pectoral limb laterally jet black, sometimes only from the elbow, its radial aspect and area above the elbow (when not black) olive green, speckled with black. A black stripe courses obliquely from the front of the shoulder to the radial side of the elbow, where it becomes continuous with the radial edge of the black of the forearm. Hands black ; nails black.

Thigh with a characteristic oblique curved white stripe, extending from the lateral limit of the ischial callosity to the knee, where it narrows and disappears. Apart from this, the thigh laterally and the shank are greyish to olive speckled with black, darker above and over the knee, contrasting sharply with the white medial side. Ankle and dorsum of foot jet black.

The white of the interramal region is continued back on the throat and thence, narrowing to a point, on the forepart of the chest. Remainder of chest and abdomen to pubic region sooty grey, sometimes with an olive-tinge from light speckling of the mesially located hairs. This hue also extends on the medial aspect of the brachium, with variable mixture of lighter grey hairs. Area below callosities white, continuous with the thigh stripe. Medial aspect of thighs white.

Naked or seminude skin of perineum light cobalt blue, darkening to Columbia blue on the globular scrotum. Distally the blue is replaced by a purple tinge over Scarpa's triangle. Callosities black. Penis 23 mm. long from preputeal reflection to tip of glans ; the latter accounting for 8·2 mm. Glans and distal part of corpus pink ; proximal part bluish, sharply defined.

ADULT FEMALE.—About one-fourth smaller than males, the largest females being smaller than the smallest males (Allen, 1925). The only constant sexual variation in pelage is in the perineum, which is brownish red in females ; but this colour has been observed by me also in immature males.

Seminude area light lilac, becoming bluer on the vulva and body of clitoris ; glans clitoridis rosy pink, diameter transversely 6 mm., sagitally 7·5 mm., with a median cleft 5 mm. long. Corpus clitoridis grooved dorsally in mid-line ; length with glans 8·5 mm.

JUVENILE.—Weight of neonatus 260 gm.

Neonatus with face, hands and feet nude, flesh-coloured. A suspicion of white tuft on chin. Natal coat of a generally uniform brown or yellowish brown ; limbs and under parts yellow. No indication of brow pattern (L. Smith, *in litt.*, Haddow, *in litt.*). A specimen born in the Paignton Zoo is described as having uniformly golden natal coat (K. Smith, *in litt.*).

In a juvenile female nineteen days old the pelage is composed of soft silky down, the hairs greyish at the base, tipped with canary yellow, giving a generally yellow effect with the greyer bases showing through. Crown and a broad median spinal tract are darker than the flanks. The brow band is uniform pale yellow, without grey bases to the hairs. Cheek hairs are stiffer, but short and pale. A trace of white fuzz around the muzzle and a distinct rudiment of the beard evident. Dorsum of hand and foot with short silvery white hairs. Tail uniformly yellowish. The face is otherwise naked, pallid around the eyes, but surrounded by a lilac zone across the brows and around orbits ; but muzzle pink. Callosities and genitalia pink.

The adult pattern commences to appear at about nine months of age. Detailed accounts of six stages from about this time onwards are given by Allen (1925, p. 381) from a series of seven skins collected during April and June, all but two from Niangara.

Allen's youngest stage ($\male$ total length 520 mm., DM$\frac{2}{2}$ not fully erupted), has the golden yellow brow-band, with black bases to the hairs, the black showing along the anterior margin of the diadem. Upper arm, lateral aspect of hind limbs and tail pale yellow, the last mentioned darker at root above and tip. Nape with a pale, thinly haired area. Rest of head and upper parts superficially yellowish, the hairs with whitish bases, broadly zoned sub-apically with thin deposit of melanin. Some black at the wrists. Radial border of forelimbs pale yellow, medial surface yellowish white with a silvery sheen; medial surface of hind-limbs similar, but darkened on thigh by greyish suffusion. Under parts sparsely haired, yellowish, with tips of hairs darkened on the pectoral region.

A much older male (Allen's No. 52437, total length 625 mm.; complete milk dentition with unworn incisors). Brow band not markedly differentiated from adjoining pelage, except mesially where the hairs are more rigid, dull reddish with paler tips. Grizzling of the entire dorsal pelage is now evident, but the paler annulations are darker than in adults. Root of tail dark chestnut passing to yellowish brown then blackish. Chestnut hairs also occur on rump and around callosities. Fore-limbs laterally yellowish grey, darker on shoulder and wrist; medially pale yellowish. Hind-limbs similar medially, but on posterior border of thigh hairs are longer and blackish. Throat and neck whitish; remainder of under parts with tips of hairs brownish. In some examples at this stage the chestnut tinge is more extensive especially around the base of the tail, rump and on the cheeks and nape.

A more advanced stage with $M\frac{1}{1}$ erupted has the brow-band much varied with black and the hairs of the forepart of the head broadly tipped with pale tawny. Rest of upper parts have the pale annuli light tawny as far as tail base, which is duskier and varied with chestnut, the rest of the tail grizzled pale tawny, except for the black tip. Fore-limbs laterally darker than back, a black area on the dorsum manus extending proximally to wrist; medial aspect yellowish white. Hind-limbs laterally pale tawny speckled with black, medially yellowish white. The white femoral stripe of the adult is now foreshadowed by an indistinct pale yellow tract. Under parts as in preceding stage.

A much older stage (total length, 865 mm.; all milk dentition replaced except DC, and $M\frac{1\,2}{1\,2}$ up). General colour now as in the adult, but yellow zones are darker, more tawny, while under parts from chest posteriorly are heavily washed with dark grey. From shoulders to bases of manual digits the lateral aspect of the fore-limb is blackish and the hind-limbs, too, are much darker than in earlier phases, though lighter than in adults.

The thigh stripe is present and buffy yellow. The brow band is bright rufous, but still lacks the black coronal bar, though the area it occupies in the mature animal is darker, due to heavier black tips to the hairs. This stage corresponds almost exactly with the original description of *C. ezrae* Pocock (1908, p. 158).

VARIATIONS.—Individual variations among adults are, according to Allen (1925), not striking compared with those in other species. However, all his material came from one area of the Congo. He did note, however, that the general colour varied somewhat according to the variation in the shade of the lighter annulations of the dorsal hairs—from nearly white to pale buff, altering the general picture from almost pure grey to buffy grey, irrespective of sex. The dark under parts also vary in intensity and in the length and tone of the buff tips, while the medial surface of the thigh varies from clear white to pale yellowish white or pale gold. The lateral thigh stripe varies in breadth and in purity of whiteness. The narrow tawny band which in most adults extends from the front of the shoulder to the elbow or proximal part of upper arm is sometimes conspicuous, but may be virtually lacking ; when present its colour varies from pale yellowish to deep tawny. The brow-band varies considerably in breadth, intensity of colour (from light ochraceous to tawny), and the adjacent black band also varies in width by as much as 50 per cent, while the narrow black line anterior to the chestnut band also varies from virtual absence to a strongly developed condition.

It is therefore clear that the differences stated by Lönnberg (1919, p. 130) to characterize the form named by him *uelensis* fall within the range of individual variation of *neglectus*, and the same may be said of Pocock's alleged race, *brazziformis*, which differed only in the modification of the colour of the lateral aspect of the hind-limb which is, distal to the thigh stripe, pale greyish green, only slightly darker than the area proximal of the stripe, and sharply defined distally from the black of the foot. Typical *neglectus* has, according to Pocock, the hind-limbs blackish olive, much darker than the area proximad of the stripe and less sharply contrasted distally from the black of the foot.

DIMENSIONS (in millimetres) :

Number	Locality	Sex	Head and Body (Crown-rump)	Head Length (Muzzle-occiput)	Tail	Foot	Ear P.H.	Weight kg.
Edin. Univ. Mus.	Bitje, S. Cameroons	♂	525		650	160	35	(Collected by G. L. Bates, 19 Feb. 1914)
M.C.Z. 31616	Kirui Mt. Elgon	♂	595		630	148	38	(Allen *et al.* 1936)
1064/55	Uganda	♂	534	140	643	155	42	7·8
56/55	,,	♂	570	140	700	165	41	5·35
PC.518	,,	♀	495	105·2	620	142	33·4	4·98
PC.536	,,	♀	480	—	—	136	37·5	4.6
94/50	,,	♀	490	104·5	530	134	33	4·5
PC.476	,,	♂ juv.	415	95	435	124·5	32·6	1·9
PC.477	,,	♀ juv.	348	85·3	340	98·3	32	1·12
Av. of 13	N.E. Congo	♂♂	540 (465-590)	—	702 (630-850)	157 (146-172)	39 (33-43)	ex Allen 1925
Av. of 8	,,	♀♀	435 (400-470)	—	587 (545-630)	134 (123-145)	38 (35-42)	

SKULL

Allen *et al.* (1936) comparing the skull with that of *C. mitis stuhlmanni* noted a number of minor differences, notably in the width of the choanae and in the form of the swollen base of the petrosal, which converges with its fellow and presents a deep keel antero-ventrally. I can confirm this from the material available to me.

Cranial measurements (in millimetres) :

Max. Cranial Length	Glabella-occiput	Condylo-basal	Biparietal	Least Frontal	Bimastoid	Basion-bregma	Bizygomatic	Biorbital	Palatal Length	Upper Cheek-teeth	Mandibular Length	Lower Cheek-teeth
107	80	82	56	44	60	45	70	58	42	28·5	70	35·5

No. 40/61 Uganda ♂

Allen gives the average (minimum-maximum) cranial dimensions of 21 skulls from the Congo as follows in millimetres :

	Max. Cranial Length	Glabella-occiput	Condylo-basal Length	Least Frontal	Bimastoid	Bizygomatic	Biorbital	Upper Molars
13 ♂♂	112·6 (1–4.5 –119)	94·4 (87·7– 98)	91·7 (84·2– 97)	44·3 (42·1– 66)	62·5 (58– 66·3)	74·2 (67·5– 78·5)	61·6 (53·6– 65·4)	19·2 (18·1– 20·2)
8 ♀♀	100·1 (95·7– 102·8)	86·8 (75·5– 90·3)	74·9 (72– 80·5)	41·7 (37·6– 44)	57·7 (54·2– 60)	65·5 (61– 68·9)	54·3 (50·7– 57·4)	17·9 (17– 19·4)

DISTRIBUTION (Map 10)

A fairly widely distributed species, which is known from the north-eastern part of the Congo basin and adjacent areas around the great lakes. It occurs on both banks of the upper and middle Congo, extending westwards into the Gabon, though failing to enter the coastal forests. Malbrant and Maclatchy, discussing its distribution in the former French territories, state that it ranges over the greater part of the forested region of the north, north-east and east of the Moyen-Congo. In the Gabon it does not appear to extend beyond the basins of the Djouah and the Ivindo up to their confluence with the Ogowé. They record material from Booué, Makokou, Kemboma, Mekambo. Northwards it probably occupies the basin of the N'Tem as far as the Cameroon border. The British Museum has specimens from the Ja (=Dja) river, Cameroons, collected by Bates. The Edinburgh University Museum also has a skin collected by Bates at Bitje, altitude

2000 feet. Perret and Aellen (1956), confirming earlier records by Bates (1905) and Jeannin (1936), record it from the southern Cameroons, while Cabrera (1929) noted its presence in Spanish Guinea (Rio Muni).

Over 120 specimens in the Tervueren Museum from localities in the Congo basin have been listed by Schouteden. The distribution is very wide, but discontinuous, there being many areas whence it has not been recorded. Schouteden's list is as follows: Lower Congo, Ilala, Tua, Kwamouth; Lake Leopold II district, Lekana, Mushie, Likongo, Oshwe, Kunungu, Dwa. Tshuapa district, Ikengo, Irebu, Mondombe, Eala, Isekombaka; Congo-Ubangi district, Bomana, Banzyville, Modjambali, Bumba, Lisala, Bokweli, Dua-river, Bosobola, Gobu, Libenge; Uellé district, Gobia, Bafuka, Poko, Mauda, Buta, Niangara, Dungu; Stanleyville district, Stanleyville; Kwango district, Kasongo Lunda, Franz-Josef Falls, Mwilambongo; Kasai district, Luluaburg, Bulenge, Basongo; Sankuru district, Lusambo, Tshipama; Lualaba district, Kazenze (= Kanzenze).

Additional localities referred to by Allen (material now in American Museum, New York) include Faradje, Niapu, Avakubi, Banalia, Ukaturaka; all in the Uellé region.

Mertens (1929) further mentions material from Angu collected by Schubotz.

Tappen (1960), analysing Schouteden's data, notes that the latter's map shows *C. neglectus* as occurring as far south as 11° S. It is not found, however, at Epulu on the river of the same name, approximately 2° N. 28° E., but it occurs along the Lindi river near Bafwasende, only 120 miles distant.

Beyond the former Belgian territory *C. neglectus* is known to extend, in suitable localities, across the whole of Uganda into Western Kenya and thence north of Lake Rudolf along the Omo river (Thomas 1900) into southern Abyssinia. The British Museum has a specimen collected by Donaldson Smith from the last mentioned locality and another from the Charada forest (6000 ft.) in Kaffa (= Kefa) to the north-west, procured by W. N. Macmillan. Pocock (1907) found no material difference between these animals and those collected by Bates on the Dja river at the extreme western limit of the range.

The only recorded locality for Uganda is the Bwamba forest (1° N. 30° E.) (Haddow).

In Kenya, *C. neglectus* is now very rare and in need of protection. According to Booth (1962) it is restricted to the lower slopes of the Cherangani hills, at altitudes around 6000 feet on privately owned farmland, where it inhabits the uncleared swampy banks of streams. Allen and Lawrence (1936), however, found it on Mt. Elgon, and Watson (1951) reported it farther north on Mt. Kadam. Tappen (1960) observed it in forest south-west of Tororo (about 1° N. 34° E.) and Haddow (*in litt.*) collected in the same locality.

ECOLOGY AND ETHOLOGY

C. neglectus is an arboreal forest species with a decided tendency to populate riverside forest and swampy terrain at relatively low altitudes (Malbrant and Maclatchy, Tappen), but it also ranges, in deep forest, up to altitudes of 6000 feet or more. It affects especially bamboo and palm-swamps.

According to Malbrant and Maclatchy, referring to the species in Gabon (especially on the Djouah) and neighbouring areas, it goes in small bands, though solitary animals are frequently met with.

On Mount Elgon, according to Tappen, it shows some considerable versatility in its ecological preferences, but favours the swampy forests along water courses. On threat of danger the bands will descend to the ground and escape along the forest floor to a safer area. Chapin informed Tappen that it was not averse to swimming across the streams in its efforts to escape danger. Haddow's statement, therefore, that *C. neglectus* is exclusively arboreal does not appear universally applicable.

Threatened danger usually results in cessation of activity and silence, but escape is accompanied by emission of a single note, a prolonged but melodious *hoon*, the only vocal utterance known according to Malbrant and Maclatchy.

The tail is characteristically carried in an even drooping curve, concave downwards or even hanging straight downward with a slight curve near the tip. The gait contrasts with that of *C. ascanius* or *C. denti* and resembles the characteristic trotting gait of *C. mitis* (Haddow, 1952) (see Plate XII).

In temperament also *C. neglectus* recalls the *C. mitis* group, especially in its sedate rather aloof mien. It is not demonstrative and therefore does not agree well in captivity with the livelier species such as *C. petaurista* or *C. ascanius*, for it resents teasing and does not participate in the frolics of the average guenons. Yet it makes a gentle and reliable pet when young and is reasonably hardy, provided a mixed diet is given, including some animal protein ; for instance, insects, especially grasshoppers and crickets, are relished (Sanderson, 1957).

The resting attitude, according to Booth (1962) is in a horizontal position lying on the side, although at night they adopt a sitting position, huddled together, like other guenons.

REPRODUCTION

Breeding in captivity has been successfully achieved in the zoological gardens of San Diego, Washington, Baltimore, Dallas, London, Paignton, Vienna, Nagoya and Takamatsu and also in the Tigoni Primate Research Centre, Limuru, Kenya, and at the Virus Research Institute, Entebbe,

Uganda. At the last mentioned, the infant was born 14 March 1959 ; the London baby was born 24 November 1960. The Tigoni infant appeared on 22 June, but in the previous 17 May the pregnant mother submitted to copulation.

The London birth was witnessed by a member of the public who reported to Head Keeper L. Smith that a baby had been born ; the mother had simply leapt to the upper part of the cage, leaving the infant on the floor. On inspection, the keeper found the mother on the upper floor peering down at the baby, which was still wet and darkly coloured, spread-eagled on the lower floor with placenta still attached and much extravasated blood around. The mother appeared nervous, but the father sat unperturbed and uninterested. After a few minutes the infant made attempts to drag itself along, but was impeded by the membranes ; it emitted feeble cries of which no notice was taken by the mother. After unsuccessful attempts to get her to accept it, the infant, a female, was hand reared by Keeper R. Willis. On recovery it weighed 260 gm. and had a body length of 110 mm., tail, 219·9 mm. Two days later the eyes of the infant were alert and it made attempts to attain a sitting posture ; it could crawl and suckled strongly. In another twelve days it weighed 332 gm. and was attempting to climb ; it could stand on all fours. At nineteen days old it was very active, hopping and running, evincing great curiosity in outside objects, using hard objects to bite on. Its voice was a lemur-like grunt followed immediately by a high-pitched flute-like note. (Plate XXXI.)

VIII. Superspecies *CERCOPITHECUS DIANA* Linnaeus, 1758 *

Bearded Guenons

(SYN. : *Cercopitheci barbati* (in part) Sclater, 1893 ; subgenus *Diana* Lesson, 1840, of Trouessart 1897 ; *Pogonocebus* (in part) Trouessart, 1906 ; Diana group of Pocock, 1907 ; by Elliot (1913) included under subgenus *Pogonocebus*)

COMMENTS

Three forms are known of this superspecies, but all may be regarded as geographical variants of a single species, *C. diana*. This is a large animal of characteristic form and pelage pattern, the subspecies merely differing in the length of the beard and in distribution and intensity of coat colour.

Agreement with *C. neglectus* is found in respect of (*a*) presence of beard, (*b*) a pale femoral stripe, but *C. diana* differs in its more gracile bodily form and (*c*) the chromosome number (60).

Sclater's original definition of his *Cercopitheci barbati* was simply " with

* *Syst. Nat.* (10th ed.), i. 27.

a long pointed white beard ", which would strictly eliminate *C. neglectus*, where the beard, although white, is neither long nor pointed.

Pocock defined his Diana group (which excluded *C. neglectus*) as having, besides the beard and thigh stripe, a white frontal diadem and markedly white chest and medial aspect of limbs. The frontal band and white under parts, coupled with the wholly black face and brightly coloured areas on the thighs, all serve to separate members of this superspecies from *C. neglectus*.

18. *CERCOPITHECUS DIANA* Linnaeus, 1758 *

Diana Monkey

(SYN. : *C. barbatus guineensis, congensibus exquima* Ray, 1693 ; ? *Simia faunus* Linnaeus, 1766, p. 36 ; *C. diana* var. Gray, 1870, p. 22 ; *C. diana ignitus* Sclater, 1893, p. 255, 1894, p. 484 ; Johnston, 1905, p. 191)

VERNACULAR NAMES : French, *diane, cercopithèque diane* ; German, *Dianameerkatze* ; Norwegian, *Dianamarekatt*.

TYPE LOCALITY : Unknown ; probably Liberia (*fide* Jentink, 1898, p. 233). Type locality of *ignitus* " West Africa ". Type skin in British Museum (No. 55.12.24.411).

CHARACTERS

PELAGE : ADULT MALE.—Face deeply pigmented, black or brownish black, becoming blue on lower cheeks, with some sparse black hairs. Among these are several groups of vibrissal type, notably forming a long fringe supraorbitally anterior to the frontal diadem, but also a lateral nasal group of 3 or 4 long hairs and more numerous, shorter, curved hairs on the upper and lower lips. Isolated long black hairs are also interspersed among the otherwise white hairs on the darkly pigmented (dark grey) external ear, especially on the tragus and crus helicis.

Behind the black supraorbital streak is the crescent-shaped white frontal diadem to which the monkey owes its name, being reminiscent of Diana's bow.

Chin with a mass of white downwardly directed hairs forming a pointed beard of varying length according to subspecies. These are continuous laterally and above with the white, backwardly directed cheek-whiskers, which more or less completely obscure the ears. Above these, separating them from the lateral end of the frontal diadem a black temporal bar extends from the lateral orbital margin to the ear.

Crown almost black, at any rate darker than rest of upper parts. Nape, shoulders and sides of back dark iron grey speckled with black ; individual hairs whitish at the roots changing gradually to pale then darker grey, the terminal half being alternately banded black and buffy white, the tips being

* *Syst. Nat.* (10th ed.), i. 27.

black. Some of the hairs show only one short light band, others two and a few more than two. In the centre of the back, commencing in the inter-scapular region and expanding posteriorly to the root of the tail, is a rich dark chestnut (acajou of French writers) unspeckled area; this is sharply demarcated from the iron-grey lateral area, but the boundary zone may be more brightly coloured and speckled. Lateral to the iron-grey area, a black unspeckled zone is continuous with the darker portion of the chest and the abdomen.

Tail with a few reddish or grey-speckled hairs at the base dorsally, otherwise wholly black above and below. Front of shoulder and arm white, continuous with that of sides of neck, sometimes extending distally on to front of forearm halfway to the wrist. Rest of pectoral limb black or nearly so both laterally and medially; where not completely black, e.g. on front of forearms in cases where the white is less extensive, the hairs are speckled iron grey.

Thigh with an oblique, arched, white stripe extending forwards and downwards from the upper lateral edge of the ischial callosity to the angle of the groin. Proximal to this the pelage is speckled iron grey. Distally the front half of the thigh is black, except proximally where a narrow tract of grey speckled hairs extends distally for a short distance from the angle of the groin. Posterior half of lateral surface of thigh and its posterior border white, yellow or even rufous and sharply demarcated from the black. Medial aspect of thigh posteriorly and the whole of the pubic and circumanal areas white, yellow or reddish, the pale area extending distally to just beyond the knee. Anterior part of medial surface of thigh black. Rest of hind-limb black on all aspects. Callosities brown black, becoming unpigmented peri-pherally. Circumanal skin with a greenish tinge.

Throat, sides of neck, chest as far as mammae and whole of front of pectoral limb to a point midway between elbow and wrist, clear shining white, rest of chest and abdomen jet black.

JUVENILE.—The neonatus has crown and back charcoal grey (Cincinnati) or brownish washed with yellow (Paris); under parts devoid of hair; white downy hairs of throat and chest appear at 4–6 weeks, and the frontal diadem, barely recognizable at two weeks, becomes fully marked at six weeks.

Change to the juvenile coat occurs slowly, beginning at the second month, and is completed at 4–5 months (data from Cincinnati birth, teste Leonora Brandt, in litt. and from the Paris Ménagerie, teste L. Strazielle).

From two births of C. d. diana at Goulds, Florida, the young is stated to be essentially like the adult (teste F. Dumond, in litt.), but this probably refers to animals after leaving their mothers.

The young suckles the two nipples independently alternately. It is completely weaned at six months (Strazielle, in litt.).

DIMENSIONS.—See under subspecies.

SKULL.—Cranial dimensions (in millimetres) Both Rode (1937) and Verheyen (1962) have published material data on skulls of *C. diana* without separating typical *diana* from *roloway*. The following are excerpted from their tables :

	Max. Cranial Length	Glabella-occiput	Condylo-basal Length	Biparietal	Least Frontal	Basion-bregma	Bimastoid	Bizygomatic	Biorbital	Palatal Length	Upper Cheek-teeth	Mandibular Length	
Average of 7 ♂♂	109		83		44·5			66·5	57·5	41		76	Rode
	110·4	76·8		58	44·4	49·5	50	70·1		37·9			Verheyen
Average of 5 ♀♀	97·1	71·8		55	41·7	45·1	44·7	61·2		31·8			

Raven and Hill (1942), comparing the skull of *C. diana* with that of *C. hamlyni*, state that the rostrum is stouter, the postorbital constriction less deep, the frontal region more elevated above the supraorbital ridge and the cheek-teeth smaller.

The skull is large and has a more prognathous muzzle than in species hitherto considered, agreeing thus with the *C. aethiops* complex.

DISTRIBUTION, ECOLOGY AND ETHOLOGY (Map 11)

The Diana monkey inhabits the West African rain-forest belt from Sierra Leone to within about 60 miles of the Volta, the Sassandra river (Ivory Coast) separating the two best-known races. A third representative (*C. d. dryas*) has been recorded from a restricted area of the Congo forest, its range being discontinuous with that of the western races. *C. diana* is the most completely arboreal member of the guenons.

Booth (1956, 1960) declares that the species is confined to primary forest and in the Gold Coast it is restricted to the high forest zone proper, and occurs only in mature forest, mainly in the west and south. Its life is spent in the middle and upper storeys and it rarely descends to the lower storey. It sleeps in, escapes to, and travels only in the upper storey, using emergents wherever possible. It thus shares an ecological niche with *Procolobus badius*. Bands are composed of up to 30 individuals which forage over a wide area.

In diet it is almost entirely frugivorous (based on 14 stomach contents examined by Booth, 1956).

In temperament the Diana monkey is lively, active, and inquisitive, comporting itself more like members of the *C. petaurista* Formenkreis than *e.g. C. neglectus*.

Hardy in captivity, the Diana monkey becomes readily tame and confiding. It spends much time in grooming, taking pride in maintaining the

PLATE XXIX

Photo: Mirrorpic

Cercopithecus hamlyni, immature, ♀♀, in London Zoo

PLATE XXX

Photo: E. Kirkland

Cercopithecus neglectus, adult ♂, in Chester Zoo

beauty and cleanliness of its coat. It is said to draw its beard aside with its hand when drinking in order to avoid soiling the adornment (Ogilby, 1838). With age the temperament becomes more aloof and wilful. This occurs at 4–5 years old (Booth, 1960). The voice is distinctive but varied. Besides the usual croaks and chuckles common to all species of *Cercopithecus*, *C. diana* emits prolonged yells. Booth (1960) renders the male's full call as a rather complicated " ki-ki-ki-ki-*kyow*-ki-ki-*kyow* ".

A characteristic display pattern observed in captive examples has the effect of emphasizing the colourful posterior aspects of the hind limbs. This is accomplished by suspending the body below a perch, which is grasped simultaneously by all four extremities, the hands medially and the feet laterally, with the ventral surface towards the observer and the tail dependent. Hereby the brightly coloured areas are effectively presented in a V-shaped design.

REPRODUCTION

Although the Diana monkey has been successfully bred in recent years in a number of public collections (Birmingham, Alabama ; Brookfield Zoo, Chicago ; Miami, Fla., Goulds Monkey Jungle, Fla. ; Seattle ; Paris ; Copenhagen ; Berlin and Colombo), no data have been published and no information is found in the literature relating to the morphology, behaviour or progress of the newborn animal.

Births in Birmingham, Alabama, occurred on the following dates : 22 October 1960, 7 January 1961, 5 March 1962, 7 June 1962 (*teste* Truett, *in litt.* 1964).

In Brookfield Zoo, Chicago, births were on 21 February 1963 and 24 April 1963 ; parents were both *C. d. roloway* (*teste* Rabb, *in litt.* 1964).

A baby Diana monkey (*C. d. diana*) born in the Cincinnati Zoo on 8 May 1950 was reared by hand from the age of two weeks when its mother died. The birth occurred during the night or early morning hours. Its eyes were open at birth. As the mother had no milk the infant made ineffectual attempts to suck the mother's food, and, for the first seven weeks, was artificially fed every two and a half hours, feeding time during the night being indicated by regular crying every 150 minutes.

DEVELOPMENT OF THE YOUNG.—The hand-reared Cincinnati infant at two weeks weighed 142 gm. and measured $3\frac{1}{2}$ inches body-length, 7 inches tail-length. All eight deciduous incisors had erupted and complete milk dentition was present at 20 months. At 27 months the permanent teeth began to replace the milk dentition, beginning with the central incisors. These erupted behind the milk predecessors, which did not fall out until the permanent successors were in a fairly advanced state of eruption. The complete change of dentition extended over more than a year, the permanent canines being the last to erupt, and their arrival coincided with sexual maturity and certain psychological changes.

Growth ceased at four-and-a-half years, at which time food intake decreased somewhat. Daily grooming played a large part in the animal's well-being, but not until she was three years old was the social impact appreciated, when the courtesy was returned by attempts to groom her keeper. The animal survived for seven years and autopsy revealed unilateral renal agenesis.

Infants were born in Goulds, Florida, in November 1962 and March 1964. Attempts to experiment with solid food occurred at six weeks.

(a) *C. diana diana* Linnaeus, 1758,* Diana Monkey

(*Syn.*: *Exquima, cercopithecus barbatus guineensis* Marcgrav, 1648, p. 227; *C. barbatus II* Clusius, 1605, p. 371; *C. diana* Linnaeus, *Act. Acad. Holmiae*, vi, p. 213; ? *C. faunus* Linnaeus, 1766, p. 36; *C. d. ignitus* Gray, 1870, p. 22)

Vernacular names: French, *cercopithèque diane*; German, *Dianameerkatze*. In Liberia " Dandy Jack " (*fide* Matschie, 1893).

CHARACTERS.—Differing from *C. d. roloway* in having a shorter beard, which is black at the base. It is not more than 25 mm. long compared with twice to thrice that length in *C. d. roloway*. This race differs further in the deeper tone of the brightly coloured portion of the thighs and adjacent areas, which are here bright chestnut to rusty brown (between hazel and chestnut of Ridgway). The frontal diadem tends to be narrower and the supraorbital black hairs are white based. Some of the hairs of the diadem proper may be annulated, the pale zones having a yellowish tinge. The same yellowish or cream tinge occurs in the pale annulations of the dorsal pelage, instead of the pure white bands occurring in *C. d. roloway*. Ears tufted with white hairs. In both male and female observed in Racine Zoo, the diadem showed yellow to reddish hairs anteriorly.

The reddish tinge of the thighs and perineum is not removable by water or organic solvents (Booth, 1956), so cannot be identified with such caused by staining from ingested food materials as remarked upon by Sanderson (1940). Iris cinnamon in male, clear amber in female.

The form labelled *ignitus* by Gray, supposedly differing in the bay coloured thighs and adjacent parts, is a typical *C. d. diana*. The name was suggested on the erroneous assumption that the Roloway was the typical form (*q.v.*). See also Sclater (1894, p. 484).

DIMENSIONS.—Elliot published measurements of a single specimen without stating age or sex; head and body, 455 mm.; tail, 820 mm.; food, 130 mm. These suggest a female or an immature male.

SKULL.—Cranial measurements of the same specimen listed by Elliot: maximum cranial length, 97·6 mm.; glabella-occiput, 83 mm.; least frontal, 42·8 mm.; bizygomatic, 62·4 mm.; palatal length, 35·6 mm.; mandibular length, 68 mm.; lower cheek-teeth, 29·6 mm.

DISTRIBUTION.—West African rain forests from Sierra Leone eastwards to the Sassandra river.

* *Syst. Nat.* (10th ed.), i. 27.

The animal, though relatively common in captivity, both in its native land and in zoological gardens, is becoming increasingly rare in the wild, due partly to its being captured for food (*e.g.* in Liberia), but even more from the reduction of its environment by encroachment from agriculture.

(b) *C. diana roloway* Schreber, 1774,* Roloway Monkey ; Palatine Guenon

(*Syn.* : *Simia roloway* Schreber, 1774, p. 186 ; *C. roloway* Erxleben, 1777, p. 42 ; *Le roloway ou la palatine*, Allamand in Buffon, 1789, xv. p. 77 and pl. xiii ; *Le diane*, Audebert, 1797, pl. vi ; *Simia diana* Shaw, 1820, p. 38 ; *C. palatinus* Wagner, 1855, p. 47 ; *C. diana* of many authors, in *errore, nec* Linnaeus ; *Lasiopyga roloway* Elliot, 1913)

Vernacular names: *exquima* (in the Congo ; *apud* Marcgrav, 1648) ; *roloway*, said to be the native name on the Gold Coast (Ogilby) ; French, *le roloway, la palatine* ; German, *Rolowaymeerkatze*.

Type locality : Guinea. No type preserved.

This form has been much confused with the preceding; many authors (*e.g.* Audebert, Ogilby, Sclater, Forbes) having treated the Roloway as the Diana. Jentink (1898) was the first to correct the error. It is perfectly clear from Linnaeus' description that the short-bearded animal was the one he had in mind. Pocock (1907) points out that the original diagnosis and figure of the Roloway indicate a white bellied animal. The account and figure were taken by Buffon from a living specimen, but since Buffon's time, no monkey answering this description has come to light, in spite of large numbers of individuals having been exhibited in European collections from the country of origin. Pocock considered the explanation of Buffon's error to be due to the fact that, when seated, the white of the medial aspect and front of the thighs appears continuous with that on the chest, giving the impression of wholly white under parts. (See Plate XXXII).

Further confusion was added by F. Cuvier (1824), who described and figured as *diane femelle* an example of *C. mitis*. He was, however, aware that his diagnosis may not have been accurate.

CHARACTERS.—Recognized at once from typical *diana* by its longer, pointed beard, which has scarcely any black hairs at the base, and by the lemon to orange-yellow colour of the posterior surface of the thighs, buttocks and perineum. Frontal diadem broader, pure white. Ears untufted.

Booth (1956) observed that an interesting colour gradation occurs in passing westwards from the Gold Coast towards the territory of *C. d. diana*. In specimens from the Gold Coast the hair of the pubic region and thighs varies from white to very pale yellow or orange. The intensity of pigmentation increases in individuals collected farther west, being bright orange in the Bandama river region and rusty red near the Sassandra, *i.e.* almost identical with true Diana from west of the Sassandra. There is, however, no corresponding gradation in the characters of the brow-band or beard.

Iris honey-coloured in female. Nipples pink in an area where skin is otherwise pale blue. Skin beneath white, under parts blue, deepening to purplish flesh colour on hinder part of chest ; abdomen sky blue with a slight greenish tinge, but inguinal region pink.

* *Säugetiere*, i. 109, 186 (Latin name), Pl. XXV.

DIMENSIONS (in millimetres) :

Number	Locality	Sex	Head and Body	Head Length	Tail	Hand	Foot	Ear	Weight (Kg.)
PC.514	Zoo (Chester)	♀ ad.	422	96	515	74·4	117·6	28·7	2·26
PC.23	Gold Coast	♀ juv.	255	78	400	63	91	26	·75
	(Elliot)	♂	512		755		135		

SKULL.—Elliot's measurements of the skull of an adult male are : maximum length, 112·8 mm. ; glabella-occiput, 92·5 mm. ; least frontal, 46·2 mm. ; biparietal, 62·4 mm. ; bizygomatic, 73·1 mm. ; palatal length, 43·6 mm. ; upper cheek-teeth, 26·7 mm. ; mandibular length, 83·5 mm. ; lower cheek-teeth, 34·1 mm.

DISTRIBUTION.—West Africa, in rain forest, from the Sassandra river eastwards to the Gold Coast, its easterly limit being about 60 miles short of the Volta. It occurs on both banks of the Pra and is probably limited in the north-east by the Afram river, a tributary of the Volta. Hayman (1935) records it from Goaso, between the Tano and Bia rivers, Gold Coast. Jeannin (1936) erroneously states that it is common in southern Cameroon, but Perret and Aellen (1956) do not report it there, nor does Rosevear (1953) list it for Nigeria. The Paris Museum has three specimens from the Ivory Coast including one from the Sassandra.

(c) *C. diana dryas* Schwarz, 1932,* Congo Diana Monkey ; Dryas Guenon

(*Syn.* : *C. dryas* Schwarz, *loc. cit.*)

Vernacular names : French, *cercopithèque diane du Congo*, *cercopithèque dryade*.

Type locality : Lomela, on Lomela river, Sankuru district, Congo. Type, male juvenile (skin and skull) in Tervueren Museum (No. 11350), collected by Guilmot.

CHARACTERS.—Differing from typical *diana*, which it otherwise closely resembles, in the greenish grey of the upper back and in the hands and feet being greyer than the back, also in lacking the femoral stripe.

Facial skin black, thickly clothed with black hairs between angle of mouth and line of whiskers, the medial hairs directed downwards and the marginal ones upwards like the whiskers. Face entirely encircled with white (cream-buff) hairs, the frontal band 15 mm. broad, crescentic, meeting the whiskers, which are white and directed upwards and backwards. Beard short and broad, white. Ears with long bushy white tufts. Crown coloured like the back, but somewhat brighter, with finer bandings of individual hairs.

PELAGE.—Upper parts moderate (5 cm. on the back) in length. Individual hairs of back speckled from alternating bands of black and old gold, each hair having two gold bands. Under wool mouse grey. Lateral aspects of limbs more weakly coloured than back ; hands and feet dirty grey. Tail above at the root like the back ; under side paler, black terminally. Hairs of throat, neck and fore part of chest directed forwards, instead of only those on chin and neck being so directed, as occurs in *C. d. diana*.

DIMENSIONS.—Crown-rump length of a young male recorded by Schouteden as 350 mm. Tail imperfect, only about 12 cm. remaining on the type skin.

SKULL.—The skull of the type specimen has a full milk dentition with $M_{\overline{1}}^{1}$ fully

* *Rev. zool. Bot. Afr.* xxi. 251.

developed in the process of eruption, $M\frac{2}{2}$ in the alveolus. Schwarz described it fully, pointing out its general agreement with skulls of *C. d. diana* of corresponding age. The few differences he mentions could be due to individual variation, but he does mention that the teeth are proportionately larger.

Cranial dimensions of the type: maximum length, 76 mm.; basal length, 48·8 mm.; glabella-occiput, 60·3 mm.; biparietal, 59·7 mm.; bizygomatic, 50·2 mm.; palatal length, 22·9 mm.; upper cheek-teeth ($dm^{\underline{3}} - M^{\underline{1}}$), 13·7; length of $M^{\underline{1}}$, 4·9 mm.

DISTRIBUTION.—Known solely from the type specimen in the Tervueren Museum, which was collected at Lomela, about 2·5° S., 23° E., on the Upper Lomela river and kept there for some time in captivity by M. Guilmot. Its photograph, when alive, was reproduced in Schwarz's original description and again by Schouteden in his great work on the Congo mammals.

IX. Superspecies *CERCOPITHECUS AETHIOPS* Linnaeus, 1758 [*]

Savannah Monkeys ; Greenish Guenons

(SYN.: =*Cercopithecus* (ss.) Erxleben, 1777 + *Chlorocebus* Gray + *Cynocebus* Gray ; *Callithrix* Reichenbach, 1862, p. 113 ; subgenus *Callithrix* Reichenbach, 1862, p. 113 ; *Cercopitheci chloronoti* of Sclater, 1893 ; and Forbes, 1894 ; *Cercopithecus* s.s. Trouessart, 1897 ; *Aethiops* group of Pocock, 1907, p. 725 ; subgenus *Chlorocebus* Elliot, 1913 ; superspecies *C. aethiops* of Dandelot, 1959, p. 361)

GENERAL COMMENTS

A well-defined and widely distributed group of guenons characterized not only by morphological peculiarities, but also by their ecological and incidental behavioural differences from all the other superspecies.

All are typical guenons as far as general appearance, size and stance are concerned, and agree with the rest of the genus in the pelage being composed of close-fitting annulated hairs of moderate length over most of the body, but with elongated side-whiskers, usually contrastedly coloured (white or sometimes yellowish) but differing from form to form in respect of their length and direction. Most forms exhibit a white frontal band (*C. sabaeus* exceptional) and usually there is a fringe of long, stiff, black hairs along the brows.

The face is typically sooty black, moderately haired, but occasionally (*e.g.* in *C. p. cynosuros*) the circumorbital region is flesh coloured.

Most characteristic of all is the generally greenish colour of the upper parts brought about by alternate banding of the individual hairs with black and some shade of yellow. Intensity of the green varies considerably, being highest in the West African *C. sabaeus*. In other races, the general effect is

[*] *Syst. Nat.* (10th ed.), i. 28.

yellower, greyish, or in rare cases with a reddish element. Schwarz emphasizes the tendency to colour mutation caused by changes in the relative proportions of the dark element (eumelanin) and the yellow or brownish phaeomelanin. In addition, erythristic individual mutants are known for some forms (*e.g.* an example of *C. aethiops hilgerti* in the Washington Zoo). A number of these individual variants have, in the past, served as basis for the description of supposedly distinct species.

Lateral surfaces of fore- and hind-limbs are speckled like the back, sometimes lighter but never darker. Tail for the most part similar to the body, but the end may be black, in the eastern and southern forms or yellow in the northern forms, while in the races of *C. pygerythrus* a patch of rusty red hairs occurs at the root inferiorly. In *C. aethiops* (s.s.) and its relatives a subcaudal tuft of light hairs projects dorso-laterally around the base of the tail each side.

Under parts and medial aspects of limbs clothed with whitish or pale yellowish hairs on a bluish skin.

The scrotum and neighbouring parts are of a bright blue or greenish tinge, the colour being remarkably constant for each form. In some cases the colour is modified to a violet tinge by virtue of the circulating blood in the subcutaneous capillary network.

Callosities are usually pigmented, but in one form (*C. p. cynosuros*) they are pink.

DISTRIBUTION AND ECOLOGY

The most widely ranging of all the superspecies of the genus, but contrasting markedly from the rest in its ecological preference for savannah country rather than forest. The range extends in the north from Senegal eastwards into Abyssinia and thence southwards, in suitable country, to Cape Province. Restriction to savannah type of terrain does not indicate that they will tolerate desert or semi-desert conditions, but merely that they prefer open park-like country and low scrub to heavy forest. They cannot survive far from water and often are to be found, therefore, in greatest concentration in gallery forests along the rivers, whence they make daily excursions into the surrounding bush. They meet and may temporarily join up with foraging bands of other species at forest fringes. Where arid or semidesert conditions prevail *C. aethiops* is absent or very rare. However, Bigourdan and Prunier (1937) record it from the Aïr Massif (18° N., 8° E.) on the edge of the Sahara, though this is not confirmed by Dekeyser (1950).

Malbrant (1952), Booth (1956 *b*) and Starck and Frick (1958) agree in their observations of the habitat of the forms of *C. aethiops* in the territories studied by them. They found them in wooded areas, but not in rain forest. The monkeys generally feed in the trees, but travel long distances across open country to their feeding areas. They rest in gallery forests. Areas with long and severe dry seasons are not precluded, nor are man-made savannah regions exempt, provided water is available. Tappen (1960) states that near Lake Victoria the animals successively occupy separate small stands of rain-forest remnants or secondary growth, whence they forage in neighbouring native cultivation.

In quadrupedal locomotion, when crossing open spaces, they adopt a characteristic cursorial gait, well represented in Dekeyser's (1955) figure (fig. 95, p. 142). The tail is held obliquely above the line of the back and slightly arched at the tip. This is also figured by Starck and Frick (1958), who in Abyssinia observed that the Grivet adopted this form of tail carriage when running through branches, but in grassland the tail is carried more vertically (see their figure 6). In these circumstances the light tail-tip in *C. aethiops* is conspicuous above the tall grass and is capable of separate motion, thereby being useful as a communicating device.

In diet, according to Booth, they are mainly frugivorous, but grass seeds are also ingested, having been recovered from stomach contents in the field. These monkeys are among the most frequent raiders of native crops.

Compared with the hylaean species, the savannah guenons are rather silent. The harsh *kek-kek-kek* of the male is the sound most commonly heard. Russell (1938) referring to a tame female Grivet mentions chirruping sounds used in defiance, and a cry of fear, emitted when accosted with a stuffed crocodile, which is described as like the sound produced by removing the cork from a champagne bottle.

The bands are not normally very large, though seasonally, when food is short, smaller bands may join up together and larger aggregations are said to be commoner in the Sudan than in the Guinea savannah (Booth, 1960).

Taxonomy

At the beginning of the present century it was customary to recognize five species of green-backed guenons, the Grivet (*C. aethiops*), Tantalus monkey (*C. tantalus*), the Vervet (*C. pygerythrus*), the Malbrouck (*C. cynosuros*) and the common West African Green monkey or Callithrix (*C. sabaeus* or *C. callitrichus*). Pocock (1907) realized that some of these were subject to regional variations accepting *ellenbecki* Neumann and *hilgerti* Neumann as races of *aethiops*, *budgetti* as a race of *tantalus*, and *rufoviridis* I. Geoffroy, *whytei* Pocock, *johnstoni* Pocock and *centralis* Neumann as races of *pygerythrus*. He also tentatively accepted, as full species, *C. matschiei* Neumann and *C. djamdjamensis* Neumann. Included in his *aethiops* group Pocock also placed his *C. nigroviridis*, afterwards found to represent a distinct genus, *Allenopithecus* (*vide infra*, p. 624).

The group was revised by Schwarz (1926) who reduced all the green-backed guenons to the status of geographical races of a single species, of which the earliest name is *C. aethiops*, the Grivet being the type. The majority of recent writers, including Tappen (1960), have accepted Schwarz's estimate. Schwarz, from his study of the morphological pecularities and the geographical range of the various forms, concluded that all had been derived from a primeval form originally located in the region of the Rift Valley, whence dispersal of derived forms has occurred in several directions. He considers the present-day races known as *rufoviridis* and *centralis* as most closely approximating to the primeval stock. One line of dispersal is regarded as having taken the route of the primitive course of the ancient Sudan drainage system (Ur-Schari) towards the Chad region, developing into *C. tantalus*, thence to the west coast, where it differentiated into *C. sabaeus*. A second radiation followed the Nile northwards, developing *en route* into *C. aethiops aethiops*, with offshoots along the Atbara and Blue Nile and eastwards to the Red Sea coast. From here, possibly via the valley of the Hawash on to the Abyssinian plateau, the forms *C. a. hilgerti* and *C. a. matschiei* have differentiated. A third or Vervet radiation went from the shores of Lake Nyasa, where it is represented by *C. rufoviridis*, towards the eastern steppe country, where *C. johnstoni* and *C. callidus* developed and gained the coastal islands, where the insular races *nesiotes* and *excubitor* subspeciated, with a branch following the valley of the Juba river which is now represented by *arenarius*, almost meeting the territory of *C. ae. hilgerti*. The most southern form, the typical Vervet (*C. p. pygerythrus*) is also a derivative of the primary *rufoviridis* stock, and from it, by migration along the Zambezi, the somewhat isolated Malbrouck (*C. p. cynosuros*) was probably derived.

Schwarz's concept of the interrelations of the members of the *aethiops* group as a single species has been challenged by Dandelot (1959). Finding the systematics of the group in a confused state on account of the prevailing similarity of coat pattern, he proceeded to define the characters of the dominant forms and to delimit their geographical ranges with finer precision than had hitherto been possible. To effect this he studied living specimens in many zoological collections as well as museum material in Paris, London and Tervueren. The study led him to adopt Mayr's concept of superspecies to cover the whole group. Within this, clarification of the relationships was possible by recognition of three basic species, *C. aethiops*, *C. pygerythrus* and *C. sabaeus*, all but the last with local subspecific variants. Dandelot's contentions are specifically confirmed by the precision of his determination of the geographical ranges, particularly at the junctional areas. For instance, his resolution of the details of distribution at the area of contact between the Vervet and the Tantalus in the Uganda-Congo boundary region reveals the fact that the local representatives of these two (*C. aethiops budgetti* and *C. p. centralis*) have previously been confused under *C. aethiops centralis*. Admittedly hybridization occurs here between Vervets and Tantalus monkeys,

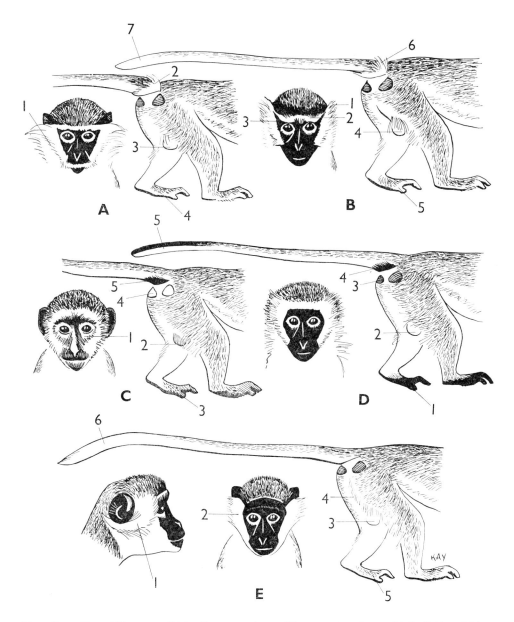

Fig. 67.—*Cercopithecus aethiops* Superspecies.   Diagram to show chief distinguishing features of the principal forms.   Redrawn from Dandelot.

A, Grivet (*C. aethiops aethiops*); 1. Elongated white whiskers; 2. Paracaudal white tuft; 3. Sky blue scrotum; 4. Pale feet. B, Tantalus (*C. ae. tantalus*); 1. Shorter brushed up whiskers with speckled tips; 2. White frontal band of peculiar shape separated by 3. black temporal bar from whiskers; 4. Sky blue scrotum; 5. Pale feet; 6. Paracaudal white tuft; 7. Pale tail tip. C, Malbrouck (*C. pygerythrus cynosuros*); 1. Partially depigmented face; 2. Azure blue scrotum; 3. Darkish feet; 4. Rose-pink Callosities; 5. Red subcaudal patch. D, Vervet (*C. pygerythrus*); 1. Black feet; 2. Scrotum turquoise blue; 3. Pigmented callosities; 4. Red subcaudal patch; 5. Black tail tip. E, Green Monkey (*C. sabaeus*); 1. Semilunar crest formed by whiskers; 2. Whiskers yellow; 3. Bluish white scrotum; 4. Yellow femoral fringe; 5. Pale feet; 6. Golden yellow tail tip.

but the hybrids, in all instances, are either predominantly the one or the other.* This all goes to prove Schwarz's belief that this particular area is a melting-pot whence lines of dispersal have emerged as indicated above.

The five main emergent types may be distinguished by the following key, based largely on Dandelot's results :

KEY TO THE PRINCIPAL FORMS OF THE SUPERSPECIES *C. AETHIOPS*

I. Whiskers sharply demarcated in colour from the crown ; extremities and caudal tip light in colour, never black.

(A) No white frontal band ; whiskers yellow, ending in a tuft of hairs in front of the ear and forming a semicircular crest on temporal region . . .   *C. sabaeus*

(B) A white frontal band present ; no parting in whiskers, all the long hairs running backwards and upwards concealing the ears

    (*a*) Face sooty black. A tuft of white hairs at root of tail ; scrotum sky blue

      (*a¹*) Frontal band pure white, constricted in centre and separated from cheeks by a bar of black extending back from the orbit. Whiskers long, radiating, yellowish, speckled at the tips ; no white hairs on lips or chin ; tip of tail creamy white . . .   *C. ae. tantalus*

      (*b¹*) Frontal band pure white, not separated from whiskers by any colour difference or by a black band. Whiskers long, soft, falciform ; some white hairs on upper lip . . . . .   *C. ae. aethiops* (Grivet)

II. Whiskers shorter, not sharply demarcated in colour from the crown, the two merging gradually. Terminal hairs of tail black or very dark grey. A patch of reddish hairs at root of tail inferiorly and around anus.

(A) Face black, without white hairs on lips or chin ; frontal band pure white, not separated from whiskers. Hands, feet and tip of tail often black, or the former speckled grey and black ; scrotum bright turquoise blue ; callosities black . . . .   *C. pygerythrus* (Vervets)

---

* See also Curry-Lindahl's (1960) observations.

(B) Face and naked palms and soles lighter in colour,
flesh-coloured around the orbits ; hands, feet and
tip of tail grizzled ; callosities rose-pink, scrotum
azure blue . . . . *C. p. cynosuros*
(Malbrouck)

19. *CERCOPITHECUS AETHIOPS* Linnaeus, 1758 *

Grivets

(SYN.: *Le Grivet* F. Cuvier, 1819, pl. vii, *C. griseoviridis* Desmarest, 1820, p. 61 ;
Simia subviridis F. Cuvier, 1821, p. 17 ; *C. griseus* F. Cuvier, 1824, p. 1 ; *C. cano-
viridis* and *C. cinereo-viridis* Gray, 1843 ; *C. sabaeus* I. Geoffroy, 1850, p. 874
(nec Linn.) ; *C. engythithia* (Hermann, 1804) Horsfield, 1851, p. 16 ; *Chlorocebus
engytitthia* Gray, 1870, p. 26, *ex* Hermann, 1804 ; *C. ellenbecki* Neumann, 1902,
p. 50 (see also under *C. aethiops hilgerti, infra*, p. 543) ; *C. (Chlorocebus) toldti*
Wettstein, 1916, p. 189 : *C. (C.) cailliaudi* Wettstein, 1918, p. 643 ; *Lasiopyga
(Cercopithecus) weidholzi* Lorenz, 1922, pl. 1)

VERNACULAR NAMES : In Egypt and Sennaar, *abellen* (*fide* Rüppell) ; Arabic, *abu-lang* ;
Amharic, *tota* ; Tigré, *alesteo* ; French, *Le grivet, cercopithèque d'Éthiopie* ; German,
Grunmeerkatze ; Italian, *cercopiteco grigioverde*.

TYPE LOCALITY : Ethiopia, Upper Egypt (=Sennaar, *fide* Schwarz, 1926, p. 35).
Linnaeus' description was based on an account by his pupil Hasselquist, 1757.†
Type locality of *engytitthia* Hermann, *Obs. Zool.* i. 1, 1804. No locality given.
Type locality of *griseo-viridis*, " Afrique ". Based on Cuvier's " le grivet ". Type
locality of *subviridis* and *griseus*, " Africa ", also based on " le grivet " of 1819.
Type locality of *cano-viridis*, unknown ; name published in *List of species of mammals
in the British Museum*, p. 5. Wrongly attributed to Rüppell. Type locality of
cinereo-viridis, also published in the above mentioned list, p. 5, and wrongly
attributed to Temminck. Type locality of *toldti*, Jebel Riful, near Kadugli, south
Kordofan. Types (two ♀♀, one adult) in Vienna Museum, collected by Wettstein.
Type locality of *cailliaudi*, Blue Nile, Anglo-Egyptian Sudan. Type, ♀ juvenile,
collected by Werne. Type in Berlin Museum. Type locality of *weidholzi* Lorenz,
Egypt. Type locality of *ellenbecki*, Suksuki river, Maki river, Lake Zwai, Abyssinia.
Type, adult ♀, in Berlin Museum (No. 35508).

CHARACTERS

PELAGE : ADULT MALE.—Face black with some white mystacial hairs on
the upper lip, and a few on the lower lip and chin. A narrow white frontal
band continuous laterally with the pure white whiskers, which sweep backwards and upwards and are elongated above so as to obscure most of the
external ear, giving a falciform appearance to the pelage of the cheek. Ears
black.

Crown strongly contrasted with cheeks, concolorous with neck and back,
which are greyish green (between dark olive buff and old gold of Ridgway),

---

* *Syst. Nat.* (10th ed.), i. 28.
† For historical note and discussion of confusion of specific name with a species of *Cercocebus*,
see Anderson (1902) and Allen (1925, p. 333).

produced by alternate banding of individual hairs with black and greyish yellow.

Lateral surfaces of limbs greyer than body (mouse-grey), the dorsum of hands and feet light grey with a brownish tinge, the colour changes being gradual.

Tail speckled greyish above and white beneath throughout, the terminal tuft wholly creamy white. A tuft of white hairs beneath the root of the tail projecting laterally and dorsally on either side of the organ ; typically no red hairs in this situation. Under parts from chin to pubes and medial surfaces of limbs white ; no yellow or red hairs on pubic or ischial regions. Callosities black ; scrotum sky blue (of one examined in the flesh between King's blue and Venetian blue ; another showed streaks of dull bluish violet) ; prepuce scarlet.

ADULT FEMALE.—No pelage differences from male.

DIMENSIONS (in millimetres) :

Number	Locality	Sex	Head and Body	Head Length	Tail	Foot	Ear	Weight (kg.)
B.M.	N.E. Africa	♂	480	115	645	135	31	4·5
6.11.1.3	Metola, Shoa	?	510	—	600	—	—	—

SKULL.—Cranial dimensions, see under subspecies.

DISTRIBUTION (Map 13)

North-east Africa from the Red Sea coast near Tokar southwards through Abyssinia as far as 5° N. The range recedes from the coast, eliminating parts of Eritrea, eastern Abyssinia and Somalia. Along the Upper Nile the range forms a salient as far as the westward loop, north of Atbara. Westwards the Grivet meets the eastern range of the Tantalus about the border between the Upper Nile and Bahr-el-Ghazal provinces of the Sudan.

Within this area four local races may be recognized : *aethiops* in the north, *hilgerti* in the south-east and *ellenbecki* and *zavattarii* in the west.

Grivets have much the same habitat preferences as the other savannah guenons, being characteristic of bush-steppe country on the tablelands of the southern Sudan and Abyssinia. They depend on the proximity of water courses or lakes for survival and have their resting places in gallery forest, whence they travel through the grasslands in their daily foraging excursions. In tall grass they stand erect to peer over the terrain, and in crossing it they run swiftly towards their goal, with the tail held vertically and its tip curved over caudally. According to Starck and Frick (1958) the pale tip of the tail is very conspicuous in these circumstances and there is evidence that it is capable of independent movement, thus serving as a semaphore. Some races, at least, ascend the mountains to comparatively high altitudes, where they resort to bamboo forest.

Taxonomy

In 1917 Wettstein (1918) revised the savannah guenons of north-eastern Africa, which he treated under the subgenus *Chlorocebus*. He maintained he was able to recognize two groups of species, a northern and a southern, each with three forms, all ranked as full species.

The northern group is described as brownish yellow in upper pelage without any greenish tinge ; the southern forms being distinctly greenish or yellowish. The range of the former is stated to cover northern Abyssinia, Eritrea, the Atbara region and also the lower Blue Nile and the White Nile below Khartoum. The southern group ranges over the area between the Blue and the White Nile, extending along the latter as far as Goz Abu Guma, and on the former as far north as Wadi Medani, failing, however, to reach Kordofan.

Both groups are stated to comprise three forms hitherto undescribed. Three are described (two as new) in the paper in question, viz. : (1) *C. (Chlorocebus) cailliaudi*. (2) *C. (C) griseoviridis* Desmarest (= *aethiops* Linnaeus). (3) *C. (C) toldti*.

Schwarz (1926) synonymized all these forms with the typical Grivet, explaining the differences as due to individual variation in melanin distribution, but he recognized Neumann's *hilgerti* and *matschiei* as distinct. He treated *ellenbecki* Neumann and *djamdjamensis* Neumann as synonyms of *hilgerti*. With new material at his disposal, de Beaux (1943) conclusively demonstrated that *ellenbecki*, *matschiei* and *djamdjamensis* all represent the same animal, the first mentioned name having priority. At the same time the Grivet of the Sagan and Lower Omo was described as new under the name *zavattarii*.

(a) *C. aethiops aethiops* Linnaeus, 1758,* Grivet, Ethiopian Grivet

    (*Syn.* : *Simia aethiops* Linnaeus in Hasselquist, 1757, p. 190 : *le grivet* F. Cuvier, 1819, pl. 39, and other synonyms as under species ; *C. sabaeus* Forbes, 1894, p. 56 ; *C. griseoviridis* Elliot, 1913, p. 336)

    CHARACTERS.—As for the species. Differing from *hilgerti* in the absence of any rufous element in the pelage, and from *ellenbecki* in its lighter colour.

    Upper parts grey-green, frequently with yellowish tinge, the lighter bands of the dorsal hairs between dark olive-buff and old gold. White frontal band distinct, but narrow, bordered anteriorly by long black brow hairs, not sharply defined from the brow-band. Whitish moustache on upper lip.

    VARIATIONS.—The differences upon which Wettstein's *cailliaudi* are based are evidently individual only, since the skin is that of a juvenile female, probably from

---

    * *Loc. cit.*

El Aes, a little west of Sennaar on the White Nile, and therefore within the range of the nominate race. It is almost identical with Neumann's specimen from Goz Abu Guma, which Wettstein himself regarded as a typical *griseo-viridis* (= *aethiops*). *C. toldti* is based upon very inadequate material (*fide* Schwarz).

DIMENSIONS.—Of a male skin from Goz Abu Guma, White Nile, in the Berlin Museum, given by Elliot as head and body 540 mm., tail 620 mm.

SKULL.—Khajuria (1954) gives the following measurements of crania in the Calcutta Museum to which are added others taken personally in the United States National Museum, Washington.

Cranial measurements (in millimetres) :

Locality	?	?	?	Anseba Valley	Umbarbit, Sudan		
Number	Zoological Survey of India				U.S. Nat. Mus.		
	11822	11892	12073	12346	252701	252703	252702
Sex	♂	♂	♂	♂	♂	♂	♀
Max. cranial length	98·8	103·4	96·9	96·7	97	95·5	85
Glabella-occiput	—	—	—	—	73	71	67
Condylo-basal	82·3	83·6	76·8	72·4	—	—	—
Biparietal	—	—	—	—	54	51	48
Least frontal	—	—	—	—	41	40	38
Bimastoid	—	—	—	—	55	53	47
Basion-bregma	—	—	—	—	47·5	47	45
Bizygomatic	63·2	67·8	65·2	66·9	67	62	55
Biorbital	44·8	48·5	47·5	45	56	53	48
Palatal length	—	—	—	—	39·5	37	32
Maxillary width	25·2	28·2	27·5	25·5	—	—	—
$C^1 - M^2$	35·6	32·5	28·6	30·5	—	—	—
Upper cheek-teeth	—	—	—	—	26	26	19
Mandibular length	72·7	71·3	—	67	70	66	55
Lower cheek-teeth	—	—	—	—	32	33	27 $M_{\bar{3}}$ not up. Socket included in measurement

DISTRIBUTION.—The most northern and most widely ranging race of the Grivet. Its distribution includes the Nile Valley as far north as, and inclusive of, the great loop north of Atbara and includes therefore the whole of southern Sudan (Darfur, Kordofan, Bahr-el-Ghazal and the Upper Nile and Equatoria provinces) and also the northern half, at least, of Abyssinia, reaching to Red Sea coast between Port Sudan and the Eritrean border, but receding to the south as indicated on the maps

12, 13, 14. Cailliaud (1826) reported it from near Moqrat island and Anderson (1902) says it occurs along the bend of the Nile at Abu-hamad. Cailliaud also found these monkeys common on the right bank of the Blue Nile between the confluences of the Rahad and Dinder rivers.

Referring to Abyssinia, Starck and Frick (1958) state that *C. aethiops* is extraordinarily widely distributed and by far the most frequently met of all the Primates of the area. With careful study they declare that four to five subspecific forms of Grivet can be recognized. They quote de Beaux (1943) as authority for the occurrence of the nominate race in the north (Eritrea, Danakil plain), but had no personal acquaintance with it. The southern extent of this form along the Hawash valley is uncertain. In the east, on the Somali tableland, the range meets that of *C. aethiops hilgerti* in the Harar province in the basin of the Webi Shebeli. In the south-west *C. aethiops* meets the area occupied by the form described by de Beaux (1943) as new under the name *C. aethiops zavattarii*, but the type locality of this form seems to be extremely close to that of the form described earlier as *matschiei* by Neumann (1894).

Starck and Frick (*loc. cit.*) state that the savannah guenons are characteristic inhabitants of the bush-steppe country, especially where marginal to the hylaea. Their survival is dependent upon the proximity of water courses or lakes and their resting places are frequently in gallery forests.

The altitudinal range extends at least as high as 1200 m. (Rode, 1937). Horsfield (1851) mentions one in the East India Company's Museum collected by Sir W. C. Harris in Abyssinia and gives the range as from sea-level up to 4000 feet. This specimen, however, may pertain to the subspecies *ellenbecki*. Material in the Calcutta Museum is listed by Khajuria (1954) as from Adigrat, Tigré, altitude 8000 feet and from the Anseba valley, Eritrea, altitude 4000 feet, collected on Blandford's expedition of 1868.

(b) *C. aethiops hilgerti* O. Neumann, 1902,[*] Abyssinian Grivet

Vernacular names : As for the species. Strand (1931) gives *fota* as native name in Abyssinia.

Type locality : Gobeli river, Webi Schebeli (= Shibeli), Galla country, East Abyssinia. Type, adult male, skin and skull in Berlin Museum (No. 35503).

CHARACTERS

PELAGE.—Very similar to typical *aethiops*, differing only in its darker colour, with a tendency to rufosity of the upper parts, which are of a general reddish-olive tone (olive lake of Ridgway). Black and white frontal bands very narrow but well defined. Whiskers long and white. Arms and legs (between knees) laterally dark iron grey. Hands and feet brownish black, not sharply defined proximally from the grey. Tail bicoloured, above blackish grey mixed with olive, below grey with a creamy white tip. A rusty brown spot or tuft on either side of the root of the tail, varying in extent and intensity. Under parts, including medial surfaces of limbs, white.

JUVENILE.—The rusty red tuft at the root of the tail is lacking ; hands and feet grey.

VARIATIONS.—The type male is the most intensely coloured of the available series. Schwarz (1926) says that an old male from the Djaffa mountains (Berlin Museum, No. 35506) comes nearest. The type of *ellenbecki* is a young female and somewhat lighter coloured than the adult males. An old female (from the Maki river, north of

[*] *Sb. Ges. naturf. Fr., Berlin,* no. 3, p. 50.

Lake Zuai, No. 35507) designated by Neumann as *ellenbecki* differs in no way from another female (No. 35508) from Abu el Kassim. On these grounds Schwarz was constrained to synonymize *ellenbecki* with *hilgerti* (see, however, *infra*, p. 545).

The type of *djamdjamensis* is different from the above, inclining towards *matschiei*, but the upper parts are paler, the reddish tone replaced by yellowish ; hind-limbs from knee ashy grey ; tail rather short, blackish grey, tinged above at the base with olive, blacker distally, paler beneath. The pelage is long especially about the shoulders, where it forms a kind of mantle and fringes on the belly and hind-limbs. The whiskers, on the other hand, are short, though no shorter than in a specimen of *hilgerti* from Gara Mulata. Schwarz declares the shortness of the tail to be due to a defect, the light-coloured tip being absent, and in any event its pelage can be considered as a local adaptation to the cold montane locality and therefore not a mutation demanding nomenclatural recognition.

On the other hand, frank erythristic individual mutants are known. An adult female of this category in the Washington Zoo was captured from a band composed of normally coloured individuals by W. T. Roth. In general colour it is reminiscent of an *Erythrocebus*, an impression which is augmented by the long white whiskers. The crown is orange red, brighter than the body. Entire length of both fore- and hind-limbs whitish on both aspects, except for a little buff on the lateral aspect of the thigh. Tail biscuit coloured above and below, but with no white tuft at the root. Under parts dirty white. Face and ears dusky ; palms and soles particoloured.

An adult male from Wahambra, Abyssinia, in the U.S. National Museum (No. 259445), collected by A. M. Bailey, April 1927, has the usual tawny dorsal pelage of *hilgerti* and is contrastedly white below ; there is a black transverse occipital band recalling that in some forms of the *petaurista* assemblage. Virtually no black hairs are present on hands or feet.

In an example assigned by Strand (1931) to this race, the rusty spot beneath the tail root is lacking, and the crown darker than the back.

DIMENSIONS.—Of an adult female from Central Abyssinia (DB 5/55) : weight 3·5 kg. ; head and body, 465 mm. ; head length, 120 mm. ; tail 530 mm. ; foot, 130 mm. ; ear, morphological length, 30 mm. ; physiognomic height, 40 mm.

SKULL.—Cranial measurements, presumably of type male, given by Elliot as : total length, 96 mm. ; occipito-nasal, 82 mm. ; least frontal, 40 mm. ; bizygomatic, 66 mm. ; upper cheek-teeth, 22 mm. ; mandibular breadth, 68 mm. ; lower cheek-teeth, 27 mm. Of a male skull from Wahambra, collected by A. M. Bailey (U.S. National Museum, No. 259445) : maximum length, 99 mm. ; glabella-occiput, 77 mm. ; biparietal, 56 mm. ; least frontal, 40 mm. ; bimastoid, 56 mm. ; basion-bregma, 53 mm. ; bizygomatic, 68 mm. ; biorbital, 57 mm. ; palatal length, 34 mm. ; upper cheek-teeth (M$\underline{3}$ not up on one side), 24 mm. ; mandibular length, 68 mm. ; lower cheek-teeth, 32 mm. Of an adult male from Belet Uen, Upper Webi Shibeli, measured by de Beaux (1924), maximum length, 95 mm. ; glabella-occiput, 71·5 mm. ; biparietal, 51 mm. ; least frontal, 40 mm. ; bizygomatic, 64 mm. ; palatal length, 36 mm. ; upper cheek-teeth, 23·4 mm.

DISTRIBUTION.—South central and south-eastern Abyssinia at higher altitudes than *C. aethiops aethiops*. Its headquarters appear to be around the headwaters of the Webi Shebeli. Schwarz records material from Gara Mulata, Gobeli river, Webi river (Abu el Kassim), Djaffa (2800 metres) and Diredawa. His records from the Lake Zuai region (Maki river ; Suksuki river ; Abera, east of Lake Abuja, 3300 metres) pertain to *ellenbecki* (*fide* de Beaux, 1943) who assigns to this form an immature female skin (No. 4182 Genoa Museum) from Colubi, a little west of Harrar,

PLATE XXXI

Cercopithecus neglectus ♂, juvenile

PLATE XXXII

Cercopithecus d. roloway (*left*) and *Cercopithecus d. diana* (*right*).   Adults in London Zoo

since it is identical with a male from the middle Webi Shebeli previously (1924) described by himself.

(c) *C. aethiops ellenbecki* O. Neumann, 1902,* Matschie's Grivet

(*Syn.* : *C. djamdjamensis* Neumann, 1902, *loc. cit.*, p. 51 ; *C. matschiei* Neumann, 1902, *loc. cit.*, p. 51 ; *Lasiopyga matschie (sic.)* Elliot, 1913, p. 326 and *L. djamdjamensis* Elliot *loc. cit.*, p. 327 ; *C. aethiops matschiei* Schwarz, 1926, p. 31)

Vernacular name : French, *cercopithèque de Matschie.*

Type locality : Suksuki and Maki rivers, Lake Zuai, Abyssinia. Type, a juvenile female, skin and skull, in Berlin Museum (No. 35504). Type locality of *djamdja-mensis* : bamboo forest, altitude 3000 metres near Abera, east of Lake Abaja, Abys-sinia. Type, an old male, skin and skull, in the Berlin Museum (No. 35505). Type locality of *matschiei* : Malo, Omo river, north of Lake Rudolf. Type, adult male, skin and skull, in the Berlin Museum (No. 35509).

PELAGE.—Longer and denser than in *zavattarii* (50 mm. long on mid back). The darkest form of the Grivet, but in all essentials similar to *aethiops* and *hilgerti*.

Upper parts speckled chestnut and black. Schwarz gives the range as between Dresden brown and cinnamon brown of Ridgway. Limbs darker than in *hilgerti*, with the golden tone of the body reaching down to the hands and feet, which are blackish.

Tail dark olive, with some yellow speckling, paler beneath, but the dorsal and ventral colours less sharply demarcated than in *aethiops* or *hilgerti* ; the tip greyish white, due to some blackish speckling. Whiskers long, white, much longer than in *zavattarii* ; under parts white with a rusty patch on the under side of the tail.

VARIATIONS.—Schwarz (1926) admits that not all specimens are as brightly coloured as the type and some fall definitely into a category intermediate between it and *hilgerti*. This applies to the type of *djamdjamensis* which has been, by different writers, synonymized either with *hilgerti* or with *matschiei* (= *ellenbecki*). Its geo-graphical provenance would certainly place it nearer to the latter.

DIMENSIONS.—Said to be larger than *C. aethiops hilgerti* (Elliot). Measurements of the type male : head and body, 670 mm. ; tail, 590 mm.

SKULL.—Cranial dimensions of type male (in millimetres) : occipito-nasal length, 93 ; least frontal, 42 ; bizygomatic, 70 ; upper cheek-teeth, 26 ; mandibular length, 75 ; lower cheek-teeth, 35.

DISTRIBUTION.—An inhabitant of dark, high altitude bamboo forests in south-western Abyssinia, especially along the upper Omo river and around the chain of lakes from Lake Zuai in the north to Lake Abaya in the south. To the east of the last mentioned lies the type locality of *djamdjamensis*, which, according to de Beaux (1943) pertains here. The vicinity of Lake Zuai provided the type of *ellenbecki*, which all previous writers have synonymized with *hilgerti*, but which de Beaux (1943) has shown to be identical with *matschiei*, and having priority, is the correct name for this race. There is clearly some confusion here and it may well be that the two races are inseparable or intergrade, so forming an east-west cline. More material is clearly required before these points can be satisfactorily settled, but for the present de Beaux's estimate is here accepted.

Schwarz assigned to this race material collected by Neumann in the Berlin Museum from Naja, Mulo ; Bolu Goschana, Doko ; Alesa, Koscha ; Schetie, Koscha ; Bonga, Kaffa ; Anderatscha, Kaffa ; Gadjir, Binescho and from the

* *Sb. naturf. Fr., Berlin*, p. 50.

2 N

Upper Gelo river. Elliot, evidently basing his information on the ticket of the type of *djamdjamensis*, gives the altitudinal range as extending up to 10,000 to 12,000 feet.

De Beaux found that material in the Genoa Museum from Shoa (males from Sciotalit and Let Marefia, Nos. 4179 and 4178) fully agreed with Neumann's *matschiei*, whilst an adult female from Let Marifia (No. 4180) perfectly matched the description of *djamdjamensis*. He found also that both these differed in no essential character from the earlier described *ellenbecki*, based on an immature female from Suksuk to the south of Lake Zuai.

(d) *C. aethiops zavattarii* de Beaux, 1943,[*] de Beaux's Grivet

Type locality : Murlé, Omo river, about 50 miles north of Lake Rudolph. Type adult male, skin and skull in the Genoa Museum (No. 81), collected by Professor E. Zavattari, 21 July 1939.

PELAGE : ADULT MALE.—Size moderate. Pelage of moderate thickness and length (hairs, 35 mm. on mid-back). Speckling distinct on upper parts and lateral aspects of limbs, individual hairs dark grey in proximal half, annulated with black bands in distal half. Cheek tufts of moderate length. General colour of crown and back olive grey suffused with reddish yellow, producing a general effect corresponding well with Ridgway's " saccardo's umber ". Distal half of arm, whole of forearm, of thigh and leg about mouse grey, strongly contrasted with the colour of the back and flanks. Dorsum of hands practically pure black ; of foot the same but relieved on the metatarsal region by some grey hairs ; digits black. Hairs at lateral side of root of tail partly white, partly reddish brown. Tail bicoloured, darker dorsally, paler beneath. Dorsal hairs annulated with black, which increases towards the tip which is almost pure black. Under parts, including medial aspects of limbs white, lightly washed with yellowish, sharply demarcated from colour of upper parts.

The paratype male (No. 79) from Asile corresponds with the type.

ADULT FEMALE.—(Paratype, No. 80), also from Asile, somewhat less grey and more reddish yellow than the type male.

The young female from Sagan (No. 78) has a somewhat lighter pelage of a bright reddish yellow tinge and a more intense and extensive reddish tuft at the root of the tail.

DIMENSIONS.—None given in original description.

SKULL.—Cranial dimensions (in millimetres) :

Number	Locality	Sex	Max. Cranial Length	Condylo-basal Length	Cranial Height with Mandible	Bizygomatic	Upper Cheek-teeth	Lower Cheek-teeth	
Genoa Mus. 81	Murlé	♂	100	77·5	66·3	68	25	31·5	Type
,, 79	Asile	♂	98·5	78·2	72·2	68·2	26	31	Paratype
,, 80	Asile	♀	91·6	72·5	70	60·5	23·5	26·5	,,

DISTRIBUTION.—The range of *zavattarii* appears to be a restricted one, lying to the south of the upland area occupied by *ellenbecki* and south-west of that of *hilgerti*. Localities mentioned for its provenance by de Beaux are, besides the type locality,

[*] *Missione Biologica Sagan-Omo*, i ; *Zoologica*, i, p. 20.

Asile and Sagan, mostly adjacent to the lower Omo river and between it and Lake Stefanie, into the north end of which the Sagan river empties.

Judging from the original description and the accompanying figure, *C. a. zavattarii* appears to be transitional between the Grivets and the Vervets, having shorter whiskers than the former and exhibiting the dark extremities of the latter. Its nearest neighbours to the south, however, are *C. pygerythrus arenarius* and *C. p. centralis* and not, as de Beaux supposed, *C. p. johnstoni*.

(e) *C. aethiops tantalus* Ogilby, 1841,* Tantalus monkey

(*Syn.*: *C. chrysurus* Blyth, 1845, p. 461; *Chlorocebus tantalus* var. f. Gray, 1870, p. 26; *C. passargei* Matschie, 1897, p. 74; *C. pousarguesi* Mitchell, 1905, p. 1 (error pro. *passargei*); *C. tantalus alexandri* Pocock, 1909, p. 545; *Cercopithecus tantalus griseistictus* Elliot, 1909, p. 259; *C. viridis* A. Schultze, 1910, p. 62 (*nomen nudum*); *Lasiopyga tantalus griseisticta* Elliot, 1913, p. 331; *C. griseitectus* Rode, 1938, p. 81 (error pro *griseistictus*)

Vernacular names: Arabic, *mongo*, *boubou*; Baguirmien, *betti kolinngo*; Bornuan, *daguelé keli*; Sara, *betti keli*; Banda,*n'djama*; Kotoko, *fili n'gaba*; Baya, *daoua*; Karre, *gâko*. From Malbrant (1952): French, *cercopithèque tantale*, *singe vert*; German, *Tantalusaffe*.

Type locality: Unknown. Type, a living animal in the London Zoo. Type locality of *chrysurus*: Unknown; based on an adult male. Type locality of *passargei*: Yola, Benue river. Type adult ♂ skin and skull in Berlin Museum $\left(\text{no. } \frac{9101}{7727}\right)$ collected by Passarge. Type locality of *alexandri*: Chad. Type skin (without skull) in British Museum (*ex* London Zoo). Type locality of *viridis*: Bornu (*nomen nudum*).

PELAGE: ADULT MALE.—Face intense black, as in *C. pygerythrus* and *C. sabaeus*, and lacking the white hairs on lips and chin of *C. aethiops*. Whiskers white, yellow at the tips, directed upwards and backwards and concealing the ears; long, but shorter than in *aethiops*, though longer than in *centralis*. Ends of longer hairs of whiskers speckled black and yellow, the tips black.

Frontal band distinct, narrowed in the centre due to recession of its anterior margin, white, and separated from the whiskers by a narrow black stripe extending posteriorly from the supero-lateral angle of the orbit. Long black brow hairs border it in front.

Crown, dorsum and sides of body golden green, rather brighter than Ridgway's old gold. Lateral aspects of limbs mouse-grey, dorsum of hands and feet scarcely darker, the fingers and toes with some white hairs.

Tail longer than head and body, with long, shiny hairs; distinctly bicolored, the whitish or yellowish golden upper surface only lightly speckled with black tips; terminal portion creamy white; a white tuft at the root on either side as in *aethiops* and an extensive rusty red patch on the pubic and perineal areas and around the scrotum. Hairs adjacent to callosities white, but beneath these, in adults and immature animals of both sexes, the rusty or orange red hairs extend. Scrotum sky blue (Amparo blue of Ridgway in one adult male; between Lyon blue and Smalt blue in another). Prepuce scarlet; glans penis pigmented. Under parts and medial aspect of limbs white.

JUVENILE.—The neonatus is uniformly dark grey, almost black, the hairs soft

* *Proc. zool. Soc. Lond.*, p. 33.

and silky in texture, each hair almost white in the basal half and black in the distal half. The colour is lighter on the limbs, becoming increasingly so distally as to be almost pure white on the digits. In a juvenile of 217 mm. C.R. length, a golden bar has developed across the forehead immediately caudal to the white frontal bar. This is the first indication of the development of adult colouring. The long black supraorbital fringe is well developed, continuous in the mid-line with an upstanding median nasal crest of black hairs. These, again, are continuous below with a patch of short, black, downwardly directed hairs on the apex of the nose. Other black hairs of vibrissal type are present on lips and chin. The hairs covering the cheeks mostly resemble those of the crown, but a downward extension of the golden frontal band is detectible, i.e. the sharp demarcation between crown and whiskers in colour seen in the adult is not here evident. Some greenish gold is also appearing on the borders of the limbs and more definitely on the tail. Face, ears, palms, soles, callosities and glans penis are unpigmented.

VARIATIONS.—Chief modification lies in the intensity of the greenish element in the pelage. Pocock (1909) described a living specimen collected by Boyd Alexander from Lake Chad as being less green than the western (i.e. Nigerian) examples, giving it subspecific rank as C. t. alexandri. As in typical animals the green is more intense on the head. Apparently also this specimen approached the Grivet in the length of its whiskers, but differed in having, as usual in tantalus, their summits tinged with yellow and somewhat indistinctly speckled. No white hairs on lips or chin. See also Pocock (1907, p. 733), who describes an abnormal specimen from Jebba, on the Niger (B.M. no. 0.2.18.1) with scarcely a trace of yellow in the whiskers and a dull brownish general colour, compared with brightly coloured living menagerie specimens from the same general area.

Variation occurs in the colour of the terminal third of the tail, a circumstance to which Blyth's (1841) description of chrysurus is due. In this example the end of the tail is described as bright yellowish ferruginous as in C. sabaeus.

DIMENSIONS (in millimetres) :

Number	Locality	Sex	Head and Body	Head Length	Tail	Foot	Ear M.L.	Ear P.L.	Weight (kg.)
24/55	Nigeria	♂ ad.	460	135	650	150	34	40	2·9
PC.488	,,	♂ juv.	204	74	287	69	27	38	

Schwarz (1926) asserts that tantalus is the largest form of the aethiops complex.

SKULL.—Schwarz gives the basal length of the skull of adult males as ranging between 73·4 and 84·7 mm.

A skull in the British Museum, supposedly that of the type, has the following dimensions (in millimetres) ; maximum length, 94 ; biparietal, 53 ; least frontal, 41 ; bizygomatic, 60 ; biorbital, 57 ; palatal length, 39 ; upper cheek-teeth, 25 ; mandibular length, 64 ; lower cheek-teeth, 30. Measurements of the skull (in millimetres) of an immature ♂, complete milk dentition + M.$\frac{1}{1}$ (no. PC.487, from Nigeria). Maximum cranial length, 82 ; glabella-opisthion, 68 ; biparietal, 54 ; least frontal, 40·5 ; bimastoid, 50 ; basion-bregma, 47 ; bizygomatic, 51 ; biorbital, 44·5 ; palatal length, 29 ; upper cheek-teeth, 17 ; mandibular length, 45 ; lower cheek-teeth, 18. Body-weight 1150 gms.

DISTRIBUTION AND ECOLOGY.—Savanna country in West and Central Africa. The western range reaches the coast in the Dahomey gap. North of the gap it meets the territory of *C. sabaeus* in longitude 0°–5° E. The northern range follows the line where the northern savanna meets the Sudanese arid zone, but embraces a salient incorporating the Lake Chad area. The specimen from here differentiated by Pocock (1909) as *C. tantalus alexandri* is considered a synonym of *tantalus*, which thus extends eastwards well into Central Africa. Malbrant (1952) considers that it probably meets and intergrades with *C. aethiops marrensis* in the extreme east of the former French territory, but had no available material to confirm the presence of this race in that territory.

The record of a savanna guenon from the Aïr massif on the edge of the Sahara by Bigourdan and Prunier (1937) presumably relates to the present form (*vide supra*, p. 534), but its presence there needs confirmation.

In the Centre africain Malbrant states that the Tantalus is less common than *Erythrocebus*. Its habitat is more localized, for it tends to be confined to gallery forests bordering the water courses, especially the Shari and its affluents. He reports it at Bahr Azoum and to the north of the Ubangi. It is more arboreal than the Patas. It lives in moderate-sized bands feeding upon wild fruit and grain.

Mertens (1929) records the Tantalus from various localities in the Middle and lower Shari, the lower Logone and also from Bagirmi and Bornu.

Schwarz (1926) recorded the Tantalus from Togoland and thought that there might be grounds for recognition of a separate race in this area (including the Gold Coast). Booth (1956), judging from freshly collected material, did not consider this step warranted as there was no significant difference from Nigerian specimens. The Tantalus does not extend west of the Volta/White Volta drainage which here separates it from *C. sabaeus*. In the eastern Gold Coast the Tantalus occurs in the savanna and also on the Accra Plain.

(f) *C. aethiops marrensis* Thomas & Wroughton, 1923,* Jebel Marra Tantalus

(*Syn.*; *C. tantalus marrensis* Thomas & Hinton, 1923, p. 248)

Type locality: Foothills of southern Jebel Marra, central Darfur, Sudan, altitude 4000 feet. Type adult, ♂, skin and skull, in the British Museum (no. 23.1.1.1), collected 1 April 1921 (Lynes-Lowe expedition). Originally described as a very well marked, brightly coloured, subspecies of *C. tantalus*.

PELAGE; ADULT MALE.—Face and chin black. White frontal band well defined, edged anteriorly with long black hairs. Whiskers yellowish-white, directed upwards and backwards, completely concealing the ears and separated from the frontal band by a sharply defined black streak extending from the lateral palpebral canthus to the neighbourhood of the ear and separated from the crown patch by a narrow tract of white whisker-hairs.

Crown, back and flanks bright buff or golden, darkened on crown and rump by black tips of individual hairs and by their slate grey bases, which are darker on crown than elsewhere. Golden tinge specially predominant on flanks and shoulders. Lateral surfaces of arms, from shoulders to hands and of legs from hips to feet, of a general light grey produced by a mixture of slate-grey and dirty white, without trace of buff.

A tuft of white hair at base of tail each side. Tail above in proximal two-thirds like rump; distal one-third dull yellow; beneath white in proximal two-thirds, distal third like the same region of the dorsum.

* *Proc. zool. Soc. Lond.*, p. 248.

Under parts, including medial aspects of limbs, well haired pure white, sharply contrasted on the flanks from the dorsal colour. The type skin shows only a few reddish hairs at the sides of the scrotum.

DIMENSIONS of type male, measured in the flesh : head and body, 830 mm. ; tail, 1140 mm. ; foot, 145 mm. ; ear, 32 mm.

SKULL.—Cranial dimensions (in millimetres) of type male : maximum cranial length, 118·6 ; condylo-basal, 88 ; biparietal, 56·5 ; least frontal, 44 ; bizygomatic, 68·2 ; biorbital, 62·6 ; C – M.$\underline{3}$ 34·2 ; P.$\underline{3}$ – M.$\underline{3}$, 25·4.

This is compared by Schwarz with the largest skull of typical *tantalus* from Bamunsa, western Cameroon, which measures 117·5 mm. long.

DISTRIBUTION.—Known only from the type locality and adjacent region. Besides the holotype male, from the foothills of the southern Jebel Marra (4000 feet) a juvenile male is mentioned in the original account, from altitude 5000 feet in the south-western Jebel Marra. Possibly intergrades with the Grivet in southern Kordofan or south-western Darfur.

(g) *C. aethiops budgetti* Pocock, 1907,* Budgett's Tantalus

(*Syn.* : *C. tantalus budgetti* Pocock, 1907, p. 733 : *C. tantalus griseistictus* Elliot, 1909, p. 259 ; *Lasiopyga t. griseisticta* Elliot, 1913, p. 331 ; *Lasiopyga tantalus budgetti* Elliot, 1913, p. 329 ; *L. tantalus beniena* Lorenz, 1914, p. 358 ; *L. t. graueri* Lorenz, *loc. cit.*, p. 358 ; *L. pygerythra griseisticta* Allen, 1925, p. 415)

Vernacular name : *nayma* (Boyd Alexander)

Type locality : Bathyaba (=Butiaba) east shore of Lake Albert, Uganda. Type, ♂, skin in British Museum (no. 3.2.12.1) ; the skull is in Cambridge University Museum. Type locality of *beniana* : Beni, Semliki river, Congo ; based on an adult ♂ and a young male. Type locality of *graueri* : Baraka, north-western Tanganyika ; type adult female in Vienna Museum. Type locality of *griseisticta* : 200 miles east of Bambara, Uelle river between Amadi and Surunga, Mongbottu country. Type, adult male, skin and skull, in British Museum (no. 7.7.8.2) collected by Boyd Alexander.

CHARACTERS.—Differing from typical specimens from Nigeria in the fact that the long upper hairs of the whiskers are more pronouncedly speckled and annulated, and in having some black hairs on the hands and feet at the roots of the digits ; also in the presence of speckling on the medial aspects of the limbs distal to the elbow and knee. The pubic area is adorned with a fiery red patch of hair. The black chin is sharply defined from the white throat.

Cercopithecus aethiops budgetti differs from its nearest neighbour, *C. pygerythrus centralis* in its darker, less green dorsal pelage, in the paler hands and feet and tail tip, in its longer, yellower whiskers, in the distal speckling of the medial aspect of the limbs and in the large extent and intensity of the pubic patch. In spite of these features, Schwarz (1926) synonymized *budgetti* with *centralis*.

The confusion has been untangled by Dandelot (1959, p. 364) who, with access to the rich material in the British and Tervueren Museums, has been able to define the respective territories of *budgetti* and *centralis* more precisely.

The type of *griseistictus*, an adult male, is much like typical *tantalus*, but has the extensive area of red around the scrotum occurring in *budgetti*. Its provenance is within the range of the last mentioned.

* *Proc. zool. Soc. Lond.*, p. 733.

DIMENSIONS (in millimetres) :

Sex	Head and Body	Tail	Foot	Ear	
Average of 4 ♂♂	473 (440–495)	598 (575–615)	145 (140–152)	41 (40–42)	Allen 1925
Average of 6 ♀♀	415 (385–440)	571 (555–600)	129 (125–135)	40	

SKULL.—Cranial dimensions (in millimetres) : (averages of two males and three females, with minima and maxima).

Sex	Max. Cranial Length	Glabella-occiput	Condylo-basal Length	Least Frontal	Bizygomatic	Bimastoid	Upper Cheek-teeth	
♂♂	104·9 98·3–111·5	90·2 86·8–93·6	84·4 77–91·8	49·1 43·3–44·9	67·6 65·3–70	59·3 56·7–61·9	34·8 33·5–36·2	from Allen
♀♀	97·9 94·4–100·8	83·1 79·4–86·5	73·6 73·1–74·2	42·6 41–45·1	63·6 61·8–65·3	52·6 50–55·2	31·8 31·6–32·2	

Cranial measurements of the type ♂ of *griseisticta* are given by Elliot as : maximum length, 113·2 mm. ; occipito-nasal, 95·5 mm. ; least frontal, 44·7 mm. ; bizygomatic 77·5 mm.

DISTRIBUTION.—Western Uganda and eastern Congo. According to Dandelot's map, specimens from Mawambi, Makala, Kilo, Nioka, Mahagui, Aru, Vankerkhoven-ville, Kaboto, Faradje, Aba, Dungu, Gangala na Bodio, Yakuluku and westwards from Gemena (Banzyville)—all in the Congo—are frankly Tantalus monkeys and probably therefore representatives of *budgetti*. He also records Tantalus monkeys from adjacent areas in the Mongalla province of the Sudan, namely Moru district, Mongalla and the Imatong mountains, but whether these represent *tantalus* or *budgetti* is not stated. In western Uganda examples of *budgetti* are known from Masindi, Butiaba, Entebbe (side by side with *C. pygerythrus centralis*) and eastwards as far as the Kerio watercourse, flowing into the southern end of Lake Rudolf, north-western Kenya. At the last mentioned locality examples of *C. p. arenarius* have been collected.

Entebbe is the extreme southern limit of the range. In addition to the above localities, Dandelot plots on his map, reproduced in modified form herewith, localities whence Tantalus monkeys have been obtained but where also the population includes Tantalus/Vervet hybrids of predominantly Tantalus facies. All these populations lie to the south of the preceding, in a triangular area between the headwaters of the Lindi and Aruwimi with the base formed by Lake Edward, namely Abok, Beni, Kiniki and Kasindi. All these places are encompassed peripherally by populations of pure Tantalus, except on the east, where another mixed population occurs composed of hybrids with a predominantly Vervet facies.

20. *CERCOPITHECUS PYGERYTHRUS* F. Cuvier, 1821 *

Vervet Monkey

(SYN. : *C. pygerythra* F. Cuvier, 1821, p. 24 ; *C. pygerythraeus* Desmarest, 1822, p. 534 ; *Simia erythropyga* G. Cuvier, 1829, p. 92 ; *C. lalandii* I. Geoffroy, 1843, p. 305)
VERNACULAR NAMES : Zulu, *pusi, nkau* ; Kiswahili, *tumbili, ngedere* ; French, *cercopithèque vervet* ; Italian, *cercopiteco giallo-verde.*

CHARACTERS

All the numerous and widely spread Vervets may be distinguished from Grivets and Tantalus monkeys by their shorter whiskers, which merge gradually into the colour of the crown, by the presence of black on the hands and feet and of a black terminal caudal pencil. A tuft of reddish hairs is invariably present on the inferior surface of the root of the tail and on the adjacent circumanal area, but there is no lateral white tuft at the tail root. Scrotum turquoise blue.

Furthermore, except for the Malbrouck (*C. p. cynosuros*), the Vervets proper retain a completely black face, the frontal band is pure white and not separated from the whiskers, the callosities are black and the extremities are completely black or, even in the palest races, heavily adorned with black hairs intermixed with pale ones.

Aside from these features the Vervets have generally a greenish or greyish ticked upper pelage, greyer on the limbs, and well furred below with white or yellowish-white hair, but they differ locally in the intensity of the green and the amount of melanin pigment in the dorsal hairs and in those of the extremities.

DISTRIBUTION (Map 13)

Vervets have a wider area of distribution than any of the other savanna guenons. In various forms they extend in East Africa from the Juba river southwards to Cape Province. For most of this range the Rift valley is their western limit, but the somewhat aberrant Malbrouck (*C. p. cynosuros*) replaces the true Vervets on the west in Angola and adjacent areas between the Congo and the Cunene rivers. Vervets also occur in the coastal islands of Patta, Manda and Pemba.

ECOLOGY AND ETHOLOGY

Field studies relate chiefly to the nominate race in South Africa, but Allen and Lawrence (1936) record data for *C. p. johnstoni* and *C. p. callidus*

* *Hist. nat. mamm.* iii, Pl. XXIV.

in East Africa. The monkeys apparently occur commonly in gallery forests fringing the rivers from 5000 feet down to the plains, sleeping in the trees but foraging in the savanna. Fitzsimons (1919) states that in South Africa they often occur also in patches of dense bush or rocky kloofs, venturing into the veld on foraging expeditions up to several hundred yards from the sleeping quarters, to which, however, they rapidly retreat at the slightest alarm. Nests of *Scopus umbretta*, the Hammer-headed stork, have been annexed as sleeping quarters. In rocky kloofs they sleep on rock ledges.

In the trees they move rapidly, leaping across gaps with great ease or running along the horizontal branches. In leaping, the extremities are extended in a fanlike way (cf. *C. l'hoesti*). In the trees they are, like most guenons, adept at concealment; they will lie flattened on the horizontal branches so as to be unobserved from beneath.

Bands vary in number from a dozen up to about a hundred, but probably these larger aggregations are due to the temporary fusion of smaller units. Adult males are agressive towards each other and often fight. Old males are often solitary.

Diet is largely vegetarian and composed essentially of wild fruits, berries, tender shoots, bark, flowers, bulbs, roots and seeds and gum of the mimosa tree, supplemented with insects, birds' eggs and nestlings. Allen and Lawrence mention *C. p. johnstoni* as resorting to wild fig trees. In South Africa, at any rate, *C. p. pygerythrus* is an inveterate raider of orchards and other cultivation, besides causing indirect damage to crops by its propensity for eating the eggs and nestlings of insectivorous birds; but some balancing of the results occurs from the fact that the monkeys also devour large numbers of caterpillars, chrysalids, locusts and phytophagous beetles, though also adding spiders to their diet. Fraternization of monkey troops with bush-dwelling antelopes is mentioned by Fitzsimons, the Vervets relieving the antelopes of ectoparasites, which they devour.

Enemies of the Vervets are listed as leopards, caracals, servals and the larger eagles (*Eutolmaëtus bellicosus*, *E. spilogaster*, *Spizaëtus coronatus* and *Aquila verreauxi*) as well as *Python sebae*. If enemies, including neighbouring troops, become too numerous, Fitzsimons declares that scouts are sent out to survey new territory and, if suitable new feeding grounds are available, the whole band migrates thereto; but if another band is met with a fight ensues in which either the old or the invading troop emerges victorious according to size or prowess.

Much has been written on the ethology of captive Vervets, for examples have been kept for centuries. Data have accrued especially from the volatile pen of Frank Buckland (1875) who kept several of them. One of these was an expert at catching mice, which he then proceeded to swallow, head first, after a preliminary grooming of its coat. Spiders, crickets and cockroaches were also captured and eaten, or removed from official traps. When large numbers of such insects were encountered a side sweep of the tail would be made to concentrate them for readier capture.

A predilection for red-hot burning coals by one captive Vervet pre-supposes the existence of some form of anting behaviour like that exhibited more regularly by capuchins (*vide* Vol. IV, p. 387, and Boulenger, 1936, p. 153). Other strange penchants that have been reported include alcohol and tobacco.

REPRODUCTION

There is no direct evidence of a special breeding season even in the nominate race of *C. pygerythrus*. Out of six London zoo births three occurred in March, two in June and one in July (Zuckerman, 1952) Fitzsimons (1919) mentions a birth in South Africa in December. This could mean the reversal of a modality on translocation across the equator, but more records are needed to substantiate such a hypothesis. Shortridge (1934) definitely states that, in South Africa, Vervets breed at all seasons of the year. Booth (1962) provides no information for East Africa, but Cooper (1964) reporting on captive examples of *C. p. callidus* in San Diego refers to births in April, May, June and July. The record of Fitzsimons was a twin birth. Several authors have referred to the fact that the newborn Vervet suckles both nipples simultaneously. The period of gestation is given by Sclater as around seven months (based on *C. p. cynosuros*).

Cooper (*loc. cit.*) has noted active solicitation of males by sexually avid females. Since they show no obvious external signs of sexual activity, the solicitation phenomenon can be of value in charting sexual cycles. Occasion-ally solicitation has been observed on the part of females in early pregnancy and also by a mother carrying a small infant apparently as a lure to divert the male's attention from the infant.

(a) *C. pygerythrus centralis* O. Neumann, 1900,* Black-faced Vervet; Bukoba Green Monkey

   (*Syn.*: *C. centralis* Neumann, 1900, p. 533; *C. aethiops centralis* Thomas, 1904, p. 459; *C. cynosurus centralis* Pocock, 1907, p. 729; *Lasiopyga centralis* Elliot, 1913, p. 344 (?); *C. (Chlorocebus) cynosurus itimbiriensis* Dubois and Matschie, 1912, p. 435)

   Type locality: Bukoba, west shore of Lake Nyanza. Swynnerton (1945) fixes this at 1° 21′ S. and 31° 48′ E. (altitude 3720 feet). Type, adult male skin and skull in Berlin Museum (no. 35502) collected by Neumann. Type locality of *itimbiriensis*: Itimbiri river, Middle Congo. Type ♀ juv. in Tervueren Museum (no. 306)

   PELAGE.—Long, especially about the shoulders. Nose and muzzle black with black hairs; whiskers short, not concealing ears, the ends of the longest hairs indistinctly banded. Frontal band of moderate breadth bordered in front by a thin line of black brow hairs, longest laterally giving the impression superficially of an incipient temporal band.

                    * *Zool. Jahrb.* xiii. 533.

Crown and back fairly uniformly greenish in general hue, due to speckling with yellow (chamois of Ridgway) and black, the bases of the hairs sooty grey on the back, paler on the flanks.

Tail grey, with some yellow speckling near the root dorsally ; its terminal portion black. Rusty red hairs at root of tail inferiorly and above callosities relatively poor in quantity.

Arms and legs laterally light iron grey, fairly sharply demarcated from the dorsal colour, changing on wrist, hand and foot to black, more or less mixed with grey, especially on the foot.

Differing from neighbouring forms of the Tantalus in its smaller size and looser, longer pelage.

DIMENSIONS (in millimetres) :

	Locality	Sex	Head and Body	Tail	
Brit. Mus.	Barumba	♂	530	445	Coll. W. G. Doggett
,,	,,	♀	614	525	

SKULL.—Cranial dimensions.

Schwarz (1926) gives the basal length of the type skull as 70·8 mm. and quotes Allen's data which, however, clearly apply to *budgetti*.

DISTRIBUTION.—Shores of Lake Victoria, including the Sesse islands, and the area between it and the chain of lakes formed by Lake Edward, Lake Kivu and the northern half of Lake Tanganyika ; also to the west of the two last mentioned.

At Entebbe *C. p. centralis* exists side by side with the Tantalus *C. aethiops budgetti*. Localities with populations of pure *C. p. centralis* are Bukoba and Kakindu on the west shore of Lake Victoria ; Tinde to the south of Lake Victoria in Tanganyika ; Kigale, Kibungu, Kisenyi, Nyanza, Astrilda, Usumbura, Kitega ; Rumonge, all in Ruanda-Urundi ; Kabare on the south-west shore of Lake Kivu and Uvira, Baraka and Fizi on the west shore of Lake Tanganyika.

In addition Dandelot (1959) found skins from the following localities showing evidences of hybridization with Tantalus, the Vervet characters predominating: Kasinga, Katebe, Burumba (all in Uganda to the north of the main localities with pure Vervet populations) and at a single locality on the south shore of the Kavirondo gulf. See also under *C. aethiops budgetti* (*supra*, p. 550).

British Museum material collected by C. R. S. Pitman is listed from Entebbe and Busesse (north-west Ankole) by St. Leger (1929).

Swynnerton and Hayman (1951) list *centralis* from Bukoba, Musoma, Mwanza, Maswa, Baha, Kigoma, Tabora and Chunya district of Tanganyika.

(b) *C. pygerythrus arenarius* Heller, 1913,* North-eastern Vervet ; Heller's Vervet ; Desert Tumbili monkey, p. 801

(*Syn.* : *C. rufoviridis* Thomas, 1900 ; *C. aff. rufoviridis* Neumann, 1902, p. 55, 53 ; *Lasiopyga pygerythra arenaria* Heller, 1913, p. 11)

Type locality : Merielle waterholes, Marsabit road, Kenya. Type, adult male in U.S. National Museum (no. 182201), collected by Edmund Heller, 25 July 1911.

PELAGE.—Face black, bedecked with numerous black hairs, forming a horizontal tract along the brows, a vertical nasal tract on the bridge of the nose expanding

---

* *Smiths. Misc. Coll.* lxi, No. 17, p. 11.

below on the nasal apex and thence over the maxillae ; also a horizontal tract on the upper lip and on the lower lip and chin, but not gaining the angle of the mouth. Frontal band of moderate depth. Whiskers almost entirely white, only the upper ones having three light grey zones and the lower ones tipped with black.

Crown and back pale olive green (in general tone about buffy citrine of Ridgway, somewhat lighter than old gold).

Arms and legs laterally deep mouse grey, speckled with whitish, the upper arm alone having some tinge of the dorsal colour. Hand and foot deep brownish-black, the middle line of the foot speckled most with lighter colour. The grey of the thigh does not encircle the root of the tail which, like the paracaudal tuft, is the same colour as the back. A brownish red subcaudal tuft radiating from the angle where the tail joins the body each side, the ventral hairs directed towards the anus and callosity. Below the callosities a few short white hairs occur on the type skin.

Tail distinctly bicoloured, grey above, with some evidence of the greenish dorsal tinge almost as far as the tip, itself intensely black ; beneath white or yellowish white.

This form displays the greatest reduction in the melanin pigmentation of the dorsal hairs. It differs from *johnstoni* in its smaller size, is much greener, has duller limbs and tail and not such intensely black hands or feet. It also has longer pelage and fuller whiskers. From *callidus* it differs in its tawnier dorsal pelage.

DIMENSIONS (in millimetres) :

Number	Locality	Sex	Head and Body	Tail	Foot	Ear
U.S. Nat. Mus. 182140	Mt. Uaraguess	♂ ad.	445	650	129	33

SKULL.—Cranial measurements (in millimetres) :

Number	U.S. Nat. Mus.	182161	182140	182142	182200
Locality	Marsabit Road	N. Uaso Nyiro	Mount Uaraguess	Mount Uaraguess	Marsabit Road
Sex	♂ old	♂	♂	♂	♀
Max. cranial length	99	92	104·5	102·3	91·4
Glabella-occiput	—	70	—	—	—
Biparietal	—	52	—	—	—
Least frontal	42·5	41	42·5	41·7	40·8
Bimastoid	—	53·5	59·4	57·2	49·3
Basion-bregma	49·5	44·5	—	—	—
Bizygomatic	70	68	68·9	67·5	59·2
Biorbital	60	57	—	—	—
Palatal length	33	34	—	—	—
Upper cheek-teeth	24	23	24·8	23·8	22·5
Mandibular length	66	62	70·1	71·2	63·1
Lower cheek-teeth	30	30	29·4	29·9	27·2

Other data are given by Hollister (1924).

DISTRIBUTION.—North-eastern Kenya from north Mount Kenya north-eastwards to the Juba river. The Rainey expedition found it common along the northern Uaso Nyiro and throughout the semi-desert to the north wherever water was available. Commonly met with in small bands in the large, flat-topped acacias, resorting daily to the water-holes for drinking. This expedition recorded specimens from Engare Ndare river, Isiola river, Marsabit road, Merelle river, Mt. Gargues (=Uaraguess) and northern Uaso Nyiro.

Pocock mentions a specimen in the British Museum from the Juba river which he tentatively assigned to *C. p. centralis*, from which he declares it differs only in minor points. Neumann (1902) also refers to material from the Juba river, but without categorically naming it, contenting himself with the statement that it was allied to *C. p. rufoviridis*.

Schwarz, whilst admitting he had not examined the type, assigned to this race material from Darre river, Daroli river, Roba Budda, Denek river, Arussi district, Wedum on the upper Juba, Bardere, Anole (middle Juba) and two skins from the lower Juba (all collected by C. von Erlanger, now in the Berlin Museum).

Material in the U.S. National Museum, mostly collected by E. Heller between July and September 1911, is derived from two principal localities, the northern Uaso Nyiro and Mount Varagess (=Uaraguess). Another from the Uaso Nyiro was collected by Roosevelt in August 1909.

(c) *C. pygerythrus callidus* Hollister, 1912,* Naivasha Vervet

(*Syn.* : *C. rubellus* Elliot, 1909, p. 260 ; *L. rubella* Elliot, 1913, p. 342 ; *Lasiopyga callida* Elliot, 1913, p. 343 ; *C. aethiops rubellus* Schwarz, 1926, p. 40)

Vernacular names : Karamojong, *akwadogot* ; Kisabei, *chokea* ; Lugishu, *musoni* (Allen and Lawrence, 1936).

Type locality : South shore of Lake Naivasha, Kenya. Type, adult ♂ skin and skull, in U.S. National Museum (No. 162843), collected by E. A. Mearns, 21 July 1909. Type locality of *rubellus*, Fort Hall, forest around Mt. Kenya, 4000 feet. Type, male in British Museum (No. 2.7.6.1), collected by S. L. Hinde.

PELAGE.—Differing only a little from *C. p. johnstoni.*

Dorsal pelage throughout somewhat paler than in *johnstoni*, the pale annuli showing little yellower than cream buff of Ridgway, but the dark speckling is somewhat heavier. Hands almost completely black ; the feet with only a narrow median pale tract. The black hairs of the extremities extend on to the digits and are sufficiently long to surpass the digital margins laterally and distally, especially on the toes. Nails black.

Arms and legs laterally iron grey, with more whitish speckling than in *johnstoni.*

Tail grey above, much speckled with black, the greenish element from the back continuing for some distance medially, even as far as the commencement of the terminal black segment (150 mm. long) but grey predominates at the sides ; tail below uniformly grey except for terminal black portion. Under parts well haired, dirty white, sharply demarcated on the flanks from the dorsal colour, the white extending back from just behind the chin, which is black haired. A few red-stained hairs in each groin in the fresh specimen, but scrotum surrounded by long white hairs. Scrotum turquoise-blue ; prepuce scarlet ; scattered crimson spots (product of cutaneous glands) on skin of corpus penis and pubic region.

The usual brick-red-chestnut hairs circumanally and at root of tail inferiorly. In the type skin they extend at least 40 mm. along the surface of the tail.

VARIATIONS.—The colour of the whiskers is individually variable. In none are they pure white, but variably lightly tinged with grey and more or less mixed anteriorly

* *Smiths. misc. Coll.* 59, 1.

with black hairs extending from the maxillary region. The tips of the longest upper hairs of the whiskers are annulated. There are also variations in the extent of the red subcaudal tract.

The differences assigned to Elliot's *rubellus* probably fall within the realm of individual variation only. Schwarz (1926) treated this form as an erythristic individual variant of *johnstoni*, but the type locality falls rather within the range of *callidus*. The general colour shows a reddish element recalling that in *C. p. rufoviridis*, but the type differs from the latter in its pinkish-buff whiskers, throat and under parts ; it also shows completely jet black hands and feet and an ochraceous tinge of the under surface of the tail. If *rubellus* proves to be a synonym of *callidus* the earlier name is *rubellus* and should then be substituted for *callidus*.

DIMENSIONS (in millimetres) :

Number	Locality	Sex	Head and Body	Head Length	Tail	Foot	Ear	
U.S. Nat. Mus. 324981	Kitale (*ex* San Diego Zoo)	♂	465		590	138	37	
,, 324982	,,	♀	436		584	119	35	
Mus. Comp. Zool. 32001	Mt. Debasien	♀	515		560	115	33	(*ex* Allen and Lawrence)
,, 31997	,,	♂ juv.	212		270	68	28	
U.S. Nat. Mus. 162843	Lake Naivasha	♂ ad.	525		610	140	27	(type) Wt. 4·35 kg.

SKULL.—Cranial dimensions (in millimetres) :

Number	Locality	Sex	Max. Cranial Length	Glabella-occiput	Condylo-basal Length	Least Frontal	Biparietal	Bimastoid	Basion-bregma	Bizygomatic	Biorbital	Palatal Length	Upper Cheek-teeth	Mandibular Length	Lower Cheek-teeth
U.S. Nat. Mus. 162843 (type)	L. Naivasha	♂ ad.	110·5	—	84	42	54·5	—	45·5	66	57	43	25·4	72	31·5
162896	do.	♂	103	75	53	43	53·5	47·5		65	59	41	27	69	31
162895	do.	♀	88	68	49·5	40	51·5	46		57	50	30	22	56	29

Hollister (1912) found the type skull, compared with that of an adult male of *C. p. johnstoni*, to be narrower, with smaller orbits and the choanae two-and-a-half times as high as wide. Palatine process of maxilla deeply concave compared with a flat surface in *C. p. johnstoni*.

DISTRIBUTION.—Kenya : area around Lake Naivasha westwards to eastern shore of Lake Victoria and thence northwards to Mount Elgon. The southernmost records are from Ikoma in Tanganyika, about 55 miles east of the Speke gulf of Lake Victoria and Wembere steppe adjacent to the Wembere river, also in Tanganyika (both records listed by Schwarz).

Allen and Lawrence (1936) collected specimens at Kirui on Mt. Elgon and at Mt. Debasien. They found the animals common in gallery forest along the Amaler river from altitude 5000 feet down to the plains of western Debasien.

Two undetermined females in the American Museum collected by W. S. Rainsford from the Cherangani Hills (altitude 6400 feet) due east of Mt. Elgon are mentioned by Allen (1914) and probably pertain here. These hills presumably form the dividing line between the range of *callidus* and *C. aethiops budgetti* in view of Dandelot's (1959) recording of a Tantalus from the Kerio water-course, which drains from the eastern flank of these hills towards Lake Rudolf.

Material in the U.S. National Museum is ticketed L. Naivasha, Amala (=Amaler) river, Telek river, Sotik, Kalialolot Hill (all collected by Heller) and Kitale (*ex* San Diego Zoo).

(d) *C. pygerythrus johnstoni* Pocock, 1907,* East African Vervet ; Yellow monkey

(*Syn.* : *C. centralis luteus* Elliot, 1910, p. 1 ; *Lasiopyga centralis johnstoni* Elliot, 1913, p. 346 ; *L. pygerythra tumbili* Heller, 1913, p. 10 ; *L. p. contigua* Hollister, 1920, p. 2 ; *C. aethiops johnstoni* Schwarz, 1926, p. 40)

Vernacular names : Kitaita, *tsavow* (Allen and Lawrence, 1936) ; Swahili, *tumbili* (Copley, 1950).

Type locality : Moshi, south side of Mt. Kilimanjaro, altitude 5000 feet. Type, an unsexed skin in the British Museum (No. 85.1.17.2), collected by Sir H. H. Johnston. According to Swynnerton (1945, p. 70) Johnston did much of his collecting at " Manderas " (*i.e.* Old Moshi) at a time before New Moshi existed. Hollister's (1924, p. 29) statement regarding the type locality (as given above) obviously refers to Old Moshi, Uchagga, Moshi district. Type locality of *luteus*, Wambugu, south-west of Mt. Kenya ; type ♀ in U.S. National Museum (No. 163086), collected by the Smithsonian African Expedition of 1910. Type locality of *tumbili*, Ndi, Taita Hills, Kenya ; type, an adult ♂ in U.S. National Museum (No. 182229), collected by E. Heller, 1 November 1911. Type locality of *contigua*, Changamwe, six miles inland from Mombassa, Kenya ; type, an adult ♂ skin and skull in U.S. National Museum (No. 163327), collected by E. A. Mearns, 30 November 1909.

PELAGE.—Of type, long, coarse. Face jet black ; frontal band distinct greyish white to tawny white, broadly continuous laterally with the paler cheek-hairs. Longer whiskers and preauricular hairs annulated and passing gradually above into colour of crown. General colour of crown and dorsal aspect of body originally described as " washed out tawny grey " with minimum of black speckling, but most fresh examples have a decidedly yellow tinge, more or less speckled, the greenish element of other races being reduced. The tone is due to the unusual length of the sub-terminal pale zone of the individual hairs. On the anterior part of the body the distal pale (honey-yellow) bands considerably exceed that of the adjacent dark bands (Pocock gives 13 mm. for the pale band, 8 mm. for the terminal black band and 10 mm. for the proximal black band in a hair from the shoulders of 60 mm. length). Posteriorly the zoning shows less discrepancy, but on the flanks it becomes more marked.

Arms laterally greyer than body ; wrists and hands black, sharply defined from arms. Legs also greyer than body, but thighs may show a little yellowish wash ; feet blackish but less pure than on hands. Tail greyish above, with scarcely any yellow wash even basally, becoming pure black at the tip ; inferiorly rusty red at the root, the remainder greyish or greyish rufous to the tip. Under parts dirty white ; some greyish-rufous hairs on the pubic region. Iris light brown (Hollister, 1924 *teste* Mearns).

VARIATIONS.—These occur in respect of the relative amounts of yellow and black in the individual dorsal hairs resulting in yellower and greyer phases of this race of the Vervet. The yellower or tawnier phase is represented by the type skin and by

* *Proc. zool. Soc. Lond.*, p. 738.

Elliot's *luteus*, the greyer phase by the type of *tumbili*. The alleged differences of *contigua* are purely of an individual nature ; the type is of a general pale sandy colour, showing a minimal amount of red subcaudally. A slight rufous wash on the flanks. In the hands only the fingers are black, speckled grey hairs occurring distally just short of the metacarpo-phalangeal joints. On the foot the toes are black with a few speckled hairs on the proximal phalangeal segments. Hollister (1924) on the basis of three specimens states that *contigua* is larger than *tumbili*, with smaller cheek-teeth and a less markedly bicoloured tail.

DIMENSIONS (in millimetres) :

Number	Locality	Sex	Head and Body	Tail	Foot	Ear	
BM.85.1.17.2	Moshi	♂	430	600	—	—	Approximate measurements from dried skins given by Pocock
PC.479	*ex* Zoo	♂	555	575	141	36·5	
PC.551	,,	♀	425	—	113·5	32	
M.C.Z. 31947	Golbanti	♂	390	500	118	33	} From Allen and Lawrence
,, 31961	Kibwezi	♀	450	530	127	33	
U.S. Nat. Mus. 163127	Wambuga	♀	420	550	120	25	Coll. J. A. Loring
,, 163086	,,	♀	420	570	120	28	Type of *luteus*
,, 163327	Changamwe	♂ old	570	720	150	—	,, ,, *contigua*

SKULL.—Cranial dimensions (in millimetres) :

Sex	♂	♂	♀	♂	♂	♀
	U.S. Nat. Mus. 163327 Changamwe	U.S. Nat. Mus. 182229 Ndi	U.S. Nat. Mus. 163086 Wambugu	U.S. Nat. Mus. 182230 Ndi	U.S. Nat. Mus. 252304 ex Zoo	U.S. Nat. Mus. 163326 Changamwe
Maximum cranial length	110	104	89	101	102	90·5
Glabella-occiput	—	—	72	74	75	72
Biparietal	—	—	55	56	56·6	52
Least frontal	46·8	43·9	43	47	42	41
Bimastoid	59·8	60	54	57	56·5	52
Basion-bregma	50	49	46	50	48	44
Bizygomatic	72·6	70	61	68	66	57
Biorbital	64	63	61	68	66	57
Palatal length	45	39	51	36·5	37	32
Upper cheek-teeth	24·8	26·4	25	25·5	26	24·5
Mandibular length	77	70·3	57	66	66	57
Lower cheek-teeth	33·5	32·5	32	31·5	32·5	22
	Type of *contigua*	Type of *tumbili*	Type of *luteus*			M^3 not erupted

PLATE XXXIII

Photos: W. C. Osman Hill

Cercopithecus diana roloway. Roloway Monkey
Below, *Cercopithecus mona*. Mona Monkey

PLATE XXXIV

Photo: E. Kirkland

Cercopithecus aethiops aethiops.   Grivet, ♂ in Chester Zoo

DISTRIBUTION.—*C. p. johnstoni* is the Vervet of the greater part of Kenya and Tanganyika from the coast to the Rift Valley. It doubtless meets and intergrades with *C. p. callidus* in the north-west. In the south-east it reaches the Uzungwa mountains to the north-east of the northern end of Lake Nyasa.

In Kenya it is especially common in the coastal hills (Taita hills) and along the Voi river and on the coastal plain (Changamwe). It also occurs along the route from Mombasa to Nairobi (*e.g.* at Kibwezi and Tsavo) (*fide* Allen and Lawrence, 1936) and near the Tanganyika border at Taveta (material in the U.S. National Museum).

Schwarz (1926) lists material in the Berlin Museum from the erstwhile German East Africa from Kibonoto (=Kibongoto) ; Arusha, (Mt. Meru) ; Middle Pangani river and Masimani mountains ; Pare ya Maboya, Lassitte mountains, Pangani ; Njiri swamp, Masai steppe ; Ngaptuk, Masai steppe ; Guaso Nyiro, Lake Natron ; near Kondoa ; Irangi ; Nai, north Ugogo ; and Kidete, east of Mpapua.

In Tanganyika Swynnerton and Hayman (1951) record *johnstoni* in the following districts : Tanga, Lushoto, Pare, Moshi, Arusha, Masai, Mbulu, Morogoro, Kilosa, Mpwapwa, Dodoma, Kondoa, Manyoni, Singida, Iringa, Kilwa, Liwale, Lindi, Mikindani, Newala, Masisi, Tundura and Songea.

(e) *C. pygerythrus excubitor* Schwarz, 1926 *

(*Syn.* : *Chlorocebus voeltzkowi* Matschie, 1923, in Voeltzkow's *Reise*, p. 47, *nomen nudum* ; *C. aethiops excubitor* Schwarz, 1926, p. 43)

Type locality : Manda island, Witu group. Type, an old male, skin and skull, in Berlin Museum (No. 35511), collected by A. Voeltzkow, February 11 1903.

CHARACTERS.—A small insular race of dull reddish pelage, very similar to *C. p. nesiotes* but redder and, in the darker phase, heavily speckled with black.

PELAGE.—*Dark phase* : Upper parts light ochre brown, very strongly but finely speckled with black, each hair alternately banded with black and cinnamon buff, the tone being purer brown on the flanks.

Face black ; frontal band broad, dirty white, the anterior black line reduced as in *johnstoni*. Whiskers brownish white, all the hairs with black tips and with at least one yellow subterminal annulus. Upper whiskers somewhat more sharply defined from the crown than in *johnstoni*. A very narrow zone of black hairs surrounding the face, but with a large black chin spot, which is continuous with the black hairs bordering the angle of the mouth. No white hairs on the upper lip or infraorbital region.

Arms and legs laterally deep mouse grey, only slightly mixed proximally by extension of the dorsal colour, more so, however, on the thighs than the arms ; but on the tail above to a lesser degree than in *johnstoni*. Hands and feet brownish black, sharply defined proximally.

Tail distinctly bicoloured, above at the root like the thigh then dull light brownish washed, with the terminal portion black ; below yellowish white.

A small, sharply-defined rusty-red area on either side of the tail root inferiorly. Under parts yellowish white

PELAGE : *Light phase.*—Similar to the preceding but with less tawny tinge, the reddish element in the dorsal pelage merging more on the thigh than in the dark phase. The tail is lighter in colour and its terminal black portion shorter.

DIMENSIONS.—No bodily measurements available.

SKULL.—Cranial measurements (in millimetres) of the type old male : maximum

---

* *Z. Säugetierk.* i. 43.

cranial length, 97·2 ; palatal length, 35·6 ; bizygomatic, 65 ; upper cheek-teeth, 23·8 ; mandibular length, 68·2 ; lower cheek-teeth, 27·5.

DISTRIBUTION.—Manda and Patta islands, Kenya coast.

(f) *C. pygerythrus nesiotes* Schwarz, 1926,* Pemba Vervet

(*Syn.*: *Chlorocebus pembae* Matschie, 1923, p. 184, *nomen nudum* ; *Tumbili* Voeltzkow, 1903, p. 583)

Vernacular name : *tumbili* (Voeltzkow, 1903, p. 583)

Type locality : Chake Chake, Pemba island. Type old male, skin and skull, in Berlin Museum (No. 35510), collected by A. Voeltzkow in 1903.

CHARACTERS.—A small reddish insular race represented only by the dark phase. Pelage short, rough.

Frontal band broad, with a light brownish wash, without dark tract in front. Whiskers relatively short, directed outwards, the upper hairs only little paler than the crown and even the lower portion often strongly washed brownish or reddish. A very narrow dark zone surrounds the face, and this is brownish rather than pure black ; chin spot large, brownish black and more or less mixed with light hairs, especially laterally, and not continuous with the black hairs near the angle of the mouth. A few short white hairs on upper lip.

Crown and back ochraceous tawny, more or less speckled with black, the individual hairs somewhat more strongly annulated than in *johnstoni* but less so than in *excubitor*. Body colour extending some distance on to the lateral surfaces of the limbs, the forearm only from the elbow and the hind limb only from the knee being purely mouse grey ; the upper arm speckled more with black and the thigh with white. Hands and feet black, sometimes mixed with a certain number of white hairs. Tail bicoloured ; above dark grey with the basal part showing extension of the colour from the back ; terminally black ; beneath yellowish white, with the usual red patch at the root. Under parts, including medial surfaces of limbs cream colour.

DIMENSIONS.—No bodily measurements available.

SKULL.—Cranial dimensions (in millimetres) of the type skull as given by Schwarz : maximum length, 100·7 ; basal length, 69·9 ; bizygomatic, 66·7 ; palatal length, 35·7 ; upper cheek-teeth (including canine), 24·3 ; mandibular length, 68·7 ; lower cheek-teeth (excluding canine), 30·3.

DISTRIBUTION.—Pemba and the adjacent island of Fundu, off the west coast of Pemba.

(g) *C. pygerythrus rufoviridis* I. Geoffroy, 1842,† Reddish-green Guenon ; Mozambique Guenon

(*Syn.*: *C. flavidus* Peters, 1852, p. 265 ; ? *C. circumcinctus* Reichenbach, 1862, p. 123 ; *Chlorocebus rufoviridis* Gray, 1870, p. 25 ; *C. rufoniger* Gray, 1870, p. 26 ; *C. pygerythrus rufoviridis* Thomas and Wroughton, 1908, p. 165, 537 ; *Lasiopyga rufoviridis* Elliot, 1913, p. 341 ; *C. aethiops rufoviridis* Schwarz, 1926, p. 38)

Vernacular names : In Mozambique *ukoro pusi* (Grant, *fide* Thomas and Wroughton, 1908). In Mashonaland *etsiko* (on ticket of U.S. National Museum No. 21656) ; French, *le cercopithèque roux-vert*.

Type locality : Unknown. Holotype, adult female in the Paris Museum (No. 253 (191)) purchased from Le Vaillant, 23 September 1842, died in the menagerie 19 November 1842 (Rode, 1938). Type locality of *flavidus*, Quitangouha, 15° S.

---

* *Z. Säugetierk.* i. 42.   † *Arch. Mus. Hist. nat. Paris*, ii. 504, Pl. XXXII.

Type, collected by Peters, no longer in the Berlin Museum where, however, there is an apparent topotype young stuffed example, with skull. Type locality of *circumcinctus* " W. Africa ". Probably a synonym of this race. Type locality of *rufoniger*, lapsus for *rufoviridis*, I. Geoffroy, 1842, to whose plate 32 Gray's page reference refers.

CHARACTERS.—A large reddish-green coloured Vervet from Mozambique. Pelage long, loose ; in some examples wiry in texture.

Frontal band white, somewhat tinged with yellow, with a narrow black zone in front of it. Face brownish black, lighter around the eyes. Whiskers long, outstanding, strongly speckled and not markedly contrasted with the crown ; individual hairs of upper whiskers with 3–4 alternating yellow and black bands ; of the lower whiskers with two black bands. Chin spot very large, brownish black, continuous laterally with hairs around angle of mouth. No pale hairs on upper lip.

General colour of crown and dorsum of body pale reddish brown, more or less heavily speckled with black, especially along the spine. According to Schwarz the speckling is heavier on the crown, nape and shoulders than on the hinder back, least marked on the flanks which are bright reddish. Pale bands on individual dorsal hairs warm-buff, the underwool, tawny.

Arms yellowish grey, much darker than in *johnstoni*, the hands from mid-dorsum distally and fingers, brownish black. Thighs much paler than arms ; toes brownish black.

Tail distinctly bicoloured, above olive greyish without any reddish tone extending from the body ; below creamy white ; terminally black. The usual deep rusty area at root of tail inferiorly and on perineum. Under parts white with tendency to yellowish, silky, sharply contrasted from the grey whiskers on the throat and from the reddish flanks. Scrotum dark blue.

VARIATIONS.—Besides the normally coloured phase, both paler and darker, greyer individuals are known. Schwarz mentions one skin where the paler elements predominate over the eumelanin, giving an ochraceous tawny effect. At the opposite extreme are dark olive grey specimens, with the reddish element limited to the flanks, where pale bands register Naples yellow with nevertheless heavy dark speckling. This latter phase is, in Schwarz's specimen, represented by Pocock's *whytei*. Both types are represented by the two skins in the U.S. National Museum.

DIMENSIONS (in millimetres) of specimen in the Paris Museum, from Bagamogo : head and body, 533·4 ; tail, 679·4 ; foot, 127 (Elliot).

SKULL.—Cranial dimensions (in millimetres) of the same specimen : maximum cranial length, 100 ; glabella-occiput, 86 ; Hensel, 70 ; biparietal, 56 ; least frontal, 42 ; bizygomatic, 60 ; basion-bregma, 50 ; biorbital, 53 ; palatal length, 33 ; upper cheek-teeth, 25 ; mandibular length, 58 ; lower cheek-teeth, 29.

DISTRIBUTION.—East Africa, in the area between Lake Nyasa and the coast.

The British Museum has skins collected by C. H. B. Grant of the Rudd expedition at Tambarara in the foothills of the Gorongoza mountains (3 ♂♂ and one ♀) and at the confluence of the Luenya and Mazoe rivers, 20 miles south of Tete (Thomas and Wroughton, 1908). Pocock had earlier assigned to this race a skin in the British Museum (No. 0.11.19.1) from Angoniland, collected by Sir A. Sharpe.

Schwarz lists material in the Berlin Museum from various localities near the Rufiji river (Ruhendo, near Mohoro ; Utete ; Kidete ; Ndirima ; Ssongea and Gumbiro) and from Mikidami ; Tendaguru ; Mkulwe ; Maliwe ; Ukinga ; Ndoe mountains ; Lake Rukwa ; Kitungulu ; Sumbawanga ; Mitora ; Bismarckburg ; Mtembwe ; New-Langenburg (north of Lake Nyasa) and Kionga (Rovuma delta).

The only skin with locality in the U.S. National Museum is ticketed Mashonaland (a male, No. 21656, collected by W. H. Brown, August 1891).

(h) *C. pygerythrus whytei* Pocock, 1907 *

> (*Syn.* : *Lasiopyga centralis whytei* Elliot, 1913, p. 345)
>
> *Type locality* : Mt. Chirangulu, Nyasaland (=Mt. Chiradzulu, Shiré highlands). Type, an unsexed skin without skull, in the British Museum (No. 95.12.7.7), collected by A. Whyte. This locality is sufficiently close to or within the range of *C. p. rufoviridis* to suggest that *whytei* is nothing more than an individual variant of that form.

CHARACTERS.—Upper parts greenish speckled with black, much the same colour as *C. p. centralis*, but differing in the colour of the under-fur, which instead of being sooty grey is a pinkish grey ; also in the greater length of the pelage, especially over the shoulders, and in the longer whiskers, which completely obscure the ears and are speckled as in *C. p. rufoviridis*.

The type skin has a deep red patch beneath the base of the tail, as in *C. p. iohnstoni*.

DIMENSIONS.—None given in the original description.

DISTRIBUTION.—Known from a single specimen from Mt. Chiradzulu, south of Lake Nyasa.

(i) *C. pygerythrus cloeti* Roberts, 1931 †

> (*Syn.* : *C. lalandei* Thomas and Schwann, 1906, p. 780 ; *C. aethiops cloeti* Roberts *loc. cit.*)
>
> *Type locality* : Mariepskop, Pilgrim's Rest district, Transvaal. Type, adult male, skin and skull, in Transvaal Museum (No. 4479), collected by G. van Dam. Original description based on nine specimens (all but one with skins).

CHARACTERS.—Differing from the nominate race in respect chiefly of its smaller average skull combined with larger teeth. It does not apparently differ in colour from the typical South African Vervet, but in this respect it differs clearly from its northern neighbour, *C. p. rufoviridis*.

DIMENSIONS (in millimetres) :

Locality	Sex	Head and Body	Tail	Foot	Ear
Lydenburg district (average of 3 ♂♂)	♂	531	625	136	37
,, ,, (minimum)	♂	470	585	130	35
,, ,, (maximum)	♂	583	650	142	40
Manetsi river	♀ ad.	380	600	130	35
Rustenburg district	♂ ad.	500	695	144	34

Average measurements (in millimetres) of the nine skulls as given by Roberts (who compared these data with the average of 40 skulls of typical *pygerythrus*) are as follows :

* *Proc. zool. Soc. Lond.*, p. 738.   † *Ann. Transv. Mus.* xiv. 223.

	Average	Minimum	Maximum
Maximum cranial length	105·6	102·5	112
Basilar length	71·6	68	76
Bimastoid	59·5	55	61·3
Biparietal	57·4	55·6	61·8
Bizygomatic	68	62·5	72·5
C – M.$\frac{3}{}$	34	31·8	35·5
P.$\frac{3}{}$ – M.$\frac{3}{}$	26	23	27·3
M.$\frac{3}{}$	5·7	5·2	6
M.$\frac{2}{}$	6·6	5·7	7·3
M.$\frac{1}{}$	6·3	5·7	7
Mandibular length	73·32	70·5	77·7
C – M.$\overline{3}$	37·9	35·5	40·3
M.$\overline{3}$	6·5	5·7	7·7
M.$\overline{2}$	6·5	6	7·1
M.$\overline{1}$	6	5·5	6·5
P.$\overline{3}$	10·5	9·2	11

DISTRIBUTION.—North Zululand to the Limpopo river. Of the nine specimens referred to in the original description, two came from the Umfolosi river, one from the Mkuzi river, two from Mariepskop near Pilgrim's Rest, two from Masiene on the coast, near the mouth of the Limpopo, and two from the Crocodile river, north of Rustenburg district. Roberts (1951) mentions one from Buffelsdraai, Pretoria.

(j) *C. pygerythrus ngamiensis* Roberts, 1932,* Okavango Vervet

Vernacular names : See under *C. p. pygerythrus*, p. 567.

Type locality : Toten-Maun road, Ngamiland, Bechuanaland. Type, adult male (skin and skull) in Transvaal Museum (No. 6616), collected 18 May 1931 by the Vernay-Lang Kalahari Expedition.

CHARACTERS.—A flavistic form similar to the type of Thomas' *helvescens*. Colour of upper parts, including flanks, yellow, contrasting with the white under parts, fore and hind limbs laterally pale grey, but the hands and feet are not whitish (*cf. helvescens*), the fingers at least more or less black and the tail black in its terminal half dorsally, with a fair amount of black hair interspersed among the grey on the rest of its dorsal region.

A male skin in the U.S. National Museum collected at Kabulabula, Bechuanaland by the Vernay-Lang Expedition in July 1930 has long, sleek pelage, especially over the shoulders. Its general tone is olive grey with black speckling, becoming greyer on the rump and tail. Lateral aspects of legs sharply contrasted from colour of back, light grey, but arms are the same tone as the back. Hands and feet are not

* *Ann. Transv. Mus. xiv. 19.*

completely black and the tail tip is black only on the dorsal side. Under parts dirty white, unspeckled. The frontal band is very narrow and has a distinct line of black hairs anteriorly.

DIMENSIONS.—Shortridge (1934) states that the Okavango Vervet appears on the average to be slightly larger than the Cunene race.

Locality	Sex	Head and Body	Tail	Foot	Ear
Toten	♂ ad.	500	680	153	38
Shorobe	♂ ad.	470	650	150	37

SKULL.—Stated by Roberts (1951) to be on the average broader than in *C. p. pygerythrus* (69–78·5 mm. as compared with 65–76 mm.) and the cheek-teeth larger (length of M.^{3} usually exceeding 6 mm.).

Cranial measurements (in millimetres) :

	Sex	Max. Cranial Length	Condylo-basal Length	Biparietal	Least Frontal	Bimastoid	Bizygomatic	Palatal Length	Upper Cheek-teeth	Mandibular Length	Lower Cheek-teeth
Average of 10	♂♂	107·7	86·6	—	43·3	60·6	72·5	39·7	26	76	33
								from Roberts (1951)			
Kabulabula (U.S. Nat. Mus. 259447)	♂	106	10	56	43	58	71	42	27	70·5	34
								ticketed " *helvescens* "			
Transvaal Mus. 6616	♂	116	77·5	65	—	—	78·5	42	26	80·2	34

DISTRIBUTION.—The present form is the Vervet of the Okavango swamps. According to Shortridge (1934) it ranges along the Okavango valley eastwards to the western Caprivi and southwards to Lake Ngami. It also inhabits the wooded hills to the north of Grootfontein town. Locally distributed, it is fairly plentiful where high trees overhang the river between Nyangana and the Popa Falls. West of Nyangana the range is discontinuous owing to the greater stretches of open country.

Vervets are unknown, except as rare wanderers, in the dry, sparsely wooded plains between Okavango and the low, rocky hills which crop up here and there within a radius of 50–60 miles of Grootfontein and Tsumeb townships, but Shortridge states that they have been reported from Berg Aukas and from forests between Guntsas and Begus (60 miles north-east of Grootfontein). In the rainy season they have been seen as far south as the first water-hole on the Grootfontein-Nuragas road. It has been suggested that a periodic migration occurs from the Okavango when surface water is sufficient. He quotes Wilhelm as authority for a record from Streitfontein (10 km. east of Grootfontein) and the Urupupa water-hole among the Grootfontein hills.

Roberts (1951) refers specimens from Shorobe and Kabulubula to this form ; a skin and skull from the last-named place was collected by the Vernay-Lang Expedition and is now in the U.S. National Museum.

These animals are difficult to approach in thick forest. They do a certain amount of damage to crops in the Upington and Louisvale districts and are consequently persecuted.

ECOLOGY.—The term swamp, as applied to the habitat of this race of the Vervet, is somewhat misleading. J. J. C. Mallinson, who has collected in the area, informs me that the terrain is not that of a mangrove swamp, but an intricate maze of crystal clear waterways and white sand. The deep heart of the Okavango is clothed with sedge, papyrus, water-grass and floating sudd. The last-mentioned constitutes a " shoreless shore " of unstable vegetable matter, and roots of swamp grasses interlaced below the water level. Bordering the swamps and larger waterways narrow strips of grass meadow occur. The sanctuaries of the monkeys lie peripheral to the last mentioned in riverine forest of mopane and wild fig trees. Specimens were captured in traps baited with seeds and an egg intended for trapping squirrel, *Paraxerus cepapi maunensis*.

(k) *C. pygerythrus marjoriae* Bradfield, 1936 *

(*Syn.* : *Cerpithecus* (*sic*) *aethiops marjoriae* Bradfield, *loc. cit.*)

Type locality : Zoetvlei, near Kuruman, Bechuanaland. Type, immature female collected by R. D. Bradfield, January 1932 and presented to the Pretoria Museum, together with a young male. Now in the Transvaal Museum (No. 6886).

CHARACTERS.—Original brief description states that this animal differs from the nominate race only in its generally paler colour. Roberts (1951) states that the type is only slightly paler than *cloeti* and this may merely be an indication of immaturity. He also adds that there are only a few black hairs on the hands and feet, while the tip of the tail is not uniformly black, due to intermingling with whitish hairs.

Roberts finds more affinity with the north-western form described by Thomas as *helvescens* in these respects, but it differs in lacking the flavistic tinge of the upper parts.

DIMENSIONS (in millimetres) of type skin as given by Roberts, 1951 : head and body, 456 ; tail, 545 ; foot, 130.

SKULL.—The skull of the type has M.$\underline{3}$ fully developed but not erupted, and is stated by Roberts (1951) to be larger than that of an old female *cloeti* from Buffelsdraai, Pretoria. He therefore regards this as evidence of the validity of *marjoriae* as a separate race.

Cranial dimensions of type (in millimetres) : maximum length, 101 ; condylobasal, 79 ; least frontal, 43 ; bimastoid, 57·2 ; bizygomatic, 63·7 ; palatal length, 31 ; upper cheek-teeth, 26·2 ; mandibular length, 66 ; lower cheek-teeth, 32.

DISTRIBUTION.—Known chiefly from the type locality in southern Bechuanaland. It is conceivable that the Vervets of this area form an eastward extension of the range of the Malbrouck, or alternatively southern representatives of the Ngamiland race described by Roberts (*supra*, p. 565). Roberts (1951) considers that the Orange river records referred to by Shortridge (1934) possibly pertain to this form (see under *C. p. ngamiensis*) and this opinion is accepted by Ockerse (1959).

(l) *C. pygerythrus pygerythrus* F. Cuvier, 1821,† Vervet ; Black-chinned Vervet ; South African Vervet

(*Syn.*: *C. glaucus* Lichtenstein, 1811, p. 645 (*nomen nudum*) ; *Simia pygerythra* Cuvier, *loc. cit.* ; *C. pygerithraeus* Desmarest, 1822, p. 534 ; *C. pusillus* Desmoulins, 1825, p. 568 ; *Simia erythropyga* G. Cuvier, 1829, p. 92 ; *C. lalandii* I. Geoffroy, 1842, p. 561 ; *Chlorocebus pygerythrus* Gray, 1870, p. 25 ; *Lasiopyga pygerythra* Elliot, 1913, p. 339 ; *C. aethiops pygerythrus* Schwarz, 1926, p. 45)

* In a privately printed booklet dated Benoni, South-west Africa, 26 Sept. 1935 ; reprinted in *The Auk*, 53, 131, Jan. 1936.
† *Hist. nat. mammifères*, livr. 24, Pl. (XXXIX) and text, p. 2, Jan. 1821.

Vernacular names: *Blue monkey* of English-speaking South Africans; *Blauaap* of Boers.

Quoted by Shortridge (1934): Amaxosa and Zulu, *unkau*; Swazi, *ingobiyana*; Basuto, *inkalatshana*; Mambakushu (Simbukushu), *joko, shoko*; Sikolo, *njoko*; Chinkoya, *kamune*; Chila, *sokwe*; Tonga, *sokwi*; Kaonde, *nkolwe*; Kung Bushman, *gei* (Zukowsky) *tei*; Sikwengo (Hukwe) Bushman, *dire*; Herero, *onjenji*; Ovambo, *ongnhima*; Bechuana, *kxabo, kxatla, thswenjane*.

Personally collected by Shortridge (1934): Ovacuangari, *intsima*; Ovadirico, *ndjima*; Nama Hottentot, //*oreb*, //*oreba*, //*oreg:b*; Berg Damara, //*oreb*.

Type locality: By substitution, the same as for *C. pusillus*, *i.e.* Keiskama, near the Great Fish river, Kaffraria (=Natal) (Schwarz, 1926, p. 45); type, adult male was a living animal in the Paris Menagerie. It died in January 1821 and is now in the Paris Museum (No. 247 (171)) (Rode, 1938).

All the other synonymies are substitute names for *pygerythrus* and therefore have the same type and type locality.

Holotype and two paratypes ($\male$ ad.; $\male$ juv.) of *lalandii* are listed by Rode (1938) in the Paris Museum. All from the Cape of Good Hope, collected by Laland.

CHARACTERS.—Pelage long, coarse, loose. Face black, covered with many black hairs, encircled by a complete white ring of hairs formed by the junction laterally of the moderately broad, pure white frontal band with the anterior hairs of the whiskers, which are likewise white throughout. Whiskers long, more or less concealing the ears, the ends of the longest upper hairs being greyish speckled with black, resulting in lack of sharp distinction between colour of crown and whiskers. Lower cheek-hairs dirty white without black tips.

Crown, neck and dorsal surface of body, also lateral surfaces of limbs greyish, uniformly speckled with black and pallid yellow, giving a general greyish-olive tinge, brighter on the flanks than on the spine.

Arms laterally dark mouse grey, thighs rather brighter (deep mouse grey). Hands jet black, except for a few lighter hairs in centre of dorsum; distal part of dorsum of foot, also toes, black.

Tail without basal tufts, but with red hairs at the root beneath (in an example examined in the flesh, these were vinaceous rufous and formed a peripheral zone around the bare circumanal skin, the dorsal hairs directed towards the tail and invading it only slightly, the ventral ones directed latero-ventrally towards the callosities). Remainder of tail above very dark grey, becoming rapidly pure black in the dorsal third; inferiorly greyish white.

Scrotum variously described as bright blue (Schwarz), turquoise blue (Zuckerman and Fulton, 1934), cobalt blue (Shortridge, 1934) and turquoise green (Pocock, 1907). Cuvier's plate of the type depicts it as green and the description gives it as *vert-de-gris pur*. According to Haagner (1920) the greenish scrotum is a sign of immaturity. In a freshly dead male I found the scrotum microcline green (of Ridgway) with patches of Nile blue, especially towards the fundus, the greenish element much more in evidence than in *C. p. callidus*, where turquoise was uniformly distributed. In the same animal the circumanal naked zone was near vinaceous brown minutely punctated with crimson papillae; callosities brownish. Prepuce scarlet.

Under parts from throat to pubic region and also medial aspects of limbs pure white, compared with yellowish white in *rufoviridis*. Mammary areola Varley's grey, fading peripherally to light, then paler Varley's grey; surrounding skin lumière blue.

VARIATIONS.—Albinos are mentioned by Fitzsimons (1919) who figures a mounted specimen which, when alive, had a blotched face, black and pink, and a few irregular patches of normally coloured fur on its body.

A living albino, adult male, observed in the Edinburgh Zoo had a completely pink face, perfectly white pelage and a typically coloured, blue-green scrotum.

DIMENSIONS (in millimetres) :

Number	Locality	Sex	Head and Body	Head Length	Tail	Foot	Ear	Weight (kg.)
PC.479	*ex* zoo	♂	555	113	575	141	36·5	—
PC.551	,,	♀	425	91	—	113·5	32	2·12
B.M. no. ?	Umfolosi	♂	309		457			
,,	,,	♂	462		—			
,,	,,	♀	403		614			
,,	Legogot	?	453		592			
,,	Hlavisa	♂	465		699			
,,	Knysna	?	446		559			
,,	,,	?	480		571			
U.S. Nat. Mus. 197158	Ubombo	♀	514		584	127		

SKULL.—Cranial measurements (in millimetres) :

	Average of 40 Specimens	Minimum	Maximum
Maximum cranial length	107	100	117
Basilar length	373	64	78
Biparietal	758·5	55	563·5
Bimastoid	60·4	55	65
Bizygomatic	70·7	65	75
C – M.$^{\underline{3}}$	32·3	30·2	34
P.$^{\underline{2}}$ – M.$^{\underline{3}}$	24·7	22	26
M.$^{\underline{3}}$	5·3	4·2	6
M.$^{\underline{2}}$	6·4	5·7	7
M.$^{\underline{1}}$	5·7	4·8	6·8
Mandibular length	74·3	68	81·2
C – M.$_{\overline{3}}$	36·6	33·8	39·3
M.$_{\overline{3}}$	6·2	5·5	7·1
M.$_{\overline{2}}$	6·6	5·9	7·3
M.$_{\overline{1}}$	5·7	5	6·3
P.$_{\overline{2}}$	9·8	8·5	11·6

Measurements of a neonatal specimen, prepared by G. Hubbel (in millimetres) : maximum cranial length, 53·3 ; glabella-opisthocranion, 50·4 ; auricular ht., 26·5 ; biparietal, 41 ; bizygomatic, 30·2 ; bimastoid, 28 ; least frontal, 34·2 ; foramen magnum length, 8·4 ; foramen magnum breadth, 8·1 ; nasion-basion, 30·5 ; basion-prosthion, 30·2 ; biorbital, 30·6 ; interorbital, 3·5 ; orbital ht. 12·6 ; orbital breadth, 12·1 ; nasal ht., 6·5 ; nasal breadth, 3·6 ; maximum breadth across canines, 14·7 ; maximum ht. (orbito-max.), 4·4 ; palatal length, 13 ; palatal breadth 10·5 ; mandibular length, 24·9 ; condylar ht., 7·9 ; coronoid ht., 10 ; symphyseal ht., 6·1 ; bigonial, 14·5 ; bicondylar, 16·9.

DISTRIBUTION.—Coastal and subcoastal areas of south-east Africa from the Limpopo to Cape Province. The southern limit according to Fitzsimons (1919) is around Swellendam and Knysna. It affects the wooded banks of the larger rivers and patches of dense bush in inland districts. It is reportedly common in the Addo Bush near Port Elizabeth, and at one time also at Table Mountain and near Pietermaritzburg in Natal. Along the Great Fish river the monkey is reported by the Namaqua Hottentots to wander a hundred miles or more up the tree-fringed valley, and although the river ceases to flow during the dry season, a chain of pools is left enabling the Vervets to survive.

Shortridge (1934) states that Vervets do not occur in the dry sand-plain and karroo regions of central and western South Africa, except along the tree-fringed valleys of the Orange and Vaal rivers.

Schwarz (1926) records material in the Berlin Museum from Entafufu, a port on the St. John's river, Pondoland and from the Addo Bush.

In South-west Africa Shortridge affirms that, in the Orange river region, Vervets are restricted to the fringing thorn-tree belt, particularly to the east of the Great Augrabies Falls, where the bordering acacia-growth is dense and continuous. It has, however, been reported on the lower Orange and this is the only point south of the Zambezi where it approaches the west coast.

(m) *C. pygerythrus cynosuros* Scopoli, 1786,* Malbrouck monkey

(*Syn.* : *Cercopithecus primus* Clusii, 1605, p. 37 ; *Simia cynosuros* Scopoli, 1786, p.44 ; *Le Malbrouck* F. Cuvier, 1819, Pl. II ; *Cercopithecus cynosurus* Desmarest, 1820, p. 60 ; *C. tephrops* Bennett, 1833, p. 109 ; *Cercopithecus faunus* Ogilby, 1838, p. 333 ; *Chlorocebus cynosurus* Gray, 1870, p. 26 ; *Cercopithecus silaceus* Elliot, 1909, p. 263 ; *C. (Chlorocebus) cynosurus weynsi* Matschie and Dubois, 1912, p. 435 ; *C. (Chlorocebus) lukonzolwae* Matschie, 1912, p. 438 ; *C. (Chlorocebus) cynosurus tholloni* Matschie, 1912, p. 438 ; *C. pygerythrus katangensis* Lönnberg 1919, p. 141 ; *C. p. helvescens* Thomas, 1926, p. 286)

Vernacular names : In eastern Congo *soko* (Frechkop, 1954 *c*) ; French, *le malbrouck, cercopithèque malbrouck.*

Type locality : Based on a living specimen of unknown provenance, probably Angola. No type specimen preserved. Schwarz, by substitution, fixed the type locality as Banana, Lower Congo, so that *weynsi* becomes an immediate synonym. Type locality of *tephrops*, unknown. Based on a specimen living in the London zoo. Type locality of *silaceus*, east bank of the Loangwa, Angoniland (altitude 2200 feet), north-eastern Rhodesia, type in the British Museum collected by S. A. Neave, number not stated by Elliot and skin not found by the present author. Two others mentioned from widely separated localities. Type locality of *weynsi*, Banana, at the

---

* *Deliciae florae et faunae insubricae*, 1786, i. 44, Tab. XIX.

mouth of the Congo ; type in Tervueren Museum—a mounted adult male skin. Paratype skin and skull from Kakongo. Type locality of *lukonzolwae*, Lukonzolwa, Lake Mweru, Tanganyika, type, mounted skin of a young male in Tervueren Museum, collected by Weyns. Type locality of *tholloni*, Brazzaville, Stanley Pool, Lower Congo, now in the Tervueren Museum. Type locality of *katangensis*, Funda Biabo and Kinda, Katanga, Congo Belge. Two specimens mentioned in the original description both in the Tervueren Museum. The second, No. 3494, an old male from Kinda is here designated as the type. Allen (1928, p. 361) gives an old male as the type, and the Kinda specimen as the paratype. Type locality of *helvescens* (altitude 3350 feet), Rua Cana Falls, Cunene river, south-west Africa. Type, female in the British Museum (No. 25.12.4.1), collected by G. C. Shortridge.

HISTORICAL.—The original description of Scopoli is barely sufficient to establish the validity of the name he gave to this monkey. Its assignment to the form of green monkey inhabiting Angola is traditional and there seems to be no reason for discarding it in favour of a more recent one. Scopoli's original diagnosis is as follows : *Simia cynosuros caudata, imberbis ; facie elongata ; fronte fuliginosa ; fascia superciliari albida ; genitalibus masculis coloratus ; unguibus convexis.*

In the more detailed account following the short diagnosis, Scopoli clearly describes a member of the *aethiops* superspecies, and such data as are given fit the Malbrouck monkey better than any other, *e.g.*, the dorsum and flanks are described as reddish fuscous, greyer on the chest and belly, a frontal band is present and the scrotum described as blue, with reddish skin around the anus and a scarlet prepuce, these colours fading in the cadaver.

Cuvier's description and plate of the Malbrouck perfectly agree with the animal now universally known by Scopoli's name. He points out that Buffon's knowledge of the animal was based on a single female (Buffon, tom xiv, pl. 29), but Scopoli's was a male and, from his reference to the colours of the genitalia, affirmed that *cynosuros* was identical with Buffon's Malbrouck.

As pointed out by Ogilby (1838) the Malbrouck was first described and figured by Buffon and Daubenton. The same writer affirms that it was " admitted into the catalogues of systematic writers by the specific appellation of *Simia faunus*, and afterwards by Scopoli under the name *Simia cynosurus* ". This would indicate that the specific name *faunus*, applied by Linnaeus, antedates Scopoli's name, for which reason Ogilby describes it under the scientific name *Cercopithecus faunus* (Linnaeus). Bennett (1833), who was unfamiliar with the Malbrouck, described as a new species under the name *tephrops* a living specimen in the London menagerie. This added further confusion, about which Ogilby makes some very penetrating and critical remarks. Subsequent writers, however, have unanimously concluded that Linnaeus's *Simia faunus* is indeterminable (*vide, e.g.*, Elliot, 1913, 2, 177), although it should be added that at least two of the five indeterminable Linnaean names listed by Elliot have since been accepted as determinable.

PELAGE : ADULT MALE.—Short, smooth. The Malbrouck is distinguished from all the Vervets by the depigmentation of the naked parts, *i.e.* face, ears, palms, soles and callosities. The face varies from dirty flesh-colour to dusky, the muzzle especially being the more darkly coloured, the circumorbital areas being pink or flesh-coloured. In a fresh specimen the circumocular areas, including the eyelids were flesh pink, and the peripheral area surrounding this, bluish, except for the nasal bridge, which is more melanized and continuous with the more darkly pigmented muzzle. The nasal bridge is adorned with the usual convergent crest of short, black hairs and there are numerous short, black bristles over the rest of the face, but not on the eyelids (except for the dense, short, black eyelashes). The nictitating membrane is deeply pigmented, but the palpebral margins are free of pigment, except for those in the eyelashes, which are so closely planted as to give an effect of marginal pigmentation. The iris is dark amber. No white hairs on the muzzle (Pocock states that his specimens had some and Schwarz agrees).

Whiskers relatively short, white, not concealing the ears and continuous above with the dirty white frontal band. Upper hairs of whiskers black-tipped and with a yellowish subterminal band blending above with the colour of the crown. No definite chin spot.

Crown, nape, back and flanks yellowish olive green (dark olive buff of Ridgway) extending peripherally some distance on the lateral aspects of the limbs, the rest of which are grey. Hands and feet dark blackish brown, except the fingers and toes, which are pale.

Tail distinctly bicoloured, above like the back, becoming darker towards the tip, which is black for some considerable distance; below greyish throughout, except for a limited area of reddish hairs at the root.

Under parts, including medial aspects of limbs, greyish white, sometimes tinged with yellow along the middle line of the abdomen. Hairs around scrotum and over pubes yellowish grey. Scrotum violet or azure blue. Callosities rose pink.

ADULT FEMALE.—Like the male but smaller. Hairs on the pubic region yellowish grey; these hairs are continued down the thighs posteriorly forming a fringe separated from the lateral colour by a parallel zone of dirty white. Labia majora distinct, lobate, bluish, enclosing flesh-coloured labia minora and preputium clitoridis. Callosities as in male.

VARIATIONS.—These affect chiefly the degree of flavism and the amount and distribution of black annulations in the pelage. Schwarz mentions a particularly flavistic specimen from Rio Cubal, Benguella, where the pale bands of the dorsal hairs registered aniline yellow. The same specimen had light hands and feet. Probably the type of Thomas's *helvescens* pertains here; it is a flavistic female with general colour pale orange yellow, whitish hands and feet, tail mixed grey and white above, dull white below and with an inconspicuous terminal black tuft. However, its provenance is well south of the area generally accepted as the limit of the range of *cynosuros*.

Elliot's *silaceus*, described from a specimen from Angoniland, east of the known range of *cynosuros*, is also a flavistic animal, yellowish green in general hue, speckled with yellow on the flanks and without distinct black speckling; its tail above is speckled cream colour and black in the proximal three-quarters, black on the distal quarter; beneath red at the root, then whitish grey, becoming buff distally and only the extreme tip black.

Pocock describes the tail beneath as grey throughout. He also describes the dorsum of the hands and feet as grey, including the digits. There is evidently considerable individual variation in this respect, as well as the amount of black at the end of the tail. I have fresh material with definitely pale, silvery feet and toes and the hands with the black confined to the metacarpal region, and here mixed with light hairs.

Two skins in the U.S. National Museum are from what is probably the extreme eastern limit of the range, namely the Kafue river in Northern Rhodesia, one from west of the railway line (collected by Haagner) and the other from Bolengwe (collected by Raven). These two, both males, show maximal divergence. The Bolengwe skin, a young male, is uniformly deep tawny above and soft, silky white below. The dorsal hairs are short and wiry. Frontal band white ; arms grizzled grey, legs similar but paler—clearly an approach to *rufoviridis*. Haagner's skin is much larger, grizzled grey above like a Grivet, but with some yellow in the pelage and not in any respect tawny. Limbs are as in Raven's skin. Under parts very sparsely haired, dirty white. The whole pelage shorter and more adpressed than in the younger male.

DIMENSIONS (in millimetres) :

Number	Locality	Sex	Head and Body	Head Length	Tail	Foot	Ear	Weight (gm.)
PC.469	? (Zoo)	♂	340	—	430	105	40	995
PC.552	? (*ex* CDC)	♀	392	85·5	—	105	24	
BM.25.12.4.1	Cunene falls	♀	485	—	505	117	34[1]	
A.M.N.H. 80787	Capelongo, Angola	♂	470	570	140			
80789	Chitau, Angola	♀	412	493	123			

[1] Type of *helvescens*.

Next to *C. ae. tantalus* the Malbrouck is the largest member of the group.

SKULL.—Cranial dimensions (in millimetrres) :

Number	Locality	Sex	Max. Cranial Length	Glabella-occiput	Biparietal	Least Frontal	Bimastoid	Basion-bregma	Bizygomatic	Biorbital	Palatal Length	Upper Cheek-teeth	Mandibular Length	Lower Cheek-teeth
U.S.N.M. 237324	Bolengwe	♂juv	92	68	55·5	41	53	49	58	48	38	26	53	25[1]
Tervueren Mus. 3493	Funda Biabo	♂old	103·5	—	—	—	—	—	—	—	—	27·6	—	—[2]
,, 35512	Rio Cubal	♀	89·3	—	—	—	—	—	—	—	—		(Schwarz)	
A.M.N.H. 80787	Capelongo	♂	108·8		57·3	45	59	50·2	73	—	37·5	33·5	Hill and Carter	
,, 80789	Chitau	♀	93·6		52·9									

[1] M.³ not up.   [2] Type of *katangensis*.

DISTRIBUTION.—The most widely distributed form of the *pygerythrus* complex and the only one reaching the west coast. It occurs, in suitable localities, from the mouth of the Congo southwards at least to the Cunene river and eastwards almost to the western shore of Lake Tanganyika. It is thus found in the southern Congo, in Angola and north-western Rhodesia.

Localities in the Congo have been recorded by Lönnberg (1918), Schwarz (1928 *a*), Schouteden (1947) and Frechkop (1954 *c*). These are all located in the South Congo savannah and include :—Lower Congo : Banana, Luali, Zambi, Kidada, Kisantu, Moanda, Bakede, Dongo, Isangila, Rocca Island, Matadi, Leopoldville. Lake Leopold II district : Inongo, Kutu (Fini river), Kwamouth. Kwango district : Franz Josef Falls, Bayaka. Kasai district : Gombe (Tshikapa river), Basongo. Sankuru district : Tshopa, Lubefu. Lualaba district : Bukama, south of Lake

Upemba; Funda Biabo, Kinda (Luina river); Sandoa (Lulua river); Nionga; Kapolowe; Kanzenze; Dilolo; Mukishi; Kadia; Lake Kisale. Upper Katanga district: Lukonzolwa; Lukafu; Kasenga; Gaye; Kilwa; Sampwe. Tanganyika district: Moba; Kabalo; Tembwe. Kivu district: Baraka.

Cabrera and Ruxton (1926) add Luluaburg to the Congolese localities. All the localities listed by Frechkop are situated in the Upemba national park and the specimens are referred to *cynosuros* on the basis of Allen's (1939) relegation of *silaceus* and *katangensis* to the synonymy of *cynosuros*.

Hill and Carter (1941), on the evidence of specimens in the American Museum, New York, give the following localities in Angola, Chitau, 35 km. east of Dunde: Chipopia and Capelongo, and mention the following places from which the Malbrouck had previously been reported: Cahama (on the Caculovar river, Jentink, 1893), Rio Cubal (Schwarz, 1926), Cangela and Cubango Mission (Monard, 1933). It would appear to be common along the rivers in Angola, but is rare in the western half of the country.

In the extreme south evidence of transgression of the Cunene river into Southwest Africa is established if Thomas's *helvescens* is truly a synonym of *cynosuros*. This was obtained on the left bank of the Cunene near the Rua Cana falls, north-west Ovamboland.

According to Shortridge (1934) these monkeys are found locally in the Cunene river region chiefly among the higher trees. They are extremely local in the Kaokoveld. The only other ascertained habitat is a thin belt of evergreen forest located around small springs flowing northwards from the base of Mt. Ehomba. The monkey also occurs along the Cunene in the extreme north-west of Ovamboland whence it seldom wanders south of the semi-tropical evergreen forest near the edge of the Rua Cana falls. Shortridge quotes an observation of Hahn to the effect that, in 1926, a small band wandered as far south as Odongwa, the sole instance known of their occurrence away from the Cunene. This still leaves a fair interval between the range of the present form and that of *C. p. ngamiensis*.

In north-western Rhodesia the Kafue river seems to be the site of possible meetings and intergradation with *C. p. rufoviridis* judging from specimens in the U.S. National Museum from the Kafue river, west of the railway and from Bolengwe farther east (*vide antea*, p. 564).

21. *CERCOPITHECUS SABAEUS* Linnaeus, 1766 [*]

Green Monkey

(SYN.: *Singe vert* Adanson, 1735, p. 178; *St. Jago monkey* Edwards, 1758, Pl. CCXV; *Simia sabaea* Linnaeus, 1766, p. 38; *Le Callitriche* F. Cuvier, 1819, p. xx; *C. werneri* I. Geoffroy, 1850, p. 874; *C. callitrichus* I. Geoffroy, 1851, p. 23, and many subsequent authors, including Forbes, 1894, p. 58)

VERNACULAR NAMES: French, *le callitriche, cercopithèque callitriche, singe vert*; German, *Grünmeerkatze, Gelbgrünmeerkatze*.

TYPE LOCALITY: Unknown, by substitution (Allen, 1925, p. 352,) Senegal. Type locality of *werneri*, West Africa, based on a live male in the Paris menagerie purchased from Vaillant, 13 July 1845, it died on 22 November 1847, and is now in the

[*] *Syst. Nat.* (12th ed.), 1766, p. 38.

Paris Museum (No. 241 (196)). Allotype female, also in the Paris Museum. Type locality of *callitrichus*, West Africa. Holotype in the Paris Museum (288 (192)), originally in the menagerie, where it died in 1834.

HISTORICAL

The West African Green Monkey was first definitely described scientifically by Michel Adanson (1735), who met with it in the woods of Podor along the Niger (= Senegal river). Vague accounts, however, of a " callithrix " had been current since the days of the ancient Greeks, who adopted a term originally introduced by Homer. There was doubtless confusion with other guenons, particularly the Grivet which, at that time, extended its range much farther north than at present. Buffon quotes Prosper Alpinus (1735) and Pietro della Valle (1665) as referring to blond guenons met with in Cairo, but these, too, may have been pale examples of *C. aethiops aethiops*. Linnaeus' description and Latin name are based mainly on Edwards' St. Jago monkey.

Writing in 1819 F. Cuvier enumerated only three representations of the Green Monkey in the literature, namely those of Edwards (1758–1764), Buffon (1767) and Maréchal—the last mentioned being described by his brother Georges (*Ménagerie du Muséum*).

Edwards labelled his monkey the St. Jago monkey since it was brought alive to England from one of the Cape Verde Islands of that name (= S. Tiago); it was a very young animal, though Buffon's figure purports it to be an adult. Though identifiable, it is a poor representation.

F. Cuvier's own plate (xix) is an excellent representation delineating all the major external features. It was the basis of later representations, for example that of Jardine (1833).

Ogilby (1838) after attempting to resolve the problem of the identity of the Callithrix of the Ancients, affirms that the species to which the name had become applied was the one otherwise known as the Green Monkey and Cape Verde Monkey and one of the most commonly imported animals in European menageries. He gives a satisfactory description and a recognizable figure.

Elliot rejected *Simia sabaea* Linnaeus as composite, substituting I. Geoffroy's *Cercopithecus callitrichus*, which was based on specimens from " Saint Yago, archipel du Cap-Vert ", and therefore essentially the same as Edwards' monkey.

CHARACTERS

Readily distinguished from all other members of the *aethiops* superspecies by obsolescence of the white frontal band, by the yellowish whiskers, which sweep upwards and backwards to form, with the forwardly directed hairs radiating from the preauricular region, a salient crest of semilunar outline with the convexity forwards and downwards ; by the pallid extremities, including a yellow terminal portion of the tail, and, finally, by the bluish white scrotum and absence of reddish hairs beneath the root of the tail.

PELAGE : ADULT MALE.—Face and ears black ; muzzle prominent. Iris dark chestnut. Whiskers lemon yellow, the uppermost hairs often black-tipped. Crown, nape and upper parts of body bright golden-green, somewhat brighter than in *C. aethiops tantalus*. Individual hairs on the mid-back average 45 mm. long, and bear two yellow annulations alternating with the black. The root is whitish followed by a 15 mm. broad black band, a 5 mm. yellow band, an 8 mm. black band, another yellow band equal to the first, and finally a slightly paler one. There may be a few whitish hairs intermingled with the black supraorbital fringe.

Beyond the elbow and knee the pelage laterally is greyer, as are also the hands and feet. On the posterior aspect of the thigh is a pure yellow fringe. Nails black.

Tail above like the back in its proximal four-fifths, below yellowish, the tip yellow for some distance both above and below ; no reddish hairs at root. Completely black tip 8 mm. in length.

Underparts, including medial aspects of limbs, dirty white. Hairs form a spiral whorl around the umbilicus.

Scrotum in adults opaque white with a bluish tinge. The blue may be confined to the root, the fundus being pure white and obscured by white hairs. In subadults it is sky blue. Testes large compared with body size.

ADULT FEMALE.—Like the male in pelage, but smaller in all bodily measurements. Nipples pink, contrasting with the bluish pectoral skin. Glans clitoridis pink, surrounded by a greenish preputium and more peripherally by lilac folds continuous dorsally with similar coloured perineal integument.

JUVENILE.—Newborn with face, ears, palms and soles unpigmented, light flesh-coloured. Dorsum of extremities also unpigmented, almost hairless and flesh-coloured. Frontal region, hinder part of crown, cheeks, arms, shanks and belly also very sparsely haired, the bluish skin apparent through the pelage. Fore part of crown and dorsum of trunk more heavily clothed with fine, dark brownish, almost black hairs, due to complete lack of yellow bands on hairs. Tail relatively shorter than in the adult, but grows rapidly to the definitive proportions. Head relatively larger and limbs relatively longer than in adults (Schlott, 1956).

Yellow appears first as a transverse frontal band. The face darkens first on the muzzle at three to four months old, being dusky at first, subsequently becoming blacker, the muzzle always preceding the other areas.

PLATE XXXV

Photo: E. Kirkland

Cercopithecus pygerythrus. Vervet, ♂ in Chester Zoo

PLATE XXXVI

Photo: Frederick Wackett

Cercopithecus sabaeus. Green Monkey. Two males, one female and young in Brighton Aquarium

According to Schlott the full adult pelage is not attained until the age of 16–17 months.

VARIATIONS chiefly relate to the extent of black annulations in the hairs of the dorsal surface. When heavy they impart a darker, almost completely black, spinal line (*e.g.* in U.S. National Museum, ♂ No. 25206). Otherwise the dark annuli are more uniformly distributed. Sometimes the tail is almost black above in the proximal two-thirds, becoming rusty-buff terminally. There is also some individual variation in the harshness of the coat ; this may be seasonal.

Two skins (61422 ♂ ; 13235 ♀) from the St. Kitts population, now in the U.S. National Museum collection, call for some remark. Both are of a general dull olive tint, but the two differ in several respects from each other. Individual hairs have grey bases, paler distal portions and black tips. One example (♂) had been in the zoo and exhibits a sleek coat with hairs adpressed. The wild example (♀) is shaggier and rougher. Underparts dirty white in the menagerie specimen, much darker, more buffy in the wild one. In the latter the tail had lost all its hair ; in the zoo animal it is incomplete, but such as is retained is almost uniformly dark grey with light speckling.

SKULL

Cranial dimensions (in millimetres). Data are derived from the statistical study by Ashton and Zuckerman (1951) on the comparison between cranial dimensions of skulls from West Africa and those from animals introduced into St. Kitts, West Indies. Adults, both sexes pooled :

	West Africa		St. Kitts	
	No. of Specimens	Average	No. of Specimens	Average
Maximum cranial length	25	106·2	55	106·9
Nasion-opisthiocranion	25	77·8	55	78·7
Biparietal	25	56	58	57·1
Basion-bregma	24	48	23	48·8
Biorbital	25	56·2	61	56·4
Palatal length	25	42·6	62	42·8
Upper cheek-teeth	30+	27·5 [1]	70+	28·2 [1]
Mandibular length	24	42·9	56	43·9
Lower cheek-teeth	20+	28·8 [1]	54+	29·5 [1]

[1] Calculated from data of Ashton and Zuckerman (1950).

2 P

Cranial dimensions of some individual skulls (in millimetres) :

Number		Locality	Sex	Max. Cranial Length	Glabella-occiput	Biparietal	Least Frontal	Basion-bregma	Bimastoid	Bizygomatic	Biorbital	Palatal Length	Upper Cheek-teeth	Mandibular Length	Lower Cheek-teeth
U.S. Nat. Mus.	268778	ex Zoo	♂ ad.	125	96	63	42	54	63	82	98	50	29	81	34
	252606	,,	♂ ad.	116	78	54·5	41·5	50	61	77·5	68	48	28·5	76·5	34
	61422	,,	♂ juv.	84	68	54	40	46	52	52	46·5	33	18	47	18·5 [1]
PC.27		Gold Coast	♀ ad.	99	72·5	54	42·5	46·5	54	64	57·2	39	29	66	32
PC.71		,,	juv.	74·5	64	51·5	39·5	40	47	47	42	23	10·5	40 [2]	11

[1] Full milk dentition + M. [1].　　　　　　[2] Full milk dentition.

Ashton and Zuckerman (1950, 1951 *a*, *b*, *c*) conclude from their studies that both skull and dentition of the St. Kitts' population, which has been isolated for some 300 years, are bigger but less individually variable in dimensions than those of the parent stock. They also reveal a greater frequency of certain dental abnormalities of an " all-or-nothing " character, such as additional teeth or loss of an individual tooth. Corresponding meristic variations in the cranium have not been noted, but only one possible one has been well studied, namely the nature of the pterion. In 23 out of 35 African specimens the frontal and temporal met at the pterion; in 11 there was a parieto-alisphenoid contact. In a single skull the two sides differed. Fronto-temporal unions were noted bilaterally in 51 out of 66 St. Kitts' skulls; in 10 a parieto-alisphenoid union was observed bilaterally. In 5 asymmetrical pterions were found. It is concluded that parieto-alisphenoid union is more frequent in the St. Kitts' population than in the African stock. However, the conclusion may not be meaningful in so far as it could be explained by errors inherent in random sampling.

" Although the cranial and dental dimensions of the St. Kitts and African green monkeys have diverged in a similar way, our analyses do not show whether the changes in the skull have directly conditioned those in the teeth (or vice versa), or whether both depend on one set of changes in some third reacting system. It is, for example, possible that the increase in the size of the teeth and skull of the St. Kitts monkey may be part of a general increase which has taken place in the size of its body. We have already suggested (Ashton & Zuckerman, 1950 *a*) that the dental changes have resulted from the action of selection on systems of multiple genes in the group of African green monkeys which became established on St. Kitts. Such an explanation appears to be adequate to account for any similar changes which have occurred in other somatic characters."

DISTRIBUTION (Map 13)

West Africa from Senegambia to the Niger, thence southwards to the fringe of the rain forest. In the east its territory meets that of *C. aethiops tantalus* without, so far as is known, any intergrading of the two species. Presumably the Volta/White Volta is a geographical barrier to intergradation. Elliot is in error in stating that the present species occurs in the Congo.

The Green Monkey also occurs on the Cape Verde islands, but it is commonly believed to have been introduced there from the adjacent mainland.

The species has been kept as a pet from time immemorial and numerous examples have been exported. In some instances these have escaped and are now living as wild populations in several West Indian islands, notably St. Kitts, one of the Leeward Islands (their history here has been recounted by Ashton and Zuckerman, 1950) and Barbados.

In Africa the range extends from the Senegal through Gambia, Guinea, Sierra Leone, Liberia and in the Ivory and Gold Coasts, but in the last five countries it is confined to the northern savannah, extending northwards to include the upper Volta area and southern Mali. According to Booth (1956) the species is restricted to the west of the Volta and White Volta, north of the forest zone, and thence ranges westwards throughout the northern Ivory Coast to the Senegal. Hayman (1936) records it from Bole, north of the Black Volta in western Gold Coast.

The most northern limit in Senegal is given by Rode (1938 *a*) as St. Louis at the mouth of the Senegal river.

ECOLOGY AND ETHOLOGY

Throughout its range the Green Monkey shows definite habitat preferences. Forest outliers, fringing forest along rivers and streams and dense bush are preferred as resting quarters, although foraging occurs in neighbouring habitats such as orchard bush and savannah. Raiding of cultivated and cleared areas is common, even to areas around village wells (Booth, 1956). Regular invasions of the high forest zone occur wherever substantial agricultural clearings have been made in Sierra Leone (*teste* T. S. Jones, quoted by Booth).

Feeding normally takes place among the trees, but animals may frequently be met with travelling on the ground between feeding sites. Their comportment when in motion agrees with that of the Grivet (*antea*, p. 535).

The Green Monkey is an apt swimmer. Cansdale (1946) reports

observing a female carrying an infant on its back swimming in the Volta ; and he states that it succeeded in crossing the river, a point of some significance in view of the remarks made above under distribution.

Diet is almost entirely frugivorous, but Booth reports having found grass seeds among the stomach contents.

Facial movements, grimacing and baring the teeth, are extensively developed. In captivity the male display consists of bouncing on the wires of the cage or on perches, after which demonstration he sits back with the spine extended and erect, the head held high with face forwards and the arms held stiffly pointing downwards and outwards. This is frequently accompanied by a penile erection. Another display pattern resembles that of *C. diana,* the head and shoulders weaving from side to side scanning the observer, the body being in the quadrupedal posture.

Lip-smacking is not evident, but instead there is grinding of the teeth by lateral mandibular movement or clacking of the teeth with an up and down mandibular movement. The latter display is frequently directed towards the female and/or young.

The male takes an interest in younger members of his family. At Orange Park, Florida, an adult pair live amicably together with their three offspring of different ages. The old male plays with younger males, apparently teaching them how to comport themselves, and also the technique of fighting. He engages in mock fights with conscious effort to avoid injury, a pattern which is clearly more purposeful than the ordinary rough and tumble play among juveniles of the same age.

REPRODUCTION AND JUVENILE DEVELOPMENT

This has been reported on by Schlott (1956) and by Moog (1957). Schlott studied a breeding pair in the Wuppertal Zoo during 1948–49, and in July of each year a male youngster was produced. Gestation was estimated at about seven months, or possibly a little less. The young was born with the eyes open. Parturition occurred without difficulty with labour pains occurring about every 35 minutes. Expulsion of the foetus was followed by that of the afterbirth. The infant was taken up by the parent, cleaned by licking off the amniotic debris and vernix and the umbilical cord bitten through. The afterbirth was licked and eaten, the male parent also partaking of this. The infant was carried against the mother's abdomen, clinging with its hands and feet. In locomotion, especially in climbing and jumping, the infant's holdfast was assisted by the mother's use of one hand and arm to support the baby. This was not observed, however, after the first ten days. At fifteen days, whilst the mother was sitting still, the young released its grip tentatively to explore with its hands its mother's arms, etc. Tentative excursions away from the mother were observed on the 21st day and from this time it was able to stand alone unsupported. A week to ten days later it was able to climb on the wire of its cage, but in this, as in walking, its movements were awkward and uncertain.

The family lived amicably together as in the Orange Park examples referred to on page 580 and the relationship between juvenile and father were identical. Play is discussed in detail by Schlott. Sometimes the mother also joined in the play behaviour.

Superspecies *INCERTAE SEDIS*

22. *CERCOPITHECUS ASNOTI* (Pilgrim,[*] 1913)

(SYN. : *Semnopithecus asnoti* Pilgrim, 1910, p. 64 ; *C.* (?) *asnoti* Pilgrim, 1913, p. 3)

Originally founded upon a fossil maxillary fragment of a cercopithecid monkey discovered in the Dhok Pathan zone of the Middle Siwalik deposits in the Salt Range, Northern India. At first placed in the colobid genus, *Semnopithecus*, Pilgrim later (1913) transferred it, with some hesitation, to the otherwise purely African genus *Cercopithecus*, admitting, however, that the fragment is probably generically indeterminable.

TYPE LOCALITY AND HORIZON : Hasnot, a village in the Salt Range area. Nature of matrix indicates derivation from the Dhok Pathan Zone of Middle Siwalik deposits. Type, a right maxillary fragment (No. D.120) with three molariform teeth (DM.^{2}, P.^{4}, M.^{1}), collected by M. Vinayak Rao. A left maxilla (No. D.121) containing two unworn molariform teeth apparently belongs to a younger individual of the same species.

An additional tooth (Indian Mus. No. D.182), exactly resembling the M.^{1} of the type, was collected by Pilgrim from about a mile north-east of Domeli railway station on the road to Chakwa—approximately twenty miles north-east of the type locality, but in the same geological horizon.

CHARACTERS

Molar cusps connected in pairs by cross ridges as in Cercopithecidae generally. Generic differences occur only in the relative proportions of the various teeth to each other, but, in the absence of available hinder molars, this criterion is not applicable to the known material.

Although first assigned to *Semnopithecus*, in view of the geographical origin, Pilgrim, even in his brief preliminary report, drew attention to the presence, on M.^{1} and DM.^{2} of a broad anterior shelf projecting slightly on the buccal aspect, which he had not observed in extant forms of the genus. The shelf is formed by the continuation of ridges running forwards from the two anterior cusps and, in the present species, the lateral portion of the shelf is separated from the anterior buccal cusp by a vertical furrow occupying half the extent of the buccal wall of the crown.

[*] *Rec. Geol. Surv. India*, xl, 64 ; also *Rec. Geol. Surv. India*, xlv. 3.

(This feature in the upper molar is constant in *Cercopithecus*, hence Pilgrim's transference of *asnoti* to the present genus. It is lacking in *Macaca*, *Cercocebus*, *Colobus*, *Presbytis*, *Mesopithecus*, *Libypithecus* and *Dolichopithecus*. In the last-named genus the anterior pair of cusps stand near the edge of the tooth, but there is a marked buccal cingulum unconnected in any way with the anterior cusps.)

Additional distinction of the present species relates to the hindmost premolar. This is characterized by the great distance between the summit of the transverse crest and the posterior border of the crown in comparison with the distance from the anterior border. In *Macaca* the two distances are about equal, and the tooth is relatively shorter. It is longer in *Presbytis*, and the posterior measure longer than the anterior, though the discrepancy is less than in *asnoti*. Neither *Mesopithecus* nor *Dolichopithecus* show this character, but somewhat similar features do occur in *Cercopithecus*.

DIMENSIONS.—Dental measurements (in millimetres) of *Cercopithecus asnoti* (Pilgrim) :

		Indian Mus. D.120 (Type)	Indian Mus. D.121	Indian Mus. D.182
P.⁴	length	6·8	—	—
	breadth	6·8	—	—
	height	—	—	—
M.¹	length	8·2	—	8·5
	breadth	8·0	—	7·4
	height	5·9	—	5·4
DM.¹	length	—	5·6	—
	breadth	—	5·5	—
	height	—	3·4	—
DM.²	length	—	6·5	—
	breadth	—	6·7	—
	height	—	4·6	—

DISTRIBUTION

Known only from the Pontian of the Siwaliks, Punjab, India. The existence in the Pontian of western Asia of a species pertaining, or at least closely allied to the African Recent *Cercopithecus*, suggests either that *Cercopithecus* emerged there, later migrating to Africa. Alternatively it might be supposed that a common cercopithecoid ancestral form occurred here whence an African migration developed into *Cercopithecus*, the local population becoming converted into *Semnopithecus* and its allies.

Pilgrim, supposing *asnoti* to be ancestral to Recent *Cercopithecus*, claims that such large dental dimensions would hardly be expected, and consequently he regarded a more probable hypothesis would be that *asnoti* represents an offshoot or lateral branch of the *Cercopithecus* stock.

The existence of this form points to a period in the Lower Miocene when free intercommunication existed between Asia and Africa. This is further supported by the close similarity between the mammalian fauna of the lower Miocene beds of the Bugti hills in Baluchistan with those of corresponding geological age in India and Africa.

Genus *MIOPITHECUS* I. Geoffroy, 1842 *

TALAPOINS or DWARF GUENONS

(SYN. : *Meiopithecus* Reichenbach, 1862, pp. 103–104, 242–243 ; *Myiopithecus* Wallace, 1876, p. 173 ; *Cercopitheci trituberculati* of Sclater, 1893)

DIAGNOSIS.—Differing essentially from *Cercopithecus* in the small size and in the occurrence in the female of a high degree of catamenial swelling.

Originally separated generically by Isidore Geoffroy on the basis of the tritubercular character of $M._{\overline{3}}$, but this feature has been shown to be inconstant (*fide* Reuvens, 1890, Pocock, 1907, 1925 ; Poll, 1940 ; James, 1960), for which reason many recent authorities have considered generic separation to be unwarranted. In spite of Pocock's assertion that in four talapoin skulls in the British Museum a quadrituberculate $M._{\overline{3}}$ was present, Elliot (1913) continued to use the generic name *Miopithecus* on the basis of the smaller size and the radiate fan-like arrangement of the hairs on the cheeks. Pocock (1925) rightly deplored this flimsy basis for separation, especially in so far as the preauricular hair pattern is hardly more definite than in, *e.g.*, *C. sabaeus*. Nevertheless, in view of the later discovery anent the catamenial swelling, some recognition of its apartness from the majority of the Cercopithecinae demands nomenclatorial emphasis over and above that of a separate group of the genus *Cercopithecus*. Possibly future serological and/or karyological studies may indicate further reasons for separation, a surmise which receives support from the apparent immunity of the Talapoin to tuberculosis—which contrasts greatly with the high incidence of the disease in captive guenons of the more typical species. Chromosome number 54 (*i.e.* as in *Erythrocebus*) (Chiarelli, 1963).

The pygmy proportions of the talapoin have been interpreted (*e.g.* Poll, 1940) as evidence of neoteny, or arrested development, similar to the somewhat parallel case mentioned by Pocock (1907) of the Pygmy Hippopotamus (*Choeropsis liberiensis*) which resembles in many characters the young stages of its larger

* *C.R. Acad. Sci. Paris*, xv. no. 15, 720, 1037.

relative *Hippopotamus amphibius*. But, whereas in Pocock's day these two were treated under the genus *Hippopotamus*, the dwarf form is now universally given full generic rank.

Thus the small size, proportionately large head, the relatively large neuro-cranium, devoid of bony ridges and crests, the short muzzle, large orbits, the slender but little bowed zygomatic arches, the delicate mandible, are all reminiscent of juvenile stages of *Cercopithecus* species, and at first sight give the impression of immaturity. Prolonged observation, however, soon reveals, in the existence of large testes in the male (larger proportionately than in adults of *Cercopithecus*) and in the development of large catamenial swellings in females, that the pygmy size is not a manifestation of immaturity. (Plates XXXVII, XXXVIII, XL, XLI, XLII.)

EXTERNAL CHARACTERS

Talapoins much resemble guenons externally, but are much smaller in size, with a proportionately larger head, shorter muzzle and infantile type of mandible. Otherwise the principal external differences from *Cercopithecus* relate to the relatively large testes and scrotum of the male and the presence of cyclical sexual swelling in the genital area of the female.

REGIONAL DETAILS

RHINAL AREA.—In the rhinal area the fronto-nasal profile is almost rectilinear, ending below in a moderately padded nose, which is strongly convex transversely. The nares are slit-like and aligned more horizontally than in *Cercopithecus*, giving an obtuse internarial angle of 105°. The septum is broad by catarrhine standards (3·2 mm. across), and the internarial region is marked by a median vertical depression. A distinct transverse groove separates the base of the septum from the upper lip. The nares are less comma-shaped in outline, being relatively straight with a raised upper margin, while the lower margin is not delimited from the contour of the upper lip. The lobate process of the medial (superior) edge is barely indicated.

BUCCAL ZONE.—In the buccal zone the upper lip is shortened vertically and highly convex from above down as well as transversely. The rima oris has approximately the same extent as in *Cercopithecus*, and lacks the sinuous course as in that genus. A short thick frenulum tethers the lip to the gum, but this is lacking on the lower lip. Buccal pouches are present, but small.

OCULAR REGION.—The superficially pallid eyelids show some pigmentation on the conjunctival aspect, and on the lower lid marginally. Numerous fine short eyelashes are present, longer on the upper than the lower lid. Lacus lachrymalis is present and unpigmented. A reduced nictitating membrane is present which is unpigmented even marginally. Marked grooves separate the eyelids peripherally from neighbouring skin, especially below.

Regarding the distribution of hair on the face, a transverse line on the bridge of the nose, 3·5 mm. above the line joining the two inner palpebral canthi, marks the divergence of two streams of short, widely spaced, black

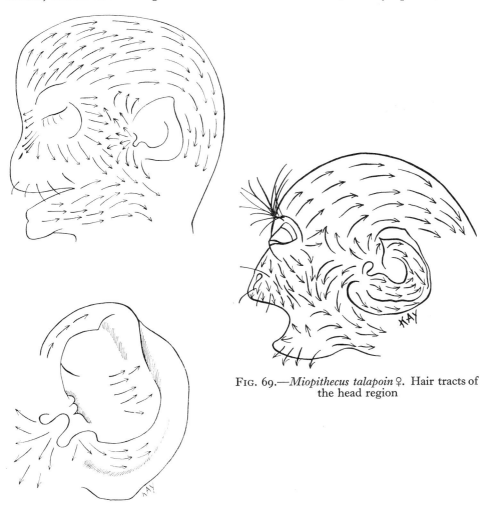

FIG. 69.—*Miopithecus talapoin* ♀. Hair tracts of the head region

FIG. 68.—*Miopithecus talapoin* foetus (107 mm. CR length). Hair tracts of head and ear (× ⅔)

hairs. Above the line these are directed upwards and medially, forming a median crest which above merges with the dark supraorbital hairs. Below the line the hairs are directed downwards and medially also forming a crest on the nasal bridge, but towards the apex nasi they become shorter and more directly downwards in slope. Laterally these are continued over the maxillary region. The supraorbital hairs elongate, some being as much as

23·5 mm. long and of vibrissal character. Other long vibrissal hairs appear on the maxillo-labial area and represent the mystacial group of the typical mammalian vibrissal system. These, like the maxillary hairs among which they occur, have a downward and lateral direction. All are blackish, but, on the lower lip, white hairs appear, mostly downwardly directed and becoming gradually longer as the chin is approached.

EXTERNAL EAR.—The external ear is of peculiar form. Large proportionately, its contour is rounded with a distinct Darwin's tubercle or point

FIG. 70.—*Miopithecus tala-poin* ♂. Left external ear (× ¼)

situated at a remarkably low level, opposite the root of the crus helicis. The helix takes at first the usual convex marginal course, but, from the summit of the pinna, it straightens taking an oblique course (13·5 mm.) downwards and backwards to the tubercle. From the tubercle the contour describes a bold semicircular sweep to the lower limit of the pinna, thence, in a still sharper curve, forwards and upwards to the base of the tragus. An extensive flattened lamina is thus circumscribed. This measures between margin and antihelix some 9–10 mm. across ; it is marked by a superficial depression, which runs parallel with the margin, somewhat deeper anteriorly, and which morphologically represents the bursa. The lowermost part of the margin is demarcated from the rest by a slight elevation. This portion is unsupported by cartilage and is homologous with the lobule of the human organ. It is better marked but more restricted in the foetus.

The anterior limit of the bursal depression is deepened by the overhanging, lobate antitragus. The latter is separated by a deep intertragic notch, 2 mm. across, from the small, lobate, subconical tragus. This, in turn, is separated by a similar notch from the crus helicis. The antihelix bifurcates above as usual, but the lower branch (inferior crus) is the better marked, the superior being, as in *Cerco-pithecus*, almost obsolete.

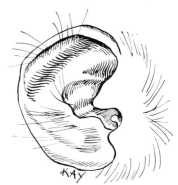

FIG. 71.—*Miopithecus talapoin* ♀. Right external ear (× ¼)

Distribution of hairs on the pinna is confined to its lateral aspect and even here they are lacking from much of the tragus and from a zone of the preauricular skin adjacent to the tragus. A few short, dark hairs radiate from the summit of the tragus, but the antitragus is much more heavily adorned, especially on its inferior border. These extend also along the edge of the antihelix, where they take an upward direction. In the bursa and along the lamina beyond the bursa the hairs take a caudal trend and increase in length towards the superior crus anti-helicis, where some of the hairs exhibit yellow annuli between the dark tip and dark base. The inferior crus antihelicis bears a few short, black hairs, directed towards the cymba. A lobate downwardly directed process on the crus helicis also bears short downwardly directed hairs, but on the ascending part of the helix a large quantity of yellow, black-tipped, upwardly directed hairs occur. These gradually give place towards the summit to shorter black hairs whose direction follows the curve of the helix and these again are followed on the descending part of the helix by yellow, downwardly directed hairs but on the ascending part of the helix a large quantity of yellow, black-tipped, upwardly directed hairs occur. These gradually give place, towards the summit, to shorter black hairs whose direction follows the curve of the helix and these again are followed on the descending part of the helix by yellow, downwardly directed hairs, which meet at Darwin's point the upwardly directed streams from the postero-inferior margin of the pinna.

CHEIRIDIA.—Palms and soles are unpigmented, as are also the nails on all digits. Digits are relatively short and stubby compared with those in *Cercopithecus*. Digital formula of manus : III>IV>II>V>I.

The proximal contour of the manus is less oblique than usual due to the lesser proximal extent of the hypothenar pad. The latter is markedly divided by a transverse sulcus into a smaller proximal and a larger distal area. The thenar pad is oval and bulbous, broader distally and narrowing to a rounded apex at its carpal extremity. Interdigital pads are almost fused into a single oblong flattened area sharply demarcated proximally from the rest of the palm by a continuous transverse flexure crease. Flexure creases on the digits are well marked at the usual situations. Interdigital webbing is obsolete.

The sole is much longer and narrower than the palm and extends proximally, in a prominent calcaneal field, 15 mm. beyond the base of the thenar area. Both thenar and hypothenar pads are long and narrow, separated by a longitudinal crease, but, whereas the hypothenar pad is parallel-sided throughout, the thenar broadens distally and becomes more elevated as it fuses with the prominent first interdigital pad. Three lateral interdigital pads are well defined from each other, but not from the rest of the sole. Flexure creases on the digits resemble those on the manual digits. Digital formula of pes III>IV>II>V>I. Interdigital webbing virtually nil.

In dermatoglyphic patterns, the palm shows no essential difference from the pattern in *Cercopithecus* as described and figured by Biegert (1961). Closed fields, with concentric ridges around a central ridge, occur on all four interdigital pads. Proximal to the first interdigital, on the thenar pad a simple pattern of parallel arches, concave distally, is found as far as the wrist. On the hypothenar pad a system of loops, open on the postaxial side, takes place around a central ridge aligned transversely. On the proximal phalanges of digits III–V duplex patterns of closed systems occur either side of a sagittal crease, but this is not found on the index finger. On the middle phalanges patterns are feeble and take the form of oblique parallel lines. Apical pads have the usual looped configurations.

On the plantar surface of the foot the dermatoglyphics are slightly simpler than in *Cercopithecus* in so far as the loops on the proximal part of the thenar pad are modified so as to constitute mainly a longitudinal system,

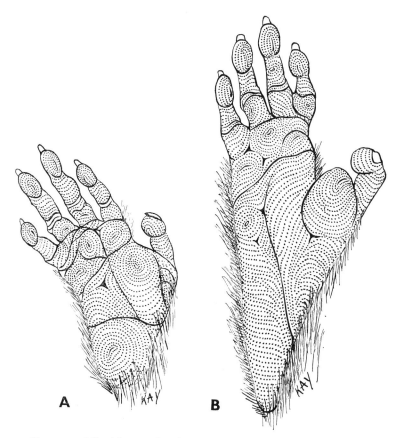

FIG. 72.—*Miopithecus talapoin* ♀. A, right manus and B, right pes

the most central members of which curve over towards the radial border at their distal ends. They enclose a series of short parallel transverse ridges running inwards from the preaxial border. The configuration on the distal part of the hypothenar pad is also simpler, there being no concentric arrangement but a pattern somewhat reciprocating that in the thenar pad. A closed system occurs on the first interdigital pad, but on the second a series of arches, open preaxially, is formed by the continuation of the parallel longitudinal ridges extending distally from the central part of the planta.

A closed system is found on the third interdigital and also on the fourth, but this is somewhat squewed so as to have its central ridge directed proximo-postaxially. Digital configurations are of the same pattern as on the manual digits.

PERINEUM AND EXTERNAL GENITALIA OF THE MALE.—Apart from the relatively large size of the scrotum and testes, the genitalia differ little from those of *Cercopithecus*. The large opaque bluish scrotum is globular, sub-pendulous and feebly divided into two halves by a shallow median sulcus.

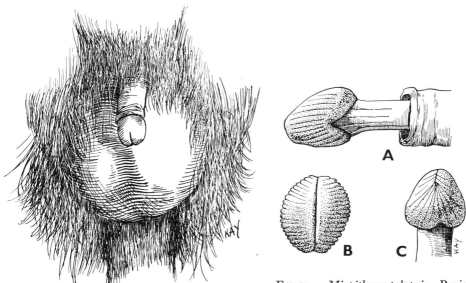

FIG. 73.—*Miopithecus talapoin*. Male external genitalia from the ventral aspect ($\times 1\frac{1}{2}$)

FIG. 74.—*Miopithecus talapoin*. Penis, A, from the left lateral aspect ; B, apical view of glans ; C, glans from above

There may be slight asymmetry of the two halves. From the root of the scrotum dorsally the perineum bears a vivid violet median triangular field with its base limited by the ventral borders of the two ischial callosities. The colouration extends dorsally between the callosities and thence around the anus and along the superior borders of the callosities. Callosities are small, oval (13·5 mm. × 10 mm.) aligned almost horizontally and separated by a space of 3 mm. They are pinkish grey in colour.

The penis is normally enclosed in its entirety in a dusky pink prepuce, which, in the immature animal, is closely adherent to the glans. The purplish glans is of the usual cercopithecine type, but slightly truncated distally. The corona projects considerably beyond the collum and is provided with a feeble median dorsal notch and deep lateral notches. The surface of the glans is marked by fine parallel grooves radiating from the meatal lips to the corona, but the lips themselves present a smooth zone. The grooves produce a fluted effect on the contour when viewed from the

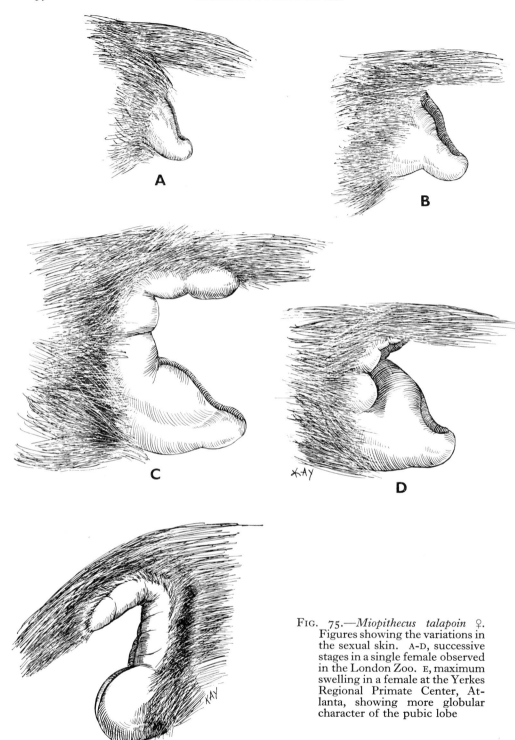

FIG. 75.—*Miopithecus talapoin* ♀. Figures showing the variations in the sexual skin. A-D, successive stages in a single female observed in the London Zoo. E, maximum swelling in a female at the Yerkes Regional Primate Center, Atlanta, showing more globular character of the pubic lobe

distal end. The meatus is a deep longitudinal cleft affecting the whole dorso-ventral extent of the glans. Within it the urethra opens to the right of the prominence formed by the tip of the baculum. The collum and pars intrapreputialis of the corpus are smooth, dusky and provided with a median keel on the perineal aspect. No frenula are present.

PERINEUM AND EXTERNAL GENITALIA OF THE FEMALE.—In the resting phase the whole ano-genital area is virtually naked, smooth and slightly purplish in colour, save the callosities, which are hornier in colour and texture. Long hairs project around the periphery of the naked area from surrounding skin. A few short, white, downwardly directed hairs are found on the perineal body.

Callosities are shaped as in the male and are approximately the same size (14 mm. × 10 mm.), but they are more widely separated (6·3 mm.). The long perineal body (8·4 mm. from above down) ends below at the commissure of the rima which is a sagittal cleft of 7 mm. extent. The dorsal part of this has no labial specializations, its margins being flush with surrounding skin. Its ventral moiety is comprised by a cleft on the glans clitoridis. This is a prominent structure projecting 8·9 mm. from the surface and unprovided with a prepuce. The glans is a globular body 4·6 mm. across, 6 mm. long and 5·1 mm. dorso-ventrally. In the foetus it is relatively even more prominent, but there is here a well-developed preputial sheath covering at least the dorsum and sides (fig. 76B).

The most remarkable feature relating to the mature animal is the periodic enlargement of the integument and subcutaneous tissues of the genital area. Phases in the establishment and increase of the sexual skin are shown in figure 75. In its fully developed condition the morphology of the swelling recalls that of *Cercocebus*, being demarcated into (i) a pendulous median ventral portion or pubic lobe, misinterpreted by Pocock (1906) as a large pendulous clitoris, yet produced by swelling of the tissues around the clitoris, and (ii) paired dorsal swellings projecting caudally, produced by engorgement of the tissues around the callosities, the perineal body, circumanal area and the skin of the root of the tail inferiorly. The pubic lobe varies individually to some degree, being sometimes subconical, in other cases more globular or pear shaped with the narrow end dorsally. In all cases it projects from the surface to a greater degree than the dorsal parts of the swelling. As in *Cercocebus* the anus, at the peak of the swelling, is carried posteriorly on to the under surface of the tail and is transformed by the swelling into a transverse slit with thickened dorsal and ventral lips. Surrounding hairs are pushed aside and erected by the pressure of the swollen skin. Phases in the appearance of the genital swelling are figured by Tomilin (1940). Mammae are two in number, pectoral rather than axillary in position. The nipples are 21·5 mm. apart and located 22·5 mm. caudal to the clavicle.

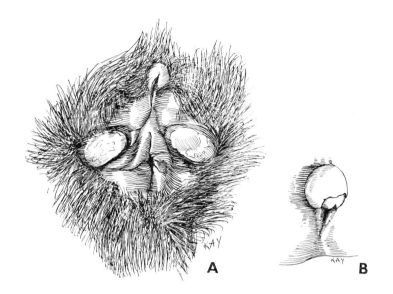

FIG. 76.—*Miopithecus talapoin*. Female genitalia of A, immature female (× ¼) ; B, advanced foetus (× ³⁄₁)

SKELETAL SYSTEM *

SKULL

The skull has been figured by Rode (1937). The mature skull recalls in many details that of the juvenile stage of *Cercopithecus*. For example, the facial portion is reduced and flattened while the neurocranium retains the smooth, globular contours with feebly developed temporal lines and relatively narrow, zygomatic arches. The mandible, too, is slenderly built with low vertical rami. These features are more applicable, however, to the female than the male.

The sagittal contour of the brain-case is arched, sloping upwards and backwards from the glabella to the vertex, which is located at the bregma or slightly anterior thereto. Thereafter it curves more gently to the lambda, whence the contour recedes rather abruptly, whereby the flattened occipital squame faces more downwards than caudad. Sometimes the occipital, immediately below the lambda, presents a transverse bulbous elevation limited inferiorly by the superior nuchal line. This feature is better marked in the female than the male. The coronal suture describes a widely open V. The sagittal suture is almost linear or slightly waved, while the lambdoid is almost transversely disposed. The metopic suture is normally lost during growth.

* The skeleton has been figured by Blainville (1839–41) whose representation has been reproduced by Gregory (1951).

PLATE XXXVII

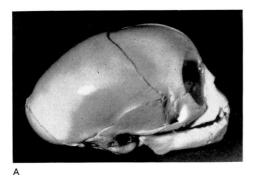

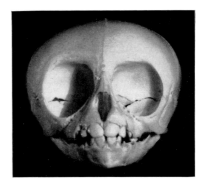

A

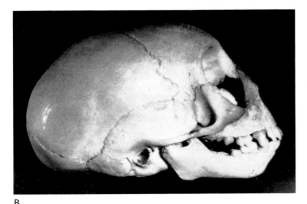

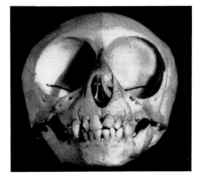

B

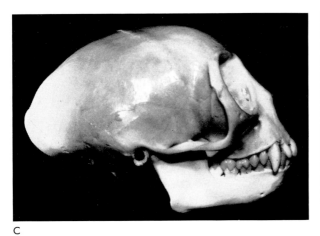

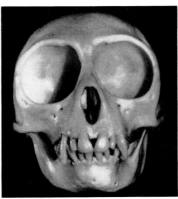

Photos: R. Q. Cox

C

Skulls in right norma lateralis and norma frontalis of A, *Cercopithecus sabaeus*, newborn ;
B, *Cercopithecus hamlyni* ♀, juvenile, 6 months old in comparison with C, *Miopithecus talapoin* ♀, adult (all × 1)

PLATE XXXVIII

Photo: I. Ashmore

Miopithecus talapoin ♀, in London Zoo

Temporal lines commence on the posterior border of the orbital rim and are well marked on the frontal. In males they proceed on to the parietal and gradually slope downwards and backward to the mastoid area, becoming almost horizontal in their final course towards the postero-superior part of the external auditory meatus. In female skulls they are scarcely discernible on the parietal and temporal bones.

At the pterion there is a broad parieto-alisphenoid union in the available skulls, but in the female a narrow pointed extension from the antero-superior angle of the temporal squame insinuates itself some distance between the two bones.

On the occipital squame a median vermian elevation extends from the middle of the bone to the margin of the foramen magnum. From the upper end of this the superior nuchal lines arch laterally and, in the male, a short supreme line is also indicated. Inferior nuchal lines are fully marked. The area below them is somewhat bulbous, except near the vermian eminence, where the bone is excavated.

Occipital condyles stand out and present the usual contour on the articular surfaces. Their long axes are aligned at an angle of 90° to each other. Between them anteriorly the margin of the foramen forms a uniform curve both in the horizontal and the vertical plane. The dorsal (posterior) edge of the foramen is subtriangular, but varies somewhat individually in this respect as well as in size, being considerably larger in a female than a male examined.

The postorbital constriction is less severe than in typical skulls of *Cercopithecus* and in front of it the fronto-malar part of the orbital wall forms a marked bulge into the temporal fossa, to which it imparts a triangular contour when viewed from above. The zygomatic arch is only moderately bowed laterally, the summit of its curve being posteriorly located just in front of its roots on the temporal bone.

On the base the axes of the two auditory meatuses align at 180°. The petrosal is strongly convex below both in transverse and longitudinal planes. The carotid foramen perforates the postero-medial part of the convexity in line with the auditory passage. A short spinous process projects anteriorly from the swollen petrosal, where it overhangs the foramen lacerum medium. The upper contour of the squamous temporal is variable ; it may be arched, sinuous or flattened.

Basioccipital, basisphenoid and presphenoid form, in adults, a continuous osseous cranial base somewhat convex longitudinally on the pharyngeal aspect. A styloid process is not present, and the small stylo-mastoid foramen lies in a depression at the medial end of a groove formed between the osseous meatus and the mastoid area of the temporal bone. A small postglenoid process is applied to the anterior wall of the bony meatus.

In the face the most striking feature is the large capacity of the orbits,

2 Q

which are separated by a thin interorbital septum. The orbital outlets are subcircular, being slightly flattened supero-medially, and marked here by shallow supraorbital notches. The orbits encroach above on the anterior cranial fossa, laterally on the temporal fossa, medially on the nasal fossa and below on the maxillary antrum. At their apices open two large pyriform foramina; the smaller medial one, apex pointing ventro-medially is the

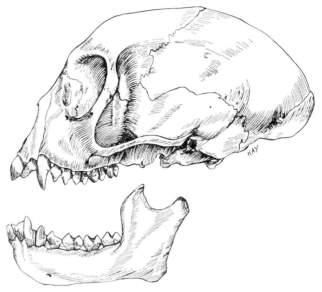

FIG. 77.—*Miopithecus talapoin.* Skull and mandible from the left side (× ¼)

optic foramen. The other, larger, with apex directed supero-laterally is the sphenoidal fissure. The inferior orbital fissure is more elongated, but narrow, cleft-like. The lateral orbital rim, formed by the malar, is perforated by several small foramina.

Infraorbital foramina number in both male and female skulls examined two on the left and three on the right.

Maxillae are narrow from side to side and shallow from above down. Prognathism is slightly greater in the male. The alveolar margin slopes slightly downwards when traced backwards, being elevated over the neck of the canine.

The palate is parallel sided, narrowing anterior to the canines. Its fore part is perforated by large paired foramina. Smaller posterior palatine foramina open obliquely at the postero-lateral angle of the hard palate. The posterior border exhibits a prominent posterior spine.

Pterygoid plates are well marked. The medial plates face downwards and medially and terminate in long curved hamular processes. The lateral plates, more extensive, are splayed outwards; they are oblong in shape, twice the length from front to back as from above down. The resulting interpterygoid fossa is very roomy and its roof is cribriform.

The nasal fossa encloses two turbinate bones each side. Its roof is cribriform. The pyriform aperture is individually variable but wider above than below.

The mandible presents a shallow horizontal ramus with a very sloping symphysis, which bears a laminar, simian shelf, separated by a deep genial depression, from the alveolar part of the bone. The vertical ramus is almost as broad as high, but proportionately less so in the female. The angular region is truncated and strongly inverted. Its medial aspect is roughened for muscular attachment. The mylohyoid groove ends posteriorly in the lower lip of the inferior dental canal. The coronoid process is short, slightly everted, and separated by a broad, shallow sigmoid notch from the condylar process. The latter has virtually no neck ; its articular surface is divided into a smaller anterior and a larger posterior area, the former of oval and the latter of triangular outline.

HYOID.—This has the same general shape as in *Cercopithecus*. The body is globose with a dorsal excavation in relation to the air-sac. Its convex surface is smooth and anteriorly is separated by an extensive bursa from the muscles of the tongue. The bursa is protected beneath by the fibrous arch connecting the two digastrics. A small ossified lesser cornu and a longer great cornu are both moveably articulated with the corpus hyoidei.

POSTCRANIAL AXIAL SKELETON

VERTEBRAL FORMULA.—C.7 ; T.13 ; L.6 ; S.3 ; Co.4 ; Ca.17.

Apart from the tail, the lumbar region is the longest segment of the spine, followed by the thoracic. The cervical region is one-third the length of the thoracic region and therefore somewhat more than one-sixth the combined thoraco-lumbar length (cf. *Cercopithecus*, p. 245). The sacrum measures 24 mm. long and therefore somewhat less than the cervical spine. The pre-sacral and sacral regions amount to only 63·8 per cent of the post-sacral.

Cervical vertebrae agree in most details with those of *Cercopithecus*, except that the axis presents, on its ventral aspect, a raised median eminence which enlarges caudally to end in a pair of rounded tubercles which overhang the body of C.3. C.7 lacks a vertebrarterial canal, but the ventral element of the transverse process of C.6 projects caudally protecting the artery as the latter courses past C.7.

In the thoracic spine, T.2 has the longest spinous process, and this slopes only slightly backwards. The first six spinous processes are long and attenuated, but increase gradually in cranio-caudal depth. On T.7 the cranio-caudal depth increases abruptly, but this and the succeeding spines as far as T.10 present a backward slope. The last thus have shorter, thicker, vertical spines and in this and other respects approach the lumbar vertebrae in character. Transverse processes, zygapophyses and centra are as in *Cercopithecus*.

In the lumbar region the centra are slenderer and relatively more elongated than in *Cercopithecus pygerythrus*, while the transverse processes are shorter and slimmer, although directed in the same fashion. Zygapophyses and other processes are exactly as in *Cercopithecus*.

The sacrum is formed as in *Cercopithecus*, but the hindmost segment (S.3) is less robust, being proportionately narrower transversely and cranio-caudally elongated. Its transverse elements make contact with those of the foremost coccygeal segment, which closely resembles a sacral vertebra, but is not fused with the sacral mass. The succeeding two vertebrae are also similar but smaller, with expanded transverse elements. The third post-sacral bears a large chevron element and this is still larger on the fourth. Remaining postsacrals resemble those of *Cercopithecus*.

Of the thirteen pairs of ribs the anterior eight pairs reach the sternum direct. The ninth, tenth and eleventh pairs of costal cartilages do so indirectly through union with their anterior neighbours. The last two pairs are " floating ", and moreover articulate only with the bodies of their respective vertebrae.

In the sternum the cranial border of the manubrium is concave. Its cranial half is oblong with concave lateral borders ; the caudal half abruptly narrows to the width of the second sternebra. A sagittal concavity is formed between the two halves ventrally, but transversely both halves of the bone are convex. The corpus sterni is composed of six sternebrae of varying length, the second being shorter than the first or third. After the third they become progressively shorter. The xiphisternum comprises an elongated more or less fusiform bony portion terminating in an expanded oval cartilaginous lamina.

The general shape of the thoracic cage is as in *Cercopithecus*. In an adult male the transverse diameter is 64 mm. and dorso-ventral 72, giving a thoracic index of 88·8.

APPENDICULAR SKELETON

In the clavicle the medial half is slender and the lateral robust. The medial half is relatively straight, but the lateral is strongly bowed with a forward convexity, arching over the shoulder joint. The sternal facet is oval with the longer axis oriented cranio-caudally. Apart from a ridge bordering the subclavius attachment ventrally, the bone is smooth. The acromial facet presents a rounded contour and a flat surface.

The scapular outline accords more closely with that of *Cercopithecus cephus* than any other among the guenons, with which it has been compared.

It favours the human rather than the classical quadrupedal form (*e.g.* that found in *C. aethiops* or *C. l'hoesti*). Scapular index 88·8. In certain features it is not matched in any other scapulae examined, notably in the obliquity of that portion of the vertebral border bordering the suprascapular fossa. This meets the cranial border in an obtuse angle (140°), the two limbs being approximately of equal length. The cranial border is straight, without coraco-scapular notch or foramen, but the coracoid arises abruptly from its lateral end to form a hook-like bony mass overhanging the glenoid ventro-medially. The suprascapular and infrascapular moieties of the vertebral border also meet at an angle of 140°, but this is more rounded than the previously mentioned angle. The infrascapular segment is straight anteriorly, but towards the caudal angle it becomes strongly convex. The caudal scapular angle is fairly acute (55°). The axillary border is complex, its glenoid three-quarters being double, with a broad groove separating the two sharp margins. The caudal one-quarter is single, but projects as a lamina beyond the rest of the axillary border, as in *Cercopithecus*. The spinous process is a thin lamina set perpendicular to the body of the scapula, but its free border is sinuous, thickening towards the acromion, which is diverted forwards and downwards. On the subscapular aspect the line of attachment of the spine is marked by a linear groove extending from the vertebral border to the neck of the glenoid process.

The humerus, 87 mm. long, exhibits a well-marked bicipital groove and the usual facets on the greater tuberosity. The shaft is divided into a proximal one-third, which exhibits a forward trend, uniting at an angle with the distal two-thirds, which is straighter. The two meet at the end of the deltoid ridge which is a distal continuation of the lateral lip of the bicipital groove. A secondary ridge located more dorsally meets the previous ridge distally but proximally is continued as a crest as far as the surgical neck. Between the two ridges the bone is flattened. Distal to the meeting point of the two ridges the shaft is cylindrical, but in the distal one-third becomes flattened from before backwards and marked by medial and lateral supracondylar ridges of which the lateral is the more pronounced. Dorsally the bone between these ridges is somewhat excavated, the cavity being continuous distally with the olecranon fossa. The coronoid fossa is shallower.

The radius is approximately of equal length with the humerus and has a well bowed shaft triangular in cross-section, the interosseous border being very sharp. The ulna is straighter, more slender and more cylindrical in its shaft. Its calibre diminishes gradually from the olecranon to the neck. Sigmoid notches are as in *Cercopithecus*.

In the carpus the pisiform is less prominent than usual in Cercopithecidae, a feature which is reflected in the contours of the palmar pads (*antea*, p. 587). Otherwise the bones are arranged as in *Cercopithecus* and are of the same proportionate size to each other.

The innominate bone has been figured by Fischer (1804) in comparison with that of *Cercopithecus mona* and *Macaca sylvana*. Though exhibiting the same general form as in *Cercopithecus*, it is smaller and more slenderly built. The iliac index (65) is about the same as in *C. pygerythrus* (63), but the proportion of the length of the sacral portion to the total iliac length is less (45 per cent in *Miopithecus*, 53·5 per cent in *C. pygerythrus*). The ventral iliac margin or crest is extremely sharp while the dorsal border is thickened. The gluteal surface is similarly excavated in both genera. The ischium is relatively thicker in *Miopithecus* and its tuberosity less everted, but the ischial index (57) is the same as in *Cercopithecus*. The axes of the two tuberosities are, like the callosities they bear, more horizontally disposed and less roughened. The symphysis is shorter and more oblique, involving scarcely any part of the ischium. The obturator foramen is smaller, more uniformly oval, with its major axis directed downwards and caudally from the region adjacent to the acetabulum. Ilio-pectineal lines are less marked especially at their anterior extremities.

The femur closely resembles that of *Cercopithecus* in all but size, especially in the short neck and large trochanters. The shaft is cylindrical, moderately bowed and comparatively smooth. The bone is 15 per cent longer than the humerus compared with 20 per cent for *Cercopithecus*. The head bears a deep fovea capitis completely occluded by the ligamentum teres. The distal articular condyles are shaped and proportioned as in *Cercopithecus*.

The ovate patella bears a quadrate articular area, narrower above than below, concave proximo-distally and convex transversely. Fabellae are present in the heads of the gastrocnemius. The tibia is approximately the same length as the femur (crural index 100), and therefore relatively longer than in *Cercopithecus*. Medio-lateral compression affects the proximal half of the shaft and the same area is evenly bowed forwards combined with medial bowing affecting the proximal two-thirds of the shaft. The platy-cnemic index is 69, based on the ratio of transverse to sagittal diameters in the proximal one-third of the shaft. The cnemial tubercle is continued distally as a ridge along the proximal one-quarter of the bone. Beyond this the anterior border is rounded ; the other borders are even less distinct. As in *Cercopithecus* the medial malleolus projects as far distad as the lateral.

The long, slender fibula presents no special peculiarity, its shape and markings agreeing fully with those of *Cercopithecus*.

The pedal skeleton is extremely narrow in proportion to its length, especially if the hallucial elements are left out of consideration. The cal-caneus is obliquely oriented, the major axis of its tuberosity inclining down-wards and medially. Its medial aspect is deeply grooved by the flexor tendons. Both talus and calcaneus present extensive articular surfaces. Other tarsal bones agree with those of *Cercopithecus*, except in their smaller size.

Metatarsals are long and slender. The fifth bears a large, outstanding styloid process. The third projects farthest distally followed by IV, and then II and V which are equal. The hallucial metatarsal extends distally as far as the junction of middle and distal thirds of the second. It is medially rotated in its resting position, articulating with a saddle-shaped facet on the entocuneiform.

DENTITION

PERMANENT DENTITION

Dental formula as for the family. The permanent dentition has been considered and magnificently illustrated by Warwick James (1960).

Upper central incisors have broad shovel-shaped crowns with the lingual surface excavated and edged by raised enamel folds. The lateral pair are, in contrast, small peg-like teeth with rounded, blunt-tipped conical crowns. Canines show marked sexual dimorphism as regards size. James figured the female and described the upper tooth as large and pointed for a female, comparing it with Rode's (1937) figure based on a male. In an adult male I find the exposed part of the upper canine 11·5 mm. long compared with 7·4 mm. in an adult female. Its crown is a three-sided pyramid with anterior, postero-medial and postero-lateral surfaces, the two latter being separated by a sharp ridge extending the whole length of the crown. The anterior surface presents a vertical groove occupying the basal half of the surface. The postero-medial aspect is con-

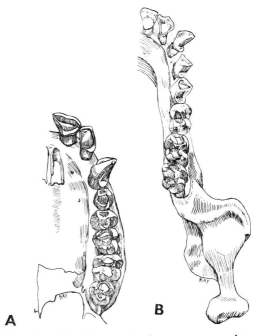

FIG. 78.—*Miopithecus talapoin.* A, upper and B, lower dentition from the occlusal aspect

cave both longitudinally and from before backwards, but the buccal (postero-lateral) surface is convex in both directions. The tooth is separated from $I.^2$ by a diastema, but is contiguous posteriorly with $P.^3$.

Upper premolars are markedly bicuspid and three-rooted ; $P.^4 > P.^3$.

Upper molars are bilophodont, except $M.^3$, which is typically 3-cusped, or more precisely the two hinder cusps are reduced and the posterior border of the crown is limited by the vestige of the loph (crista transversa posterior). Schwarz (1928) maintained that the metacone is retained and the hypocone absent or minute. The lophs are, in all the molars, short on account of the approximation of the lingual and buccal cusps—resulting in bulbous buccal and lingual aspects of the crown, a feature linking *Miopithecus* with *Allenopithecus*.

Lower incisors are smaller than the uppers, having narrow crowns. In the unworn condition all four have sharp incisive margins and spade-like

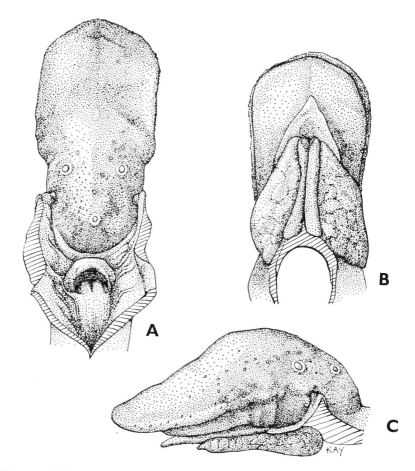

Fig. 79.—*Miopithecus talapoin* ♀. Tongue from A, dorsal; B, ventral and C, left lateral aspect

lingual surfaces. There is less discrepancy in size and shape between $I.\overline{1}$ and $I.\overline{2}$ than between the corresponding upper teeth, but $I.\overline{2}$ has its distal angle bevelled off.

Lower canines in the female are but little larger than the incisors, but in the male their crowns are almost double the height of the incisor crowns. In occlusion the crown is received into the diastema in front of the upper canine. The pyramidal crown of the lower canine presents a smooth convex buccal aspect, while the lingual aspect is divided into mesial and distal surfaces by a ridge, which ends below in a prominent posterior talon or heel forming a sharp angle with the ridge. The surface mesial to the ridge is grooved, whereas that lateral to it is smooth.

In the female the two lower premolars differ little from each other. Both are bicuspid with a tall buccal cusp and a short lingual cusp situated postero-medial to it, the two separated by a shallow talonid basin. The only difference between $P_{\bar{3}}$ and $P_{\bar{4}}$ is a slightly longer anterior edge on the buccal cusp. In the male, however, in correlation with the larger canines, $P_{\bar{3}}$ has the more characteristic cynomorph feature, with a long oblique mesial ridge to the buccal cusp ; this occludes with the upper canine ridge forming a shearing surface.

$M_{\bar{1}} < M_{\bar{2}} = M_{\bar{3}}$. All are bilophodont, but there has been much difference of opinion as to the details of the cusps on $M_{\bar{3}}$. It was on the basis of the supposedly constant tritubercular $M_{\bar{3}}$ that the genus *Miopithecus* was founded. As already noted (p. 583) several workers have found the character inconstant, quite a high proportion of Talapoin mandibles bearing a quadricuspidate $M_{\bar{3}}$.

There seems to be some confusion in the literature as to whether the trituberculal condition affects principally $M_{\bar{3}}$ or $M^{\underline{3}}$, or both. Pocock states that Geoffroy's original diagnosis of *Miopithecus* applied to trituberculy of $M_{\bar{3}}$ and that this concept has been copied by later authors *ad nauseam*. Schwarz knew of the frequent trituberculy of $M^{\underline{3}}$, maintaining that, although the hypocone is usually absent or minute, it is occasionally well developed— yet the same holds true of many *Cercopithecus* skulls, especially *C. cephus* and *C. pygerythrus arenarius*.

Rode (1937) affirms there may be only three cusps on $M_{\bar{3}}$, but the female specimen in the British Museum (No. 97.7.1.1) illustrated by James shows four fully developed cusps. Quadritubercular $M_{\bar{3}}$ occurs bilaterally in both male and female skulls examined by me.

Pulp cavities have been studied by Senyurek (1953) who found $M_{\bar{1}}$ – $M_{\bar{3}}$ two-rooted and typically cynodont, but in one specimen $M_{\bar{1}}$ was moderately taurodont, while $M_{\bar{2}}$ and $M_{\bar{3}}$ were moderately taurodont in two. He also recorded hypertaurodonty in $P_{\bar{4}}$ of one Talapoin ; $P_{\bar{3}}$ may be two-rooted.

SPLANCHNOLOGY

PERITONEUM

The elongated, relatively narrow great omentum depends over the intestines in the usual fashion. Its dorsal layer gains a limited colic adhesion in the neighbourhood of the hepatic flexure, without an extension along the transverse colon. To the left, however, it is adherent to the mesocolon as far dorsad as the tail of the pancreas.

The gastric attachment of the omentum is dorsad of the major curvature and, on the right, it is continued on to the ventral wall of the duodenum in a sagittal direction as far as the level where this gut takes a cranial bend before ending at the duodeno-jejunal flexure.

Mesenterium commune and mesocolon are as in *Cercopithecus*. The region of the hepatic flexure is anchored by an extensive parieto-colic fold to the right flank. This presents a semilunar free edge caudally. Dorsally this is attached to the posterior pole of the right kidney and to the dorsal parietes behind this for some 5 mm. Elsewhere the colon is freely mobile, the caecum and ascending colon in a continuation of the mesenterium commune and the transverse and left colons in a mesocolon of their own. A trace of the recto-duodenal fold connects the duodeno-jejunal flexure with the right side of the descending mesocolon and supports a branch of the posterior mesenteric artery.

The falciform ligament of the liver is a delicate triangular sheet whose free edge carries a thin fibrous ligamentum teres. The anterior end of the latter becomes deeply embedded in the liver.

A lieno-renal ligament or fold carries the left extremity of the pancreas, but the rest of this organ is entirely retro-peritoneal.

Alimentary System

The thickish *lips* are covered on the vestibular aspect by unpigmented mucosa. A short thick frenum tethers the upper lip in the mid-line, but the vestige of this in the lower lip is represented merely by a median rise in the line of attachment to the gum. Buccal pouches are well developed for the size of the animal, being about 25 mm. deep and 16 mm. broad, with the medial and lateral walls in contact when not in use. Their openings occupy the whole length of the lower alveolo-buccal groove from the level of the canine backwards.

The *hard palate* is relatively short and broad. It is marked anteriorly by bulbous incisive papilla of pyriform outline, the narrow end pointed and directed towards the interdental space between the two central incisors. Behind this are six pairs of transverse rugae forming double arches, convex rostrally. The last pair are fainter than the others and incomplete medially. No rugae occur in relation to the incisive papilla.

The *tongue*, according to Schneider (1958), has a strikingly smooth surface. In a subadult female, I find it measures 26·5 mm. from tip to median vallate papilla and 12 mm. wide. Papillae fungiformes occur only near the apex and near the lateral margins. The three vallate papillae are arranged in a V with the apex aborally. Filiform papillae are short conical bodies with blunt tips ; some have bifurcated tips. The pharyngeal one-third is provided with a layer of mucus glands beneath the lymphoid stratum.

A lateral organ extends from the hinder part of the lateral margin on to the inferior part of the glosso-palatine fold. It consists of alternating vertical grooves and ridges ; a total of nine grooves includes four on the tongue and five on the glosso-palatal fold. Beneath the free part of the tongue is a fringe-like plica fimbriata enlarging in the median line to form a prominent broadened lappet. The latter is connected to the tongue by a frenal fold and another fold occupies the angle between it and the floor of the mouth.

Salivary Glands.—The parotid is a soft, lobulated organ covered superficially with a dense fascial layer, which sends septa inwards between the lobules. It is as broad antero-posteriorly as from above down, but presents the same general relations as in *Cercopithecus*. The superficial surface is markedly convex. Its apex is separated by a small space (containing a lymph gland) from the submandibular gland. The latter is comprised by a

FIG. 80.—*Miopithecus talapoin* ♀. Parotid and submandibular glands of the left side
(× 1½)

mass of rounded discrete lobules, only the hinder ones being compacted into a single glandular mass. One lobule ascends superficially on the masseter, others pass along the deep aspect of the mylohyoid. The duct opens as usual on the parafrenular papilla. The sublingual gland is a smooth almond-shaped mass occupying the usual position, but it is compound in structure, its fore part consisting of a number of oblique elongated lobules from whose apices the Rivinian ducts proceed upwards to open directly into the mouth cavity. They lie superficial to the greater or Bartolinian gland whose duct runs alongside Wharton's duct, as in *Cercopithecus*.

Pharynx.—The smooth soft palate ends behind in an ovate, markedly defined, sessile uvula. The glosso-pharyngeal fold bears some of the papillae foliatae. The tonsil is of the pocket type and occupies the upper part of the interval between the anterior and posterior faucial pillars.

There are no glosso-epiglottidean folds ; the anterior wall of the oro-pharynx presents, at the base of the tongue, a transverse groove which separates an area of smooth mucosa from the anterior aspect of the epiglottis. This area comprises two triangular fields united by their apices in the median line. They are swollen and serve to diminish the height of the epiglottis. The latter presents a curved, swollen free border without median notch. It guards the triradiate aditus laryngis, whose dorsal lip is formed

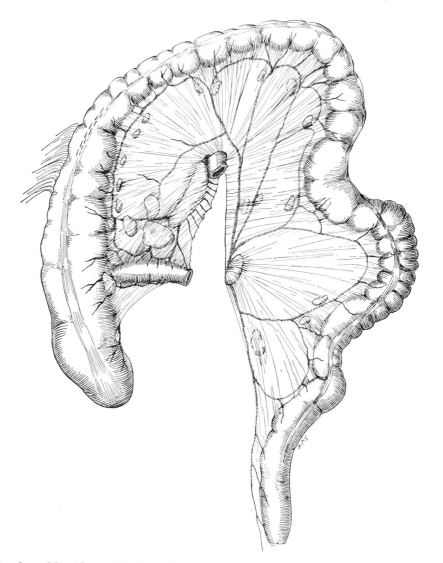

FIG. 81.—*Miopithecus talapoin* ♂ adult. General disposition of the colon and mesenteries

by the two convexities produced by the corniculate cartilages. A peculiarity of the retropharyngeal connective tissues are numerous deposits of melanin pigment.

Oesophagus.—This presents nothing noteworthy. Its lower cervical portion makes a very definite leftward shift before entering the thorax. Otherwise it is as in *Cercopithecus*.

Stomach.—This resembles the organ in *Cercopithecus*, being a simple pyriform sac with a globular fundus and narrow, thick-walled pyloric segment. The two are separated on the lesser curvature by an incisura angularis. The pylorus is marked externally by an annular constriction. It lies well to the right of the median line in contact with the liver. No notches on the greater curve were observed in the material examined.

Intestine.—The duodenum turns caudally in the right flank immediately after leaving the stomach. Its ventral wall gives attachment to a dextral extension of the great omentum which here connects the duodenum to the hepatic flexure of the colon. Its walls are completely surrounded by peritoneum in the first 10 mm., where the gut forms the ventral boundary of the oval foramen of Winslow. Aboral to this the duodenum is attached to the right kidney by a short thick sagitally aligned mesentery-like fold which, however, contains no vessels. An extension of the peritoneum of this fold becomes the parieto-colic fold already referred to (p. 602). The common bile duct opens with the pancreatic duct 7·5 mm. beyond the pylorus at the junction of medial and dorsal walls of the duodenum in a relatively avascular zone of the mucosa, which forms a raised annulus around the orifice. The patulous orifice is rounded to oval, approximately 0·8 mm. in diameter. In contrast, the villi of the regular duodenal mucosa are highly vascular.

The duodeno-jejunal flexure lies to the left of the lumbar spine. From here the small intestine is carried in a mesentery which at first is short, lengthening progressively in relation to the aboral coils. There is no sharp line of demarcation between jejunum and ileum. The mesenteric vessels are partly concealed by large lymphoid masses, including one specially large one of sausage-shaped form lying alongside the main anterior mesenteric vessels—a primitive feature. Others of smaller size occur on the distal branches as shown in figure 81.

The ileo-colic junction is placed relatively far craniad in the right flank, the angle of union of ileum with colon being slightly more obtuse than a right angle. The opposite angle between ileum and caecum is occupied by a triangular peritoneal fold. This fold receives a dorsal caecal artery delivered from a fold which crosses the ileo-colic junction dorsally. On entering the mesotyphlon it supplies a recurrent ileal branch to the terminal ileum, continuing thereafter towards the apex of the caecum. This vessel also has, in relation to its course within the mesotyphlon, a small lymph node projecting dorsally.

Caecum and colon are much as in *Cercopithecus*, except for the relatively shorter ascending colon due to the forward site of the caecum and terminal ileum. The caecum is a subconical sac 24·5 mm. long and 17 mm. in diameter. Its proximal two-thirds is sacculated, and apical one-third smooth walled and unsacculated. The apex of the distended organ is directed slightly to the left.

The colon is sacculated, the haustra forming a triple series separated by three taenae coli. They become indistinct in the posterior third of the descending colon, which assumes a cylindrical form. The transition to the rectum is therefore indefinite.

The anal canal takes a dorsad direction in relation to the rectum and its dorsal wall is longer than the ventral, being carried backwards on to the base of the tail. The orifice is therefore oblique. Its lining is sharply demarcated into cutaneous, intermediate and mucosal zones from without inwards. The cutaneous zone is bluish, like the perineal skin and terminates in a series of lobes, which are more darkly pigmented with melanin. These interdigitate, in the transitional zone, with columns descending from the mucosal zone. The mucosal columns are oblong. Indefinite pockets or valves are formed by this interdigitation. There is a marked constriction level with the transitional zone. Usual relations are established with pubo-rectalis and ilio-caudalis fibres.

Liver.—This differs in several minor details from the liver of *Cerco-pithecus*. In general form it is relatively reduced in the sagittal diameter, especially ventrally, but elongated in the transverse dimension. The left lateral lobe is entirely independent, having no connection by hepatic tissue with the rest of the organ, being anchored solely by a pedicle of vessels near the dorsal border.

The central lobe forms by far the largest portion of the viscus. It comprises a wedge-shaped left portion separated from the larger right portion by the shallow umbilical notch and the line of the attachment of the falciform ligament. The right portion of the central lobe curves into the right flank and dorsally overlaps the right lateral lobe. The latter is deeply excavated by the impression for the right kidney, but it also receives the caudate process, which is itself excavated to form part of the renal impression. The marginal part of the renal impression is therefore formed by right lateral lobe and the central part by caudate process.

On the visceral aspect the left lateral lobe is related to the stomach and therefore markedly concave ; its caudal margin is especially extended and thin, giving rise medially to a large processus triangularis. On the extreme right border of the right half of the central lobe lies the fossa for the gall-bladder. The fossa is deepened by the left margin of the right lobe so that the gall-bladder makes contact with both. The gall-bladder is more exposed therefore than in *Cercopithecus*, but shows the same sinuous character. The visceral aspect of the right lobe has no fissura praecaudalis, but a low ridge separates the renal from the duodenal area.

The Spigelian complex is closely related to the postcaval vein bridging over it dorsally to meet the dorsal aspect of the right lobe. It has the usual oblong outline with its flat surface facing more medially than dorsally. Both caudal angles bear processes. On the left a curled lappet-like processus papillaris embraces the portal vein as it enters the liver. On the right an extensive lamina of hepatic tissue covers the ventral wall of the prehepatic part of the postcaval vein, expanding on the right into a pyramidal caudate lobe which, as already noted, is applied to the dorsal surface of the right lobe and, by its dorsal aspect, to the kidney. Its ventral or visceral aspect is related to the duodenum. The sharp border between renal and duodenal aspects is markedly notched, producing a forked appearance. (See Plate XXXIX.)

Pancreas.—This is a short, relatively compact structure, extending left-wards from the left wall of the duodenum to the upper pole of the left kidney. Cranially the blunt tail is related to the spleen. No part of the tail projects into the greater sac of the peritoneum. The left extremity is sagitally elongated in relation to the duodenum.

RESPIRATORY TRACT

The hyoid has been described above (p. 295). The thyroid cartilage is of the same general shape as in *Cercopithecus*, but the union is not produced cranially, though a median notch is present relative to the emergent air-sac.

The cranial border is highly concave and ends behind in a large superior cornu, articulated by diarthrodial union with the tip of the greater hyoid cornu. The dorsal border is relatively straight and continued caudally as a large inferior cornu, which articulates with the cricoid. The most striking feature is the enormous tubercle at the caudal end of the oblique line. This forms a hook-like projection overhanging the ventral extremity of the inferior border of the thyroid cartilage. It not only receives fibres from sterno-thyroideus and thyro-hyoideus, but also the ventral fibres of crico-thyroideus.

The petaloid epiglottis presents the same relations to the thyroid and air-sac as in *Cerco-pithecus*. The stem is highly concave on its vestibular aspect giving a funnel-like entrance to the air-sac.

The cricoid has no special peculiarity. Aryte-noids rest upon the cranial border of its expanded

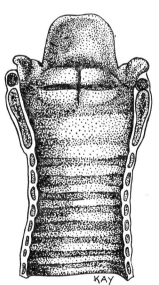

FIG. 82.—*Miopithecus talapoin* ♀. Larynx, opened from behind (× 4)

dorsal lamina and present the usual processes. Their summits are low and rounded, producing two cushion-like processes guarding the aditus, separated by a median cleft. No cartilage of Santorini is developed, but a small nodule representing Wrisberg's cartilage is found in the aryteno-epiglottidean fold, lying deeply without forming a conspicuous bulge.

The vestibule is produced into a capacious air-sac which emerges through the thyro-hyoid membrane and embraces the narrowed tendon of insertion of the sterno-hyoideus. It fills the capacious hollow on the dorsum of the corpus hyoidei and expands in the superficial tissues of the neck as far laterally as the sterno-mastoids and caudally to the suprasternal notch. Above and laterally it is related to the submandibular salivary glands. Superficially, in the median line of the neck, it is covered only by skin, superficial and deep fascia, but laterally the platysma also intervenes and antero-laterally the buccal pouch.

Vestibular folds are striking pyriform swellings lying with their narrow ends dorsally in relation to the arytenoids. Their swollen ventral extremities are separated by a median depression, which communicates above with the mouth of the air-sac and below with the ventral limits of the two ventricles. Ventricles are elliptical depressions between the vestibular and vocal folds each side. They are overhung by both folds which, in the resting condition, are in contact. The ventricles are lined by laryngeal epithelium which expands cranially in the cellular tissues beneath the vocal folds to form a saccule of some 4·5 mm. total depth. Vocal folds are extremely thin, transparent folds of watch-pocket type.

The trachea has a diameter of 4 mm. and bifurcates at the level of the fifth thoracic vertebral body.

Lungs.—The left lung is three lobed and the right four lobed. The caudal border of the left lung gains the level of the seventh rib in the midmammary line and as its border is horizontal, with the animal in the erect posture, it crosses successive ribs as traced dorsally. The middle lobe of the left lung is fully separated from the basal lobe, but incompletely differentiated from the apical lobe, the interlobar fissure being confined to the ventral one-third, thus agreeing rather with *Erythrocebus* than *Cercopithecus*. The right lung is larger than the left and all four lobes are fully differentiated. The infracardiac lobe is completely independent, being connected only by its vessels to the hilum of the lung. It has a pyramidal form and its dextral surface is deeply grooved by the postcaval vein.

Pleurae are exactly as in *Cercopithecus*.

URINARY TRACT

The right kidney lies at a more cranial level than the left, its caudal pole being level with the caudal limit of the hilum of the left. In an adult male the right kidney measures 26·8 mm. long, 14·2 mm. transversely and 7·7 mm. dorso-ventrally. Same measurements on the left are 23·8 mm., 16 mm. and 8·5 mm. The right kidney is therefore distinctly longer and narrower. Both are flattened dorsally and highly convex on the ventral aspect. The medulla ends medially in a single undivided pyramid.

PLATE XXXIX

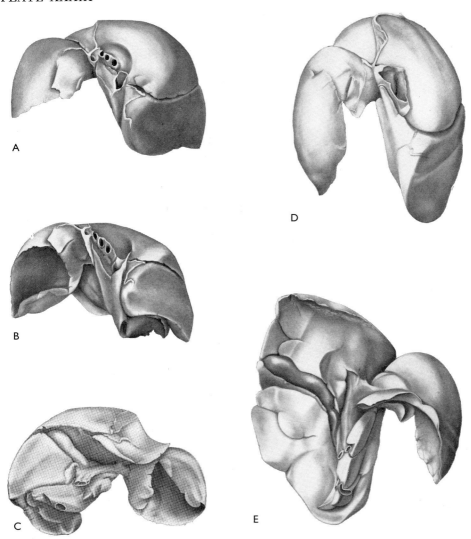

Miopithecus talapoin. Adult ♂. Liver. A, from the diaphragmatic aspect ; B, from the dorsal aspect ; C, from the visceral aspect

Cercopithecus preussi. Adult ♂. Liver. D, from the diaphragmatic aspect. E, from the visceral aspect

PLATE XL

Miopithecus talapoin ♀, in London Zoo

The left ureter is 75 mm. long, the right being somewhat longer. Their course and direction are typical. The bladder is pyriform with the fundus and body of the collapsed organ both situated craniad of the symphysis pubis. Mesocyst and urachus are lacking, as in *Cercopithecus*. Internally a definite interureteric muscular bar is recognizable ; a branch of the inferior vesical artery courses beneath its mucous layer to form an anastomosis with its fellow. The trigone is therefore more clearly demarcated than in *Cercopithecus*.

The male urethra has the same divisions as in *Cercopithecus*, the prostatic portion measuring 5 mm. long, the membranous 3·5 and the bulbo-penile tract 50 mm. In the prostatic portion the mucosa is highly vascular, but in the membranous and bulbo-penile portions it has a greyish appearance. The prostate lies wholly dorsal and lateral to the urethra. The membranous portion has a thick, muscular wall.

REPRODUCTIVE SYSTEM

MALE GENITAL ORGANS.—Testes are relatively larger than in *Cercopithecus*, but in details do not differ materially from the organs in that genus. Each testis measures 10 mm. long ; 15 mm. if the epididymis is included. Each lies in a roomy saccus vaginalis, which remains open as far proximally as the internal abdominal ring. Peritoneal relations within the sac are exactly as in *Cercopithecus*. On the medial border of the gonad a spiral artery ascends, having four loops in each direction. Between testis and epididymis a much finer vessel ascends on the ventro-lateral aspect. The epididymis presents a large pyramidal caput, but the cauda and body are of the same diameter. The whole organ is slightly lobulated. The vas has the usual appearance, relations and course.

Vesiculae seminales lie between bladder and rectum, embracing the latter. They form compact fusiform masses composed of coils held together by connective tissue and vessels. Each is 15·5 mm. long in the adult male. As in *Cercopithecus*, the single main tube is supplemented by a small accessory uncoiled secreting pocket, 1·5 mm. long, located more laterally than in *Cercopithecus* in the angle between the main organ and the base of the prostate and unrelated to the termination of the ductus deferens.

Ejaculatory ducts are formed by the union of ductus deferens and duct of seminal vesicle each side. These perforate the prostatic tissue and open on the lips of the utriculus masculinus. The openings are very conspicuous in so far as their margins are relatively avascular, contrasting with the highly vascular mucosa covering the colliculus seminalis and that of the prostatic urethra.

The prostate is a firm pyramidal mass with its base at the neck of the

2 R

bladder, clothing the dorsal and lateral walls of the prostatic urethra. It measures 5 mm. long and 6 mm. transversely at its base.

Well developed bulbo-urethral glands of brownish colour occupy the usual position and drain into the bulbous urethra.

The penile urethra expands within the glans in a fossa navicularis lined with longitudinally grooved mucous membrane. This opens into the cleft on the summit of the glans. A baculum is present ; its tip forms a prominent, rounded projection in the wall of the left half of the meatal cleft above the urethral opening.

FEMALE GENITAL ORGANS.—*Ovary.*—This is a smooth oval in shape, 5·8 mm. long, 3·4 mm. across and 2·5 mm. thick. It is partly concealed along its cranial border by a fold derived from the anterior mesosalpinx. The organ is attached to the dorsal aspect of the mesometrium by a very short mesovarium. The maximum diameter is aligned more transversely than in *Cercopithecus*. The ovario-pelvic ligament is broad and its free border aligned almost transversely. There is a short, wide ovario-uterine ligament.

Uterine Tube.—This is greatly coiled, the loops being held together by connective tissue within a fold derived from the anterior mesosalpinx. Laterally the mesosalpinx is connected with the ovarian fimbria. The tube narrows considerably as it enters the uterine wall.

Uterus.—This is a dorso-ventrally compressed viscus of triangular outline, the cranial border being straight and without median notch. The organ is 10 mm. long by 9·5 mm. across the fundus. 8·3 mm. of its length lie craniad of the symphysis pubis. Body and cervix are not well differentiated, the caudal limit of the uterus being marked merely by lateral cushion-like thickenings with the least possible indication of fornices. Ligamentum teres, markedly flattened, connects the utero-tubal angle with the internal abdominal ring. Peritoneum clothes only the cranial 3·3 mm. of the ventral surface, slightly more dorsally.

Vagina.—Approximately 25 mm. long, this passage is wide at first, but narrows abruptly in the distal one third. Its ventral wall is adherent to the urethra and a common sphincter surrounds the two passages distally. The vaginal lining was quite smooth in the specimen examined, but patent throughout. It could appear therefore to be post-pubertal but as yet immature.

DUCTLESS GLANDS

The *spleen* resembles that of *Cercopithecus*, being relatively short and trihedral. The dorsal pole is pointed and the base broad and entire. All the other borders are also entire. The organ is supported caudally by a peritoneal fold or sustentaculum lienis passing from the duodeno-jejunal flexure to the ventral aspect of the left kidney.

The *hypophysis* is relatively large, being 4·5 mm. in transverse diameter, 3·5 mm. antero-posteriorly and 2·8 mm. from above down. The infundibulum is surrounded by a collar of tuberalis tissue. The anterior lobe is reniform, embracing the pars nervosa, the latter has a triangular outline and its base is 3·5 mm. across.

Thyroid.—This is remarkable for its length, for the gland extends from a point lateral to the upper end of the thyroid cartilage as far as the sixth ring of the trachea. Its caudal part is somewhat narrower than the cranial. There is no isthmus or connecting strand across the mid-line. It receives blood vessels from both poles, and these anastomose on the dorsal surface of the organ. Parathyroids have not been grossly demonstrated.

Adrenals are relatively large. The left, triangular in outline, sits upon the cranial pole of the left kidney. It measures 9·2 mm. in height and the same across its base. It receives arteries from the inferior phrenic and renal arteries, mainly the latter. The right is also more or less triangular, but set more obliquely so that its medial border faces more ventrad. It is partly covered by postcaval vein, and the remainder by liver. Its maximum height is 10·4 mm., but its base is only 7 mm. across. The cortico-medullary boundary is sharply defined.

ANGEIOLOGY

HEART AND PERICARDIUM

Located in the median line, the long axis of the pericardium lies in the sagittal plane, while the cardiac apex is only a few millimetres to the left of the median line, opposite the fourth costal cartilage. The pericardium is connected to the sternum by a double-layered serous fold produced by the union of layers from the right and left pleurae. It is connected to the diaphragm by bilaminar folds of pleura related to the azygos lobe of the right lung.

The serous pericardium presents a transverse sinus, but no oblique sinus. A shallow pocket is formed between the postcaval vein and the right pulmonary vein and a deeper one between the left and right pulmonary veins. Although an oblique vein of Marshall can be seen, no fold continues this on the back of the left atrium.

The shape of the heart corresponds closely with that of *Cercopithecus*. The apex is bifid equally shared between left and right ventricles, and lies opposite the fourth costal cartilage or the anterior part of the following interspace. The cranial limit gains the hinder border of the level of the first costal cartilage.

Atria are thin walled and are provided with capacious appendices, that on the left with strongly crenated margins. The right shows feeble development of musculi pectinati while externally the sulcus terminalis is not indicated. On the other hand the auriculo-ventricular sulci are markedly developed in spite of the large size of the vessels occupying them.

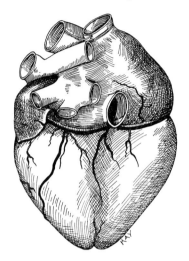

FIG. 83.—*Miopithecus talapoin.* Heart from the dorsal aspect ($\times \frac{2}{1}$)

Internally, the right atrium presents a single large semilunar fold at the entrance of the postcaval vein. The fold is continued to the left to form a hood over the cranial border of the opening of the coronary venous sinus, *i.e.* there is no separate Thebesian valve. Fenestra ovalis is rounded and deep.

The right ventricle presents two papillary muscles, both springing from the septal wall, a short one (M. papillaris subarterialis), and a long one (M. papillaris septalis proprius). A thin moderator band leaves the septal wall near the root of the short papillary muscle, passing obliquely across to the lateral wall. The left ventricle has two papillary muscles, anterior and posterior (or ventral and dorsal) each arising from the corrresponding wall near its junction with the septal wall.

Only three pulmonary veins open into the left atrium, one from the left, and two from the right lung.

CORONARY VESSELS

Coronary arteries are arranged almost exactly as in *Cercopithecus* (*antea*, p. 346). The ventral interventricular branch of the left coronary proceeds to the apical notch and then along the dorsal interventricular groove for about one-third its extent. Circumflex and atrial branches are as in *Cercopithecus*. The right coronary gives a large infundibular branch and proceeds to the crux, where it supplies a large oblique atrial branch to the wall of the right atrium.

The aortic arch is two-branched. From its summit a large innominate arises, which bifurcates into brachiocephalic (which divides into right subclavian and right common carotid), and left common carotid. The left subclavian arises from the aortic arch as it curves into its descending portion, sot hat a space exists between the roots of the two branches (Keith's type B).

NEUROLOGY

Central Nervous System

BRAIN.—Weight of brain of an adult male (body weight 519 g.) 36 gm., *i.e.* one-fourteenth of body-weight.

Cerebral hemispheres are produced posteriorly 5 mm. beyond the most prominent part of the cerebellum. The normal degree of asymmetry occurs

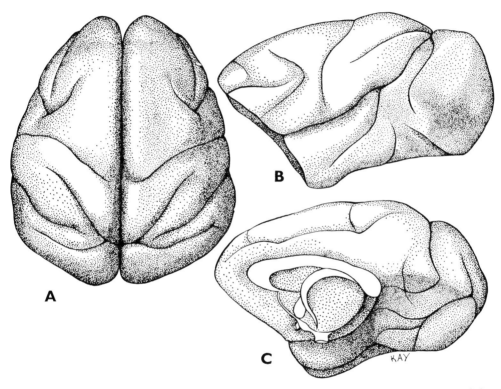

FIG. 84.—*Miopithecus talapoin* ♂. Three views of brain (× 1½). A, from above ; B, left hemisphere, lateral aspect ; C, right hemisphere, medial aspect

between the two hemispheres. The right temporal pole, for example, is considerably bulkier than its fellow, the difference being largely due to that part formed by the hippocampal gyrus.

The fissural pattern on the hemispheres is in close accord with that of *Cercopithecus*. The frontal lobe shows the same curved prefrontal sulcus, more acutely bent, however, and enclosing a short inferior frontal sulcus. The remainder of the lateral surface of the lobe is quite smooth. The long central sulcus is directed forwards and downwards in sinuous fashion and incises the superior margin. Sylvian and parallel sulci unite, the latter joining at about the mid-point of the Sylvian. The top of the fused fissures is embraced by the bifurcated parieto-occipital as in *Cercopithecus*. The occipital area is quite smooth, apart from the deep inferior occipital sulcus, which curves upwards and forwards from the inferior margin.

On the medial aspect the calloso-marginal, calcarine and collateral sulci are as in *Cercopithecus*, the first mentioned turning upwards behind to incise the upper margin. Between the upturned end and the upper part of the calcarine, commencing at the posterior extremity of the corpus callosum and extending to the upper margin, is a large medial limb of the parieto-occipital—largely unrepresented in *Cercopithecus*.

BEHAVIOURAL CHARACTERS

HABITAT : ECOLOGY

The Talapoin inhabits rain forest belts and is said to be frequently seen in forests of the southern Cameroons (Jeannin, 1936; Perret & Aellen, 1956) and Rio Muni (Cabrera, 1929). It is also said to be common in forested areas of the lower Congo especially the area north of the river mouth.

According to Malbrant and Maclatchy (1949), the Talapoin affects swamp-forests and forests along streams, as well as coastal and estuarine mangrove swamps. It is also frequently found in low secondary brush on abandoned farms. The existence of high altitude swamps in the Ruwenzori range offers confirmatory evidence for the occurrence there of a race of Talapoin (*M. t. pilettei*) so far known from a single specimen in the Tervueren Museum, collected at an altitude of 2500 metres (Lönnberg, 1919).

Although apparently fully adapted to an arboreal existence, it is interesting to report that captive specimens show a preference for resting on the cage floor in the shade of the perch rather than upon the perches themselves.

Malbrant and Maclatchy state that the animals move freely about the tangle of stems of mangroves feeding upon aquatic plants, the troops being composed of up to 60–80 individuals, although the usual number in a band is much less. Presumably, as with *Cercopithecus*, the larger bands are the result of temporary fusion of smaller family units or clans.

Being essentially timid animals they seldom approach human settlements, although Malbrant and Maclatchy report a troop taking up residence at night near the entrance to a native village at the mouth of the Ofoubour river.

Troops are somewhat sedentary, remaining long periods in their preferred range, strictly maintaining their territories.

The nocturnal resting place is frequently located in the middle of the dense tangle of adventitious roots whose ends are bathed in water, thereby serving as a protection against predators.

FOOD AND FEEDING

In the wild state the diet is composed largely of palm-nuts, seeds of various plants growing in secondary bush, seeds of the Uapaea and of the

Umbrella-tree (*Musanga cecropioides*) and also the leaves and petals of the Miani, a plant which bears a red and white flower, growing abundantly on old plantations. Talapoins are also extremely fond of the fruit of the Pawpaw (*Carica papaya*), overcoming their natural timidity to the extent of entering native cultivation to obtain it (Malbrant and Maclatchy).

In captivity most readily available fruits and vegetables are eaten, though individual items vary, at irregular intervals, in their order of acceptance. Apples, grapes, oranges, tomatoes, bananas, peaches, plums, carrots, lettuce and corn cobs are accepted; but whereas, at one time, the last mentioned was taken in preference to the others, soon this order changed and corn cobs fell to the lowest priority. Banana is preferred sliced and best of all if rolled in a protein concentrate powder (Gevral). That some animal protein is a natural dietetic requirement is indicated in the avidity with which crickets, mealworms, egg-yolk and newborn mice are seized and eaten. Other items offered and accepted more or less readily are ground-nuts and sunflower seeds.

A curious pattern of behaviour has been noted in the preparatory treatment of grapes, ground-nuts and similar sized comestibles. These are taken in the hand and then repeatedly rolled bimanually on the substrate without banging or bruising the fruit. In the case of grapes, an eager desire for the seed rather than the pulp is manifested; the seeds having been cleared of pulp, are then cracked by dental action to obtain the kernel. The same applies to the seeds of cucurbitaceous fruits (melon, pumpkin, etc.), and also of orange.

Coprophagy has been observed once by a female when frustrated by refusal of proffered food.

MOTILE ACTIVITIES

Talapoins are extremely lively monkeys which move rapidly and dexterously through their arboreal milieu. Their movements are often jerky.

In resting they sit upright using their hands the while in exploring the environment, manipulating food or grooming.

The tail is used in the normal manner of guenons, but an interesting manifestation in the male, when in aggressive mood, is a rapid twitching of the terminal third, recalling the similar pattern met with in felines.

The display posture consists of jerky side to side and up and down movements of the fore part of the body, which is held in a crouched position on the extended and abducted arms.

A challenging gesture adopted by males as a threat display and by females toward cage companions consists of opening the mouth widely, displaying the canines, the tongue being drawn backwards and upwards, and the ears pressed back and to the side of the head. The mouth is kept open for a few seconds with the head held up and thrust forward, the fore body being held in the same crouched posture as in the display pattern. The facial display cannot be described as a yawn, though functioning in the same way as the so-called yawning pattern of guenons and other cynomorphs.

Movements of the eyebrows are somewhat more marked than in typical guenons, but less noticeable than in mangabeys, macaques or baboons. Ear movements are very limited in spite of their large relative size.

Handedness is individually variable, but a preference for the use of one hand seems general. My female, though to some extent ambidextrous, is predominantly right handed; the male is more ambidextrous, but shows some preference towards left-handedness. The male, too, is expert in catching food objects, especially crickets, thrown to him; he grasps them bimanually, afterwards pulling them apart.

VOICE

Talapoins are relatively silent monkeys. Malbrant and Maclatchy (*loc. cit.*) describe a feeble emission symbolized by *ti ti ti*, recalling slightly the whistle-like alarm note of *C. nictitans*.

I have not observed this in captive examples, where the commonest utterance is a single *ahk* or *arkh*, used by both sexes when disturbed. A more definite alarm note, emitted when a cat was introduced in their neighbourhood, is a *chrrk*. This was more emphatically used when a green hose pipe was first introduced; presumably it was mistaken for a serpent. The only other vocal emission is a keening note heard solely during copulation.

TOILET

This consists principally of self-grooming and mutual grooming. Grooming is not as intensive or frequent as in other guenons. Mutual grooming is probably more of social than hygienic significance. Scratching with hands or feet occurs as in *Cercopithecus*.

SOCIAL STRUCTURE

Nothing has been recorded of the social relationships in the wild state, but this may be presumed to be as in *Cercopithecus*. Male dominance does not appear to be a marked feature. In a pair maintained in the Yerkes Primate Center, the female was the bolder at first and definitely dominated the more timid male. She has always remained tamer and will accept food from the hand of her keeper, whereas the male, though constantly exhibiting aggressive postures and displays, will not make friendly approaches even when enticed with food. He allows the female first choice from the feeding trough.

On the other hand, on one occasion, when both had escaped into the laboratory and the female had been recaptured, the male, in order to protect her, attacked her captor, leaping upon him in efforts to bite and scratch to the accompaniment of the sharp alarm note above mentioned.

REPRODUCTIVE BEHAVIOUR

The most striking feature in the reproductive physiology of *Miopithecus* is the occurrence of a genital swelling in the mature female. This was first reported by Zuckerman (1930) in a female under observation for twelve months in the London Zoo. Five irregular cycles of sexual swelling occurred without, however, noticeable evidence of menstruation.

Tomilin (1940) reported on two females (one adult, one young, supposedly daughter of the adult) in the Philadelphia Zoo. The older animal commenced menstruation with copious sanguineous discharge soon after arrival. The sexual swelling was considerable. Serosanguineous discharge occurred at intervals of a few hours, active flow ceasing during the intervals. A second menstrual flow took place about three weeks later and was associated with partial deturgescence of the sexual skin. Subsequent observations over the next ten months led to the following conclusions :

1. Fluctuations in size and contours of sexual skin are irregular.
2. Correlation between sexual skin turgescence and menstruation is not exact, some menses taking place when the swelling is in abeyance, others during advance of turgescence and some during deturgescence.
3. Menses are of irregular duration, lasting from 1–4 days.
4. Although spaced more or less at monthly intervals, the cycles varied— 27, 28, 32, 36 and 43 days apart.
5. There is a seasonal amenorrhoea. A period of 120 days lapsed between the October menstruation and the next succeeding one in February. Possibly this is indicative of seasonal cessation of ovarian activity and therefore of reproductive capacity.

In figure 75 are shown stages in the size and conformation of the genital swelling in two mature female talapoins, one observed over a period of ten years in the London Zoo and another more intensively studied for seven months in the Yerkes Laboratories. General conclusions are in agreement with Tomilin's findings. Sexual swelling is assumed gradually taking approximately one week, and detergescence varies in the degree of its completion. Once established, some degree of turgescence appears to persist, the dorsal lobe generally collapsing to a greater degree than the pubic lobe, which always remains large. No consistent correlation is noted between menstrual flow and state of turgescence. Flow is somewhat irregular, commencing as a sero-mucoid discharge from the vulva, followed by bleeding on the next day. Bleeding may cease for a day, but becomes copious on the succeeding day, after which cessation takes place until the next cycle is due. Histological appearances of the endometrium on the first day of the menses have been figured by Zuckerman (1937).

COPULATION.—Copulation has been observed two days after a profuse menstrual flow and also at the height of the sexual swelling. It occurs as in *Cercopithecus*. The female emits a low keening note during the process. The male is more agressive in these circumstances. He will make ineffectual attempts at copulation when frustrated, *e.g.* by withholding expected food. After coition the female adopts a smug, self-satisfied expression.

PREGNANCY AND PARTURITION.—Little information is available concerning breeding. Talapoins have been bred, according to the International Zoo Yearbook, in the menageries at Barcelona, Frankfurt and Prague. The Barcelona record is apparently erroneous in so far as births have, in all cases been from mothers pregnant on arrival from Rio Muni (Jonch, 1964, *in litt.*). Some of these are reared by their mothers, others discard their babies.

In Frankfurt birth took place on 4 March 1963 (*Internat. Zoo News*, x. 132), but no further data has been published. See, however, Hill (1965, in press).

LONGEVITY.—Once it is established in captivity the expectation of life of the Talapoin is considerable. A record has been established for the species by a male *M. t. ansorgei* in the Philadelphia Zoo, where it arrived fully adult 6 October 1939, and was still alive in February 1964 (Marvin Jones, 1964, *in litt.*). A female in the London Zoo, received 4 February 1950, was still alive when I left London in October 1962 ; she survived the 1954 tuberculosis epizootic which killed all her cage companions. Flower (1931) records a Talapoin of over 19 years of age which was received in the Amsterdam Zoo in 1888 and was still living in the summer of 1907.

1. *MIOPITHECUS TALAPOIN* (Schreber), 1774 *

(SYN. : *Talapoin* Buffon, 1766, xiv, p. 287 ; *Simia talapoin* Schreber, 1774 ; *Cercopithecus talapoin* Erxleben, 1777, p. 36 ; *S. (Cercopithecus) niger* Kerr, 1792, p. 71 ; *Cercopithecus pileatus* Desmarest, 1820, p. 57 (*nec* Shaw, 1800, p. 53) ; Rode, 1937, p. 111 ; *Simia melarhina* F. Cuvier, 1829, p. 92 ; *Miopithecus capillatus* I. Geoffroy, 1842, p. 720 ; *Cercopithecus melarhinus* Schinz, 1844, p. 47 ; *Miopithecus talapoin* Geoffroy, 1849, p. 308 ; *Cercopithecus coronatus* Rode, *Ann. Mus.* xix., 94.)

VERNACULAR NAMES : in West Africa, *ozem* ; French, *le talapoin, singe des paletuviers, mélarhine*. In Fernando Po and the Canary Isles Talapoins are imported and offered for sale under the erroneous name of *titi* (Cabrera, 1929).

* *Säugetiere*, i. 101, Pl. XVII.

TYPE LOCALITY : Unknown. Schreber's description is based on a male specimen, now in the Paris Museum (no. 295 (136)), which is the type of the genus, but not of the species (*fide* Rode, 1938). It is the individual to which Buffon first applied the name *talapoin*. According to Rode the label also mentions *C. coronatus* and it has also been mistakenly called *C. pileatus*. The skull is in the anatomical collection in Paris. Type locality of *niger*, unknown, but reference is made in description to Bosman's voyage ; therefore some part of Guinea. Type locality of *capillatus*, none stated ; species retracted later (p. 1037) by author. Type locality of *melarhinus* " Africa ".

CHARACTERS

All forms of the Talapoin agree in their small size, disproportionately large, globular brain-case, very short muzzle with large eyes and relatively wide internarial septum, separating the oblique laterally directed nares.

The face is hairy and for the most part light in colour, but localized blackish hairs occur, especially over the nasal area and on the lips. There is no frontal band, but the bristle-like dark frontal hairs are erect, forming a distinct curved crest. The bright yellow whiskers are arranged in a radiating fashion from a point on the cheek level with the nares.

Ears are naked and sometimes blackish, but largely obscured by the whiskers.

Crown, nape and upper surface of trunk clothed with speckled olive-green hairs, individual hairs having basal two-thirds grey, a single olive-green middle section and black tips. The black speckling darkest along the spinal tract, less evident on the flanks and lateral aspects of the limbs and obsolete on the dorsum of hands and feet. Tail ashy grey above, yellower beneath.

Under parts whitish or somewhat washed with yellow.

Perineum violet.

SKULL.—Relatively large to body size ; with rounded neuro-cranium lacking ridges and crests, except for supraorbital ridges. Orbits large, separated by a very thin partition. M.$\frac{3}{3}$ smaller than other molars and often with hinder pair of cusps reduced to one, though not constantly so (see also under genus, *supra*, p. 592).

DISTRIBUTION (Map 6)

The Talapoin is essentially a West African form occupying the rain forest belt from the southern Cameroons and Gabon to Angola, thence inland along the Lower Congo at least as far as the Kasai river. Its existence farther east in the Ruwenzori range is based solely on the evidence of the type specimen of *M. t. pilettei* described by Lönnberg (1919) from an animal collected by Pilette. There is no evidence that this animal had been transported there from elsewhere. Like *Allenopithecus*, the Talapoin seems to favour lowland swamp forest (*vide antea*, p. 614).

(a) *M. talapoin talapoin* Schreber, 1774 *

(*Syn* : *Simia talapoin* Schreber, 1774 ; *Cercopithecus talapoin* Erxleben, 1777, p. 36 and many recent authors ; *Simia melarhina* F. Cuvier, 1829, p. 92)

Vernacular names : Eschira and Bapounou, *tsiengui* ; Pahouin mazouma, *ouzem* ; Pahouin makima, *n'zem* ; Bakota, *inziembi* ; Bakoulé, *n'zem* or *ezienze* ; Adouma, *munzimbi* ; Lingomo, *zimbi*.

Type locality : See under species.

CHARACTERS.—Face pallid, especially around the eyes, where the skin tends towards an orange hue, that of the lips being yellowish. Nose and lips clothed with short black hairs giving a smudged appearance to the face ; a blackish area also infraorbitally ; no pale frontal band present. Iris maroon.

Cheek hairs for the most part golden yellow, but some of these have their apices brownish or black-tipped. A thin black tract separates the whiskers from the crown, passing from the supero-lateral angle of the orbit as far as the middle of the ear. Anterior whiskers directed backwards ; the posterior preauricular ones fanwise, some upwards, some directly backwards and some downwards, from a point immediately anterior to the tragus, thus forming a distinct semicircular field. Hairs of inferior part of cheek somewhat elongated and directed straight backwards.

Ears flesh-coloured or lightly pigmented, decorated with a few short hairs either black or banded yellow and black.

Crown, nape and back bright olive yellow, individual hairs with basal two-thirds grey, black at the extremity and a single yellow band subterminally, narrower than the terminal black band. On shoulders and hips the yellow bands are broader and this colour tends to predominate over the black ; this becomes still more exaggerated on the limbs which are, on their lateral aspects, golden yellow, as also are the dorsum of hands and feet.

Tail dorsally similar to back, becoming duskier towards the extremity ; below golden yellow proximally, then more greyish and finally at the tip blackish.

Hairs around anus, scrotum, pubes and upper parts of medial aspect of thighs, golden yellow.

ADULT FEMALE.—Similar to the male, but less richly coloured.

JUVENILE.—Resembles the adult except for absence of black maxillary patches and lesser amount of yellow in the pelage, especially on the limbs ; callosities blackish.

DIMENSIONS (in millimetres) :

Number	Locality	Sex	Head and Body	Head Length	Tail	Foot	Ear	Weight in Gm.
B.M.	30 miles above mouth of Rio Benito	♂	350	—	375	—	—	—
,,	R. Como	♀	340	—	385	—	—	—
PC.554	*ex* Miami Zoo	♂	267	69·3	307	86·6	18·8	519
PC.548	*ex* Frankfurt Zoo	♀	228	69	258	75	16·5	—
PC.557	*ex* Baltimore Zoo	♂	326	78	400	91	20	1346

* *Säugethiere*, i. 101, Pl. XVII.

SKULL.—Cranial measurements (in millimetres) :

Number	Locality	Sex	Max. Cranial Length	Glabella-occiput	Biparietal	Least Frontal	Basion-bregma	Bimastoid	Bizygomatic	Biorbital	Palatal Length	Upper Cheek-teeth	Mandibular Length	Lower Cheek-teeth
U.S. Nat. Mus. 220349	Ogouma, R. N'kami	♂	69	58	45	33	36	43	41	37	22	13·5	35	15
												M.³ lacking		
U.S. Nat. Mus. 220330	N'tyonga	♀	67	56	45	32	37	43·5	40	36	20	15	35	17
												M.³ present		
,,	Rio Muni	♂	77·7	59	46·4	35·2	39·5	47·4	50·5	44·5	24·5	16·3	43·3	20·4
Royal Free Hospital OW 6	Zoo	?	67·2	59	43	34·3	—	43·4	42·5	39·3	21	15	37·3	17

In the last-mentioned skull there are two infraorbital foramina each side, one malar foramen on the left, two on the right. The mandible shows a single large mental foramen each side below P.$\overline{4}$.

DISTRIBUTION.—Southern Cameroons and Gabon as far south as the right bank of the Congo. Specific localities given by Perrett and Aellen (1956) are Ambam and Foulassi, both in Cameroons. Mertens (1929) mentions one from Bange forest, southern Cameroon. Rochebrune (1883–5, p. 26) includes the Talapoin in the fauna of Senegambia, stating it occurs in the forests along the Gambia and Casamance and Somone rivers, in the country of Den-y-dack and at Douzar. He also records the local name as *Pindojh*. No modern evidence of the species so far north is recorded however.

(b) *M. talapoin ansorgei* Pocock, 1907,* Ansorge's Talapoin

(*Syn.* : *Cercopithecus talapoin ansorgei* Pocock, 1907 ; Poll, 1940 ; *C. talapoin* Bocage, 1889)

Type locality : Camboka (=Canhoca), Angola. Type, adult male, in British Museum (No. 4.4.9.1), collected by W. J. Ansorge, December 1903.

CHARACTERS.—Generally characterized by the slightly greater size, by lesser amount of black on cheek-hairs, by whiteness of the radiating hairs of the preauricular region, and by the greater predominance of yellow in the dorsal pelage.

PELAGE.—Nose covered with black hairs ; hairs on upper lip adjacent to nose long, black, bristly. Hairs on fore part of cheeks golden yellow with tips slightly darker, directed downwards ; those on preauricular area forming a fan-like arrangement, almost white ; inferior whiskers longer, backwardly directed. Ears black.

Crown, nape and back, yellowish olive green, the yellow annuli on each hair broad, almost as broad as the black. Lateral aspects of limbs chrome yellow ; hands and feet less bright—chamois yellow.

Tail above in basal one-third blackish brown, becoming purer brown in distal two-thirds, each hair, however, tipped with yellow or chamois ; inferiorly yellowish grey basally, remainder buff. Underparts pure white.

DIMENSIONS of type ♂ : head and body, 400 mm. ; tail, 525 mm. ; hind foot, 105 mm. ; ear, 35 mm.

* *Proc. zool. Soc. Lond.*, p. 742.

Skull.—Cranial dimensions (in millimetres) :

Number	Locality	Sex	Max. Cranial Length	Biparietal	Least Frontal	Bimastoid	Basion-bregma	Bizygomatic	Biorbital	Palatal Length	Upper Cheek-teeth	Mandibular Length	Lower Cheek-teeth
B.M. 4.4.9.1	Canhoca	♂	—	—	—	—	—	—	43·4	23·6	16·4	41·5	18·6 [1]
AMNH 80779	Hanha	♂	74·1	48·6	38·3	48·6	39·1	51·1	—	20·4	—	—	—
Leiden Mus.	Benguela	♂	77·8	49·6	39·8	51·3	40·5	55·2	—	21·1	—	—	—
,,	,,	♀	72·7	47·1	37·1	48·2	38·3	50·2	—	19·3	—	—	—

[1] Type.

The type skull has four infraorbital foramina each side and a single malar foramen.

Distribution.—Angola. Besides the type locality, specimens have been recorded from Ambaca (Bocage, 1889), Cassoalala (Elliot, 1913). Hanha, Benguela (Leiden Museum) and Harba (Hill and Carter, 1941). Appears to be uncommon in Angola.

(c) *M. talapoin vleeschowersi* Poll, 1940 *

> (*Syn.* : *Cercopithecus talapoin vleeschowersi* Poll, 1940)
> *Vernacular names* : *ntela* (Leopoldville area) ; *nkene* (Lake area).
> *Type locality* : Kinseke, Lower Congo (? = Kinsele on right bank of Lukunga). Original description based on two individuals, an immature male from Kinseke (the first mentioned) and an adult female from Bomu, both collected July 1939 by C. Vleeschowers. Both skins (with skulls) in Tervueren Museum.

Characters.—Distinguished by the body proportions and by hair colour, especially the short white hairs on the centre of the upper lip, long and black only at the sides. General colour brighter than in *talapoin* or *pilettei* due to the broader yellow zone in individual hairs, yellow and black zones being of approximately the same length, as also in *ansorgei*.

Pelage (both sexes).—Facial skin pallid, the nose and medial parts of cheeks furnished with black hairs ; upper lip with grey hairs below nostrils, black at the sides ; lower lip with grey or white hairs. Whiskers for the most part golden yellow, but some hairs with brownish tips ; a thin black tract from lateral palpebral canthus to ear ; frontal tract in two parts arching over brows, also black. Anterior preauricular hairs deep yellow, the more posterior ones disposed radially from a point situated level with the middle of the ear forming a well defined semicircular area of somewhat paler colour, the central hairs almost white but becoming increasingly yellow peripherally. Hairs of lower part of cheeks more elongated and directed straight backwards.

Ears black, decorated with few hairs, black, grey and yellow.

Crown, nape and back yellow olive, the hairs greyish in their basal two-thirds, black-tipped with a single golden yellow band between or about the same width as the apical black zone.

On shoulders and hips the yellow bands are augmented at the expense of the black tips ; this effect is still further exaggerated on the limbs, the yellow colour

* *Rev. zool. bot. Afr.* (Tervueren), xxxiii. 131.

predominating, though somewhat less on the hind- than the fore-limbs. Hands and feet similar, a little greyer on the feet than the hands.

Chin, throat, chest and abdomen, also medial aspects of limbs, white with a slight greyish tinge.

Tail above similar to back, but distinctly darker, greyer, especially in terminal half ; beneath grey from the root, the grey becoming darker in the distal half where dorsal and ventral tones merge.

Hairs around anus and pubic region grey, with a slight yellowish tinge.

DIMENSIONS.—Immature male : head and body, 320 mm. ; tail, 305 mm. Adult female : head and body, 370 mm. ; tail, 360 mm.

SKULL.—Cranial measurements (in millimetres) :

M.t. vleeschowersi	♀ ad.	♂ immat.
Maximum cranial length	71	66
Occipito-nasal length	63	59
Condylo-basal length	47	—
Palatal length	—	21
Biorbital breadth	40	38
Least frontal breadth	35	34
Bizygomatic	47	44
Bitemporal	47	45
L. nasal bones	7	6
Upper cheek-teeth	26	25
Lower cheek-teeth	25	26

DISTRIBUTION.—South bank of Lower Congo. The two specimens referred to in the original description were respectively from Kinseke and Bomer, both collected in July 1939 by C. Vleeschowers. The former is an immature male and the latter an adult female.

According to an anonymous writer in *Zooleo*, 1953 (n.s. No. 18, p. 495) the distribution of the Talapoin in Leopoldville province embraces the whole of the territories of Muschie and Banningville. It was first found at Monkana in the lower Kwango country and seemed, at that time, to be localized there, but during World War II, specimens were obtained on the opposite bank of the Kasai. Subsequently, material has been collected from the immediate environs of Leopoldville, at Sabuka, and in the Panzi region in the upper Kwango.

(d) *Miopithecus talapoin pilettei* Lönnberg, 1919 *

Type locality : Kabawaki, Mt. Ruwenzori, 2500 m. Holotype skin in Tervueren Museum, collected by André Pilette.

Known only from the type specimen, which has been described by Lönnberg and re-examined by Schwarz (1928)† and Poll (1940)

* *Rev. zool. bot. afr.* vii. 119.　　† *Loc. cit.*, xvi. 40.

Differing from typical race by the presence of a shiny black patch on either side of the forehead contiguous laterally with the black temporal streak, and in the absence of yellow on the under surface of the tail.

CHARACTERS.—Face pallid, the nose covered with black hairs ; upper lip with short yellowish hairs and long black bristles ; lower lip with slightly yellowish hairs with black tips.

Hairs on cheeks golden yellow, some with black tips, separated by narrow tract of black hairs passing from supero-lateral angle of orbit to middle of ear. From the last mentioned a shiny black patch extends over each side of the forehead, contrasting markedly with the predominating yellow of the rest of the forehead.

General colour of upper parts like the typical race with the yellowish tinge predominating on the crown and flanks and the darker element along the spinal tract. Individual hairs dark grey basally, with black tips and a single golden yellow subapical band which, on the back, is narrower than the apical black band. On the shoulders and lateral aspects of arms the yellow predominates, becoming distally more ochraceous, especially on the hands. On the hind limbs the lighter colour also predominates, but is somewhat more olive, while the feet are somewhat paler than the hands.

Tail above basally differing from colour of back, the yellow zones being paler, yellowish white, distally the hairs becoming dirty brownish grey, but in the type the hairs are damaged and many are lost. Inferiorly the tail is grey without trace of yellow, sharply demarcated from the dorsal colour, except towards the end.

Underparts and medial aspect of limbs white, with a slight yellowish suffusion only on the distal parts of the limbs.

Callosities surrounded by pale buff hairs.

DIMENSIONS of type : head and body, 365 mm. ; tail, 460 mm. Size apparently intermediate between *ansorgei* and *talapoin*.

SKULL.—No skull accompanies the type skin.

DISTRIBUTION.—Known only from the type locality, Kabawaki on the Congo versant of Mount Ruwenzori, altitude 2500 metres.

Genus *ALLENOPITHECUS* Lang, 1923 *

SWAMP GUENONS

(SYN. : *Cercopithecus* Pocock, 1907 ; *Lasiopyga* Elliot, 1913)

DIAGNOSIS.—Guenons of more macaque or baboon-like habitus, with body shorter and heavier, the limbs stouter, more muscular and tail shorter than in *Cercopithecus*. Head roundish, but thickset with short rostrum ; molars more hypsodont, much broader basally, with buccal and lingual cusps more approximated to each other towards their apices and with narrow longitudinal depression between them ; $M.\overline{\underline{1}}$–$M.\overline{\underline{3}}$ with small buccal cusplet (mesostylid) at base of groove between anterior and posterior cusp. Females with a moderate catamenial swelling. Chromosome number 60 (Chiarelli, 1962, 1963).

* *Amer. Mus. Novit.* No. 87, 1.

PLATE XLI

Photo: W. C. Osman Hill

Miopithecus talapoin, adult ♂ and ♀. Note the threat display of the male

PLATE XLII

Photo: W. C. Osman Hill

Miopithecus talapoin, ♂ ♀ and young

AFFINITIES.—Lang (*loc. cit.*) on the basis of a single adult male could not assess the affinities of his new genus. He noted, however, that it was widely separated from *Macaca sylvana* or other species of *Macaca*, although certain dental features pointed in their direction. He affirmed it to be totally different from other African genera, notably from *Erythrocebus* and *Miopithecus*.

Hill (1964) on the basis of external anatomy, notes features linking *Allenopithecus* with *Macaca* and *Cercocebus* whilst others suggest alignment with *Cercopithecus*.

HISTORICAL

First recognized as a distinct species of guenon by Pocock, who knew the type specimen, a juvenile female, when it was living in the Zoological Society's menagerie. After its death, its skin was sent to the British Museum. Until then it had been exhibited tentatively as an example of *C. albogularis*, and afterwards, on grounds of its bodily proportions, changed to *C. talapoin* (*teste* label on type-skin). It was still later recognized as differing from *talapoin* in the direction of the hairs on the cheeks.

A second living example was subsequently acquired by the Hon. Walter Rothschild from the dealer, J. D. Hamlyn, and deposited in the London Zoo. According to Hamlyn it had arrived at Brazzaville (700 miles up the Congo) from still farther inland in Belgian territory.

No further material was forthcoming until the American Museum Congo Expedition (1909–1915) collected, in July 1909, an adult male near Bolobo on an island in the Congo river. This was the first Primate collected by the expedition. It was recognized by Lang as an example of Pocock's *C. nigroviridis*, but showed differences due to maturity which rendered it necessary to separate the species generically from *Cercopithecus*. Lang named the new genus in honour of the well-known American mammalogist, J. A. Allen, who devoted much time to the study of the collections of the Congo Expedition.

Since 1945 the species has been exhibited in many zoological collections and in the San Diego Zoo has successfully bred on several occasions.

EXTERNAL CHARACTERS

A stockily built monkey with robust torso, short, stout limbs and a relatively short, thick tail which, in the adult, is only a little longer than the crown-rump length, compared with, *e.g.*, *C. cephus*, where the crown-rump length is only 75 per cent of the tail length. In addition to its shortness the tail is also markedly thickened, especially at its base (see Hill, 1964).

2 S

Allenopithecus differs from *Cercopithecus* in respect of its hair tracts, notably in the head region. Pocock (1907) noted that the hairs on the cheeks lacked the upward trend seen in the *aethiops* group of *Cercopithecus* (with which he associated his *C. nigroviridis*), but he did not recognize the complexity manifested in this area in the adult (fig. 85). A vertical crest is produced in the preauricular region from the level of the root of the helix to that of the buccal cleft. This is formed by the convergence of two hair streams, an anterior sweeping downwards and backwards from the temporal and malar regions, and a posterior directed upwards and forwards from the region below the ear, including the whole of the area over the masseter. The last-mentioned stream is separated from the posteriorly directed hairs of the neck and postauricular areas by a curved line of divergence which sweeps around the postero-inferior margin of the head following, more or less, the edge of the mandible.

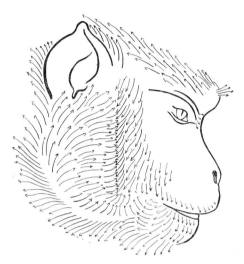

FIG. 85.—*Allenopithecus nigroviridis* ♂ adult. Head from the right side to show arrangement of hair tracts

These arrangements are only vaguely foreshadowed in the foetus and had probably still not attained their adult definitive arrangement in the juvenile animal examined by Pocock. In the adult male the arrangement, combined with the length of the hairs forming the crest, imparts an appearance reminiscent of some examples of *Macaca irus*.

Elsewhere the hair streams depart little from a generalized cranio-caudal plan and demand no special consideration. A striking feature in the foetal and neonatal hair pattern is the sharp line of demarcation between dorsal and ventral pelage extending from the dorsal axillary fold to the lateral angle of the groin. The terminal black pencil on the tail is striking in the infant, while in the adult the contrastedly pale chin is equally noteworthy.

On the intermammillary region and the area immediately craniad of the nipples is a sparsely haired region, the hairs of which are different in character from the neighbouring pelage, being pure white, unspeckled and more bristle-like. Presumably these form a tuft related to a subjacent glandular patch. Hairs over the anterior chest between the two acromia are soft, silky and provided with several dark annulations on the distal part of the shaft. The same applies to the hairs posterior to the supposed glandular area. The arrangement is less well marked in the female.

REGIONAL DETAILS (Hill, 1964)

FACE.—The face is guenon-like in immature specimens, but with a more prominent muzzle in mature animals, giving a more macaque-like appearance. Pigmentation produces a dusky facial appearance, somewhat more pallid on the eyelids (especially the upper), and completely lacking on the chin, which is markedly defined from the pigmented area of the lower lip.

Nictitating membranes reasonably well developed, with deeply pigmented free margins. Puncta lachrymalia oval to slit-like on free margins of each eyelid near medial canthus. Ocular conjunctiva darkly pigmented, palpebral merely dusky. Irides uniformly ochre.

Dorsum nasi raised 8–10 mm. above level of palpebral area and triangular in section at the bridge ; marked by transverse flexure lines. Towards the apex nasi the skin becomes smoother and the elevation more rounded. In an adult male the internarial septum is 5 mm. thick and each external naris 8 mm. long by 3 mm. across. Corresponding values in the adult female are 4·8 mm., 5·7 mm. and 3·5 mm. The nares are directed forwards and slightly laterad ; they show a prominent, sharp upper margin, whereas the lower margin is not defined from the integument of the face. The narial angle is 85° in the adult male, 83° in the female, 70° in a neonatus.

Relatively thick lips guard the horizontal rima oris. The upper lip is highly convex in both diameters. Pigment is heavy on the cutaneous aspect and the free margin but less deep on the mucosal surface. Cheek pouches are of moderate size as in *Cercopithecus*. Their cleft-like orifices are located level with the distal end of M.^{2}.

EXTERNAL EAR.—Differing from the external ear of *Cercopithecus* in the greater degree of retention of the morphological apex, which gives a high grade of angularity between superior and posterior borders and a consequent similarity to the ear of *Macaca*. The apex is more produced, everted and separated from the posterior border by a slight notch. The helix commences with a broad crus in the cavum conchae immediately dorsad of the lobate tragus, rapidly expanding upwards and then backwards, but thereafter narrowing gradually to disappear at the morpho-

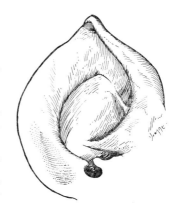

FIG. 86.—*Allenopithecus nigroviridis* ♂ adult. Right external ear

logical apex. The posterior border of the pinna is thin, smooth and slightly convex. Below, it merges into the inferior border, the two forming a semicircular outline bounding the lamina. The last mentioned is marked by a very shallow depression parallel with the margin, representing all that remains of the bursa. The intertragic notch has a flask-shaped outline due to the approximation of the tragus and antitragus. From the base of the antitragus posteriorly the anti-helix takes the usual course, but becomes weaker above and barely traceable into the upper fold bordering the fossa triangularis.

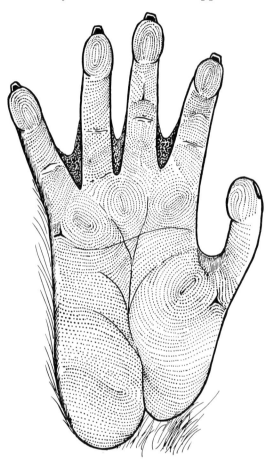

The latter is bounded below by a well marked horizontal supratragal fold, which lies parallel with the crus helicis.

CHEIRIDIA.—Lang (1923) noted the baboon-like habitus and robust, stocky limbs, without giving details of manus or pes. The manus especially recalls the short, broad hand of the baboons, particularly in the male, but the foot is less altered. Detailed measurements, compared with certain forms of *Cercopithecus*, are recorded by Hill (1964). Length/breadth ratios of hand in adults significantly greater in *Allenopithecus* than *Cercopithecus*, but the difference is less marked in juveniles.

Digital formula of manus III>IV>II>V>I. Digits stubby and united at their bases by extensive interdigital webs whose extremities gain the distal interphalangeal joints. Nails almost black, convex in both directions, but flatter on pollex, longer than wide,

FIG. 87.—*Allenopithecus nigroviridis* ♂ adult. Palmar aspect of the right hand to demonstrate dermatoglyphics. Based partly on palm prints, partly on direct observation

narrowing somewhat distally, extending beyond tips of digits (except on pollex).

Digital formula of pes III>IV>II>V>I, but the discrepancy between IV and II slightly greater than on manus. Interdigital webbing less marked than on manus. Nails as on manual digits, but on hallux longer and flatter.

Naked areas of palms and soles deeply pigmented, except that the summits of the torulae may be pallid. Torulae tactiles are well defined and prominent, being separated by deep creases. Number and arrangement of pads as in *Cercopithecus*. On the manus the radial interdigital pad is confluent with the thenar pad. The hypothenar pad is subdivided into proximal and distal parts by a transverse crease. Small central torulae may occur in the triangular field proximal to the middle of the main transverse crease.

Papillary ridge systems closely recall those in *Cercopithecus* as delineated by Bychowska (1930), Midlo and Cummins (1942) and Biegert (1961).

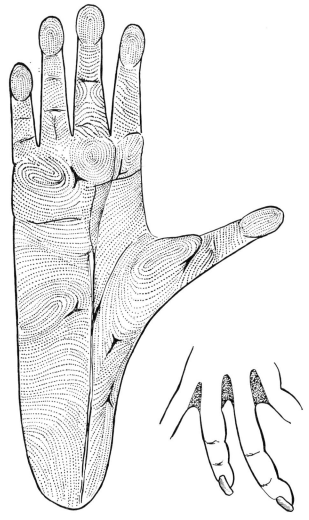

Fig. 88.—*Allenopithecus nigroviridis* ♀ adult. Palmar aspect of the right foot to demonstrate dermatoglyphics. Inset shows pedal digits from the dorsal aspect spread apart to show interdigital webbing.

Manual palmar ridge patterns conform exactly with the arrangement depicted and described by Biegert in *Cercopithecus*, except for the presence of a symmetrical V-pattern on the intermediate phalanx of III. The same applies to the planta, with, again, more complication on digit III, but in this case affecting the proximal phalangeal area (see fig. 88). A further difference affects the postaxial interdigital pad where the pattern of a twisted loop replaces the normal whorl.

CALLOSITIES AND SEXUAL SKIN.—Schwarz (1928 *a*) described and figured the callosities in both sexes. He found that in the male they were horn-coloured, elongated, almost rectangular, approximated and contiguous ventro-medially, in contrast to the small rounded, elliptical callosities of *Cercopithecus*. In the female he found them larger, of elongated pyriform shape, approximated but not contiguous.

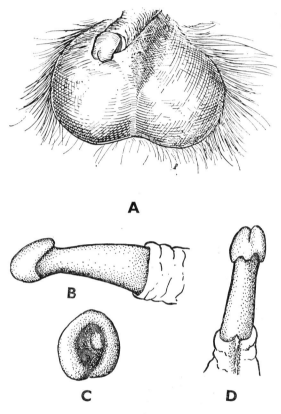

A

B

C   D

FIG. 89.—*Allenopithecus nigroviridis* ♂ adult. External genitalia. A, Penis and scrotum viewed from the ventral aspect ; B, Penis in left lateral view ; C, Apical view of glans penis with the meatal lips parted ; D, Penis from the perineal aspect

In my male the callosities, though approximated, fail to make contact in the median line and they are more rounded than in Schwarz's diagram and furthermore show a certain degree of asymmetry. My newborn male has small, narrowed but contiguous callosities.

A sexual skin is present in both sexes. In the male it takes the form of a transverse, sausage-shaped cushion between the root of the tail and the dorsal margins of the callosities. The anus is a transverse, puckered depression in the centre of the cushion. The swelling is rosy red, contrasting markedly with the horn-coloured callosities and the pale skin on the under surface of the root of the tail. The lateral extremities of the cushion are rounded. The area is already differentiated in the newborn, but here it lacks the bright rosy tinge.

In the female the sexual skin is more extensive and, as in *Miopithecus*, undergoes cyclical turgescence. The exact form of the structure when fully turgescent has not been described, but in the adult female examined by me the area was somewhat obscured by the effects of recent parturition. The subcaudal sausage-shaped swelling is present as in the male, but oedema arising from recent parturition affects the whole circumvulvar area and also the callosities and integument surrounding them. The skin peripheral to the inferior and lateral margins of the callosities shows a purplish discolouration. Whether or not a dependent pubic lobe is present during normal catamenial swelling is uncertain.

FIG. 90.—*Allenopithecus nigroviridis* ♀ adult. Perineum viewed from behind, animal in prone position—to show callosities and external genitalia in the post-parturient state

EXTERNAL GENITALIA OF THE MALE.—Testes are relatively large, agreeing rather with *Macaca* than *Cercopithecus* in this respect. They descend fully into a subglobular scrotum which is coloured a pale bluish shade. The two lateral sacs are separated by a shallow median sulcus which anteriorly is differentiated as a pale pink median strip. Towards the root of the scrotum the pink band widens into a triangular field to form a partial or complete pink collar around the root of the free part of the penis.

In the adult male the scrotum measures 66·7 mm. in transverse diameter, 25 mm. dorso-ventrally and 43 mm. from root to fundus. It is subpendulous and is the only part of the genitalia visible from the rear.

The penis closely resembles that of *Cercopithecus*. Its free portion, 52·6 mm. long, is capped by a glans 10 mm. long, 8·4 mm. broad and 9·2 mm. high. The glans is covered by a lax pinkish preputial sheath whose reflected layer is attached near the root of the pars libera. The attachment is annular, but exhibits a well-defined median fraenum on the perineal aspect.

Glans and pars intrapraeputialis are purplish in colour, except for an opaque white bar on the side of the corpus. The collum is elongated and laterally compressed, and, after an initial constriction, widens again as the glans is approached. The integument of the pars libera from the collum proximally to the attachment of the prepuce is finely papillated by low horny excrescences irregularly arranged. The glans is of the usual helmet-shape with a sinuous corona, without lateral notches, which are, however, represented by slight recession of the corona. Otherwise the organ closely resembles that of *Cercopithecus ascanius*.

EXTERNAL GENITALIA OF THE FEMALE.—Apart from the occurrence of a sexual skin and the fact that, in mature females, this undergoes cyclical turgescence, the external genitalia depart in no marked respect from those of *Cercopithecus*. A short (7 mm.) perineal body of purplish colour separates the anus from the vaginal opening. The rima pudendi from dorsal commissure to apex of glans clitoridis measures 28 mm. long. The acorn-like glans is deeply cleft on its perineal aspect giving a bilobed appearance. The two lobes diverge during turgescence. There is some evidence of both labia majora and labia minora (Hill, 1964).

Nipples are closely approximated as in *Cercopithecus* and are, therefore, as in that genus, probably used by the suckling simultaneously.

SKELETAL SYSTEM

SKULL (Lang, 1923 ; Allen, 1925 ; Verheyen, 1962)

Brain-case of similar form and size as in *Cercopithecus*, but facial skeleton much more prominent and oblique. The contention of Schwarz (1928) and Rode (1937) that the skull is, except for that of the Talapoin, the smallest of that of any African monkey, cannot be maintained.

Brain-case elongated, narrowed, with rather flattened superior profile ; without pronounced curvature anywhere ; the fossa supraglabellaris practically obsolete in males though well marked in females. Supraorbital arcades narrow and flattened in males ; narrow and curved in females.

Course of temporal lines much as in *Cercopithecus*, coming nearest to the *C. aethiops* group; but old males produce a well marked sagittal crest 2–3 mm. high, which may be of irregular development (see fig. 91).

On the base, compared with *Cercopithecus*, the basi-sphenoid and presphenoid portion, from the basilar suture, form a more abrupt inclination,

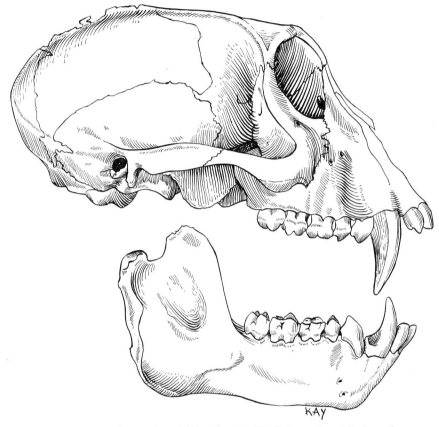

FIG. 91.—*Allenopithecus nigroviridis* ♂ (× $\frac{1}{1}$). Skull from the right lateral aspect.
Redrawn and modified from Lang

resembling rather the condition in *Erythrocebus*. These parts of the base are, furthermore, narrowed in the transverse dimension. Petrosal bulbous, smooth, narrowing towards its pointed apex, where it may show a longitudinal crest; but a true spina tubaria is lacking. Styloid process always well developed. As in *C. aethiops* and *Erythrocebus*, the floor of the auditory passage presents a V-shaped cleft or incision laterally, but in some cases this is difficult to determine on account of the antero-posterior flattening of the canal. On account of this flattening the postglenoid process is large and wide.

Orbital region much as in *Cercopithecus*, especially *C. aethiops*. Lachrymo-maxillary suture exactly on border of orbital opening and on the anterior border of the fossa sacci lacrimalis; it almost constantly presents a small fissure on its course below the level of the fossa.

Nasal bridge narrow transversely, flattened and standing out but little ahead of the orbital plane. Viewed from above, the planes of the two orbital openings form an obtuse angle as in most species of *Cercopithecus*.

The lateral cleft-like portion of the spheno-maxillary fissure is normally closed, but may persist as a small discrete orifice. Sphenoidal fissure in form of a reversed comma.

Nasals long and very narrow, pointed below, with persistent internasal suture even in old animals ; apertura pyriformis narrow, generally lozenge-shaped (as in *C. aethiops*).

Malar with several foramina zygomatico-faciales ; its zygomatic process heavy, much widened in front, rounded below, with a broad area of attachment for the masseter reaching as far as the maxillo-malar suture. Zygomatic arch strongly developed, with the maxillary root and anterior part of malar strongly bent forward level with the anterior surface of $M.^{2}$. Zygomatic process of temporal widening at base.

Prosthion-nasospinale dimension very high—higher than in any form of *Cercopithecus*.

Palate characteristically narrow, rugose, with the palatal processes of the two maxillae meeting at an angle with each other and so forming in the median line a slight crest. Posterior palatine canals opening within deep gutters, as in *Erythrocebus* ; posterior palatal spine very sharp.

Medial pterygoid plate with larger hamular process than in *Cercopithecus*. Lateral plate expanded, with convex free border presenting at its base but a single large foramen. Interpterygoid fossa deep and narrow, unperforated. Vomer with free posterior border not forming a curve as in *Cercopithecus*, but presenting a deep angular incision. Above, it becomes swollen as it approaches the presphenoid, resulting in an anomalous outline of the choanae. The alae vomeris diverge acutely, but just fail to reach the presphenoid-basiosphenoidal suture.

Mandible with short, wide ascending ramus, rising at an angle of approximately 105° from a line parallel with base of tooth-row. Posterior edge of ascending ramus with strong, laterally everted notch some distance below the wide condylar process. Angular process strongly inflected. Coronoid process wide and with an irregularly rounded contour, higher than condyle, from which it is separated by a deep, narrow notch.

Verheyen (1962) further draws attention to the following features of the mandible : (*a*) presence of a median sagittal symphyseal foramen (as in *Erythrocebus*), (*b*) fusion in the median plane of the two digastric fossae, (*c*) development of a transverse crest beneath the fossa sublingualis and (*d*) the existence of 1–3 mental foramina situated beneath $P._{\overline{3}}$–$P._{\overline{4}}$.

DENTITION

Dental formula as for *Cercopithecus*. The dentition is well figured by James (1960). Incisors and canines much as in *Cercopithecus*. Median upper incisors not quite twice as wide as I.$\underline{2}$. Lower incisors long, narrow, somewhat procumbent.

Canines larger in males, strongly curved, but slender; details as in *Cercopithecus*. A wide diastema between I.$\underline{2}$ and canine. Upper cheek teeth radically differing from those of *Cercopithecus*, and approaching those of *Cercocebus* and *Papio*. Crowns are broader, but lack the rudimentary buccal cusplets between anterior and posterior cusps.

P.$\underline{3}$ approximately two-thirds size of M.$\underline{2}$; P.$\underline{4}$, bicuspid.

M.$\underline{2}$ broadest, slightly wider at its base than long.

M.$\underline{3}$ broader than M.$\underline{1}$, with two markedly developed hinder cusps.

Individual molar cusps sloping strongly from their bases

FIG. 92.—*Allenopithecus nigroviridis* ♂ ($\times \frac{2}{1}$). A, upper dentition of the left side; B, lower molar series. Redrawn from Lang

towards the apex of the tooth, thereby forming a narrow longitudinal trench between buccal and lingual cusp series.

Tips of cusps of M.$\underline{1}$ and M.$\underline{2}$ with dentine exposed in mature animals.

Mandibular premolars relatively large, the foremost lacking the sloping surface for occlusion with maxillary canine. P.$\overline{3}$<P.$\overline{4}$ (James, 1960).

Mandibular molar series strongly reminiscent of those in *Cercocebus*, but lacking the fifth cusp on M.$\overline{3}$. Buccal cusps sloping strongly inward, bringing their tips close to those of the lingual cusps.

In adults M.$\overline{2}$ and M.$\overline{3}$ have more pointed lingual cusps, and the anterior higher than the posterior. At the base of the groove on the buccal surface between anterior and posterior cusps is a small stylid. As in upper molars the dentine is exposed at the tips of the principal cusps, especially on M.$\overline{1}$, less so on M.$\overline{2}$ and least on M.$\overline{3}$.

SPLANCHNOLOGY

PERITONEUM

The great omentum is broader than in *Miopithecus*, but has similar attachments. It is firmly attached over a distance of 25 mm. to the hepatic flexure of the colon, but sinistrally the transverse colon depends as a broad loop in an extensive mesocolon, to the cranial aspect of which the great omentum is attached along an oblique line, which becomes increasingly dorsal in position as it is traced to the left, while a final ventrad extension almost to the mesocolic attachment to the gut occurs on the left. As a result a fossa is formed facing to the right between omentum and mesocolon. Ventral and dorsal (or returning) laminae of the omentum remain distinct, enclosing a capacious extension of the lesser sac. Both laminae carry large blood vessels derived from the splenic artery, those in the dorsal lamina being directed mainly sagittally, whereas those in the ventral layer take arch-like courses from left to right, with only minute sagittally directed branches therefrom.

Cranially the lesser sac presents a narrow recessus oesophageus, 45 mm. deep, extending on the left and dorsal to the abdominal portion of the oesophagus, between it and the left crus of the diaphragm.

On the dorsal wall of the lesser sac, at the extreme right, a strongly marked fold connects the pylorus with that part of the returning lamina of the great omentum which adheres to the transverse mesocolon, but no gastro-pancreatic folds are developed.

In the greater sac the hepatic connections are as in *Cercopithecus*. No special plicae are developed at the neighbourhood of the duodeno-jejunal flexure nor around the ileo-colic junction, the caecum being quite free, as is also the ascending colon as far as the hepatic flexure, which is firmly adherent to the caudal half of the right kidney. No trace of a recto-duodenal fold has been found, but a strong transverse plica, constituting a sustentaculum lienis, crosses from the left side of the descending mesocolon to the ventral surface of the left kidney. The whole of the pancreas is retroperitoneal.

ALIMENTARY SYSTEM

The highly convex lips are deeply pigmented on the cutaneous aspect and dusky on the vestibular side, where the pigmentation extends to the gums, except for the marginal strip adjacent to the teeth. There is no frenum to either lip. Buccal pouches extend the vestibular mucosa some 36 mm. in a downward and backward direction. Each sac is greyish in colour from the subcutaneous aspect due to the extension of the vestibular pigmentation into its mucous membrane. The lining membrane is thrown into folds which present a reticular pattern recalling that seen in the body of the collapsed stomach. Its vestibular opening is oval, 3·4 mm. in major diameter, opposite $P.\overline{\underline{4}}-M.\overline{\underline{1}}$.

The hard palate is unpigmented except for the incisive papilla and more especially its surrounding depressed areola. Seven pairs of rugae arranged in detached arches are present, but the hindmost, opposite $M.\underline{1}$, tends to be vestigial on one or both sides. No rugae are related to the incisive papilla, the foremost being based opposite the forepart of the canine. The oval incisive papilla lies in a depression into which open the naso-palatine canals ; the depression is deeper and more pigmented laterally.

The tongue narrows slightly towards its apex, which is rounded rather than quadrate. A deep median sulcus marks the ventral surface of the free portion. A remarkable feature is, at the apex, the complete carpet of low, broad topped fungiform papillae to the almost total exclusion of filiform papillae. Along the lateral margins and in the zone just short of the apex, fungiform papillae become sparser and filiforms fill the interspaces. Along the sides a few fungiform papillae transgress the lateral margin. A single very large and prominent vallate papilla occupies the median line of the dorsum at the junction of oral and pharyngeal portions of the organ. Much smaller papillae, intermediate between vallate and fungiform in structure, occur along the lines of a V, whose apex is at the large vallate papilla. In the female examined two such minor vallate papillae occur on the right and only one on the left. They are no more prominent than fungiform papillae, but are provided with a shallow vallum. Lateral organs are well developed and are divisible into two distinct regions. The anterior part, comprised of five thick laminae with four intervening grooves, is succeeded behind by a region with shorter, less prominent, laminae and grooves. All are confined to the tongue proper, *i.e.* not trespassing on to the palato-glossal fold (cf. *Miopithecus*).

A triangular plica fimbriata occupies the angle between the tongue and the buccal floor. It is connected to the former by a frenal fold and its margin is entire.

Salivary Glands.—Parotid glands are large. Of the usual outline, the base or superior border embraces the auditory passage and then extends forwards over the masseter. The posterior border follows the anterior edge of the sterno-mastoid, meeting the oblique anterior border below in a prolonged apex, which is level with the angle of the mandible. The superficial aspect is distinctly convex ; the deep is irregular and sends forth a large oval lappet on the deep aspect of the medial pterygoid. The whole gland is greyish in colour, and a socia parotidis of similar appearance lies adjacent to the duct as the latter crosses the masseter.

The submandibular gland is a bulky mass of ovoid to pyramidal form occupying a depression below the angle of the mandible anterior to the sterno-mastoid. Its duct takes the usual course in relation to the mylohyoid and the sublingual gland, opening on the parafrenular papilla.

The sublingual is also relatively large and pyramidal in shape with the apex anteriorly. The base is directed backwards and its postero-inferior angle somewhat produced. There is no major division into two parts, the whole gland forming a compact mass of lobules. Nevertheless, both Bartholinian and Rivinian ducts are present, the former from the hinder part of the gland and the latter from the apical region.

Pharynx.—The soft palate is marked by large pores draining mucous glands and ends in the midline in a large, globular uvula similar to that of *Miopithecus*. The glosso-palatine fold is thin and smooth and the palatopharyngeal thicker and more oblique. The tonsil is located in a pocket near the insertion of the interfaucial mucosa to the base of the tongue. The pharyngeal one-third of the tongue is beset, behind the median vallate papilla, with numerous modified filiform papillae whose apices break into three or more filamentous appendages. Laterally, near the angle between the tongue and the lateral pharyngeal wall, occur a number of large lobate growths, which partly obscure the tonsillar recess. Others, somewhat less prominent, occupy the area adjacent to the epiglottis (fig. 95). Glosso-epiglottidean folds are lacking, as in *Miopithecus*.

Oesophagus.—This totals 136 mm. long in an adult female, of which 28 mm. are cervical, 96 mm. thoracic, and 12 mm. abdominal. The course taken resembles that in *Cercopithecus*.

Stomach.—Besides being very capacious, the stomach differs in several respects from that of *Cercopithecus* or *Miopithecus*, having incipient sacculation towards the condition characteristic of the Colobidae and therefore probably a parallel development in adaptation to some dietary specialization.

The parts most affected are the fundus and body, but there is some individual variation in detail. In all cases the cardia and pylorus are relatively close together and the greater curvature correspondingly very extensive. In an adult male the fundus and body form a globular chamber, with the right part of the greater curvature prolonged caudally into a subconical sac separated by a distinct sulcus from the pyloric segment. The latter narrows gradually, with some minor notches on its major curve, towards the pylorus. In an adult female the conical sac on the aboral part of the greater curve is much more developed and separated by a deeper constriction from the fundus, giving a suspicion of hour-glass stomach. In addition, the greater curve over the fundus is subdivided by two lesser sulci. No taenia formation occurs.

The fundal portion is vascularized by branches of the coronary artery descending from the lesser curvature and dorsally by branches from the splenic artery. The conical sac is supplied by branches from the right gastro-epiploic artery.

Internally the oesophageal mucosa is continued on to the cardiac extremity of the stomach for a variable distance (up to 11 mm. on the fundal side) in the form of a radially grooved surface with fluted margins. There is

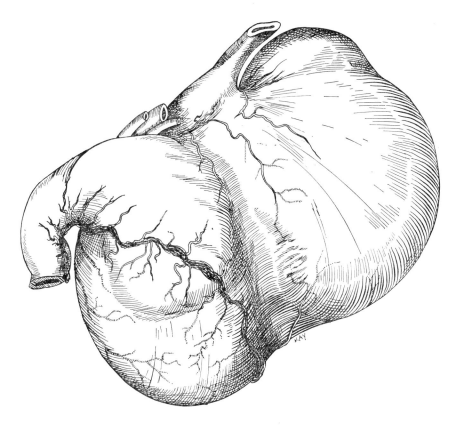

FIG. 93.—*Allenopithecus nigroviridis* ♀. Stomach from the ventral aspect (× 1)

a strong annular fold, based on muscle, at the junction of body and pyloric segment, better developed over the lesser curvature. Appearances of the mucosa are not remarkable.

Intestine.—The duodenum is relatively short, but C-shaped, and entirely retroperitoneal. The common bile duct opens with the main pancreatic duct, 16 mm. beyond the pylorus on the left half of the dorsal wall. It is not provided with a papilla, but lies buried among the villi, guarded by a horseshoe-shaped fold around its aboral edge. A papilla minor with an orally directed frenulum lies 11 mm. aboral to the preceding at the junction of medial and ventral duodenal walls. The jejuno-ileum is slung in a mesentery carrying 10–11 main rami intestini tenuis, of which the hindmost enters into loop-formation with the ileo-colic artery (fig. 105B).

The caecum is of the usual cercopithecine type, quite free, but tethered

to the terminal ileum by an anangious mesotyphlon.   The caecum is supplied
mainly by two vessels, branches of a single trunk which crosses the ileo-caecal
junction on the ventral side.   Opposite the antimesenteric border of the

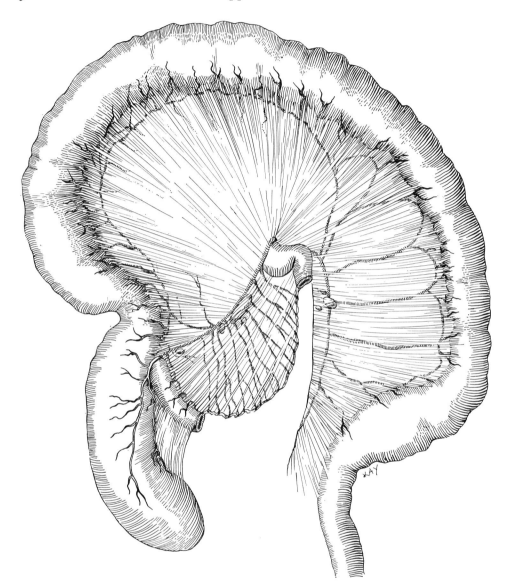

FIG. 94.—*Allenopithecus nigroviridis,* ♂ adult.
Disposition of the large intestine and associated mesenteries (× ½)

ileum, it bifurcates into a larger right and smaller left branch, the latter
coursing on the gut wall adjacent to the attachment of the mesotyphlon,
raising a fold of peritoneum.   A smaller dorsal caecal artery crosses the
ileo-caucal junction in a fatty fold sending radiating branches to the dorsal

PLATE XLIII

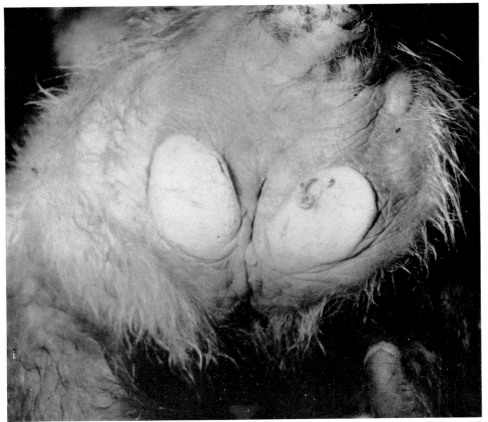

Photo: W. C. Osman Hill

Allenopithecus nigroviridis ♀. Post-partum. General view of perineum showing
callosities, sexual skin and vulva

PLATE XLIV

Photo: H. J. Kuhn

Allenopithecus nigroviridis, adult ♂, with *Cercopithecus neglectus* in Munich Zoo

wall of the caecum (not, however, as far as the apex) and adjacent parts of the ascending colon. Branches pass deep to the dorsal taenia.

The colon departs in no important respect from that of *Cercopithecus*. The transverse colon is a capacious, dependent loop freely suspended in an ample mesocolon. This carries a single vascular arcade coursing near the attachment of mesocolon to gut and formed by anastomoses between the right colic branch of the anterior mesenteric and the most cranial branch of the posterior mesenteric, *i.e.* there is no middle colic artery. A local attempt at a secondary loop occurs in relation to the right half of the transverse colon—a condition which is further elaborated in *Cynopithecus niger*.

The rectum, 60 mm. long in an adult female, is somewhat fusiform in shape and covered with peritoneum as far caudad as the level of the symphysis pubis. It displays a single dilatation and no specialization of the muscular coat. Both superior and middle haemorrhoidal vessels occur, the latter near the pelvic diaphragm. The anal canal, 13 mm. long, shows no sharp angulation with the rectum. Internally it displays the usual three zones of which the intermediate or transitional zone is marked by anal columns, 6 mm. long, separating pockets whose aboral ends are limited by transverse mucosal folds forming anal valves. The mucous zone is more vascular than the intermediate and transitional zone.

Liver.—Both relatively and absolutely larger than in *Miopithecus* and more markedly divided by secondary fissures than in *Erythrocebus* or most species of *Cercopithecus*, the nearest approach being that of *C. preussi*. Weight of liver in an adult female (body-weight 2920 gm.) 112 gm., giving a ratio of 1/26 of the body-weight, compared with 1/34 in a male Talapoin.

The large left lobe expands farther over the stomach than in any of the other genera mentioned above. Dorsally it presents a shallow but well-defined oesophageal notch and groove, bordered laterally by a lobate process. Medially and somewhat more ventrally a short, thick, but distinct processus triangularis borders the left side of the lesser omental attachment at the angle between its transverse and sagittal components.

The central lobe is divided by the deep umbilical fissure, which is more extensive on the visceral than the parietal aspect, into a flattened left portion and a thicker right part, the latter forming, on the visceral aspect, a highly convex quadrate lobe lying to the left of the fossa for the gall-bladder.

To the right of the gall-bladder lies a wedge-shaped mass with a conical free tip caudally but largely obscured on the visceral aspect by the massive right lobe. At its dorsal end this area presents a localized rounded tubercle (omental tubercle) around which the common bile duct courses in a raised fold of lesser omentum.

On the parietal aspect the base of the wedge is separated from the central

2 T

lobe by a wide, but shallow, fissure over the whole cranio-caudal extent of the organ in the female, but failing to gain the free border in the male.

The main right lobe (right lateral lobe) has the usual form. It is by far the bulkiest part of the liver. Its visceral aspect presents several irregularly disposed minor fissures mostly lying caudal to the concavity lodging the caudate lobe.

The Spigelian complex consists of the usual oblong Spigelian area proper ending caudally in a large, undivided, tongue-shaped caval lappet. On the ventral side of the caval channel arises the neck of the caudate process, which extends as a prismatic stem to the right, expanding on the visceral surface of the right lobe into a prismatic caudate lobe. On the visceral surface of this a small accessory (paracaudate) lobe is sometimes demarcated by a curved sulcus sweeping around its caudal margin. On the whole the liver of the male is less subdivided than in the female.

Pancreas.—This has the usual relations and structure. The left extremity is blunt, abuts on the spleen and does not project into the greater sac. The right extremity shows a rudimentary uncinate process; it adjusts snugly to the lesser curve of the duodenum. Along the cranial border two short extensions embrace the portal vein as the latter enters the lesser omentum, but the rest of the border is entire, contrasting with the serrate caudal border. The main duct joins the common bile duct near its entrance to the duodenum. An accessory duct of considerable size drains the caudal part of the head of the pancreas, opening independently into the duodenum upon a papilla minor, situated 11 mm. aboral to the common duct and somewhat more ventrad (fig. 105C).

RESPIRATORY TRACT

Larynx.—The thyroid cartilage is shaped like a jug without a back. The spout is formed by the pomum Adami—well marked in the male. There is a long narrow superior cornu and a short, broad inferior cornu. The dorsal border is slightly concave. A small tubercle marks the lower end of the oblique line, to which are attached sterno-thyroid (by a narrow insertion), thyro-hyoid (by a broad origin) and inferior constrictor pharyngis muscles.

The cricoid has the usual form. Arytenoids are short and broad with scarcely the trace of a median notch in the covering mucosa. No corniculate cartilages are present, but well-marked cuneiform nodules occur in the aryteno-epiglottidean folds. The epiglottic cartilage is leaf-shaped and at its root the large oval orifice of the air-sac is found.

The air-sac is very large, extending subcutaneously over the neck and for at least (in the male) 30 mm. over the anterior pectoral region beyond the suprasternal notch. Its cranial end is protected by the corpus hyoidei, as in *Cercopithecus*.

Vestibular folds are as in *Cercopithecus*, while the highly elastic opaque vocal folds resemble watch-pockets, guarding a roomy ventricle each side. No saccular derivative of the ventricle has been encountered.

Trachea.—This has a transverse diameter in the adult male of 12 mm.

Lungs.—The left is three-lobed and the right four-lobed as in *Cercopithecus*. On the left both interlobar fissures extend to the hilum. The cranial interlobar fissure of the right lung also completely severs the apical lobe

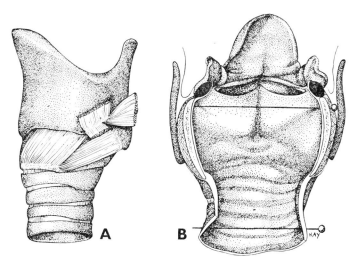

FIG. 95.—*Allenopithecus nigroviridis* ♂.
Larynx, A, from the left side ; B, opened from the dorsal side (×⅔)

from the remainder ; moreover, it widens ventrally to produce a V-shaped cardiac notch. A sagittal sulcus divides the intermediate lobe, but is medially adherent to the dorsal portion of the lobe, which embraces the vein of the basal lobe, to which it closely adheres. A minor fissure incises the costo-diaphragmatic margin of the basal lobe.

The azygos or subpericardial lobe is small, forming a pyramidal lappet on the medial side of the hilum of the right basal lobe. Its apex is bifid. It is connected by only a narrow neck of pulmonary tissue to the hilum of the right lobe.

URINARY TRACT

Relations between right and left kidneys are not the same as in *Miopithecus* or *Cercopithecus* in so far as both lie at the same level, presumably in correlation with the large size of the right liver lobe. Renal measurements in *Allenopithecus* are as follows (in millimetres) :

	♂		♀	
	Left	Right	Left	Right
Length	48	50	46	47
Breadth	29	28	25	22
Dorso-ventrally	22	19	14	18

A single renal pyramid is developed, dome-like and undivided or secondarily grooved. It projects into the funnel-like pelvis of the ureter.

The ureteric openings into the urinary bladder are very oblique, 8 mm. apart in the female, 10 mm. in the male. There is no interureteric bar and the trigone is not well demarcated, apart from its finer rugosities, compared with those in the fundus.

The female urethra is 24 mm. long and opens into the vestibule inconspicuously 13 mm. proximal to the glans clitoridis. The male urethra measures from the neck of the bladder to the external meatus 131 mm., made up of 14 mm. prostatic, 9 mm. membranous and 108 mm. penile portions.

REPRODUCTIVE SYSTEM

MALE GENITAL ORGANS.—Testes are remarkable for their large size compared with those in *Cercopithecus*. They are fully scrotal in position in the mature animal, but the subpendulous scrotum is largely parapenial and contains a fair quantity of fat around the testes. In the full term foetus the testes lie just outside the external abdominal ring, the scrotum being small and occupied by myxoid tissue.

The testis of the adult male measures 31 mm. between its poles, 25 mm. wide and 19 mm. dorso-ventrally. With the epididymis the total length is 41 mm. Testis and spermatic cord are surrounded by the usual invest-ments, which include a heavily developed cremaster muscle and a tunica vaginalis, which is open as far proximad as the external abdominal ring. Fusion between testis, epididymis and cord dorsally with the parietal layer of the tunica takes place.

The caput epididymidis is conical and compressed ; distally it narrows to the corpus and remains narrow to include the cauda, which sweeps around the caudal pole of the testis dorsally for some distance before becoming the first, highly convoluted, part of the ductus deferens.

Vesiculae seminales are much as in *Cercopithecus*. Each consists of a single unbranched tube, highly convoluted to form a solid three-sided pyramidal mass with the base posteriorly, the apex anteriorly and two concave surfaces (vesical and rectal) and one convex (parietal). Short accessory tubules were found at the same site as in *Cercopithecus*. Ducts unite with the deferent ducts to form common ejaculatory ducts, which open inconspicuously into the prostatic urethra after perforating the prostate. The openings bear the usual relation to the colliculus, which bears a median slit-like opening leading into a shallow utriculus masculinus. Lateral to the colliculus lie the openings of about half a dozen conspicuous ducts from the prostate.

The prostate is of the usual form and consistence, extending 15 mm. cranio-caudally, 14 mm. across at its base, and 10 mm. dorso-ventrally. Its base is somewhat concave and its dorsal surface presents a distinct median sulcus. It does not extend ventral to the urethra. The basal portion each side forms a partly separated wedge-shaped lobe of darker colour than the rest and demarcated by a sulcus in the coronal plane.

Bulbo-urethral glands are well developed, occupying the angle between the membranous urethra and the pelvic diaphragm. Their ducts pass through the diaphragm to open into the bulbous urethra. The membranous urethra is surrounded by a strongly developed compressor urethrae.

The body of the penis leaves the symphysis earlier than usual in cyno-morphs, at about the junction of the anterior and middle thirds. In the angle between the dorsum penis and the cranial one-third of the symphysis a triangular fibrous septum connects the bone with the corpora cavernosa ; this is a modification of the suspensory ligament. Alongside it are slender levator penis muscles running parallel with the insertion of the ischio-cavernosi. The pars libera has already been described (*antea*, p. 630).

FEMALE GENITAL ORGANS.—These are known to me only in the post-partum condition (fig. 96). The flask-shaped uterus is smooth-walled with indications of hypertrophy of the myometrium, the direction of the fibres being demarcated by minor surface grooves. The dome-like fundus rises 40 mm. cranial to the uterine end of the Fallopian tubes, but 26 mm. of tube lie apposed to the uterine wall, having been taken up with it during enlarge-ment. The apparent tubal insertion lies farther back, level with the ovary. The total height of the post-partum uterus, from summit to utero-vaginal constriction, is 86 mm. ; maximum breadth 41 mm. and dorso-ventral diameter 25 mm.

Ovaries are relatively small, the left measuring 12 ×4·5 ×2 mm. Each shows the usual relations to the uterine tube and mesometrium, but the plica vasculosa is greatly stretched and to a lesser degree also the ovario-uterine ligament.

The round ligament is reduced to a flattened band passing from the level of the apparent utero-tubal junction to the ventral parietes, a peritoneal pouch being formed laterally between it and the serous coat of the uterine wall.

Another pouch, of cleft-like form, is developed between the anterior mesosalpinx ventrally and the ovarian ligament, mesovarium and plica vasculosa dorsally. Anterior mesosalpinx is carried forwards for a few millimetres on the uterine wall, parallel with the elongated isthmic part of the tube. Laterally it forms a free-edged fold which fails to form a hood over the ovary.

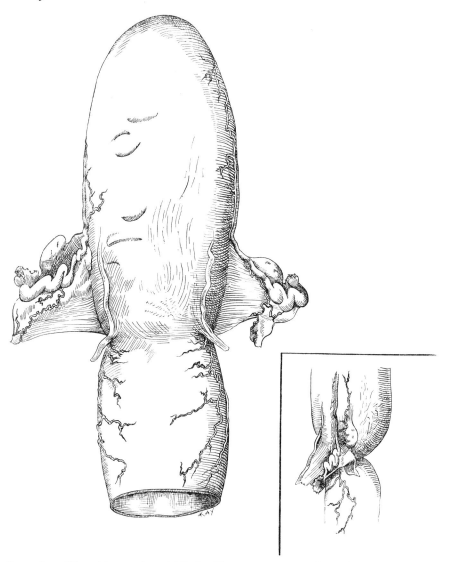

FIG. 96.—*Allenopithecus nigroviridis* ♀. Postpartum uterus from the dorsal aspect. Inset shows the utero-vaginal junctional region from the lateral aspect

The uterine tube consists of the usual parts. The lateral portion between infundibulum and isthmus is highly convoluted ; the coils are held in place by the anterior mesosalpinx. The isthmus is stretched out of all proportion by the enlargement of the uterus.

The vagina, 74 mm. long, is distended to a diameter of 32 mm. The dorsal fornix is retained, but the ventral has been obliterated during parturition.

Ductless Glands

The *spleen*, of pyramidal form, has rounded poles and entire borders. In the foetus, however, the postero-ventral angle forms a recurved hook-like process.

Hypophysis.—This resembles the same organ in *Cercopithecus* and *Miopithecus*. It is shaped like a minute cerebellum, in which the vermis is represented by the pars nervosa. The reniform pars buccalis is draped around the front and sides of the pars nervosa and shows, anteriorly, a deep groove formed by the pressure of the internal carotid artery.

Thyroid.—A relatively large sausage-shaped thyroid lies on either side of the larynx ; it is 24 mm. long in the adult male. Its caudal end covers the first two tracheal rings and a fibrous isthmus connects the lower poles of the two glands across the first tracheal ring.

Adrenals.—These lie in direct contact with the corresponding kidney. The left is crescent shaped and the right like a cocked hat. Dimensions are as follows (in millimetres) :

	Adult Male		Adult Female		Full Term Male	
	Left	Right	Left	Right	Left	Right
Height	12	19	11	13	4	7
Breadth at base	19	15	20	12	4·5	9
Thickness at base	5·5	6	3	3	3	3

The right is deeply grooved on its ventral aspect by the posterior vena cava.

ANGEIOLOGY

Heart and Pericardium

As in *Cercopithecus* and *Miopithecus*, the pericardium has a median position with the cardiac apex, but slightly to the left. The pericardium is connected to the sternum by a bilaminate pleural fold extending from the root of the aorta to the pericardial apex.

The serous pericardium resembles that of *Miopithecus*.

The cardiac apex is formed by the left ventricle, but the right sweeps beneath it almost to the apex without, however, producing any notch.

The thin walled atria possess large auricular appendages, both visible from the ventral aspect. A sulcus terminalis is present. Within the right atrium the muscle bands form a reticulum rather than definitive musculi pectinati, though a basal band, corresponding to the sulcus terminalis, is present. A watch-pocket type of Eustachian valve occurs at the entrance of the posterior vena cava. Its medial cornu meets the dorsal cornu of the small Thebesian valve, the two forming a V, the Thebesian valve lying wholly to the ventral side of the Eustachian. In the female heart examined, the fossa ovalis was but feebly indicated (cf. *Miopithecus*).

Two main papillary muscles occur in the right ventricle, both arising from the apical region of the septum with their chordae tendineae expanding fanwise to insert on the lateral cusp of the tricuspid valve. The more distally arising muscle has a bifid apex. A third short muscle lying in

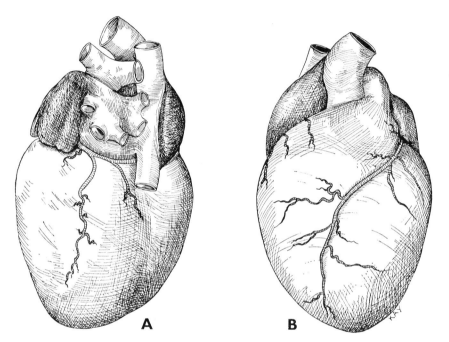

FIG. 97.—*Allenopithecus nigroviridis* ♀. Heart from A, dorsal and B, ventral aspects
(× 1½)

almost coronal plane springs from the basal part of the septum and also inserts on the lateral cusp. The smaller septal cusp has most of its chordae attached directly to the septal wall, but a few inserting on its dorsal extremity are derived from a tall, slender papillary muscle, which arises on the dorsal part of the septal wall, midway along its length and near the junction of septal and dorsal walls.

Two more short papillary muscles, the medial one with a deeply bifid apex, spring from the dorsal part of the lateral wall and supply chordae to the right (dorsal) cusp. No moderator band was found.

In the left ventricle two papillary muscles are found, of approximately equal size, a dorsal and a ventral, the latter supplying chordae to the septal cusp, while the dorsal supplies principally the other cusp of the mitral valve.

Five pulmonary veins enter the right atrium, two on the left, three on the right, of which the hindmost is the largest, draining the basal and azygos lobes.

Coronary Vessels

The left coronary artery is much larger than the right, giving a large interventricular branch, which reaches the apex, but does not transgress on to the diaphragmatic surface. Its circumflex branch sends a large dorsal interventricular branch and then terminates in a branch on the dorsal aspect of the right ventricle, after supplying a septal branch.

An atrial branch is sent to the ventral wall of the left atrium.

The right coronary is small, ending on the margo obtusus as a right marginal artery. Its collateral branches are short and include a right atrial branch and an infundibular branch.

The aortic arch is two branched, the branches being arranged as in *Miopithecus*. The descending aorta gives pairs of aortic intercostals of which the most cranial is a long, oblique vessel ending in the caudal part of the second interspace. The superior intercostal from the subclavian supplies branches to the first two spaces.

NEUROLOGY

Central Nervous System

Brain.—Weight of the brain of an adult female (body-weight, 2·92 kg.) 57 gm., *i.e.* 1/51 of body-weight.

Fissural pattern of the hemispheres shows no significant departure from that in *Cercopithecus*. The frontal lobe presents a large, highly curved prefrontal sulcus without an inferior frontal, the rest of the lateral surface of the lobe being quite smooth. There is a long central sulcus and the usual relative configuration of the Sylvian, parallel and parieto-occipital fissures. The occipital lobe laterally is quite smooth, save for the large inferior occipital sulcus, whose anterior end curves upwards at right angles to its previous horizontal course, approaching the hinder end of the parallel sulcus. Parallel to the inferior occipital, on the ventral aspect, is a long collateral sulcus.

The medial aspect of the hemisphere presents calloso-marginal and calcarine sulci with the usual arrangements.

The fused anterior cerebral arteries extend back, lying on the right hemisphere, almost as far as the upturned end of the calloso-marginal. As in *Cercopithecus* the internal parieto-occipital is obsolete, being buried in the deep fissure produced by the union of the upper limb of the calcarine with the superior border.

BEHAVIOURAL CHARACTERS

Beyond the fact that it inhabits swamp forests, especially in the Lake Leopold II area on the right bank of the Congo, and on islands in the main river, nothing has been recorded of the ecology of *Allenopithecus*.

Lang, who collected the adult male now in the American Museum, shot it in a low tree. It was accompanied by an unspecified number of others who escaped by leaping to the ground, barking loudly (*vide* Allen, 1925).

Tappen (1960) comments on the alleged adaptation to swamps, noting that the manner of this adaptation has not been reported upon.

Schouteden's photograph (fig. 79) shows a quadrupedal stance in which the hands are aligned in the coronal plane with thumbs and index digits divergent from the three ulnar digits—a posture reminiscent of *Papio*.

Its ecological relationship with other swamp-dwelling monkeys, such as *Miopithecus talapoin* and *Cercopithecus neglectus*, needs to be determined. Tappen declares that the geographical range is separated from that of *Miopithecus*, though there may be some overlap in the former French Equatorial Africa. On the other hand the ranges of *Allenopithecus* and *C. neglectus* overlap, though the distribution of the latter (map 10) is much more extensive. Tappen, therefore, suggests that *Allenopithecus* may have similar ecologic preferences to the Talapoin while *C. neglectus* is not essentially a competitor.

The condition of the stomach suggests that some adaptation to a specialized diet has occurred, probably a highly vegetarian one. Pournelle (1959), however, states that small fish, shrimp and snails are included in their menu in addition to the more usual comestibles like fruit, nuts and insect larvae. It is also believed that they are capable swimmers—a necessary adjunct to successful survival in their chosen environment.

In captivity *Allenopithecus* is hardy and quite active and entertaining in its behaviour. Solicitation of food from visitors by holding forth a hand, and on occasion catching the proffered nut or fruit, is shared with other monkeys, and is soon learned by juveniles from their parents.

In San Diego Zoo the *Allenopithecus* family was provided in summer with a tub of water in which they disported for hours on end, especially playing with a floating ball. Their diet in captivity consisted of fruits, vegetables, hard-boiled eggs and a daily ration of fresh shrimps, with vitamin supplements. On this regime breeding was successfully accomplished.

REPRODUCTION

Apart from the occurrence of a regular catamenial swelling in the female (first reported by Schwarz in 1928 *a*) the only information available is based on a series of successful births in the San Diego Zoo (Pournelle, 1959, 1962).

A young pair was received in San Diego on 14 May 1953, approximately six months after their capture in the Lake Leopold II area. They were estimated to be three years of age. On 10 June 1959 a male offspring was born, apparently the first in captivity. Successive offspring from the same pair were born 15 July 1960, 27 July 1961 and 29 September 1962. All the young were males as was also one stillborn produced during the night of 7/8 September 1963 and discovered dead next morning. The placenta was not found, nor were any remains left *in utero*.

DEVELOPMENT OF YOUNG

The above-mentioned stillborn infant weighed 190 gm. Body pelage in the newborn closely resembles that of the mature animal, but with more predominance of the yellow annulations of individual hairs ; but the head is noticeably paler than the rest, the crown hairs being fine and silky in texture, long and almost white, matching closely the light grey throat ruff of the mother, the two blending closely when the infant is carried by the mother and therefore serving for concealment.

Replacement of the natal coat begins with a clearly defined semicircular supraorbital area extending posteriorly over the crown and thence as a median dark spinal streak. At ten weeks all the natal coat has been replaced. In one case the moult was completed on the sixty-seventh day (Pournelle 1962).

The neonatus clings tightly to its mother's ventral surface and seeks the nipple within a few hours after birth. Earliest noted separation of infant from mother was on fourteenth day, at which time this particular baby was playing at a distance of several feet from its parent. The mother raised no objection, but kept very careful watch on her offspring, ready to reclaim it at the earliest indication of danger. Times and distances of separation become daily more extended.

Experimental testing of food by the infant was noted earliest at thirty-three days and within a further two weeks solid food was being regularly ingested. Weaning takes place at two and a half months, with only occasional resort to the nipple thereafter (Pournelle, 1962).

The father was caged with the rest of the family and showed no aggressive tendencies towards his sons.

DISTRIBUTION

See under species (p. 654).

1. *ALLENOPITHECUS NIGROVIRIDIS* (Pocock),* 1907

Swamp Guenon ; Blackish-green Guenon
Allen's Baboon-like Monkey

(SYN.: *Cercopithecus nigroviridis* Pocock, 1907 ; *Lasiopyga* (*Chlorocebus*) *nigriviridis* Elliot, 1913, ii. p. 348)

VERNACULAR NAMES : French, *cercopithèque noir et vert* ; German, *Sumpf meerkatz*.

TYPE LOCALITY : Upper Congo. Type, a half-grown female which lived in the London Zoo for one and a half years (from 29 November 1892 till 15 May 1894), now in the British Museum (no. 9/7/19/3).

A second specimen was later received alive in London from the dealer Hamlyn who stated that it "was brought with other monkeys to Brazzaville from further inland ".

A third specimen, an adult male, was collected 16 July 1909 near Bolobo on an island in the Congo river, 150 miles north of Brazzaville. Upon this the genus *Allenopithecus* was based by Lang.

PELAGE : ADULT MALE.—Pelage coarse above, softer and sparser below.

Face and ears dark greyish-brown ; chin pinkish white, beset with stiff greyish white hairs. Hairs on upper lip and adjacent areas of face, black, sparse.

Supraciliary band with stiff black hairs, scarcely indicated medially but increasing in width over eyes and continuing as a black band to ears. Ears with a few soft black hairs.

Whiskers basally light grey, tipped with black and annulated with yellow to produce a golden subapical band near their edges.

Crown, nape, shoulders, centre of back and dorsum of tail darker than flanks ; all hairs dark grey at base, elsewhere black, with two golden-yellow bands narrower than the black space between them or the black-tip.

Pectoral limbs with hairs gradually shortening distally ; laterally speckled like the back, but paler ; dorsum of hands grizzled. Thighs laterally more golden than back, but passing gradually into more greyish speckled appearance distally and on feet.

Under parts paler, except for a darker shade across breast. Throat light grey ; under parts of body speckled black and yellow, but portion near flanks bright rusty red.

Scrotum whitish-blue. A tuft of hair on perineum dark rusty brown.

Tail short-haired, darker dorsally, pale yellowish speckled below, but the extreme tip black.

ADULT FEMALE.—Much like the male but smaller and less robust.

SUBADULT FEMALE (based on type specimen).

Pelage softer and silkier than in adult.

Superciliary band narrow, black, continued laterally from outer canthus

* *Proc. zool. Soc. Lond.*, 739.

of eye to ear. Hair on cheeks directed straight backwards, blackish grey anteriorly with obscure golden subapical bands on hairs nearer to ears. Ear-tufts lacking.

Hairs of crown, neck, shoulders, back and sides of body with two narrow rich golden bands, narrower than the intervening black zone or the apical band, black therefore predominating. Frequently the proximal golden band is not, or only poorly differentiated from the basal grey-brown zone.

Compared with the adult, the hairs of the forearms, thighs and shanks are paler, with the golden tinge more in evidence. Throat, cheeks and sides of neck dirty white. Under parts sparsely haired with dirty white hairs.

Some reddish hairs on perineum and base of tail.

Nails chestnut.

Neonatus.—See above p. 651. Pournelle (1962) describes the newborn young as closely resembling the adult in pelage, but of a somewhat lighter colour, having a more yellowish-brown cast. The head differs in that the crown hairs are fine and silky, long and almost white. Replacement of this by the juvenile pelage begins with a clearly defined semicircular area on the frontal region, extending backwards as a median dorsal streak which fans out at the occiput. Moulting above the cheeks converges with the median streak. Natal coat is entirely replaced by the tenth week. In one case it was completed by the 67th day. Concurrently with the changes on the head, there is a general darkening of the body pelage.

DIMENSIONS (in millimetres) :

Number	Locality	Sex	Head and Body	Tail	Foot	Ear	
B.M. No. 9.7.19.3	Upper Congo	♀ subad.	290	defective	—	—	Type [1]
A.M.N.H. 52467	Bolobo	♂ ad.	460	500	135	—	*ex* Lang
PC.537	Lake Leopold II	♂ ad.	510	525	135	42	*ex* San Diego Zoo
PC.540	,,	♀ ad.	410	355	111	33	,,
PE.137		♂ newborn	153	152	49·1	23·3	,,

[1] Elliot (1913) gives total length 540, tail 230, but Pocock had already remarked on the defective tail.

SKULL (described under genus, *antea*, p. 632). Cranial measurements (in millimetres) : locality, Bolobo ; ♂ maximum cranial length, 111 ; occipito-nasal length, 95 ; condylo-basal length, 85·4 ; least frontal, 39·5 ; bimastoid, 56 ; bizygomatic, 71·5 ; biorbital, 57·7 ; l. nasals, 24 ; upper cheek-teeth, 27·6 ; mandibular length, ? ; lower cheek-teeth, 31·9.

DISTRIBUTION (Map 17)

Allenopithecus appears to be sparsely distributed over a large area of the middle Congo basin (see map), especially in the Lake Leopold II area. Its southern limit is the Fini river, which coincides with the southern end of Lake Leopold II. To the west the boundary of the range follows the Fini and the Kasai to its confluence with the Congo, which it crosses into former French territory, where Malbrant and Maclatchy (1949) report its range as including the lower Likouala-Mossaka and lower Sangha basins. It is also reported from Pakama by Powell-Cotton (*fide* Malbrant and Maclatchy). Presumably the range is thereafter limited by the Ubangi river as far east as the confluence of the Uele, the south bank of which it follows for some distance. Thereafter the territory is limited by a north–south line east of Stanleyville, enclosing the lower reaches of the Tshopo, Maiko and Lualaba rivers, and the whole of the basin of the Tshuapa, thence turning westwards to the southern end of Lake Leopold II.

Besides the aforementioned localities in former French territory, the above range is based on the localities whence was obtained the material in the Tervueren Museum. These have been listed by Schwarz (1928 *a*) and Schouteden (1944, 1947). Schouteden summarizes them as follows :

Tschuapa district : Eala (near Coquilhatville), Tschombaka, Lulonga, Mondombe, Evenaar ; Congo-Ubangi district : Karawa, Bumba, Lisala.

The American Museum has a single male from an island near Bolobo in the main Congo stream, north of the confluence of the Kasai.

Genus *ERYTHROCEBUS* Trouessart, 1897 *

RED GUENONS, DANCING RED MONKEYS, HUSSAR MONKEYS

(SYN. : *Chlorocebus* Gray, 1870, pp. 5, 24, in part ; *Cercopitheci erythronoti* of Sclater, 1893 and Forbes, 1894, ii. 63 ; Patas group of *Cercopithecus* of Pocock, 1907, p. 742)

DIAGNOSIS.—Large (head and body 500–700 mm. long), harsh-furred guenons in which the dorsal colouration is predominantly reddish and the ventral surface white. Differing from *Cercopithecus*, *Miopithecus* and *Allenopithecus* in having proportionately longer, slenderer limbs with short thickly-padded hands and feet bearing short, stubby digits including an especially abbreviated hallux—all adaptations to cursorial activity on the ground.

An approach to the baboons is seen in the greater frequency with which, on palm and sole, the free radiant from triradius 13 at the base of the first interdigital pad sweeps clean across the palm (or sole) to the postaxial border, resulting in the transverse pattern of ridges proximal thereto. Duckworth (1915) claimed this as

---

* *Cat. Mamm. viv. foss.*, i. 19.

undoubtedly an adaptation to terrestrial progression, but Biegert (1961) contends that, as the transverse ridging occurs in such an arboreally adapted monkey as *Cebus*, this explanation is not acceptable. Moreover, it occurs sometimes, though less frequently, in *Cercopithecus*. Tail longer than head and body.

Chromosome number 54 (Chu and Giles, 1957 ; Chiarelli, 1962, 1963).

EXTERNAL CHARACTERS

PELAGE.—In addition to the preponderance of a reddish element in the dorsal pelage, *Erythrocebus* differs from all the preceding genera of the present subfamily in the absence of speckling. Individual dorsal hairs are reddish throughout, paler basally, darkening peripherally. A few hairs, however, chiefly on the head, may have black tips, below which a pale yellowish annulation is sometimes seen. Similarly the whitish hairs of the under parts and limbs are uniformly coloured throughout.

Cutaneous pigment is lacking from the face and ears, which are typically pallid, whitish, adorned with scattered black hairs, especially on the nose. These nasal hairs are at maturity, however, replaced by white in some races. On the ventral surface and on the limbs cutaneous (dermal) pigment imparts a bluish tinge to the skin, readily visible through the relatively sparse whitish pelage. On the abdomen the effect is Nile blue, but on the thighs parula blue (of Ridgway).

Ischial callosities are yellowish-white to greyish-white, sometimes pallid flesh-colour with some irregular grey mottling. The pallid area extends dorsal to the callosities and on to the under surface of the root of the tail, but is a shade more brownish, sometimes slaty, around the anus. The scrotum is pale sky-blue (between lumière blue and Bremen blue of Ridgway), becoming slightly greenish laterally and on the perineum.

Cutaneous glands have not been located, but a characteristic odour is discernible over the dorsal surface. This lacks the garlic-like quality exuded by *Cercopithecus* and may be likened to the smell of a new carpet. A brown waxy secretion has been observed on occasion in the inguinal region, probably indicative of the local occurrence of apocrine glands.

REGIONAL DETAILS

Crown flat ; with the supraorbital area prominent, especially in adult males, and adorned with a line of long black hairs projected forwards in the centre and laterally at the sides. The median nasal profile is concave, ending below in a well-padded, raised, almost rectangular external nose ; but the muzzle is no more prominent than in *Cercopithecus*, though more prognathous in males than females. The free edge of the nasal septum is vertically disposed and level with the contour of the upper lip without any line of demarcation. The comma-shaped external nares face downwards and somewhat laterad, with the large, rounded end rostrally. No special lobation of their upper bounding fold is indicated.

Lips differ in no way from those of *Cercopithecus*. They are unpigmented and provided with sparse longish curved black hairs of vibrissal type. On the upper lip, these are directed downwards and constitute a definite moustache. On the lower lip they are disposed more vertically to the skin surface and radiate from a point over the mental prominence. Labial frenulae are lacking.

Eyelids are pallid and well provided with eyelashes. The nictitating membrane is developed to the same degree as in *Cercopithecus*. Irides olive, but varying in exact shade in the different subspecies.

The relatively large external ear is unpigmented. A few longish white or pale yellowish hairs adorn the flattened area (scapha) on the lateral surface adjacent to the morphological apex. The general form of the organ resembles that of *Cercopithecus*, but there are minor differences in detail. Notably the crus helicis is greatly developed and marked off by a notch (better marked in the foetus) from the infolded edge of the helix proper. Traced into the cavum the crus makes a horseshoe-shaped turn, concentric with the antihelix, dividing the cavum into an upper and a lower depression. The upper portion is limited above by a simple horizontal supratragal fold virtually divorced from the upper end of the antihelix. The lower depression is of semicircular outline commencing above as a trough between crus helicis and antihelix, ending below in the deeper cavum proper which joins with the auditory meatus. The helix proper presents a broad ascending portion and an oblique, rapidly narrowing superior portion, which disappears at the morphological apex. The tragus is prominent and conical, separated by a semicircular intertragic notch from the shorter antitragus. The latter, however, is thickened, presenting a rounded tubercle on its outer face. A little behind and below the tubercle the lamina is marked by a depression (bursa) which is deep in front but, becoming shallower, follows the contour of the rounded lamina, disappearing at the junction of inferior and superior borders.

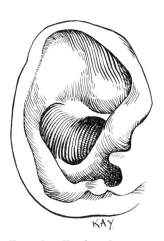

FIG. 98.—*Erythrocebus patas* ♀. Right external ear

CHEIRIDIA.—The extremities differ in several important characters from those of *Cercopithecus*, as first pointed out by Pocock (1928). In the manus the palm is long, the elongation affecting especially the area proximal to the pollex ; but the digits are short and stubby. The palm is thickly padded

PLATE XLV

Allenopithecus nigroviridis.   Juveniles in San Diego Zoo

PLATE XLVI

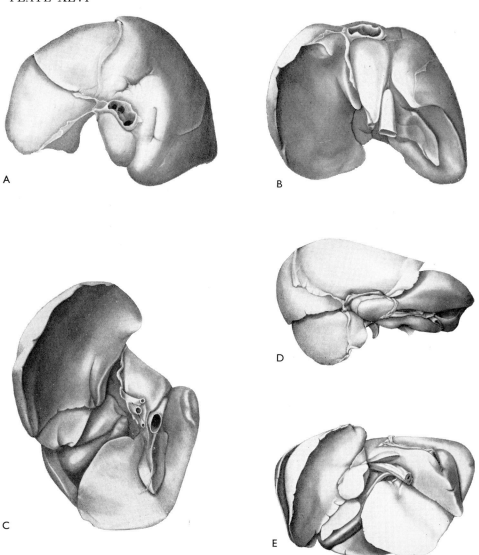

Erythrocebus patas. ♀ infant. Liver. A, from the diaphragmatic aspect ; B, from the dorsal aspect ; C, from the visceral aspect

Cercopithecus cephus. Adult. Liver. D, from the diaphragmatic aspect ; E, from the visceral aspect

encroaching distally on the bases of the four ulnar digits, giving them a shallowly webbed appearance. The pollex is shorter and weaker than in *Cercopithecus*, with a poorly developed basal lobe. Digital formula III>IV

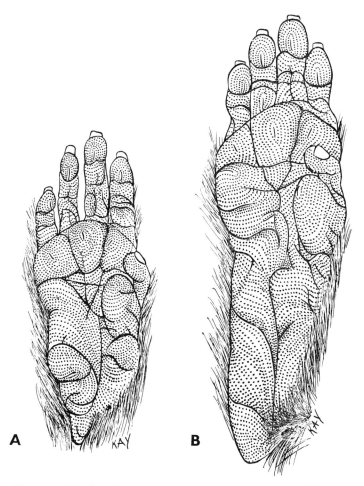

FIG. 99.—*Erythrocebus patas* ♀. A, right manus and B, right pes

II>V>I. Digit IV is only very slightly shorter than III, but II is considerably shorter.

The usual palmar pads are recognizable and these, with their ridge patterns, are depicted in figure 99. Interdigital pads present concentric figurations. The main distinction lies in the course of the principal radiant from triradius 13. This, as already indicated (*antea*, p. 654), proceeds across the palm to the ulnar border, with the result that ridge patterns on the carpal side of this follow parallel transverse courses. Nails are short, broad and convex on digits I to III, more elongated on digits IV and V; in colour dark brown.

2 U

The pes is modified in much the same fashion as the manus. The region proximal to the root of the hallux is narrow and elongated. The plantar pads are thickly cushioned and spread over the bases of digits II–V. The hallux is noticeably shorter and weaker than in *Cercopithecus*, and, when opposed, its tip falls considerably short of the distal end of the second interdigital pad (fig. 99B). Configurations of plantar papillary ridges agree with those on the manus, especially with reference to the principal radiant of triradius 13. Toe nails are short, broad, spatulate, strongly convex transversely and of yellowish-brown colour. Digital formula of pes III>IV>II = V>I (*vide* also Midlo, 1934).

PERINEUM AND EXTERNAL GENITALIA OF THE MALE.—Callosities in *Erythrocebus* agree in all essentials with those in *Cercopithecus*, but the surrounding integument is less hairy, so they are more conspicuous. They are, moreover, pallid, with only occasional mottling with light melanin deposits. The skin between the callosities, which are never confluent, is provided with only a narrow median hairy tract, the rest being hairless. The circumanal area is also, in general, less hairy than is the rule in *Cerco-pithecus*, although individuals of the latter genus may show relatively naked circumanal zones.

Testes are fully scrotal in the adult, but capable of retraction to the external abdominal ring, where, in immature animals, they may be temporarily located, in which event a scrotum barely exists. The adult scrotum is a pendulous, subglobular sac of opaque bluish colour, with sparse hairs.

The penis is essentially like that in *Cercopithecus* both in size and shape. In an adult male of *E. p. patas* the free portion measured, from preputial reflexion to tip of glans, 36·5 mm. ; of which the glans accounts for 14·5 mm. The sagittal diameter of the corpus is 9 mm., but distally this narrows somewhat abruptly to the retroglandic collum, where the vertical diameter is only 6·5 mm. and the transverse diameter only 5 mm. compared with 8 mm. proximally.

The glans penis differs in several details from that of *Cercopithecus*. It is acorn-shaped and its dorsal profile slopes in *E. p. patas* evenly from corona to summit, but in an example of *E. p. pyrronotus* a highly convex profile was noted. Transversely the glans becomes greatly compressed in passing from corona to apex, so that the lips of the meatus project distad in a spout-like manner. Hence Pocock's description of the glans as more pyriform than in *Cercopithecus*. The glans measures 9 mm. in sagittal diameter, 7·3 mm. transversely at the corona.

The corona projects markedly on the dorsum, its lateral margins sloping evenly distad to the lateral notch, which is moderately well marked but situated remarkably low down near the ventral border. Between the two lateral notches the corona projects proximad as a bilobed swelling, having a slight median notch. Proximal to this is a median raphe traceable back to the preputial reflexion. The corona also presents a slight dorsal median incisura. The meatal cleft is vertically disposed, extending over some 8 mm., and may be slightly sinuous. The depth of the contained fossa is 6·7 mm. The tip of the baculum projects in the middle of the upper part of the fossa. (See fig. 24, p. 228.)

EXTERNAL GENITALIA OF THE FEMALE.—The rima pudendi, 7·5–10 mm.

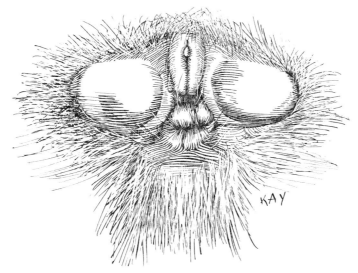

FIG. 100.—*Erythrocebus patas*. Female external genitalia (adult)

long, is flanked by cutaneous folds providing a feebly prominent vulva 9 mm. across. The folds show incipient division into outer and inner labia. Ventrally they merge in the projection of the clitoris of which they form an integumentary sheath. The folds fail to form a dorsal commissure, the dorsal end of the rima being distant 10–11 mm. from the anus. The latter occupies a circular prominence 14 mm. in diameter. The glans clitoridis is rosy red and globular, projecting but little beyond the general level of the labial folds.

SKELETAL SYSTEM

SKULL (Verheyen, 1962)

In the full-grown male the skull is larger than the average of any species of *Cercopithecus*. It is further distinguished by the more elongated and narrowed brain-case, which is remarkably flat over the vault, the dorsal contour, passing almost horizontally back from the prominent supraorbital ridge. In females there is a slight frontal elevation and then a low convexity all the way to the lambda. In the male, after a short horizontal course, the profile shows a slight coronal depression (fossa supraglabellaris) continued up from the postorbital constriction, and thereafter a slight elevation, followed by an even slope to the lambda. Behind the lambda, in both sexes, the contour curves abruptly and from the opisthion the profile slopes downwards and forwards at approximately 45° as far as the foramen magnum. This nuchal area is elongated, the condyles being placed relatively far forward, giving a prominent occiput.

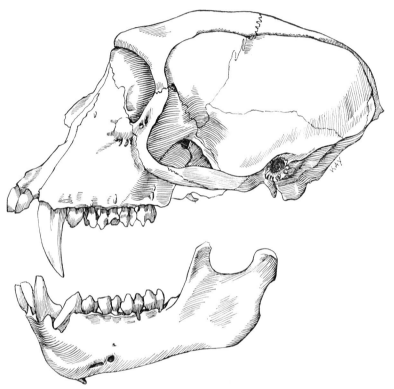

FIG. 101.—*Erythrocebus patas patas* ♂ adult. Skull and mandible in left norma lateralis ($\times \frac{1}{1}$)

In norma verticalis the frontal contour presents an arcade, angled in the median line, with the brows sloping at a wide angle (140°) in the male, more acutely (130°) in the female. From the point of most lateral projection of the supraorbital ridge the contour slopes back somewhat abruptly to the bottom of the postorbital constriction. This is slight in the female, where the constriction reaches its maximum depth 10 mm. posterior to the lateral orbital margin, but much more pronounced in the male where the maximum depth lies 19·3 mm. behind the lateral orbital margin. Furthermore, in the male, the bone between the orbital edge and the constriction is bulbous, forming the lateral wall of the orbit. The contour of the female brain-case behind the postorbital constriction is a uniform oval. In the male it is more pyriform, widening gradually to the maximum biparietal width, which lies level with the bimastoid diameter, *i.e.* behind the level of the external auditory passage, where the biparietal diameter is greatest in the female.

Verheyen found the course of the temporal line the same as in *Cercopithecus*. This worker found in males that the lines of the two sides fused to form a median crest over a short distance (1 mm.) over the posterior one-third of the parietal region.

In my material the lines run parallel some 26 mm. apart over the whole vault. They turn abruptly laterad before reaching the lambda, joining the superior nuchal line 17·5 mm. from the lambda.

Nuchal crests are well developed in males, sometimes attaining a height of 5 mm. The external occipital crest is likewise well marked, especially in its middle section.

On the base the basioccipital, basisphenoid and presphenoid are narrower and, especially

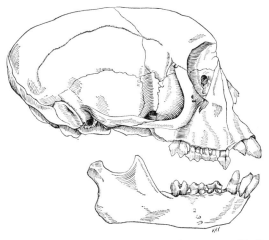

FIG. 102.—*Erythrocebus patas* ♂ immature. Skull and mandible in right norma lateralis ($\times \frac{1}{1}$)

the two last, form a much more marked upward declivity than in **any** form of *Cercopithecus*. Lateral to the basioccipital the petrous element**s** present a smooth, bulbous surface, separated by a concavity from the auditory tube. The axis of the latter is almost truly transverse or with a slight backward trend. Its terminal orifice presents a finely serrated margin and a V-shaped cleft on its ventral wall. Its posterior wall is fused firmly with the mastoid part of the temporal, but its anterior wall is separated by a deep cleft from the strongly developed postglenoid process, but the tube extends laterad some distance beyond the most lateral point of the post-glenoid process. The spina tubaria on the petrosal is variably developed, but never very sharp. A sharply pointed styloid process is developed lateral to the jugular foramen.

The facial skeleton is transversely compressed and not particularly prominent, though prognathism is considerably greater in males than females. With the skull oriented in the Frankfurt plane, the upper orbital margin lies well anterior to the lower, an arrangement seen in *Cercopithecus* only in the *C. aethiops* group, where it is much less extreme. The nasal profile is long and somewhat concave. Premaxillae extend upwards between nasals and nasal processes of maxillae, but just fail to gain the frontal. The internasal suture persists well into adult life.

Nasals and nasal processes of premaxillae stand out markedly rostral to the plane of the orbital openings forming, with the lachrymals, a thick interorbital septum. The lachrymo-maxillary suture runs along the margin of the orbital opening or even slightly rostrad thereto. Along it a distinct foramen or cleft is constantly present. The opening of the lachrymo-nasal duct is large, oval and oblique.

Within the orbit the spheno-maxillary fissure is of considerable size and dendriform shape with the bole postero-medially dividing in front into two narrower branches with the rounded continuation of the main stem between them. The medial anterior limb becomes the infraorbital canal. The arrangement appears to be characteristic. The sphenoidal (superior orbital) fissure is distinct ; its lateral cleft-like portion may become obliterated.

The apertura pyriformis is long, narrow and, in the adult male, on a considerable slope, due to the beak-like prognathism of the alveolar part of the premaxillae. According to Verheyen the floor of the nasal fossa passes insensibly on to the face in a sulcus prenasalis, but in adult males I have found a sharp sill, rostral to the prenasal fossae. Maxillae are deep from above down, flat to concave from before backwards on their lateral aspects. They are perforated by up to five infraorbital foramina, although three (arranged in a line, sloping from above downwards and laterally) is the more usual number. The alveolar border of the maxilla is rectilinear, horizontal or only feebly convex.

The facial aspect of the malar is perforated by two or more foramina.

The palate is long, narrow, deep and, like that of *Allenopithecus*, very rough (according to Verheyen). In the median line the union of the two maxillae forms a crest as in *Allenopithecus*. It is perforated by large oval anterior palatine foramina, while the posterior palatine canals open into a deep gutter bearing a sharp, spinose medial margin. The posterior nasal spine is always sharp.

The interpterygoid fossa is a deep but narrow cleft-like space. The medial pterygoid lamina is proportionately greater in extent compared with the lateral lamina than in any species of *Cercopithecus*. The inferior extremity of the medial lamina bears a well-developed hamular process visible in norma lateralis, since it projects beyond the free concave inferior border of the lateral lamina.

The high, narrow choanae are separated by a very thin vomer, whose posterior border is almost rectilinear. Above, the thickened alae of the vomer almost entirely conceal the presphenoid from below.

The mandible gives a general impression of being weak and slender for the size of the cranium. It differs from that of all forms of *Cercopithecus* in its greater length, lesser relative bicondylar diameter and relatively feebler dentition. The horizontal ramus narrows in depth from front to back where it joins a lower but very wide ascending ramus set obliquely at an angle of 125°, bearing a wide, shallow sigmoid notch and very rounded condylar process. The angular region is bluntly rounded. The mental eminence is markedly prominent and the symphyseal region relatively vertical. Mental foramina (one or more) are located very low down, almost on the inferior border, level with P.$_{\overline{4}}$. Additionally a median sagittal foramen perforates the symphysis midway between alveolar and lower borders and often a second, smaller foramen occurs above the main one. On the lingual aspect of the symphysis, immediately behind the incisors, two or three very small canals perforate the bone. The digastric fossae are confluent, with sometimes a spina digastrica at the point of union. A deep genial pit penetrates the symphysis at the upper limit of the fused fossae.

HYOID.—This differs but little from that of *Cercopithecus cephus* (fig. 32). It has the same bulbous body, highly convex ventrally and hollowed on the pharyngeal aspect, united laterally with the rod-like cornua each side. The shorter cornu lies parallel with the greater cornu, the two being closely bound together. At birth the apparatus is wholly cartilaginous and remains so for at least three weeks.

POSTAXIAL SKELETON

Vertebral formula of an adult male C.7, T.13, L.6, S.3, Co.4, Ca.? Schultz and Straus (1945), quoting from Flower (1855), give the formula C.7, T.12, L.7, S.3, Ca.28. Thoraco-lumbars appear constantly to number 19 ; total precaudals 29. Robustness of vertebral bodies in thoracic and lumbar regions, as represented by the smallest transverse diameters in mid-thoracic and mid-lumbar regions, expressed in percentage of trunk length as given by Schultz (1953) differ little from the corresponding values in *Cercopithecus*. In the latter the value for males is 3·3 (thoracic), 4·7 (lumbar), for females 3·5 (thoracic), 5·3 (lumbar). Corresponding values based on two females of *Erythrocebus* are given as 3·4 (thoracic), 5·3 (lumbar). In an adult male *Erythrocebus* I find the thoracic value 2·5 only and the lumbar value 3·2.

Cervical vertebrae, apart from their larger size, closely resemble those of *Cercopithecus*. Their sagittally widened spinous processes form a median septum and their directions, on the individual vertebrae, are as in *Cerco-pithecus*. Their apices, however, are less acutely pointed. The spinous process of the axis is not proportionately as robust as in *Cercopithecus*, and shows marked division by a semicircular notch into a smaller anterior and larger posterior moiety. Strong imbrication affects the ventral part of the cervical centra, diminishing in the posterior segments. Transverse processes show the same features as in *Cercopithecus* in exaggerated degree, the sagittal widening of the ventral tubercle on C.6 being more robustly developed and affecting to some degree that of C.5 also. Dorsal tubercles are as in *Cerco-pithecus*, being very large on C.7, where the costal element is lacking.

Characters of the atlas in respect of foramina, etc., are as in *Cercopithecus*.

In the thoracic region all the spinous processes are broad-tipped and all from T.1 to T.10 slope backwards. In T.11 and T.12 they are practically vertical. That of T.13 resembles a lumbar spine. All but the last three bear large transverse processes. In the last three they are much reduced but supplemented by pointed pleurapophyses as in *Cercopithecus*. The last four also resemble lumbar vertebrae in their raised zygapophyses, which are strengthened and thickened by mammillary processes.

Except in their greater size and robusticity, lumbar vertebrae match, in all particulars, those of *Cercopithecus*. Their costal processes resemble those of the *aethiops* section of *Cercopithecus* rather than the L-shaped form seen in *C. l'hoesti* or *C. cephus*. The postero-lateral angle of the costal process of L.6 is blunt and thickened. From this tubercle an oblique ridge extends along the ventral face towards the cranial border of the centrum. This tubercle is also developed in *C. aethiops*, where it is even larger, but the ventral ridge is correspondingly shorter and less oblique than in *Erythrocebus*. All the lumbar bodies are perforated ventrally by a pair of venous foramina, one each side the median ventral keel.

The sacrum, approximately one and a half times the size of that of *Cercopithecus pygerythrus*, resembles it in most respects. A most notable difference concerns the prezygapophyses of S.1, which have larger, flatter, articular surfaces, which face more dorsad, allowing freer movement at the lumbo-sacral articulation, especially laterally. The dorsal edge of the ala, instead of being sharp throughout, is provided at its base with a rough thickening, which continues back on the dorsal surface of the lamina as far as the first dorsal foramen.

The foremost five post-sacral vertebrae retain complete neural canals and the first four are provided with chevron bones. The first four are short and present a lumbar pattern in miniature. The fifth post-sacral differs markedly in its elongation and in the flange-like character of its transverse process, which is perforated in the middle by a large oval foramen. Remaining caudals are as in *Cercopithecus*, elongated bodies without neural arches, the anterior members retaining blunt processes representing zygapophyses and lateral ridges homologous with transverse elements. They also bear sharp median dorsal and ventral ridges.

Haemal spines on the first two chevron bones are directed backwards. The third is provided with both backwardly and forwardly directed processes. The fourth, more elongated, is directed strongly forwards. The fifth vertebra is provided with tubercles at the site of the haemal arch.

The thoracic cage is of the elongated, laterally compressed type with the sternum sloping steeply downwards and backwards at an angle of 50° with the thoracic spine. (Maximum depth in an adult male 170 mm. ; maximum breadth 110 mm. Thoracic index 65.)

The first two pairs of ribs are uniformly curved, but thereafter the ribs become increasingly straighter, after their initial sharp spinal curvature, so that the thorax becomes progressively deeper from the first to the ninth or tenth thoracic segment.

The sternum is of the long, narrow type. The manubrium is longer than wide, with a thickened horizontal front border, and the clavicular and first costal facets widely spaced. A median ventral ridge marks the manubrium, but the mesosternal segments are smooth and rounded, narrow in the middle and broadening at each end. The fifth mesosternal sternebra is somewhat different, being shorter and thicker than the others, the thickening posteriorly affecting its dorso-ventral as well as its transverse diameter. The sixth is shorter still, whilst the bony xiphisternum is longer again. Eight pairs of costal cartilages reach the sternum direct, while the ninth pair overlie the xiphisternum without fusing with it or with the eighth pair. The tenth and eleventh pairs join their cranially located neighbours, leaving ribs 12 and 13 floating.

Appendicular Skeleton

The scapula (fig. 103C) is of the quadrupedal type, longer in the coronal than the sagittal plane. In an adult male it measures 106 mm. from glenoid to vertebral border and 83 mm. from the highest point on the anterior border to the posterior angle, giving a scapular index of 129, *i.e.* higher than in any species of *Cercopithecus*, that of *C. l'hoesti* coming nearest.

Nearest approach, not only in general shape, but in certain minor details to the scapula of *Erythrocebus* is attained by *C. l'hoesti* and members of the *C. aethiops* superspecies, especially the latter. In all three the long spinous processes run perpendicular to the vertebral border. *Erythrocebus* and *C. aethiops* agree in the increased area of the supraspinous fossa by forward advance of the cranial border. In *Erythrocebus* this border rises more abruptly from the coraco-scapular depression to a rounded summit, situated slightly nearer the glenoid than the vertebral end of the blade. The lateral two-thirds of the axillary border exhibits the usual double ridge with an intervening gutter. The medial one-third is a single blade-like expansion for the teres major, but this bears no unciform spicule, instead, passing smoothly into the deeper ridge of the axillary border. The more superficial axillary border is more prominent and is continued dorsally, as a ridge, between the areas for infraspinatus and teres major.

The glenoid has a pyriform contour and is highly concave in its cranio-caudal diameter. The coracoid presents a short thick stem and a long medio-laterally compressed hook, extending beyond the glenoid margin and as far caudad as the notch between narrower and broader regions of the glenoid.

The subscapular fossa resembles that of *Cercopithecus*—relatively flat with a broad, shallow gutter corresponding to the line of attachment of the spinous process.

The powerful clavicle presents a rectilinear medial two-thirds with the acromial one-third bent rather abruptly dorsad thereto. The sternal facet

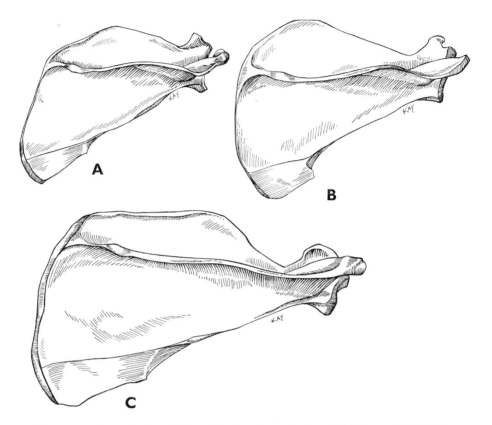

FIG. 103.—Scapula viewed from the dorsal aspect of A, *Miopithecus talapoin* ♂; B, *Allenopithecus nigroviridis* ♀; C, *Erythrocebus patas* ♂; (A and B ×$\frac{1}{1}$, C ×$\frac{3}{4}$)

is convex with a convex ventral and straight dorsal border. A very strong coraco-clavicular ligament of triangular outline has its base attached to the clavicle opposite the angle between sternal two-thirds and acromial one-third. The acromial end presents the usual flattened form and attains a major diameter of 9·5 mm.

The brachial index is recorded by Gabis (1960) as 100, *i.e.* higher than in any species of *Cercopithecus*, where the highest values are recorded for members of the *C. aethiops* superspecies and for *C. n. nictitans*. The humero-femoral index is given by the same authority as 84. This is exceeded among guenons only in *C. pogonias* (85) and *C. mona* (86). The maximum length of the humerus is given by Botez (1926) as 167–186·5 mm. whence a humero-radial index of 105·6–110 is derived (compared with 96 in *C. cephus*). *Erythrocebus* therefore stands apart from *Cercopithecus* in regard to its humeral relationships. The bone is very stout and markedly bowed forwards and laterally, the summit of the curve being at the most distal point of the long deltoid ridge. Robusticity index is valued at 27–29·3 by Botez compared with 25·2 for *C. cephus*. Schultz (1953) gives a robusticity index of 22·8 for females of *Erythrocebus* compared with 25·0 for males of *Cercopithecus* and 22·9 for females. Botez gives the superior angle of deviation as varying from 22° to 28°. In my adult male it is 28°, so that Botez' lesser value probably relates to immature animals. The adult male value surpasses that of any adult *Cercopithecus*. (Botez gives 24° for *C. cephus*.) The inferior angle of deviation is poorly marked, the distal half of the shaft being virtually straight.

In general it may be stated that the curvature of the humeral shaft is adapted to that of the chest wall against which its excursion takes place during quadrupedal walking and running. On the concave (thoracic) aspect the shaft is smooth, but on the lateral aspect the bone, in the proximal half, presents a broad flattened area with its base above at the epiphyseal line joining shaft and epiphysis of the great tuberosity. Distally the area narrows, and, distal to the summit of the curve, gradually merges with the more cylindrical part of the shaft. The margins of the flattened area are raised into ridges of which the more dorsal is the sharper, forming an attachment for the lateral head of the triceps. Beyond the ridge the shaft is marked by a longitudinal gutter. The ventral or more medial ridge is less prominent, more rounded and forms the anterior lip of the bicipital groove.

The distal half of the shaft and the inferior extremity present nothing unusual. Torsion of the shaft is estimated by Botez as up to 100°.

The radio-humeral index of 105·6–110 given by Botez is higher than in any *Cercopithecus* and the great length of the forearm is indeed a marked feature in the present genus. Robusticity index of the radius is recorded by Schultz (1953) as 16·2, indicating a relatively slenderer bone than in *Cercopithecus* (index in males 17·9, females 18·6). The radial shaft is of triangular cross section and uniformly bowed longitudinally. Botez gives the index of incurvation as 11·2 to 12·3, compared with 16·6 for *C. cephus* and 11·7 for *Cercocebus*. The angle of deviation of the collum is 160°–162°—*i.e.* rather greater than in *Cercopithecus* (*C. cephus* = 156°). In other respects the details of the markings and processes of the radius agree well with the description given for *Cercopithecus* (*antea*, p. 256).

As in *Cercopithecus* the ulna also is relatively straight, but is proportionately slenderer. Schultz gives the robusticity index as 12·8 compared with 15·5 to 16·7 for *Cercopithecus*. Botez records it at 11·7 to 13·1 in comparison with 11·7 for *C. cephus*. The bone of *Erythrocebus* is figured by Botez, who records the index of incurvation as 6·8–7·1 compared with 7·7 for *C. cephus*.

In my adult male the bone is 215 mm. long. Flattening of the bone at the level of the brachialis insertion is equally marked as in *Cercopithecus*, the index of platoleinia being given by Botez as varying from 50 to 53·7, which is a lesser degree than he recorded for any other cynomorph monkey, *Cercopithecus* being nearest with index 57. Flattening otherwise appears to be greater in quadrupedal than in orthograde primates.

The lower end of the ulna is provided with a large styloid process which projects as far distad as the radial styloid. Its distal and flexor aspects are clothed with articular cartilage for articulation with the pisiform bone and the cuneiform. The cuneiform also articulates with the distal surface of the head of the ulna, by a separate facet. Moreover the entire ulno-pisicuneiform joint cavity communicates freely with that of the radio-carpal joint.

The pisiform is by far the largest carpal bone. In the adult male it is 13·5 mm. long and has a minimum diameter of 7 mm. It projects directly in a volar direction and exhibits an oblong base and a quadrate summit with rounded corners. Scaphoid and semilunar are of the usual form and both are large. Level with the trapezium is a small lentiform radial sesamoid some 5·2 mm. long. The capitate is relatively small and transversely compressed, but the hamate is very large, with an extensive dorsal surface of trapezoidal outline ; ventrally it narrows to the uncinate process, whilst the disto-postaxial surface is cartilage-covered for articulation with the large styloid process at the base of the fifth metacarpal.

In the manus the pollex is small, reaching distally only slightly beyond the metacarpo-phalangeal joint of the index finger. Metacarpals are but moderately bowed, the third projecting farthest distally, the second and fourth slightly less. All have large rounded heads. Opposite the metacarpo-phalangeal joints of digits II–V, on the palmar side, are pairs of large lentiform sesamoids developed within the joint capsules. A small pair also occurs in the pollex.

Proportionate lengths between digital bones of II and I differ in *Erythrocebus* from the corresponding values in *Cercopithecus*. Gabis (1960) gives 44 for the ratio between the digital bones of I and III compared with values ranging from 46 to 54 among species of *Cercopithecus*—except for *C. aethiops*, where the ratio is the same as in *Erythrocebus*. Ratio between the phalangeal length and the total digital length of III is listed as 53 in *Erythrocebus*. Again *C. aethiops* is nearest with 54 ; other species of *Cercopithecus* having values ranging between 49 and 60.

The innominate bone recalls that of *Cercopithecus*, except for its larger size. Total length from iliac crest to most posterior point of the ischium in the adult male is 163·1 mm. Of this, the iliac length accounts for 103 mm. compared with Waterman's (1929) estimate of 60–7·7 mm. for *Cercopithecus* sp., where the ratio to total body length is 18. The same ratio for *Erythrocebus* is 21.

The gluteal plane faces laterally and slightly dorsad ; it is highly concave to the degree of becoming translucent. Its dorsal edge is thickened and its ventral sharp, but becoming roughened towards the acetabulum. The iliac plane is narrow, facing ventrally and scarcely at all medially ; it is separated by a sharp longitudinal ridge from the sacral surface. Posteriorly it curves medially to join the pubic bone craniad to the acetabulum. This part is separated from the pelvic surface of the body of the ilium by the ilio-pectineal line, which here is smooth and little raised, contrasting with its pubic portion, which is high and razor-sharp. The great sacro-sciatic notch is rather more deeply excavated than in *Cercopithecus*. The acetabulum differs little, except in size from that of *Cercopithecus*, but the dorsal margin recedes to a greater degree permitting wider abduction of the thigh, while the cotyloid notch is relatively wider.

The obturator foramen is distinctly more pyriform in shape with the narrow end lying ventral to the acetabulum. From its apex a well-marked transverse crest crosses the ventral surface of the pubis. This is but feebly represented in *Cercopithecus*. It divides the pubis into an oblong cranial portion, continuous with the body of the ilium, and a broad triangular lamina, which is confluent with the ischium. Both pubis and ischium participate in the symphysis.

The ischium is 56 per cent the length of the ilium, *i.e.* higher than in *Cercopithecus* or *Macaca*, but in general form it closely resembles that of *Cercopithecus*, with its prismatic body and expanded tuberosity. The dorsal outline of the tuberosity is, however, more evenly rounded than in, for example, *C. pygerythrus*.

The femur is both long and robust. The humero-radial index is 84 (Gabis ; confirmed by personal observation) and the crural index 96, *i.e.* very near to *Cercopithecus* and higher than in *Macaca* or *Papio* (*vide* Gabis). The average robusticity index of the femur, based on two females, is stated by Schultz (1953) to be 20·9, compared with 21·1 for females and 21·3 for males of *Cercopithecus*. In all gross morphological particulars the bone closely resembles that of members of the *C. aethiops* group, *i.e.* in form and proportions of head, neck, trochanters, bowing of shaft, degree of torsion and characters of the condylar processes. The linea aspera is better marked, however, and more extensive longitudinally.

The somewhat pyriform patella is 23 mm. long in the adult male, but only 16 mm. broad. Otherwise it resembles closely the patella of *Cercopithecus aethiops*. Behind the femoral condyles are two huge fabellae, one in each gastrocnemius attachment. These are laterally compressed, rising 9–10 mm. above the level of the knee-joint capsule, with rounded summits, concave on the inner (popliteal) and convex on their outer surfaces. The medial fabella is larger than the lateral and has a deeper excavation on its popliteal aspect.

The tibia has much the same length in proportion to the femur as in *Cercopithecus*. Its robusticity index is recorded by Schultz (1953) as 20·4—the same as in females of *Cercopithecus*. The cnemial crest is somewhat better developed, giving a relatively more expansive area for attachment of the extensor muscles on the lateral surface of the proximal half of the shaft. The medial convexity is less acutely marked than in the tibia of *C. aethiops*, but the sagittal curvature, approximately the same. Transverse compression of the shaft is continued farther distally, the terminal fourth at most having a cylindrical form.

The long, slender fibula is less straight than in *Cercopithecus*, being bowed towards the tibia at mid-shaft, with resultant diminution in the interosseous interval in the distal half. In its morphological features it is a longer counterpart of the fibula of *Cercopithecus*.

Relations between the lengths of the main parts of the pedal skeleton have been recently studied by Schultz (1963) who records the average pedal length/trunk length for three specimens of *Erythrocebus* as 39·5 compared with 39·3 for *Cercopithecus* (six specimens) and 43·4 for *Cercocebus* (two specimens). The lever length (*i.e.* distance between tuber calcis and head of metatarsal III) reaches 27·8 per cent of the trunk length in *Erythrocebus* compared with 25·7 in *Cercopithecus* and 28 in *Cercocebus*. The higher values seem to point to a more terrestrial habit, the highest of all being found in *Theropithecus*.

As regards relative lengths of tarsus, metatarsus and phalanges, Schultz (*loc. cit.*) records the undermentioned averages :

	Tarsal Length	Metatarsal III	Phalanges III	Phalanx III / Metatarsal III
Erythrocebus	36·9	33·3	29·8	89·1
Cercopithecus	32	33·1	34·9	107·7
Cercocebus	31·7	32·9	35·4	108

These data show the remarkable shortness of the phalangeal segments in proportion to the rest of the pedal skeleton and especially in relation to the metatarsus.

Relative proportions between lengths of proximal, middle and distal phalanges do not differ appreciably from the ratios in *Cercopithecus*. Ratio of total length of digital bones of hallux and medius differ slightly, the index being recorded by Schultz as 52·6 for *Erythrocebus* compared with 54·5 for *Cercopithecus*. There is also a wide divergence in the ratio between metatarsal I and its two phalangeal segments ; this is only 68·6 in *Erythrocebus* compared with 75·7 in *Cercopithecus*.

Morphological features in the tarsus and pedal digits show no significant departure from conditions in *Cercopithecus*.

DENTITION

The permanent dentition of *E. patas pyrronotus* has been described and well illustrated by James (1960). Dental formula as for the family.

$I.^{\underline{1}}$ much larger than $I.^{\underline{2}}$, the latter with more oval crowns with sloping lateral edges.

Upper canine very long and pointed, relatively large in proportion to the other teeth; in occlusion about half the length of its crown projects below the line of the necks of the adjacent lower teeth.

Upper premolars small, bicuspid and two-rooted. $P.^{\underline{3}} < P.^{\underline{4}}$.

$M.^{\underline{1}} < M.^{\underline{2}} < M.^{\underline{3}}$, but James states that $M.^{\underline{2}}$ is sometimes equal to or slightly larger than $M.^{\underline{3}}$. Molar crowns bilophodont, without approximation of buccal and lingual cusps. Lingual aspects with deep vertical grooves separating protocones and hypocones. Hinder pair of cusps reduced and approximated on $M.^{\underline{3}}$.

$I.^{\overline{1}}$ and $I.^{\overline{2}}$ subequal, the crown of $I.^{\overline{2}}$ curved so that its lateral border is convex and medial concave. Both are vertically implanted.

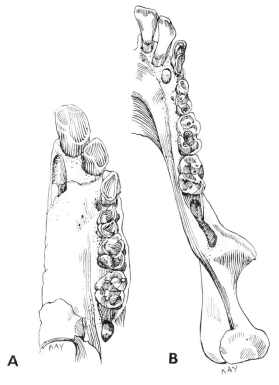

A   **B**

FIG. 104.—*Erythrocebus patas*. Dentition from the occlusal aspect, A, of left upper jaw; B, of right mandible ($\times \frac{1}{1}$)

Lower canine smaller than upper, nevertheless elongated with convex anterior and concave posterior border to crown. A prominent heel at base of crown posteriorly.

$P.^{\overline{3}}$ with laterally compressed crown ending in a pointed summit, from which the sharp sectorial border slopes downwards and forwards overlapping the hindmost part of the crown of the canine.

$P.^{\overline{4}}$ smaller and more molariform; the crown bearing a single pointed cusp anteriorly with a shallow talonid basin at its base posteriorly.

$M.^{\overline{1}} < M.^{\overline{2}} < M.^{\overline{3}}$. $M.^{\overline{1}}$ imperfectly bilophodont; though Rode (1937) states all lower molars are quadrituberculate.

PERITONEUM

The general arrangement of the peritoneum resembles that in other Cercopithecoidea, especially *Cercopithecus*.

The great omentum is usually draped over the coils of small intestine and the colon and its two principal laminae remain distinct to the free margin. The dorsal sheet gains a rather more extensive attachment to the colon, the increase being to the right along the ascending colon where the line of attachment extends midway to the caeco-colic junction (*vide* also *antea*, p. 314). The corresponding part of the colon is firmly attached to the parietes without any intervening mesocolon. The caecum, however, is quite free dorsally, and the parieto-colic attachment forms a broad reflexion dorsal to the caeco-colic junction.

The mesenterium commune presents no unusual feature. It contains a chain of large lymphatic glands along the course of the anterior mesenteric vessels. Others lie more peripherally on both sides of the ileo-colic junction. The mesocolon is a broad bilaminar membrane connecting the transverse, descending and pelvic colons with the dorsal abdominal wall. It, too, contains lymphatic glands in association with the posterior mesenteric vessels, some of the smaller ones being located near the gut.

The duodenum is entirely retroperitoneal, the serous membrane passing over it to the right on to the surface of the right kidney. From the cranial pole of this kidney a well-marked fold anchors the tip of the caudate lobe of the liver. From here the mesohepar continues the hepatic attachment forwards sagittally, along the line of the sunken postcaval vein, as far as the diaphragm, where the peritoneum surrounds the emergent vein and is reflected on to the diaphragm. To the left the coronary ligament is continued dorsally along the diaphragmatic surface of the left lobe as far as its apex. The falciform ligament has the usual attachments and contains, besides the round ligament, some slender arteries passing from the liver towards the umbilicus, branching as they proceed.

The lesser omentum is broad sagittally and shows the usual two parts, which are set at a slight angle with each other ; but the angle is less acute than usual, in so far as the mesial aspect of the Spigelian lobe has no dorsal inclination, consequently the porta hepatis is virtually in alignment with the oesophageal notch.

The lesser sac exhibits a roomy recessus oesophageus broad enough to admit the handle of a scalpel. Its dorsal wall, posterior to this recess, is formed by a broad peritoneal sheet, which constitutes a gastro-pancreatic ligament. To the left this is continuous with the gastro-splenic omentum. The epiploic foramen shows the usual boundaries and relations.

PLATE XLVII

Photos: Chester Zoo

Erythrocebus patas patas. Above, adult ♀. Below, adult ♂ (right) and adult ♀ (left)

PLATE XLVIII

Erythrocebus patas baumstarki ♀. Juvenile, 8 months old,
Ikoma, Tanganyika

In the pelvis the utero-vesical pouch is shallow and the pouch of Douglas deeper.

ALIMENTARY SYSTEM

Lips closely resemble those in *Cercopithecus*, but are somewhat thinner. Neither has a frenum, merely a median elevation at the line of attachment to the gum.* There is no mucosal pigmentation. Buccal pouches are of moderate size—about the same as in *Cercopithecus*, and open by a slit-like passage into the inferior bucco-alveolar sulcus.

The *hard palate* shows several peculiarities. Firstly, the incisive papilla scarcely warrants the name, since its surface, though extensive, is not raised above the general level of the palate. It is sharply circumscribed and oval to pyriform in outline, with the narrow end posteriorly. Laterally it presents a firm convex outline separated by a deep cleft each side from the neighbouring mucoperiosteum. This margin forms an overhanging lip, which can be artificially raised to expose an underlying fossa, into which opens the corresponding naso-palatine canal. Apart from some minor depressions the surface of the papilla is flat. It is more prominent in the foetus.

Secondly, the transverse rugae may be reduced to six pairs, although Schultz (1949) found seven pairs in a juvenile female, where incidentally they showed some asymmetry. In a juvenile female and a full-term foetal male I found a very short pair opposite the posterior end of the incisive papilla passing obliquely to the neck of I.$^{\underline{2}}$, followed by six normal pairs of which the foremost ends at the hinder part of the neck of the canine, two pairs lead towards DM.$^{\underline{1}}$, one interspaces between DM.$^{\underline{1}}$ and DM.$^{\underline{2}}$ and the last two lead towards the neck of DM.$^{\underline{2}}$.

Finally, the lateral ends of the first two or three ridges, on reaching the gum, turn sharply backwards, parallel with the gum, for a short distance before fading out. The last two or three are feebler than the others and fade before gaining the alveolar border.

The *tongue* is, by Sonntag (1921), recorded as 4·8 cm. long (oral part 4·3 cm.) and 1·9 cm. wide in the largest of his three specimens, but in an adult male I found it measures 6·65 cm. long (oral part 4·94) and 2·68 cm. broad opposite the lateral organs. Colour varies from yellowish-brown to bright pink, being sometimes slightly pigmented sometimes without pigment. In some examples the mucosa is darkened by food-stains.

The general form of the tongue is much as in *Cercopithecus*, at least in young animals, but in old males it is relatively longer, due to the longer muzzle, and more parallel-sided. The apex is spatulate and stated by Sonntag to present a median notch, as in *Cercopithecus mona*, but this is not invariably present. A median dorsal sulcus is lacking, but a deep median

---

* A frenum is present on the lower lip of the neonatus.

2 X

ventral sulcus is characteristic ; within the latter lies buried a median crest.

Three vallate papillae are arranged in a V, apex posteriorly, but Sonntag records one with four and one with six papillae. These supernumerary papillae are not truly vallate, but enlarged papillae of fungiform type or somewhat intermediate between fungiform and vallate papillae, being smaller than the latter and slightly larger than the former. Three such intermediates occur on the right side only of one of my specimens, the hindmost lying immediately in front of the median vallate papilla, the others in a line between it and the right anterior vallate. Vallate papillae are prominent, but the posterior may be more or less prominent than the lateral pair. All are conical with the bases superficially projecting beyond the vallums ; the surfaces are granular.

Fungiform papillae occur all across the dorsum, but tend to form a cluster at the apex and along the lateral margins. All are hemispherical with granular surfaces. Conical papillae are arranged in clusters and rows with their tips pointing in all directions. Most are filiform, but the number of points varies from one to many, giving in the latter case a brush-like appearance.

Lateral organs are marked by wide sulci so that the laminae, which are small and rounded, appear as a row of small oval bodies. Each lamina is marked by a broad, shallow secondary sulcus. From the medial end of each ridge an oblique row of filiform papillae crosses the dorsum posterior to the lateral vallate papilla. This appearance is characteristic. Six main laminae occur on each side in my adult male animal.

The frenal lamella presents a bilobed apex, the two halves tapering from a broad base. The edges are entire, running postero-laterally to the level of the middle of the lateral organs. In *E. patas pyrronotus* Pocock (1926) figures an oval lamella with bifid apex.

Plicae fimbriatae are present in juveniles, but disappear with maturity. Anteriorly they begin level with the apex of the free part of the frenal lamella, running postero-laterally for 18 mm. The mucosa of the venter, and adjacent structures is smooth and shiny.

Salivary Glands.—These are relatively large. The parotid is even more bulbous than in *Miopithecus*, its lateral and posterior aspects forming an almost uniform convexity, resulting in a superficial elevation over the pre-auricular region. The gland measures more from front to back than from above downwards. Its superior border presents a broad, shallow groove for the auditory meatus. Anterior to this it proceeds extensively over the zygoma on to the temporal fascia. Its anterior border is irregular ; several lobules project along the course of the duct, in addition to the presence of an independent socia parotidis over the masseter (cf. *Cercopithecus*).

The submandibular gland comprises two main compact masses of coarse lobules, and is also therefore a relatively large structure. The two main masses lie one ahead of the other, the larger anterior mass extending forwards beneath the lower edge of the mandible beyond the anterior limit of the masseter. Its duct emerges from its deep surface and takes the usual course.

The sublingual, also large, has representatives of Bartholinian and Rivinian elements. The latter are limited to a small area postero-dorsally adjacent to the level of the lateral organ of the tongue. The main mass appears entirely Bartholinian and lies along Wharton's duct, which deeply grooves its medial aspect.

Pharynx.—The thick, glandular soft palate ends behind in a lobate pyriform uvula, which is apposed to the front of the tip of the epiglottis. The lower aspect of the velum is marked by numerous pores leading from the palatal glands. On the lateral wall of the oro-pharynx lies the pocket-shaped tonsil some 5 mm. deep, opening by a slit-like orifice, bearing a thickened inferior lip. The opening is directed upwards and posteriorly. Lymphoid patches also extend on to the infratonsillar area of the lateral wall from the pharyngeal surface of the tongue. Faucial pillars are not specially marked ; papillae foliatae extend on to the root of the anterior fold. A median glosso-epiglottidean mucosal fold is developed.

The epiglottis differs in no way from that of *Cercopithecus*. Thickened summits of the two arytenoids project dorsally into the laryngo-pharynx, whose ventral wall caudal to them is rendered markedly concave. Para-laryngeal pyriform fossae are also well defined.

Oesophagus.—This has the same divisions, course and relations as in *Cercopithecus*. When collapsed, its mucosa is thrown into upwards of a dozen fine longitudinal folds. The abdominal portion is 5·5 mm. long, measured along its dextral wall. On the left the fundus ascends to the diaphragm, so there is virtually no oesophagus at that point.

Stomach.—This resembles the organ in *Cercopithecus*, but there is a tendency for the pyloric segment to be flexed dorsally on the axis of the body of the stomach, which lies in the coronal plane. An incisura angularis is present on the lesser curve and another notch occurs on the greater curve at the junction of body and pyloric segment, somewhat to the left of the level of the incisura angularis. The omental attachment is located somewhat to the ventral side of the major curvature.

Internally the keratinized gular epithelium ends in an abrupt, coarsely crenated margin at the cardia. The rest of the gastric epithelium is of the usual soft velvety texture and is raised into the usual pattern of folds. Both circular and longitudinal muscular fibres can be seen from the exterior. The pylorus is marked externally by a very distinct annular constriction.

Small Intestine.—The duodenum is retroperitoneal, except for the first few millimetres. As in *Miopithecus*, it turns directly caudad after a very short transverse initial course, the whole tube describing a C-shaped curve.

The main or descending portion is compressed between the prehepatic part of the vena cava and the hepatic flexure of the colon.

The common bile duct opens, after a long (9 mm.) oblique intramural

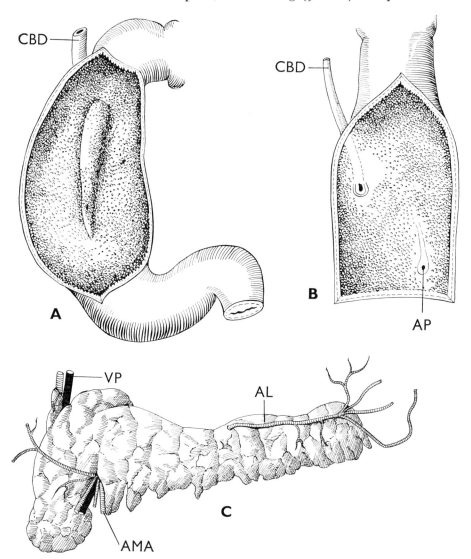

FIG. 105.—A, Duodenum, opened, of *Erythrocebus patas* ($\times\frac{1}{4}$); B, The same of *Alleno-pithecus nigroviridis*, showing opening of accessory pancreatic duct; C, Pancreas, from the ventral aspect, of *Allenopithecus*

CBD, common bile duct; *AP*, accessory pancreatic duct; *VP*, vena portae; *AL*, arteria lienalis; *AMA*, arteria mesenterica anterior

course, among the thick carpet of coarse duodenal villi on the dorsal wall of the gut. The intramural section of the duct raises a distinct fold, which extends aborally without formation of a special papilla. The pancreatic duct joins the bile duct as the latter enters the duodenal wall, so that the intramural passage acts as a common receptacle for both biliary and pancreatic secretions. No accessory pancreatic duct has been found.

The rest of the small intestine shows no sharp division between jejunum and ileum. In a juvenile female of 27 cm. crown-rump length, the tract measured 130 cm., *i.e.* over four times the body length. Other details are as in *Cercopithecus*.

Large intestine.—Taking a horseshoe-shaped course around the small intestinal coils, the colon is markedly sacculated, displaying haustra and taeniae as in other cynomorph monkeys. The ascending colon is fixed dorsally between the caeco-colic junction and the hepatic flexure, the remainder of the colon being provided with mesenteries, that on the left colon being particularly extensive and the left colon itself thrown into several wide coils. Three taeniae extend aborally as far as the commencement of the rectum, *i.e.* at the level of the entrance to the pouch of Douglas. Here their fibres diverge to provide the rectum with a complete investment of longitudinal fibres. Orally the taeniae are continued on to the basal caecal sac, thereafter fusing to give a complete investment to the apical part of the caecum.

Hill and Rewell (1948) found the caecum short, subcylindrical and conical at the apex with only two distinct taenae on its proximal sac. The ileum joins at an acute angle, which is bridged, on the antimesenteric side, by a triangular mesotyphlon. This is flanked either side by vessel-bearing fatty folds (caeco-colic folds) which convey the dorsal and ventral caecal branches of the ileo-colic artery, accompanied by lymphatic glands. The vessel in the dorsal fold is the larger and, on gaining the caecal wall, enters the caecal attachment of the mesotyphlon to be carried therein as far as the caecal apex. It also supplies a branch to the distal ileum.

Internally the terminal ileum is telescoped a short distance into the colon, but appearances vary according to physiological state. When dilated, an annular thickening with a large central opening is seen ; when contracted the marginal mucosa is puckered and the orifice indistinct. No special frenular folds are developed.

The rectum is short and bulbous, with a complete muscular coat. It is well differentiated from the colon (cf. *Miopithecus*, p. 606). Its cranial one-third is related ventrally to peritoneum ; the remainder is extraperitoneal. Wider transversely than dorso-ventrally, it describes a curve, convex dorsally in relation to the hollow of the sacrum. A dorsal flexure takes place at the junction of rectum and anal canal ; and the gut becomes markedly constructed by the action of internal and external sphincters. Internally the anal canal is marked by about a dozen columns descending from the mucous zone, interdigiting with a corresponding number in the cutaneous zone. No valves, however, occur at the junction. The anal opening is placed on the summit of a low circular anal hillock.

Liver.—The organ is markedly compressed in the transverse dimension. Its greatest area is the right aspect, which lies in the right flank extending dorsally in the deep paravertebral hollow. In the midline dorsally is a deep notch occupied by bodies of vertebrae and oesophagus. Compression may reach the degree where the medial edge of the left lobe almost makes contact with the right half of the central lobe. The left part of the central lobe is then sandwiched between them near the diaphragm, though caudally the margin of the left lobe recedes, leaving the left central lobe exposed.

The left lobe is deeply separated from the remainder, but not quite to the full extent met with in *Miopithecus*, there being a small bridge of hepatic tissue at the junction of dorsal and diaphragmatic surfaces connecting the left with the central lobe. Another feature is the presence of a deep transverse fissure on the diaphragmatic aspect of the left lobe, convex ventrally, and continuing along the right face of the lobe within the interlobar fissure. On the visceral aspect a small processus triangularis is present.

The left central lobe is a more or less cuboidal mass without special features. Convex ventrally, its visceral aspect is concave transversely but convex in the sagittal diameter. The fissure between right central and right lateral lobes incises the right aspect of the organ passing obliquely from the free margin upwards and cranially at 45°, but failing by 1 cm. to gain the diaphragmatic aspect. The caudate lobe is completely overshadowed by the right lateral lobe, its tip falling short of the margin by a few millimetres. Otherwise the caudate has the usual prismatic form. It is connected by its broad base with the postero-lateral (postero-dorsal) angle of the Spigelian lobe. The latter is small, of scalene triangular outline, and its surface directed entirely mediad. Its base is directed forwards and apex backwards, with the root of the caudate attached from the apex forwards for 5–10 mm. Neither papillary process nor caval lobule is present. (Plate XLVI.)

The gall-bladder occupies the usual site on the left central lobe alongside the central interlobar fissure.

Pancreas.—This consists of head and body, the former comprising a few sagittally elongated lobules aligned along the duodenal wall, the latter constituting a band of more rounded lobules extending across the spine to the hilum of the spleen, where it ends bluntly after slight narrowing. The cranial border is grooved by the splenic vein. Anterior mesenteric vessels emerge through a fissure between head and body. A smaller fissure on the head permits the passage of the gastro-duodenal artery which, on reaching the duodenum, bifurcates into an oral and an aboral branch. No uncinate process or omental lobule is developed.

RESPIRATORY TRACT

The thyroid cartilage is more bulbous than in *Cercopithecus*, both in front and laterally. Despite the emergence of the air-sac at its cranial end, there is no median notch on the superior border. The latter is highly convex ventrally becoming concave dorsally, ending in a short superior cornu, which articulates directly with the greater hyoid cornu. The inferior border is slightly concave, but ends dorsally in a long, stout inferior cornu, which descends almost to the lower border of the cricoid before entering into articulation therewith. The oblique line is placed unusually low down near the inferior border and almost parallel with it, turning upwards slightly at its dorsal extremity, where it gives origin to the lowest fibres of the constrictor pharyngis inferior.

The cricoid is stoutly built; of the usual general form, but strongly convex from above down in front and hollowed at the sides in relation to the origin of the crico-thyroideus muscle. The caudal site of the facet for the inferior thyroid cornu has been mentioned. The cranial pole of the thyroid gland overlaps the inferior margin of the cricoid and crico-thyroid joint.

Arytenoids are short, rather thin, except at their rolled free margins, and highly flexible. No corniculate cartilages are present, but cuneiform cartilages form prominent rounded nodules in the aryteno-epiglottidean folds and also project internally into the vestibule of the larynx. The epiglottis has the usual leaf-like form, with relations as in *Cercopithecus*. The free end is feebly notched in the median line. The anterior (oral) aspect lies on the dorsal surface of the soft palate.

The interior of the larynx shows little difference from that of *Cercopithecus*. In the vestibule a horizontal fold forms a distinct line of demarcation of the lower limit of the epiglottic cartilage, running parallel with the adjacent vestibular fold. Ventrally, at the root of the epiglottis, is the large opening into the air-sac. This, though small in juveniles, becomes relatively enormous in adult males, extending over the front of the neck as far laterally as the sterno-mastoids and caudally to beyond the suprasternal margin. Cranially it extends superficial to the supra-hyoid muscles as far as the lower border of the mandible.

Vestibular folds are highly elastic as are also the thinner vocal folds. The relations of these structures are as in *Cercopithecus*.

The trachea presents a broad dorsal area between the ends of the cartilaginous annuli.

The left lung is incipiently three-lobed and the right four-lobed. On the left the fissure dividing the apical from the middle lobe incises the ventral border and courses from one-third to two-thirds the distance from ventral to dorsal border. Minor notches sometimes cut into the ventral border more anteriorly. The apex is broad and dome-shaped. The ventral border of the middle lobe may show additional tongue-shaped projections over the pericardium. The interlobar fissure between middle and basal lobes incises the whole thickness of the pulmonary tissue, the two being held together by pleural reflexion only. There is no ventral border to the basal lobe, the cranial and costo-diaphragmatic borders meeting in an acute angle ventrally.

On the right lung the apical and basal lobes make contact dorsally, the fusiform middle lobe being sandwiched between them in the ventral five-eighths of the lung. In one example, a young female, the apical and middle lobes are united for a short distance in the dorsal half of their extent, the interlobar fissure being interrupted. Imbrication of middle by apical lobe and of basal by middle lobe is the rule. The apex is shaped as on the left and there may be minor incisures on the ventral border of the apical lobe. The middle lobe is prolonged ventrally in a tongue-shaped flap overlying the pericardium. The basal lobe resembles that on the left, but its ventral apex is less acute. Its mediastinal aspect is hollowed for reception of the azygos lobe. This is independent of its hilum and deeply grooved by the postcaval vein, around the dorsal aspect of which it proceeds before enlarging within the infracardiac bursa. (See also Narath, 1901.)

URINARY TRACT

As in *Allenopithecus* the two kidneys are located virtually at the same level. They are unipyramidal with the pyramid flattened dorso-ventrally and with its apex marked by a series of grooves, which produce an effect of three parallel summits (Straus's type D). The upper pole, on both sides, makes direct contact with the adrenal. Other relations are as in *Cercopithecus*.

The ureters take the usual course and open into the bladder some 4 mm. apart. They have a long intra-mural course, resulting in a raised fold of the bladder mucosa and producing a Y-shaped trigone. The two short limbs of the Y form an acute angle and the ureteric orifices are located on the distal one-third of the ridge. There is no interureteric muscular ridge. The bladder is pyriform and in the adult male attains a length of 95 mm.

The prostatic urethra is 7 mm. long, membranous 9 mm. and penile 92 mm. in the adult male.

REPRODUCTIVE SYSTEM

MALE GENITAL ORGANS.—Testes are, in the adult, fully descended into the pendulous post-penile scrotum. The usual coverings are present, the thickest sheath being the cremasteric fascia, which is uniformly provided throughout with pale muscular fibres. The tunica vaginalis is open for some distance along the spermatic cord and, over a triangular area, subtended by the distal part of the cord and proximal part of the epididymis, forms a mesentery-like structure (mesorchium). Distal to this the epididymis and lower pole of the testes are firmly adherent to the wall of the sac.

The testis in the adult measures 35 mm. between its poles ; 40 mm. if the caput epididymidis is included. The dorso-ventral diameter is 24 mm. and the medio-lateral 21 mm. The epididymis resembles that of *Cercopithecus*. The ductus deferens emerges from the cauda epididymidis and is at first highly convoluted. It leaves the epididymis to run in the parietal attachment of the mesorchium and then joins the spermatic cord.

At the neck of the bladder the two ducts converge and, before entering the prostate, each dilates slightly and is provided with two small, blind accessory vesicular bodies, one dorsal to the other and sometimes some-what asymmetrically arranged. Lateral to the terminal portion of each ductus is the elongated highly coiled vesicular gland, measuring some 38–40 mm. long. Their ducts unite with the deferent ducts to form the ejaculatory ducts, which proceed through the prostate to open in relation to the colliculus seminalis. The latter is a prominent rounded projection in the floor of the prostatic urethra, with vascular arrangements as in *Cercopithecus*. Its summit is marked by the slit-like opening of the utriculus masculinus. The hillock terminates distally in a low median fold of mucous membrane.

The prostate is markedly divided by a deep transverse fissure into a smaller proximal and larger distal lobe, each furrowed in the median line so that a paired character is presented. The proximal lobe lies wholly dorsal to the urethra, but the distal lobe extends around the sides also. Two sausage-shaped compact bulbo-urethral glands embrace the distal part of the membranous urethra.

FEMALE GENITAL ORGANS.—Ovaries are flattened, bean-shaped bodies, with a rectilinear attached margin, a highly convex free margin and two pointed poles. In the resting state an ovary measures 12 mm. between the poles, 6 mm. across and 3 mm. thick. The cranial pole is connected to the ovarian fimbria of the tube ; the caudal pole to the utero-tubal angle by a peritoneal thickening. The hilum is connected to the dorsum of the meso-metrium by a free mesovarium.

The tube is provided with a narrow anterior mesosalpinx, which does not connect with its fellow across the fundus uteri. Laterally the fold maintains the coiled portion of the tube in relation to the ovary, but no hood is formed over the latter.

The uterus is flask-shaped, dorso-ventrally compressed, and has a flattened fundus. Caudally it narrows to an elongated cervix, which is not internally specialized (cf. *Macaca*). The corpus uteri is 12 mm. across. Distance from fundus to external os is 28 mm., and from fundus to vaginal outlet 66 mm. The cervix presents an internal and an external os, the latter on the summit of a dome-like intravaginal portio, with shallow dorsal and ventral fornices.

The vagina is highly rugose internally. At its outlet, in the vestibule, the urethra opens upon a prominent conical caruncle, which is flanked by (? glandular) pockets. Externally the vaginal oullet is guarded by large erectile bodies (vaginal bulbs).

DUCTLESS GLANDS

Spleen.—This is relatively simple. Its dorsal pole is roundly pointed and its ventral pole broad. Margins are entire. The cross section is triangular.

Pituitary.—A rounded, pea-sized object deeply seated in the sella turcica and overhung posteriorly by the dorsum sellae and posterior clinoid processes. The organ is less flattened dorso-ventrally than in *Miopithecus*. The firm pars buccalis is sharply differentiated from the more spongy textured pars nervosa. The pars tuberalis forms a collar round the infundibulum as in some specimens of *Cercopithecus* (*vide antea*, p. 342).

Thyroid.—Consists of two pyramidal lateral lobes united by an isthmus comprised of two triangular laminae which meet at their apices in the median line. The lateral pyramids have their bases cranially, level with the lower border of the cricoid, or even slightly overlapping it. They extend some 16 mm. cranio-caudally in an adult male. Veins from the dorsum of the gland drain cranially via the superior thyroid veins; those from the isthmus and ventral aspect of the lateral lobes drain caudally to the inferior thyroid vein.

Adrenals.—Relatively large in juveniles, these become reduced with maturity in proportion to the size of the kidney. In shape they agree with the organs in *Cercopithecus*.

ANGEIOLOGY

HEART AND PERICARDIUM

These structures are neither as gracile in form as in *Cercopithecus* nor as broad and robust as in *Macaca* and *Papio*. Moreover, there is more departure from the median, symmetrical position in so far as the cardiac apex is located well to the left of the median plane and is comprised solely by left ventricle, the interventricular furrow being approximately midway between margo acutus and margo obtusus. The long axis of the heart makes an angle of 28° with the median sagittal plane, compared with 20° in *Cercopithecus*.

The ventral aspect is contributed to about equally by right and left ventricles. The right atrium presents only a narrow, uncrenated border of its appendix on the ventral surface, but the crenated margin and a fairly extensive part of the wall of the left atrial appendage are visible ventrally.

Its caudal margin is more highly crenated than the medial. On the right atrium externally there is no sulcus terminalis, nor is the crista well defined internally, though pectinate bundles are visible ventrally. At the postcaval entrance a large Eustachian valve cusp sweeps ventro-medially, and its free margin bifurcates at the medial cornu to form the free margin of the smaller Thebesian valve. A tall fossa ovalis forms a feeble depression on the inter-atrial septum.

In the right ventricle three major papillary muscles spring from the distal part of the septum wall. They decrease in size from the ventral to the dorsal. The most dorsal, as in *Cercopithecus*, is two-rooted. All send chordae to the ventro-lateral cusp of the tricuspid valve. The most ventral part of this cusp also receives chordae from a short but stout m. papillaris subarterialis. Chordae of the septal cusp connect directly with the septal wall musculature. The moderator band is present. Cusps of the pulmonary valve are arranged as in *Cercopithecus*.

The left ventricle presents two short, thick papillary muscles, dorsal and ventral, each supplying chordae to both cusps of the mitral valve. Aortic cusps are arranged as in *Cercopithecus*. The left atrium receives six pulmonary veins, three each side. Two from the right lung, the cranial and caudal are large, the intermediate being very small and entering close to the caudal vein. On the left also large cranial and caudal veins are present, the caudal being particularly long. The small intermediate vein opens alongside the cranial vein in a common sinus. A deep sagittal sulcus separates the terminal portions of the left and right caudal pulmonary veins.

CORONARY VESSELS AND AORTA

Although slightly the larger, the left coronary artery is not so dis-proportionately greater than the right as it is in *Cercopithecus*. The short wide trunk of the left coronary divides into interventricular, left ventricular and circumflex branches. The first gives immediately a branch to the root of the pulmonary artery, then continues in the interventricular sulcus to the margo acutus, then, turning aside to the apex of the left ventricle. The left ventricular stem is large and sinks almost at once into the muscular tissue. The circumflex provides an atrial branch to the ventral wall of the atrium and then continues in the atrio-ventricular groove almost to the crux. Its largest terminal branch, however, is the left marginal.

The right coronary continues around the atrio-ventricular groove as far as the crux, where it bifurcates into dorsal interventricular and septal branches. The interventricular courses in the interventricular sulcus to the margo acutus. Numerous collateral ventricular branches are supplied to the right ventricular wall, but no specific right marginal branch is developed.

Coronary veins show the usual arrangement. A small oblique vein of Marshall occurs on the dorsal wall of the left atrium without associated fold.

As in *Cercopithecus* the aortic arch is two-branched. The two trunks arise in close proximity—virtually touching—from the summit of the arch. Subsequent branching of the innominate is exactly as in *Cercopithecus*.

From the descending thoracic aorta are given off the intercostal stems as single trunks, which afterwards bifurcate into right and left. They supply intercostal spaces from the second onwards. The first vessel is small, the second large, with an oval mouth aligned transversely. The next three are small and relatively close together; thereafter the vessels are larger and more widely spaced.

Coeliac and anterior mesenteric arise separately but close together from the commencement of the abdominal aorta. Their openings are large, oval, transversely aligned and set in pocket-like depressions of the aortic wall.

NEUROLOGY

CENTRAL NERVOUS SYSTEM

BRAIN.—The cerebrum, in conformity with the shape of the cranial vault, is rather flattened above. Fissuration on the lateral surface of each hemisphere closely recalls that of *Cercopithecus*. The central sulcus is more sinuous instead of forming a simple curve with a forward convexity. The frontal lobe is marked by a parabolic sulcus, open forwards, with a horizontally aligned inferior frontal sulcus enclosed within its arch. A small horizontal superior frontal sulcus occurs, marked only by a dimple in *Cercopithecus*. Sylvian and parallel sulci unite above, as in *Cercopithecus*, and around the termination of the united sulci the angular gyrus is demarcated by a horseshoe-shaped system derived from intraparietal and parieto-occipital sulci. A small postcentral sulcus marks the parietal lobe. Both lateral and inferior occipital sulci are well marked, as is also the second temporal, parallel with the first.

Elliot Smith (1902) mentions three sagittally directed sulci on the orbital surface of the frontal lobe, the most lateral being a mere depression on the right, but a definite sulcus on the left. On the left hemisphere in my material only one sagittal fissure is found.

The medial aspect of the hemisphere shows considerable complication in the calcarine area. The main stem of the calcarine fissure sweeps forwards from a deep depression at the occipital pole towards the hinder end of the corpus callosum, describing an arc convex downwards. Its posterior end turns dorsally almost parallel with the occipital contour. It is not joined by the parieto-occipital. The latter passes down from the superior margin and its inferior end is circumscribed by a U-shaped gyrus, whose posterior limb is virtually buried through infolding of the occipital cortex. Hereby the parieto-occipital has the appearance of turning forwards in a loop, whereas the fissure bounding this loop is part of the intercalary series—as explained

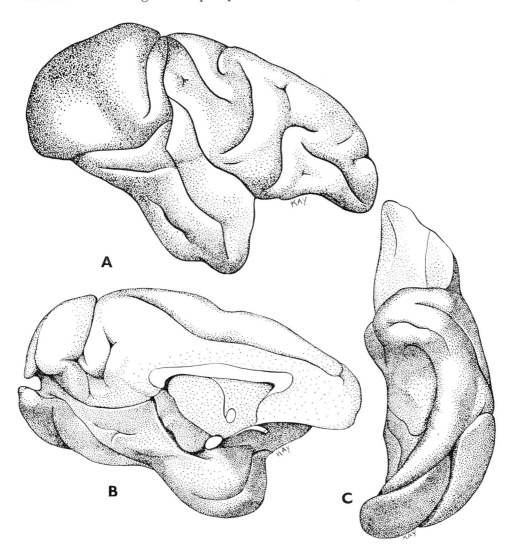

FIG. 106.—*Erythrocebus patas* ♀. Brain (×¼). A, right cerebral hemisphere from the lateral aspect; B, left hemisphere from the medial aspect; C, left hemisphere from below

by Elliot-Smith (p. 413) in describing the brain of *Macaca sinica*. It is in fact the compensatory or post-limbic sulcus of Broca. A large intercalary is developed in the usual position, with its hinder end turned upwards obliquely but often failing to gain the superior margin. A long collateral and long sinuous rhinal fissure mark the medial surface of the temporal lobe.

Sense Organs

In the nasal fossa a supranarial organ is well developed with the upper lip exceeding the lower in length with a resulting oblique posterior limit. The floor of the intervening groove is pigmented, but pigment does not extend to the rest of the vestibular mucosa (Hill, 1965, in the press).

The remainder of the nasal fossa resembles that of *Cercopithecus*. There is an elongated, oblong inferior concha and a small tongue-shaped superior concha, the latter with an everted lower margin, which shuts off the subtended meatus. Above the superior concha the otherwise smooth mucosa is marked by a short sagittal sulcus, the rudiment of a third meatus. The Eustachian opening lies 16 mm. behind the posterior end of the inferior concha.

In the eyeball the iris is a light hazel in colour and the pupil circular.

BEHAVIOURAL CHARACTERS

Habitat and Ecology

Pocock's (1907) early suspicion that the Patas is an open country rather than a forest animal received further support from his later (1925) morphological studies, which led him to the conclusion that the limbs were adapted for cursorial progression on the ground. These suspicions have been amply confirmed by field studies of more recent years. Thus Jeannin (1936), Malbrant (1952) and Dekeyser (1955) all agree that the Patas is a ground dwelling guenon, not depending, even to the same extent as *C. aethiops*, on the presence of trees or water. Hall (1963, verbal communication),* who has observed the animal in the field, also supports this contention. Jeannin states that the Patas occurs in drier regions of the Cameroons, where its mode of life is more terrestrial than arboricolous. Malbrant observed that it is common in the Chad area, where it occurs in more or less wooded terrain south of the 15° parallel ; but spends more of its time on the ground than in trees. Dekeyser notes that these are the commonest monkeys of deforested areas up to the northern limits of the Sahel. They sometimes frequent the borders of isolated patches of forest, where they make their headquarters, sallying forth into the grassland to forage each day. They penetrate into the forest periodically, but never sojourn there.

According to Booth (1960) this penetration occurs only in search of water. Hall found them spending the daytime in long grass—the bands dispersing at nightfall to sleep in neighbouring scrub or forest margin. He found the diurnal range to average up to three miles, whereas the night range of a band would be around 400 yards.

* The later (1965) valuable contribution by Hall *et al.* appeared too late to incorporate more than a few brief points herein.

Dekeyser found them often in the neighbourhood of termite mounds ; sometimes one would perch on the summit of such a mound surveying the environment, whilst its companions foraged or frolicked in the neighbouring scrub or grassland.

Opinions differ as to the numbers constituting a band. Jeannin speaks of bands of around twenty in the Cameroons, but Malbrant found aggregations of fifty or more. Dekeyser states that the bands are composed of small numbers, ten to twenty individuals, but occasionally larger groups are met with, sometimes up to a hundred. These, as Dekeyser observes, are probably due to temporary fusion of smaller units at the feeding sites or watering places. In the smaller units a large adult male appears to dominate the band. On the move he follows the line of march in the rear. Hall (*et al.*, 1965) in Uganda encountered groups varying from four to thirty-one in number, each group with only one full-grown male.

According to Malbrant the Patas is not particularly ferocious and is often to be found adjacent to human settlements. All observers agree, however, that, away from such areas, the Patas is extremely difficult to observe or to stalk. As with baboons, one member of the band is always located where he can observe the terrain and give warning to the others on the approach of danger. A leader, for example, will ascend a tree while the band is feeding or passing below, then he will descend and bring up the rear of the migrating band while another takes his turn as watch-dog (Booth). When danger threatens the youngest members of the band may be temporarily left in hiding behind the clumps of grass till danger is past.

FOOD AND FEEDING BEHAVIOUR

Little is known of the diet in the truly wild state, as most of those killed have been surprised whilst raiding crops. Booth, however, claims that it is mainly a fruit-eater. Jeannin states that the diet consists of fruits and grain, supplemented by fodder obtained by raiding crops, especially ground-nuts. Malbrant reports similar findings, pointing out that ground-nuts are obtained during night raids. Besides wild fruits and seeds, Dekeyser mentions that insects form part of the diet. In captivity Booth mentions that roots are taken, and this may therefore indicate that the same occurs in the wild. In zoological collections the diet given is the same as the other African cercopithecoids. A youngster reared by Bolwig (1963) at the time of weaning off an artificial milk diet stole porridge from the dogs, after which he was placed on a cereal diet, which was thereafter preferred to milk. Later, he passed to mashed banana and paw-paw without ill effect. Gradually a much wider variety of mainly vegetable foods was presented and accepted. In some cases gravy was added. Still later variety was increased by the addition of more animal food in the form of small quantities of raw or cooked meat, combined with bread, lettuce, cabbage. These were supplemented by items which he found for himself—brightly coloured flowers, seeds, fruits, leaves and insects, all of which were subjected to trial and error so that he learned which were suitable to eat and which not. New foods were always stored in the buccal pouches and then chewed and swallowed in minute portions when suitable. Stings from bees and wasps and bites from spiders produced little ill effect, but they often made him aggressive towards an insect until experience taught him which kinds he should eschew.

Dietary deficiencies, especially salts, absent in the artificial diet, are to some extent replaced by eating soil, licking stones, or drinking urine, either its own or that of some other animal. Soap also had an appeal to Bolwig's animal. Bolwig concluded that, as with children, there is an instinctive tendency to balance the diet.

MOTILE ACTIVITIES

In locomotion, *Erythrocebus*, with its long limbs, typifies the cursorial method. Booth (*loc. cit.*) describes it as the greyhound among monkeys, while Hollister (1924) quotes Lönnberg (1912) who records one having been shot by Dr. Walsh near Ulu, Uganda, after having mistaken the animal for a cheetah!

In progression the tail is carried arched upwards above the line of the back; the hind feet are completely plantigrade.

In ambulatory progression the attitude is dignified, unhurried and stately. In captivity much time is spent parading the cage to and fro in this pattern. In normal stance the position is dandified, with the pectoral supports resting on the palmar interdigitial pads, the proximal pads being raised (*i.e.* incompletely plantigrade).

The trivial name Dancing Red Monkey, often applied to the Patas, is derived from a curious display pattern (often employed in captivity for soliciting food or in greeting). This consists of a rapid rhythmic jumping up and down, the body at each bound being raised several inches above the ground and all four extremities cleared of the substrate. Sometimes only the fore-legs are raised and on the return are brought down first to one side, then to the other of the initial position, whereby a swaying movement is imparted to the body. In the all fours pattern of the " joy dance ", as Boulenger (1936) terms it, the substrate is alternately struck by fore and hind extremities, thus imparting a see-saw motion to the body. No change of facial expression or vocalization accompanies the procedure.

Bolwig (1963) has carefully recorded the postural expressions and expressive actions of his young male Patas, which he affirms to be identical with those of the adult. They involve part or the whole of the body, but especially the face.

Threat, anger and attack postures involve the depression of the occipital region, with chin raised, open mouth and steady gaze with widely opened eyes ; body and limbs are held stiffly and lashing forth with the hands often accompanies the attack. Anger may be expressed purely by facial movements—lowered brows, tightening of the lips by contraction of the orbicularis oris and the angle of the mouth slightly depressed by the platysma. In anger of high intensity the upper lip may be elevated locally, revealing the canine in a snarl, either on one or both sides ; if unilateral on the side facing the enemy or offender. Pilo-erection on head, nape or shoulders was not observed to accompany this expression.

Fear, if of slight intensity, is expressed by ducking and looking at the opponent, the extent of the lowering of the body increasing with the intensity of the fear. At the same time the ears are adpressed and, in fear of high intensity, the upper edge of the ear may be folded down. In intense fear, horror or despair the youngster would rush to the foster-parent for protection, clutching the neck with his arms and pressing his cheek and chest against its keeper. Extent of bodily contact and degree of pressure varied directly with the intensity of the emotion. Lessening of the stimulus effected reduction of the activity and often ended by sucking the keeper's ear-lobule. If prevented from sucking, the intensity of the reaction was more prolonged. Facial expression in this emotion involves depression of the angles of the mouth, or the lips may be pouched to the accompaniment of soft cries. In greater degrees of horror both platysma and zygomatici would be tensed drawing the lips away from the teeth, exposing them and, in extreme cases, the pull of the zygomatici would depress the lateral part of the lower eyelids also, as well as the lateral limit of the eyebrow—the latter combined with a raising of their medial ends through contraction of the occipito-frontalis.

In pleasurable states small love-bites and licks, not always clearly distinguishable from suction, are recorded. These are clearly early representations of the kisses employed by humans. Such affection is frequently expressed during abrupt interruption of some other activity.

VOICE

Booth (1960) describes the voice as normally harsh, but the repertoire includes an eerie, moaning sound. Malbrant also refers to a plaintive note which, in anger, is converted into a strident call. Bolwig (1963) found his young Patas to be very vocal in comparison with most other monkeys. On first receipt it cried a lot with pouched and rounded lips, the note being designated as a rounded *ooo-ooo* in the region of A, B on the piano. Fear was expressed by shrill cries and anger with an explosive guttural sound *aa-aa-aa*. A similar sound was emitted if separated from its foster-parent—followed, on reunion, by a joyful twittering note or whistle. This latter

2 Y

note was also used in recognition of friends, whether human or other animal. A final note referred to by Bolwig, emitted when the animal is relieved or happy, or when snuggling close to its foster-parent, is a rather long drawn-out tremulous treble noise, wavering up and down and then fading on slightly lower notes.

TOILET

This consists as in *Cercopithecus*, essentially of self or mutual grooming. In self-grooming the parts not accessible by hand are scratched with the toes.

RECEPTIVE CAPACITIES

Visual powers are evidently acute judged by the activities of sentinels, and the same is probably applicable to auditory acuity. Olfaction is developed to an equal degree as in *Cercopithecus*, especially in selection of food substances. As regards taste, Chiarelli (1960, 1963) has shown that the proportion of tasters of pheno-thio-carbamide is only 60 per cent compared with 90 per cent in *Cercopithecus*.

REPRODUCTIVE BEHAVIOUR

Erythrocebus, like *Cercopithecus*, is reticent in its sexual behaviour, but nevertheless has been reported as having bred in captivity (Paris ; Tel Aviv ; Colorado ; Hamamatsu, Japan ; Nishinomiuya, Japan ; Dudley ; Khartoum ; Vienna ; Portland, Oregon ; and Memphis, Tennessee), and even to have hybridized with *C. cephus* (St. Paul, Minnesota), which is remarkable in view of the disparity in chromosome numbers. Unfortunately no data have been published concerning any of these births ; the records are taken from the International Zoo Yearbooks for 1960, 1961 and 1962.

The female produces a single infant after a gestation estimated at 7 months' duration (Jeannin). According to Jennison (1927) duration of pregnancy is 213 days.

Sexual play is not very frequent among Patas monkeys, according to Bolwig, who seldom saw play mounting among his animals ; but an immature male attempted to mount a serval (*Leptailurus serval*) and make contact with its hindquarters with the erected penis whilst gripping manually the serval round the middle. He never attempted this from the wrong position as is sometimes observed with young baboons. In copulation the male uses no foot-clasp on the female, but stands upon the substrate (Hall *et al.*, 1965).

In the female sexual cycle there is no trace of catamenial swelling (Pocock, 1906, 1925). Slight external bleeding occurs during menstruation, but there are no recorded continuous observations on the duration or periodicity of the phenomenon.   Failing these phenomena, the female solicits sexual intercourse by posture and facial expression (Hall *et al.*).

Births are said by Dekeyser and Villiers (1951) to take place in April in the Casamance region, for newborn young are particularly abundant in May. This agrees with their findings in *C. sabaeus* in the same region.

BEHAVIOURAL DEVELOPMENT OF THE YOUNG

This has been made the subject of a very careful study by Bolwig (1963), to which reference should be made for details.   Bolwig received his animal when it was estimated at only five days old, but at any rate under two weeks. Its gait was unsteady and movements inco-ordinate.   It was not afraid of humans, yet panicked if left alone.   In its earliest days the young Patas exhibited three types of behaviour corresponding to those described by Harlow (1960) for the Rhesus monkey.   These, however, do not correspond to three clearly defined periods in the animal's life, since the patterns were to some extent simultaneous, although not equally pronounced at any given period.   They are recognized as (*a*) reflex phase, (*b*) phase of attachment and (*c*) phase of exploration.

In the reflex phase a firm, manual grip on any object is automatic; removal results in screaming, the reaction being stronger if removed from the hand rather than the foot.   Hairy objects are not specially preferred over other soft objects.   A sucking reflex is also developed early; any object applied to the mouth is sucked, but discrimination soon develops whereby hard objects are discarded in preference to softer ones, which may be sucked persistently.   Bolwig gives a scale of preference in respect of softer objects available for sucking.

Another early reflex is the tendency to press the ventral aspect of the body against larger objects, after first clasping them with its hands or arms similar to the so-called Moro Umklammerungs reflex of human infants (clasping or embrace reflex of Freudenberg).   At this stage some epileptoid phenomena are recorded in which the body becomes rigid, the limbs stretched and the head thrown into opisthotonus, but with time they become less frequent and finally cease.   They are exhausting and usually followed by sleep.

In the phase of attachment a bond is developed towards the individual most frequently contacted, whereas prior to this (within the first three weeks), any one on whom the embracing reflex can be applied is acceptable. The restriction of attachment to a single individual eventually becomes very close, until eventually it is virtually unbreakable.   A sense of insecurity develops if separation from the desired individual is effected, and is accompanied by screams; the crying ceases as soon as reattachment takes place. This phase lasts for over three months, but after that the infant becomes less particular, though always making sure of the whereabouts of the favoured guardian, and rushing madly towards him if he had been lost.

The phase of exploration has its beginnings during the reflex phase, the infant from the first taking an interest in its surroundings. Exploration is at first purely visual, but shortly hands and lips come into contact with outside objects, which are subjected to examination. Exploration of inanimate objects gradually increases in proportion to physical development, and is directly opposite to the phenomena observed in the phase of attachment.

Exploration begins with increased power of walking and jumping, enabling wider fields to be investigated, including the taking and testing of new food substances, contact with other animals of its own or other species sharing the environment. Exploratory powers remain limited until the power of climbing is perfected, when more adventurous excursions become possible ; this occurs at approximately the fourth week.

An interesting side issue from Bolwig's study is the revelation of a distinct colour preference in his Patas. Within a couple of weeks of arrival an attraction to brightly coloured objects was noted. Soon it was revealed that blue objects were preferred to all others, *e.g.* attraction to persons wearing blue apparel, preference for blue toys, flowers or stones.

Longevity

Patas monkeys are not particularly hardy in captivity at least in northern climes, but instances of attaining an age of 14 or even 20 years have been recorded (Dekeyser, 1955).

DISTRIBUTION

Erythrocebus in one form or another is likely to occur in suitable savanna or scrub country across the width of Africa from Mauretania and Senegal to the Nile and thence southwards, in the east, as far as northern Tanganyika. The exact range is not definable in all districts, but in general its southern distribution is limited by the edge of the forest belt.

Patas monkeys are particularly common in the Lake Chad area in relatively dry terrain and extend westwards in what French writers term the Sahelian and Sudanian zones into southern Mauretania. To the east of Lake Chad the Nisnas (*E. p. pyrronotus*) ranges in similar terrain into Kordofan and thence southwards into Uganda. An isolated population occurs in the Aïr massif to the north-west of Lake Chad. Otherwise the northern limit of the range is approximately the 15° parallel, although locally transgressing this, *e.g.* as far as the Mourdi depression to the north of the Ennedi plateau (Malbrant, 1952).

In the Congo no records are known south of the Uelle river.

Tappen (1960), in discussing the differences between the distribution of *Erythrocebus* and that of other savanna monkeys, is inclined to the opinion that in the east, at any rate, the Patas may still be extending its range and will eventually spread more to the south—or would, if European civilization had not changed an earlier ecological situation. Its occurrence on the edge of the Kenya highlands may indicate such an expansion. Tappen feels that this extension of the range is fairly recent. If this is the case, the present adaptations must be recent, or severe barriers to its expansion must have been of long standing.

Absence of *Erythrocebus* from apparently suitable areas east and south of its known range is difficult to explain. Possible competition with baboons and other savanna-dwelling Primates may be a factor, or there may be a lack of some specific food requirement, although no clue to such is to be gathered from the vegetational maps. That elevation is too great is dismissed as a hypothesis by Tappen in view of his encounter with persistent colonies on high plateaux at the edge of the Kenya highlands.

TAXONOMY

Most specimens in museums, at any rate until recent years, have their origins in zoos. Collection of properly documented material in the field is notoriously difficult on account of the elusive nature of these animals and the character of their preferred environment, their rapid dispersal and consequent difficulty of close encounter.

Many different supposed species of *Erythrocebus* have been described, mostly on the basis of single specimens. Speaking of East Africa alone, Hollister (1924) states that several species of the Hussar monkey have been recognized. Almost hopeless confusion was introduced by Elliot (1909), who described two new species from the Nile region both based on menagerie specimens of uncertain history and probable abnormal colouration.

Matschie (1905) admitted five species of *Erythrocebus* previously described and added four more, bringing the total up to nine; but Pocock (1907) recognized but one, with an eastern and a western subspecies, as his material was too scanty to assess the validity of Matschie's new forms. Elliott (1913) recognized twelve species including all those described by Matschie and two further ones added in 1909 by himself on the basis of menagerie specimens. Two more were described by Matschie in 1912, bringing the total to fourteen. Of these, eight were based on single individuals, six of them from menagerie sources.

Schwarz (1926 *b*) examined all the available material in European museums and came to the conclusion that most of the described forms could be reduced to synonymy and fitted into two series, eastern and western, which could be regarded as subspecies of a single species, *E. patas*. One from *E. baumstarki* he considered might, on the receipt of fresh material, be validated as a third race. Subsequent writers have accepted Schwarz's conclusions, but in 1950 Dekeyser discovered an isolated population of Patas monkeys inhabiting the Aïr massif, differing in their smaller size and other minor features. To these he gave the name *E. patas villiersi*. It seems reasonable, therefore, at the present time, to allow four valid races of *E. patas*.

1. *ERYTHROCEBUS PATAS* (Schreber, 1775) *

Patas Monkey

(SYN. : *Simia patas* Schreber, 1775, p. 98 ; *Cercopithecus patas* Erxleben, 1777, Schlegel, 1876, Sclater, 1893, Forbes, 1894 ; *Simia rubra* Gmelin, 1788, p. 34 ; Fischer, 1829 ; *Cercopithecus ruber* E. Geoffroy, 1812, Desmarest, 1820, Martin, 1841, Wagner, 1855 ; *Chlorocebus ruber* Gray, 1870, p. 25)

VERNACULAR NAMES : Arabic, *abaleigne, boubou* ; Baguirmien, *betti atché* ; Bornuan, *daguelé kimé* ; Sara, *betti kaké* ; Banda, *tagoua* ; Kanura, *dagull* (Gosling, *fide* Thomas, 1906) ; Kotoko, *filigamoa* ; Baya, *m'boro* ; Karré, *loukou* ; Haussa, *birija* ; Fula, *suaülé* ; French, *singe rouge, singe pleureur* ; Portuguese, *macaco fula*.

TYPE LOCALITY : Senegal. For details see under subspecies.

CHARACTERS

PELAGE ; ADULT MALE.—Face hairy with a patch of downwardly directed hairs on the nose, either black or white or a mixture of the two ; above, the tract is continuous with a black superciliary band, which also may contain a few white hairs. Laterally the superciliary band is continued back as a temporal band to the ear, but showing a slight dorsal angulation over the temple, from which a thin parietal line is sometimes continued across the scalp. This may or may not meet its fellow on the crown. Hairs on lips and chin white, at any rate in the adult. Facial skin pink. Ears pink, white tufted. Irides light hazel. Whiskers elongated, directed downwards and backwards ; those nearest the face black, the others greyish white, but becoming yellower and annulated or tipped with black in the subauricular region.

Hair on crown short, adpressed, varying from bright coppery red to light orange in front and posteriorly becoming speckled with black, the coppery tint blending gradually with the colour of the rest of the crown.

Occiput, nape, shoulders and thoracic region clothed with coarse hairs which are red at the base and tipped with black and show a subterminal yellowish annulus. Over the shoulders the hairs are more elongated and

* *Säugetiere*, i. 98, Pl. XVI.

blackish, with a broader subapical annulus imparting an iron-grey effect to this area. Lumbar and sacral regions and root of tail above, also thighs, uniformly red.

On the sides of the neck the hairs are washed with yellow and along the flanks they are longer than on the back, forming a dependent fringe, redder than over the back. Tail rich dark red above, yellowish below, the apical portion paler. Chin, chest, belly, medial aspects of limbs and also the lateral aspect as far as the shoulders and knees, white or greyish-white. Callosities unpigmented.

ADULT FEMALE.—Like the male, but smaller.

JUVENILE.—Except for some longish pale hairs around the mouth, the face at birth and up to seventeen days old is naked and pink. Ears also pink with a few scattered black hairs. Crown and sides of head, all the way back to the occiput, clothed with soft uniformly coloured dark hairs giving a deep mole-grey effect. The same applies to the arms and forearms laterally. Shoulders and the whole dorsal surface to root of tail yellowish, the hairs black tipped. A rufous tinge appears on the root of the tail above and extends distally over all but the terminal fourth ; sides of tail yellowish, like the back ; apical region whitish, mixed with a few black hairs, which form a terminal tassel. A yellow patch on the dorsum of the wrist. Thighs and shanks laterally yellow, mixed with a few black hairs, which are more numerous on the thighs and hips.

Under parts with some patchy pigmentation on chest and belly ; more uniformly pigmented, giving a bluish effect, on medial aspects of arms, both aspects of forearms and on dorsum and palms of hands. Deeper blue pigmentation occurs on the scrotum, and callosities, fading to grey laterally on thighs. Area of Scarpa's triangle unpigmented, but the remainder bluish grey—continuing distally on to both surfaces of crural segment and both dorsum and planta of foot. Area around anus and root of tail bluish. Testes inguinal, situated just outside external abdominal ring. (*Vide supra*, also p. 658.)

Pocock (1907, p. 744) describes the young (presumably the juvenile after shedding the natal coat) as having the lips clothed with black hairs instead of white as in the adult ; also differing in the lateral aspects of the arms and legs being pale yellowish red. Pocock suspected, but had no proof, that the hairs of the lips turn from black to white and those of the limbs from yellowish to white, during subsequent growth.

Variations.—Many writers have remarked upon the great range of individual variation in colour and pattern. From the beginning, Buffon (1766) distinguished two forms, both from West Africa, the *patas à bandeau noir*, and the *patas à bandeau blanc*, distinguished solely by the colour of the hairs forming the frontal band.

Jeannin (1936) discusses variations in the whiskers, which he declares to be sometimes whitish yellow, in others blackish. Many of the variations concern the amount and distribution of black hairs in the pelage, especially on the head and their variable replacement by white, *e.g.* on the nose, in the superciliary and temporal bands, the existence or absence of a parietal extension from the latter. In some individuals the temporal band fails to reach the ear, but from its end a thin parietal bar may be continued which may or may not gain the vertex.

Variations also affect the depth of the coppery tone, which may be replaced by a paler shade, especially on the forepart of the head.

There is some evidence that, at least in some races, there are age variations in the colour of the hairy nose patch. In the past much reliance has been placed on the colour of the nose in differentiation of the Nisnas from the true Patas, but, as suspected by Pocock, the white nose of the eastern form is black in the juvenile, and therefore it may be assumed that all intermediate stages may be found (*a*) during adolescence of the Nisnas and (*b*) in passing geographically from the western black-nosed Patas to the eastern white-nosed Nisnas—a conclusion also arrived at by Schwarz (1960, personal communication).

DIMENSIONS.—See under subspecies.

DISTRIBUTION (Map 18)

Since only a single species of *Erythrocebus* is now recognized, the geographical range is the same as that of the genus (p. 692).

(a) *E. patas patas* Schreber, 1775,* Patas Monkey; West African Red Monkey

(*Syn.* : *Simia rubra* Gmelin, 1788, p. 34 ; *Simia* (*Cercopithecus*) *ruber nigrofasciatus* Kerr, 1792, p. 71, and *S.* (*C.*) *ruber albofasciatus* Kerr, 1792, p. 71 ; *Erythrocebus rufa* Schreber, 1801, Pl. XVIB (no text) ; *Erythrocebus zechi* Matschie, 1905, p. 274 ; *Erythrocebus kerstingi* Matschie, 1905, p. 274 ; *Erythrocebus langheldi* Matschie, 1905, p. 276 ; *Cercopithecus patas sannio* Thomas, 1906, p. 173)

Vernacular names : See under species.

Type locality : Tuabo (? = Tuba), Upper Senegal. Based on Buffon's *patas à bandeau noir* and *patas à bandeau blanc.* Buffon's data in turn are based on Brue (1746, p. 520). Type locality of *nigrofasciatus* and *albofasciatus* Senegal. Both described as varieties of *Simia rubra* Gmelin (=*S. patas* Schreber) and based on the two figures given by Buffon (1766). Type locality of *zechi*, Keti Kradji, western Togoland. Type a young female living in the Berlin Zoo. Type locality of *kerstingi*, Sokode, Togoland. Type a very old male lacking tail and skull. Type locality of *langheldi*, Garua, upper Benue river, Cameroon. Type, an immature female in Berlin Museum (No. 13213), collected by Langheld. Type locality of *sannio*, Yo, Lake Chad. Type, adult male in British Museum Original No. 61. Collected 3 December 1904, and presented by Captain G. B. Gosling.

* *Säugethiere*, i. 98, Pl. XVI.

PELAGE : ADULT MALE.—Face pink ; hairs of nose black, on lips and chin white ; hairs of front part of whiskers and on cheeks, black.

Fore part of crown chestnut red to orange, not sharply defined from rest of crown ; shoulders iron grey.

Irides maroon (*fide* Jeannin) or hazel (Gosling, *fide* Thomas).

Ears bordered with a fringe of black hairs above and whitish hairs internally. Tail bicoloured, red above, whitish below.

VARIATIONS.—As for the species. The type of *E. zechi* is a juvenile female from the Berlin Zoo in the beginning of the coat change. Much black hair on face ; nose spot black ; a black moustache and a large black chin spot.

E. kerstingi, based on an old male, shows much grey on the shoulders, much black speckling on the head and face, but the chin spot is pure white, as in the type of *sannio*.

E. langheldi, another juvenile female, is very similar to the type of *E. zechi*, but the moustache has less black and the chin spot is smaller. Head and neck more brightly coloured.

Thomas (1906) separated an old male from Lake Chad under the name *sannio*. The type is a magnificent animal with generally sandy close-fitting coat, a black nose and no ear-tufts. Thighs and legs are snowy white, strongly demarcated at the hips from the red upper parts. The moustache is also pure white. The sandy tinge of the back and extensive white of the moustache and hind limbs indicate transition towards the eastern race, as might be anticipated on geographical grounds. Schwarz compared it with the type of *kerstingi* and considered the two almost identical. A similar specimen (a half grown male in the Berlin Museum) is recorded by Schwarz from the Strasse Gulfei-Afade, on Lake Chad.

DIMENSIONS (in millimetres) :

Number	Locality	Sex	Head and Body	Head Length	Tail	Foot	Ear; Morphol. Length	Ear; Morphol. Breadth	Physiognomic Length	Physiognomic Breadth	Weight in grams
PC.509	Chessington Zoo	♂ ad.	625	135	—	168·5	41	35	48	37	7482·7
—	Lake Chad	♂	630		720	172	(Type of *sannio*)				
PC.498	Chester Zoo	♀	510	114·5	—	137			48		4081·5
PE.165	Miami Zoo	♂ newborn	211	81·7	240	71	30	24	31·5	26·8	1
PE.170	,,	,,	245	80	269	75·8	35	21·4	32·4	21·8	—
PC.539	San Diego Zoo	♂ 17 days old	215	77	254	73·7	28·8	19·8	26·8	30·6	—
—	Cameroon (average)	ad.	750	—	700	—	(Jeannin, 1936)				
—	Bignona	♂	750	—	630	165	(Dekeyser and Villiers, 1947)				
—	,,	♂	670	—	700	—	—	—	—	—	12 Kg.

[1] Caesarian section : head moulded.

Skull.—Cranial dimensions (in millimetres) :

Number Locality and Sex			Max. Cranial Length	Condylo-basal Length	Glabella-m.o.p.	Biparietal	Least Frontal	Basionbregma	Bimastoid	Bizygomatic	Biorbital	Palatal Length	Upper Cheek-teeth	Mandibular Length	Lower Cheek-teeth
PC.517	Chester Zoo	♂	134	101	98	64·5	49·5	59	67·5	86	70	53	30	89	37·5
	Bignona	♂	138	101	—	71	50	—	—	90	73	56	52	97	52 [1]
	,,	♂	123	93	—	68	53	—	—	82	67	50	51	85	49 [1]
	Lake Chad	♂	143	98·2	—	63	47·3	—	—	88·5	—	—	30	—	—

Type of *sannio* Thos.

[1] Dekeyser and Villiers, 1947.

Distribution.—West Africa, south of the Sahara, from Senegambia at least as far east as Lake Chad. Southwards the range is limited by the edge of the rain forest.

Dekeyser and Villiers (1947) record the typical Patas from Bignona near the Casamance, in Senegal.

In Portuguese Guinea, Monard (1938) found the Patas confined to the savanna districts of the east and north. He records it existing in bands of 20–30 individuals around Cutia and Mansoa, near Contubo-el, in the Sama territory, near Pitché and near Sabéré Dandun and also 3 km. from Madina Boé. It seems to have disappeared along the coastal tract, and Monard disbelieves its occurrence on the Bissau island.

Ingoldby (1929) states that the animal is common in the northern territories of the Gold Coast. In the same territory Booth (1956) found that it is confined to the orchard-bush, rarely, if ever, entering the forest outliers or fringing forest. His distribution map indicates occurrence on both sides of the Volta and extending southwards to the Afram river, which it does not cross. A similar map for Nigeria is given by Rosevear (1953) showing the range of the Patas as extending south to the northern limit of the marginal coastal rain forest.

In the Dahomey Gap the range extends to the coast, as witness the Berlin material, collected in Togoland.

In the Cameroons the Patas is recorded by Jeannin (1936) Sanderson (1940) and by Perret and Aellen (1956). According to Jeannin it is restricted to the north and centre of the country, especially in the region of Garoua and Maroua. Sanderson obtained two males, one from Bamenda, another from Afikpo (350–5000 ft.). He encountered large bands roaming the grasslands in northern Assumbo. Perret collected a single native prepared skin from Meyomajôm, which lies in the forested zone, but it is suspected that this had been brought in from farther north.

Malbrant (1952) found the Patas common around Lake Chad and as far north as the 15th parallel. To the north-east it ranges into the Ennedi Plateau as far north as the Mourdi depression. It also occurs in the northern part of the Ubangi.

(b) *E. patas villiersi* Dekeyser, 1950,* Aïr Red Monkey

Vernacular names : Tamacheq, *awirkitwaza garane* ; Haussa, *biri-ja.*

Type locality : Irabellaben, Aïr, French West Africa (=Niger) ; altitude 1200–1300 m. Type, an adult male collected by A. Villiers.

* *Mém. inst. franç. Afr. noire*, No. 10, p. 422.

PELAGE : ADULT MALE.—Similar to the typical race, but smaller ; no colour differences recorded.

DIMENSIONS.—Of type male ; length of head and body, 620 mm. (compared with 750 mm. for a male of *E. p. patas* from Casamance ; both skulls stated to be fully adult and if anything the Aïr specimen is the older, judged by the greater wear on the molar crowns and the more acute lambdoid crests).

SKULL.—Dimensions in millimetres : maximum cranial length, 130 ; bizygomatic, 89 ; length of upper canines, 31 (compared with 26 in the Casamance male). The exceptionally long canines are noteworthy ; but this may be an individual anomaly. The skull has been figured by Dekeyser.

DISTRIBUTION.—The Aïr population of *Erythrocebus patas* is isolated from the sahelian range of the species and is itself composed of several isolated pockets. Dekeyser (1950) states, on the authority of Lhote, that this monkey is common in the Aïr massif, where it inhabits the larger valleys in the southern part of the area. The same observer is authority for the fact that the distribution is discontinuous. One zone of occupation extends along the north of the bend of the Niger, the other occupying the southern part of the Aïr massif. This is in accord with Villiers' observations, who found no evidence of the animal in the intermediate area, *e.g.* between Zinder and Agadez. The latter zone pertains to the sahelian floristic type (savanna with acacias), but is unprovided with termitaries, etc., which are favoured by the Patas, whilst water is virtually lacking during the dry season.

Dekeyser lists the following localities whence this race has been found : Irabellaben (1200–1300 m.) ; Dahaga (600 m.) ; between Tessouma and Abardagh ; Teouar (800–900 m.) ; Tabello ; plateau des Baguezans (1600 m.) ; Tassesset and Kori Bedeï.

The animals cause considerable havoc in the maize plantations and in date-growing areas.

(c) *E. patas pyrronotus* (Hemprich *et* Ehrenberg), 1829*, Nisnas ; Dancing Red Monkey ; Blue Nile Hussar Monkey

(*Syn.* : *Le nisnas* F. Cuvier, 1830, Pl. XXVII ; *Cercopithecus pyrrhonotus* Hemprich and Ehrenberg, 1838,† Sclater, 1893, p. 250 ; deWinton, 1902, p. 25 ; *C. ruber* Rüppell, 1835, p. 8 ; Martin, 1841, p. 509 (in part) ; *C. poliophaeus* Heuglin (*nomen nudum*), 1861, p. 13 ; *Chlorocebus ruber* Gray, 1870, p. 25 ; *E. whitei* Hollister, 1910, p. 11 ; *C. (E.) patas albosignatus*, 1912, p. 433 and *C. (E.) patas poliomystax* Matschie, 1912, p. 434 ; *E. phyrrhonotus* Wettstein, 1917, p. 646 ; *E. formosus* Elliot, 1909, p. 264 ; *E. albigenus* Elliot, 1909, p. 265 ; *E. albigenis* Elliot, 1913, 3, p. 14 (emendation of *albigenus*).

Vernacular names : Arabic, *nisnas* (in Egypt), *abulang el achmar* (Upper Nile), *nango* (Kordofan, teste Rüppell) ; German, *Husarenaffe*. The name *nisnas* was first used scientifically by Forskål (1775) (*teste* Anderson, 1902).

Type locality : Kordofan. Type, male, brought alive from Kordofan to Berlin and now preserved in Berlin Museum. Type locality of *poliophaeus*. Type, a male brought alive by Heuglin from Jebel Fazogli (=Fazoql) on the Blue Nile, near Abyssinia frontier, to Vienna, where it lived four years and was preserved in the

---

* *Verh. Ges. naturf. Fr. Berlin*, i. 407.   † *Symbolae Physicae*, pl. X (1838).

Vienna Museum. Described by Reichenbach (1862) and Fitzinger (1866). Name later changed to *poliolophus* Heuglin (1877). Type locality of *formosus* " Uganda ". Type, adult male in British Museum (No. 9.2.21.2), received from the London Zoo, where it lived from 4 March 1904 until 28 April 1904. Type locality of *albosignatus*, Bornu river, Belgian Congo. Type, adult female skin in Tervueren Museum. Type locality of *albigenus*, " Egyptian Sudan, exact locality not known ". Based on an adult male skin and skull in British Museum (No. 8.6.15.1). Collected by Colonel S. S. Flower. Died in Giza Zoo, 2 February 1908. Type locality of *whitei*, Nzoia river, Guas Ngishu plateau, Kenya. Type, adult male, skin and skull, in U.S. National Museum (No. 155340). Collected by J. J. White. Paratype in British Museum (No. 11.1.13.1). Type locality of *poliomystax*, Upper Congo, exact locality unknown. Based on an adult male skin and skull in the Tervueren Museum. Type locality of *phyrrhonotus*, Jebel Debri, south Kordofan (about 30 miles north of Kadugli). Type, a juvenile female (skin and skull), in Vienna Museum.

PELAGE : ADULT MALE.—Differing principally in the completely white nasal patch and in the fact that the hairs of the whiskers nearest the cheeks are also white ; the red patch on the fore part of the crown is sharply differentiated and bordered in front by a black brow band, which extends laterally and defines the crown patch. The shoulders are the same rich tinge as the back, showing little tendency to the iron-grey tint of typical *patas*. Distal parts of limbs both medially and laterally white.

ADULT FEMALE.—Resembling the male, but considerably smaller.

JUVENILE.—Allen (1925) describes a male in " first pelage " (total length 495 mm., maximum cranial length 69·3 mm. with DM.$\frac{2}{2}$ still unerupted) as having thick soft pelage above, scanty below, silky and not concealing the skin. The nose is black with a creamy-buff spot either side. Frontal band of rigid black hairs, bordered behind by a broader band of ochraceous buff, which becomes paler posteriorly ; cheeks faintly yellowish, grizzled with black ; head washed with tawny, the hairs with slaty-grey bases, at first pale, then darkening, annulated subterminally with tawny and the extreme tips black ; nape and shoulders similar, but hairs basally creamy white, passing distally into pale grey. Rest of upper parts similar, but with tawny subterminal rings more extensive.

Tail proximally deep cinnamon buff, becoming paler towards the end. Underparts and medial aspects of limbs with hairs whitish from base to apex. Lateral aspects of limbs tawny, blackening on the hands and feet.

At the completion of eruption of milk dentition a coarser pelage is found. Allen refers to two specimens in this stage. The pelage has the general colouration of the adult, all markings being the same except on nose, shoulders and limbs. The nose is still black ; whiskers are softer and less grizzled with black than in the adult and those at the base of the ear are curved upwards. Ears strongly tufted with white hairs up to 25 or 30 mm. long. Crown dark red, with many hairs minutely black-tipped, especially towards the occiput, where the black extends 3–5 mm. Upper parts pale reddish, the red reaching the bases of individual hairs, some of which are black-tipped, these tips being longer and more conspicuous over the shoulders. Limbs laterally paler than upper parts of body, but not white as in adult ; hands and feet only slightly darkened with blackish.

Underparts faintly greyish white with a slight reddish wash over chest and lower abdomen.

In another specimen, scarcely older, the whiskers are more suffused with black, especially towards the face, and the ear-tufts are sparser—evidently features liable to individual variation. This specimen also shows a grey suffusion over the front of the shoulders, while the back is redder, with less soft under fur.

An older female with M.$\frac{1}{1}$ fully erupted in addition to the complete milk dentition (maximum cranial length, 93·6 mm.), resembles the two preceding, but the colour is somewhat brighter, with the interscapular region much greyer. Medial surfaces of limbs purer white and the lateral showing more restriction of the reddish areas. Grey of shoulders extends along anterior border nearly to the wrist. Nose still black.

VARIATIONS.—Although the adult colour pattern is substantially the same in all specimens, the tones and relative extent of the different areas is subject to considerable individual variation. This has resulted in the large number of names given to individual variants.

The type of Elliot's *formosus* is a typical Nisnas with white nose, a dark red crown, bordered sharply in front and at the sides by a band of black hairs ; an almost obsolete black line also represents the temporal band of certain *Cercopitheci*. A few white hairs are intermixed in the black frontal band. Ear-tufts have been lost. (? as a result of captivity.)

Elliot's *albigenus*, based on a male from the Anglo-Egyptian Sudan that died in the Gizeh Zoo, Cairo, displays a loose, shaggy pelage. It still has a black nose, but the ear-tufts are large and white. The elongated shoulder mantle contains many predominantly black hairs, which bear widely spaced narrow black annuli. Forearms and practically the entire pelvic limb clothed with white hairs. Sacral region richer than in the type of *formosus*.

The type of Hollister's *whitei* closely resembles the preceding, but its nose patch is white ; crown patch dark bay bordered by black in front and laterally ; shoulders with much grey speckling ; spinal line expanding posteriorly into a sacral triangle, deep chestnut ; remainder of back cinnamon-rufous with black speckling ; distal parts of limbs white. Examples from Kenya, Uganda and north-eastern Congo have usually been assigned to this form (*e.g.* by J. A. Allen, 1914, p. 344, 1925, p. 428 ; and Hollister, 1924, p. 24). Both Hollister (1924) and Allen (1925) discuss in considerable detail individual variation in this subspecies.

DIMENSIONS (in millimetres) :

Number	Locality	Sex	Head and Body	Head Length	Tail	Foot	Ear; Morphological Length	Ear; Physiognomic Length	Remarks
PC.4	?	♂	490	117	540	141	35	38·5	Kept in captivity at Colombo, Ceylon
	—	♂	670	—	740	145	—	—	Type of *formosus*
,,	Fazogli	♂	620	—	680	175	—	—	Type of *poliophaeus*
B.M.8.6.15.1	Sudan	♂	640	—		140	—	—	Type of *albigenus*
U.S. Nat. Mus.	Uganda	old ♀	1318	—	547	167	—	—	Coll. W. S. Rainsford. Referred by J. A. Allen (1914) to *E. whitei*
U.S. Nat. Mus. 52576	Faradje	♂	575	—	620	165	49	—	—

SKULL.—Cranial dimensions (in millimetres) :

	Nzoia R Guas Ngishu	Guas Ngishu	Nimule	Sudan	Upper Congo	Upper Congo	Upper Congo	Faradje
Locality								
Number	U.S.N.M. 155340	U.S.N.M. 173009	U.S.N.M. 164684	B.M. 8.6.15.1	U.S.N.M. 34714	U.S.N.M. 34713	Tervueren Museum	U.S.N.M. 52576
Sex	♂	♀	♂	♂	♂	♂	♂	♂
Max. Cranial Length	149	147	145	135	147·3	143·8	150	141
Glabella-opisthocranion	99	—	—	—	—	—	—	107·2
Condylo-basal Length	—	118	114	—	117·8	115	—	—
Biparietal	64	—	—	59·3	—	—	—	—
Least Frontal	50	—	—	47·3	49·4	48·3	53	49·3
Bimastoid	72	69·8	72·8	—	72·5	70	73	65·6
Basion-bregma	58	—	—	80	—	—	—	—
Bizygomatic	89·1[1]	84	91	—	89·3	86·3	93	88·3
Biorbital	71·5[1]	—	—	—	74·2	73·3	—	73·9
Palatal Length	61·5[1]	62·2	58·3	47·7	—	—	—	—
Upper Cheek-teeth	—	32	31·8	29·7	43·4	43·1	—	44·3
Mandibular Length	105	106	103	81·8	—	—	—	—
Lower Cheek-teeth	42	—	—	36·6	—	—	—	—
Remarks	Type of *Whitei* (personal measurements)	From Hollister 1924	From Hollister 1924	Type of *albigenus*	Basal suture obliterated	Basal suture closed	Type of *poliomystax*	Basal suture closed

[1] Erroneously printed as 99 in original description.

DISTRIBUTION.—Sudan (including Darfur, Kordofan and Bahr-el-ghazal), southwards to the Uelle river in north-eastern Congo; Uganda and western Kenya. Westwards the range presumably meets and intergradation occurs with E. p. *patas*. Eastwards the range transgresses the Blue Nile, probably as far as the Abyssinian frontier.

In the Sudan, Setzer (1956) records specimens from Torit, Kinyeti Valley (Imatong mountains) and from the foothills of the southern Jebel Marra. Furthermore the type of *poliophaeus* was from Jebel Fazoql, Blue Nile. Roosevelt (1910) collected a specimen, now in the U.S. National Museum, 60 miles north of Nimule.

Mertens (1929) mentions a specimen from Tambura, between the Mbomu and Sueh rivers.

In north-eastern Congo, Allen (1925) records examples from Faradje and Niangara collected by Lang and Chapin. Schouteden (1947) lists material in the Tervueren Museum from Manda, Mbomu, Sassa and Uelle (all in the Uele district); Abok and Mahagi port (Kibali-Ituri district).

In Kenya the animal is common on the Uasin Gishu plateau as attested by material in the U.S. National Museum. The type of *whitei* was shot near the Nzoia river, another was collected near Mount Elgon and one from 12 miles east of Sirgoit rock on the plateau. A form of Nisnas occurs south-east of Nairobi, presumably *E. p. pyrronotus*. Heller, in his journal of the Rainey expedition (1911), refers to a group of five seen about 100 yards from the railway between Kui and Ulu in March 1911, whilst Lönnberg (1912) also records it from near Ulu station.

In Uganda, the Nisnas has been collected by Rainsford (*fide* J. A. Allen, 1914), the exact locality being unrecorded.

Schwarz (1928 *a*) mentions a specimen in the Tervueren Museum collected by Bayer, merely ticketed " British East Africa ".

Anderson (1902) gives an excellent summary of the literature on the ecology of the Nisnas.

(d) *E. patas baumstarki* Matschie, 1905,* Ikoma Patas Monkey

(*Syn.* : *Cercopithecus baumstarki* Pocock, 1907, p. 745)
Vernacular names : None recorded.
Type locality : Ikoma, south-east end of Lake Victoria, Tanganyika. According to Swynnerton (1945) this is a village on the Kilimafeza–Musoma road at the crossing of the Grummetti river, 2° 05′ S., 34° 38′ E. Type, adult male (No. 13718) in Berlin Museum, together with two topotype females (Nos. 13717, 13719).

PELAGE : ADULT MALE.—Closely resembling *pyrronotus*, but differing principally in lacking the black frontal band and the lateral black streaks bordering the crown patch ; also in its somewhat paler general colour.

Crown patch described by Matschie as orange rufous (Elliot says orange buff); occipital region buff, mixed with long black hairs ; whiskers and sides of neck yellowish white ; back with median spinal stripe, redder than flanks, which are orange buff; shoulders and arms greyish white with interspersed black hairs ; thighs laterally buff; hands and feet dorsally greyish-white intermingled with brownish hairs.

Tail basally with continuation of spinal stripe above, remainder ochraceous buff, paler below.

Underparts and medial surfaces of limbs yellowish white, this colour spreading on the hind-limbs to the lateral aspect also—except for a basal triangular area on the thigh.

ADULT FEMALE.—Heller (quoted by Hollister, 1924) examined the topotype immature female (Berlin Museum No. A5575) and found it pale coloured, with the spinal stripe sorrel, the flanks ochraceous, and the underparts of belly and legs whitish.

Schwarz (1926 *b*) states that the older female has an almost completely black face except for a few white hairs in the moustache.

* *Sb. Ges. naturf. Fr. Berlin*, p. 273.

DIMENSIONS.—Of type as given by Elliot (1913): head and body, 580 mm.; tail 500 mm.

SKULL.—Cranial dimensions (in millimetres):

Berlin Museum Number	Locality	Sex	Max. Cranial Length	Basal Length	Occipito-nasal Length	Hensel	Least Frontal	Bizygomatic	Upper Cheek-teeth	Mandibular Length	Lower Cheek-Teeth
13718	Ikoma	♂	109		93	70	47	66	28	76·5	28
13717	,,	♀	—	84·1	—	—	—	—	—	—	—
A5575 =13719	,,	♀ subad.	109	75·6	—	—	—	—	—	—	—

DISTRIBUTION.—Masailand.

In addition to the type locality, which is located in the area south-east of Lake Victoria in the Musoma district of Tanganyika, Swynnerton and Hayman (1951) record this race from Engare Nairobi; Kisongo; between Banagi and Ikoma and Handajega. So far as is known this population is isolated, being unconnected with the population of *E. p. pyrronotus* to the south-east of Nairobi. Presumably it does not spread over the Serengeti plateau.

REFERENCES TO LITERATURE

Abel, O. 1931. *Die Stellung des Menschen im Rahmen der Wirbeltiere,* Jena; G. Fischer.

Adachi, B. 1903. *Z. Morph. Anthrop.,* **6**, 1-131.

Adanson, M. 1735. *Voyage au Sénégal,* Paris.

1759. English Edition : *A Voyage to Senegal, the Isle of Goree and the River Gambia.* London; J. Nourse & W. Johnston.

1749–1753. *Histoire naturelle du Sénégal, avec la relation abrégée de son voyage au Sénégal,* Paris.

Aeby, C. 1883. *Arch. Anat. Physiol.* 312-327.

Aelian, C. 1616. *de Natura animalium,* Coloniae Allobrogum ; P. Albertum.

Aelian, C. 1744. *Aeliani de Natura animalium Libri XVII cum animadversionibus Conradi Gesneri, et Danielis Wilhelmi Trilleri,* 2 vols., London.

Africanus, Leo (see Leo Africanus).

Albrecht, P. 1833. *Bull. Mus. Belg.,* **2**, 287-296.

Ali, S., and Santapau, H. 1956. *J. Bombay nat. Hist. Soc.,* **53**, 687.

Allen, E. 1926a. *Proc. Soc. exp. Biol. and Med.,* N.Y., **23**, 381-383.

1926b. *Proc. Soc. exp. Biol.,* **23**, 434-436.

1926c. *Anat. Rec.,* **32**, 226.

1927. *Contr. Embryol., Carneg. Instn.,* Washington, **19**, 1-44.

1928a. *Proc. Soc. exp. Biol. and Med.,* N.Y., **25**, 325-327.

1928b. *Amer. J. Physiol.,* Baltimore, **85**, 471-475.

1928c. *J. Morph. Physiol.,* Boston, **46**, 479-495.

1928d. *Amer. J. Anat.,* Pa., **42**, 467-486.

1928e. *Anat. Rec.,* **37**, 351-356.

Allen, G. M. 1930. *Amer. Mus. Nov.,* N.Y., **430**, 1-19.

1939. *Bull. Mus. comp. Zool.,* Harvard, **83**, 1-763.

Allen, G. M., and Coolidge, H. 1930. *Mammals of Liberia* in Vol. 2 of Strong, R. P., *The African Republic of Liberia and the Belgian Congo,* Cambridge, Mass.; Harvard University Press.

Allen, G. M., Lawrence, B., and Loveridge, A. 1936. *Bull. Mus. comp. Zool.,* Harvard, **79**, 31-126.

Allen, G. M., and Loveridge, A. 1933. *Bull. Mus. comp. Zool.,* Harvard, **75**, 47-140.

1942. *Bull. Mus. comp. Zool.,* Harvard, **89**, 147.

Allen, J. A. 1914. *Bull. Amer. Mus. nat. Hist.,* **33**, 337-344.

1925. *Bull. Amer. Mus. nat. Hist.,* **47**, 283-499.

Allison, A. C. 1959. *Amer. Naturalist,* **93**, 5-16.

Alpinus, Prosper. 1553–1617. *Historiae Aegypti naturalis; opus postumum,* 2 vols., Ludg. Batav. ; G. Potvliet.

Altmann, S. A. 1962a. *Current Anthrop.,* **3**, 100.

1962b. *Ann. N.Y. Acad. Sci.,* **102**, 338-435.

Ameghino, F. 1889. *Acta Acad. Nac. Cienc. Córdoba,* 547.

Amoroso, E. C. 1952. In Marshall, F. H. A., *Physiology of Reproduction*, ed. 3, vol. 2, chapter 15, Placentation, p. 278 *et seq.*, London ; Longmans.

— 1961. In Marshall, F. H. A., *Physiology of Reproduction*, ed. 3, new imp., London ; Longmans.

Anderson, J. 1872. *Proc. zool. Soc. Lond.*, 203-212.

— 1902. *Zoology of Egypt*, vol. 2, Mammals. London ; Rees.

Anderson, R. J. 1903. The premaxilla in Primates, *14th Int. Congr. Med., Madrid, Sect. Anat.*, 147-154.

— 1906. Some notes on the mandible and jugal in Primates, *15th Int. Congr. Med., Lisbonne, Sect. 1 Anat.*, 291-308.

Andrew, R. 1962. *Ann. N.Y. Acad. Sci.*, **102**, Art. 2, 296-315.

— 1963. *Symp. zool. Soc. Lond.*, No. 10, 89-102.

Anon. 1953. *Zooleo*, n.s., No. 18, 495.

Anoutchine, D. 1878. *Bull. Soc. Anthrop. Paris*, (3), **1**, 330-333.

Ansell, W. F. H. 1956. *Ann. Mag. nat. Hist.* (12), **10**, 529-551.

— 1960a. *Occ. Pap. Nat. Mus. S. Rhodesia*, No. 24B, 351-398.

— 1960b. *Mammals of Northern Rhodesia*, Lusaka ; Government Printer.

— 1961. *Mammalia*, Paris, **25**, 190-191.

— 1964. *Puku*, No. 2, 14-52.

Ansell, W. F. H., Benson, C. W., and Mitchell, B. L. 1962. *Nyasaland J.*, **15**, 38-54.

Anthony, J. 1952a. *Ann. paléont.*, **38**, 71-79.

— 1952b. *La Biologie Médicale*, **41**, No. 5, 17 pp.

Anthony, R., and Villemin, F. 1923. *Mission Rohan-Chabot (Angola et Rhodésie, 1912–1914)*, 4 (Histoire naturelle), fasc. 1, Mammifères (Anat. comp. et Embryologie) 1-106, Paris ; Imprimerie nationale.

Appelman, F. J. 1953. *Zool. Gart. Lpz.*, **20**, 95-98.

— 1957. *Zool. Gartn. Lpz.*, **23**, 246-247.

Apstein, C. 1915. *Sb. Ges. naturf. Fr. Berlin*, No. 5, 119-202.

Arends, T., and Rodriguez, M. L. G. 1960. *Nature*, Lond., **185**, 325-326.

Aristotle. 1910. *Historia animalium* (Vol. 4 of works), translated by D'Arcy W. Thompson, Oxford; University Press.

Aronson, L. R., and Papez, J. W. 1933. *Arch. Neurol. Psychiat.*, Chicago, **32**, 1-26.

— 1934. *Arch. Neurol. Psychol.*, **32**, 72-74.

Artus, Gothard. 1603. *Relation d'Artus; histoire générale des voyages*, tome 4, 238 (A translation by Artus of J. T. de Bry, Part VI).

Asdell, S. A. 1946. *Patterns of Mammalian Reproduction*, London ; Constable.

Ashley-Montagu, M. F. 1933. *Amer. J. phys. Anthrop.*, **18**, 159-336.

— 1943. *Amer. J. phys. Anthrop.*, n.s. **1**, 129-140.

— 1950. *J. Mammal.*, **31**, 150-153.

Ashton, E. H. 1957. *Proc. zool. Soc. Lond.*, **129**, 61-74.

Ashton, E. H., and Oxnard, C. E. 1958. *Proc. zool. Soc. Lond.*, **131**, 457-470.

— 1963. *Trans. zool. Soc. Lond.*, **29**, 553-650.

— 1964a. *Proc. zool. Soc. Lond.*, **142**, 1-28.

— 1964b. *Proc. zool. Soc. Lond.*, **142**, 49-66.

Ashton, E. H., and Zuckerman, S. 1950–1951. *Proc. roy. Soc.*, B. **137**, 212-238 ; **138**, 205-213, 214-218, 354-374.

— 1956. *Proc. zool. Soc. Lond.*, **126**, 581-634.

Athias, M. 1915. *Bull. soc. Portug. Sci. nat.*, **7**, 67-76.

Aubert, E. 1929a. *Ann. Mus. Hist. nat. Marseille*, **22**, 1-30.

Aubert, E. 1929b. *C.R. Ass. Anat.*, **24**, 573-575.

Audebert, J. B. 1797. *Histoire naturelle des singes et des makis*, Paris; Desray.

Auge, P. (ed.). 1930. *Larousse du XXᵉ siècle*, Paris; Librairie Larousse, **3**, 775.

Auskaps, A. M., and Shaw, J. H. 1957. *J. Dent. Res.*, **36**, 432-436.

Avis, V. 1962. *Southw. J. Anthrop.*, **18**, 119-148.

Ayer, A. A. 1948. *The Anatomy of Semnopithecus entellus*, Madras; The Indian Publishing House Ltd.

Aykroyd, O. E., and Zuckerman, S. 1938. *J. Physiol.*, **94**, 13-25.

Ayukawa, T. 1960. *Fol. anat. Jap.*, **35**, 243-255.

Bachman, C., Collip, J. B., and Selye, H. 1935. *Proc. roy. Soc.*, B, **117**, 16-21.
1936. *Proc. Soc. exp. Biol.*, N.Y., **33**, 549-551.

Bachmann, R. 1958. Nebennieren; in Höfer, Schultz, Starck (eds.), *Primatologia*, **3**, (1) 752-798, Basel; Karger.

Baitsch, H. 1960. *Anthrop. Anz.*, **24**, 63-69.

Baker, A. B. 1927. *Ann. Rept. Nat. Zool. Park for* 1926, Washington, D.C.

Baker, W. E., and Durand, H. M. 1836. *J. Asiat. Soc.*, **5**, 739.

van Balen Blanken, G. C. 1912. *Bijdrage tot de Kennis der Anatomie van Pancreas en Lymphaatstelsel der Primaten*, Amsterdam.

Barbot, J. 1746. In Churchill's *Voyages*, **6**, 1-420, London.

Bardeleben, K. von. 1894. *Proc. zool. Soc. Lond.*, 354-376.

Bargmann, R. 1958. Thyroidea und Parathyroidea in *Primatologia*, 3 ed., Höfer, Schultz, Starck (eds.), Basel; Karger.

Bargmann, W. 1943. Der Thymus; in *Handbuch der mikroskopischen Anatomie des Menschen*, 6/4, Berlin; Springer.

Baron, A., and Littman, R. A. 1961. *Genetic Psychol. Monogr.*, **64**, 129-209.

Barros Machado, A de. 1957. *Naturalia*, **7**, 1-12.

Bartels, P. 1911. *Arch. mikr. Anat.*, Abt. 1, **78**, 529-564.

Bartlakowski, J. 1930. *Morph. Jb.*, **65**, 129-163.

Bates, G. L. 1905. *Proc. zool. Soc. Lond.*, 65-85.

Bateson, W. 1894. *Materials for the Study of Variation treated with especial regard to discontinuity in the origin of species*, London; Macmillan.

Baylet, R., and Grattepanche, H. 1964a. *C.R. Soc. Biol.*, **159**, 1382-1383.

Bayley, R., and Grattepanche, H. 1964b. *C.R. Acad. Sci. Paris*, **259**, 3096-3099.

Bearcroft, W. G. C., and Jamieson, M. F. 1958. *Nature*, Lond., **182**, 195-196.

Beattie, J. 1927. *Proc. zool. Soc. Lond.*, 593-718.

de Beaux, O. 1917a. *G. Morf.*, **1**, 1-12.
1917b. *G. Morf.*, **1**, 222-227.
1917c. *Arch. Ital. Anat. Embr.*, **15**, 467, 541.
1924. *Atti Soc. Ital. Sci. Nat. e Mus. Civ. Stor. Nat.*, Milano, **62**, 247-254.
1943. Missione biologica Sagan-Omo, *R. Accad. Ital. Roma, Centro studi Africa Orient. Ital.*, **7**, 15-57.

Beaven, G. H., and Gratzer, W. B. 1959. *Nature*, Lond., **184**, 1730.

Beckman, L., and Cedermark, G. 1960. *Nature*, Lond., **186**, 643-644.

Beddard, F. E. 1903. *Proc. zool. Soc. Lond.*, 12-21.
1907. *Proc. zool. Soc. Lond.*, 181-223.
1909a. *Proc. zool. Soc. Lond.*, 496-526.
1909b. Mammalia in *Cambridge Natural History*, **10**, London; Macmillan.

Beebe, W. 1934. *Half-mile Down*. London; Bodley Head.

Beeckman, D. 1718. *A Voyage to and from the Island of Borneo*, London.

Bemmel, A. C. V. van, Peters, J. C., and Zwart, P. 1960. *Tijdschr. Diergeneesk.*, **85**, aft. 19, 1203-1213.

Bemmel, A. C. V. van, Zwart, P., and Peters, J. C. 1962. *Tijdschr. Diergeneesk.*, **87**, aft. 12, 826-836.

Bender, M. A., and Mettler, L. E. 1958. *Science*, **128**, 186-190.

Bennett, E. J. 1833. *Proc. zool. Soc. Lond.*, 109-110.

Benton, R. S., and Gavan, J. A. 1960. *Amer. J. phys. Anthrop.*, **18**, 273-279.

Benzien, J. 1959. *Zool. Gart. Lpz.*, **24**, 521-522.

Berg, W. 1903. *Z. Morph. Anthrop.*, **5**, 315-345.

Bernstein, H. 1923. *Abh. Senckenb. Naturf. Ges.*, **38**, 105-128.

Bernstein, I. S., and Schusterman, R. J. 1964. *Folia primat.*, **2**, 161-170.

Berry, P. S. M. 1965. *Puku*, No. 3 (in press).

Biedl, A. 1913. *Innere Sekretion*, Berlin und Wien ; Urban & Schwarzenberg.

Biegert, J. 1957. *Morph. Jb.*, **98**, 77-199.

    1961. Volarhaut der Hände und Füsse : in Höfer, Schultz and Starck (eds.), *Primatologia*, **2**, Teil 1, Lfg. 3, Basel ; Karger.

Bierens de Haan, J. A. 1925a. *J. comp. Psychol.*, **5**, 417-453.

    1925b. *Zool. Jb.*, Abt. 3, **42**, 272-306.

    1925c. *Biol. Zbl.*, **45**, 727-734.

Bierens de Haan, J. A., and Frima, M. J. 1930a. *Z. vergl. Physiol.*, **11**, 630-655.

    1930b. *Z. vergl. Physiol.*, **12**, 603-631.

Bierens de Haan, J. A., and Heubel, F. 1938. *Z. Morph. Ökol. Tiere*, **34**, 89-128.

Bigourdan, J. 1950. *C.R. Ière Conf. Int. des Africanistes de l'Ouest* (Dakar, 1945), **1**, 189.

Bigourdan, J., and Prunier, R. 1937. *Les Mammifères sauvages de l'Ouest Africain et leur milieu*, Montrouge ; Rudder.

Bingham, H. C. 1932. Gorillas in a native habitat. *Publ. Carneg. Instn.*, No. 426, 66 pp.

Birch, S. 1839. *Charlesworth's Mag. nat. Hist.*, 537.

    1840. *Charlesworth's Mag. nat. Hist.*, 35.

Bischoff, T. L. W. von. 1870. *Abh. Bayer. Akad. Wiss.*, **10**, 3. Abt., 198-297.

Blainville, H. M. D. de. 1839–1864. *Ostéographie*, 1, Paris ; J. B. Baillière & fils. Also English translation by R. Knox in *Lancet*, 1839–40.

Bland Sutton, J. 1884. *J. Anat. Lond.*, **18**, 225-238.

    1885. *J. Anat. Lond.*, **19**, 27-50 ; 241-265.

    1886a. *J. Anat. Lond.*, **20**, 39-75.

    1886b. *Brit. Gynecol. J.*, **2**, 285-292.

    1887. *Ligaments*, London ; Lewis.

    1897. do. 2nd ed.

    1902. do. 3rd ed.

    1920. do. 4th ed.

    1888. *J. Anat. Lond.*, **22**, 542-553.

    1889. *Amer. J. med. Sci.*, **97**, 247-257.

Blanford, W. T. 1887. *Proc. zool. Soc. Lond.*, 620-638.

    1888. Mammalia in *Fauna of British India*, London ; Taylor & Francis.

Blumenbach, J. F. 1779. *Handbuch der Naturgeschichte*, Göttingen ; J. C. Dieterich.

Bluntschli, H. 1906. *Morph. Jb.*, **36**, 276-461.

    1910. *Morph. Jb.*, **41**, 110-148.

Blyth, E. 1843. *J. r. Asiatic Soc. Bengal*, **12**, 173.

1845. *Ann. Mag. nat. Hist.* (1), **15**, 461.

1875. *J. Asiatic Soc. Bengal*, **44**, Pt. 2, extra number pp. i-xiv, 1-167.

Bocage, J. V. B. du. 1889. *J. Sci. Math. Phys. Nat.*, Lisbon (2), **1**, 8-14.

Boerner-Patzelt, D. 1922. *Anat. Anz.*, **55**, 162-187.

Bolk, L. 1897. *Morph. Jb.*, **25**, 305-361.

1902a. *Morph. Jb.*, **31**, 44-84.

1902b. *Ned. Bijdr. Anat.*, **1**, 371-567.

1907. *Z. Morph. Anthrop.*, **10**, 250-316.

1921. *Lancet*, 588-592.

1926. *Beitr. path. anat.*, **76**, 238-253.

Bolwig, N. 1957. *Suid-Afrikaanse J. Wetenskap.* (*South Afr. J. Sc.*), **53**, 255-260.

1959. *Koedoe*, **2**, 60-69.

1961. *South Afr. J. Sci.*, **57**, 147-152.

1963a. *Behaviour*, **21**, (3-4), 300-330.

1963b. *Behaviour*, **22**, (1-2), 24-40.

1964. *Behaviour*, **22**, (3-4), 167-192.

Bonin, G. von. 1942. *J. comp. Neurol.*, **77**, (2), 405-430.

1943. Abstr. from Suppl. *Anat. Rec.*, **35** (3) March 1943.

Booth, A. H. 1955. *J. Mammal.*, **36**, 434-449.

1956a. *J. W. Afr. Sci. Assoc.*, **2**, 122-133.

1956b. *Ann. Mag. nat. Hist.* (12), **9**, 476-480.

1956c. *Proc. zool. Soc. Lond.*, **129**, 421-430.

1957. *J. Mammal.*, **39**, 434.

1958. *Bull. Inst. franç. Afr. noire*, **20**, 587-622.

1960. *Small Mammals of West Africa*, West African Nature Handbooks, London ; Longmans.

Booth, C. P. 1957. *Afr. Wild Life*, **12**, 313-318.

1962. *Ann. N.Y. Acad. Sci.*, **102**, 477-487.

Bopp, P. 1953. *Rev. Suisse Zool.*, **60**, 441-446.

1954. *Rev. Suisse Zool.*, **61**, 83-151.

Bordy, J. 1962. *Mammalia*, Paris, **26**, 402-407.

Boreman, T. 1739. *A Description of some Curious and Uncommon Creatures . . . for the Entertainment of Young People*, London.

Bortolami, R., and Callegari, E. 1957. *Riv. Biol.*, **49**, 163-179.

Botar, J. 1931a. *Bull. Mus. Hist. nat. Paris* (2), **3**, 579-585.

1931b. *Bull. Mus. Hist. nat. Paris* (2), **3**, 727-736.

1932. *Acta Univ. Szeged.*, Sect. medic. **6**, 150-222.

Botar, J., Vilaghi, M., and Sere, G. 1950. *Acta anat.*, Basle, **9**, 235-250.

Botez, G. 1926. *Arch. Morph. gén. exp.*, Paris, **24**, 1-174.

Boulenger, E. G. 1936. *Apes and Monkeys*, London ; Harrap.

Bourdelle, E., and Matthias, P. 1928. *Bull. Mus. Hist. nat.*, **34**, No. 5, 306-310.

Bourdelle, E., Mouquet, A., and Mathias, P. 1929. *Bull. Mus. Hist. nat. Paris* (2), **1**, 234-238.

Bourlière, F. 1961. Patterns of social grouping among wild Primates: in Washburn (ed.) *Social Life of Early Man*, Chicago ; Aldine Press.

Bourne, G. H. 1936. *Amer. Naturalist*, **70**, 159-178.

1949. *The Mammalian Adrenal Gland*, Oxford ; Clarendon Press.

Bowden, R. E. M., Mahran, Z. Y., and Gooding, M. R. 1960. *Proc. zool. Soc. Lond.*,
    135, 587-611.
Boyden, A. A. 1926. *Biol. Bull.*, Woods Hole, **50**, 73-107.
Bradfield, R. D. 1935. *The Auk* (1936), **53**, 131.
Bradley, O. C. 1903. *Proc. roy. Soc. Edinb.*, **24**, 505-543.
Brambell, F. W. R. 1956. In Marshall's *Physiology of Reproduction*, 3 ed., **1**, Pt. 1,
    397-542.
Brandt, L. 1964. *Monkey Business* (Simian Soc. of America Inc.), Dec. 1963–Jan.
    1964, 3.
Brandt, W. 1940. *Hum. Biol.*, **12**, 203-231.
Brecher, G. A. 1935. *Z. vergl. Physiol.*, **22**, 539-547.
    1936. *Z. vergl. Physiol.*, **23**, 771-780.
Breitinger, E. 1951. *Umschau*, **51**, 563-565.
Breschet, G. 1845. *Mém. Acad. Sci. Paris*, **19**, 401-490.
von Breydenbach, B. 1486. *Reyss in das gelobt Land*, folio, Mainz.
Brisson, M. J. 1756. *Regnum animale in classis IX distributum, sive synopsis methodica*,
    Paris ; C. J. B. Baunche.
    1762. *Regnum animale in classis IX distributum sive synopsis methodica*, Leiden ; T.
    Haak.
Broca, P. 1869. *Bull. Soc. anthrop. Paris*, (2), **4**, 228-401.
    1871. *Bull. Soc. anthrop. Paris*, (2), **6**, 225-230.
    1872. *Rev. anthrop.*, Paris, **1**, 577-605.
    1877. *L'ordre des Primates, Mém. anthrop.*, Paris, **3**, 1-28.
    1878. *Bull. Soc. anthrop. Paris*, (3), **1**, 66-92.
Brodmann, K. 1909. *Vergleichende Localisationslehre der Grosshirnrinde in ihren
    Prinzipien dargestellt auf Grund des Zellenbaues*, Leipzig ; Barth.
van den Broek, A. J. P. 1907. *Morph. Jb.*, **37**, 202-288.
    1908. *Morph. Jb.*, **38**, 532-589.
    1911. *Arch. anat. Physiol.*, Anat. Abt., 163-184.
    1914. *Morph. Jb.*, **49**, 1-118.
Brooks, W. T. 1883. *J. Anat. Lond.*, **17**, 329-332.
Brown, C. E. 1936. *J. Mammal.*, **17**, 10-13.
Brown, J. Macdonald. 1881. *J. Anat. Lond.*, **15**, 523-535.
Brue, Sieur André. *c.* 1697. *Voyages and Travels along the Western Coast of Africa on
    Account of the French Commerce*, in *Astley's New Collection of Voyages*, Vol. 2.
Brünnich, M. T. 1772. *Zoologiae Fundamenta*, Hafniae et Lipsiae ; Frider, Christ ;
    Pelt, pp. 34, 40.
Bry, J. T. de. 1603. *India orientalis*, Part VI, Frankfurt ; Richtern.
Buchbinder, L. 1933. *J. Immunol.*, **25**, 33-59.
Buchi, E. C. 1953. *Nature*, Lond., **172**, 873.
Buckland, F. T. 1859. *Curiosities of Natural History*, 4 ed., London ; Bentley.
    1875. *Log Book of a Fisherman and Zoologist*, London ; Chapman & Hall.
Buettner-Janusch, J. 1962. *Ann. N.Y. Acad. Sci.*, **102**, 235-248.
Buffon, G. L. le Comte de. 1749–1804. *Histoire naturelle générale et particulière*,
    Paris ; L'imprimerie du Roi.
    1776. 14, (Orangs, Catarrhini).
Bullerman, R. 1950. *J. Mammal.*, **31**, 93-94.
Burdach, E. 1838. *Beitr. zur vergl. Anat. der Affen; Bericht von d. K. Akad. Königs-
    berg.*

Burkl, W. 1958. In Höfer, Schultz and Starck (eds.), *Primatologia*, **3**, (1) 41-61, Basel ; Karger.

Burnett, G. T. 1828. *Quart. J. Sci. Lit. Art.*, **26**, 301-307.

Büttikofer, J. 1900. *Notes Leyden Mus.*, **12**, 197-206.

1911. *Notes Leyden Mus.*, **34**, 1-3.

Buxton, A. P. 1951. *J. anim. Ecol.*, **20**, 31-32.

Buytendijk, F. J. J., and Revesz, G. 1923. *Arch. néerl. Physiol.*, **8**, 14-19.

Bychowska, M. 1930. *Folia morph. Warszawa*, **2**, 69-121.

Cabrera, A. 1929. *Mem. Soc. Españ. hist. nat. Madrid*, **16**, 121 pp.

Cabrera, A., and Ruxton, A. E. 1926. *Ann. Mag. nat. Hist.* (9), **17**, 591-602.

Cailliaud, F. 1826. *Voyage à Méroë, au Fleuve Blanc, au delà de Fazoql dans le midi du Royaume de Sennâr, à Syouah et dans cinq autres Oasis, 1812-22*, 4 vols., Paris ; L'imprimerie royale.

Camerano, L. 1896. *Boll. Mus. Zool. Anat. comp. Torino*, **11**, 3 pp.

Candela, P. B., Wiener, A. S., and Goss, L. J. 1940. *Zoologica*, N.Y., **25**, 513-521.

Cansdale, G. S. 1946. *Animals of West Africa*, London ; Longmans.

Cantor, T. 1846. *J. Asiatic Soc. Bengal*, **15**, 71-241.

Capobianco, F., and Maziotti, L. 1899. *G. int. Sci. Med.*, **21**, 337-364.

Carlisle, A. 1805. *Phil. Trans. roy. Soc.*, 198-210.

Carpenter, C. R. 1938. A survey of wildlife conditions in Atjeh, North Sumatra, with special reference to the orang-utans, *Commun. No. 12 Netherlands Comm. for International Nature Protection*, 34 pp.

1940. *Comp. Psychol. Monogr.*, **16**, (5), 1-212.

1942. *J. comp. Psychol.*, **33**, 133-142, 143-162.

Carreri, J. F. G. 1707-1747. *Voyages round the World in Turkey, Persia, India, China, the Philippine Islands and New Spain*, in Churchill, A. & J., *Collection of Voyages*, Vol. 4.

Carter, J. Thornton. 1922. *Proc. zool. Soc. Lond.*, 599-608.

Cautley, P. J., and Falconer, H. 1837. *Trans. Geol. Soc. Lond.*, **5**, (2), 499. (Reprinted in Falconer's *Palaeontological Memoirs*, ed. by Murchison, C., London ; Hardwicke (1868)).

Cave, A. J. E. 1948. *B.M.A. Proc. Ann. Mtg.*, 363-366, London ; Butterworth.

Cave, A. J. E., and Haines, R. W. 1940. *J. Anat. Lond.*, **74**, 493-523.

Chaine, J. 1926. *Act. Linn. Soc.*, Bordeaux, **78**, 5-195.

Champion, F. W. 1929. *J. Bombay nat. Hist. Soc.*, **33**, 424, 921.

1930. *J. Bombay nat. Hist. Soc.*, **34**, 543.

Champneys, F. 1871. *J. Anat. Lond.*, **6**, 176-211.

Chance, M. R. A. 1956. *Brit. J. Anim. Behav.*, **4**, 1-13.

Chance, M. R. A., and Mead, A. P. 1952. *Soc. exp. Biol. Symp.*, **7**, 395.

Chapin, J. P. 1923. *Amer. Nat.*, **57**, 106-125.

1925. *Nat. Hist.*, N.Y., **25**, 459.

1932. *Bull. Amer. Mus. Nat. Hist.*, **65**, pp. x + 756.

Chapman, H. C. 1874. *Proc. Acad. nat. Sci.*, Philad., 94-95.

1879. *Proc. Acad. nat. Sci.*, Philad., 146-147.

1880. *Proc. Acad. nat. Sci.*, Philad., 52-63.

Chase, R. E. 1938. *Amer. J. phys. Anthrop.*, **23**, 299-320.

1942. *Amer. J. phys. Anthrop.*, **29**, 267-286.

Chase, R. E., and de Garis, C. F. 1938–1939. *Amer. J. phys. Anthrop.*, **24**, 427-448.

Chasen, F. N. 1940. Handlist of Malaysian Mammals, *Bull. Raffles Mus.*, Singapore, No. 15, xx + 209 pp.

Chiarelli, B. 1958. *Caryologia*, **11**, 99-104.

1959. *Arc. Antr. Etn.*, **89**, 148-167.

1960. *Atti A.G.I.*, 275-280.

1961. *Atti A.G.I.*, **6**, 213-220.

1962a. *Experientia*, **18**, 405-407.

1962b. *Caryologia*, **15**, 401-420.

1963a. *Rivista di Antropologia*, **50**, 87-124.

1963b. *Symp. zool. Soc. Lond.*, No. 10, 277-280.

Chiodi, V. 1932. *Clin. vet. Milano*, **55**, 689-714 ; 799-823.

Chopra, S. R. K. 1957. *Proc. zool. Soc. Lond.*, **128**, 67-112.

Chu, E. H. Y., and Bender, M. A. 1961. *Science*, **133**, 1399-1405.

1962. *Ann. N.Y. Acad. Sci.*, **102**, 253-266.

Chu, E. H. Y., and Giles, N. H. 1956. *Rec. Genet. Soc. Amer.*, **25**, 637.

1957. *Amer. Nat.*, **91**, 273-282.

Church, W. S. 1861. *Nat. Hist. Rev.*, **1**, 510-516.

1862. *Nat. Hist. Rev.*, **2**, 82-94.

Clark, O. H., and Corner, G. W. 1935. *Anat. Rec.*, **63**, 247-252.

Clark, W. E. Le Gros. 1930. *Nature*, Lond., **125**, 236-7.

1934. *Early Forerunners of Man*, London ; Baillière, Tindall & Cox.

1935. *Man*, No. 2, 5 pp.

1936. *Proc. zool. Soc. Lond.*, (**1**), 1-24.

1945. *J. Anat. Lond.*, **79**, 123-126.

1959. *The Antecedents of Man*, Edinburgh ; University Press.

Clark, W. E. Le Gros, and Boggon, R. H. 1933. *J. Anat. Lond.*, **67**, 215-227.

1935. *Phil. Trans. roy. Soc.* (B), **224**, 313-359.

Clark, W. E. Le Gros, and Leakey, L. S. B. 1951. *Fossil Mammals of Africa*, I. Brit. Mus. (Nat. Hist.) 1-117, London.

Clark, W. E. Le Gros, and Northfield, D. W. C. 1937. *Brain*, **60**, 126-142.

Clermont, Y., and Leblond, C. P. 1955. *Amer. J. Anat.*, **96**, 229-253.

Clusius, C. (L'Écluse, C.). 1605. *Exoticorum libri decem. quibus animalium plantarum . . . etc.*, Leyden; Raphelengii.

Coiter, V. 1578. *Analogia ossium humanorum simiae at verae et caudatae quae Cynocephali similis est, atque vulpis.*

Colbert, E. H. 1937. *Amer. Mus. Novit.*, No. 951, 1-18.

1938. *Bull. Amer. Mus. Nat. Hist.*, **74**, 255-436.

Cole, J. 1952. *J. Comp. Physiol. Psychol.*, **45**, 226.

1953a. *J. Comp. Physiol. Psychol.*, **46**, 16.

1953b. *Behaviour*, **2**, 121.

1956. *Behaviour*, **11**, 202-208.

1957. *J. Comp. Physiol. Psychol.*, **50**, 296.

1963. *Symp. zool. Soc. Lond.*, No. 10, 105-114.

Collings, M. R. 1926. *Anat. Rec.*, **33**, 271-278.

Collins, H. B. 1925. *Amer. J. phys. Anthrop.*, **8**, 261-274.

Colyer, J. F. 1936. *Variations and Diseases of the Teeth of Animals*, London ; Bale Sons & Danielsson.

Colyer, F. 1948. *Proc. roy. Soc. med.*, **41**, 845-848.

Connolly, C. J. 1950. *External Morphology of the Primate Brain*, Springfield, Ill. ; Thomas.

Cooper, R. W. 1964. *Second annual report on experimental breeding of subhuman Primates. N.I.H. Cancer Institute, Contract* PH 43-63-56.

Copley, H. 1950. *Small mammals of Kenya*, Nairobi ; Highway Press.

Cordier, P., Couloumas, P., and van Varseveld. 1936. *C.R. Ass. Anat.*, 124-132.

Corner, E. J. H. 1946. *Zoo Life*, **1**, 89.
1955. *Proc. roy. Institn. G.B.*, **36**, 1.

Corner, G. W. 1923. Ovulation and Menstruation in *Macacus rhesus*, *Contr. Embryol. Carneg. Instn.*, no. 332, **15**, 73-101.
1927. *J. Amer. med. Ass.*, **89**, 1838-1840.
1932. *Anat. Rec.*, **52**, 401-410.
1942. The fate of the corpora lutea in the ovary of the monkey, *Contr. Embryol. Carneg. Instn.*, **30**, 85-96.
1951. *Amer. Scientist*, **39**, 50-73.

Corner, G. W., Hartman, C. G., and Bartelmez, G. W. 1945. Development, organization and breakdown of the corpus luteum in the rhesus monkey, *Contrib. Embryol. Carneg. Instn.*, **31**, 117-146.

Cornish, C. J. 1895. *Life at the Zoo, Notes and Traditions*, London ; Seely & Co.

Correnti, V. 1952. *Rend. Accad. Lincei.*, ser. viii, **12**, 618-623.

Coruch, R. L. 1934. *J. comp. Neurol.*, **59**, 451-485.

Coventry, A. F. 1923. *Anat. Rec.*, **25**, 237-255.

Crisp, E. 1862. *Proc. zool. Soc. Lond.*, 132-139.

Cruickshank, J. C., and Bray, R. 1950. *Mon. Bull. Minist. Hlth. Lab. Serv.*, **9**, 278-279.

Cunningham, D. J. 1879. *J. Anat. Lond.*, **13**, 1-16.
1882. *Challenger Repts.* Zool., **5**, pt. 16, 1-192.
1886. *Cunningham Mem. R. Irish Acad.*, **2**, 148 pp.
1888. *Proc. roy. Irish Acad.*, (3), **1**, 78-91.
1891. *J. Anat. & Phys.*, n.s. 5, 286-291.
1892. *Cunningham Mem., Roy. Irish. Acad. Sci.*, 7
1896a. *J. Anat. Lond.*, **31**, (n.s.) i-ii.

Curry-Lindahl, K. 1961. *Expl. Parc. nat. Albert et du Parc. nat. de la Kajera II*, fasc. 1, 1 331.

Cuvier, F. 1818. *Mém. Mus. Hist. nat. Paris*, 4, 419-426.
1819. *Histoire naturelle des mammifères*, liv. IV, Plate XX. Paris ; Belin.
1824. In Geoffroy and Cuvier's *Histoire naturelle des mammifères*, 7 vols. in 4, Folio, Paris ; Belin.

Cuvier, G. L. C. F. D. 1800–1805. *Leçons d'anatomie comparée*, Paris ; Bauduin, xxxi + 540 pp.
1801. in Lacépède and Cuvier, *La Ménagerie du Muséum National d'Histoire Naturelle.* Paris ; Miger, Patris, Grandchier et Dentu.
1817. *Le Règne animal*, Paris ; Déterville, 1, xxxvii + 540 pp.

Dahl, F. 1907. *Zool. Jb.*, Abt. 1, **25**, 329-338.

Dahlbom, A. G. 1856–1857. *Zoologiska Studier, afhandlande Djurrikets naturliga familjer*, Lund.

Dandelot, P. 1956. *Mammalia*, Paris, **20**, 330-331.
1959. *Mammalia*, Paris, **23**, 357-368.
1962. *Mammalia*, Paris, **26**, 447-449.

Dapper, O. 1676. *Naukeurige Beschrijvinge der Afrikaensche gevesten van Egypten . . . ,* Amsterdam ; J. van Meurs.

1686. (French ed.), *Description d'Afrique,* (*traduit du Flammand*), Amsterdam.

Darlington, C. D., and Haque, A. 1955. *Nature,* Lond., **175**, 32.

Dart, R. A. 1925. *Nature,* Lond., **115**, 95.

1953. *Int. Anthrop. Linguist Rev.,* **1**, 210-217.

1960. Africa's place in the emergence of civilization, *Van Riebeck Lectures,* S. African Broadcasting Corp. publ., 96 pp.

1963. *Symp. zool. Soc. Lond.,* No. 10, 49-56.

Darwin, C. R. 1871. *Descent of Man,* London ; Murray.

1872. *The Expressions of the Emotions in Man and Animals,* London ; Murray.

Daubenton, L. J. M. 1764. In Buffon's *Histoire naturelle,* **15**, 43.

1776. See Buffon.

Dawson, A. B. 1948. *Anat. Rec.,* **102**, 103-121.

Day, M. H., and Napier, J. R. 1963. *Folia primat.,* **1**, 122-134.

Debrunner, I. M. 1955. *Z. Morph. Anthrop.,* **47**, 187-210.

Dekeyser, P. L. 1950. *Mém. Inst. franç. Afr. noire,* No. 10, 388-425.

1955. *Les Mammifères de l'Afrique noire française,* Dakar ; Inst. français d'Afrique noire.

Dekeyser, P. L., and Derivot, J. 1960. *Bull. Inst. franç. Afr. noire,* **14**, 537-544.

Dekeyser, P. L., and Villiers, A. 1951a. *Trab. 2a Conf. int. Afr. occid.,* Bissau, 1947, 3, 2, 66-72.

1951b. Idem, 73-92.

Delfs, E. 1941. *Anat. Rec.* (Suppl.), **79**, 17.

Demeter, G., and Matyas, J. 1928. *Z. Anat. EntwGesch.,* **87**, 45-99.

Deniker, J. 1885. *Arch. zool. exp. gén.,* (2) 3 bis, Suppl., No. 3, 265 pp.

Denon, D. V., Baron de. 1802. *Voyage dans la basse et la haute Égypte,* Paris.

Denzer, H. W. 1938. *Tabulae biologicae,* **15**, Pts. 3 and 4, 260-322, Haag.

Depéret, C. 1890. *Mém. Soc. géol. France,* Paléontologie, **3**, 11.

1928. *C.R. Congr. Geol. Internat.,* Madrid, **14**, Pt. 3, 999-1000.

1929. *Trav. Lab. Géol. Univ. Lyon,* **15**, Mém. 12 ; 12.

Dick, G. W. A. 1948. *Brit. J. exp. Path.,* **29**, 559-577.

Dobson, G. E. 1881. *Proc. zool. Soc. Lond.,* 812-818.

1882. *Trans. Linn. Soc.,* (2) II, 259-264.

Dollman, J. G. 1931a. *Primates,* series 1, London ; British Museum (Nat. Hist.), Pl.B 139.

1931b. Mammalia in *The Standard Natural History,* ed. W. P. Pycraft, London ; F. Warne.

Doran, A. H. G. 1876. *Proc. roy. Soc.,* **25**, 101-109 (Abstr.).

1879. *Trans. Linn. Soc. Lond.,* Zool., 1878 (2) **1**, 371-497.

Dubois, E., and Matschie, P. 1912. *Rev. zool. Afric.,* **1**, 439-440.

Duckworth, W. L. H. 1904a. In *Studies from the Anthropological Laboratory in the Anatomy School,* Cambridge ; Cambridge University Press, 80-90.

1904b. Idem, 91-97.

1907. *Proc. Camb. phil. Soc.,* **14**, 299-312.

1910. *J. Anat. Lond.,* **44**, 349-353.

1912. *J. Anat. Lond.,* **67**, 80-115.

1915. *Morphology and Anthropology,* 2 ed., Cambridge ; University Press.

Duncan, P. M. 1876. Quadrumana in *Cassell's Natural History*, 1, London ; Cassel, Petter and Galpin. (Quotations are taken from the later undated edition.)

Dzwonkowski, L. 1935–1936. *Folia morph. Warszawa*, 6, 147-202.

Eckstein, P. 1944. *J. Anat., Lond.*, 78, 147.

1948. Thesis, Cambridge University, quoted in Eckstein, P. 1958, Internal reproductive organs in Höfer, Schultz and Starck (eds.), *Primatologia*, 3/1 Basel ; Karger.

1958. Internal reproductive organs in Höfer, Schultz and Starck (eds.), *Primatologia*, 3/1, Basel ; Karger, 542-629.

Eckstein, P., and Zuckerman, S. 1956. Morphology of the reproductive tract : in Marshall's *Physiology of Reproduction*, 1, 3 ed. i, 43-155, London ; Longmans.

1959. Monkeys : in Worden, A. N., and Lane-Petter, W. (eds.), *U.F.A.W. Handbook*, 2 ed. (second impression), London ; U.F.A.W.

1962. Oestrous cycle in the Mammalia : in Parkes, A. S. (ed.) Marshall's *Physiology of Reproduction*, 3 ed., new imp., London ; Longmans.

Edwards, G. 1758-1764. *Gleanings of Natural History*, 3 vols., London ; G. Sidney.

Eggeling, H. von. 1896. *Morph. Jb.*, 24, 311-631, 768-774.

1922. *Anat. Anz.*, 55, 33-94.

Eggeling, W. J., and Dale, I. R. 1947. *Notes on the Forests of Uganda and their Products*, Entebbe (paper prepared by Forest authority for the fifth British Empire forestry conference, London).

Ehrenberg, C. G. 1835. *Abh. Akad. Wiss. Berlin*, 1833 ; phys. Klasse, 337-367.

Elftman, H. O. 1932. *Amer. J. Anat.*, 51, 307-346.

Eller, H. 1932. *Z. Anat. EntwGesch.*, 97, 725-756.

Ellerman, J. R., and Morrison Scott, T. C. S. 1951. *Checklist of Palaearctic and Indian Mammals, 1758–1946*, London ; British Museum (Nat. Hist.).

Ellerman, J. R., Morrison Scott, T. C. S., and Hayman, R. W. 1953. *Southern African Mammals, 1758–1951, a reclassification*, London ; British Museum (Nat. Hist.).

Elliot, D. G. 1907. *Ann. Mag. nat. Hist.* (7), 20, 185-196.

1909. *Ann. Mag. nat. Hist.* (8), 4, 244-274.

1910. *Smiths. misc. Coll.*, 56, No. 7, 1.

1913. *Review of the Primates*, 2, New York ; Amer. Mus. Nat. Hist. Monogr.

Elliot-Smith, G. 1902a. *J. Anat. Lond.*, 36, 309-319.

1902b. *Descriptive and Illustrated Catalogue of the Physiological Series of Comparative Anatomy contained in the Museum of the Royal College of Surgeons of England*, 2 (2 ed.), London ; Taylor and Francis.

1903a. *Anat. Anz.*, 24, 74-83.

1903b. *Trans. Linn. Soc. Lond.*, Zool., 8, 319-432.

1904a. *Proc. roy. Soc.*, 73, 59.

1904b. *Anat. Anz.*, 24, 436-451.

1919a. *J. Anat. Lond.*, 53, 271-291.

1919b. *J. Anat. Lond.*, 53, 361-362.

1929. *Nature*, Lond., 124, 876-877.

Emlen, J. T., and Schaller, G. B. 1960. *Animal Kingdom ; Bull. N.Y. Zool. Soc.*, 63, 98-108.

Engle, E. T. 1932. *Endocrinology*, 16, 513-520.

Erikson, G. E. 1963. Brachiation in the New World monkeys, *Symp. zool. Soc. Lond.*, No. 10, 135-165.

Erxleben, J. C. P. 1777. *Systema Regni animalis Classis I Mammalia*, Lipsiae ; Impensis Weygandiansis.

von Eschscholtz, J. F. 1821. In von Kotzebue, O., *Entdeckungs-Reise in die Sud-See und nach den Berings-Strasse zur Erforschung einer nordostlichen Durchfahrt Unternommen in der Jahren 1815–1818*, 3 vols. Weimar.

L'Escluse, C. de (Carolus Clusius). 1605. *Exoticorum libri x, quibus animalium, plantarum, aromatum, aliorunque peregrinorum fructuum historie describuntur*, fol. Antwerp.

Ewing, H. E. 1935. *J. Mammal.*, **16**, 303-306.

Fahrenholz, C. 1937. Drüsen der Mundhöhle: in Bolk, Göppert, Kallius & Lubosch, *Hbd. d. vergl. Anat. d. Wirbeltiere*, **3**, 115-210, Berlin-Wien ; Urban & Schwarzenburg.

Falconer, H. 1868a. *Palaeont. Memoirs*, **1**, 307-309, London ; Hardwicke.
1868b. *Palaeont. Memoirs*, **1**, 309-314, London ; Hardwicke.

Falconer, H., and Cautley, P. J. 1837. *J. Asiatic Soc.*, **6**, 354-360.

Farris, E. J. 1950. *The Care and Breeding of Laboratory Animals*, New York ; Wiley.

Ferrier, D. 1876. *The Function of the Brain*, London ; Smith, Elder & Co.

Fieandt, E. 1914. *Morph. Jb.*, **48**, 513-643.

Fiedler, W. 1956. In Höfer, Schultz and Starck (eds.), *Primatologia*, **1**, Basel ; Karger.
1957. *Z. Säugetierk.*, **22**, 57-76.

Fischer, E. 1903. *Z. Morph. Anthrop.*, **5**, 383-414.

Fischer, G. 1804. *Anatomie der Maki*, Frankfurt ; Andreaischen Buchhandlung.

Fischer, J. von. 1876. *Zool. Gart. Frankft.*, **17**, 116-127, 174-179.

Fischer, J. B. 1829. *Synopsis mammalium*, Stuttgart.

Fischer, R. B., Krohn, P. L., and Zuckerman, S. 1936. *Biochem. J.*, **30**, 2219-2223.

Fitzinger, L. J. 1866. *Sitzber. Akad. Wiss. Wien*, **54**, 4.

Fitzsimons, F. W. 1911. *The Monkey Folk of South Africa*, London ; Longmans, Green & Co.
1919. *The Natural History of South Africa*, I : Mammals, London ; Longmans, Green & Co.

Fitzsimons, V. 1955. *Fauna & Flora*, Pretoria, No. 6, 79-83.

Fleming, J. 1822. *The Philosophy of Zoology; or a General View of the Structure, Functions and classification of animals*, Edinburgh ; A. Constable.

Flower, S. S. 1931. *Proc. zool. Soc. Lond.*, 145-234.

Flower, W. H. 1862. *Phil. Trans.*, **152**, 185-201.
1870. *An Introduction to the Osteology of the Mammalia*, London ; Macmillan.
1872. *Med. Times Lond.*, **1**, 215-219.
1885. *Osteology of the Mammalia*, 3 ed., 78-79.

Flower, W. H., and Lydekker, R. 1891. *An Introduction to the Study of Mammals, Living and Extinct*, London ; Black.

Folley, S. J., Guthkelch, A. N., and Zuckerman, S. 1939. *Proc. roy. Soc. Lond.*, (B), **126**, 469-491.

Folley, S. J., and Zuckerman, S. 1938. *Proc. Anat. Soc. in J. Anat. Lond.*, **72**, 613.

Follis, R. H. 1957. *Proc. Soc. exp. Biol. N.Y.*, **96**, 523-528.

Forbes, H. O. 1894. *Handbook to the Primates*, London ; Allen's Natural History.
1905. *Nature*, Lond., **72**, 630.

Forbes, W. A. 1881. *Rept. Brit. Assoc.*, 718.

Forskål, P. 1775. *Descriptiones animalium*, post mortem auctoris edidit C. Niebuhr, Hauniae ; Mälleri.

Förster, A. 1903. *Arch. Anat. Physiol. Lpz.*, Anat. Abt., 257-320.

1904. *Arch. Anat. Physiol. Lpz.*, Anat. Abt., 197-298.

1916a. *Z. Morph. Anthrop.*, **19**, 27-148, 271-352.

1916b. *Z. Morph. Anthrop.*, **20**, 111-224, 339-456.

1916c. *Arch. Anat. Physiol. Lpz.*, Anat. Abt., 101-378.

1918. *Anat. Hefte*, **56**, 1-170.

1919. *Z. Morph. Anthrop.*, **21**, 23-102.

1922. *Arch. Anat. Strasb.*, **1**, 205-244.

1923. *Arch. Anat. Strasb.*, **2**, 393-428.

1924. *Arch. Anat. Strasb.*, **3**, 193-246.

1925. *Arch. Anat. Strasb.*, **4**, 45-99.

1928. *Arch. Anat. Strasb.*, **8**, 359-432.

Förster, A., and Lacroix, M. 1926. *Rev. anthrop. Paris*, **36**, 49-52.

Forsyth, D. 1908. *J. Anat. Lond.*, **42**, 141-169.

Forsyth-Major, C. I. 1901. *Proc. zool. Soc. Lond.*, 129-153.

Fox, H. 1941. *Rept. Penrose Res. Lab.*, 14-25.

Fraas, O. 1870. *Ver. Vaterl. Naturk. Württemb.*, **26**, 148-306.

Franke, H. J. I. B. 1902. *Ned. Bijdr. Anat.*, **1**, 326-370.

Franz, S. I. 1913. *J. Anim. Behav.*, **3**, 140-144.

Franz, V. 1934. In Bolk, Göppert, Kallius and Lubosch (eds.), *Handbuch vergleichenden Anatomie der Wirbeltiere*, **2**, 2, Berlin ; Urban & Schwarzenburg.

Fraser, L. 1849. *Zoologia typica*, London.

Frassetto, F. 1903. *Ann. Sci. nat. Zool.* (8), **17**, 143-363.

Frechkop, S. 1927 (1928). *Ann. Soc. zool. Belg.*, **58**, 109-116.

1937. *Bull. Mus. Hist. nat. Belg.*, **13**, No. 40, 21 pp.

1940. *Bull. Mus. Hist. nat. Belg.*, **16**, 1-22.

1947. *Animaux protégés au Congo Belge et dans le territoire sous mandat du Ruanda-Urundi*, Bruxelles.

1951. *Assoc. franç. adv. Sci.*, *70e congrès*, Tunis, fasc. 4, 15 pp.

1953. *Animaux protégés au Congo Belge et dans le territoire sous mandat du Ruanda-Urundi*, Bruxelles, 4 ed.

1954a. *Vol. Jubilaire V. van Straelen*, Bruxelles.

1954b. *Bull. Inst. roy. Soc. nat. Belg.*, **30**, 11 pp.

1954c. *Exploration du Parc National de l'Upemba Mission G. F. de Witte; Mammifères*, Bruxelles, 84 pp.

Freedman, L. 1956. *Ann. Trans. Mus.*, **23**, 121-262.

1960. *Paleont. Afr.*, **7**, 7-45.

1961. *Ann. S. Afr. Mus.*, **46**, 1-14.

Frets, G. P. 1908. *Morph. Jb.*, **38**, 135-193.

Freund, L. 1939. Das Urogenitalsystem der Säugetiere : in Bronn's *Klassen und Ordnungen des Tierreichs*, **6**, Abt. 5, Buch 2, T. 5, Lief. 5, 49-143. Leipzig ; Akademische Verlagsesellschaft.

Frey, H. 1923. *Z. Anat. Entw. Ges.*, **74**, 240-284.

Friant, M. 1947. *Anatomie comparée de cerveau*, Paris ; Orion.

1952. *C.R. Acad. Sci. Paris*, **235**, 1334-1335.

1953. *Ann. Soc. roy. Zool. Belg.*, **84**, (1), 39-59.

Frick, H. 1957. *Anat. Anz.*, **104**, 305-333.

1960. In Höfer, Schultz, and Starck (eds.), *Primatologia*, **3/2**, Basel ; Karger, 163-272.

Friedemann, M. 1911. *J. Psychol. Neurol. Lpz.*, **18**, 309-378.

Friedenthal, H. 1908, 1910. *Beiträge zur Naturgeschichte des Menschen*, Lfg. I-V, Jena ; Fischer.

Froger, Sieur. 1699. *Relation d'un voyage fait en 1656-57 aux côtes d'Afrique . . .*, Paris. 1715. Amsterdam ; l'Honoré & Châtelain.

Frommolt, G. 1934. *Z. Geburtsh. Gynäk.*, **107**, 165-178.

Funaoka, S., and Shinosaki, S. 1908. *Folia anat. Japon*, **6**, 599.

Fürst, C. M. 1903. *Lunds Univ. Årsskr.*, **39**, (2) art. 1, 134 pp. (in 1904).

Gabis, R. V. 1960. *Mammalia*, Paris, **24**, 577-607.

Galton, J. C. 1875. *J. Anat. Lond.*, **9**, 169-175.

Garis, C. F. de. 1936. *J. Anat. Lond.*, **70**, 149-158.

1938. *Anat. Rec.*, **70**, 251-262.

1941. *Amer. J. phys. Anthrop.*, **28**, 41-74.

Garner, R. L. 1892. *The Speech of Monkeys*, New York ; Webster, 217 pp.

1900. *Apes and Monkeys; their Life and Language*, Boston ; Ginn.

Garnham, P. C. C. 1947. *E. Afr. med. J.*, **24**, 47-51.

1948. *Trans. R. Soc. trop. Med. Hyg.*, **41**, 601-616.

Garnham, P. C. C., Harper, J. O., and Highton, R. B. 1946. *Bull. ent. Res.*, **36**, 473-494.

Gegenbaur, C. 1898. *Lehrbuch der Anatomie des Menschen*, Leipzig ; Engelmann.

Geist, F. D. 1933. In Hartman and Straus (eds.), *The Anatomy of the Rhesus Monkey*, Baltimore ; Williams & Wilkins.

Geoffroy Saint-Hilaire, E. 1812. *Ann. Mus. Hist. Nat. Paris*, **19**, 157-170.

Geoffroy Saint-Hilaire, I. 1830. Mammifères : in Bélanger, C., *Voyage aux Indes-Orientales par le Nord de l'Europe . . . pendant les années 1825-1829*, Zoologie, Paris. A. Bertrand.

1842. *C.R. Acad. Sci.*, **15**, 1037-1038.

1843. In d'Orbigny, A., *Dictionnaire universelle d'histoire naturelle*, **3**, 296 et seq.

Gerber, R. 1957. *Zool. Gart. Lpz.*, **53**, 247.

Gerhardt, U. 1904. *Jena Zeitschr. Naturw.*, **39**, 43-117.

Gervais, F. P. 1847. *Ann. Sci. nat. Zool.*, sér. 3, **8**, 203-224.

Gesner, C. 1551. *Historiae animalium*, lib. I. De quadrupedibus viviparis, Tiguri.

Gibbett, E. R. 1959. *Nature*, Lond., **183**, 192.

Giebel, C. G. 1877. Mammalia : in Bronn's *Klassen und Ordunugen des Thierreichs*, **6**, Abt. 5, Leipzig ; Akademische Verlagsgesellschaft.

Gijzen, A. 1962. *Zoo*, Anvers, **27**, 88-90.

1963. *Zool. Meded.*, **39**, 522-525.

Gilbert, C., and Gillman, J. 1951. *S. Afr. J. Med. Sci.*, 16, 115-124.

Gill, J. 1872. *Smiths. misc. Coll.*, No. 230, 98 pp.

Gillman, J. 1935. *S. Afr. J. Sci.*, **32**, 342-355.

1939. *S. Afr. J. Sci.*, **36**, 406.

1942. *S. Afr. J. med. Sci.*, **16**, 115-124.

Gillman, J., and Gilbert, C. 1946. *S. Afr. J. med. Sci.*, **11**, Suppl. 1-54.

Girard, L. 1923. *Bull. Soc. Anthrop. Paris*, (7), **4**, 14-33.

1924. *Ot. etc. internat.* (Lyon), **8**, 257-266.

1930. *Ot. etc. internat.* (Lyon), **14**, 517-537.

Gisler, D. B., Benson, R. E., and Young, R. J. 1960. *Ann. N.Y. Acad. Sci.*, **85**, 758-768.

Glees, P., and Cole, J. 1951. *Experientia*, Basel, **7**, 224-230.

Gluckmann, F. 1946. *C.R. Acad. Sci. Paris*, **223**/**10**, 517-519.

Gmelin, C. G. 1805. *Gemeinnützige systematische Naturgeschichte für gebildete Leser. Nach dem Linneischen Natursystem*, **1**, Säugethiere, Mannheim ; Rechnungs-Rathes Neudeck.

Goodall, J. M. 1962. *Ann. N.Y. Acad. Sci.*, **102**, 455-467.

1963. *Symp. zool. Soc. Lond.*, No. 10, 39-47.

Goodman, M. 1960. *Amer. Nat.*, **94**, 184-186.

Goodman, M., Poulik, E., and Poulik, M. D. 1962 (?) Seen only in typescript.

Goulay, R. N. 1960. *J. comp. Path. Ther.*, **70**, 339-345.

Grafflin, A. L. 1940. *J. Morphol.*, **67**, 471-476.

1940. *J. Morphol.*, **70**, 535-543.

Gratiolet, P. 1850. *C.R. Acad. Sci. Paris*, **31**, 366-369.

1854. *Mémoire sur les plis cérébraux de l'homme et les primates*, Paris ; Arthus Bertrand, 104 pp. +atlas.

Gray, A. A. 1907. *The Labyrinth of Animals, including Mammals, Birds, Reptiles and Amphibians*, London ; Churchill.

Gray, A. P. 1954. *Mammalian Hybrids, a Checklist with Bibliography*, Farnham Royal ; Commonwealth Agricultural Bureau.

Gray, J. E. 1821. *London Med. Reposit.*, **15**, Pt. 1, 296-310.

1825. *Ann. Philos.*, n.s. **10**, 337-344.

1848. *Proc. zool. Soc. Lond.*, 56-57.

1849. *Proc. zool. Soc. Lond.*, 7-10.

1866. *Proc. zool. Soc. Lond.*, 168-169.

1866. *Proc. zool. Soc. Lond.*, 202-203.

1868. *Proc. zool. Soc. Lond.*, 180-182.

1870. *Catalogue of Monkeys, Lemurs and Fruit-eating Bats in the Collection of the British Museum*, London ; British Museum (Nat. Hist.).

Gregory, P. W. 1930. *Contrib. Embryol. Carneg. Instn.*, **21**, 141-168.

Gregory, W. K. 1916. *Bull. Amer. Mus. Nat. Hist.*, 35, 239-355.

1920. *Mem. Amer. Mus. Nat. Hist.*, n.s. 3, Pt. 2, 49-243.

1920-1921. *J. dent. Res.*, **2**, 89-183, 215-283, 357-426, 607-711 ; **3**, 87-228. (Also published in 1922 as a separate work by Williams and Wilkins, Baltimore, 548 pp.)

1922. *The Origin and Evolution of the Human Dentition*, Baltimore ; Williams and Wilkins.

1951. *Evolution Emerging*, New York ; Macmillan, 2 vols.

Gregory, W. K., and Hellman, M. 1939. *Ann. Transv. Mus.*, **29**, 339-373.

Gronov, L. T. 1763. *Zoophylaceum Gronovianum*, fasc. 1, 5.

Grünthal, E. 1934. *J. Psychol. Neurol.*, **46**, 41-112.

1949. *Dtsch. med. Wschr.*, **74**, 943.

Grzybowsky, J. 1926. *C.R. Séances Soc. Sc. Lettres de Varsovie*, 276-282.

Guillaume, P., and Meyerson, I. 1930a. *J. Psychol. norm. path.*, **27**, 92-97.

1930b. *J. Psychol. norm. path.*, **27**, 117-236.

1931. *J. Psychol. norm. path.*, **28**, 481-555.

1934. *J. Psychol. norm. path.*, **31**, 497-554.

1937. *J. Psychol. norm. path.*, **34**, 425-448.

Gunning, J. W. B. 1910. *Zool. Gart. Frankft.*, **51**, 54.

Gyldenstolpe, N. 1918–1920. *List of Mammals at present known to inhabit Siam*, *J. Siam Soc.*, **3**, 127-175.

Haagner, A. K. 1920. *South African Mammals*, London ; Witherby.
Haddow, A. J. 1945. *Proc. zool. Soc. Lond.*, **115**, 1-13.
    1952. *Proc. zool. Soc. Lond.*, **122**, 297-394.
Haddow, A. J., Dick, G. W. A., Lumsden, W. H. R., and Smithburn, K. C. 1951. *Trans. R. Soc. trop. Med. Hyg.*, **45**, 189.
Haddow, A. J., Gillet, J. D., and Highton, R. B. 1947. *Bull. ent. Res.*, **37**, 301-330.
Haddow, A. J., Smithburn, K. C., Mahaffy, A. F., and Bugher, J. C. 1947. *Trans. R. Soc. trop. Med. Hyg.*, **40**, 677-700.
Haeckel, E. H. 1866. *Generelle Morphologie der Organismen*, Berlin ; Reimer, 2 vols.
Hafferl, A. 1929. *Z. Anat. Entw.*, **88**, (5/6), 749-784.
Haggerty, M. E. 1909. *J. comp. Neurol.*, **19**, 337-455.
Haines, R. W. 1934. *J. Morphol.*, **56**, No. 1, 21-49.
Halde, J. B. du. 1736. *The General History of China*, London (English trans. from French by R. Brookes), 4 vols.
Hall, K. R. L. 1960. *Behaviour*, **16**, 261-294.
    1961. *Advancement Sci.*, **17**, (70) 559-567.
    1962. *Proc. zool. Soc. Lond.*, **139**, 181-220, 283-327.
    1963. *Symp. zool. Soc. Lond.*, No. 10, 1-28.
Hall, K. R. L., Boelkins, R. C., and Goswell, M. J. 1965. *Folia primat.*, **3**, 22-49.
Hamerton, A. E. 1937. *Proc. zool. Soc. Lond.*, (B) **107**, 443-478.
    1938. *Proc. zool. Soc. Lond.*, (B) **108**, 489-526.
    1942. *Brain*, **65**, 193-204.
Hamerton, J. L. 1963. *Symp. zool. Soc. Lond.*, No. 10, 211-219.
Hamilton, G. V. 1914. *J. Anim. Behav.*, **4**, 295-318.
Hamilton, J. B. 1938. *Anat. Rec.*, **70**, 533-540.
Hamlett, G. W. D. 1937. *Amer. J. Physiol.*, **118**, 664-666.
Hammack, B. A. 1960. *J. genet. Psychol.*, **96**, 275-299.
Hänel, H. 1932. *Morph. Jb.*, **71**, 1-76.
Hänström, B. 1948. *Acta Univ. Lund.*, n.s., Avd. 2, **44**, 10, 1-36.
    1952. *Ark. Zool. Stockholm*, **4**, 187-294.
    1958. In Höfer, Schultz and Starck (eds.), *Primatologia*, **3**, (1), 705-751, Basel ; Karger.
Hardy, A. 1960. *New Scientist*, **7**, 642-645, 730-733.
Harlow, H. F. 1932. *J. comp. Psychol.*, **4**, 241-252.
    1958. In Roe, A., and Simpson, G. G. (eds.), *Behaviour and Evolution*, New Haven ; Yale Univ. Press.
Harlow, H. F., 1960. *Amer. J. Orthopsychiatry*, **30**, 676-684.
Harlow, H. F., and Zimmerman, R. R. 1959. *Science*, **130**, (3373) 421-432.
Harman, P. J. 1943. *Proc. Soc. exp. Biol.*, N.Y., **54**, 297-298.
Harms, J. W. 1956a. In Höfer, Schultz and Starck (eds.), *Primatologia*, **1**, 561-660, Basel ; Karger.
    1956b. In Höfer, Schultz and Starck (eds.), *Primatologia*, **1**, 661-722, Basel ; Karger.
Harris, W. 1904. *J. Anat. Lond.*, **38**, 399-422.
    1939. *The Morphology of the Brachial Plexus*, Oxford ; University Press.
Harrison, R. G. 1949. *Proc. zool. Soc. Lond.*, **119**, 325-344.
Harrisson, B. 1962. *Orang-utan*, London ; Collins.

Hartman, C. G. 1927. *J. Mammal.*, **8**, 96-106.

    1928a. *Johns Hopk. Hosp. Bull.*, **43**, 33-51.

    1928b. *Science*, n.s. **67**, 15.

    1928c. *J. Mammal.*, **9**, 181-194.

    1929. *Quart. Rev. Biol.*, **4**, 373-388.

    1931. *J. Mammal.*, **12**, 129-142.

    1932. *Contr. Embryol. Carneg. Instn.*, **23**, 1-162.

    1938. In L. Brouha (ed.), *Les Hormones sexuelles*, Paris ; Hermann et Cie, 15-31.

Hartman, C. G., and Corner, G. W. 1941. *Contrib. Embryol. Carneg. Instn.*, **29**, 1-6.

Hartman, C. G., and Straus. 1933. *The Anatomy of the Rhesus Monkey* (*Macaca mulatta*), London ; Baillière, Tindall & Cox.

Hasselquist, F. 1757. *Iter Palestinum; eller resa til Heliga Landet*, Stockholm, also 1762, Rostock ; J. C. Koppe.

Haughton, S. 1864. *Proc. R. Irish Acad.*, **8**, 467-471.

von Hayek, H. 1960. In Höfer, Schultz and Starck (eds.), *Primatologia*, **3/2**, 588-625, Basel ; Karger.

Hayman, R. W. 1936. *Proc. zool. Soc. Lond.*, for 1935, 915-937.

    1940. See Sanderson, 1940.

Heape, W. 1894. *Phil. Trans.*, B., **185**, 411-471.

    1896. *Proc. roy. Soc.*, **60**, 202-205.

    1897. *Phil. Trans.*, B., **18**, 135-166.

    1898. *Trans. obstet. Soc. Lond.*, **40**, 161-174.

    1900. *Quart. J. micr. Sci.*, **44**, 1-70.

Heberer, G. 1956. In Höfer, Schultz and Starck (eds.), *Primatologia*, **1**, 379-561, Basel ; Karger.

Hecker, P. 1922. *Arch. Anat. Strasbourg*, **1**, 413-435.

    1927. *Arch. Anat. Strasbourg*, **6**, 283-320.

Hediger, H., and Zweifel, F. 1962. *Bibl. primat.*, **1**, 252-276.

Heller, E. 1913. *Smiths. misc. Coll.*, **61**, No. 17, 1-12.

Heller, J., and Sprinz, O. 1921. *Z. urol. Chir.*, **7**, 196-258.

Henckel, K. O. 1929. *Morph. Jb.*, **61**, 43-48.

Henderson, T. 1926. *Trans. ophthal. Soc. U.K.*, **46**, 280-286.

    1950. *Principles of Opthhalmology*, London ; Heinemann.

Hepburn, D. 1892. *J. Anat. Lond.*, **26**, 149-186, 324-356.

Herberg, H. P. 1935. *Z. mikr.-anat. Forsch.*, **37**, 1-15.

Hervé, G. 1882. *Bull. Soc. anthrop. Paris* (3), **5**, 792-794.

Hett, G. S., and Butterfield, H. G. 1909. *J. Anat. Lond.*, **44**, 35-55.

Hett, M. L. 1929. *Proc. zool. Soc. Lond.* (for 1928) ; (2), 843-915.

Heuglin, T. 1877. *Reise in Nord-Ost Afrika*, Braunschweig ; G. Westermann, 2 vols.

Heuser, C. H., and Streeter, G. L. 1941. *Contrib. Embryol. Carneg. Instn.*, Washington, **29**, 15-55.

Hill, J. E., and Carter, T. D. 1941. *Bull. Amer. Mus. nat. Hist.*, **78**, 1-211.

Hill, J. P. 1932. *Phil. Trans.*, B **221**, 45-178.

Hill, W. C. Osman. 1930. *J. Anat. Lond.*, **64**, 479-502.

    1933. *J. Anat. Lond.*, **68**, 19-38.

    1937a. *Ceylon J. Sci.* (B), **20**, 211-251.

    1937b. *Ceylon J. Sci* (B), **20**, 257.

    1937c. *Ceylon J. Sci.* (B), **20**, 369-389.

    1938. *Ceylon J. Sci.* (B), **21**, 66-67.

3 A

Hill, W. C. Osman. 1939a. *Ceylon J. Sci.*, (D), **5**, 9-15.

1939b. *Ceylon J. Sci.*, (D), **5**, 21-36.

1944. *Nature*, **153**, 199.

1949. *Proc. zool. Soc. Lond.*, **119**, 19-32.

1952. *Proc. zool. Soc. Lond.*, **122**, 127-186.

1953a. *Primates, Comparative Anatomy and Taxonomy, 1, Strepsirhini*, Edinburgh ; University Press.

1953b. *Proc. zool. Soc. Lond.*, **123**, 227-251.

1954a. *Proc. Anat. Soc. in J. Anat. Lond.*, **88**, 582.

1954b. *Man's Ancestry*, London ; Heinemann.

1955a. Glandes cutanées chez les primates. *VIe Congrès fédératif d'anatomie, Paris.* Résumés des communications, 102-103.

1955b. *Säuget. Mitt.*, **3**, 145-151.

1955c. *Primates, Comparative Anatomy and Taxonomy, 2, Haplorhini, Tarsioidea*, Edinburgh ; University Press.

1956. *Proc. Roy. Soc. Edinb.*, (B), **66**, 94-110.

1957a. *Primates, Comparative Anatomy and Taxonomy, 3, Platyrrhini, Hapalidae*, Edinburgh ; University Press.

1957b. *Proc. zool. Soc. Lond.*, **129**, 431-446.

1958. In Höfer, Schultz and Starck (eds.), *Primatologia*, **3**, 139-203, Basel ; Karger.

1960. *Primates, Comparative Anatomy and Toxonomy, 4, Platyrrhini, Cebidae*, Part A, Edinburgh ; University Press.

1962. *Primates, Comparative Anatomy and Taxonomy, 5, Platyrrhini, Cebidae*, Part B, Edinburgh ; University Press.

1964. *Proc. R. Soc. Edinb.*, **68**, (4), 302-326.

1965. *Morph. Jb.* (in the press).

Hill, W. C. Osman, and Booth, A. H. 1957. *J. Bombay nat. Hist. Soc.*, **54**, 309-321.

Hill, W. C. Osman, and Rewell, R. E. 1948. *Trans. zool. Soc. Lond.*, **26**, 119-256.

Hinde, R. A., and Rowell, T. E. 1962. *Proc. zool. Soc. Lond.*, **138**, 1-21.

Hines, M. 1933. In Hartman and Straus (eds.), *Anatomy of the Rhesus Monkey*, London ; Baillière, Tindall and Cox, 275-289.

1942. *Contrib. Embryol. Carneg. Instn.*, Washington, **196**, 155-209.

Hingston, R. W. G. 1920. *A Naturalist in Himalaya*, London ; Witherby.

Höfer, H. 1954a. *Morph. Jb.*, **94**, 275-334.

1954b. *Homo*, **5**, 52-72.

Hoffman, E. F., and Bast, T. H. 1930. *Anat. Rec.*, **46**, 333-347.

Hofmann, L. 1926. *Arch. Anat. Strasb.*, **6**, 141-186.

Hollister, N. 1912a. *Proc. biol. Soc.*, Washington, **25**, 93.

1912b. *Smiths. misc. Coll.*, **59**, No. 3, 1-2.

1920. *Smiths. misc. Coll.*, **72**, No. 2, 2.

1924. *Bull. U.S. nat. Mus.*, No. 99, 164 pp.

Hongo, T. T., and Luck, C. P. 1953. *J. Physiol.*, **122**, 570-581.

van Hoof, J. A. R. A. M. 1962. *Symp. zool. Soc. Lond.*, No. 8, 97-125.

1963. *Symp. zool. Soc. Lond.*, No. 10, 103-104.

Hoogstraal, H. 1956. Research Rep. N M 005 050.29.27, Cairo, Egypt : U.S. Naval Medical Res. Unit No. 3, 1101 pp.

Hooton, E. A. 1947. *Up from the Ape*, New York ; Macmillan. Revised ed.

Hopkins, G. H. E. 1949. *Proc. zool. Soc. Lond.*, **119**, 387-604.

Horsfield, T. 1851. *Catalogue of the Mammalia in the Museum of the Hon. East India Company*, London ; J. & H. Cox.

Howard-Miller, E. 1930. *Anat. Rec.*, **46**, 93-104.

Howell, A. B., and Straus, W. L. 1933a. *Proc. U.S. nat. Mus.*, **80**, No. 13, 31 pp.

1933b. In Hartman and Straus (eds.), *The Anatomy of the Rhesus Monkey*, London ; Baillière, Tindall & Cox.

Howell, F. C. (Ed.). 1962. *African Ecology and Human Evolution*, Viking Fund Publications in Anthropology, Chicago ; Aldine Press.

Hüber, E. 1933. In Hartman & Straus (eds.), *The Anatomy of the Rhesus Monkey*, London ; Baillière, Tindall & Cox, 176-188.

Hunt, W. A., Landis, C., and Jacobsen, C. F. 1937. *J. Psychol.*, Provincetown, **3**, 339-343.

Huntington, G. S. 1897. *Trans. N.Y. Acad. Sci.*, **16**, 82-95.

1913. *Stud. Cancer Columb. Univ.*, **4**, 73-113, 117-154a.

Hurme, V. O., and Van Wagenen, G. 1961. *Proc. Amer. Phil. Soc.*, **105**, No. 1, 105-140.

Hürzeler, J. 1948. *Schweiz. paläont. Abh.*, **66**, 1-46.

1958. *Verhandl. naturforsch. Ges.*, Basel, **69**, 1-48.

Huxley, T. H. 1863. *Man's Place in Nature*, London ; Williams and Norgate.

1872. *The Anatomy of Vertebrated Animals*, London ; Churchill.

Hyrtl, J. 1845. *Vergl. anat. und topogr. Studien über das innere Gehörorgan des Menschen und der Säugetiere*, Prague ; Ehrlich.

1872. *Denkschr. Akad. Wien*, **31**, Abt. 1, 107-140.

Illiger, J. K. W. 1811. *Prodromus systematis mammalium et avium*, Berolini ; Salfeld.

Imai, S. 1939. *Jap. J. med. Sci.*, **7**, 193.

Imanishi, K. 1957. *Primates: J. Primatol.*, **1**, 47-54.

1960. *Current Anthrop.*, **1**, 393-407.

Inay, M., Ruch, T. C., Finan, S., and Fulton, J. F. 1940. *Endocrinology*, **27**, 58-67.

Ingoldby, C. M. 1929. *Ann. Mag. nat. Hist.* (10), **3**, 511-529.

Inoue, M. 1958. *J. Primatol.*, **1**, 160 (in Japanese) summary.

Iperen, J. von, and Schoutman, F. 1784. *Verh. batavia Genoot.*, 1826, **2**, 235-256.

Itani, J. 1951. *Shezen*, **6**, No. 10, 45-49.

1959. *Primates: J. Primatol.*, **2**, 61-93.

Izawa, K., and Nishida, T. 1963. *Primates: J. Primatol.*, **4**, 67-88.

Jacob, G. F., and Tappen, N. C. 1957. *Nature*, Lond., **180**, 241-242.

1958. *Nature*, Lond., **181**, 197-198.

James, W. W. 1960. *The Jaws and Teeth of Primates*, London ; Pitman.

Janson, H. W. 1952. *Apes and Ape Lore in the Middle Ages and the Renaissance*, London ; The Warburg Institute, University of London.

Jardine, W. 1933. Mammalia, i, Monkeys : in *The Naturalist's Library*, Edinburgh ; Lizars, Stirling and Kennedy.

Jay, P. C. 1962. *Ann. N.Y. Acad. Sci.*, **102**, art. 2, 468-476.

1963. In Rheingold, H. L. (ed.), *Maternal Behaviour in Mammals*, New York ; John Wiley.

Jazuta, K. 1930. *Anat. Anz.*, **70**, 212-213.

1932. *Z. Anat. EntwGesch.*, **97**, 588-609.

Jeannin, A. 1936. *Les Mammifères sauvages du Caméroun*, Paris ; Paul Lechevalier.

Jennison, G. 1927. *Table of Gestation Periods and Number of Young*, London ; A. & C. Black.

Jentink, F. A. 1886. *Notes Leyden Mus.*, **8**, 55-57.

 1893. *Notes Leyden Mus.*, **15**, 265.

 1898. *Notes Leyden Mus.*, **20**, 233.

Joachimovits, R. 1928. *Biol. Generalis*, Vienne, **4**, 447-540.

 1931. *Zbl. Gynäk.*, **55**, 2697-2703.

 1935. *Biol. Generalis*, Vienne, **11**, 281-348.

Jobson, R. 1623. *The Golden Trade or a Discovery of the River Gambra*, London ; sold by N. Bourne.

Johnson, G. L. 1897. *Proc. zool. Soc. Lond.*, 183-188.

 1901. *Philos. Trans.*, (B), **194**, 1-82.

Johnstone, J. (Johnstonus ; Jonstonus). 1657. *Historiae naturalis de quadripedibus insectis, serpentibus, avibus, piscibus et cetis* etc., folio, Amstelodami, I. Jacob Fil. Schiffer.

Joleaud, L. 1931. *Bull. Soc. Accl., Paris*, 153-155.

Jones, M. L. 1962. *Lab. Primate Newsletter*, **1**, No. 3, 3-14.

Jones, T. S. 1950. *Sierra Leone Agriculture Notes*, No. 22.

Jost, A. 1922. *Arch. Anat. Strasb.*, **1**, 245-277.

Jouffroy, F. K. 1959a. *Bull. Mus. Hist. nat. Paris*, **31**, 330-333.

 1959b. *Bull. Mus. Hist. nat. Paris* (sér. 2), **31**, 209-216.

Jouffroy, F. K., and Lessertisseur, J. 1959. *Ann. Sci. nat. Zool.* (12 sér.), 211-235.

Kälin, J. 1960. *C.R. Acad. Sci. Paris*, **250**, 3359-3361.

 1961. *Z. wiss. Zool.*, **165**, 35-46.

 1962. *Bibl. primat.*, **1**, 32-42.

Katz, D., and Katz, R. 1936. *Proc. zool. Soc. Lond.*, 579-582.

 1937. *Proc. zool. Soc. Lond.*, **107A**, 183-186.

Kaup, J. J. 1835. *Das Thierreich in seinen Hauptformen sytematisch beschrieben*, Darmstadt ; J. P. Diehl, 1835-1837, 3 vols.

Kawamura, S. 1954. *Seibutu Sinka*, **2** (1) (in Japanese).

 1959. *Primates: J. Primatol.*, **2**, 43-60.

Keith, A. 1894. *J. Anat. Lond.*, **28**, 149-168.

 1895. *J. Anat. Lond.*, **29**, 453-458.

 1896a. *J. Anat. Lond.*, **30**, 275-279.

 1896b. *J. Anat. Lond.*, **30**, ii-iv.

 1899. *Proc. zool. Soc. Lond.*, 296-312.

 1902. *J. Anat. Lond.*, **37**, 18-40.

 1907. *Nature*, Lond., **65**, 16-21.

 1933. *Human Morphology and Embryology*, London ; Arnold.

Kelemen, G. 1932. *Monats. Ohrenheilk. u. Laryngo-Rhinol.*, **66.** Jhrg., 953-963.

 1939. *Arch. Sprach- und Stimmphysiol.*, **3**, 213-237.

Keller, O. 1887. *Thiere des Classischen Altertums in Culturgeschichtlicher Beziehung*, Innsbruck.

Kellogg, W. N., and Kellogg, L. A. 1933. *The Ape and the Child. A Study of Environmental Influence on Behaviour*, New York & London ; McGraw-Hill.

Kelly, H. A., and Hurdon, E. 1905. *The Vermiform Appendix and its Diseases*, Philadelphia & London ; W. B. Saunders.

Kempf, E. J. 1917. *Psychoanal. Rev.*, **4**, 127-154.

Kennard, M. A., and Willner, M. D. 1914. *Endocrinology*, **28**, 977-984.

Kenneth, J. H. 1947. *Gestation Periods. Technical Communication No. 5*, Imp. Bureau of Animal Breeding and Genetics, Edinburgh, 2 ed.

Khajuria, H. 1954a. *Rec. Ind. Mus.*, **52**, 95-99.

1954b. *Rec. Ind. Mus.*, **52**, 101-127.

1956. *Rec. Ind. Mus.*, **52**, 195-220.

Kidd, W. 1907. *The Sense of Touch in Mammals and Birds*, London ; A. & C. Black.

Kiesselbach, A., and Steiner, H. 1961. *Z. wiss. Zool.*, **165**, 88-107.

Kihara, T., and Teshima, G. 1935. *Fol. anat. japon.*, 303-324.

Kinsky, M. 1960. *Anat. Anz.*, **108**, 65-82.

Kirk, J. 1864. *Proc. zool. Soc. Lond.*, 649-660.

Kiss, F. 1931. *Arch. Mus. Paris* (6), **7**, 147-172.

1932. *Acta Univ. Szeged*, Sectio medicorum, **6**, 129-150.

Klaar, J., and Krasa, F. C. 1921. *Z. Anat. EntwGesch.*, **61**, 41-75.

Klaatsch, 1888. *Anat. Anz.*, **3**, 679-686.

1892. *Morph. Jb.*, **18**, 609-716.

Klaauw, C. J. van der. 1922. *Tijdsch. Ned. Dierk. Ver.* (2), D1. **18**, 135-176.

1923. *Z. Anat. EntwGesch.*, **69**, 32-83.

1924. *Ned. Tijdsch. Geneeskunde*, **68**, 2de heft, No. **15**.

Kleinschmidt, A., 1939. *Anat. Anz.*, **88**, 49-112.

Kluver, H. 1933. *Behaviour Mechanisms in Monkeys*, Chicago ; University Press.

Knottnerus-Meyer, T. C. B. 1909. *Sb. Ges. naturf. Fr. Berlin*, 84.

1928. *Birds and Beasts of the Roman Zoo*, London ; Allen & Unwin.

Knox, R. 1681. *Historical Relation of Ceylon, an Island in the East Indies*, Fol. London.

Koford, C. B. 1963. *Primate Social Behaviour*, Princeton ; N. J. van Nostrand Pub. Co.

Kohlbrugge, J. H. F. 1897. *Verh. Akad. Wet. Amst.*, Sect. 2, **5**, No. 6, 246 pp.

1903. *Z. Morph. Anthrop.*, **6**, 191-250.

Köhler, W. 1925. *The Mentality of Apes*, London ; Kegan Paul.

Kohne, G. 1944. *Veröff. Konstitutions-Wehrpathol.*, Jena, **53**, 78 pp.

Kohno, S. 1925. *Z. Anat. EntwGesch.*, **77**, 419-480.

Kohts, N. 1928a. *J. Psychol.*, **25**, 255-275.

1928b. *Sci. Mem. Mus. Darwinianum*, 368 pp.

1935. *Infant Ape and Human Child*, Moscow, Sci. Mem. Mus. Darwinianum.

1959. *Acad. Nauk. SSSR*, Moscow, 399 pp.

Kollmann, J. 1894. *Anat. Anz.*, **9**, ErgH., 198-205.

1900. *Anat. Anz.*, **17**, 465-479.

Kollmann, M. 1919. *Voyage de M. Guy Babault dans l'Afrique orientale anglaise. Mammifères*, Paris (no publisher indicated).

Kolmer, W. 1909. *Arch. mikr. Anat.*, **74**, 259-310.

1918. *Arch. mikr. Anat.*, **91**, 1-139.

1930. *Z. Anat. EntwGesch.*, **93**, 679-722.

Kortlandt, A., and Kooij, M. 1963. *Symp. zool. Soc. Lond.*, No. 10, 61-88.

Kosinki, C. 1927. *C.R. Ass. Anat.*, **22**, 121-133.

Kostanecki, K. 1926. *Bull. int. Acad. Cracovie* ; Cl. Sci. math. nat. ; Sér. B. Sci. nat., Supplément, 295 pp.

Kounin, J. S. 1938. *J. genet. Psychol.*, **52**, 375-383.

Kraus, R. 1897. *Wien. klin. Wochenschr.*, **10**, 736-738.

Krieg, W. J. S. 1964. *Collected Papers on the Cerebrum*, Springfield, Ill. ; C. C. Thomas, 320 pp.

Krise, G. M.   1960.   *Ann. N.Y. Acad. Sci.*, **85**, 803-810.

von Krogh, C.   1936.   *Anthrop. Anz.*, **13**, 89-100.

Krogman, W. M.   1930.   Studies in the growth-changes in the skull and face of Anthropoids and Old World Apes, *Amer. J. Anat.*, **46**, 315-353.

   1931.   *Amer. J. Anat.*, **47**, 89-115.

Krohn, P. I., and Zuckerman, S.   1937.   *J. Physiol.*, **88**, 369-387.

Kummer, H.   1956.   *Rev. Suisse Zool.*, **63**, 288-297.

   1957.   *Schweiz. Z. Psychol.*, Beiheft, **33**,

Kuntz, A.   1933.   In Hartman & Straus (eds.), *Anatomy of the Rhesus Monkey*, London ; Baillière, Tindall & Cox.

Lacroix, M. R.   1926.   *Arch. Anat. Strasb.*, **6**, 33-63.

Lai, L. Y. C., and Kirk, R. L.   1960.   *Nature*, Lond., **188**, 673-674.

Lancaster, D. G.   1953.   *A Check List of the Mammals of Northern Rhodesia*, Lusaka ; Govt. Printer.

Landsteiner, K.   1928.   *J. Immunol.*, **15**, 589-599.

Landsteiner, K., and Levine, P.   1928.   *J. exp. Med.*, **47**, 757-775.

Landsteiner, K., and Miller, C. P.   1925a.   *J. exp. Med.*, **42**, 841-852.

   1925b.   *J. exp. Med.*, **42**, 853-862.

   1925c.   *J. exp. Med.*, **42**, 863-872.

Landsteiner, K., and Wiener, A. S.   1937.   *J. Immunol.*, **33**, 19-23.

   1940.   *Proc. Soc. exp. Biol. Med.*, **43**, 223.

   1941.   *J. exp. Med.*, **74**, 309-320.

Lang, H.   1923.   *Amer. Mus. Nov.*, No. 87, 1-5.

Langley, J. N., and Sherrington, C. S.   1891.   *J. Physiol.*, Lond., **12**, 278-291.

Lapin, B. A., and Yakoleva, L. A.   1957.   *Tez. Dok. ras. Zas. Bur. med-biol. Nauk, A. M. N.*, U.S.S.R., 55-59 (in Russian).

Lashley, K. S.   1917.   *J. Anim. Behav.*, **7**, 178-186.

Lasinski, W.   1960.   In Höfer, Schultz and Starck (eds.), *Primatologia*, **2**, Teil 1, Lfg. **5**, Basel ; Karger.

Latreille, P. A.   1801.   *Histoire naturelle des singes*, Paris ; Dufart.

Leakey, L. S. B.   1962.   *Ann. Mag. nat. Hist.*, (13), **14**, 689-696.

Leakey, L. S. B., and Whitworth, T.   1958.   *Coryndon Mem. Mus. Occ. Pap.*, No. 6, 1-14.

Leboucq, G.   1928.   *C.R. Ass. Anat.*, **23**, 268-273.

   1929.   *Mem. Acad. R. Belg. Cl. Sci.* (2), **10**, No. 9, 1-56.

Leche, W.   1898-9.   Der Darmkanal und seine Anhänge : in Bronn's *Klassen u. Ordnungen des Thier-Reichs*, 5, Mammalia, 1037-1151, Leipzig ; Akademische Verlagsgesellschaft.

Leconte, J.   1857.   *Proc. Acad. Nat. Sci. Philadelphia*, **9**, 10-11.

Ledingham, J. C. G.   1904.   *Proc. anat. anthrop. Soc. Aberdeen*, 136-155.

Leger, M.   1922.   *C.R. Soc. Biol. Paris*, **86**, 835-837.

Le Guat, F.   1708.   *Voyages et aventures de François Leguat, et de ses compagnons en deux îles désertes des Indes Orientales*, London ; R. Bonwick, *et al.*

Lehmann, H.   1960.   *Intermedica*, **3**, 11 pp.

Leo Africanus.   1550.   *Descriptio Africae*, Roma ; Ramusio.

Lessertisseur, J.   1958.   *Ann. Sci. nat. Zool.*, Sér. 11, 77-104.

   1959.   *Bull. Mus. Nat. Hist. nat. Paris*, **31**, 322-329.

Lewis, W. H., and Hartman, C. G.   1933.   *Contrib. Embryol. Carneg. Instn.*, **24**, 187-201.
   1941.   *Contrib. Embryol. Carneg. Instn.*, **29**, 7-14.

Lichtenstein, A. A. H.   1791.   *Commentatio philologica de simiarum quotquot veteribus innotuerunt formis eorunque nominibus pro specimine methodi qua historia naturalis veterum ad systema naturae Linnaeanum exigenda atque adornanda*, Hamburg.

Lichtenstein, H.   1814.   *Ges. Nat. Freunde, Berlin*, Mag. 6, 152-171.

Lineback, P.   1933.   In Hartman and Straus (eds.), *The Anatomy of the Rhesus Monkey*, London ; Baillière, Tindall & Cox.

Linnaeus, C.   1748.   *Systema Naturae*, 6 ed., Holmiae ; L. Salvii.
   1758.   *Systema Naturae*, 10 ed., Holmiae ; L. Salvii.

Linton, R. G.   1905.   *Vet. J. Lond.*, n.s., **12**, 220-252.

Lipp, W.   1958.   In Höfer, Schultz and Starck (eds.), *Primatologia*, **3**, (1), 383-445, Basel ; Karger.

Locchi, R.   1932.   *Fol. clin. biol. S. Paulo*, **4**, 91-93.

Loghem, J. J. van.   1903.   *Petrus Camper*, **2**, 350-437.

Lönnberg, E.   1912.   *K. Svensk. Vet. Akad. Handl Stockholm*, **48**, 38.
   1917.   *K. Svensk. Vet. Akad. Handl. Stockholm*, **58**, No. 2, 32-35.
   1919.   *Rev. Zool. Bot. Afr.*, **7**, 107-154.

Lordat, J.   1804.   *Observations sur quelques points de l'anatomie de singe vert, et réflexions physiologiques sur le même sujet*, Paris ; l'imprimerie de Feugueray.

Lorenz, L. L. von.   1914.   *Anz. K. Akad. Wiss. Wien*, No. 18, 1-3.
   1915.   *Anz. K. Akad. Wiss. Wien*, **52**, 172.
   1917.   *Ann. Naturhist. Hofmus. Wien*, **31**, 227.
   1922.   *Ann. Naturhist. Hofmus. Wien*, **36**.

Lorin-Epstein, M.   1932.   *Z. Anat. EntwGesch.*, **97**, 68-144.

Loth, E.   1907.   *Korresp. Bl. dtsch. Ges. Anthrop.*, **38**, 169-172.
   1931.   *Anthropologie des parties molles*, Paris ; Masson.

Loveridge, A.   1928.   *Proc. U.S. Nat. Mus.*, **73**, 1-69.

Lubosch, W., and Schaller, J.   1928.   *Z. Anat. EntwGesch.*, **85**, 400-445.

Lucas, A. M.   1932.   *Amer. J. Anat.*, **50**, 141-177.

Luck, C. R.   1957.   In Worden and Lane-Petter (eds.), *U.F.A.W. Handbook on the Care and Management of Laboratory Animals*, London ; U.F.A.W.
   1959.   In Worden and Lane-Petter (eds.), *U.F.A.W. Handbook on the Care and Management of Laboratory Animals*, London, U.F.A.W., 2 ed.

Lumsden, W. H. R.   1951.   *J. Anim. Ecol.*, **20**, 11-30.

Lydekker, R.   1885.   *Catalogue of Fossil Mammals in the British Museum*, **1**, 7 et seq.
   1893.   *Royal Natural History*, **1**, London ; Warne.
   1902.   *Novit. Zool.*, **9**, 138-140.

Macalister, A.   1867.   *Proc. R. Irish Acad.*, **9**, 444-467.
   1868.   *Ann. Mag. nat. Hist.* (4), **1**, 313-322.
   1871.   *Ann. Mag. nat. Hist.* (4) **7**, 341-351.
   1878.   *Proc. R. Irish Acad.* (2) **1**, 501-506.
   1878.   *An Introduction to the Systematic Zoology and Morphology of Vertebrate Animals*, Dublin ; Hodges, Foster & Figgis : London ; Longmans.

Macfie, J. W. S.   1915.   *Ann. trop. Med. Parasit.*, **9**, 507-512.

Mackenzie, A. F.   1952.   *Proc. zool. Soc. Lond.*, **122**, 541.

Maclatchy, A. R., and Malbrant, R.   1947.   *Bull. Mus. Hist. nat. Paris* (2), **19**, 3, 254-256.

Macleod, J. 1881. *Arch. Biol.*, **2**, 127-144.

McCann, C. 1928. *J. Bombay nat. Hist. Soc.*, **33**, 192-194.

1933. *J. Bombay nat. Hist. Soc.*, **36**, 618-628.

McClure, C. F. W., and Silvester, C. F. 1909. *Anat. Rec.*, **3**, 534-552.

McDermott, W. C. 1935. *Trans. Amer. philol. Ass.*, **66**, 165-176.

1938. *The Ape in Antiquity*, Baltimore ; Johns Hopkins Press.

McDowell, A. A., Davis, R. T., and Steele, J. P. 1956. *Percept. motor skills.* Monogr. Suppl. 3.

McInnes, D. G. 1943. *J. East Afr., Uganda nat. Hist. Soc.*, **17**, 141-181.

Machado, A. B. M., and de Dio, J. A. 1963. *An. Fac. Med. Univ. Minas Gerais*, **20**, 123-229.

Machado, A. B. M., and Liberato, J. A. 1963. *Anat. Anz.* **113**, 45-57.

Mäkelä, O., Renkonen, O.-V., and Salonen, E. 1960. *Nature*, Lond., **185**, 852-853.

Makino, S. 1952. *Cytologia*, **16**, 288-301.

Malbrant, R. 1952. *Faune du centre africain français*, Paris ; Lechevalier.

Malbrant, R., and Maclatchy, A. 1949. *Faune de l'Équateur africain français*, Paris ; Lechevalier.

Mangubi-Kudrjavtzewa, A. 1909. *Arb. anat. Wiesbaden*, **39**, 697-736.

Mann, W. M. 1938. *Nat. Geogr. Mag.*, **73**, 615-655.

Manners-Smith, T. 1910, 1912. *J. Anat. Lond.*, **44**, 271-302 ; **45**, 23-64 ; **46**, 95-172.

Manteuffel-Szoege, L. 1933. *Arch. Nauk. Anthropol. Znych.*, **3**, No. 5, 1-40.

Marcgrav, G. L. 1648. *Historia rerum naturalium Brasiliae*, Amsterdam ; J. de Laet.

Marit, C. 1960. *Acta Anat.*, **41**, 115-130.

Marker, R. E., and Hartman, C. G. 1940. *J. biol. Chem.*, **133**, 529-537.

Marshall, F. H. A. 1922. *The Physiology of Reproduction*, 2 ed., 57 *et seq.*, London ; Longmans.

Martin, W. C. L. 1841. *General Introduction to the Natural History of Mammiferous Animals*, London ; Wright.

Maslow, A. H. 1933. *J. comp. Psychol.*, **16**, 187-197.

1936. *J. genet. Psychol.*, **48**, 261-277, 310-338.

Maslow, A. H., and Flanzbaum, S. 1936. *J. genet. Psychol.*, **48**, 278-309.

Mason, W. A. 1960. *J. abnorm. soc. Psychol.*, **60**, 100-104.

1963. In Southwick (ed.), *Primate Social Behaviour*, Princeton ; van Nostrand.

Mason, W. A., and Riopelle, A. J. 1964. *Ann. Rev. Psychol.*, **15**, 143-180.

Matschie, P. 1893. *Sb. Ges. naturf. F. Berlin*, 212-216.

Matschie, P. 1893. *Säugethiere des Togogebietes.* Mitt. aus den deutschen Schutzgebieten, **6**, 19 pp.

1898. *Sb. Ges. naturf. Fr. Berlin*, 75-81.

1905. *Sb. Ges. naturf. Fr. Berlin*, 262-276.

1913. *Ann. Soc. zool. Malac.*, Bruxelles, **47**, 45-81.

Matthews, W. D. 1915. *Bull. Amer. Mus. nat. Hist.*, **34**, 429-483.

Matthews, L. H. 1946. *Proc. zool. Soc. Lond.*, **116**, 339-346.

1956. *Trans. zool. Soc. Lond.*, **28**, 543-545.

Matthews, L. H., and Baxter, J. S. 1948. *Proc. zool. Soc. Lond.*, **118**, 144-145.

Mayr, E. 1942. *Systematics and the Origin of Species*, New York ; Columbia University Press.

Meckel, J. F. 1806. *Abhandlungen aus der menschlichen und vergleichenden Anatomie und Physiologie*, Halle ; Rengerschen Buchhandlung.

Meijere, J. C. H. de. 1894. *Morph. Jb.*, **21**, 312-424.

Meisenhelder, J. E., and Thompson, P. E. 1963. *J. Parasitol.*, **49**, 567.

Mergner, H. 1961. *Z. wiss. Zool.*, **165**, 140-185.

Mertens, R. 1929. *Z. Säugetierk.*, Berlin, **4**, 129-141.

Meyer, A. B. 1891. *Notes Leyden Mus.*, **13**, 63-64.

　1894. *Proc. zool. Soc. Lond.*, 83-84.

Miall, L. 1911. *History of Biology*, London ; Watts & Co.

Midlo, C. 1934. *Amer. J. phys. Anthrop.*, **19**, 337-389.

Midlo, C., and Cummins, H. 1942. Palmar and Plantar dermatoglyphics in Primates ; *Amer. Anat. Mem.*, No. 20, Philadelphia ; Wistar Inst.

Mijsberg, W. A. 1923. *Verh. k. Akad. Wetenschappen*, Amsterdam, Ser. 2, Pt. 13, No. 1, 1-92.

Miller, G. S. 1931. *Smiths. misc. Coll.*, **85**, No. 10, 13 pp.

　1933. In Hartman & Straus, *The Anatomy of the Rhesus Monkey* (Macaca mulatta), London ; Baillière, Tindall & Cox.

Miller, G. S., and Kellogg, R. 1955. *Bull. U.S. Nat. Mus.*, No. 205, 128.

Miller, R. A. 1947. *Amer. J. Anat.*, **80**, 117-142.

Minkowski, M. 1913. *Arb. hirnanat. Inst. Zürich*, **7**, 253-362.

　1920. *Verh. Schw. naturforsch. Ges.*, 101 sess., 231.

Mitchell, P. C. 1905a. *Proc. zool. Soc. Lond.*, **1**, 1.

　1905b. *Trans. zool. Soc. Lond.*, 17, 347-536.

　1916. *Proc. zool. Soc. Lond.*, **1**, 183-251.

Mivart, St. G. 1865a. *Proc. zool. Soc. Lond.*, 43-46.

　1865b. *Proc. zool. Soc. Lond.*, 545-592.

　1865c. *Proc. zool. Soc. Lond.*, 744.

　1868. *Philos. Trans.*, 1867, **157**, 299-429.

　1873. *Man and Apes*, London ; Hardwicke.

　1875. Art. APE in *Encyclopaedia Britannica*, ed. 9.

Miyadi, D. 1959. *Proc. 15th Inter. Confr. Zoology*, 857-860.

Mizuhara, H. 1957. Japanese Monkey, *San'iti-Syobo, Kyoto* (in Japanese).

Mizutani, A. 1960. *Folia anat. japon.*, **34**, 615-627.

Mollinson, T. *Arch. anthrop. Braunschw.*, **41**, 388-396.

　Z. Morph. Anthrop., **24**, 206-210.

Monard, A. 1933. *Bull. Soc. Neuchâtel Sci. Nat.*, **57**, 45-66.

　1938. *Arq. Mus. Bocage*, **9**, 121-149.

Monod, T. 1963. In Howell and Boulière (eds.), *African Ecology and Human Evolution*, Chicago ; Aldine Press.

Montagu, M. F. A. See Ashley-Montagu, M. F.

Monteiro, J. J. 1960. *Proc. zool. Soc. Lond.*, **28**, 112.

Moog, G. 1957. *Zool. Gart. Lpz.*, **23**, 220-223.

Moor, E. 1810. *The Hindu Pantheon*, London ; J. Johnson.

Moreau, R. E. 1952. *Proc. zool. Soc. Lond.*, **121**, 869-913.

Moreau, R. E., Hopkins, G. H. E., and Hayman, R. W. 1946. *Proc. zool. Soc. Lond.*, **115**, 387-447.

Moreau, R. E., and Pakenham, R. H. W. 1941. *Proc. zool. Soc. Lond.*, **110A**, 97-128.

Moreaux, R. 1909. *C.R. Soc. Biol. Paris*, **67**, 369-371.

Mori, M. 1959. *Folia anat. japon.*, 241-274.

Morton, D. J. 1922. *Amer. J. phys. Anthrop.*, **5**, 305-336.

　1924. *Amer. J. phys. Anthrop.*, **7**, 1-52.

　1926. *J. Morph.*, **43**, 149-179.

Mott, F., and Schuster, E. 1924. *Proc. zool. Soc. Lond.*, 1161-1170.

Muir, G. B. F. 1916. *J. Bombay nat. Hist. Soc.*, **24**, 353.

Müller, E. 1904. *Arb. anat. Inst. Wiesbaden*, **27**, 71-242.

Muller, S., and Schlegel, H. 1839–45. *Verhandelingen over de Natuurlijke Geschiedenis der Nederlandsche overzeesche bezittingen*, Leiden ; Luchtmans & van der Koek.

Münch, F. 1896. *Morph. Arb.*, **6**, 605-690.

Murie, J. 1866. *Proc. zool. Soc. Lond.*, 380-382.

Mussen, A. T. 1923. *J. Psychol. Neurol.*, **29**, 451-518.

Muthmann, E. 1913. *Arb. anat. Inst. Wiesbaden*, **48**, 65-114.

Napier, J. R. 1956. *J. Bone Joint Surg.*, **38B**, 902-913.

   1960. *Proc. zool. Soc. Lond.*, **134**, 647-657.

   1961. *Sym. zool. Soc. Lond.*, No. 5, 115-132.

   1962. *New Scientist*, **15**, 88-92.

   1963. *Symp. zool. Soc. Lond.*, No. 10, 183-196.

Napier, J. R., and Davis, P. R. 1959. *Fossil Mammals of Africa*, No. 16, Brit. Mus. (Nat. Hist.), London.

Narath, A. 1901. *Bibl. med. Verl. Stuttgart.*

Negus, V. E. 1929. *The Mechanism of the Larynx*, London ; Heinemann.

   1949. *The Comparative Anatomy and Physiology of the Larynx*, London ; Heinemann.

Neumann, O. 1902. *Sb. Ges. naturf. Fr. Berlin*, No. 3, 49-59 ; 93-102.

Neuville, H. 1922. *Anthropologie*, Paris, **32**, 409-451.

Newstead, R., and Todd, J. O. 1906. *Mem. Lpool Sch. trop. Med.*, **18**, 41-44.

Nieremberg, J. E. 1635. *Historia naturae*, Antverpiae ; B. Moreti.

Nishi, S. 1937. *Fol. anat. japon.*, **15**, 49-57.

Nissen, H. W. 1931. *Comp. Psychol. Monogr.*, 1931-32, **8**, No. 1, 122 pp.

Noback, C. R. 1943. Abstr. from Suppl. *Anat. Rec.*, **35** (3).

Nolte, A. 1955a. *Z. Tierpsychol.*, **12**, 77-87.

   1955b. *J. Bombay nat. Hist. Soc.*, **53**, 177-184.

Nonaka, I. 1959. *Folia anat. japon.*, **33**, 105-118.

Norris, C. E. 1955. *Loris*, **7**, 179-180.

Nuttall, G. H. F. 1904. *Blood Immunity and Blood Relationship*, Cambridge ; University Press.

Ockerse, T. 1959. *J. Dent. Assoc. S. Afr.*, **14**, 209-226.

   1963. *J. Dent. Ass. S. Afr.*, **18**, 1-6.

Oettlé, A. G. 1958. *S. Afr. J. med. Sci.*, **23**, 225-230.

   1959. *S. Afr. med. J.*, **33**, 327.

Ogilby, W. 1838. *The Menageries; the Natural History of Monkeys, Opossums and Lemurs*, London ; C. Knight.

Ogston, A. G., Philpot, J. St. L., and Zuckerman, S. 1939. *J. Endocrinol.*, **1**, 231-238.

Ohtsuka, N. 1937. *Acta psychol. Keijo*, **3**, 33-44.

Olivier, G., and Fontaine, M. 1956. *Mammalia*, Paris, **21**, 142-189.

Olivier, G., and Libersa, C. 1954. *Mammalia*, Paris, **18**, 287-328.

Olivier, G., and Piganiol, G. 1956. *Mammalia*, Paris, **21**, 430-451.

Olivier, G., and Pineau, H. 1957. *C.R. Acad. Sci. Paris*, **246**, 1292-1294.

Onelli, C. 1905. *Rev. Jard. zool. B. Aires* (2), **1**, 15-19.

Ono, M. 1936. *Fol. anat. japon.*, **14**, 537-543.

  1937. *Hokuetsu Ig. Z. Niigata*, **52**, 163-177.

  1939. *Abst. Jap. J. med. Sci.*, I, Anat., **7**, 258.

Ortmann, R. 1958. In Höfer, Schultz and Starck, *Primatologia*, **3**, (i), 355-382, Basel ; Karger.

Osborn, H. F. 1908. *Bull. Amer. Mus. nat. Hist.*, **24**, 265-272.

Osgood, W. H. 1932. *Field Mus. nat. Hist. Publ.*, **10**, 193-339.

Ottley, W. 1879. *Proc. zool. Soc. Lond.*, 121-128.

Oudemans, J. T. 1892. *Natuurk. Verh. Holland. Maatsch. Wet.*, (3) **5**, 96 pp.

Owen, R. 1832. *Proc. zool. Soc. Lond.*, 18-20.

  1843. *Rept. Brit. Assoc. Adv. Sci. for 1842*, 54-74.

  1846. *A History of British Fossil Mammals and Birds*, London ; van Voorst.

  1859. *On the Classification and Geographical Distribution of the Mammalia; to which is added an appendix "on the Gorilla"*, London ; Parker.

  1862. *Ann. Mag. nat. Hist.* (3), **10**, 240.

  1868. *Comparative Anatomy and Physiology of Vertebrates*, London ; Longmans, 3 vols.

Oxnard, E. E. 1863. *Symp. zool. Soc. Lond.*, No. 10, 165-182.

Ozansoy, F. 1956. *Bull. Min. Res. Expl. Inst. Turkey*, No. 49, 11-28, 29-48.

Pagenstecher, H. A. 1867. *Zool. Gart. Frankft.*, **8**, 121-137, 161-172.

Painter, T. S. 1924. *J. exp. Zool.*, **39**, 433-463.

Palay, S. L. 1953. *Amer. J. Anat.*, **93**, 107-142.

Palmer, T. S. 1904. Index generum mammalium, *U.S. Dept. Agric.: Div. Biol. Survey, North American Fauna*, No. 23, Washington.

Panerazi, G. 1931. *Atti Soc. Nat. Mat. Modena*, **62**, 135-153.

Pang-Chieh, T. 1956. *Zoo Life*, **12**, 61-63.

Park, W. W. 1957. *J. Anat.*, **91**, 369-373.

Parker, A. J. 1896. *J. Acad. nat. sci. Philad.*, **10**, 247-365.

Parker, G. H. 1922. *Smell, Taste and Allied Senses in the Vertebrates*, Philadelphia ; Lippincott.

Parkes, A. S. 1931. *Proc. Roy. Soc.*, B, **109**, 185-196.

Parkes, A. S., and Zuckerman, S. 1931. *J. Anat. Lond.*, **65**, Pt. 2, 272-276.

Parsons, F. G. 1899. *J. Anat. Lond.*, **34**, 41-68, 302-233.

Patten, C. J. 1899. *Trans. R. Acad. Med. Ire.*, **17**, 562-677.

Patterson, B. 1954. *Hum. Biol.*, **26**, 191-209.

Patterson, T. L. 1930. *Ann. N.Y. Acad. Sci.*, **32**, 53-86.

Paugger, J. 1923. *Z. Morph. Anthrop.*, **23**, 185-226.

Paulicki, A. 1872. *Mag. ges. Thierheilk.*, **38**, 1-117.

Paulicki, A., and Hilgendorf, F. 1869. *Virchows Arch.*, **46**, 60-67.

Paulli, S. 1900. *Morph. Jb.*, **28**, 483-564.

Pearson, K., and Bell, J. 1919. *Drap. Co. Mem. biom. Ser.*, Ser. 11, Pt. 1, Sect. 2, 225-539.

Pehrson, R. 1914. *Anat. Anz.*, **46**, 161-179.

Pennant, T. 1781. *History of Quadrupeds*, London ; White.

Perizzi, M. 1927. *Publ. League of Nations*, III, Health, **13**, 254-323.

Perrault, C. 1676. *Suite des mémoires pour servir à l'histoire des animaux*, Paris.

  1733. *Mém. Acad. r. Sci. Paris* (1666-1699), **3**, (2), 51-64.

Perret, J. L., and Aellen, V. 1956. *Rev. suisse Zool.*, **63**, 395-450.

Peters, H. B. 1932. *Z. Morph. Anthrop.*, **30**, 317-372.

Peters, W. 1865. *Proc. zool. Soc. Lond.*, 400-401.

Petrov, N. N., Krotkina, N. A., Vadova, A. V., and Postuikova, Z. A. 1951. *Dynamics of the Origin and Development of Malignant Growths in Monkeys*, Moscow ; Academy of Sciences.

Petter-Rousseau, A. 1962. *Mammalia*, Paris, **26**, (1), 88 pp.

Pettit, A. 1896. *J. Anat. Paris*, **32**, 301-361, 369-419.

Philippe, J. 1948. *Bull. Soc. Path. exot.*, **41**, 597-600.

Phillips, W. W. A. 1925. *Ceylon J. Sci.*, **13**, 261.

Pick, J. 1943. *Zoologica N.Y.*, **28**, 145-148.

Pilgrim, G. E. 1910. *Rec. Geol. Surv. India*, **40**, 63-71.

   1915. *Rec. Geol. Surv. India*, **45**, 1-174.

   1927. *Palaeont. India*, n.s., **14**, 1-24.

Pina, L. de. 1930. *Ann. Anat. path. Med.*, **7**, 783-788.

   1930 (1931). *15th Congr. int. Anthropol.*, Portugal, 73-78.

Pischinger, A. 1937. In Bolk, Göppert, Kallius and Lubosch (eds.), *Handbuch der vergleichenden Anatomie der Wirbeltiere*, **3**, Berlin und Wien.

Pitman, C. R. S. 1929. *Ann. Rep. Game Dept.*, Entebbe.

   1931. *A Game Warden among His Charges*, London ; Nisbet.

   1938. *Ann. Rept. Game Dept.*, Entebbe.

   1942. *A Game Warden takes Stock*, London ; Nisbet.

Piveteau, J. 1957. *Traité de paléontologie*, **7**, 1-675, Paris ; Masson.

Platzer, W. 1960. In Höfer, Schultz and Starck (eds.), *Primatologia*, **3/2**, 273-387, Basel ; Karger.

Plinius, C. Secundus. 23-79 A.D. *Plinius secundus noucomensis equestribus*, etc. (edition of 1516 consulted).

Plutchik, R. 1964. *Folia primat.*, **2**, 67-92.

Pocock, R. I. 1904. *Proc. zool. Soc. Lond.*, 433-436.

   1905. *Proc. zool. Soc. Lond.*, 169-180.

   1906. *Proc. zool. Soc. Lond.*, 558-570.

   1907. *Proc. zool. Soc. Lond.*, i, 677-746.

   1908. *Proc. zool. Soc. Lond.*, 158-160.

   1909. *Proc. zool. Soc. Lond.*, 545-546.

   1925. *Ann. Mag. nat. Hist.* (9), **16**, 264-268.

   1926a. *Proc. zool. Soc. Lond.*, 1925, 1479-1579.

   1926b. *Field*, **148**, 1154.

   1932. *J. Bombay nat. Hist. Soc.*, **35**, 530-551.

   1936. In Regan, C. T. (ed.), *Natural History*, London ; Ward Lock.

   1939. *The Fauna of British India* ; Mammalia I, London ; Taylor and Francis.

Pohl, L. 1928. *Z. anat. EntwGesch.*, **86**, 71-119.

Polak, C. 1908. *Verh. Akad. Wet. Amst.*, Sect. 2, **14**, No. 2, x+247 pp.

Poll, M. 1939. *Rev. zool. bot. Afr.*, **32**, 33-41.

   1940. *Rev. zool. bot. Afr.*, **33**, 126-135.

Pollak, W. 1926. *Anat. Anz.*, **61**, 202-204.

Polyak, S. 1957. *The Vertebrate Visual System. Its origin, structure and function and its manifestations in disease with an analysis of its role in Man.* Chicago ; University Press.

Ponder, E. O., Yeager, J. F., and Charipper, H. A. 1928. *Quart. J. exp. Physiol.*, **19**, 181-195.

   1929. *Zoologica*, N.Y., **11**, 9-18.

Poole, A. J., and Schantz, V. S. 1942. *Bull. U.S. nat. Mus.*, No. 178, xiii+705 pp.

Popowski, I. S. 1903. *Bull. Soc. Anthrop. Paris* (5), **4**, 596-607.

Popowsky, J. 1889. *Anat. Anz.*, **10**, 55-80, 99-114.

Pournelle, G. H. 1959. *Zoonooz*, **32**, 3-5.

    1960. *Sarawak Mus. J.*, **9**, 458-460.

    1962. *J. Mammal.*, **43**, 265-266.

Pousargues, E. 1896a. *Ann. Soc. nat.* (8), **3**, 211.

    1896b. *Bull. Mus. Paris*, **2**, 55-58.

    1897. *Bull. Mus. Paris*, **3**, 52.

Prakash, I. 1957. *J. Bombay nat. Hist. Soc.*, **55**, 154.

Prosper Alpinus (see Alpinus, Prosper).

Przibram, H. 1910. Bastardierung: in *Experimental-Zoologie*, **3**, 27-129, Leipzig and Vienna ; Deuticke.

Pucheran, J. 1857. *Rev. Mag. Zool.*, 195.

Purchas, S. 1625. *Hakluytus postumus, or Purchas his pilgrimes*, 4 ed., London ; Stansky and Fetherstone.

Pycraft, W. P. 1925. *Camouflage in Nature*, 2 ed., London ; Hutchinson.

Quain, R. 1895. *Elements of Anatomy*, London ; Longmans.

Rabb, G. B. 1958. *J. Mammal.*, **41**, 114.

Radlauer, C. 1908. *Morph. Jb.*, **38**, 322-447.

Raffles, T. S. 1821. *Trans Linn. Soc.*, **13**, 239-340.

Ranke, J. 1898. *S.B. bayer. Akad. Wiss.*, **28**, 227-270.

von Rapp, W. 1839. *Arch. Anat. Physiol. wiss. Med.*, 189-199.

Ratcliffe, H. L. 1942. *Rep. Penrose Res. Lab.*, Philadelphia, 11-25.

Raven, H. C. 1935. *Bull. Amer. Mus. nat. Hist.*, **68**, 179-293.

    1950. *The Anatomy of the Gorilla*, Raven Memorial Volume, New York ; Columbia University Press.

Raven, H. C., and Hill, J. E. 1942. *Amer. Mus. Nov.*, No. 1177, 1-6.

Ray, J. 1693. *Synopsis methodica animalium quadrupedum et serpenti generis*, London ; S. Smith & B. Walford.

Reade, W. W. 1864. *Savage Africa*, New York; Harpers.

Regan, C. T. 1930a. *Nature, Lond.*, **125**, 125-126.

    1930b. *Ann. Mag. nat. Hist.* (10), **6**, 383-392.

Regendanz, P., and Hoeppli, R. 1929. *Arch. Schiffs.- u. Tropenhyg.*, **33**, 376-387.

Reichenbach, H. G. L. 1862. *Die vollständigste Naturgeschichte der Affen*, Dresden ; Expedition des vollständigsten Naturgeschichte.

Reider, N. 1936. *Proc. zool. Soc. Lond.*, 433-453.

Remane, A. 1951. *Anat. Anz.*, **98**, 161-165.

    1960. In Höfer, Schultz and Starck (eds.), *Primatologia*, **3/2**, Basel ; Karger.

Retterer, E. 1907. *C.R. Soc. biol. Paris*, **63**, 148-150.

Retterer, E., and Neuville, H. 1914. *C.R. Soc. biol. Paris*, **77**, 535-538.

    1916. *C.R. Soc. biol. Paris*, **79**, 490-495.

Retzius, G. 1909. *Biol. Untersuch.*, n.f., **14**, 201-204.

    1912. *Biol. Untersuch.*, n.f., **17**, 100-108.

    1914. *Biol. Untersuch.*, n.f., **18**, 91-94.

Reuvens, C. L. 1890. *Notes Leyden Mus.*, **12**, 41-46.

Rex, H. 1887. *Morph. Jb.*, **12**, 275-285.

Ridgway, R. 1886. *A Nomenclature of Colors for Naturalists*, Boston ; Little, Brown & Co.

Rieffenstuhl, G. 1960. In Höfer, Schultz and Starck (eds.), *Primatologia*, **3/2**, 388-422.

Riegele, L. 1926. *Z. Anat. EntwGesch.*, **80**, 777-858.

Ripley, S. *Field Work on Langurs in Ceylon* (in press).

Ristori, G. 1890. *Boll. r. Com. Geol. Ital.*, (3), **1**, 178-226.

Roberts, A. 1931. *Ann. Transvaal Mus.*, **14**, 221-224.

   1932. *Ann. Transvaal Mus.*, **15**, 1-19.

   1948. *Ann. Transvaal Mus.*, **21**, 63-69.

   1951. *Mammals of South Africa*, Johannesburg ; Trustees of " The Mammals of South Africa " book fund.

Robinson, H. C., and Kloss, C. B. 1914. *Ann. Mag. nat. Hist.* (8) (13), 389-399.

Robinson, M., Richards, T. W., and Anderson, M. 1942. *Growth*, Ithaca, **6**, 127-133.

Rochebrune, A. T. 1883–5. *Faune de Sénégambie*, Paris ; Octave Doin.

Rode, P. 1936. *Mammalia*, Paris, **1**, 59-64.

   1937. *Les Primates de l'Afrique*, Paris ; Larose.

   1938a. *Mammalia*, Paris, **2**, 182-186.

   1938b. *Bull. Mus. Paris*, 2e sér., **10**, 202-251.

   1938c. *Scientia Bologna*, **64**, 27-36.

   1943. *Bull. Mus. Hist. nat. Paris* (2), **15**, 4, 151-154.

Rodriguez, H. 1937. *Endokrinologie*, **19**, 151-160.

Roginski, G. S. 1939. Quoted by Dembowski, J., *Die Psychologie der Affen*, Berlin, 1956, and by Bolwig (1961).

Rohen, J. W. 1961a. *Amer. J. Ophthal.*, **52**, 529-953.

   1961b. *Amer. J. Ophthal.*, **52**, 384-396.

   1962. In Höfer, Schultz and Starck (eds.), *Primatologia*, **2** (1), 6, Basel ; Karger.

Rojecki, F. 1889. *J. Anat. Paris*, **25**, 513-561.

Roosevelt, T. 1910. *African Game Trails*, Amer. ed., p. 474, London ed., p. 486.

Rosenfeld, M. C. 1898. *Arb. Anat. Inst. Wiesbaden*, **11**, 359-390.

Rosevear, D. R. 1953. *Check-list and Atlas of Nigerian Mammals*, Lagos ; Nigerian Govt. publ.

Rothfils, K. H., and Siminowitch, L. 1958. *Chromosoma*, **9**, 163-175.

Rowell, T. E., and Hinde, R. A. 1962. *Proc. zool. Soc. Lond.*, **138**, Pt. 2, 279-294.

Ruch, T. C. 1959. *Diseases of Laboratory Animals*, Philadelphia and London ; Sanders.

   1941. *Bibliographia primatologica*, Springfield, Ill., and Baltimore, Md. ; Thomas.

Ruge, G. 1887. *Untersuchungen über die Gesichtsmuskulatur der Primaten*, Leipzig ; Engelmann.

   1892. *Morph. Jb.*, **19**, 149-249.

   1893a. *Morph. Jb.*, **20**, 149-249.

   1893b. *Morph. Jb.*, **20**, 376-427.

   1906. *Morph. Jb.*, **36**, 93-275.

   1912. *Morph. Jb.*, **44**, 371-402.

   1917. In *Festschr. zum 70. Geburtstag von Dr. Emil Grasser*, Berlin ; Springer.

   1918. *Z. angew. Anat.*, **2**, 233-284.

   1920. *Morph. Jb.*, **51**, 141-146.

Rüppell, E. 1835–1840. *Neue Wirbelthiere zu der Fauna von Abyssinien gehörig entdeckt und beschrieben*, 1, Säugethiere und Vögel, Frankfurt ; S. Schmerber.

Russell, C. E. B.   1938.   *My Monkey Friends*, Bristol ; Arrowsmith.
Russell, J. S. R.   1893.   *Proc. Roy. Soc.*, **53**, 459-462.

Sachs, E.   1909.   *Brain*, **32**, 95-186.
Sahlins, M. D.   1959.   *Hum. Biol.*, **31**, 54-73.
Sahs, A. L.   1942.   *J. comp. Neurol.*, **76**, (3), 403-416.
de Saint-Denys, d'H.   1881.   *Bull. Soc. Acclim.* (3), **8**, 1-4.
St. Leger, J.   1929.   *Ann. Mag. nat. Hist.* (10), **4**, 290-294.
Sakurai, M., and Montagna, W.   1964.   *J. Invest. Dermat.*, **43**, 279-285.
Sanderson, I. T.   1940.   *Trans. zool. Soc. Lond.*, **24**, 623-725.
   1957.   *The Monkey Kingdom*, New York ; Hanover House.
   1961.   *Abominable Snowman*: *legend come to life*, Philadelphia and New York ; Chilton Co.
Sandys, O. C., and Zuckerman, S.   1938.   *J. Anat. Lond.*, **72**, 352-357.
Sauer, R. M., and Fegley, H. C.   1960.   *Ann. N.Y. Acad. Sci.*, **85**, 866-888.
Sawalischin, M.   1911.   *Morph. Jb.*, **42**, 557-663.
Schaefer, U.   1954.   *Z. Morph. Anthrop.*, **46**, 12-23.
Schaeffer, J. P.   1920.   *The Embryology, Development and Anatomy of the Nose, Para-nasal sinuses, Nasolacrimal Passageways and Olfactory Organ in Man*, Philadelphia ; Blakistons.
Schaller, G. B.   1963.   *The Mountain Gorilla; ecology and behaviour*, Chicago ; University Press.
Schlaginhaufen, O.   1905.   *Morph. Jb.*, **33**, 577-671.
Schlegel, H.   1876.   *Les singes, Monogr. 40 of Mus. Pays-bas*, **7**, Leyden.   356 pp.
Schlosser, M.   1911.   *Beitr. Paläont. Geol. Öst-Ung.*, **24**, 51-167.
Schlott, M.   1956.   *Zool. Gart. Lpz.*, **21**, 270-274.
Schneider, R.   1958a.   In Höfer, Schultz and Starck (eds.), *Primatologia*, **3**, (1), 5-40 ; Basel ; Karger.
   1958b.   In Höfer, Schultz and Starck (eds.), *Primatologia*, **3**, (1), 61-126, Basel ; Karger.
Schoeller, W., Dohrn, M., and Hohlweg, W.   1932.   *Arch. Gynäk.*, **150**, 126-134.
   1933.   *J. Lab. clin. Med.*, **18**, 926-932.
Schouteden, H.   1934.   *Rev. zool. bot. Afr.*, Tervueren, **25**, 291-304.
   1943.   *Rev. zool. bot. Afr.*, Tervueren, **36**, 102-125.
   1944.   *Rev. zool. bot. Afr.*, Tervueren, **38**, 192-196.
   1947.   *Ann. Mus. Congo Belge*, (2), **3**, 1.
Schouten, W.   1676.   *Ost-Indische Voyagie*, Amsterdam ; J. van Meurs.
Schouten, G.   1707.   *Voiage de Gautier Schouten aux Indes Orientales commencé l'an 1658 et fini l'an 1665*.   Traduit de Hollandais ; Amsterdam.
Schreiber, H.   1931.   *Morph. Jb.*, **67**, 621-676.
   1932.   *Morph. Jb.*, **69**, 221-315.
   1934.   *Anat. Anz.*, **78**, 369-429.
Schrier, A. M. (ed.).   1965.   *Lab. Primate Newsletter*, **4**, 2, 2.
Schultz, A. H.   1924.   *Amer. J. phys. Anthrop.*, **7**, 149-164.
   1926.   *Quart. Rev. Biol.*, **1**, 465.
   1929.   *Contr. Embryol. Carneg. Instn.*, No. 117, 213.
   1930.   *Hum. Biol.*, **2**, No. 3, 303-438.
   1931a.   *Scientific Monthly*, **33**, 385-412.
   1931b.   *Hum. Biol.*, **3**, No. 3, 304-321.

Schultz, A. H.   1933.   In Hartman and Straus (eds.), *The Anatomy of the Rhesus Monkey*, Baltimore ; Williams & Wilkins : London ; Baillière, Tindall & Cox.

1934.   *J. Mammal.*, **15**, 51-61.

1935.   *Amer. J. phys. Anthrop.*, **19**, 489-581.

1938.   *Anat. Rec.*, **72**, 387-394.

1940.   *Contrib. Embryol. Carneg. Instn.*, No. 518, 1-63.

1941.   *Contrib. Embryol. Carneg. Instn.*, No. 525, 57-110.

1948.   *Amer. J. phys. Anthrop.*, n.s., **6**, 1-23.

1949.   *Contr. Embryol. Carneg. Instn.*, **33**, 43-66.

1952.   *Homo*, **3**, 105-109.

1953.   *Amer. J. phys. Anthrop.*, n.s., **11**, 277-311.

1956.   In Höfer, Schultz and Starck (eds.), *Primatologia*, **1**, 887-964, Basel ; Karger.

1958.   In Höfer, Schultz and Starck (eds.), *Primatologia*, **3**, (1), 127-238, Basel ; Karger.

1958.   *Proc. zool. Soc. Lond.*, **130**, 79-105.

1963a.   *Folia primat.*, **1**, 150-171.

1963b.   *Symp. zool. Soc. Lond.*, No. 10, 199-206.

Schultz, A. H., and Straus, W. L.   1945.   *Proc. Amer. philos. Soc.*, **89**, 601-626.

Schultze, A.   1910.   *The Sultanate of Bornu*, trans. from German with additions by P. Askell Benton, London, New York, etc. ; H. Milford, 1913.

Schwalbe, G.   1889a.   *Anat. Anz.*, **4**, 176-189.

1889b.   *Arch. Anat. Physiol. Lpz.*, Anat. Abt., Suppl. Bd., 241-269.

1916a.   *Z. Morph. Anthrop.*, **19**, 149-254.

1916b.   *Z. Morph. Anthrop.*, **19**, 545-668.

Schwarz, E.   1910a.   *Ann. Mag. nat. Hist.* (8), **5**, 527-530.

1910b.   *Sb. Ges. naturf. Fr. Berlin*, 452-459.

1926a.   *Z. Säugetierk.*, **1**, 28-47.

1926b.   *Sb. Ges. naturf. Fr. Berlin*, 24-41.

1927a.   *Sb. Ges. naturf. Fr. Berlin* (for 1926), 32.

1927b.   *Ann. Mag. nat. Hist.* (9), **19**, 151-155.

1928a.   *Rev. zool. bot. Afr.*, **16**, 1-48.

1928b.   *Verh. V. internat. Kongr. Vererbungswiss.* Berlin, 1927, 1299-1319.

1928c.   *Ann. Mag. nat. Hist.*, (10), **1**, 649.

1932.   *Rev. zool. bot. Afr.*, **21**, (2), 251-254.

1933.   *Z. Säugetierk.*, **8**, 279.

1935.   *Bull. Soc. Portug. Sci. nat.*, **12**, 27-28.

1954.   *Rev. zool. bot. Afr.*, **49**, 328-336.

Sclater, P. L.   1860.   *Proc. zool. Soc. Lond.*, 245-247.

1866.   *Proc. zool. Soc. Lond.*, 79-80.

1893a.   *Proc. zool. Soc. Lond.*, 243-258.

1893b.   *Proc. zool. Soc. Lond.*, 441-444.

1893c.   *Proc. zool. Soc. Lond.*, 615-616.

1893d.   *Proc. zool. Soc. Lond.*, 691.

1894a.   *Proc. zool. Soc. Lond.*, 1.

1894b.   *Proc. zool. Soc. Lond.*, 484.

1894c.   *Proc. zool. Soc. Lond.*, for 1893, 723-729.

1896.   *Proc. zool. Soc. Lond.*, 780.

1898.   *Proc. zool. Soc. Lond.*, 586.

1902.   *Proc. zool. Soc. Lond.*, 237-238.

Sclater, W. L. 1900. *The Mammals of South Africa*, London ; Porter.

Scotin, —. 1739. *Nova Acta eruditorum*, Lipsiae, **8**, 564-565.

Scott, H. H. 1927. *Proc. zool. Soc. Lond.*, **48**, 560-563.

Scott, J. 1963. *Symp. zool. Soc. Lond.*, No. 10, 127-134.

Scott, J. P. 1958. *Animal Behaviour*, Chicago ; University Press.

Seib, G. A. 1931/1932. *Anat. Rec.*, **51**, 285-297.

Selenka, E. 1891/1892. *Stud. EntwGesch. Tiere*, **1**, 195-208.

   1898. *Biol. Zentrbl.*, **18**, 552-557, 808-809.

   1899. *Biol. Zentrbl.*, **19**, 175-176.

   1901. *S.B. bayer. Akad. Wiss.*, **31**, 3-14.

   1903. *Stud. EntwGesch. Tiere*, **3**, 329-373.

Sen, N. N., Das, K. C., and Aikat, B. K. 1960. *Nature*, Lond., **186**, 977-988.

Senyürek, M. S. 1953. *Belleten, Ankara*, **17**, 321-365.

   1960. *Anatolia, Ankara*, **5**, 47-85.

Sera, G. L. 1947. *Riv. Sci. Preistor.*, **2**, 2-29.

Setzer, H. W. 1956. *Proc. U.S. nat. Mus.*, **106**, 447-587.

Seydel, O. 1891. *Morph. Jb.*, **17**, 44-99.

Shantz, H. L., and Marbut, C. F. 1923. *Amer. Geogr. Soc.*, Research Series, No. 13.

Shellshear, J. 1927. *J. Anat., Lond.*, **61**, 268-279.

Sherborn, C. D. 1923. *Index Animalium*, **2**, London ; Trustees of British Mus.

Sherrington, C. S. 1892. *J. Physiol.*, **13**, 621-772.

   1893. *Phil. Trans.* (B), **184**, 641-763.

Shiwago, P. I. 1939. *Bull. biol. med. expl., U.R.S.S.*, **9**, 3-8.

Shortridge, C. C. 1934. *The Mammals of South-west Africa*, 2 vols., London ; Heinemann.

Shufeldt, R. W. 1914. *Ann. Carneg. Mus.*, **9**, 58-85.

Sidman, R. L., and Wislocki, G. B. 1954. *J. Histochem. Cytochem.*, **2**, 413-433.

Siepi, J. 1925. *Ann. Mus. Hist. nat. Marseille*, **20**, 107-115.

Sigel, W. L. 1883. *Zool. Gart. Frankft.*, **24**, 235-237.

Simonetta, A. 1957. *Att. Soc. Tosc. Sci. nat., B.*, **64**, 53-112.

Simons, E. L. 1951. *Amer. Mus. Nov.*, **1976**, 1-16.

   1960. *Nature*, Lond., **186**, 824-826.

   1962. *Postilla*, Yale, No. 64, 12 pp.

   1963. In Buettner-Janusch, J. (ed.), *Evolutionary and Genetic Biology of Primates*, **1**, 65-129, New York & London ; Academic Press.

   1964. *Scientific American*, **211**, 50-62.

Simpson, G. G. 1931. *Bull. Amer. Mus. nat. Hist.*, **59**, 259-293.

   1945. *Bull. Amer. Mus. nat. Hist.*, **85**, xvi + 1-350.

Singh, I. 1963. *J. Anat. Lond.*, **97**, 107-110.

Sjöstrand, F. S. 1959. *Erg. Biol.*, **21**, 128-160.

   1961. In Smelser (ed.), Electron microscopy of the retina, *The Structure of the Eye*, New York ; Academic Press.

Smith, L. 1958. *Longevity Records of Monkeys*, M.S.S.

Smith, R. M., and Rubinstein, B. B. 1940. *Endocrinology*, **26**, 667-679.

Smith, W. 1744. *A New Voyage to Guinea*, London.

Sommer, A. 1906. *Das Muskelsystem des Gorilla*, Habilitationschrift (Med.), Würzburg, Jena, 128 pp.

   1907. *Jena Z. Naturw.*, **42**, 181-308.

3 B

Sonntag, C. F. 1921a. *Proc. zool. Soc. Lond.*, 277-322.

 1921b. *Proc. zool. Soc. Lond.*, 757-767.

 1922. *Proc. zool. Soc. Lond.*, (1), 429-453.

 1924. *The Morphology and Evolution of the Apes and Man*, London ; Bale Sons & Danielsson.

 1925. *Proc. zool. Soc. Lond.*, (1), 701-762.

Southwick, C. H. 1962. *Ann. N.Y. Acad. Sci.*, **102**, 181-514.

Southwick, C. H. (ed.). 1963. *Primate Social Behaviour*, Princeton, N.J. ; D. van Nostrand.

Southwick, F. L., Beg, M. A., and Siddiqui, R. 1961. *Ecology*, **42**, Pt. 3, 538-547 ; **42**, 698-710.

Speransky, A. D. 1926. *Z. Anat. EntwGesch.*, **78**, 111-135.

Sperber, I. 1944. *Zool. Bidrag.*, Uppsala, **22**, 249-432.

Sperino, G. 1827. *Anatomia del cimpanze* (Anthropopithecus troglodytes, Trouessart) *in rapporto con quella degli altri antropoide e dell' uomo.* Torino ; Unione tipografico.

Spiegel, A. 1929. *Zool. Anz.*, **81**, 45-65.

 1930. *Arch. Gynäk.*, Berlin, **142**, 561-591.

 1950. *Arch. Gynäk.*, **177**, 590-629.

 1954. *Zool. Gart. Lpz.*, **20**, 227-270.

Spiert, H. 1942. *Quart. Rev. Biol.*, **17**, 59.

Spinage, C. A. 1962. *Animals of East Africa*, London ; Collins.

Sprague, J. M. 1944. *Anat. Rec.*, **90**, 197-208.

Ssokolow, P. 1933. *Z. Anat. EntwGesch.*, 100, 194-217.

Stamm, T. T. 1931. *J. Anat. Lond.*, **66**, 80-83.

Starck, D. 1956. *Mitt. naturf. Ges. Bern*, N.F., **14**, 21-32.

 1957. *Z. Säugetierk.*, **22**, 77-86.

 1958. In Höfer, Schultz and Starck (eds.), *Primatologia*, **3/1**, 446-506, Basel ; Karger.

 1960. In Höfer, Schultz and Starck (eds.), *Primatologia*, **3/2**, Basel ; Karger.

Starck, D., and Frick, H. 1958. *Zool. Jb. Abt. Syst. Ökol. Geogr. Tiere*, **86**, 41-70.

Stechow, E. 1949. *Nature*, Lond., **164**, 484.

Stephan, H. 1963. In Bargmann and Schade (eds.), *Progress in Brain Research*, 3, Amsterdam and London and New York ; Elsevier.

Steslicka, W. 1957. *Przegl. zool.*, **1**, 124-135.

Stevenson, H. J. 1947. *Wild Life in South Africa*, London ; Cassell.

Stewart, T. D. 1933. In Hartman and Straus (eds.), *The Anatomy of the Rhesus Monkey*, London ; Baillière, Tindall & Cox.

Stewart, W. H. 1886. *Zoologist*, (3), **10**, 483.

Stiles, C. W., and Nolan, M. O. 1929. *Hygienic Lab. Bull.*, No. 152, U.S. Treasury Dept., Public Health Service, Washington, 491-580.

Stiles, C. W., and Orleman, M. B. 1926. *J. Mammal.*, **7**, 48-53.

Stilwell, D. L. 1956. *Anat. Rec.*, **125**, 138-170.

Stott, K. 1960. *J. Mammal.*, **41**, 400-401.

Strabo. 1st cent. b.c. *Geographia*, Aldine ed. 1516, Venice.

Strand, E. 1931. *Fol. zool. hydrobiol.*, Riga, 23, 12, Vol. 3, 191-198.

Straus, W. L. 1930. *Quart. Rev. Biol.*, **5**, 261-317.

 1934. *J. Anat. Lond.*, **69**, 93-108.

 1936. *Proc. Amer. phil. Soc.*, **76**, 1-85.

 1960. *Anat. Rec.*, **138**, 93-104.

 1962. *Bibl. primat.*, **1**, 197-216.

Straus, W. B., and Arcadi, J. A. 1958. In Höfer, Schultz and Starck (eds.), *Primato-logia*, **3**/**1**, 507-541, Basel ; Karger.

Struthers, J. 1893–1894. *Edinb. med. J.*, **39**, 289, 438.

Swindler, D. R., Gavan, J. A., and Turner, W. M. 1963. *Hum. Biol.*, **35**, 104-122.

Swindler, D. R., and Sassoumi, V. 1962. *The Angle Orthodontist*, **32**, 27-37.

Swynnerton, G. H. 1945. *Proc. zool. Soc. Lond.*, **115**, 49-84.

Swynnerton, G. H., and Hayman, R. W. 1951. *J. E. Afr. nat. Hist. Soc.*, **20**, 274-392.

Sykes, W. H. 1831. *Proc. zool. Soc. Lond.*, **99**, 105-106.

   1832. *Proc. zool. Soc. Lond.*, 18-20.

Tachibana, O. 1936. *Kaibo Z.*, Tokyo, **9**, 238-294 (in Japanese).

Takeshita, H. 1962. *Primates*, **3**, No. 1, 59-72.

Tanaka, R. 1961. *Folia anat. japon.*, **37**, 1-17.

Tanja, T. 1891. *Morph. Jb.*, **17**, 145-197.

Tappen, N. C. 1958. *J. Mammal.*, **39**, 584.

   1960a. *Current Anthrop.*, **1**, 91-120.

   1960b. *S. Afr. J. Sci.*, **56**, 57-63.

   1960c. *Bull. Tulane Univ. Med. Fac.*, **20**, 17-22.

   1963. *Sym. zool. Soc. Lond.*, No. 10, 267-276.

   1964. *Current Anthrop.*, **5**, 339-340.

Tate, G. H. H. 1944. *A List of the Mammals of the Japanese War Area*, Pts. 1-4, Amer. Mus. nat. Hist., New York.

Tennent, J. E. 1861. *Sketches of the Natural History of Ceylon*, London ; Longmans, Green.

Teshima, G. 1935. *Fol. anat. japon.*, **13**, 251-288.

Theile, W. 1852. *Arch. Anat. Physiol. wiss. Med.*, 419-449.

Themido, A. 1928. *Mem. Est. Mus. Zool. Univ. Coimbra*, Ser. 1, No. 19, 1-30.

Thomas, O. 1893. *Proc. zool. Soc. Lond.*, 3.

   1900. *Proc. zool. Soc. Lond.*, 800-807.

   1902. *Ann. Mag. nat. Hist.* (7), **10**, 243-244.

   1904. *Proc. zool. Soc. Lond.*, ii, 183-193.

   1906. *Ann. Mag. nat. Hist.* (7), **17**, 173-179.

   1907. *Proc. zool. Soc. Lond.*, 2-3.

   1909. *Ann. Mag. nat. Hist.* (8), **4**, 542-543.

   1916. *Ann. Mag. nat. Hist.* (8), **17**, 179-181.

   1923. *Ann. Mag. nat. Hist.* (9), **11**, 607.

   1926. *Proc. zool. Soc. Lond.*, 285-312.

Thomas, O., and Hinton, M. A. C. 1923. *Proc. zool. Soc. Lond.*, 247-271.

Thomas, O., and Schwann, H. 1904. *Proc. zool. Soc. Lond.*, i, 459-465.

   1906. *Proc. zool. Soc. Lond.*, 779-782.

Thomas, O., and Wroughton, R. C. 1908. *Proc. zool. Soc. Lond.*, 164-173.

   1910. *Trans. zool. Soc. Lond.*, **19**, 485.

Thomsen, O., and Kemp, T. 1930. *Z. Immunitätsforsch.*, Jena, **67**, 251-265.

Tinklepaugh, O. L. 1931. *J. Mammal.*, **12**, 430.

Tinklepaugh, O. L., and Hartman, C. G. 1932. *J. genet. Psychol.*, **40**, 257-286.

Todd, T. W. 1912. *Anat. Anz.*, **42**, 129-144.

   1922. *Anat. Rec.*, **24**, 261-286.

Tokarski, S. 1931. *C.R. Ass. Anat.*, **26**, 507-510.

   1935–1936. *Fol. morph. Warszawa*, **6**, 58-65.

Tokuda, K. 1962. *Primates*, **3**, No. 2, 1-40.

Toldt, K. 1921. *Mitt. Anthrop. Ges. Wien*, **51**, 161-183.

Tomilin, M. I. 1940. *Proc. zool. Soc. Lond.*, **110A**, 43-45.

Topsell, E. 1658. *The History of Four-footed Beasts and Serpents . . . collected out of the Writings of Conradus Gesner and other Authors.* London ; E. Cotes.

Trendelenburg, W., and Schmidt, J. 1930. *Z. vergl. Physiol.*, **12**, 249-278.

Treves, F. 1885. *Brit. med. J.*, **1**, 415-419, 470-474, 527-530, 580-583.

Trevor, J. C. 1963. *Symp. zool. Soc. Lond.*, No. 10, 197-198.

Trouessart, E. L. 1897–1899. *Catalogus mammalium tam viventium quam fossilium.* Nova editio, Berlin ; Friedländer.

Truex, R. C., and Warshaw, L. J. 1942. *Anat. Rec.*, **82**, 361-372.

Trumble, H. C. 1934. *Brit. J. Surg.*, **21**, 664-676.

Tschachmachtschjan, H. 1912. *Morph. Jb.*, **44**, 297-370.

Tsouras, J. I. 1954 (1955). *Prakt. Akad. Athens*, **29**, 383-410.

Tsubouchi, R. 1961. *Folia anat. japon.*, **37**, 161-168.

Tuckerman, F. 1890. *J. Anat. Lond.*, **25**, 505.

  1892. *J. Anat. Lond.*, **26**, 391-393.

Tulp, N. 1641. *Observationum medicarum*, III, Amsterdam ; L. Elzevirum.

Turner, C. W., and Allen, E. 1933. *Anat. Rec.*, **55**, Suppl., 80.

Turner, W. 1878 (1879). *Philos. Trans.*, **169**, 523-562.

  1890. *The Convolutions of the Brain*, London ; Williams and Norgate. Also in *J. Anat. Lond.*, **25**, 105-133 (1891).

Tyson, E. 1699. *Orang-utang, sive homo sylvestris: or the Anatomy of a Pygmie compared with that of a Monkey, an Ape and a Man. To which is added a philological essay concerning the pygmies, the cynocephali, the satyrs and the sphinges of the ancients*, London ; Thomas Bennet.

Ullrich, W. 1961. *Zool. Gart. Lpz.*, **25**, 305-368.

Urbain, A. 1933. *Bull. Ass. franç. Sci.*, **62**, 191.

  1940. *Sciences*, **35**, 53.

  1942. *C.R. Soc. Biol. Paris*, **136**, 637-638.

  1944. *Bull. Soc. sci. Hyg. aliment.*, **32**, 137.

  1949. *Bull. Acad. vet. franç.*, **22**, 349-351.

Urbain, A., and Nouvel, J. C. G. 1954. *Endeavour*, **13**, 184-189.

Utschneider, A. 1892. *Münch. med. Abh.*, **26**, VII R. (1), 1-32.

della Valle, P. 1665. *Travels in East India and Arabia deserta*, etc., London ; Translated by G. Havers.

  1745. *Voyages de Pietro della Valle*, Paris ; d'Espilly.

Vallois, H. V. 1912. *Bull. Soc. anthrop. Paris*, (6), **3**, 247-291.

  1914. *Étude anatomique de l'articulation du genou chez les Primates*, Montpellier ; L'Abeille.

  1919. (1920). *Bull. Mém. Soc. anthrop. Paris*, (6), **10**, 21-45, 80-107.

  1927. *Bull. Mus. Hist. nat. Paris*, **33**, 65-70.

  1955. In Grassé (ed.), *Traité de zoologie*, **17**, Paris ; Masson.

Verheyen, W. 1957. *Ann. Mus. Congo belge, zool.*, **62**, 1-94.

  1959. *Rev. zool. bot. Afr.*, **60**, 28-30.

  1962. *Ann. Mus. roy. Afr. centr.*, Tervueren, (8), No. 105, 255 pp.

Vermes, E., and Weidholz, A. 1930. *Zool. Gart. Lpz.*, **3**, 28-34.

Verneau, R. 1903. *Les Anciens Patagons*, Monaco ; Contribution à l'étude des races précolombiennes de l'Amérique de Sud, 342 pp.

Verschuren, J. (n.d.) *Exploration du Parc National de Garumba*, (9), Inst. Parcs Nat. Congo Belge, Bruxelles, 1-225.

Vicq d'Azyr, F. 1792. Système anatomique in *Encyclopédie méthodique*, Paris, **2**,

de Visme, S. 1769. *Philos. Trans.*, **59**, 71-73.

Voeltzkow, A. 1903. *Z. Ges. Erdkunde*, Berlin, 560-591.

Vogel, C. 1962. *Z. Morph. Anthrop.*, **52**, 306-332.

Vogt, C. 1909. *J. Psychol. Neurol.*, **12**, 285-324.

de Vore, I. 1962. *The Social Behaviour and Organization of Baboon Troops*, Ph.D. thesis, University of Chicago.

    1963a. In Rheingold (ed.), *Maternal Behaviour in Mammals*, New York ; John Wiley.

    1963b. In Washburn (ed.), *Classification and Human Evolution*, Chicago ; Aldine Press.

de Vore, I., and Lee, R. 1963. *Folia primat.*, **1**, 66-72.

de Vore, I., and Washburn, S. L. 1960. *Baboon Behaviour*, 16-mm. film, Berkeley ; University Extension, University of California.

    1962. *La Terre et la vie* (2), 133-149.

    1963. In Howell and Bourlière (eds.), *African Ecology and Human Evolution*, Chicago ; Aldine Publ. Co.

Voronoff, S., and Alexandresco, G. 1930. *1er Congr. Internat. Microbiol.*, Paris, **2**, 198.

Vrolik, W. 1847. Art. ' Quadrumana ' in Todd, R. B., *Cyclopaedia of Anatomy and Physiology*, London ; Longman, Brown.

van Wagenen, G. 1936. *Anat. Rec.*, **66**, 411-421.

    1941. *Proc. Soc. expl. Biol.*, N.Y., **48**, 133-134.

    1945. *Endocrinology*, **37**, 307-312.

    1949. *Endocrinology*, **45**, 544-546.

    1950. In Farris (ed.), *The Care and Breeding of Laboratory Animals*, New York.

    1954. *Anat. Rec.*, **118**, 231-243.

Wagner, R. 1855. *Säugethiere*, **5**, 38 et seq.

Waldeyer, W. 1889. *S.B. preuss. Akad. Wiss.* (2), 679-710.

Walker, A. E. 1937. *J. comp. Neurol.*, **66**, 145-155.

Wallis, H. M. 1897. *Proc. zool. Soc. Lond.*, 298-310.

Walton, A. 1960. In Marshall, F. H. A. (ed.), *Physiology of Reproduction*, 3 ed., I, (Pt. 2), 130-160.

Wang, P. H. 1960. *Acta med. Nagasakiensia*, **5**, 67-75.

Washburn, S. L. 1942. *Hum. Biol.*, **14**, 444-472.

    1943. *Amer. J. Anat.*, **72**, 339-360.

Washburn, S. L. 1963. In *Classification and Human Evolution*, Viking Fund Publ. Anthrop., **37**, 190-203, Chicago ; Aldine Press.

Washburn, S. L., and de Vore, I. 1961. *Sci. Amer.*, **204**, 62-71.

Waterhouse, G. R. 1838. *Proc. zool. Soc. Lond.*, 61-62.

    1841. *Proc. zool. Soc. Lond.*, 71.

Waterman, H. C. 1929. *Bull. Amer. Mus. nat. Hist.*, **58**, 585-642.

Watson, J. M. 1951. *Uganda J.*, **15**, 193-202.

Wegner, R. N. 1956. Studien über Nasennebenhöhlen des Schädels. *Wiss. Zts. der Ernst Moritz Arndt-Universität*, Greifswald.

Weidenreich, F., Baum, H., and Trautmann, A. 1933. In *Handbuch d. vergl. Anat. d. Wirbeltiere*, Wien ; Urban & Schwarzenburg.

Weinberg, M. 1906. *C.R. Soc. Biol. Paris*, **60**, 844-845.

Weinbrenn, C. 1930. *S. Afr. J. Sci.*, **26**, 501-520.

Weinert, H. 1925. *Z. Morph. Anthrop.*, **25**, 243-357.

Wen, I. C. 1930. *Contr. Embryol. Carneg. Instn.*, **22**, 109-134.

Werner, C. F. 1960. In Höfer, Schultz and Starck (eds.), *Primatologia*, **2/1**, Basel ; Karger.

Werth, E. 1918. *S.B. Ges. naturf. Fr. Berlin*, 327-345.

von Wettstein, O. 1918. *Denksch. Akad. Wiss. Wien*, **19**, 535-693.

Whitnall, S. E. 1911. *J. Anat. Lond.*, **46**, 36.

Wiener, A. S. 1938. *J. Immunol.*, **34**, 11-18.

    1943. *Amer. Naturalist*, **77**, 199-210.

Wiener, A. S., Candela, P. B., and Goss, L. J. 1942. *J. Immunol.*, **45**, 299-235.

Wiener, A. S., Gavan, J. A., and Gordon, E. B. 1953. *Amer. J. phys. Anthrop.*, **11**, 39-45.

Wilder, B. G. 1861. *Boston J. nat. Hist.*, **7**, 353-384.

Wilhelmi, R. W. 1942. *Biol. Bull.*, **82**, (2), 179-189.

William, R. 1912. *Anat. Anz.*, **42**, 145-153.

Wilson, H. G. 1910. *Ann. Otol. Rhin. Laryng.*, **19**, 951.

Wilson, M. 1937. *Just Monkeys*, London ; Country Life Ltd.

Winckler, G. 1926. *Arch. Anat. Strasb.*, **6**, 1-32.

    1930. *Arch. Anat. Strasb.*, **12**, 151-227.

    1932. *Arch. Anat. Strasb.*, **14**, 301-386.

    1934. *Arch. Anat. Strasb.*, **18**, 181-219.

    1936. *Arch. Anat. Strasb.*, **23**, 127-164.

Windle, B. C. A. 1887. *Proc. Bgham. nat. Hist. Soc.*, **6**, 22-25.

    1889. *J. Anat. Lond.*, **24**, (n.s.4), 72-84.

Windle, F. W. 1931. *J. comp. Neurol.*, **53**, 115-127.

Winge, H. 1924. *Pattedyr Slaegter*, II, Copenhagen ; H. Hagerups Forlag.

Wislocki, G. B. 1929. *Contr. Embryol. Carneg. Instn.*, **20**, 51-80.

    1932. *Contr. Embryol. Carneg. Instn.*, **135**, 163-204.

    1933a. *Anat. Rec.*, **57**, 133-148.

    1933b. In Hartman and Straus (eds.), *The Anatomy of the Rhesus Monkey*, London ; Baillière, Tindall & Cox.

    1936. *Hum. Biol.*, **8**, 309-347.

    1952. *Amer. J. Anat.*, **91**, 233-262.

Wislocki, G. B., and Bennet, H. S. 1943. *Amer. J. Anat.*, **73**, 335-449.

Wislocki, G. B., and Hartman, C. G. 1929. *Johns Hopkins Hosp. Bull.*, **44**, 165-185.

Wislocki, G. B., and Sidman, R. L. 1954. *J. comp. Neurol.*, **101**, 53-100.

Wislocki, G. B., and Streeter, G. L. 1938. *Contr. Embryol. Carneg. Instn.*, **27**, 1-66.

Wolf, J. 1822. *Abhildungen und Beschreibungen merkwürdiger naturgeschichtlichter Gegenstände*, Nürnberg ; C. Tyroff.

Wolfe, J. B. 1936. *Comp. Psychol. Monogr.*, **12**, No. 5, 72 pp.

Wolff, E. 1938a. *Proc. zool. Soc. Lond.*, 1937A, **107**, 347-350.

    1938b. *Proc. zool. Soc. Lond.*, 1938A, **108**, 143-161.

Wood, J. 1867. *J. Anat. Lond.*, **1**, 44-59.

Wood-Jones, F. 1929a. *Hum. Biol.*, **1**, 214-228.

 1929b. *Man's Place among the Mammals*, London ; Arnold.

 1940. *J. Anat. Lond.*, **74**, 147-170.

 1944. *Structure and Function as seen in the Foot*, London ; Baillière, Tindall & Cox.

Wörner, R. 1940. *Z. angew. Psych. Charakterkunde*, **59**, 257-318.

Woskresensky, L. N., and Ivanow, N. S. 1932. *Biol. gen.*, **8**, 597-606.

Wunderlich, L. 1884. *Zool. Gart. Frankft.*, **25**, 317-318.

Yerkes, R. M., and Yerkes, A. W. 1929. *The Great Apes*, Newhaven ; Yale University Press.

Yoffey, J. M., and Drinker, C. K. 1938. *J. exp. Med.*, **68**, 629-640.

Yoshimi, T. 1956. *Folia anat. japon.*, **29**, 181-209.

Yoshioka, K. 1936. *Folia anat. japon.*, **14**, 545-602.

Ziegler, A. C. 1964. *Amer. J. phys. Anthrop.*, **22**, 15-31.

Zlabek, K. 1936. *Bull. Mus. Hist. nat. Paris*, (2), **8**, 118-124.

Zuckerkandl, E. 1895. *Arb. anat. Inst. Wiesbaden*, **5**, 207-291.

 1897. *Arb. anat. Inst. Wiesbaden*, **8**, 707-799.

 1900. *S.B. Akad. Wiss. Wien*, **109**, 405-458.

Zuckerman, S. 1930. *Proc. zool. Soc. Lond.*, 691-754.

 1931. *Proc. zool. Soc. Lond.*, 325-343.

 1932a. *Proc. zool. Soc. Lond.*, 1059-1075.

 1932b. *Proc. zool. Soc. Lond.*, 1080-1081.

 1932c. *The Social Life of Monkeys and Apes*, London ; Kegan Paul, Trench.

 1933. *Functional Affinities of Man, Monkeys and Apes*, London ; Kegan Paul.

 1937a. *Proc. zool. Soc. Lond.*, 1937A, 315-329.

 1937b. *Proc. roy. Soc. B.*, **123**, 457-471.

 1938a. *Trans. zool. Soc. Lond.*, **23**, 315-378.

 1938b. *Proc. Anat. Soc. in J. Anat. Lond.*, **72**, 471.

 1953a. *Proc. zool. Soc. Lond.*, **122**, 827-950.

 1953b. In Huxley, Hardy and Ford (eds.), *Evolution as a Process*, London ; Allen and Unwin.

Zuckerman, S., Ashton, E. H., and Pearson, J. B. 1962. *Bibl. primat.*, **1**, 217-228.

Zuckerman, S., and Burr, H. S. 1934. *Anat. Rec.*, **61**, 53-56.

Zuckerman, S., and Fisher, R. B. 1938. *Proc. zool. Soc. Lond.*, (B), **107**, 529-538.

Zuckerman, S., and Fulton, J. F. 1934. *The Nomenclature of Primates commonly used in Laboratory Work*, New Haven, Conn.

Zuckerman, S., and Krohn, C. L. 1937. *Philos. Trans.*, B, **228**, 147-172.

Zuckerman, S., and Parkes, A. S. 1930. *Proc. physiol. Soc. in J. Physiol.*, 69.

 1931. *J. Anat. Lond.*, **65**, 272-276.

 1932. *Proc. zool. Soc. Lond.*, (1), 139-191.

 1935. *J. Anat. Lond.*, **69**, 484-496.

 1938. *J. Anat. Lond.*, **72**, 277-279.

 1939. *J. Endocrinol.*, **1**, 430-438.

Zuckerman, S., and Sandys, O. C. 1939. *J. Anat. Lond.*, **73**, 597-616.

Zuckerman, S., and Sudermann, A. 1935. *J. exp. Biol.*, **12**, 222-228.

Zuckerman, S., van Wagenen, G., and Gardiner, R. H. 1938. *Proc. zool. Soc. Lond.*, **108**, 385-401.

Zwaardemaker, H. 1895. *Die Physiologie des Geruchs*, Leipzig ; Engelmann.

INDEX

Principal references are in bold type. **Text** *figures are indicated by an asterisk*

3 C

Text set in Monotype Imprint series 101 and printed letterpress by
R. AND R. CLARK, LTD., EDINBURGH

Letterpress blocks by
CITY ENGRAVING CO., LTD., HULL

Map section printed offset litho by
R. CUNNINGHAM AND SONS, LTD., ALVA, CLACKMANNANSHIRE

Offset plates by
EDINBURGH PHOTOLITHO CO.

Text paper, Basingwerk Parchment; art paper, Basingwerk Art, by
GROSVENOR, CHATER AND CO., LTD., LONDON

Bound by
HUNTER AND FOULIS, LTD., EDINBURGH

DISTRIBUTION MAPS

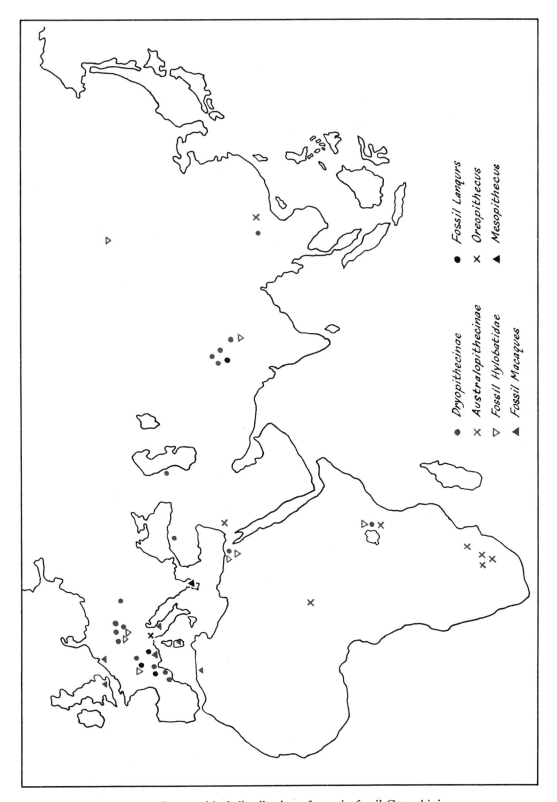

MAP I. Geographical distribution of certain fossil Catarrhini

Legend:

● Dryopithecinae   ● Fossil Langurs
× Australopithecinae   × Oreopithecus
▷ Fossil Hylobatidae   ▲ Mesopithecus
▲ Fossil Macaques

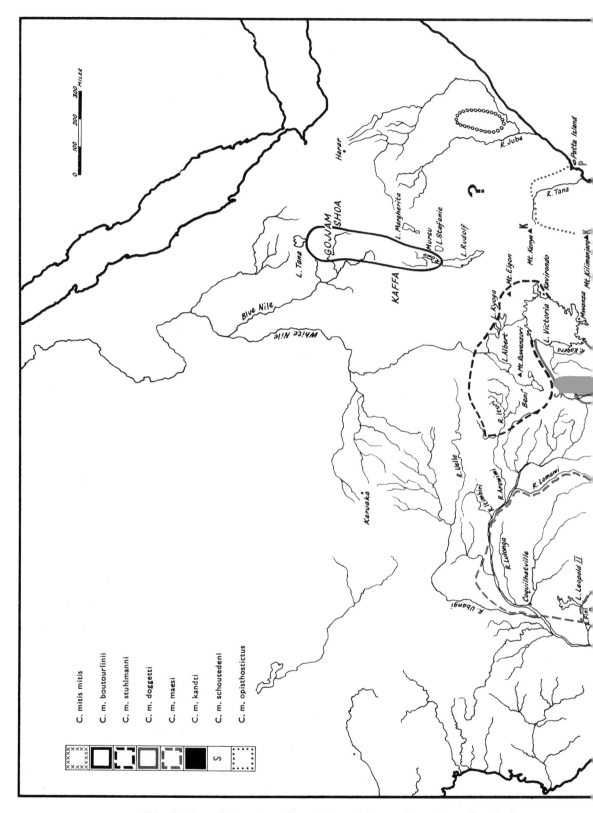

MAP 2. Distribution of the subspecies of *Cercopithecus mitis* and *C. albogularis*

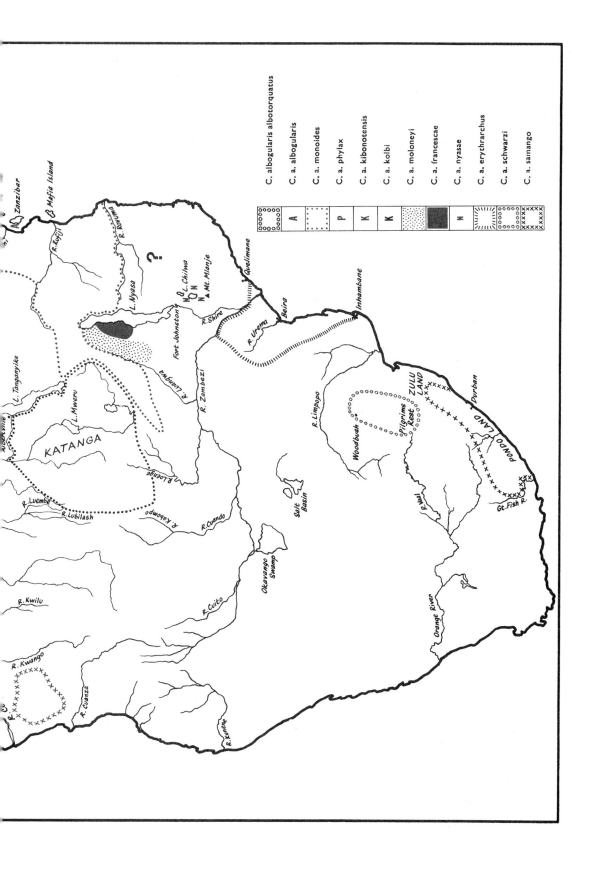

C. albogularis albotorquatus

C. a. albogularis

C. a. monoides

C. a. phylax

C. a. kibonotensis

C. a. kolbi

C. a. moloneyi

C. a. francescae

C. a. nyasae

C. a. erythrarchus

C. a. schwarzi

C. a. samango

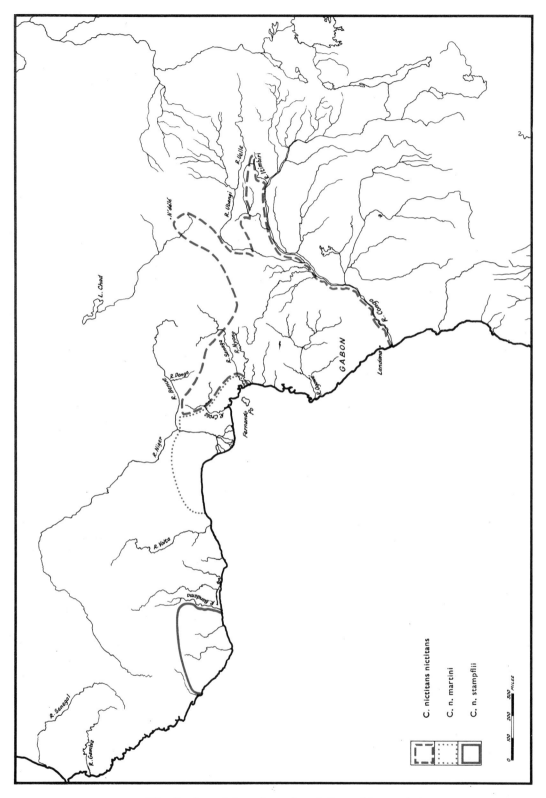

MAP 3. Distribution of the subspecies of *Cercopithecus nictitans*

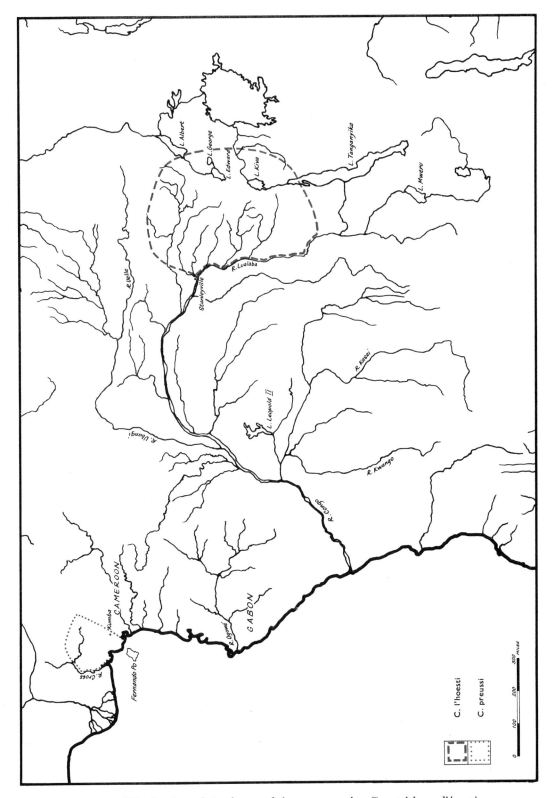

MAP 4. Distribution of the forms of the superspecies *Cercopithecus l'hoesti*

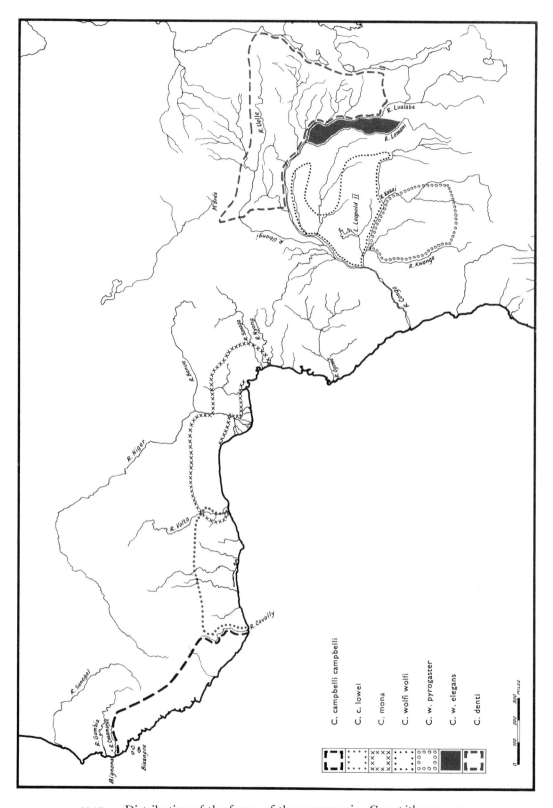

C. campbelli campbelli

C. c. lowei

C. mona

C. wolfi wolfi

C. w. pyrogaster

C. w. elegans

C. denti

MAP 5. Distribution of the forms of the superspecies *Cercopithecus mona*

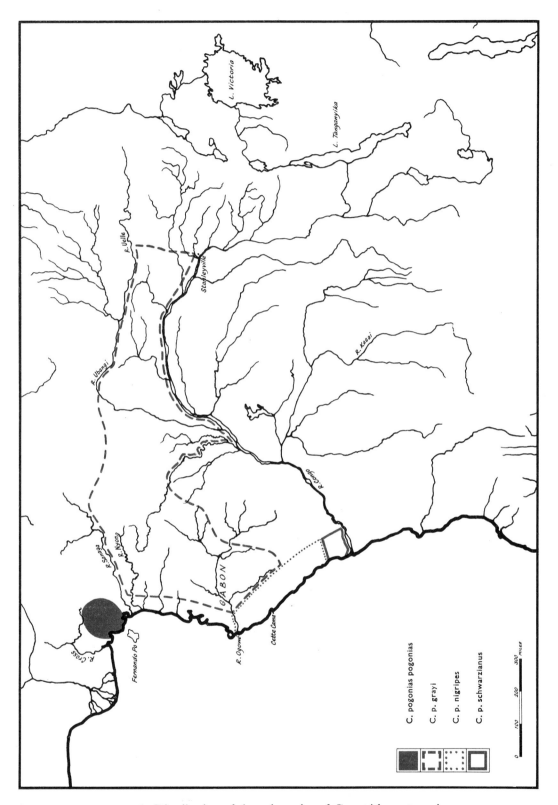

MAP 6. Distribution of the subspecies of *Cercopithecus pogonias*

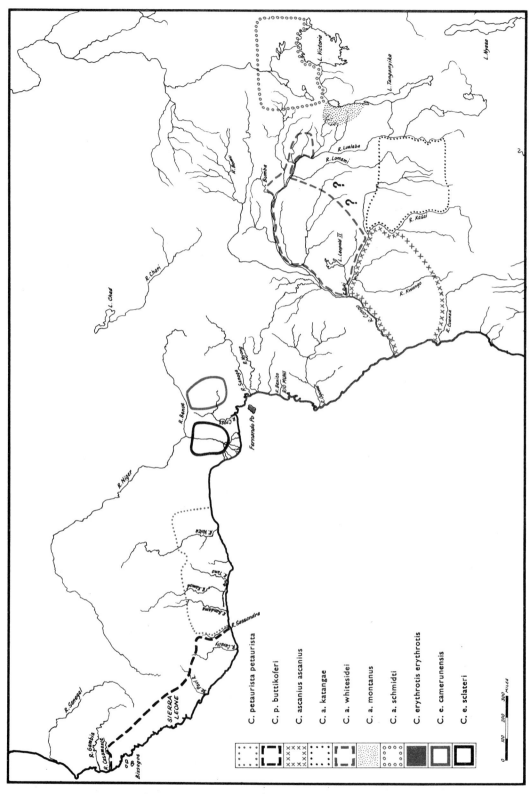

MAP 7. Distribution of the subspecies of *Cercopithecus petaurista*, *C. ascanius* and
C. erythrotis

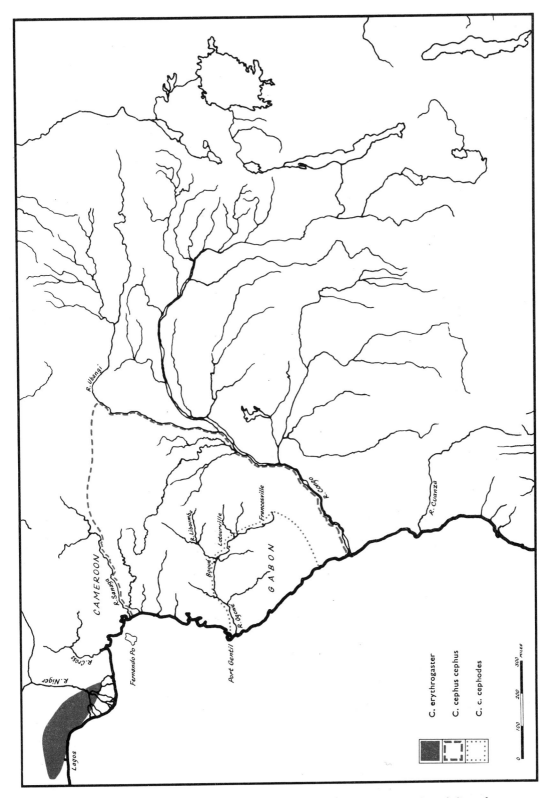

MAP 8. Distribution of *Cercopithecus erythrogaster* and the subspecies of *C. cephus*

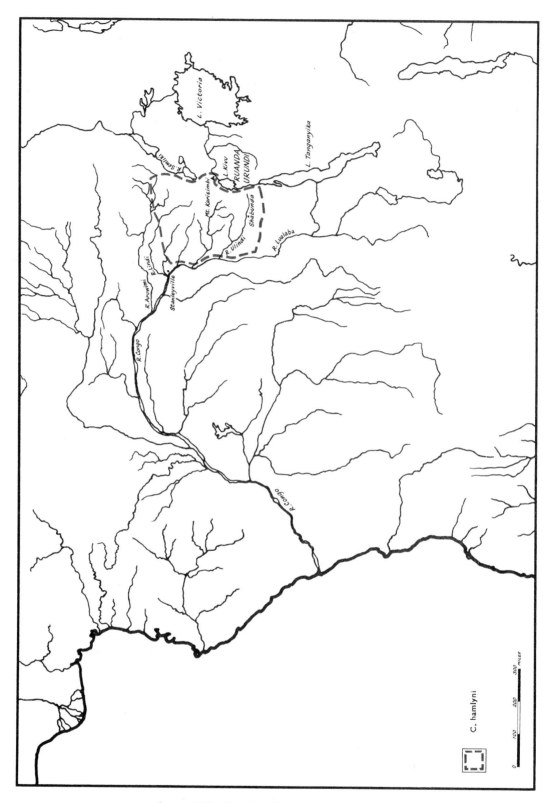

MAP 9. Distribution of *Cercopithecus hamlyni*

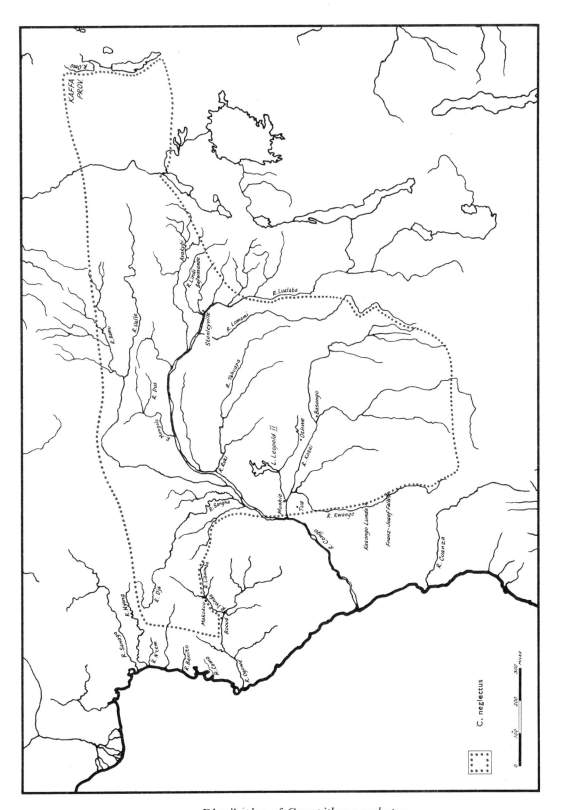

MAP 10. Distribution of *Cercopithecus neglectus*

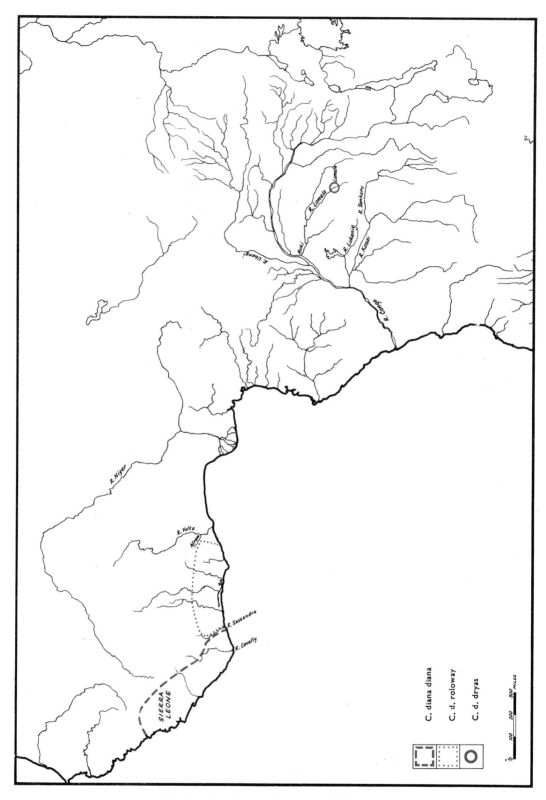

MAP 11. Distribution of the subspecies of *Cercopithecus diana*

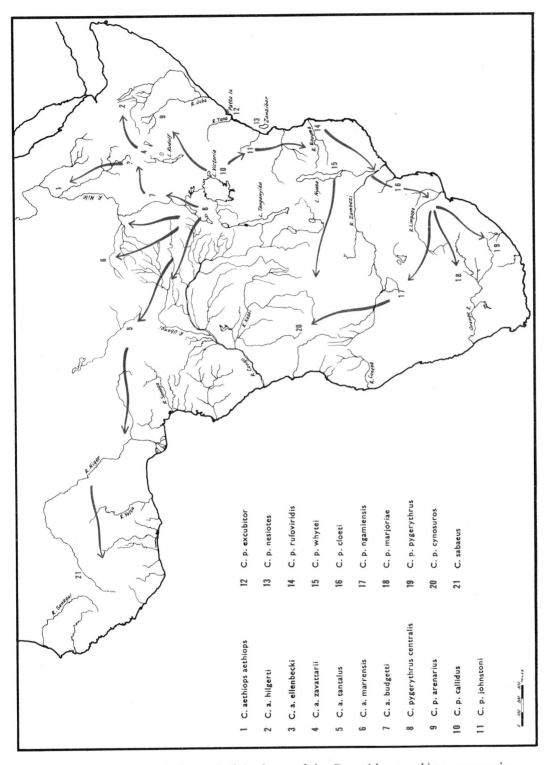

MAP 12. Theoretical dispersal of the forms of the *Cercopithecus aethiops* superspecies

1 C. aethiops aethiops
2 C. a. hilgerti
3 C. a. ellenbecki
4 C. a. zavattarii
5 C. a. tantalus
6 C. a. marrensis
7 C. p. budgetti
8 C. pygerythrus centralis
9 C. p. arenarius
10 C. p. callidus
11 C. p. johnstoni

12 C. p. excubitor
13 C. p. nesiotes
14 C. p. rufoviridis
15 C. p. whytei
16 C. p. cloeti
17 C. p. ngamiensis
18 C. p. marjoriae
19 C. p. pygerythrus
20 C. p. cynosuros
21 C. sabaeus

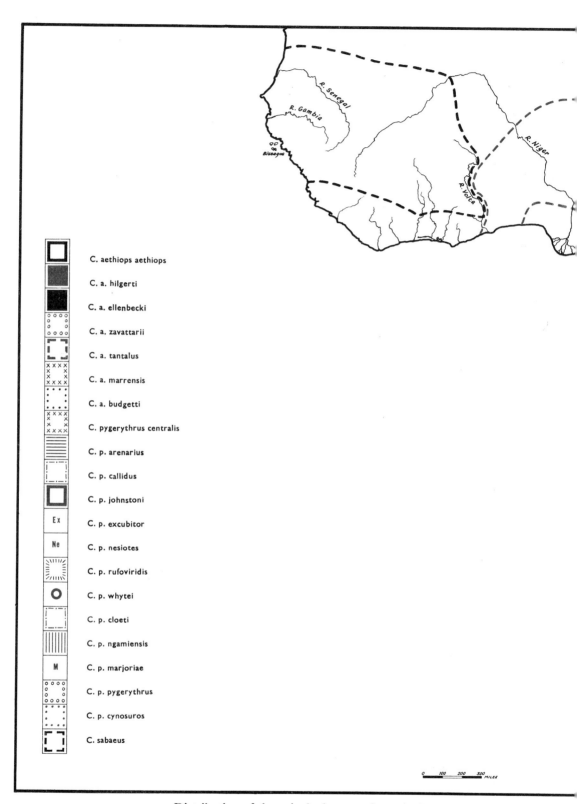

C. aethiops aethiops

C. a. hilgerti

C. a. ellenbecki

C. a. zavattarii

C. a. tantalus

C. a. marrensis

C. a. budgetti

C. pygerythrus centralis

C. p. arenarius

C. p. callidus

C. p. johnstoni

C. p. excubitor

C. p. nesiotes

C. p. rufoviridis

C. p. whytei

C. p. cloeti

C. p. ngamiensis

C. p. marjoriae

C. p. pygerythrus

C. p. cynosuros

C. sabaeus

MAP 13. Distribution of the principal types of savannah guenons
(*C. aethiops* superspecies)

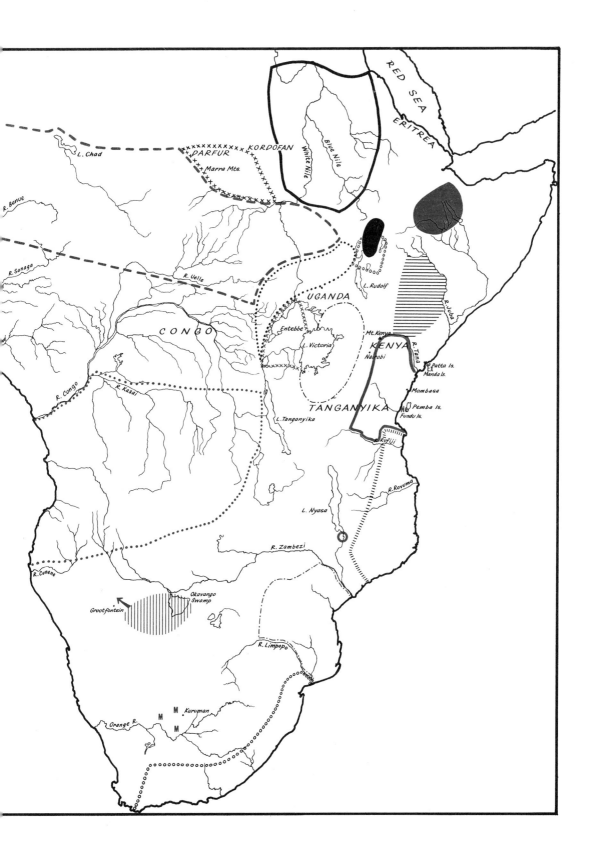

RED SEA

ERITREA

L. Chad

KORDOFAN

DARFUR

Marra Mts.

White Nile

Blue Nile

R. Benue

R. Sanaga

R. Uelle

CONGO

UGANDA

L. Rudolf

R. Juba

Entebbe

L. Victoria

Mt. Kenya

KENYA

R. Tana

Nairobi

Patta Is.

Manda Is.

R. Congo

R. Kasai

TANGANYIKA

Mombasa

Pemba Is.

Fundu Is.

L. Tanganyika

Rufiji

R. Rovuma

L. Nyasa

R. Cunene

R. Zambezi

Okavango
Swamp

Grootfontein

R. Limpopo

M Kuruman

Orange R.

M

M

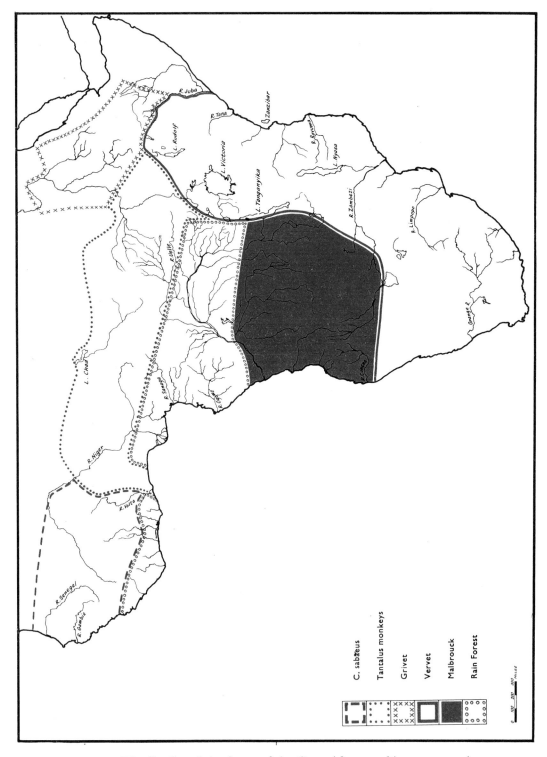

MAP 14. Distribution of the forms of the *Cercopithecus aethiops* superspecies

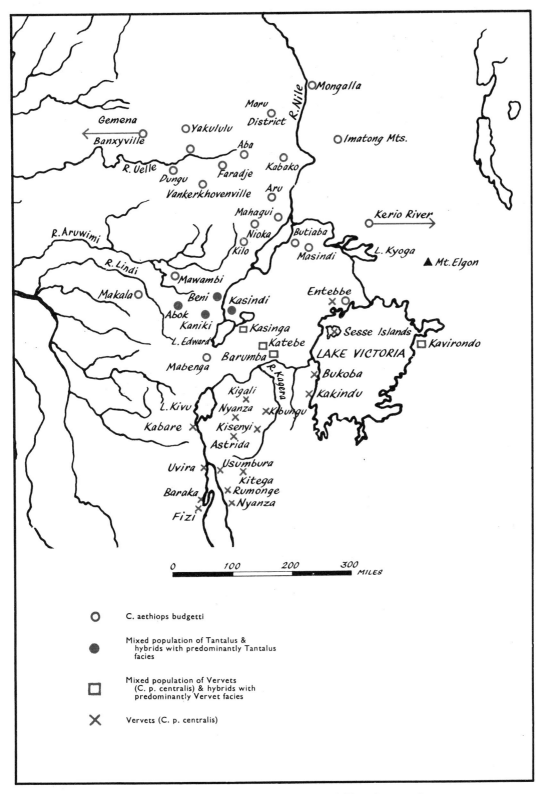

MAP 15. Area of integration of Vervet and Tantalus monkeys
(based on Dandelot, 1959)

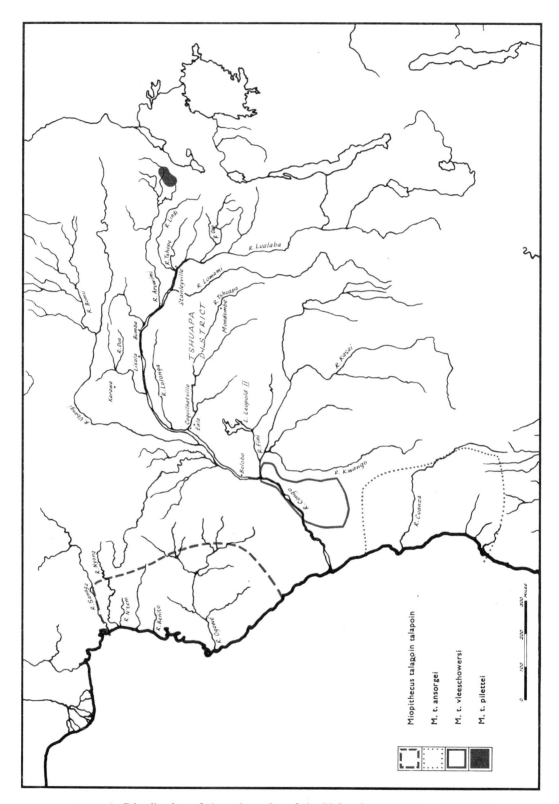

MAP 16. Distribution of the subspecies of the Talapoin (*Miopithecus talapoin*)

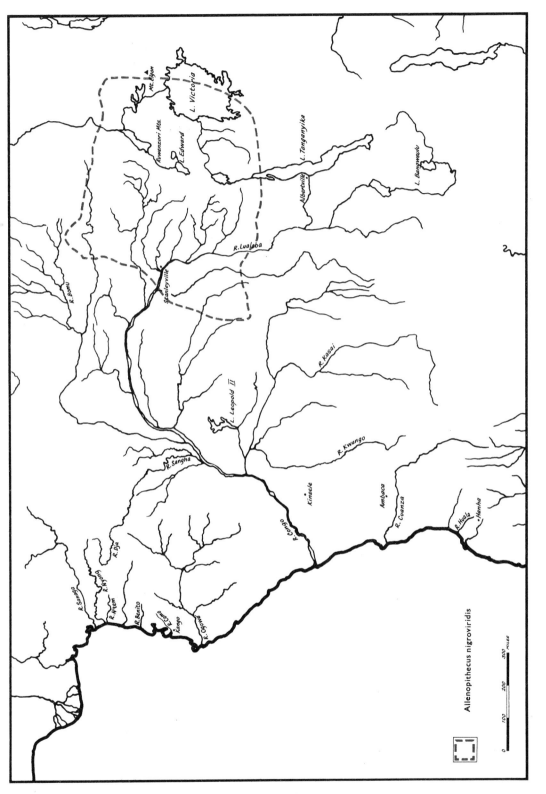

MAP 17. Distribution of *Allenopithecus nigroviridis*

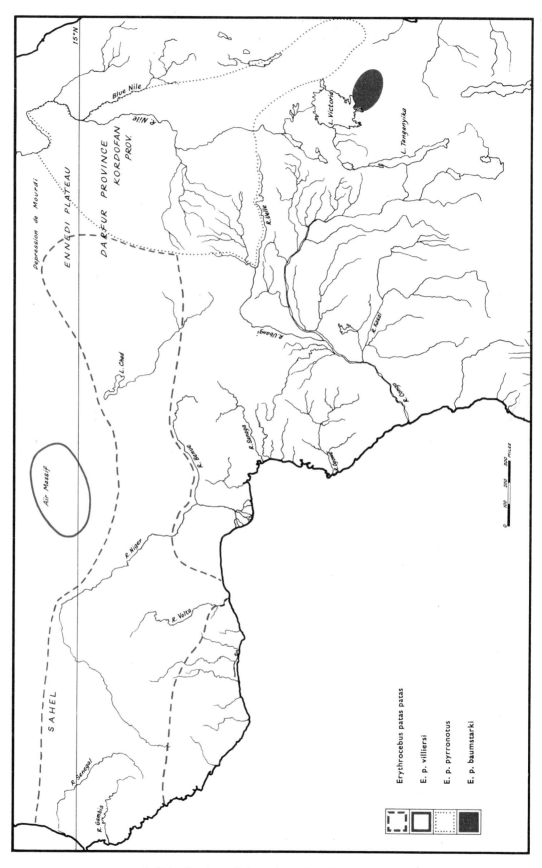

MAP 18. Distribution of the subspecies of *Erythrocebus patas*

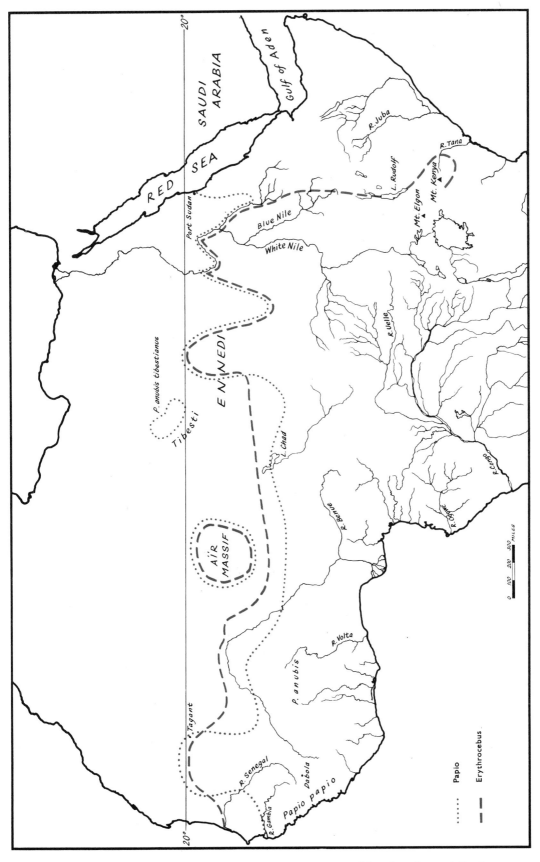

MAP 19. Map to show the northern limit of the range of *Erythrocebus* and *Papio*